PB
G
9-14-16

PEARSON

ALWAYS LEARNING

Marvin L. Bittinger • Judith A. Beecher

Developmental Math
MATV 0018/0022

Custom Edition for Brevard Community College

D1311664

Taken from:
Developmental Mathematics, Eighth Edition
by Marvin L. Bittinger and Judith A. Beecher

Cover Art: Courtesy of Pearson.

Taken from:

Developmental Mathematics, Eighth Edition
by Marvin L. Bittinger and Judith A. Beecher
Copyright © 2012, 2008, 2004, 2000 by Pearson Education, Inc.
Published by Addison-Wesley
San Francisco, California 94111

All rights reserved. No part of this book may be reproduced, in any form or by any means, without permission in writing from the publisher.

This special edition published in cooperation with Pearson Learning Solutions.

All trademarks, service marks, registered trademarks, and registered service marks are the property of their respective owners and are used herein for identification purposes only.

Pearson Learning Solutions, 501 Boylston Street, Suite 900, Boston, MA 02116
A Pearson Education Company
www.pearsoned.com

Printed in the United States of America

1 2 3 4 5 6 7 8 9 10 V303 17 16 15 14 13 12

000200010271309605

ML

ISBN 10: 1-256-77115-5
ISBN 13: 978-1-256-77115-9

Contents

Photo Credits

Photo Credits

1, Six Flags Great Adventure 3, Jim McIsaac/Getty Images 4, Guy Reynolds/Staff Photographer/Dallas Morning News/Corbis 7, Corbis 8 (left), Purestock/SuperStock 8 (right), Tannen Maury/epa/Corbis 9 (top left), Rick Dole/Getty Images 9 (top right), Louis Lopez/CSM/Landov 9 (bottom left), Tim Pannell/Corbis 9 (bottom right), Red Chopsticks/Getty Images 24, K-King Photography Media Co. Ltd/Getty Images 34, Dana Hoff/Beateworks/Corbis 50, Simon Jarratt/Corbis 58, Brand X/Corbis 60, Six Flags Great Adventure 61 (left), Laurence Mouton/PhotoAlto/Corbis 61 (right), Tyler Stableford, The Image Bank/Getty Images 63 (top left), Thinkstock/Corbis 63 (top right), Pete Saloutos/Corbis 63 (bottom left), James Leynse/Corbis 63 (bottom right), Reuters/Corbis 64, Associated Press 94, Don Farrall, Photodisc/Getty Images 98, Gail Mooney/Corbis 99, Richard Shock/Corbis 103, Tom Sears www.tomsears.com 104, Jeffrey Racette/Icon SMI/Corbis 130 (left), Phil Schermeister, National Geographic Stock/Getty Images 130 (right), William Thomas Cain/Getty Images 142, Dorling Kindersley © Jamie Marshall 143, David Frazier/Corbis 144, MedioImages/Corbis 146, Micheal Simpson, Taxi/Getty Images 148, Ben Blankenburg/Corbis 149 (top right), James Shaffer/PhotoEdit 149 (bottom left), Focus on Sport/Getty Images 149 (bottom right), Bettmann/Corbis 150, Abode/Beateworks/Corbis 153, Dorling Kindersley Media Library 154 (top), Kim Carson, Digital Vision/Getty Images 154 (bottom), Juice Images/Corbis 156, Corbis Royalty-Free 158 (top), Pete Starman, Photonica/Getty Images 158 (bottom), Blend Images/SuperStock 165, Tom Sears www.tomsears.com 172, Comstock Select/Corbis 173 (top), Creatas/SuperStock 173 (bottom), Charles & Josette Lenars/Corbis 177, Michael Jones, Alaskastock/Photolibrary New York 178, Yves Herman/Reuters/Corbis 179, Blaine Harrington III/Corbis 180 (left), Faytok, Chris/Star Ledger/Corbis 180 (right), Robert Laberge/Getty Images 185 (left), Sara D. Davis/Getty Images 185 (right), Thinkstock/SuperStock 199 (left), Photodisc/SuperStock 199 (right), Construction Photography/Corbis 220, Royalty-Free/Corbis/JupiterImages 223, Chuck Savage/Corbis 224, Tetra Images/Corbis 227, Paul Sakuma/Associated Press 230, Ablestock/Images/IPNStock 232, Blend Images/SuperStock 238, Radius Images/Corbis 249, Joe Raedle/Getty Images 250, David Joel, Photographer's Choice Royalty-Free/Getty Images 255, Richard Drew, Associated Press 256, Viviane Moos/Corbis 258, Tim Pannell/Corbis 263, Tom Grill/Corbis 264, Ant Strack/Corbis 266, Dean Krakel II/Photo Researchers, Inc. 267 (left), EADS Astrium/Master Image/2008 267 (right), PictureNet/Corbis 268 (top right), NBAE/Getty Images 268 (bottom left), Sebastian Kaulitzki/Shutterstock 268 (bottom right), DLILLC/Corbis 269 (left), Polka Dot Images/SuperStock 269 (right), AGE Fotostock 270 (left), Raymond Gehman/Corbis 270 (right), Reuters/Corbis 272, Corbis 273, Aldo Pavan/Grand Tour/Corbis 276 (left), Corbis RF 276 (right), NASA 277 (left), Cultura Limited/SuperStock 277 (right), Pixland/SuperStock 280, Frank and Helena/Cultura/Corbis 288, Corbis/SuperStock 289 (top), Photodisc/SuperStock 289 (bottom), Sergio Urday/epa/Corbis 293, moodboard/Corbis 301 (top left), Paul A. Souders/Corbis 301 (top middle), Icun/Xinhua Press/Corbis 301 (top right), SuperStock 301 (bottom left), AGE Fotostock/SuperStock 301 (bottom middle), D. Robert & Lorri Franz/Corbis 301 (bottom right), Jenny E. Ross/Corbis 302, Comstock/SuperStock 305, Richard Drew, Associated Press 306 (top), Tomasz Szymanski/Shutterstock 306 (bottom), Corbis 307, Uden Graham/Redlink/Corbis 309, Andrew Sacks/AgStock Images/Corbis 310 (left), Dave Bartruff/Corbis 310 (right), Tom & Dee Ann McCarthy/Corbis 312, Corbis/SuperStock 313 (left), Bettmann/Corbis 313 (right), Hill Street Studios/Brand X/Corbis 318, Perry Mastrovito/Corbis 319, Photodisc/SuperStock 321, Christian Science Monitor/Getty Images 326, Jose Luis Pelaez, Inc./Blend Images/Corbis 336, fStop/SuperStock 337 (top), Nevada Wier/Corbis 337 (bottom), James Hardy, PhotoAlto Agency RF Collections/Getty Images 343, Sharon Pearson, GAP Photos/Getty Images 344, Tom Carter/PhotoEdit 346 (top), Steve Lipofsky/Corbis 346 (bottom), Car Culture/Corbis 347, Jennie Woodcock; Reflections Photolibrary/Corbis 350, Thinkstock Images/JupiterImages 352 (left), George D. Lepp/Corbis 352 (right), Markus Moellenberg/zefa/Corbis 356, Reuters/Corbis 360, Tom Uhlman/Alamy 364, Corbis/SuperStock 369, Sharon Pearson, GAP Photos/Getty Images 374, Tony Dejak, Associated Press 382, David Young-Wolff/PhotoEdit 389, Gideon Mendel/Corbis 404 (left), Digital Vision/Getty Images 404 (right), Thinkstock/Corbis 410, Gideon Mendel/Corbis 422 (left), Comstock/Thinkstock 422 (right), Wisconsin Department of Natural Resources 436 (left and right), Associated Press 437 (left), Thinkstock/SuperStock 437 (right), Deborah Gilbert/Getty Images 485, Curlypinky/Dreamstime 488, Fancy/Veer/Corbis 502 (left), Raymond Gehman/National Geographic Stock/Getty Images 502 (right), Melissa Farlow/National Geographic Stock/Getty Images 511, Curlypinky/Dreamstime 515, Purestock/Getty Images 565, Thinkstock/Getty Images 569, AGE Fotostock/SuperStock 605, Glow Images/SuperStock 606, MedioImages/Photodisc/Getty Images 608 (left), Jochen Sand, Digital Vision/Getty Images 608 (right), Don Mason/Blend Images/Corbis 609, Tetra Images/Corbis 610 (left), Fancy/Veer/Corbis 610 (right), AGE Fotostock/SuperStock 617, C. Jess Yu/Shutterstock 619, AFP/Getty Images 620, Visual Ideas/Camilo Morales/JupiterImages 623 (left), AGE Fotostock/SuperStock 623 (right), Photodisc/SuperStock 626, Glow Images/SuperStock 641, Aladdin Color, Inc./Corbis 644, Charles O'Rear/Corbis 645, Tetra Images/JupiterImages 646 (left), A. Ramey/PhotoEd 646 (right), Spencer Grant/Alamy 652, Rob Van Petten, Digital Vision/Getty Images 655, David Sailors/Corbis 689, Digital Vision/Getty Images 693 (left), David Sailors/Corbis 693 (right), D. Robert & Lorri Franz/Corbis 694 (left), Jim West/PhotoEdit 694 (right), Photodisc/SuperStock 726, Federal Highway Administration and Washington Infrastructure Services, Inc. 733, Larry W. Smith/epa/Corbis 746, Francesca Yorke © Dorling Kindersley 747 (top), NASA 747 (bottom), Eyewire Collection 750 (left), NASA 750 (right), Alfred Pasieka/Peter Arnold, Inc. 752, Larry W. Smith/epa/Corbis 753 (left), NASA 753 (right), Dennis MacDonald/PhotoEdit 754, Creatas/SuperStock 801, Time & Life Pictures/Getty Images 821, Stockbyte/SuperStock 854, GSFC/NASA 886, SW Productions/Brand X/Corbis 889, Fredrik Nyman, Johner Images Royalty-Free/Getty Images 892 (top), Shaffer Smith Photo LLC/JupiterImages 892 (bottom), JupiterImages 893 (left), Corbis 893 (right), Hans Neleman, Taxi/Getty Images 905, AGE Fotostock/SuperStock 924, Tetra Images/SuperStock 952, Alamy Images 956, Associated Press 957 (top), Joel Sartore, National Geographic Stock/Getty Images 957 (bottom), Istock 958, AGE Fotostock/SuperStock 963, Tim Pannell/Corbis 964 (left), Pearson Student Photo Archive 964 (right), Tom Turpin, Purdue University 965 (left), Matthew Cavanaugh/epa/Corbis 965 (right), Noah K. Murray/Star Ledger/Corbis 966, Axiom Photographic Agency/Getty Images 976, U.S. Mint 979, Heather Charles/The Indianapolis Star 980, Myrleen Pearson/PhotoEdit, Inc. 981 (left), Anthony West/Corbis 981 (right), Fancy/Veer/Corbis 984, Kevin Burke/Corbis 989 (left), Billie E. Barnes/PhotoEdit, Inc. 989 (right), PhotoLink/Getty Images 993, Alan Carey/Corbis 1018, Comstock/Getty Images 1019, Peter Essick/Aurora Photos 1023, Steve Skjold/PhotoEdit, Inc. 1025 (left), Alan Carey/Corbis 1025 (right), Richard Hutchings/PhotoEdit, Inc. 1027 (top), Rick D'Elia/Corbis/Corbis 1027 (bottom), Jeff Smith/Getty Images 1029, Car Culture/Corbis 1037, Corbis/Bettmann 1045, Fancy Collection/SuperStock 1047, David Frazier/PhotoEdit 1051 (left), Photodisc/Getty Images 1051 (right), Michael Newman/PhotoEdit 1069, Getty Images-Photodisc-Royalty-Free 1078, Steve Smith/SuperStock 1085, National Geographic Stock/Photolibrary New York 1089, LandWave Products, Inc. 1092, *Untitled* (1989), Frederick Lane Sandback. Tile-red acrylic yarn, 105 × 237 × 273 in. Indianapolis Museum of Art, Ann M. Stack Fund for Contemporary Art [2004.153]/Copyright © Estate of Fred Sandback Frederick McKinney/Getty Images 1115, David McNew/Getty Images 1138, Johner Images Royalty-Free/Getty Images 1139, Image Source/JupiterImages 1155, Doug Menuez/Photodisc/Getty Images 1157, MedicalRF/The Medical File 1176 (top), Alissa Crandall/Corbis 1176 (bottom), AFP/Getty Images 1177, AGE Fotostock/SuperStock 1185, Tom & Dee Ann McCarthy/Corbis 1186 (left), AGE Fotostock/SuperStock 1186 (right), Bork/Shutterstock 1188, Eli Lilly and Company

Index of Applications

Authors' Note to Students

Welcome to *Developmental Mathematics: College Mathematics and Introductory Algebra*. Having a solid grasp of the mathematical skills taught in this book will enrich your life in many ways, both personally and professionally, including increasing your earning power and enabling you to make wise decisions about your personal finances.

As we wrote this text, we were guided by the desire to do everything possible to help you learn its concepts and skills. The material in this book has been developed and refined with feedback from users of the seven previous editions so that you can benefit from their class-tested strategies for success. Regardless of your past experiences in mathematics courses, we encourage you to consider this course as a fresh start and to approach it with a positive attitude.

One of the most important things you can do to ensure your success in this course is to allow enough time for it. This includes time spent in class and time spent out of class studying and doing homework. To help you derive the greatest benefit from this textbook, from your study time, and from the many other learning resources available to you, we have included an organizer card at the front of the book. This card serves as a handy reference for contact information for your instructor, fellow students, and campus learning resources, as well as a weekly planner. It also includes a list of the Study Tips that appear throughout the text. You might find it helpful to read all of these tips as you begin your course work.

Knowing that your time is both valuable and limited, we have designed this objective-based text to help you learn quickly and efficiently. You are led through the development of each concept, then presented with one or more examples of the corresponding skills, and finally given the opportunity to use these skills by doing the interactive margin exercises that appear on the page beside the examples. For quick assessment of your understanding, you can check your answers with the answers placed at the bottom of the page. This innovative feature, along with illustrations designed to help you visualize mathematical concepts and the extensive exercise sets keyed to section objectives, gives you the support and reinforcement you need to be successful in your math course.

To help apply and retain your knowledge, take advantage of the new Skill to Review exercises when they appear at the beginning of a section and the comprehensive mid-chapter reviews and the summary and reviews. Read through the list of supplementary material available to students that appears in the preface to make sure you get the most out of your learning experience, and investigate other learning resources that may be available to you.

Give yourself the best opportunity to succeed by spending the time required to learn. We hope you enjoy learning this material and that you will find it of benefit.

Best wishes for success!
Marv Bittinger
Judy Beecher

Related Bittinger Paperback Titles

- Bittinger: *Fundamental College Mathematics,* 5th Edition
- Bittinger: *Basic College Mathematics,* 11th Edition
- Bittinger/Penna: *Basic College Mathematics with Early Integers,* 2nd Edition
- Bittinger/Ellenbogen/Johnson: *Prealgebra,* 6th Edition
- Bittinger: *Introductory Algebra,* 11th Edition
- Bittinger: *Intermediate Algebra,* 11th Edition
- Bittinger/Ellenbogen/Beecher/Johnson, *Prealgebra and Introductory Algebra,* 3rd Edition
- Bittinger/Beecher: *Introductory and Intermediate Algebra,* 4th Edition

Accuracy

Students rely on accurate textbooks, and our users value the Bittinger reputation for accuracy. All Bittinger titles go through an exhaustive checking process to ensure accuracy in the problem sets, mathematical art, and accompanying supplements.

Preface

New in This Edition

To maximize retention of the concepts and skills presented, five highly effective review features are included in the 8th edition. Student success is increased when review is integrated throughout each chapter.

Four Types of Integrated Review

Skill to Review exercises, found at the beginning of most sections, link to a section objective. These exercises offer a just-in-time review of a previously presented skill that relates to new material in the section. For convenient studying, section and objective references are followed by two practice exercises for immediate review and reinforcement. Exercise answers are given at the bottom of the page for immediate feedback.

Skill Maintenance Exercises, found in each exercise set, review concepts from other sections in the text to prepare students for their final examination. Section and objective references appear next to each Skill Maintenance exercise. All Skill Maintenance answers are included in the text.

A Mid-Chapter Review reinforces understanding of the mathematical concepts and skills just covered before students move on to new material. Section and objective references are included. Exercise types include Concept Reinforcement, Guided Solutions, Mixed Review, and Understanding Through Discussion and Writing. Answers to all exercises in the Mid-Chapter Review are given at the back of the book.

The Chapter Summary and Review at the end of each chapter is expanded to provide more comprehensive in-text practice and review.

- **Key Terms, Properties, and Formulas** are highlighted, with page references for convenient review.
- **Concept Reinforcement** offers true/false questions to enhance students' understanding of mathematical concepts.
- Important Concepts are listed by section objectives, followed by *worked-out examples* for reference and review and *similar practice exercises* for students to solve.
- **Review Exercises**, including Synthesis exercises and two new multiple-choice exercises, are organized by objective and cover the whole chapter.
- **Understanding Through Discussion and Writing** exercises strengthen understanding by giving students a chance to express their thoughts in spoken or written form.

Section and objective references for all exercises are included. Answers to all exercises in the Summary and Review are given at the back of the book.

Chapter Tests, including Synthesis questions and a new multiple-choice question, allow students to review and test their comprehension of chapter skills prior to taking an instructor's exam. Answers to all questions in the Chapter Tests are given at the back of the book. Section and objective references for each question are included with the answers.

Other New Elements

A new design enhances the Bittinger guided-learning approach. Margin exercises are now located next to examples for easier navigation, and answers for those exercises are given at the bottom of the page for immediate feedback.

Content changes include streamlined coverage in Sections 1.2 and 1.3. Material on simple interest and compound interest has been moved from Section 4.7 to Section 4.8 in this edition. Appendix K, *Inequalities and Interval Notation*, and Appendix O, *The Complex Numbers*, are new to this edition. In addition, we have added over 240 new examples and 1900 new exercises.

Hallmark Features

Revised!   The **Bittinger Student Organizer** card at the front of the text helps students keep track of important contacts and dates and provides a weekly planner to help schedule time for classes, studying, and homework. A helpful list of study tips found in each chapter is also included.

New!   **Chapter Openers** feature motivating real-world applications that are revisited later in the chapters. This feature engages students and prepares them for the upcoming chapter material. (See pages 103, 177, and 905.)

New!   **Real-Data Applications** encourage students to see and interpret the mathematics that appears every day in the world around them. (See pages 71, 257, 301, 354, 664, and 752.) Many applications are drawn from the fields of business and economics, life and physical sciences, social sciences, medicine, and areas of general interest such as sports and daily life.

Study Tips appear throughout the text to give students pointers on how to develop good study habits as they progress through the course, encouraging them to get involved in the learning process. (See pages 11, 179, 546, and 875.) For easy reference, a list of all Study Tips, organized by category and page number, is included in the Bittinger Student Organizer.

Algebraic–Graphical Connections To provide a visual understanding of algebra, algebraic–graphical connections are included in each chapter beginning with Chapter 9. This feature gives the algebra more meaning by connecting it to a graphical interpretation. (See pages 665, 879, and 997–998.)

Caution Boxes are found at relevant points throughout the text. The heading "*Caution!*" alerts students to coverage of a common misconception or an error often made in performing a particular mathematics operation or skill. (See pages 112, 184, and 861.)

Revised!   Optional **Calculator Corners** are located where appropriate throughout the text. These streamlined Calculator Corners are written to be accessible to students and to represent current calculators. A calculator icon indicates exercises suitable for calculator use. (See pages 190, 279, 555, and 666.)

Immediate Practice and Assessment in Each Section

OBJECTIVES ➡ SKILL TO REVIEW ➡ EXPOSITION ➡ EXAMPLES WITH DETAILED ANNOTATIONS AND VISUAL ART PIECES ➡ MARGIN EXERCISES ➡ EXERCISE SETS

Objective Boxes begin each section. A boxed list of objectives is keyed by letter not only to section subheadings, but also to the section exercise sets and the Mid-Chapter Review and the Summary and Review exercises, as well as to the answers to the questions in the Chapter Tests. This correlation enables students to easily find appropriate review material if they need help with a particular exercise or skill at the objective level. (See pages 76, 178, and 582.)

New!   **Skill to Review** exercises, found at the beginning of most sections, link to a section objective and offer students a just-in-time review of a previously presented skill that relates to new material in the section. For convenient studying, objective references are followed by two practice exercises for immediate review and reinforcement. Answers to these exercises are given at the bottom of the page for immediate feedback. (See pages 196, 287, and 695.)

Revised! **Annotated Examples** provide annotations and color highlighting to lead students through the structured steps of the examples. The level of detail in these annotations is a significant reason for students' success with this book. This edition contains over 240 new examples. (See pages 150, 584, and 1079.)

Revised! The **art and photo program** is designed to help students visualize mathematical concepts and real-data applications. Many applications include source lines and feature graphs and drawings similar to those students see in the media. The use of color is carried out in a methodical and precise manner so that it conveys a consistent meaning, which enhances the readability of the text. For example, the use of both red and blue in mathematical art increases understanding of the concepts. When two lines are graphed using the same set of axes, one is usually red and the other blue. Note that equation labels are the same color as the corresponding line to aid in understanding. (See pages 55, 106, 312, 369, 689, 709, 952, and 1089.)

Revised! **Margin Exercises**, now located next to examples for easier navigation, accompany examples throughout the text and give students the opportunity to work similar problems for immediate practice and reinforcement of the concept just learned. Answers are now available at the bottom of the page. (See pages 220, 583, and 1047.)

Exercise Sets

To give students ample opportunity to practice what they have learned, each section is followed by an extensive exercise set *keyed by letter to the section objectives* for easy review and remediation. In addition, students also have the opportunity to synthesize the objectives from the current section with those from preceding sections. **For Extra Help** icons, shown at the beginning of each exercise set, indicate supplementary learning resources that students may need. This edition contains over 1900 new exercises.

- **Skill Maintenance Exercises**, found in each exercise set, review concepts from other sections in the text to prepare students for their final examination. Section and objective codes appear next to each Skill Maintenance exercise for easy reference. All Skill Maintenance answers are included in the text. (See pages 278, 694, and 1132.)

- **Vocabulary Reinforcement Exercises** provide an integrated review of key terms that students must know to communicate effectively in the language of mathematics. These appear once per chapter in the Skill Maintenance portion of an exercise set. (See pages 160, 713, and 895.)

- **Synthesis Exercises** help build critical-thinking skills by requiring students to use what they know to synthesize, or combine, learning objectives from the current section with those from previous sections. These are available in most exercise sets. (See pages 75, 610, and 796.)

Mid-Chapter Review

New! A **Mid-Chapter Review** gives students the opportunity to reinforce their understanding of the mathematical skills and concepts just covered before they move on to new material. Section and objective references are included for convenient studying, and answers to all the Mid-Chapter Review exercises are included in the text. The types of exercises are as follows:

- **Concept Reinforcement** are true/false questions that enhance students' understanding of mathematical concepts. These are also available in the Summary and Review at the end of the chapter. (See pages 131, 701, and 941.)

- **Guided Solutions** present worked-out problems with blanks for students to fill in the correct expressions to complete the solution. (See pages 131, 701, and 941.)

- **Mixed Review** provides free-response exercises, similar to those in the preceding sections in the chapter, reinforcing mastery of skills and concepts. (See pages 132, 701, and 941.)

- **Understanding Through Discussion and Writing** lets students demonstrate their understanding of mathematical concepts by expressing their thoughts in spoken and written form. This type of exercise is also found in each Chapter Summary and Review. (See pages 132, 702, and 942.)

Matching Feature

Translating for Success problem sets give extra practice with the important "Translate" step of the process for solving word problems. After translating each of ten problems into its appropriate equation or inequality, students are asked to choose from fifteen possible translations, encouraging them to comprehend the problem before matching. (See pages 239, 622, and 1035.)

Visualizing for Success problem sets ask students to match an equation or inequality with its graph by focusing on characteristics of the equation or inequality and the corresponding attributes of the graph. This feature appears at least once in each chapter that contains graphing instruction and reviews graphing skills and concepts with exercises from all preceding chapters. (See pages 718, 792, and 1145.)

End-of-Chapter Material

Revised! The **Chapter Summary and Review** at the end of each chapter is expanded to provide more comprehensive in-text practice and review. Section and objective references and answers to all the Chapter Summary and Review exercises are included in the text. (See pages 167, 648, and 813.)

- **Key Terms, Properties, and Formulas** are highlighted, with page references for convenient review. (See pages 167, 648, and 813.)

- **Concept Reinforcement** offers true/false questions to enhance student understanding of mathematical concepts. (See pages 167, 648, and 813.)

- **New!** Important Concepts are listed by section objectives, followed by *a worked-out example* for reference and review and *a similar practice exercise* for students to solve. (See pages 167–170, 648–650, and 813–816.)

- **Review Exercises**, including Synthesis exercises and two new multiple-choice exercises, covering the whole chapter are organized by objective. (See pages 170–174, 650–652, and 816–818.)

- **Understanding Through Discussion and Writing** exercises strengthen understanding by giving students a chance to express their thoughts in spoken or written form. (See pages 174, 652, and 818.)

Chapter Tests, including Synthesis questions and a new multiple-choice question, allow students to review and test their comprehension of chapter skills prior to taking an instructor's exam. Answers to all questions in the Chapter Test are given at the back of the book. Section and objective references for each question are included with the answers. (See pages 175, 340, and 991.)

For Extra Help

Student Supplements

New! MyWorkBook (ISBN: 978-0-321-73090-9)

MyWorkBook can be packaged with the textbook or with the MyMathLab access kit and includes the following resources for each section of the text:

- Key vocabulary terms and vocabulary practice problems
- Guided examples with stepped-out solutions and similar practice exercises, keyed to the text by learning objective
- References to textbook examples and section lecture videos for additional help
- Additional exercises with ample space for students to show their work, keyed to the text by learning objective

Student's Solutions Manual (ISBN: 978-0-321-73157-9)
By Judith Penna
Contains completely worked-out annotated solutions for all the odd-numbered exercises in the text. Also includes fully worked-out annotated solutions for all the exercises (odd- and even-numbered) in the Mid-Chapter Reviews, the Summary and Reviews, and the Chapter Tests.

Chapter Test Prep Videos

Chapter Tests can serve as practice tests to help you study. Watch instructors work through step-by-step solutions to all the Chapter Test exercises from the textbook. These videos are available on YouTube (search using BittingerDevMath) and in MyMathLab. They are also included on the Video Resources on DVD described below and available for purchase at www.MyPearsonStore.com.

Video Resources on DVD Featuring Chapter Test Prep Videos
(ISBN: 978-0-321-73084-8)

- Complete set of lectures covering every objective of every section in the textbook
- Complete set of Chapter Test Prep videos (see above)
- All videos include optional English and Spanish subtitles
- Ideal for distance learning or supplemental instruction
- DVD-ROM format for student use at home or on campus

InterAct Math Tutorial Website (www.interactmath.com)

Get practice and tutorial help online! This interactive tutorial website provides algorithmically generated practice exercises that correlate directly to the exercises in the textbook. Students can retry an exercise as many times as they like with new values each time for unlimited practice and mastery. Every exercise is accompanied by an interactive guided solution that provides helpful feedback for incorrect answers, and students can also view a worked-out sample problem that steps them through an exercise similar to the one they're working on.

Instructor Supplements

Annotated Instructor's Edition (ISBN: 978-0-321-73082-4)

Includes answers to all exercises printed in blue on the same page as the exercises. Also includes the student answer section, for easy reference.

Instructor's Solutions Manual (ISBN: 978-0-321-73080-0)
By Judith Penna

Contains brief solutions to the even-numbered exercises in the exercise sets. Also includes fully worked-out annotated solutions for all the exercises (odd- and even-numbered) in the Mid-Chapter Reviews, the Summary and Reviews, and the Chapter Tests.

Instructor's Resource Manual with Printed Test Forms
(ISBN: 978-0-321-73085-5)
By Laurie Hurley

- Features resources and teaching tips designed to help both new and adjunct faculty with course preparation and classroom management.
- **New!** Includes a mini-lecture for each section of the text with objectives, key examples, and teaching tips.
- Additional resources include general first-time advice, sample syllabi, teaching tips, collaborative learning activities, correlation guide, video index, and transparency masters.
- Contains one diagnostic test, plus two cumulative tests per chapter, beginning with Chapter 2.
- Provides eight test forms for every chapter and six test forms for the final exam.
- For the chapter tests, four free-response tests are modeled after the chapter tests in the main text, two test forms are designed for a 50-minute class period, and two test forms are multiple-choice.
- For the final exam, four test forms are free-response and two are multiple-choice.
- Also includes extra practice exercises for select sections.

Additional Media Supplements

MyMathLab | **MyMathLab® Online Course (access code required)**

MyMathLab® is a text-specific, easily customizable online course that integrates interactive multimedia instruction with textbook content. MyMathLab gives you the tools you need to deliver all or a portion of your course online, whether your students are in a lab setting or working from home.

- **Interactive homework exercises,** correlated to your textbook at the objective level are algorithmically generated for unlimited practice and mastery. Most exercises are free-response and provide guided solutions, sample problems, and tutorial learning aids for extra help.

- **Personalized homework** assignments that you can design to meet the needs of your class are included. MyMathLab tailors the assignment for each student on the basis of their test or quiz scores. Each student receives a homework assignment that contains only the problems he or she still needs to master.

- **Personalized Study Plan,** generated when students complete a test or quiz or homework, indicates which topics have been mastered and links to tutorial exercises for topics students have not mastered. You can customize the Study Plan so that the topics available match your course content.

- **Multimedia learning aids,** such as video lectures and podcasts, animations, interactive games, and a complete multimedia textbook, help students independently improve their understanding and performance. You can assign these multimedia learning aids as homework to help your students grasp the concepts.

- **Homework and Test Manager** lets you assign homework, quizzes, and tests that are automatically graded. Select just the right mix of questions from the MyMathLab exercise bank, instructor-created custom exercises, and/or TestGen® test items.

- **Gradebook,** designed specifically for mathematics and statistics, automatically tracks students' results, lets you stay on top of student performance, and gives you control over how to calculate final grades. You can also add offline (paper-and-pencil) grades to the gradebook.

- **MathXL Exercise Builder** allows you to create static and algorithmic exercises for your online assignments. You can use the library of sample exercises as an easy starting point, or you can edit any course-related exercise.

- **Pearson Tutor Center** (www.pearsontutorservices.com) access is automatically included with MyMathLab. The Tutor Center is staffed by qualified math instructors who provide textbook-specific tutoring for students via toll-free phone, fax, email, and interactive Web sessions.

Students do their assignments in the Flash®-based MathXL Player, which is compatible with almost any browser (Firefox®, Safari™, or Internet Explorer®) on almost any platform (Macintosh® or Windows®). MyMathLab is powered by CourseCompass™, Pearson Education's online teaching and learning environment, and by MathXL®, our online homework, tutorial, and assessment system. MyMathLab is available to qualified adopters. For more information, visit www.mymathlab.com <http://www.mymathlab.com/> or contact your Pearson representative.

Math XL | **MathXL® Online Course (access code required)**

MathXL® is a powerful online homework, tutorial, and assessment system that accompanies Pearson Education's textbooks in mathematics or statistics.

With MathXL, instructors can

- create, edit, and assign online homework and tests using algorithmically generated exercises correlated at the objective level to the textbook.
- create and assign their own online exercises and import TestGen tests for added flexibility.
- maintain records of all student work tracked in MathXL's online gradebook.

With MathXL, students can

- take chapter tests in MathXL and receive personalized study plans and/or personalized homework assignments based on their test results.
- use the study plan and/or the homework to link directly to tutorial exercises for the objectives they need to study.
- access supplemental animations and video clips directly from selected exercises.

MathXL is available to qualified adopters. For information, visit our website at www.mathxl.com, or contact your Pearson representative.

TestGen® (www.pearsoned.com/testgen) enables instructors to build, edit, and print tests using a computerized bank of questions developed to cover all the objectives of the text. TestGen is algorithmically based, allowing instructors to create multiple but equivalent versions of the same question or test with the click of a button. Instructors can also modify test bank questions or add new questions. The software and test bank are available for download from Pearson Education's online catalog.

PowerPoint® Lecture Slides present key concepts and definitions from the text. Slides are available to download from within MyMathLab and from Pearson Education's online catalog.

Pearson Math Adjunct Support Center (www.pearsontutorservices.com/math-adjunct.html) is staffed by qualified instructors with more than 100 years of combined experience at both the community college and university levels. Assistance is provided for faculty in the following areas: suggested syllabus consultation, tips on using materials packed with your book, book-specific content assistance, and teaching suggestions, including advice on classroom strategies.

Acknowledgments

Our deepest appreciation to all of you who helped to shape the 8th Edition of *Developmental Mathematics* by reviewing and spending time with us on your campuses. In particular, we would like to thank the following reviewers:

Galen Adams, *Texas State Technical College, Harlingen*
Kim Banks, *Florence Darlington Technical College*
Alfred Basta
Jerry Becan, *University of Texas, San Antonio*
Susan Haley, *Florence Darlington Technical College*
Donna Harbin, *Maui Community College*
Greg Millican, *Northeast Alabama Community College*
Suzette Takas, *Central Arizona College*

The endless hours of hard work by Martha Morong and Geri Davis have led to products of which we are immensely proud. We also want to thank Judy Penna for writing the *Student's* and *Instructor's Solutions Manuals* and for her strong leadership in the preparation of the printed supplements and the index. Other strong support has come from Laurie Hurley for the *Instructor's Resource Manual with Printed Test Forms* and for accuracy checking, along with checker Holly Martinez and proofreader Patty LaGree. Michelle Lanosga assisted with applications research, and Becky Troutman provided the glossary and the index of applications. We also wish to recognize Tom Atwater and Patty Schwarzkopf, who wrote video scripts and presented videos along with Margaret Donlan, Clem Vance, and authors Judy Penna, Barbara Johnson, and David Ellenbogen.

In addition, a number of people at Pearson have contributed in special ways to the development and production of this textbook, including the Developmental Math team: Vice President, Executive Director of Development Carol Trueheart, Senior Development Editor Dawn Nuttall, Production Manager Ron Hampton, Senior Designer Beth Paquin, Associate Content Editor Christine Whitlock, Assistant Editor Jonathan Wooding, and Associate Media Producer Nathaniel Koven. Executive Editor Cathy Cantin and Executive Marketing Manager Michelle Renda encouraged our vision and provided marketing insight. Kari Heen, Executive Content Editor, deserves special recognition for overseeing every phase of the project and keeping it moving.

Whole Numbers

Real-World Application

Kingda Ka, in Six Flags Great Adventure, New Jersey, and Top Thrill Dragster, in Cedar Point, Ohio, are the two fastest roller coasters in the world. Kingda Ka is 3118 ft long, and Top Thrill Dragster is 2800 ft long. How much longer is Kingda Ka than Top Thrill Dragster?

Source: ultimaterollercoaster.com

This problem appears as Exercise 1 in Section 1.5.

1.1

Standard Notation; Order

OBJECTIVES

a Give the meaning of digits in standard notation.

b Convert from standard notation to expanded notation.

c Convert between standard notation and word names.

d Use < or > for ☐ to write a true sentence in a situation like 6 ☐ 10.

TO THE STUDENT

At the front of the text, you will find the Bittinger Student Organizer card. This pullout card will help you keep track of important dates and useful contact information. You can also use it to plan time for class, study, work, and relaxation. By managing your time wisely, you will provide yourself the best possible opportunity to be successful in this course.

What does the digit 2 mean in each number?

1. 526,555

2. 265,789

3. 42,789,654

4. 24,789,654

5. 8924

6. 5,643,201

Answers

1. 2 ten thousands **2.** 2 hundred thousands
3. 2 millions **4.** 2 ten millions **5.** 2 tens
6. 2 hundreds

We study mathematics in order to be able to solve problems. In this section, we study how numbers are named. We begin with the concept of place value.

a Place Value

Consider the numbers in the following table.

Three Most Populous Countries in the World

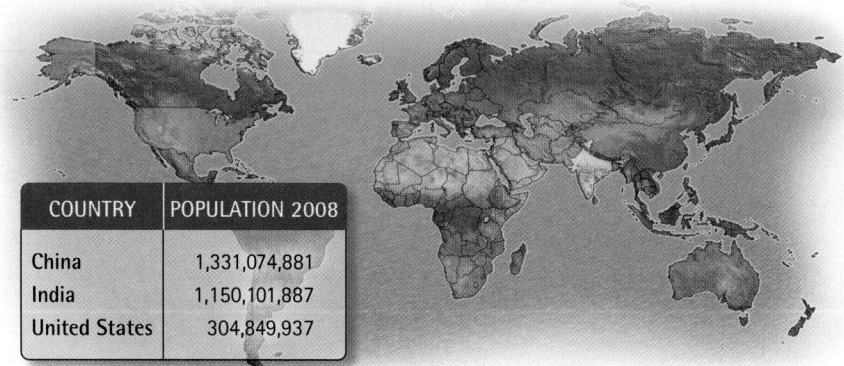

COUNTRY	POPULATION 2008
China	1,331,074,881
India	1,150,101,887
United States	304,849,937

SOURCE: msnu.edu

A **digit** is a number 0, 1, 2, 3, 4, 5, 6, 7, 8, or 9 that names a place-value location. For large numbers, digits are separated by commas into groups of three, called **periods**. Each period has a name: *ones, thousands, millions, billions, trillions,* and so on. To understand the population of India in the table above, we can use a **place-value chart**, as shown below.

PLACE-VALUE CHART														
Periods →	Trillions			Billions			Millions			Thousands			Ones		
						1	1	5	0	1	0	1	8	8	7
	Hundreds	Tens	Ones	Hundreds	Tens	Ones	Hundreds	Tens	Ones	Hundreds	Tens	Ones	Hundreds	Tens	Ones

1 billion   150 millions   101 thousands   887 ones

EXAMPLES In each of the following numbers, what does the digit 8 mean?

1. 278,342   8 thousands
2. 872,342   8 hundred thousands
3. 28,343,399,223   8 billions
4. 1,023,850   8 hundreds
5. 98,413,099   8 millions
6. 6328   8 ones

Do Margin Exercises 1–6 (in the margin at left).

EXAMPLE 7 *Hurricane Relief.* Private donations for relief for Hurricanes Katrina and Rita, which struck the Gulf Coast of the United States in 2005, totaled $3,378,185,879. What does each digit name?

Source: The Center on Philanthropy at Indiana University

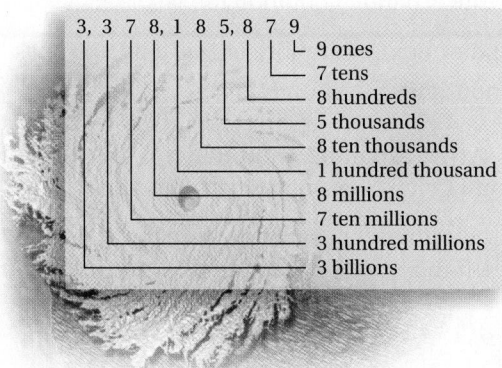

3, 3 7 8, 1 8 5, 8 7 9
- 9 ones
- 7 tens
- 8 hundreds
- 5 thousands
- 8 ten thousands
- 1 hundred thousand
- 8 millions
- 7 ten millions
- 3 hundred millions
- 3 billions

Do Exercise 7.

Do Exercise 7.

b Converting from Standard Notation to Expanded Notation

To answer questions such as "How many?", "How much?", and "How tall?", we often use whole numbers. The set, or collection, of **whole numbers** is

0, 1, 2, 3, 4, 5, 6, 7, 8, 9, 10, 11, 12, ...

The set goes on indefinitely. There is no largest whole number, and the smallest whole number is 0. Each whole number can be named using various notations. The set 1, 2, 3, 4, 5, . . . , without 0, is called the set of **natural numbers**.

Consider the data in the table below showing the Advanced Placement exams taken most frequently by the class of 2007.

EXAM	NUMBER TAKEN
U.S. History	333,561
English Language and Composition	282,230
Calculus AB	211,693
Biology	144,796

SOURCE: The College Board

The number of Biology exams taken was 144,796. This number is expressed in **standard notation**. We write **expanded notation** for 144,796 as follows:

144,796 = 1 hundred thousand + 4 ten thousands
+ 4 thousands + 7 hundreds
+ 9 tens + 6 ones.

7. Federal Payroll. In December 2006, the payroll for civilian employees of the federal government was $13,896,346,626. What does each digit name?

Source: U.S. Census Bureau

Answer

7. 1 ten billion; 3 billions; 8 hundred millions; 9 ten millions; 6 millions; 3 hundred thousands; 4 ten thousands; 6 thousands; 6 hundreds; 2 tens; 6 ones

Write expanded notation.

8. 1895

9. 333,561, the number of Advanced Placement U.S. History exams taken by the class of 2007

10. 1670 ft, the height of the Taipei 101 Tower in Taiwan

11. 2718 mi, the length of the Congo River in Africa

12. 104,094 square miles, the area of Colorado

EXAMPLE 8 Write expanded notation for 1815 ft, the height of the CN Tower in Toronto, Canada.

$$1815 = 1 \text{ thousand} + 8 \text{ hundreds} + 1 \text{ ten} + 5 \text{ ones}$$

EXAMPLE 9 Write expanded notation for 3400.

$$3400 = 3 \text{ thousands} + 4 \text{ hundreds} + 0 \text{ tens} + 0 \text{ ones,} \quad \text{or}$$
$$3 \text{ thousands} + 4 \text{ hundreds}$$

EXAMPLE 10 Write expanded notation for 211,693, the number of Advanced Placement Calculus exams taken by the class of 2007.

$$211,693 = 2 \text{ hundred thousands} + 1 \text{ ten thousand}$$
$$+ 1 \text{ thousand} + 6 \text{ hundreds} + 9 \text{ tens} + 3 \text{ ones}$$

Do Exercises 8–12.

(c) Converting Between Standard Notation and Word Names

We often use **word names** for numbers. When we pronounce a number, we are speaking its word name. Russia won 72 medals in the 2008 Summer Olympics in Beijing, China. A word name for 72 is "seventy-two." Word names for some two-digit numbers like 36, 51, and 72 use hyphens. Others like 17 use only one word, "seventeen."

2008 Summer Olympics Medal Count

COUNTRY	GOLD	SILVER	BRONZE	TOTAL
United States of America	36	38	36	110
People's Republic of China	51	21	28	100
Russia	23	21	28	72
Great Britain	19	13	15	47
Australia	14	15	17	46

SOURCE: beijing2008.cn

Answers

8. 1 thousand + 8 hundreds + 9 tens + 5 ones
9. 3 hundred thousands + 3 ten thousands + 3 thousands + 5 hundreds + 6 tens + 1 one
10. 1 thousand + 6 hundreds + 7 tens + 0 ones, or 1 thousand + 6 hundreds + 7 tens
11. 2 thousands + 7 hundreds + 1 ten + 8 ones
12. 1 hundred thousand + 0 ten thousands + 4 thousands + 0 hundreds + 9 tens + 4 ones, or 1 hundred thousand + 4 thousands + 9 tens + 4 ones

EXAMPLES Write a word name.

11. 36, the number of gold medals won by the United States

Thirty-six

12. 15, the number of silver medals won by Australia

Fifteen

13. 100, the total number of medals won by the People's Republic of China

One hundred

Do Exercises 13-15.

For word names for larger numbers, we begin at the left with the largest period. The number named in the period is followed by the name of the period; then a comma is written and the next number and period are named. Note that the name of the ones period is not included in the word name for a whole number.

EXAMPLE 14 Write a word name for 46,605,314,732.

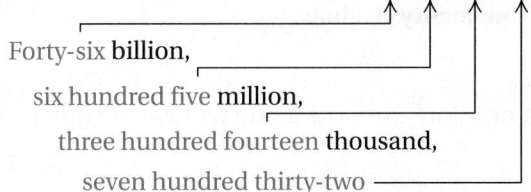

Forty-six **billion,**

six hundred five **million,**

three hundred fourteen **thousand,**

seven hundred thirty-two

The word "and" *should not* appear in word names for whole numbers. Although we commonly hear such expressions as "two hundred *and* one," the use of "and" is not, strictly speaking, correct in word names for whole numbers. For decimal notation, it is appropriate to use "and" for the decimal point. For example, 317.4 is read as "three hundred seventeen *and* four tenths."

Do Exercises 16-19.

EXAMPLE 15 Write standard notation.

Five hundred six **million,**

three hundred forty-five **thousand,**

two hundred twelve

Standard notation is 506,345,212.

Do Exercise 20.

Write a word name. (Refer to the table on the previous page.)

13. 46, the total number of medals won by Australia

14. 13, the number of silver medals won by Great Britain

15. 28, the number of bronze medals won by Russia

Write a word name.

16. 204

17. $52,177, the average salary offered to computer science majors who graduated from college in 2007
Source: CollegeRecruiter.com

18. 1,879,204

19. 6,677,602,292, the world population in 2008
Source: U.S. Census Bureau

20. Write standard notation.

Two hundred thirteen million, one hundred five thousand, three hundred twenty-nine

Answers

13. Forty-six **14.** Thirteen **15.** Twenty-eight **16.** Two hundred four **17.** Fifty-two thousand, one hundred seventy-seven **18.** One million, eight hundred seventy-nine thousand, two hundred four **19.** Six billion, six hundred seventy-seven million, six hundred two thousand, two hundred ninety-two **20.** 213,105,329

 Order

We know that 2 is not the same as 5. We express this by the sentence $2 \neq 5$. We also know that 2 is less than 5. We symbolize this by the expression $2 < 5$. We can see this order on the number line: 2 is to the left of 5. The number 0 is the smallest whole number.

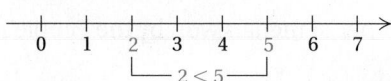

> ### ORDER OF WHOLE NUMBERS
>
> For any whole numbers a and b:
>
> 1. $a < b$ (read "a is less than b") is true when a is to the left of b on the number line.
> 2. $a > b$ (read "a is greater than b") is true when a is to the right of b on the number line.
>
> We call $<$ and $>$ **inequality symbols**.

EXAMPLE 16 Use $<$ or $>$ for ☐ to write a true sentence: $7 \ \square \ 11$.

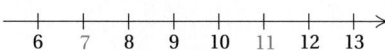

Since 7 is to the left of 11 on the number line, $7 < 11$.

EXAMPLE 17 Use $<$ or $>$ for ☐ to write a true sentence: $92 \ \square \ 87$.

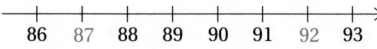

Since 92 is to the right of 87 on the number line, $92 > 87$.

A sentence like $8 + 5 = 13$ is called an **equation**. It is a *true* equation. The equation $4 + 8 = 11$ is a *false* equation. A sentence like $7 < 11$ is called an **inequality**. The sentence $7 < 11$ is a *true* inequality. The sentence $23 > 69$ is a *false* inequality.

| Do Exercises 21–26. |

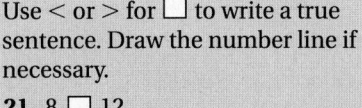

Use $<$ or $>$ for ☐ to write a true sentence. Draw the number line if necessary.

21. $8 \ \square \ 12$

22. $12 \ \square \ 8$

23. $76 \ \square \ 64$

24. $64 \ \square \ 76$

25. $217 \ \square \ 345$

26. $345 \ \square \ 217$

> ### STUDY TIPS
>
> #### TEXTBOOK SUPPLEMENTS
>
> Are you aware of all the supplements that exist for this textbook? See the preface for a description of each supplement including the *Student's Solutions Manual.*

Answers

21. $<$ 22. $>$ 23. $>$ 24. $<$
25. $<$ 26. $>$

a What does the digit 5 mean in each number?

1. 235,888
2. 253,777
3. 1,488,526
4. 500,736

Movie Receipts. Box-office receipts on the opening weekend of *Shrek the Third* were $121,629,270.
Source: Box Office Mojo

What digit names the number of:

5. thousands?
6. ten millions?

7. tens?
8. hundred thousands?

b Write expanded notation.

9. 5702
10. 3097
11. 93,986
12. 38,453

Stair-Climbing Races. The figure below shows the number of stairs in four buildings in which stair-climbing races are held. In Exercises 13–16, write expanded notation for the number of stairs in each race.

Stair-Climbing Races

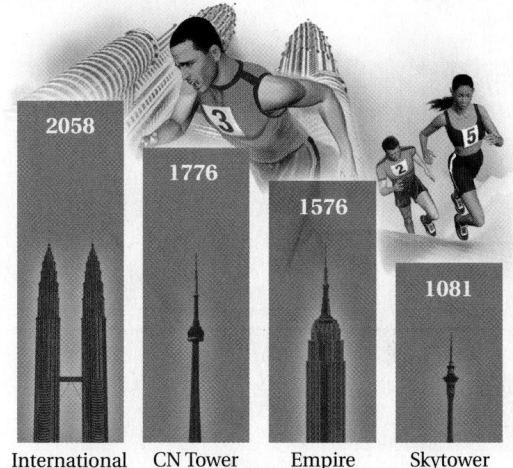

| 2058 | 1776 | 1576 | 1081 |

International Towerthon, Kuala Lumpur, Malaysia | CN Tower Stair Climb, Toronto, Ontario, Canada | Empire State Building Run-Up, New York | Skytower Vertical Challenge, Auckland, New Zealand

SOURCE: towerrunning.com

13. 2058 steps in the International Towerthon, Kuala Lumpur, Malaysia

14. 1776 steps in the CN Tower Stair Climb, Toronto, Ontario, Canada

15. 1576 steps in the Empire State Building Run-Up, New York City, New York

16. 1081 steps in the Skytower Vertical Challenge, Auckland, New Zealand

Population Projections. The table below shows the projected population in 2050 for six countries. In Exercises 17–22, write expanded notation for the population of the given country.

PROJECTED POPULATION IN 2050

COUNTRY	POPULATION
China	1,424,161,948
Hong Kong	6,172,725
Japan	99,886,568
Monaco	32,964
Surinam	617,249
United States	420,080,587

SOURCES: International Programs Center, U.S. Census Bureau, U.S. Department of Commerce

17. 1,424,161,948 in China

18. 6,172,725 in Hong Kong

19. 99,886,568 in Japan

20. 32,964 in Monaco

21. 617,249 in Surinam

22. 420,080,587 in the United States

 Write a word name.

23. 85

24. 48

25. 88,000

26. 45,987

27. 123,765

28. 111,013

29. 7,754,211,577

30. 43,550,651,808

Write a word name for the number in each sentence.

31. *Wilderness Areas.* In 2009, in the most sweeping land-protection law passed in fifteen years, all development was banned on huge swaths of land in nine states. The largest was in California, where 700,634 acres were newly designated as wilderness.
Source: The Wilderness Society

32. *Busiest Airport.* In 2006, the world's busiest airport, Hartsfield in Atlanta, had 84,846,639 passengers.
Source: Airports Council International World Headquarters, Geneva, Switzerland

Copyright © 2012 Pearson Education, Inc.

33. *Auto Racing.* Helio Castroneves, winner of the 2009 Indianapolis 500 auto race, won a record prize of $3,048,005.
Source: ESPN

34. *College Football.* The 2008 Rose Bowl game was attended by 93,923 fans.
Source: Fox Sports

Write standard notation.

35. Two million, two hundred thirty-three thousand, eight hundred twelve

36. Three hundred fifty-four thousand, seven hundred two

37. Eight billion

38. Seven hundred million

39. Fifty thousand, three hundred twenty-four

40. Twenty-six billion

41. Six hundred thirty-two thousand, eight hundred ninety-six

42. Seventeen thousand, one hundred twelve

Write standard notation for the number in each sentence.

43. *Ice Cream Purchases.* Americans buy one billion, six hundred million gallons of ice cream and frozen desserts each year.
Source: International Dairy Foods Association

44. *Learning a Language.* There are two hundred million Chinese children studying English.
Source: U.S. Department of Education

45. *Pacific Ocean.* The area of the Pacific Ocean is sixty-four million, one hundred eighty-six thousand square miles.

46. The average distance from the sun to Neptune is two billion, seven hundred ninety-three million miles.

d   Use < or > for ☐ to write a true sentence. Draw the number line if necessary.

47. 0 ☐ 17   **48.** 32 ☐ 0   **49.** 34 ☐ 12   **50.** 28 ☐ 18

51. 1000 ☐ 1001   **52.** 77 ☐ 117   **53.** 133 ☐ 132   **54.** 999 ☐ 997

55. 460 ☐ 17   **56.** 345 ☐ 456   **57.** 37 ☐ 11   **58.** 12 ☐ 32

New Book Titles.   The number of new book titles published in the United States in each of three recent years is shown in the table below. Use this table to do Exercises 59 and 60.

YEAR	NEW BOOK TITLES
2004	190,078
2005	172,000
2007	276,649

SOURCE: R. R. Bowker

59. Write an inequality to compare the number of new titles published in 2004 and in 2005.

60. Write an inequality to compare the number of new titles published in 2005 and in 2007.

61. *Wind-Power Capacity.*   Wind-power capacity in the United States has increased from 1694 megawatts installed in 2001 to 5249 megawatts installed in 2007. Write an inequality to compare these numbers of megawatts of wind power installed.

U. S. Wind-Power Boom

SOURCE: American Wind Energy Association

62. *Life Expectancy.*   The life expectancy of a female in the United States in 2015 is predicted to be about 82 yr and that of a male about 76 yr. Write an inequality to compare these life expectancies.

Life Expectancy in the United States

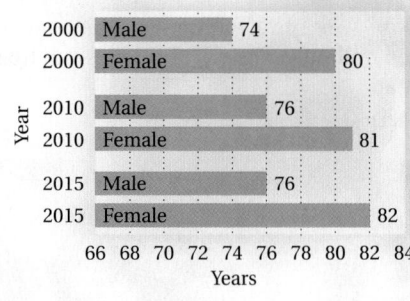

SOURCE: U.S. Census Bureau

Synthesis

To the student and the instructor: The Synthesis exercises found at the end of every exercise set challenge students to combine concepts or skills studied in that section or in preceding parts of the text. Exercises marked with a ▦ symbol are meant to be solved using a calculator.

63. How many whole numbers between 100 and 400 contain the digit 2 in their standard notation?

64. ▦ What is the largest number that you can name on your calculator? How many digits does that number have? How many periods?

Copyright © 2012 Pearson Education, Inc.

1.2 Addition and Subtraction

a Addition of Whole Numbers

Addition of whole numbers corresponds to putting things together.

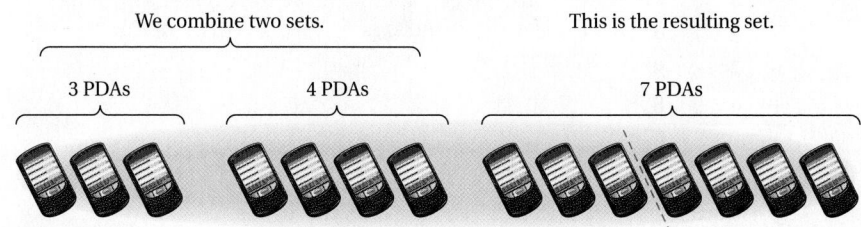

We combine two sets.   This is the resulting set.

3 PDAs   4 PDAs   7 PDAs

We say that the **sum** of 3 and 4 is 7. The numbers added are called **addends**. The addition that corresponds to the figure above is

$$3 + 4 = 7.$$
$$\downarrow \quad\quad \downarrow \quad\quad \downarrow$$
Addend   Addend   Sum

To add whole numbers, we add the ones digits first, then the tens, then the hundreds, then the thousands, and so on. Adding 0 to a number does not change the number: $a + 0 = 0 + a = a$. That is, $6 + 0 = 0 + 6 = 6$, or $198 + 0 = 0 + 198 = 198$. We say that 0 is the **additive identity**.

EXAMPLE 1   Add: $6878 + 4995$.

Place values are lined up in columns.

$$
\begin{array}{r}
\;6\;8\;7\;\overset{1}{8} \\
+\;4\;9\;9\;5 \\
\hline
3
\end{array}
$$

Add ones. We get 13 ones, or 1 ten $+$ 3 ones. Write 3 in the ones column and 1 above the tens. This is called *carrying*, or *regrouping*.

$$
\begin{array}{r}
\;6\;8\;\overset{1}{7}\;\overset{1}{8} \\
+\;4\;9\;9\;5 \\
\hline
7\;3
\end{array}
$$

Add tens. We get 17 tens, so we have 10 tens $+$ 7 tens. This is also 1 hundred $+$ 7 tens. Write 7 in the tens column and 1 above the hundreds.

$$
\begin{array}{r}
\;6\;\overset{1}{8}\;\overset{1}{7}\;\overset{1}{8} \\
+\;4\;9\;9\;5 \\
\hline
8\;7\;3
\end{array}
$$

Add hundreds. We get 18 hundreds, or 10 hundreds $+$ 8 hundreds. This is also 1 thousand $+$ 8 hundreds. Write 8 in the hundreds column and 1 above the thousands.

$$
\begin{array}{r}
\;\overset{1}{6}\;\overset{1}{8}\;\overset{1}{7}\;8 \\
+\;4\;9\;9\;5 \\
\hline
1\;1\;8\;7\;3
\end{array}
$$

Add thousands. We get 11 thousands.

We show you these steps for explanation. You need write only this.

$$
\begin{array}{r}
\overset{1}{}\;\overset{1}{}\;\overset{1}{} \\
6\;8\;7\;8 \\
+\;4\;9\;9\;5 \\
\hline
1\;1\;8\;7\;3
\end{array}
$$

$\leftarrow$ Addends

$\leftarrow$ Sum

OBJECTIVES

a Add whole numbers.

b Use addition in finding perimeter.

c Subtract whole numbers.

STUDY TIPS

One of the most important ways in which to improve your math study skills is to learn the proper use of the textbook. Here we highlight a few points that we consider most helpful.

USING THIS TEXTBOOK

Be sure to note the symbols **a**, **b**, **c**, and so on, that correspond to the objectives you are to master in each section. The first time you see them is in the margin at the beginning of the section; the second time is in the subheadings of each section; and the third time is in the exercise set for the section. You will also find symbols like [1.1a] or [1.2c] next to the skill maintenance exercises in each exercise set, in the mid-chapter review, and in the review exercises at the end of the chapter, as well as in the answers to the chapter tests. These objective symbols allow you to refer to the appropriate place in the text when you need to review a topic.

EXAMPLE 2 Add: 391 + 276 + 789 + 498.

$$
\begin{array}{r}
\overset{\scriptstyle 2}{} \\
3\;9\;|\;1 \\
2\;7\;|\;6 \\
7\;8\;|\;9 \\
+\;4\;9\;|\;8 \\
\hline
|\;4
\end{array}
$$

Add ones. We get 24, so we have 2 tens + 4 ones. Write 4 in the ones column and 2 above the tens.

$$
\begin{array}{r}
\overset{\scriptstyle 3}{}\overset{\scriptstyle 2}{} \\
3\;|\;9\;|\;1 \\
2\;|\;7\;6 \\
7\;|\;8\;9 \\
+\;4\;|\;9\;8 \\
\hline
|\;5\;|\;4
\end{array}
$$

Add tens. We get 35 tens, so we have 30 tens + 5 tens. This is also 3 hundreds + 5 tens. Write 5 in the tens column and 3 above the hundreds.

$$
\begin{array}{r}
\overset{\scriptstyle 3}{}\overset{\scriptstyle 2}{} \\
|\;3\;|\;9\;1 \\
|\;2\;7\;6 \\
|\;7\;8\;9 \\
+\;|\;4\;9\;8 \\
\hline
1\;9\;5\;4
\end{array}
$$

Add hundreds. We get 19 hundreds.

Do Exercises 1–4.

Add.

1. 6203 + 3542

2.
$$
\begin{array}{r}
7\;9\;6\;8 \\
+\;5\;4\;9\;7 \\
\end{array}
$$

3.
$$
\begin{array}{r}
9\;8\;0\;4 \\
+\;6\;3\;7\;8 \\
\end{array}
$$

4.
$$
\begin{array}{r}
1\;9\;3\;2 \\
6\;7\;2\;3 \\
9\;8\;7\;8 \\
+\;8\;9\;4\;1 \\
\end{array}
$$

Calculator Corner

Adding Whole Numbers   This is the first of a series of *optional* discussions on using a calculator. A calculator is *not* a requirement for this textbook. Check with your instructor about whether you are allowed to use a calculator in the course.

There are many kinds of calculators and different instructions for their usage. We have included instructions here for a low-cost calculator. Be sure to consult your user's manual as well.

To add whole numbers on a calculator, we use the $\boxed{+}$ and $\boxed{=}$ keys. For example, to find 314 + 259 + 478, we press $\boxed{3}\;\boxed{1}\;\boxed{4}\;\boxed{+}\;\boxed{2}\;\boxed{5}\;\boxed{9}\;\boxed{+}\;\boxed{4}\;\boxed{7}\;\boxed{8}\;\boxed{=}$. The display reads $\boxed{1051}$, so 314 + 259 + 478 = 1051.

Exercises: Use a calculator to find each sum.

1. 73 + 48

2. 925 + 677

3. 826 + 415 + 691

4. 253 + 490 + 121

Answers

1. 9745   2. 13,465   3. 16,182
4. 27,474

b Finding Perimeter

Addition can be used when finding perimeter.

> ### PERIMETER
>
> The distance around an object is its **perimeter**.

EXAMPLE 3 Find the perimeter of the figure.

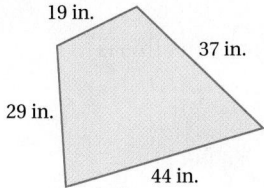

We add the lengths of the sides:

Perimeter = 29 in. + 19 in. + 37 in. + 44 in.

We carry out the addition as follows.

$$
\begin{array}{r}
\overset{2}{2}\,9 \\
1\,9 \\
3\,7 \\
+\,4\,4 \\
\hline
1\,2\,9
\end{array}
$$

The perimeter of the figure is 129 in.

> Do Exercises 5 and 6.

EXAMPLE 4 Find the perimeter of the octagonal (eight-sided) resort swimming pool.

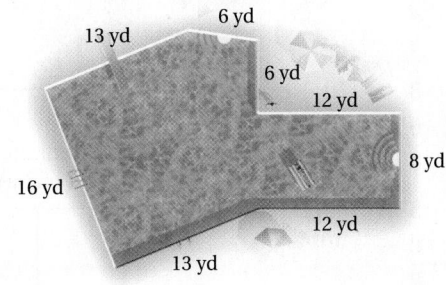

Perimeter = 13 yd + 6 yd + 6 yd + 12 yd + 8 yd
                   + 12 yd + 13 yd + 16 yd

The perimeter of the pool is 86 yd.

> Do Exercise 7.

Find the perimeter of each figure.

5.

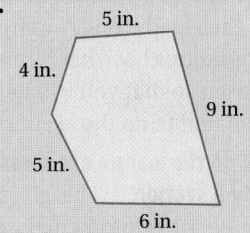

6.

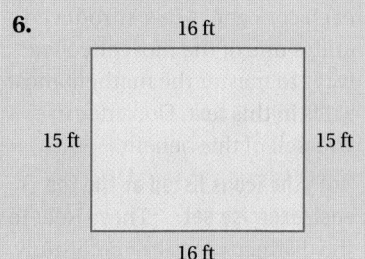

Solve.

7. Index Cards. Two standard sizes for index cards are 3 in. (inches) by 5 in. and 5 in. by 8 in. Find the perimeter of each type of card.

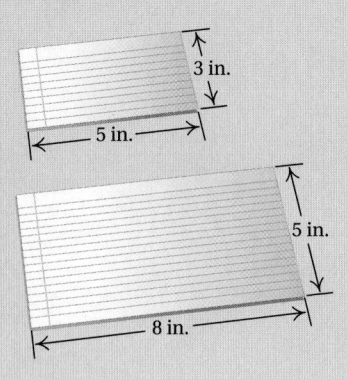

Answers

5. 29 in.   **6.** 62 ft   **7.** 16 in.; 26 in.

(c) Subtraction of Whole Numbers

Subtraction is finding the difference of two numbers. Suppose you pick 6 pints of blueberries and give your neighbor 2 pints.

The subtraction that represents this is

6   –   2   =   4.
↓   ↓   ↓
Minuend Subtrahend Difference

The **minuend** is the number from which another number is being subtracted. The **subtrahend** is the number being subtracted. The **difference** is the result of subtracting the subtrahend from the minuend.

In the subtraction above, note that the difference, 4, is the number we add to 2 to get 6. This illustrates the relationship between addition and subtraction and leads us to the following definition of subtraction.

> **SUBTRACTION**
>
> The difference $a - b$ is that unique whole number c for which $a = c + b$.

We see that $6 - 2 = 4$ because $4 + 2 = 6$.

To subtract numbers, we subtract the ones digits first, then the tens digits, then the hundreds, then the thousands, and so on.

EXAMPLE 5 Subtract: $9768 - 4320$.

$$
\begin{array}{r}
9\;7\;6\;\mathbf{8} \\
-\;4\;3\;2\;\mathbf{0} \\
\hline
8
\end{array}
$$
Subtract ones.

$$
\begin{array}{r}
9\;7\;\mathbf{6}\;8 \\
-\;4\;3\;\mathbf{2}\;0 \\
\hline
4\;8
\end{array}
$$
Subtract tens.

$$
\begin{array}{r}
9\;\mathbf{7}\;6\;8 \\
-\;4\;\mathbf{3}\;2\;0 \\
\hline
4\;4\;8
\end{array}
$$
Subtract hundreds.

We show these steps for explanation. You need write only this.

$$
\begin{array}{r}
\mathbf{9}\;7\;6\;8 \\
-\;\mathbf{4}\;3\;2\;0 \\
\hline
5\;4\;4\;8
\end{array}
$$
Subtract thousands.

$$
\begin{array}{r}
9\;7\;6\;8 \\
-\;4\;3\;2\;0 \\
\hline
5\;4\;4\;8
\end{array}
$$

STUDY TIPS

USING THIS TEXTBOOK

Read and study each step of each example. The examples include important side comments that explain each step. These examples and annotations have been carefully chosen so that you will be fully prepared to do the exercises.

Stop and do the margin exercises as you study a section. This gives you immediate reinforcement of each concept as it is introduced and is one of the most effective ways to master the mathematical skills in this text. Don't deprive yourself of this benefit!

Note the icons listed at the top of each exercise set. These refer to the distinctive multimedia study aids that accompany the book.

Because subtraction is defined in terms of addition, we can use addition to *check* subtraction.

Subtraction:

```
    9 7 6 8
 −  4 3 2 0
    5 4 4 8
```
?

Check by Addition:

```
    5 4 4 8
 +  4 3 2 0
    9 7 6 8
```

Do Exercise 8.

Do Exercise 8.

8. Subtract. Check by adding.

```
    7 8 9 3
 −  4 0 9 2
```

EXAMPLE 6 Subtract: 348 − 165.

We have

$$
\begin{array}{rl}
3 \text{ hundreds} + 4 \text{ tens} + 8 \text{ ones} = & 2 \text{ hundreds} + 14 \text{ tens} + 8 \text{ ones} \\
- 1 \text{ hundred} \ - 6 \text{ tens} - 5 \text{ ones} = & -1 \text{ hundred} \ - \ 6 \text{ tens} - 5 \text{ ones} \\
= & 1 \text{ hundred} \ + \ 8 \text{ tens} + 3 \text{ ones} \\
= & 183.
\end{array}
$$

First, we subtract the ones.

```
    3 4 8
 −  1 6 5
        3
```
Subtract ones.

We cannot subtract the tens because there is no whole number that when added to 6 gives 4. To complete the subtraction, we must *borrow* 1 hundred from 3 hundreds and regroup it with the 4 tens. Then we can do the subtraction 14 tens − 6 tens = 8 tens.

```
    2 14
    3 4 8
 −  1 6 5
        3
```
Borrow one hundred. That is, 1 hundred = 10 tens, and 10 tens + 4 tens = 14 tens. Write 2 above the hundreds column and 14 above the tens.

```
    2 14
    3 4 8
 −  1 6 5
    1 8 3
```
Subtract tens; subtract hundreds.

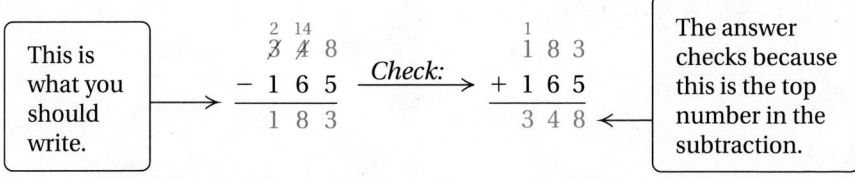

This is what you should write.

```
    2 14
    3 4 8
 −  1 6 5
    1 8 3
```
Check:
```
      1
    1 8 3
 +  1 6 5
    3 4 8
```

The answer checks because this is the top number in the subtraction.

Calculator Corner

Subtracting Whole Numbers To subtract whole numbers on a calculator, we use the [−] and [=] keys. For example, to find 63 − 47, we press [6][3][−][4][7][=]. The calculator displays [16], so 63 − 47 = 16. We can check this result by adding the subtrahend, 47, and the difference, 16. To do this, we press [1][6][+][4][7][=]. The sum is the minuend, 63, so the subtraction is correct.

Exercises: Use a calculator to perform each subtraction. Check by adding.

1. 57 − 29

2. 81 − 34

3. 145 − 78

4. 612 − 493

5.
```
    4 9 7 6
 −  2 8 4 8
```

6.
```
   1 2 , 4 0 6
 −    9 8 1 3
```

Answer

8. 3801

EXAMPLE 7 Subtract: 6246 − 1879.

```
        3 16
    6 2 4 6
  − 1 8 7 9
  ─────────
            7
```
We cannot subtract 9 ones from 6 ones, but we can subtract 9 ones from 16 ones. We borrow 1 ten to get 16 ones.

```
          13
      1   3 16
    6 2 4 6
  − 1 8 7 9
  ─────────
        6 7
```
We cannot subtract 7 tens from 3 tens, but we can subtract 7 tens from 13 tens. We borrow 1 hundred to get 13 tens.

```
    11  13
    5  1  3 16
    6 2 4 6
  − 1 8 7 9
  ─────────
    4 3 6 7
```
We cannot subtract 8 hundreds from 1 hundred, but we can subtract 8 hundreds from 11 hundreds. We borrow 1 thousand to get 11 hundreds. Finally, we subtract the thousands.

This is what you should write. →
```
    11  13
    5  1  3 16
    6 2 4 6
  − 1 8 7 9
  ─────────
    4 3 6 7
```
Check: →
```
    1 1 1
    4 3 6 7
  + 1 8 7 9
  ─────────
    6 2 4 6
```
← The answer checks because this is the top number in the subtraction.

Do Exercises 9 and 10.

Subtract. Check by adding.

9.
```
    8 6 8 6
  − 2 3 5 8
```

10.
```
    7 1 4 5
  − 2 3 9 8
```

EXAMPLE 8 Subtract: 902 − 477.

```
    8  9 12
    9 0 2
  − 4 7 7
  ───────
    4 2 5
```
We cannot subtract 7 ones from 2 ones. We have 9 hundreds, or 90 tens. We borrow 1 ten to get 12 ones. We then have 89 tens.

Do Exercises 11 and 12.

Subtract.

11.
```
    7 0
  − 1 4
```

12.
```
    5 0 3
  − 2 9 8
```

EXAMPLE 9 Subtract: 8003 − 3667.

```
    7  9  9 13
    8 0 0 3
  − 3 6 6 7
  ─────────
    4 3 3 6
```
We have 8 thousands, or 800 tens. We borrow 1 ten to get 13 ones. We then have 799 tens.

EXAMPLES

10. Subtract: 6000 − 3762.
```
    5  9  9 10
    6 0 0 0
  − 3 7 6 2
  ─────────
    2 2 3 8
```

11. Subtract: 6024 − 2968.
```
           11
    5  9  1 14
    6 0 2 4
  − 2 9 6 8
  ─────────
    3 0 5 6
```

Do Exercises 13–16.

Subtract.

13.
```
    7 0 0 7
  − 6 3 4 9
```

14.
```
    6 0 0 0
  − 3 1 4 9
```

15.
```
    9 0 3 5
  − 7 4 8 9
```

16.
```
    2 0 0 1
  −   1 2 4
```

Answers

9. 6328 **10.** 4747 **11.** 56 **12.** 205
13. 658 **14.** 2851 **15.** 1546 **16.** 1877

a Add.

1.
```
  3 6 4
+   2 3
```

2.
```
  1 5 2 1
+   3 4 8
```

3.
```
  8 6
+ 7 8
```

4.
```
  7 3
+ 6 9
```

5.
```
  1 7 1 6
+ 3 4 8 2
```

6.
```
  7 5 0 3
+ 2 6 8 3
```

7.
```
  4 8 2 5
+ 1 7 8 3
```

8.
```
  3 6 5 4
+ 2 7 0 0
```

9. 8113 + 390

10. 271 + 3338

11. 356 + 4910

12. 280 + 34,902

13.
```
  2 3,4 4 3
+ 1 0,9 8 9
```

14.
```
  4 5,8 7 9
+ 2 1,7 8 6
```

15.
```
  7 7,5 4 3
+ 2 3,7 6 7
```

16.
```
  9 9,9 9 9
+       1 1 2
```

17.
```
  1 2,0 7 0
    2,9 5 4
+   3,4 0 0
```

18.
```
  4 2,4 8 7
  8 3,1 4 1
+ 3 6,7 1 2
```

19.
```
  4 8 3 5
    7 2 9
  9 2 0 4
  8 9 8 6
+ 7 9 3 1
```

20.
```
  9 8 9
  5 6 6
  8 3 4
  9 2 0
+ 7 0 3
```

b Find the perimeter of each figure.

21.

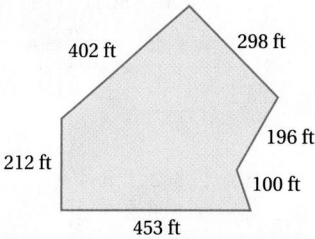

22.

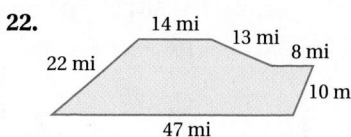

23. Find the perimeter of a standard hockey rink.

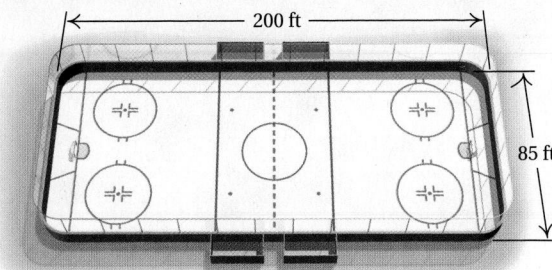

200 ft

85 ft

24. In Major League Baseball, how far does a batter travel in circling the bases when a home run has been hit?

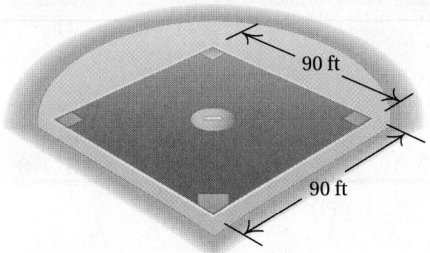

90 ft

90 ft

C   Subtract. Check by adding.

25.   6 5
     − 2 1

26.   8 7
     − 3 4

27.   8 6 6
     − 3 3 3

28.   5 2 6
     − 3 2 3

29.   5 6 3
     − 1 9 4

30.   7 9 5
     − 3 9 8

31.   3 9 1
     − 3 6 5

32.   3 1 6
     − 2 4 7

33. 981 − 747

34. 887 − 698

35. 683 − 266

36. 342 − 217

37.   7 7 6 9
     − 2 3 8 7

38.   6 4 3 1
     − 2 8 9 6

39.   4 5 1 2
     − 1 7 3 4

40.   8 3 6 4
     − 5 3 7 5

41. 5318 − 2249

42. 9241 − 5643

43. 3947 − 2858

44. 7583 − 3641

45.   1 2,6 4 7
     − 4,8 9 9

46.   1 6,2 2 2
     − 5,8 8 8

47.   5 1,3 4 2
     − 4 7,1 9 8

48.   3 2,1 9 4
     − 2 9,2 3 6

Copyright © 2012 Pearson Education, Inc.

49. 7 6 4 0
  − 3 8 0 9

50. 5 2 8 0
  − 3 0 9 1

51. 6 8 0 8
  − 3 0 5 9

52. 9 4 0 5
  −   2 5 8

53. 2 3 0 0
  −   1 0 9

54. 7 5 0 0
  − 3 6 0 4

55. 6 0 0 7
  − 1 5 8 9

56. 8 0 0 3
  −   5 9 9

57. $90{,}237 - 47{,}209$

58. $84{,}703 - 298$

59. $101{,}734 - 5760$

60. $15{,}017 - 7809$

61. 7 0 0 0
  − 2 7 9 4

62. 8 0 0 1
  − 6 5 4 3

63. 3 9,0 0 0
  − 3 7,6 9 5

64. 1 7,0 0 0
  − 1 1,5 9 8

65. $10{,}008 - 19$

66. $40{,}006 - 147$

67. $50{,}001 - 1984$

68. $30{,}004 - 6749$

Skill Maintenance

The exercises that follow begin an important feature called *Skill Maintenance exercises*. These exercises provide an ongoing review of topics previously covered in the book. You will see them in virtually every exercise set. It has been found that this kind of continuing review can significantly improve your performance on a final examination.

69. Write a word name for 6,375,602.   [1.1c]

70. What does the digit 7 mean in 6,375,602?   [1.1a]

Synthesis

71. Fill in the missing digits to make the subtraction true:
        $9{,}\square 48{,}621 - 2{,}097{,}\square 81 = 7{,}251{,}140.$

72. A fast way to add all the numbers from 1 to 10 inclusive is to pair 1 with 9, 2 with 8, and so on. Use a similar approach to add all numbers from 1 to 100 inclusive.

1.3 Multiplication and Division; Rounding and Estimating

OBJECTIVES

a Multiply whole numbers.

b Use multiplication in finding area.

c Divide whole numbers.

d Round to the nearest ten, hundred, or thousand.

e Estimate sums, differences, products, and quotients by rounding.

SKILL TO REVIEW

Objective 1.2c: Subtract whole numbers.

Subtract.

1. $\begin{array}{r} 5\,6\,4 \\ -\,3\,9\,7 \end{array}$ 2. $\begin{array}{r} 7\,0\,3\,5 \\ -\,2\,9\,4\,4 \end{array}$

a Multiplication of Whole Numbers

Repeated Addition

The multiplication 3×5 corresponds to this repeated addition.

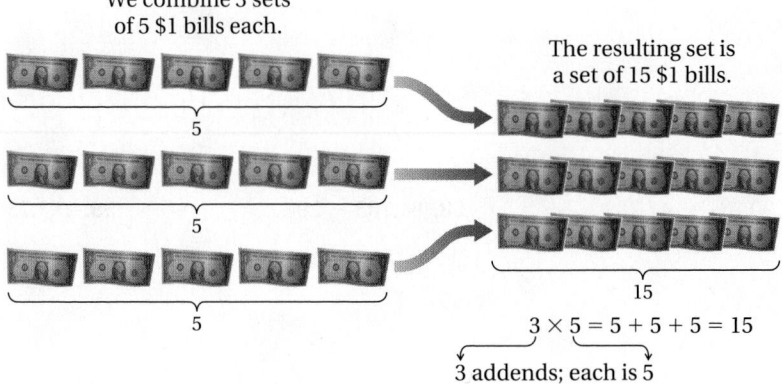

We combine 3 sets of 5 $1 bills each.

The resulting set is a set of 15 $1 bills.

$$3 \times 5 = 5 + 5 + 5 = 15$$

3 addends; each is 5

The numbers that we multiply are called **factors**. The result of the multiplication is called a **product**.

$$3 \quad \times \quad 5 \quad = \quad 15$$

Factor   Factor   Product

Rectangular Arrays

Multiplications can also be thought of as rectangular arrays. Each of the following corresponds to the multiplication 3×5.

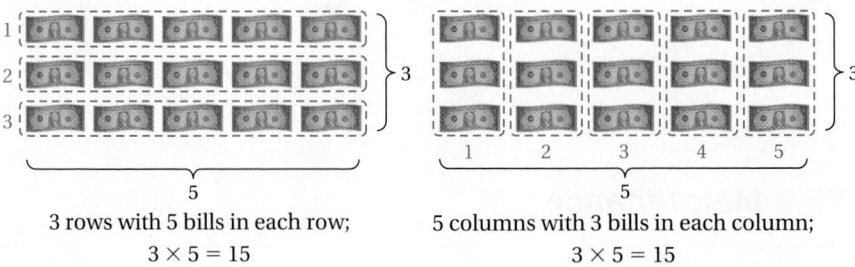

3 rows with 5 bills in each row; $3 \times 5 = 15$

5 columns with 3 bills in each column; $3 \times 5 = 15$

When you write a multiplication sentence corresponding to a real-world situation, you should think of either a rectangular array or repeated addition. In some cases, it may help to think both ways.

We have used an "×" to denote multiplication. A dot " · " is also commonly used. (Use of the dot is attributed to the German mathematician Gottfried Wilhelm von Leibniz in 1698.) Parentheses are also used to denote multiplication. For example,

$$3 \times 5 = 3 \cdot 5 = (3)(5) = 3(5) = 15.$$

Answers

Skill to Review:
1. 167   2. 4091

The product of 0 and any whole number is 0: $0 \cdot a = a \cdot 0 = 0$. For example, $0 \cdot 3 = 3 \cdot 0 = 0$. Multiplying a number by 1 does not change the number: $1 \cdot a = a \cdot 1 = a$. For example, $1 \cdot 3 = 3 \cdot 1 = 3$. We say that 1 is the **multiplicative identity**.

EXAMPLE 1 Multiply: 5×734.

We have

$$
\begin{array}{r}
7\ 3\ 4 \\
\times \qquad 5 \\
\hline
2\ 0 \\
1\ 5\ 0 \\
3\ 5\ 0\ 0 \\
\hline
3\ 6\ 7\ 0
\end{array}
$$

$2\ 0 \leftarrow$ Multiply the 4 ones by 5: $5 \times 4 = 20$.
$1\ 5\ 0 \leftarrow$ Multiply the 3 tens by 5: $5 \times 30 = 150$.
$3\ 5\ 0\ 0 \leftarrow$ Multiply the 7 hundreds by 5: $5 \times 700 = 3500$.
$3\ 6\ 7\ 0 \leftarrow$ Add.

Instead of writing each product on a separate line, we can use a shorter form.

$$
\begin{array}{r}
\overset{2}{7}\ \ 3\ \ 4 \\
\times \qquad 5 \\
\hline
0
\end{array}
$$

Multiply the ones by 5: $5 \cdot (4\ \text{ones}) = 20\ \text{ones} = 2\ \text{tens} + 0\ \text{ones}$. Write 0 in the ones column and 2 above the tens.

$$
\begin{array}{r}
\overset{1}{7}\ \overset{2}{3}\ \ 4 \\
\times \qquad 5 \\
\hline
7\ 0
\end{array}
$$

Multiply the 3 tens by 5 and add 2 tens: $5 \cdot (3\ \text{tens}) = 15\ \text{tens}$, $15\ \text{tens} + 2\ \text{tens} = 17\ \text{tens} = 1\ \text{hundred} + 7\ \text{tens}$. Write 7 in the tens column and 1 above the hundreds.

$$
\begin{array}{r}
\overset{1}{7}\ \overset{2}{3}\ \ 4 \\
\times \qquad 5 \\
\hline
3\ 6\ 7\ 0
\end{array}
$$

Multiply the 7 hundreds by 5 and add 1 hundred: $5 \cdot (7\ \text{hundreds}) = 35\ \text{hundreds}$, $35\ \text{hundreds} + 1\ \text{hundred} = 36\ \text{hundreds}$.

$$
\left.
\begin{array}{r}
\overset{1}{7}\ \overset{2}{3}\ \ 4 \\
\times \qquad 5 \\
\hline
3\ 6\ 7\ 0
\end{array}
\right\}
$$

You should write only this.

Do Exercises 1–4.

Multiplication of whole numbers is based on a property called the **distributive law**. It says that to multiply a number by a sum, $a \cdot (b + c)$, we can multiply each addend by a and then add like this: $(a \cdot b) + (a \cdot c)$. Thus, $a \cdot (b + c) = (a \cdot b) + (a \cdot c)$. For example, consider the following.

$4 \cdot (2 + 3) = 4 \cdot 5 = 20$ Adding first; then multiplying

$4 \cdot (2 + 3) = (4 \cdot 2) + (4 \cdot 3) = 8 + 12 = 20$ Multiplying first; then adding

The results are the same, so $4 \cdot (2 + 3) = (4 \cdot 2) + (4 \cdot 3)$.

STUDY TIPS

TIME MANAGEMENT

Time is the most critical factor in your success in learning mathematics. Have reasonable expectations about the time you need to study math.

Balancing work and study. Working 40 hours per week and taking 12 credit hours is equivalent to having two full-time jobs. It is challenging to handle such a load. If you work 40 hours per week, you will probably have more success in school if you take 3 to 6 credit hours. If you are carrying a full class load, you can probably work 5 to 10 hours per week. Be honest with yourself about how much time you have available to work, attend class, and study.

Multiply.

1. $\begin{array}{r} 5\ 8 \\ \times \quad 2 \\ \hline \end{array}$ 2. $\begin{array}{r} 3\ 7 \\ \times \quad 4 \\ \hline \end{array}$

3. $\begin{array}{r} 8\ 2\ 3 \\ \times \qquad 6 \\ \hline \end{array}$ 4. $\begin{array}{r} 1\ 3\ 4\ 8 \\ \times \qquad\quad 5 \\ \hline \end{array}$

Answers
1. 116   **2.** 148   **3.** 4938   **4.** 6740

Let's find the product 51×32. Since $32 = 2 + 30$, we can think of this product as

$$51 \times 32 = 51 \times (2 + 30) = (51 \times 2) + (51 \times 30).$$

That is, we multiply 51 by 2, then we multiply 51 by 30, and finally we add. We can write our work this way.

$$
\begin{array}{r}
5\ 1 \\
\times\ 3\ 2 \\
\hline
1\ 0\ 2 \\
1\ 5\ 3\ 0
\end{array}
$$

Multiplying by 2

Multiplying by 30. (We write a 0 and then multiply 51 by 3.)

> You may have learned that such a 0 need not be written. You may omit it if you wish. If you do omit it, remember, when multiplying by tens, to start writing the answer in the tens place.

We add to obtain the product.

$$
\begin{array}{r}
5\ 1 \\
\times\ 3\ 2 \\
\hline
1\ 0\ 2 \\
1\ 5\ 3\ 0 \\
\hline
1\ 6\ 3\ 2
\end{array}
$$

Adding to obtain the product

EXAMPLE 2 Multiply: 457×683.

$$
\begin{array}{r}
{}^{5}\ {}^{2}\ \ \\
6\ 8\ 3 \\
\times\ 4\ 5\ 7 \\
\hline
4\ 7\ 8\ 1
\end{array}
$$

Multiplying 683 by 7

$$
\begin{array}{r}
{}^{4}\ {}^{1}\ \ \\
{}^{5}\ {}^{2}\ \ \\
6\ 8\ 3 \\
\times\ 4\ 5\ 7 \\
\hline
4\ 7\ 8\ 1 \\
3\ 4\ 1\ 5\ 0
\end{array}
$$

Multiplying 683 by 50

$$
\begin{array}{r}
{}^{3}\ {}^{1}\ \ \\
{}^{4}\ {}^{1}\ \ \\
{}^{5}\ {}^{2}\ \ \\
6\ 8\ 3 \\
\times\ 4\ 5\ 7 \\
\hline
4\ 7\ 8\ 1 \\
3\ 4\ 1\ 5\ 0 \\
2\ 7\ 3\ 2\ 0\ 0 \\
\hline
3\ 1\ 2,\ 1\ 3\ 1
\end{array}
$$

Multiplying 683 by 400. (We write 00 and then multiply 683 by 4.)

Adding

Do Exercises 5–8.

Calculator Corner

Multiplying Whole Numbers   To multiply whole numbers on a calculator, we use the $\times$ and $=$ keys. For example, to find 13×47, we press $\boxed{1}\ \boxed{3}\ \boxed{\times}\ \boxed{4}\ \boxed{7}\ \boxed{=}$. The calculator displays 611, so $13 \times 47 = 611$.

Exercises: Use a calculator to find each product.

1. 56×8
2. 845×26
3. $5 \cdot 1276$
4. $126(314)$
5. $$\begin{array}{r} 3\ 7\ 6\ 0 \\ \times\ \ \ \ 4\ 8 \\ \hline \end{array}$$
6. $$\begin{array}{r} 5\ 2\ 1\ 8 \\ \times\ \ \ 4\ 5\ 3 \\ \hline \end{array}$$

Multiply.

5. $$\begin{array}{r} 4\ 5 \\ \times\ 2\ 3 \\ \hline \end{array}$$

6. 48×63

7. $$\begin{array}{r} 7\ 4\ 6 \\ \times\ \ 6\ 2 \\ \hline \end{array}$$

8. 245×837

Answers

5. 1035   **6.** 3024   **7.** 46,252   **8.** 205,065

EXAMPLE 3   Multiply: 306 × 274.

Note that 306 = 3 hundreds + 6 ones.

```
      2 7 4
    × 3 0 6    ┌ Multiplying by 6
    1 6 4 4   ←┤ Multiplying by 3 hundreds. (We write 00
  8 2 2 0 0   ←┘ and then multiply 274 by 3.)
  8 3,8 4 4     Adding
```

Do Exercises 9–12.

EXAMPLE 4   Multiply: 360 × 274.

Note that 360 = 3 hundreds + 6 tens.

```
      2 7 4    ┌ Multiplying by 6 tens. (We write 0 and
    × 3 6 0    │ then multiply 274 by 6.)
  1 6 4 4 0   ←┤ Multiplying by 3 hundreds. (We write 00
  8 2 2 0 0   ←┘ and then multiply 274 by 3.)
  9 8,6 4 0     Adding
```

Do Exercises 13–16.

b Finding Area

The area of a rectangular region can be considered to be the number of square units needed to fill it. Here is a rectangle 4 cm (centimeters) long and 3 cm wide. It takes 12 square centimeters (sq cm) to fill it.

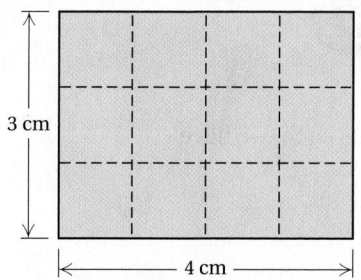

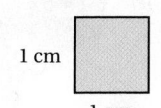

This is a square centimeter (a square unit).

1 cm
1 cm

In this case, we have a rectangular array of 3 rows, each of which contains 4 squares. The number of square units is given by 3 · 4, or 12. That is, $A = l \cdot w = 3\,\text{cm} \cdot 4\,\text{cm} = 12\,\text{sq cm}$.

EXAMPLE 5   *Table Tennis.*   Find the area of a standard table tennis table that has dimensions of 9 ft by 5 ft.

9 ft
5 ft

Multiply.

9.   4 7 2
       × 3 0 6

10. 408 × 704

11.   2 3 4 4
       × 6 0 0 5

12.   1 0 0 6
       ×   7 0 3

Multiply.

13.   4 7 2
        × 8 3 0

14.   2 3 4 4
       × 7 4 0 0

15. 100 × 562

16. 1000 × 562

Answers

9. 144,432   **10.** 287,232
11. 14,075,720   **12.** 707,218
13. 391,760   **14.** 17,345,600
15. 56,200   **16.** 562,000

Do Exercise 17.

17. Professional Pool Table. The playing area of a pool table used in professional tournaments is 50 in. by 100 in. (There are 6-in. wide rails on the outside that are not included in the playing area.) Determine the playing area.

If we think of filling the rectangle with square feet, we have a rectangular array. The length $l = 9$ ft and the width $w = 5$ ft. Thus the area A is given by the formula

$$A = l \cdot w = 9 \text{ ft} \cdot 5 \text{ ft} = 45 \text{ sq ft.}$$

c Division of Whole Numbers

Repeated Subtraction

Division of whole numbers applies to two kinds of situations. The first is repeated subtraction. Suppose we have 20 doughnuts, and we want to find out how many sets of 5 there are. One way to do this is to repeatedly subtract sets of 5 as follows.

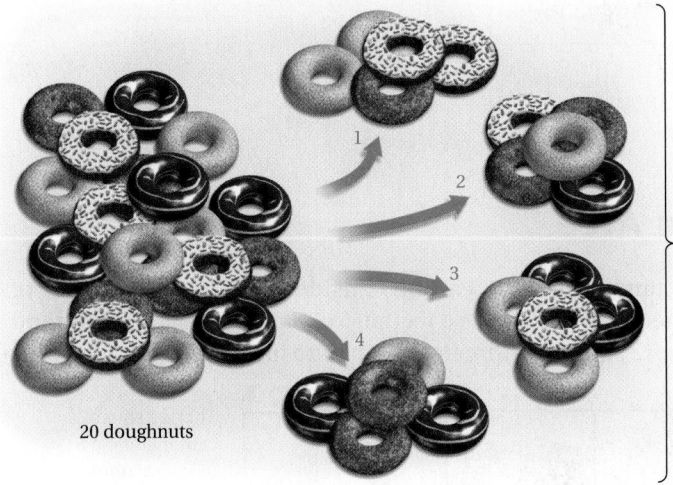

20 doughnuts

How many sets of 5 doughnuts each?

Since there are 4 sets of 5 doughnuts each, we have

$$20 \div 5 = 4.$$

Dividend   Divisor   Quotient

The division $20 \div 5$ is read "20 divided by 5." The **dividend** is 20, the **divisor** is 5, and the **quotient** is 4. We divide the *dividend* by the *divisor* to get the *quotient*.

We can also express the division $20 \div 5 = 4$ as

$$\frac{20}{5} = 4 \quad \text{or} \quad 5\overline{)20}.$$

Rectangular Arrays

We can also think of division in terms of rectangular arrays. Consider again the 20 doughnuts and division by 5. We can arrange the doughnuts in a rectangular array with 5 rows and ask, "How many are in each row?"

We can also consider a rectangular array with 5 doughnuts in each column and ask, "How many columns are there?" The answer is still 4.

Answer

17. 5000 sq in.

In each case, we are asking, "What do we multiply 5 by in order to get 20?"

Missing factor   Quotient

$$5 \cdot \boxed{} = 20 \qquad 20 \div 5 = \boxed{}$$

This leads us to the following definition of division.

DIVISION

The quotient $a \div b$, where $b \neq 0$, is that unique number c for which $a = b \cdot c$.

This definition shows the relation between division and multiplication. We see, for instance, that

$$20 \div 5 = 4 \quad \text{because} \quad 20 = 5 \cdot 4.$$

This relation allows us to use multiplication to check division.

EXAMPLE 6 Divide. Check by multiplying.

a) $16 \div 8$ 　　　　 b) $\dfrac{36}{4}$ 　　　　 c) $7\overline{)56}$

We do so as follows.

a) $16 \div 8 = 2$ 　　 *Check*: $8 \cdot 2 = 16.$

b) $\dfrac{36}{4} = 9$ 　　 *Check*: $4 \cdot 9 = 36.$

c) $\begin{array}{r} 8 \\ 7\overline{)56} \end{array}$ 　　 *Check*: $7 \cdot 8 = 56.$

Do Exercises 18–20.

Divide. Check by multiplying.

18. $9\overline{)45}$

19. $27 \div 3$

20. $\dfrac{48}{6}$

Let's consider some basic properties of division.

DIVIDING BY 1

Any number divided by 1 is that same number: $a \div 1 = \dfrac{a}{1} = a.$

For example, $6 \div 1 = 6$ and $\dfrac{15}{1} = 15.$

DIVIDING A NUMBER BY ITSELF

Any nonzero number divided by itself is 1: $a \div a = \dfrac{a}{a} = 1, \quad a \neq 0.$

For example, $7 \div 7 = 1$ and $\dfrac{22}{22} = 1.$

DIVIDENDS OF 0

Zero divided by any nonzero number is 0: $0 \div a = \dfrac{0}{a} = 0, \quad a \neq 0.$

For example, $0 \div 14 = 0$ and $\dfrac{0}{3} = 0.$

EXCLUDING DIVISION BY 0

Division by 0 is not defined: $a \div 0$, or $\dfrac{a}{0}$, is **not defined**.

For example, $16 \div 0$, or $\dfrac{16}{0}$, is not defined.

Why can't we divide by 0? Suppose the number 4 could be divided by 0. Then if ☐ were the answer, we would have

$4 \div 0 = $ ☐,

and since 0 times any number is 0, we would have

$4 = $ ☐ $\cdot 0 = 0.$ False!

Thus, the only possible number that could be divided by 0 would be 0 itself. But such a division would give us any number we wish. For instance,

$$0 \div 0 = 8 \quad \text{because} \quad 0 = 8 \cdot 0;$$
$$0 \div 0 = 3 \quad \text{because} \quad 0 = 3 \cdot 0; \quad \left.\right\} \quad \text{All true!}$$
$$0 \div 0 = 7 \quad \text{because} \quad 0 = 7 \cdot 0.$$

We avoid the preceding difficulties by agreeing to exclude division by 0.

Do Exercises 21–24.

Division with a Remainder

Suppose we have 22 cans of soda and want to pack them in cartons of 6 cans each. We could fill 3 cartons and have 4 cans left over.

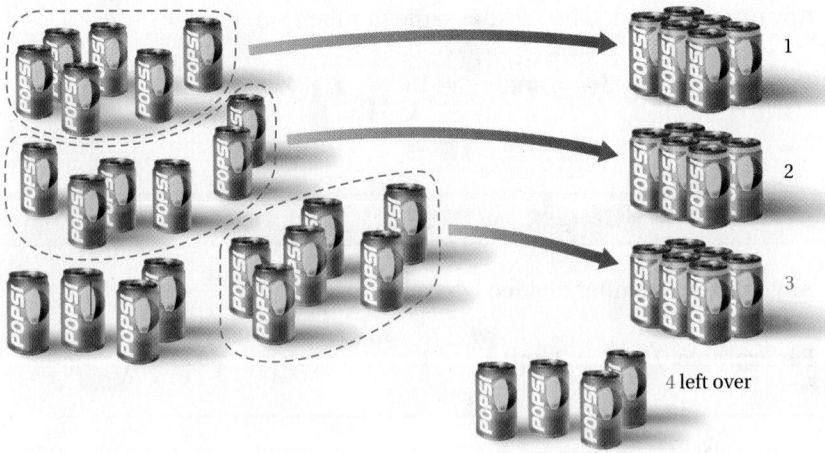

1
2
3
4 left over

Divide, if possible. If not possible, write "not defined."

21. $\dfrac{9}{9}$ **22.** $5 \div 0$

23. $0 \div 20$ **24.** $\dfrac{8}{1}$

STUDY TIPS

HIGHLIGHTING

- **Highlight important points.** You are probably used to highlighting key points as you study. If that works for you, continue to do so. But you will notice many design features throughout this book that already highlight important points. Thus you may not need to highlight as much as you generally do.
- **Highlight points that you do not understand.** Use a special mark to indicate trouble spots that can lead to questions to be asked during class or in a tutoring session.

Answers

21. 1   22. Not defined
23. 0   24. 8

We can think of this as the following division. The leftover cans are the **remainder**.

$$
\begin{array}{r}
3 \leftarrow \text{Quotient} \\
6\overline{)2\ 2} \\
\underline{1\ 8} \\
4 \leftarrow \text{Remainder}
\end{array}
$$

We express the result as

$$
\underset{\text{Dividend}}{22} \div \underset{\text{Divisor}}{6} = \underset{\text{Quotient}}{3} \text{ R } \underset{\text{Remainder}}{4}.
$$

Note that

Quotient · Divisor + Remainder = Dividend.

Thus we have

$3 \cdot 6 = 18$ Quotient · Divisor

and $18 + 4 = 22.$ Adding the remainder. The result is the dividend.

We now show a procedure for dividing whole numbers.

EXAMPLE 7   Divide and check: $4\overline{)3\ 4\ 5\ 7}$.

First, we try to divide the first digit of the dividend, 3, by the divisor, 4. Since $3 \div 4$ is not a whole number, we consider the first *two* digits of the dividend.

$$
\begin{array}{r}
8 \\
4\overline{)3\ 4\ 5\ 7} \\
\underline{3\ 2} \\
2
\end{array}
$$

Since $4 \cdot 8 = 32$ and 32 is smaller than 34, we write an 8 in the quotient above the 4. We also write 32 below 34 and subtract.

What if we had chosen a number other than 8 for the first digit of the quotient? Suppose we had used 7 instead of 8 and subtracted $4 \cdot 7$, or 28, from 34. The result would have been $34 - 28$, or 6. Because 6 is larger than the divisor, 4, we know that there is at least one more factor of 4 in 34, and thus 7 is too small. If we had used 9 instead of 8, then we would have tried to subtract $4 \cdot 9$, or 36, from 34. That difference is not a whole number, so we know 9 is too large. When we subtract, the difference must be smaller than the divisor.

Let's continue dividing.

$$
\begin{array}{r}
8\ 6 \\
4\overline{)3\ 4\ 5\ 7} \\
\underline{3\ 2} \\
2\ 5 \\
\underline{2\ 4} \\
1
\end{array}
$$

Now bring down the 5 in the dividend and consider $25 \div 4$. Since $4 \cdot 6 = 24$ and 24 is smaller than 25, we write 6 in the quotient above the 5. We also write 24 below 25 and subtract. The difference, 1, is smaller than the divisor, so we know that 6 is the correct choice.

STUDY TIPS

EXERCISES

- **Odd-numbered exercises.** Often an instructor will assign some odd-numbered exercises as homework. When you complete these, you can check your answers at the back of the book. If you miss any, check your work in the *Student's Solutions Manual* or ask your instructor for help.

- **Even-numbered exercises.** Whether or not your instructor assigns the even-numbered exercises, always do some on your own. Remember, there are no answers given for the chapter tests, so you need to practice doing exercises without answers. Check your answers later with a friend or your instructor.

Continuing, we have

$$
\begin{array}{r}
8\ 6\ 4 \\
4\ \overline{)\ 3\ 4\ 5\ 7} \\
3\ 2 \\
\overline{2\ 5} \\
2\ 4 \downarrow \\
\overline{1\ 7} \\
1\ 6 \\
\overline{1}
\end{array}
$$

Bring down the 7 and consider $17 \div 4$. Since $4 \cdot 4 = 16$ and 16 is smaller than 17, we write 4 in the quotient above the 7. We also write 16 below 17 and subtract.

$\leftarrow$ The remainder is 1.

Check: $864 \cdot 4 = 3456$ and $3456 + 1 = 3457$.

The answer is 864 R 1.

Do Exercises 25–27.

Do Exercises 25–27.

Divide and check.

25. $3\ \overline{)\ 2\ 3\ 9}$

26. $5\ \overline{)\ 5\ 8\ 6\ 4}$

27. $6\ \overline{)\ 3\ 8\ 5\ 5}$

Calculator Corner

Dividing Whole Numbers

To divide whole numbers on a calculator, we use the $\div$ and $=$ keys. For example, to divide 711 by 9, we press $\boxed{7}\ \boxed{1}\ \boxed{1}\ \boxed{\div}$ $\boxed{9}\ \boxed{=}$. The display reads $\boxed{79}$, so $711 \div 9 = 79$.

When we enter $453 \div 15$, the display reads $\boxed{30.2}$. Note that the result is not a whole number. This tells us that there is a remainder. The number 30.2 is expressed in decimal notation. Decimal notation will be studied in Chapter 3.

Exercises: Use a calculator to perform each division.

1. $19\overline{)532}$

2. $7\overline{)861}$

3. $9367 \div 29$

4. $12{,}276 \div 341$

EXAMPLE 8 Divide: $8904 \div 42$.

Because 42 is close to 40, we think of the divisor as 40 when we make our choices of digits in the quotient.

$$
\begin{array}{r}
2 \\
4\ 2\ \overline{)\ 8\ 9\ 0\ 4} \\
8\ 4 \downarrow \\
\overline{5\ 0}
\end{array}
$$

$\leftarrow$ *Think:* $89 \div 40$. We try 2. Multiply $42 \cdot 2$ and subtract. Then bring down the 0.

$$
\begin{array}{r}
2\ 1 \\
4\ 2\ \overline{)\ 8\ 9\ 0\ 4} \\
8\ 4 \\
\overline{5\ 0} \\
4\ 2 \downarrow \\
\overline{8\ 4}
\end{array}
$$

$\leftarrow$ *Think:* $50 \div 40$. We try 1. Multiply $42 \cdot 1$ and subtract. Then bring down the 4.

$$
\begin{array}{r}
2\ 1\ 2 \\
4\ 2\ \overline{)\ 8\ 9\ 0\ 4} \\
8\ 4 \\
\overline{5\ 0} \\
4\ 2 \\
\overline{8\ 4} \\
8\ 4 \\
\overline{0}
\end{array}
$$

$\leftarrow$ *Think:* $84 \div 40$. We try 2. Multiply $2 \cdot 42$ and subtract.

The remainder is 0, so the answer is 212.

Do Exercises 28 and 29.

Do Exercises 28 and 29.

------------------------------ *Caution!* ------------------------------

Be careful to keep the digits lined up correctly when you divide.

Divide.

28. $4\ 5\ \overline{)\ 6\ 0\ 3\ 0}$

29. $5\ 2\ \overline{)\ 3\ 2\ 8\ 8}$

Answers

25. 79 R 2   **26.** 1172 R 4
27. 642 R 3   **28.** 134
29. 63 R 12

Zeros in Quotients

EXAMPLE 9 Divide: 6341 ÷ 7.

```
        9
    7 ) 6 3 4 1   ←  Think: 63 ÷ 7 = 9. The first digit in the quotient
        6 3 ↓        is 9. We do not write the 0 when we find 63 − 63.
            4        Bring down the 4.
```

```
        9 0
    7 ) 6 3 4 1
        6 3 ↓
            4 1   ←  Think: 4 ÷ 7. If we subtract a group of 7's, such
                     as 7, 14, 21, etc., from 4, we do not get a whole
                     number, so the next digit in the quotient is 0.
                     Bring down the 1.
```

```
        9 0 5
    7 ) 6 3 4 1
        6 3
            4 1   ←  Think: 41 ÷ 7. We try 5. Multiply 7 · 5 and
            3 5      subtract.
              6   ←  The remainder is 6.
```

The answer is 905 R 6.

Do Exercises 30 and 31.

Do Exercises 30 and 31.

EXAMPLE 10 Divide: 8169 ÷ 34.

Because 34 is close to 30, we think of the divisor as 30 when we make our choices of digits in the quotient.

```
         2
   3 4 ) 8 1 6 9   ←  Think: 81 ÷ 30. We try 2. Multiply 34 · 2 and subtract.
         6 8 ↓        Then bring down the 6.
         1 3 6
```

```
         2 4
   3 4 ) 8 1 6 9
         6 8
         1 3 6   ←  Think: 136 ÷ 30. We try 4. Multiply 34 · 4 and
         1 3 6 ↓     subtract. The difference is 0, so we do not write it.
               9     Bring down the 9.
```

```
         2 4 0
   3 4 ) 8 1 6 9
         6 8
         1 3 6
         1 3 6
               9   ┌ Think: 9 ÷ 34. If we subtract a group of 34's, such as
               9 ←   34 or 68, from 9, we do not get a whole number, so the
               0     last digit in the quotient is 0.
               9   ← The remainder is 9.
```

The answer is 240 R 9.

Do Exercises 32 and 33.

Do Exercises 32 and 33.

Divide.

30. 6) 4 8 4 6

31. 7) 7 6 1 6

Divide.

32. 2 7) 9 7 2 4

33. 5 6) 4 4 , 8 4 7

Answers

30. 807 R 4   **31.** 1088
32. 360 R 4   **33.** 800 R 47

STUDY TIPS

TIME MANAGEMENT

- **A rule of thumb on study time.** Budget about 2–3 hours for homework and study for every hour you spend in class each week.

- **Scheduling your time.** Make an hour-by-hour schedule of your typical week. Include work, school, home, sleep, study, and leisure times. Try to schedule time for study when you are most alert. Choose a setting that will enable you to focus and concentrate. Plan for success and it will happen!

Round to the nearest ten.

34. 37

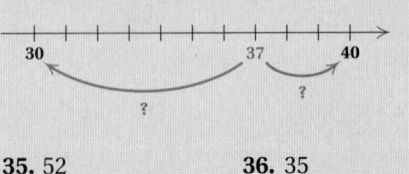

35. 52   **36.** 35

37. 73   **38.** 75

39. 88   **40.** 64

(d) Rounding

We round numbers in various situations when we do not need an exact answer. For example, we might round to see if we are being charged the correct amount in a store. We might also round to check if an answer to a problem is reasonable or to check a calculation done by hand or on a calculator.

To understand how to round, we first look at some examples using the number line. The number line displays numbers at equally spaced intervals.

EXAMPLE 11 Round 47 to the nearest ten.

47 is between 40 and 50. Since 47 is closer to 50, we round up to 50.

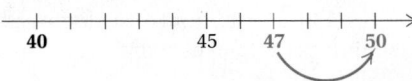

EXAMPLE 12 Round 42 to the nearest ten.

42 is between 40 and 50. Since 42 is closer to 40, we round down to 40.

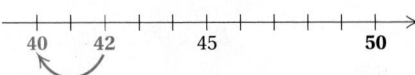

EXAMPLE 13 Round 45 to the nearest ten.

45 is halfway between 40 and 50. We could round 45 down to 40 or up to 50. We agree to round up to 50.

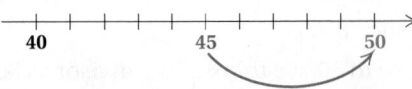

When a number is halfway between rounding numbers, round up.

Do Exercises 34–40.

We round whole numbers according to the following rule.

ROUNDING WHOLE NUMBERS

To round to a certain place:

a) Locate the digit in that place.

b) Consider the next digit to the right.

c) If the digit to the right is 5 or higher, round up. If the digit to the right is 4 or lower, round down.

d) Change all digits to the right of the rounding location to zeros.

Answers

34. 40   **35.** 50   **36.** 40   **37.** 70
38. 80   **39.** 90   **40.** 60

EXAMPLE 14 Round 6485 to the nearest ten.

a) Locate the digit in the tens place, 8.

    6 4 8 5
        ↑

b) Consider the next digit to the right, 5.

    6 4 8 5
        ↑

c) Since that digit, 5, is 5 or higher, round 8 tens up to 9 tens.

d) Change all digits to the right of the tens digit to zeros.

      6 4 9 0 ← This is the answer.

Do Exercises 41–44.

Round to the nearest ten.

41. 137   **42.** 473

43. 235   **44.** 285

EXAMPLE 15 Round 6485 to the nearest hundred.

a) Locate the digit in the hundreds place, 4.

    6 4 8 5
     ↑

b) Consider the next digit to the right, 8.

    6 4 8 5
     ↑

c) Since that digit, 8, is 5 or higher, round 4 hundreds up to 5 hundreds.

d) Change all digits to the right of hundreds to zeros.

      6 5 0 0 ← This is the answer.

Do Exercises 45–48.

Round to the nearest hundred.

45. 641   **46.** 759

47. 1871   **48.** 9325

EXAMPLE 16 Round 6485 to the nearest thousand.

a) Locate the digit in the thousands place, 6.

    6 4 8 5
   ↑

b) Consider the next digit to the right, 4.

    6 4 8 5
   ↑

c) Since that digit, 4, is 4 or lower, round down, meaning that 6 thousands stays as 6 thousands.

d) Change all digits to the right of thousands to zeros.

    6 0 0 0 ← This is the answer.

Do Exercises 49–52.

Round to the nearest thousand.

49. 7896   **50.** 8459

51. 19,343   **52.** 68,500

-------------------------------- *Caution!* --------------------------------

7000 is not a correct answer to Example 16. It is incorrect to round from the ones digit over, as follows:

    6485 → 6490 → 6500 → 7000.

Note that 6485 is closer to 6000 than it is to 7000.

Answers

41. 140   **42.** 470   **43.** 240   **44.** 290
45. 600   **46.** 800   **47.** 1900   **48.** 9300
49. 8000   **50.** 8000   **51.** 19,000
52. 69,000

Sometimes rounding involves changing more than one digit in a number.

EXAMPLE 17 Round 78,595 to the nearest ten.

a) Locate the digit in the tens place, 9.

$$7\ 8,5\ \underset{\uparrow}{9}\ 5$$

b) Consider the next digit to the right, 5.

$$7\ 8,5\ 9\ \underset{\uparrow}{5}$$

c) Since that digit, 5, is 5 or higher, round 9 tens to 10 tens. To carry this out, we think of 10 tens as 1 hundred + 0 tens and increase the hundreds digit by 1, to get 6 hundreds + 0 tens. We then write 6 in the hundreds place and 0 in the tens place.

d) Change the digit to the right of the tens digit to zero.

$$7\ 8,6\ 0\ 0\ \leftarrow \text{ This is the answer.}$$

Note that if we round this number to the nearest hundred, we get the same answer.

Do Exercises 53 and 54.

(e) Estimating

Estimating can be done in many ways. In general, an estimate made by rounding to the nearest ten is more accurate than one rounded to the nearest hundred, and an estimate rounded to the nearest hundred is more accurate than one rounded to the nearest thousand, and so on.

EXAMPLE 18 Estimate this sum by first rounding to the nearest ten:

78 + 49 + 31 + 85.

We round each number to the nearest ten. Then we add.

7 8	8 0
4 9	5 0
3 1	3 0
+ 8 5	+ 9 0
	2 5 0 ← Estimated answer

Do Exercises 55 and 56.

EXAMPLE 19 Estimate the difference by first rounding to the nearest thousand: 9324 − 2849.

We have

9 3 2 4	9 0 0 0
− 2 8 4 9	− 3 0 0 0
	6 0 0 0 ← Estimated answer

Do Exercises 57 and 58.

---

53. Round 48,968 to the nearest ten, hundred, and thousand.

54. Round 269,582 to the nearest ten, hundred, and thousand.

55. Estimate the sum by first rounding to the nearest ten. Show your work.

```
  7 4
  2 3
  3 5
+ 6 6
```

56. Estimate the sum by first rounding to the nearest hundred. Show your work.

```
  6 5 0
  6 8 5
  2 3 8
+ 1 6 8
```

57. Estimate the difference by first rounding to the nearest hundred. Show your work.

```
  9 2 8 5
− 6 7 3 9
```

58. Estimate the difference by first rounding to the nearest thousand. Show your work.

```
  2 3,2 7 8
− 1 1,6 9 8
```

Answers

53. 48,970; 49,000; 49,000
54. 269,580; 269,600; 270,000
55. 70 + 20 + 40 + 70 = 200
56. 700 + 700 + 200 + 200 = 1800
57. 9300 − 6700 = 2600
58. 23,000 − 12,000 = 11,000

EXAMPLE 20 Estimate the following product by first rounding to the nearest ten and then to the nearest hundred: 683×457.

Nearest ten

$$
\begin{array}{r}
6\ 8\ 0 \\
\times\quad 4\ 6\ 0 \\
\hline
4\ 0\ 8\ 0\ 0 \\
2\ 7\ 2\ 0\ 0\ 0 \\
\hline
3\ 1\ 2{,}8\ 0\ 0
\end{array}
\qquad
\begin{array}{l}
683 \approx 680 \\
457 \approx 460
\end{array}
$$

Nearest hundred

$$
\begin{array}{r}
7\ 0\ 0 \\
\times\quad 5\ 0\ 0 \\
\hline
3\ 5\ 0{,}0\ 0\ 0
\end{array}
\qquad
\begin{array}{l}
683 \approx 700 \\
457 \approx 500
\end{array}
$$

Exact

$$
\begin{array}{r}
6\ 8\ 3 \\
\times\quad 4\ 5\ 7 \\
\hline
4\ 7\ 8\ 1 \\
3\ 4\ 1\ 5\ 0 \\
2\ 7\ 3\ 2\ 0\ 0 \\
\hline
3\ 1\ 2{,}1\ 3\ 1
\end{array}
$$

We see that rounding to the nearest ten gives a better estimate than rounding to the nearest hundred.

Do Exercise 59.

59. Estimate the product by first rounding to the nearest ten and then to the nearest hundred. Show your work.

$$
\begin{array}{r}
8\ 3\ 7 \\
\times\ 2\ 4\ 5 \\
\end{array}
$$

EXAMPLE 21 Estimate the following quotient by first rounding to the nearest ten and then to the nearest hundred: $12{,}238 \div 175$.

Nearest ten

$$
\begin{array}{r}
6\ 8 \\
1\ 8\ 0\ \overline{)\ 1\ 2{,}2\ 4\ 0} \\
1\ 0\ 8\ 0 \\
\hline
1\ 4\ 4\ 0 \\
1\ 4\ 4\ 0 \\
\hline
0
\end{array}
$$

Nearest hundred

$$
\begin{array}{r}
6\ 1 \\
2\ 0\ 0\ \overline{)\ 1\ 2{,}2\ 0\ 0} \\
1\ 2\ 0\ 0 \\
\hline
2\ 0\ 0 \\
2\ 0\ 0 \\
\hline
0
\end{array}
$$

Do Exercise 60.

60. Estimate the quotient by first rounding to the nearest hundred. Show your work.

$$64{,}534 \div 349$$

In the sentence $7 - 5 = 2$, the equals sign indicates that $7 - 5$ is the *same* as 2. When we round to make an estimate, the outcome is rarely the same as the exact result. Thus we cannot use an equals sign when we round. Instead, we use the symbol $\approx$. This symbol means "**is approximately equal to**." In Example 19, for instance, we could write

$$9324 - 2849 \approx 6000.$$

Answers
59. $840 \times 250 = 210{,}000$;
$800 \times 200 = 160{,}000$
60. $64{,}500 \div 300 = 215$

61. Microwave Ovens. Suppose Ellen chooses a smaller model of microwave oven that costs $198. Estimate, by rounding to the nearest ten, the total cost of 12 ovens.

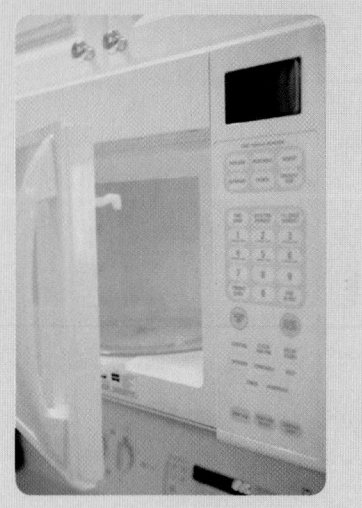

The next two examples show how estimating can be used in making a purchase.

EXAMPLE 22 *Microwave Ovens.* Ellen manages a small apartment building and is planning to purchase a new over-the-range microwave oven for each of the 12 units in the building. One model that she is considering costs $248. Estimate, by rounding to the nearest ten, the total cost of the purchase.

We have

$$
\begin{array}{r}
2\ 5\ 0 \\
\times\quad 1\ 0 \\
\hline
2\ 5\ 0\ 0.
\end{array}
$$

The microwave ovens will cost about $2500.

Do Exercise 61.

EXAMPLE 23 *Purchasing a New Car.* Jon and Joanna are shopping for a new car. They are considering buying a Saturn ASTRA 5-Door XE. The base price of the car is $16,495. A 4-speed automatic transmission package can be added to this, as well as several other options, as shown in the chart below. Jon and Joanna want to stay within a budget of $20,000.

Estimate, by rounding to the nearest hundred, the cost of the ASTRA with the automatic transmission package and all other options and determine whether this will fit within their budget.

Refer to the chart at right to do Margin Exercises 62 and 63.

62. By eliminating at least one option, determine how Jon and Joanna can buy an ASTRA and stay within their budget. Keep in mind that purchasing the sunroof also requires the purchase of air conditioning.

63. Elizabeth and C.J. are also considering buying a Saturn ASTRA 5-Door XE. Estimate, by rounding to the nearest hundred, the cost of this car with automatic transmission, air conditioning, and StabiliTrak Stability Control.

First, we list the base price of the car and then the cost of each of the options. We then round each number to the nearest hundred and add.

$$
\begin{array}{rr}
1\ 6,4\ 9\ 5 & 1\ 6,5\ 0\ 0 \\
1\ 3\ 2\ 5 & 1\ 3\ 0\ 0 \\
3\ 5\ 0 & 4\ 0\ 0 \\
9\ 6\ 0 & 1\ 0\ 0\ 0 \\
1\ 2\ 0\ 0 & 1\ 2\ 0\ 0 \\
2\ 5\ 0 & 3\ 0\ 0 \\
+\quad 4\ 9\ 5 & +\quad 5\ 0\ 0 \\
\hline
& 2\ 1,2\ 0\ 0 \leftarrow \text{Estimated cost}
\end{array}
$$

The estimated cost is $21,200. This exceeds Jon and Joanna's budget of $20,000, so they will have to forgo at least one option.

Do Exercises 62 and 63.

Answers

61. $2000   **62.** Eliminate either the automatic transmission or the sunroof. There are other correct answers as well.   **63.** $19,300

a Multiply.

1.
$$\begin{array}{r} 6\,5 \\ \times\ \ 8 \\ \hline \end{array}$$

2.
$$\begin{array}{r} 8\,7 \\ \times\ \ 4 \\ \hline \end{array}$$

3.
$$\begin{array}{r} 8\,7 \\ \times 1\,0 \\ \hline \end{array}$$

4.
$$\begin{array}{r} 2\,3\,4\,0 \\ \times 1\,0\,0\,0 \\ \hline \end{array}$$

5. $3 \cdot 509$

6. $7 \cdot 806$

7. $7(9229)$

8. $4(7867)$

9. $90(53)$

10. $60(78)$

11. $(47)(85)$

12. $(34)(87)$

13.
$$\begin{array}{r} 6\,4\,3 \\ \times\ \ 7\,2 \\ \hline \end{array}$$

14.
$$\begin{array}{r} 7\,7\,7 \\ \times\ \ 7\,7 \\ \hline \end{array}$$

15.
$$\begin{array}{r} 4\,4\,4 \\ \times\ \ 3\,3 \\ \hline \end{array}$$

16.
$$\begin{array}{r} 5\,4\,9 \\ \times\ \ 8\,8 \\ \hline \end{array}$$

17.
$$\begin{array}{r} 5\,6\,4 \\ \times 4\,5\,8 \\ \hline \end{array}$$

18.
$$\begin{array}{r} 4\,3\,2 \\ \times 3\,7\,5 \\ \hline \end{array}$$

19.
$$\begin{array}{r} 8\,5\,3 \\ \times 9\,3\,6 \\ \hline \end{array}$$

20.
$$\begin{array}{r} 3\,4\,6 \\ \times 6\,5\,9 \\ \hline \end{array}$$

21.
$$\begin{array}{r} 6\,4\,2\,8 \\ \times 3\,2\,2\,4 \\ \hline \end{array}$$

22.
$$\begin{array}{r} 8\,9\,2\,8 \\ \times 3\,1\,7\,2 \\ \hline \end{array}$$

23.
$$\begin{array}{r} 3\,4\,8\,2 \\ \times\ \ 1\,0\,4 \\ \hline \end{array}$$

24.
$$\begin{array}{r} 6\,4\,0\,8 \\ \times 6\,0\,6\,4 \\ \hline \end{array}$$

25.
$$\begin{array}{r} 8\,7\,6 \\ \times 3\,4\,5 \\ \hline \end{array}$$

26.
$$\begin{array}{r} 3\,5\,5 \\ \times 2\,9\,9 \\ \hline \end{array}$$

27.
$$\begin{array}{r} 7\,8\,8\,9 \\ \times 6\,2\,2\,4 \\ \hline \end{array}$$

28.
$$\begin{array}{r} 6\,5\,2\,1 \\ \times 3\,4\,4\,9 \\ \hline \end{array}$$

29.
$$\begin{array}{r} 5\,6\,0\,8 \\ \times 4\,5\,0\,0 \\ \hline \end{array}$$

30.
$$\begin{array}{r} 4\,5\,0\,6 \\ \times 7\,8\,0\,0 \\ \hline \end{array}$$

31.
$$\begin{array}{r} 5\,0\,0\,6 \\ \times 4\,0\,0\,8 \\ \hline \end{array}$$

32.
$$\begin{array}{r} 6\,0\,0\,9 \\ \times 2\,0\,0\,3 \\ \hline \end{array}$$

b Find the area of each region.

33.
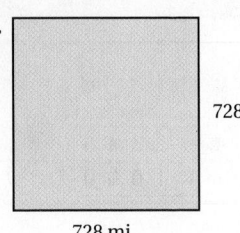
728 mi
728 mi

34.
129 yd
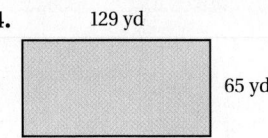
65 yd

35. Find the area of the region formed by the base lines on a Major League Baseball diamond.

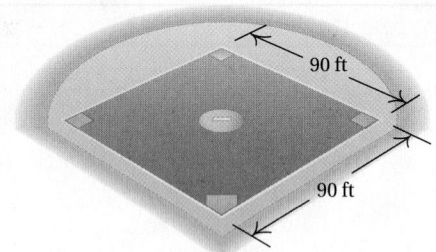
90 ft
90 ft

36. Find the area of a standard-sized hockey rink.

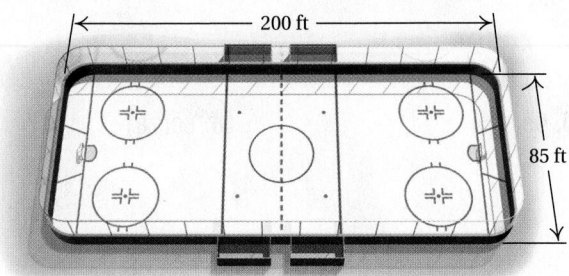
200 ft
85 ft

c Divide, if possible. If not possible, write "not defined."

37. $72 \div 6$

38. $54 \div 9$

39. $\dfrac{23}{23}$

40. $\dfrac{37}{37}$

41. $22 \div 1$

42. $\dfrac{56}{1}$

43. $\dfrac{0}{7}$

44. $\dfrac{0}{32}$

45. $\dfrac{16}{0}$

46. $74 \div 0$

47. $\dfrac{48}{8}$

48. $\dfrac{20}{4}$

Divide.

49. $277 \div 5$

50. $699 \div 3$

51. $864 \div 8$

52. $869 \div 8$

53. $4\overline{)1\ 2\ 2\ 8}$

54. $3\overline{)2\ 1\ 2\ 4}$

55. $6\overline{)4\ 5\ 2\ 1}$

56. $9\overline{)9\ 1\ 1\ 0}$

Copyright © 2012 Pearson Education, Inc.

57. 297 ÷ 4

58. 389 ÷ 2

59. 738 ÷ 8

60. 881 ÷ 6

61. 5) 8 5 1 5

62. 3) 6 0 2 7

63. 9) 8 8 8 8

64. 8) 4 1 3 9

65. 127,000 ÷ 10

66. 127,000 ÷ 100

67. 127,000 ÷ 1000

68. 4260 ÷ 10

69. 7 0) 3 6 9 2

70. 2 0) 5 7 9 8

71. 3 0) 8 7 5

72. 4 0) 9 8 7

73. 852 ÷ 21

74. 942 ÷ 23

75. 8 5) 7 6 7 2

76. 5 4) 2 7 2 9

77. 1 1 1) 3 2 1 9

78. 1 0 2) 5 6 1 2

79. 8) 8 4 3

80. 7) 7 4 9

81. 5) 8 0 4 7

82. 9) 7 2 7 3

83. 5) 5 0 3 6

84. 7) 7 0 7 4

85. 1058 ÷ 46

86. 7242 ÷ 24

87. 3425 ÷ 32

88. 4 8) 4 8 9 9

89. $24 \overline{)8880}$ **90.** $36 \overline{)7563}$ **91.** $28 \overline{)17,067}$ **92.** $36 \overline{)28,929}$

93. $80 \overline{)24,320}$ **94.** $90 \overline{)88,560}$ **95.** $285 \overline{)999,999}$

96. $306 \overline{)888,888}$ **97.** $456 \overline{)3,679,920}$ **98.** $803 \overline{)5,622,606}$

(d) Round to the nearest ten.

99. 48   **100.** 532   **101.** 463   **102.** 8945

103. 731   **104.** 54   **105.** 895   **106.** 798

Round to the nearest hundred.

107. 146   **108.** 874   **109.** 957   **110.** 650

111. 9079   **112.** 4645   **113.** 32,839   **114.** 198,402

Round to the nearest thousand.

115. 5876   **116.** 4500   **117.** 7500   **118.** 2001

119. 45,340   **120.** 735,562   **121.** 373,405   **122.** 6,713,255

(e) Estimate each sum or difference by first rounding to the nearest ten. Show your work.

123.
```
   7 8
 + 9 2
```

124.
```
   6 2
   9 7
   4 6
 + 8 1
```

125.
```
   8 0 7 4
 - 2 3 4 7
```

126.
```
   6 7 3
 -   2 8
```

Copyright © 2012 Pearson Education, Inc.

Estimate each sum or difference by first rounding to the nearest hundred. Show your work.

127. 7 3 4 8
        + 9 2 4 7

128. 5 6 8
         4 7 2
         9 3 8
        + 4 0 2

129. 6 8 5 2
        − 1 7 4 8

130. 9 4 3 8
        − 2 7 8 7

Estimate each sum or difference by first rounding to the nearest thousand. Show your work.

131. 9 6 4 3
         4 8 2 1
         8 9 4 3
        + 7 0 0 4

132. 7 6 4 8
         9 3 4 8
         7 8 4 2
        + 2 2 2 2

133. 9 2,1 4 9
        − 2 2,5 5 5

134. 8 4,8 9 0
        − 1 1,1 1 0

135. *Banquet Attendance.* Tickets to the annual awards banquet for the Riviera Swim Club cost $28 each. Ticket sales for the banquet totaled $2716. Estimate the number of people who attended the banquet by rounding the cost of a ticket to the nearest ten and the total sales to the nearest hundred.

136. *School Fundraiser.* For a school fundraiser, Charlotte sells trash bags at a price of $11 per box. If her sales total $2211, estimate the number of boxes sold by rounding the price per box to the nearest ten and the total sales to the nearest hundred.

Estimate each product by first rounding to the nearest ten. Show your work.

137. 4 5
        × 6 7

138. 5 1
        × 7 8

139. 3 4
        × 2 9

140. 6 3
        × 5 4

Estimate each product by first rounding to the nearest hundred. Show your work.

141. 8 7 6
        × 3 4 5

142. 3 5 5
        × 2 9 9

143. 4 3 2
        × 1 9 9

144. 7 8 9
        × 4 3 4

Estimate each quotient by first rounding to the nearest ten. Show your work.

145. 347 ÷ 73   **146.** 454 ÷ 87   **147.** 8452 ÷ 46   **148.** 1263 ÷ 29

Estimate each quotient by first rounding to the nearest hundred. Show your work.

149. 1165 ÷ 236   **150.** 3641 ÷ 571   **151.** 8358 ÷ 295   **152.** 32,854 ÷ 748

Planning a Kitchen.   Perfect Kitchens offers custom kitchen packages with three choices for each of four items: cabinets, countertops, appliances, and flooring. The chart below lists the price for each choice. Customers design their kitchens by making one selection from each group of items.

CABINETS	TYPE	PRICE
(a)	Oak	$7450
(b)	Cherry	8820
(c)	Painted	9630
COUNTERTOPS	TYPE	PRICE
(d)	Laminate	$1595
(e)	Solid surface	2870
(f)	Granite	3528
APPLIANCES	PRICE RANGE	PRICE
(g)	Low	$1540
(h)	Medium	3575
(i)	High	6245
FLOORING	TYPE	PRICE
(j)	Vinyl	$625
(k)	Travertine	985
(l)	Hardwood	1160

153. Estimate the cost of remodeling a kitchen with choices (a), (d), (g), and (j) by rounding to the nearest hundred dollars.

154. Estimate the cost of a kitchen with choices (c), (f), (i), and (l) by rounding to the nearest hundred dollars.

155. Sara and Ben are planning to remodel their kitchen and have a budget of $17,700. Estimate by rounding to the nearest hundred dollars the cost of their kitchen remodeling project if they choose options (b), (e), (i), and (k). Can they afford their choices?

156. The Davidsons must make a final decision on the kitchen choices for their new home. The allotted kitchen budget is $16,000. Estimate by rounding to the nearest hundred dollars the kitchen cost if they choose options (a), (f), (h), and (l). Does their budget allotment cover the cost?

157. Suppose you are planning a new kitchen and must stay within a budget of $14,500. Decide on the options you would like and estimate the cost by rounding to the nearest hundred dollars. Does your budget support your choices?

158. Suppose you are planning a new kitchen and must stay within a budget of $18,500. Decide on the options you would like and estimate the cost by rounding to the nearest hundred dollars. Does your budget support your choices?

Copyright © 2012 Pearson Education, Inc.

Skill Maintenance

In each of Exercises 159–166, fill in the blank with the correct term from the given list. Some of the choices may not be used and some may be used more than once.

159. The distance around an object is its _____ . [1.2b]

160. The _____ is the number from which another number is being subtracted. [1.2c]

161. For large numbers, _____ are separated by commas into groups of three, called _____ . [1.1a]

162. In the sentence $28 \div 7 = 4$, the _____ is 28. [1.3c]

163. In the sentence $10 \times 1000 = 10{,}000$, 10 and 1000 are called _____ and 10,000 is called the _____ . [1.3a]

164. The number 0 is called the _____ identity. [1.2a]

165. The number 1 is called the _____ identity. [1.3a]

166. We can use the following statement to check division: quotient · _____ + _____ = _____ . [1.3c]

addends

factors

area

perimeter

minuend

subtrahend

product

digits

periods

additive

multiplicative

dividend

quotient

remainder

divisor

Synthesis

167. Complete the following table.

a	b	$a \cdot b$	$a + b$
	68	3672	
84			117
		32	12

168. Find a pair of factors whose product is 36 and:
   a) whose sum is 13.
   b) whose difference is 0.
   c) whose sum is 20.
   d) whose difference is 9.

169. A group of 1231 college students is going to take buses for a field trip. Each bus can hold 42 students. How many buses are needed?

170. ▦ Fill in the missing digits to make the equation true:

$$34{,}584{,}132 \div 76\,\square = 4\,\square{,}386.$$

171. ▦ An 18-story office building is box-shaped. Each floor measures 172 ft by 84 ft with a 20-ft by 35-ft rectangular area lost to an elevator and a stairwell. How much area is available as office space?

1.4 Solving Equations

OBJECTIVES

a Solve simple equations by trial.

b Solve equations like $t + 28 = 54$, $28 \cdot x = 168$, and $98 \cdot 2 = y$.

Find a number that makes each sentence true.

1. $8 = 1 + \square$ $\quad 7$

2. $\square + 2 = 7$ $\quad 5$

3. Determine whether 7 is a solution of $\square + 5 = 9$. $\quad Not$

4. Determine whether 4 is a solution of $\square + 5 = 9$. $\quad yes$

Solve by trial.

5. $n + 3 = 8$ $\quad 5$

6. $x - 2 = 8$ $\quad 10$

7. $45 \div 9 = y$ $\quad 5$

8. $10 + t = 32$ $\quad 22$

Answers

1. 7   2. 5   3. No   4. Yes   5. 5
6. 10   7. 5   8. 22

a Solutions by Trial

Let's find a number that we can put in the blank to make this sentence true:

$$9 = 3 + \square.$$

We are asking "9 is 3 plus what number?" The answer is 6.

$$9 = 3 + 6$$

Do Exercises 1 and 2.

A sentence with $=$ is called an **equation**. A **solution** of an equation is a number that makes the sentence true. Thus, 6 is a solution of

$$9 = 3 + \square \quad \text{because} \quad 9 = 3 + 6 \text{ is true.}$$

However, 7 is not a solution of

$$9 = 3 + \square \quad \text{because} \quad 9 = 3 + 7 \text{ is false.}$$

Do Exercises 3 and 4.

We can use a letter in an equation instead of a blank:

$$9 = 3 + n.$$

We call n a **variable** because it can represent any number. If a replacement for a variable makes an equation true, it is a **solution** of the equation.

> ### SOLUTIONS OF AN EQUATION
>
> A **solution of an equation** is a replacement for the variable that makes the equation true. When we find all the solutions, we say that we have **solved** the equation.

EXAMPLE 1 Solve $y + 12 = 27$ by trial.

We replace y with several numbers.

If we replace y with 13, we get a false equation: $13 + 12 = 27$.
If we replace y with 14, we get a false equation: $14 + 12 = 27$.
If we replace y with 15, we get a true equation: $15 + 12 = 27$.

No other replacement makes the equation true, so the solution is 15.

EXAMPLES Solve.

2. $7 + n = 22$
(7 plus what number is 22?)
The solution is 15.

3. $63 = 3 \cdot x$
(63 is 3 times what number?)
The solution is 21.

Do Exercises 5-8.

b Solving Equations

We now begin to develop more efficient ways to solve certain equations. When an equation has a variable alone on one side and a calculation on the other side, we can find the solution by carrying out the calculation.

EXAMPLE 4 Solve: $x = 245 \times 34$.

To solve the equation, we carry out the calculation.

$$
\begin{array}{r}
2\ 4\ 5 \\
\times\ \ 3\ 4 \\
\hline
9\ 8\ 0 \\
7\ 3\ 5\ 0 \\
\hline
8\ 3\ 3\ 0 \\
\end{array}
\qquad
\begin{array}{l}
x = 245 \times 34 \\
x = 8330
\end{array}
$$

The solution is 8330.

Look at the equation

$$x + 12 = 27.$$

We can get x alone by subtracting 12 *on both sides*. Thus,

$$
\begin{array}{ll}
x + 12 - 12 = 27 - 12 & \text{Subtracting 12 on both sides} \\
x + 0 = 15 & \text{Carrying out the subtraction} \\
x = 15.
\end{array}
$$

SOLVING $x + a = b$

To solve $x + a = b$, subtract a on both sides.

If we can get an equation in a form with the variable alone on one side, we can "see" the solution.

EXAMPLE 5 Solve: $t + 28 = 54$.

We have

$$
\begin{array}{ll}
t + 28 = 54 \\
t + 28 - 28 = 54 - 28 & \text{Subtracting 28 on both sides} \\
t + 0 = 26 \\
t = 26.
\end{array}
$$

To check the answer, we substitute 26 for t in the original equation.

Check:
$$
\begin{array}{c}
t + 28 = 54 \\
\hline
26 + 28\ ?\ 54 \\
54\ \mid \quad \text{TRUE}
\end{array}
\qquad \text{Since } 54 = 54 \text{ is true, 26 checks.}
$$

The solution is 26.

Do Exercises 13 and 14.

Solve.

9. $346 \times 65 = y$

10. $x = 2347 + 6675$

11. $4560 \div 8 = t$

12. $x = 6007 - 2346$

Solve. Be sure to check.

13. $x + 9 = 17$

14. $77 = m + 32$

Answers

9. 22,490   **10.** 9022   **11.** 570   **12.** 3661
13. 8   **14.** 45

1.4 Solving Equations   **43**

EXAMPLE 6 Solve: $182 = 65 + n$.

We have

$$182 = 65 + n$$
$$182 - 65 = 65 + n - 65 \qquad \text{Subtracting 65 on both sides}$$
$$117 = 0 + n \qquad \text{65 plus } n \text{ minus 65 is } 0 + n.$$
$$117 = n.$$

Check: $\qquad \dfrac{182 = 65 + n}{182 \; ? \; 65 + 117}$
$$\qquad\qquad\qquad\quad |\; 182 \qquad \text{TRUE}$$

The solution is 117.

Do Exercise 15.

15. Solve: $155 = t + 78$. Be sure to check.

EXAMPLE 7 Solve: $7381 + x = 8067$.

We have

$$7381 + x = 8067$$
$$7381 + x - 7381 = 8067 - 7381 \qquad \text{Subtracting 7381 on both sides}$$
$$x = 686.$$

Check: $\qquad \dfrac{7381 + x = 8067}{7381 + 686 \; ? \; 8067}$
$$\qquad\qquad\qquad 8067 \;| \qquad \text{TRUE}$$

The solution is 686.

Do Exercises 16 and 17.

Solve. Be sure to check.

16. $4566 + x = 7877$

17. $8172 = h + 2058$

We now learn to solve equations like $8 \cdot n = 96$. Look at

$$8 \cdot n = 96.$$

We can get n alone by dividing by 8 *on both sides*. Thus,

$$\frac{8 \cdot n}{8} = \frac{96}{8} \qquad \text{Dividing by 8 on both sides}$$
$$n = 12. \qquad \text{8 times } n \text{ divided by 8 is } n.$$

To check the answer, we substitute 12 for n in the original equation.

Check: $\qquad \dfrac{8 \cdot n = 96}{8 \cdot 12 \; ? \; 96}$
$$\qquad\qquad\qquad 96 \;| \qquad \text{TRUE}$$

Since $96 = 96$ is a true equation, 12 is the solution of the equation.

> **SOLVING** $a \cdot x = b$
>
> To solve $a \cdot x = b$, divide by a on both sides.

EXAMPLE 8   Solve: $10 \cdot x = 240$.

We have

$$10 \cdot x = 240$$

$$\frac{10 \cdot x}{10} = \frac{240}{10} \qquad \text{Dividing by 10 on both sides}$$

$$x = 24.$$

Check: $\dfrac{10 \cdot x = 240}{\begin{array}{c|c} 10 \cdot 24 \ ? \ 240 \\ 240 & \ \text{TRUE} \end{array}}$

The solution is 24.

EXAMPLE 9   Solve: $5202 = 9 \cdot t$.

We have

$$5202 = 9 \cdot t$$

$$\frac{5202}{9} = \frac{9 \cdot t}{9} \qquad \text{Dividing by 9 on both sides}$$

$$578 = t.$$

Check: $\dfrac{5202 = 9 \cdot t}{\begin{array}{c|c} 5202 \ ? \ 9 \cdot 578 \\ 5202 & \ \text{TRUE} \end{array}}$

The solution is 578.

Do Exercises 18-20.

Solve. Be sure to check.

18. $8 \cdot x = 64$

19. $144 = 9 \cdot n$

20. $5152 = 8 \cdot t$

EXAMPLE 10   Solve: $14 \cdot y = 1092$.

We have

$$14 \cdot y = 1092$$

$$\frac{14 \cdot y}{14} = \frac{1092}{14} \qquad \text{Dividing by 14 on both sides}$$

$$y = 78.$$

The check is left to the student. The solution is 78.

EXAMPLE 11   Solve: $n \cdot 56 = 4648$.

We have

$$n \cdot 56 = 4648$$

$$\frac{n \cdot 56}{56} = \frac{4648}{56} \qquad \text{Dividing by 56 on both sides}$$

$$n = 83.$$

The check is left to the student. The solution is 83.

Do Exercises 21 and 22.

Solve. Be sure to check.

21. $18 \cdot y = 1728$

22. $n \cdot 48 = 4512$

Answers

18. 8   **19.** 16   **20.** 644   **21.** 96   **22.** 94

a Solve by trial.

1. $x + 0 = 14$

2. $x - 7 = 18$

3. $y \cdot 17 = 0$

4. $56 \div m = 7$

b Solve. Be sure to check.

5. $x = 12{,}345 + 78{,}555$

6. $t = 5678 + 9034$

7. $908 - 458 = p$

8. $9007 - 5667 = m$

9. $16 \cdot 22 = y$

10. $34 \cdot 15 = z$

11. $t = 125 \div 5$

12. $w = 256 \div 16$

13. $13 + x = 42$

14. $15 + t = 22$

15. $12 = 12 + m$

16. $16 = t + 16$

17. $10 + x = 89$

18. $20 + x = 57$

19. $61 = 16 + y$

20. $53 = 17 + w$

21. $3 \cdot x = 24$

22. $6 \cdot x = 42$

23. $112 = n \cdot 8$

24. $162 = 9 \cdot m$

25. $3 \cdot m = 96$

26. $4 \cdot y = 96$

27. $715 = 5 \cdot z$

28. $741 = 3 \cdot t$

29. $8322 + 9281 = x$

30. $9281 - 8322 = y$

31. $47 + n = 84$

32. $56 + p = 92$

33. $45 \cdot 23 = x$

34. $23 \cdot 78 = y$

35. $x + 78 = 144$

36. $z + 67 = 133$

Copyright © 2012 Pearson Education, Inc.

37. $6 \cdot p = 1944$ **38.** $4 \cdot w = 3404$ **39.** $5 \cdot x = 3715$ **40.** $9 \cdot x = 1269$

41. $x + 214 = 389$ **42.** $x + 221 = 333$ **43.** $567 + x = 902$ **44.** $438 + x = 807$

45. $234 \cdot 78 = y$ **46.** $10{,}534 \div 458 = q$ **47.** $18 \cdot x = 1872$ **48.** $19 \cdot x = 6080$

49. $40 \cdot x = 1800$ **50.** $20 \cdot x = 1500$ **51.** $2344 + y = 6400$ **52.** $9281 = 8322 + t$

53. $m = 7006 - 4159$ **54.** $n = 3004 - 1745$ **55.** $165 = 11 \cdot n$ **56.** $660 = 12 \cdot n$

57. $58 \cdot m = 11{,}890$ **58.** $233 \cdot x = 22{,}135$ **59.** $491 - 34 = y$ **60.** $512 - 63 = z$

Skill Maintenance

Divide.   [1.3c]

61. $1283 \div 9$ **62.** $1278 \div 9$ **63.** $1\,7\,)\,\overline{5\,6\,7\,8}$ **64.** $1\,7\,)\,\overline{5\,6\,8\,9}$

Use > or < for ☐ to write a true sentence.   [1.1d]

65. 123 ☐ 789   **66.** 342 ☐ 339   **67.** 688 ☐ 0   **68.** 0 ☐ 11

69. Round 6,375,602 to the nearest thousand.   [1.3d]   **70.** Round 6,375,602 to the nearest ten.   [1.3d]

Synthesis

Solve.

71. ▦ $23{,}465 \cdot x = 8{,}142{,}355$ **72.** ▦ $48{,}916 \cdot x = 14{,}332{,}388$

Mid-Chapter Review

Concept Reinforcement

Determine whether each statement is true or false.

_____ **1.** If $a - b = c$, then $b = a + c$. [1.2c]

_____ **2.** We can think of the multiplication 4×3 as a rectangular array containing 3 columns with 4 items in each column. [1.3a]

_____ **3.** The product of two whole numbers is always greater than either of the factors. [1.3a]

_____ **4.** Zero divided by any nonzero number is 0. [1.3c]

_____ **5.** Any number divided by 1 is the number 1. [1.3c]

Guided Solutions

Fill in each blank with the number that creates a correct statement or solution.

6. Write a word name for 95,406,237. [1.1c]

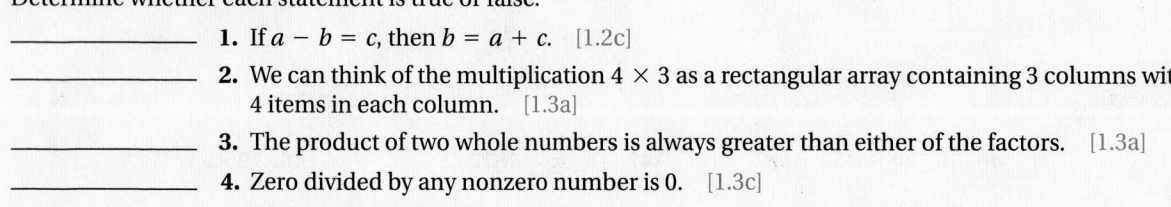

7. Subtract: $604 - 497$. [1.2c]

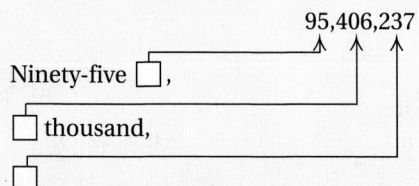

Mixed Review

In each of the following numbers what does the digit 6 mean? [1.1a]

8. 2698

9. 61,204

10. 146,237

11. 586

Consider the number 306,458,129. What digit names the number of: [1.1a]

12. tens

13. millions

14. ten thousands

15. hundreds

Write expanded notation. [1.1b]

16. 5602

17. 69,345

Write a word name. [1.1c]

18. 136

19. 64,325

Write standard notation. [1.1c]

20. Three hundred eight thousand, seven hundred sixteen

21. Four million, five hundred sixty-seven thousand, two hundred sixteen

Use $<$ or $>$ for $\square$ to write a true sentence. [1.1d]

22. 61 $\square$ 16

23. 100 $\square$ 101

24. 0 $\square$ 18

25. 380 $\square$ 327

Solve. [1.4b]

26. $4 \cdot b = 72$

27. $45 = 23 + x$

28. $t = 725 \div 25$

29. $3902 - 260 = y$

Copyright © 2012 Pearson Education, Inc.

Add. [1.2a]

30. 3 1 6
       + 4 8 2

31. 5 9 3
       + 4 3 7

32. 2 6 3 8
       + 5 2 8 4

33. 4 6 1 7
         2 4 3 6
       +   4 8 1

Subtract. [1.2c]

34. 7 8 6
       − 3 2 1

35. 6 2 4
       − 2 8 5

36. 3 6 0 2
       − 1 7 4 8

37. 5 0 0 4
       −   6 7 6

Multiply. [1.3a]

38. 3 6
       ×   6

39. 5 6 7
       ×   2 8

40. 4 0 7
       × 3 2 5

41. 9 4 3 5
       ×   6 0 2

Divide. [1.3c]

42. 4) 1 0 1 2

43. 3 8) 4 2 6 1

44. 6 0) 1 3 9 9

45. 5 6) 8 0 9 5

46. Find the perimeter of the figure. [1.2b]

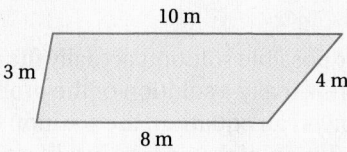

47. Find the area of the region. [1.3b]

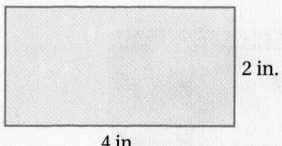

48. Round 647 to the nearest hundred. [1.3d]

49. Round 823,502 to the nearest thousand. [1.3d]

50. Estimate the product 218 × 865 by first rounding to the nearest hundred. [1.3e]

Understanding Through Discussion and Writing

To the student and the instructor: The Discussion and Writing exercises are meant to be answered with one or more sentences. They can be discussed and answered collaboratively by the entire class or by small groups.

51. Explain how estimating and rounding can be useful when shopping for groceries. [1.3e]

52. Explain why we use commas when writing large numbers. [1.1a]

53. Describe a situation that corresponds to each multiplication: 4 · $150; $4 · 150. [1.3a]

54. Suppose a student asserts that "0 ÷ 0 = 0 because nothing divided by nothing is nothing." Devise an explanation to persuade the student that the assertion is false. [1.3c]

1.5

Applications and Problem Solving

OBJECTIVE

a Solve applied problems involving addition, subtraction, multiplication, or division of whole numbers.

a A Problem-Solving Strategy

One of the most important ways in which we use mathematics is as a tool in solving problems. To solve a problem, we use the following five-step strategy.

> **FIVE STEPS FOR PROBLEM SOLVING**
>
> 1. **Familiarize** yourself with the problem situation. If the problem is presented in words, this means to read and reread it carefully until you understand what you are being asked to find. Some or all of the following can also be helpful.
>   a) Make a drawing, if it makes sense to do so.
>   b) Make a written list of the known facts and a list of what you wish to find out.
>   c) Assign a letter, or *variable*, to the unknown.
>   d) Organize the information in a chart or a table.
>   e) Find further information. Look up a formula, consult a reference book or an expert in the field, or do research on the Internet.
>   f) Guess or estimate the answer and check your guess or estimate.
> 2. **Translate** the problem to an equation using the variable.
> 3. **Solve** the equation.
> 4. **Check** to see whether your possible solution actually fits the problem situation and is thus really a solution of the problem. Although you may have solved an equation, the solution of the equation might not be a solution of the original problem.
> 5. **State** the answer clearly using a complete sentence and appropriate units.

The first of these five steps, becoming familiar with the problem, is probably the most important. It provides a solid foundation for translating the problem to an equation that represents the situation accurately.

EXAMPLE 1 *Community Colleges and New Jobs.* Community colleges are playing an increasingly large role in educating America's work force. The numbers of new jobs requiring a community college degree that will be created between 2004 and 2014 are shown in the table on the next page. Find the total number of new jobs for registered nurses, nursing aides and orderlies, and medical assistants.

New Jobs Created, 2004–2014

JOB	NUMBER
Registered nurse	703,000
Customer service	471,000
Nursing aide; orderly	325,000
Heavy-truck driver	223,000
Maintenance; repair	202,000
Medical assistant	202,000
Executive secretary/assistant	192,000
Sales representative	187,000
Carpenter	186,000

SOURCES: U.S. Bureau of Labor Statistics;
College Board Center for Innovative Thought

1. **Familiarize.** First, we assign a letter, or variable, to the number we wish to find. We let n = the total number of new jobs created for registered nurses, nursing aides and orderlies, and medical assistants. Since we are combining numbers, we will add.

2. **Translate.** We translate to an equation:

Registered nurses' jobs	plus	Nursing aides' and orderlies' jobs	plus	Medical assistants' jobs	is	Total number of jobs
703,000	+	325,000	+	202,000	=	n.

3. **Solve.** We solve the equation by carrying out the addition.

$$\begin{array}{r} 703{,}000 \\ 325{,}000 \\ +\ 202{,}000 \\ \hline 1{,}230{,}000 \end{array}$$

$$703{,}000 + 325{,}000 + 202{,}000 = n$$
$$1{,}230{,}000 = n$$

4. **Check.** We check 1,230,000 in the original problem. There are many ways in which this can be done. For example, we can repeat the calculation. (We leave this to the student.) Another way is to check whether the answer is reasonable. In this case, we would expect the total to be greater than the number of each individual type of new job, and it is. We can also estimate the expected result by rounding. Here we round to the nearest hundred thousand:

$$703{,}000 + 325{,}000 + 202{,}000 \approx 700{,}000 + 300{,}000 + 200{,}000$$
$$\approx 1{,}200{,}000.$$

Since $1{,}200{,}000 \approx 1{,}230{,}000$, our answer seems reasonable. If the estimate had differed greatly from the possible solution found in step (3), we would suspect that the possible solution is incorrect.

5. **State.** The total number of new jobs created for registered nurses, nursing aides and orderlies, and medical assistants between 2004 and 2014 is 1,230,000.

Do Exercises 1–3.

Refer to the table above to do Margin Exercises 1–3.

1. Find the total number of new jobs that will be created for customer-service representatives, executive secretaries/assistants, and sales representatives.

2. Find the total number of new jobs that will be created for heavy-truck drivers, maintenance and repair workers, and carpenters.

3. Find the total number of new jobs listed in the table.

Answers

1. 850,000 new jobs   2. 611,000 new jobs
3. 2,691,000 new jobs

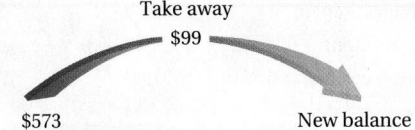

EXAMPLE 2 *Checking Account Balance.* The balance in Francisco's checking account is $573. He uses his debit card to buy a juicer that costs $99. Find the new balance in his checking account.

1. **Familiarize.** We first make a drawing or at least visualize the situation. We let B = the new balance in Francisco's checking account. We start with $573 and take away $99.

Take away
$99

$573   New balance

2. **Translate.** We translate to an equation:

Money in the account	minus	Money spent	is	New balance
↓	↓	↓	↓	↓
573	−	99	=	B.

3. **Solve.** This equation tells us what to do. We subtract.

$$\begin{array}{r} \overset{16}{4\ \overset{}{\cancel{6}}\ 13} \\ \cancel{5}\ 7\ \cancel{3} \\ -\ \ 9\ 9 \\ \hline 4\ 7\ 4 \end{array}$$

$573 - 99 = B$
$474 = B$

4. **Check.** To check our answer of $474, we can repeat the calculation. We can also note that the answer should be less than the original amount, $573, and it is. Another way to check is to add the money spent, $99, to the new balance, $474: $99 + $474 = $573. We get the original balance, so the answer checks. We can also estimate:

$573 − $99 ≈ $570 − $100 = $470 ≈ $474.

This tells us that the answer is reasonable.

5. **State.** The new balance in Francisco's checking account is $474.

Do Exercise 4.

In the real world, problems may not be stated in written words. You must still become familiar with the situation before you can solve the problem.

EXAMPLE 3 *Travel Distance.* Abigail is driving from Indianapolis to Salt Lake City to attend a family reunion. The distance from Indianapolis to Salt Lake City is 1634 mi. In the first two days, she travels 1154 mi to Denver. How much farther must she travel?

1. **Familiarize.** We first make a drawing or at least visualize the situation. We let d = the remaining distance to Salt Lake City.

4. Checking Account Balance. The balance in Laura's checking account is $457. She uses her debit card to buy a digital-picture frame that costs $49. Find the new balance in her checking account.

Answer
4. $408

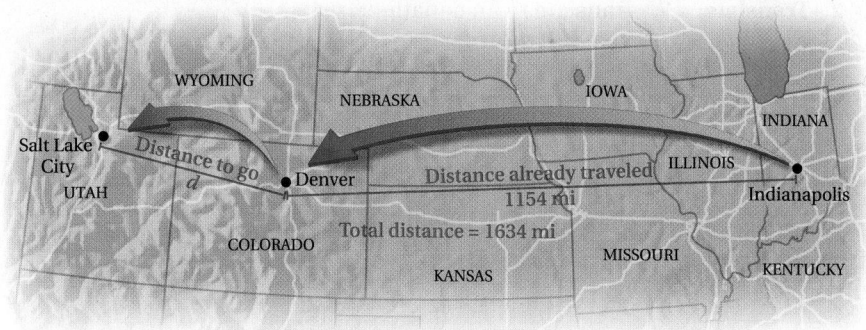

2. **Translate.** We want to determine how many more miles Abigail must travel. We translate to an equation:

Distance already traveled	plus	Distance to go	is	Total distance of trip
↓	↓	↓	↓	↓
1154	+	d	=	1634.

3. **Solve.** To solve the equation, we subtract 1154 on both sides.

$$1154 + d = 1634$$
$$1154 + d - 1154 = 1634 - 1154$$
$$d = 480$$

$$\begin{array}{r} \overset{5\ \ 13}{1\ \cancel{6}\ \cancel{3}\ 4} \\ -\ 1\ 1\ 5\ 4 \\ \hline 4\ 8\ 0 \end{array}$$

4. **Check.** We check our answer of 480 mi in the original problem. This number should be less than the total distance, 1634 mi, and it is. We can add the distance traveled, 1154, and the distance left to go, 480: 1154 + 480 = 1634. We can also estimate:

$$1634 - 1154 \approx 1600 - 1200$$
$$= 400 \approx 480.$$

The answer, 480 mi, checks.

5. **State.** Abigail must travel 480 mi farther to Salt Lake City.

Do Exercise 5.

> **5. Reading Assignment.** William has been assigned 234 pages of reading for his history class. He has read 86 pages. How many more pages does he have to read?

EXAMPLE 4 *Total Cost of Chairs.* What is the total cost of 6 Adirondack chairs if each one costs $169?

1. **Familiarize.** We first make a drawing or at least visualize the situation. We let $C =$ the cost of 6 chairs.

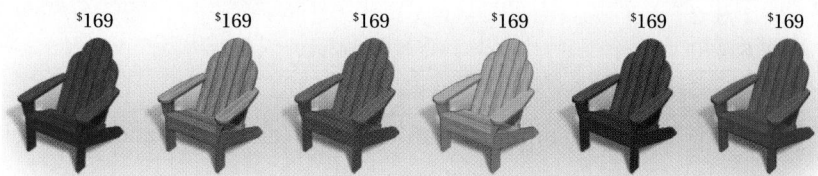

$169 $169 $169 $169 $169 $169

Answer

5. 148 pages

2. Translate. We translate to an equation:

Number
of chairs   times   Cost of
each chair   is   Total
cost

6   × $169   =   C.

3. Solve. This sentence tells us what to do. We multiply.

$$
\begin{array}{r}
1\ 6\ 9 \\
\times \quad 6 \\
\hline
1\ 0\ 1\ 4
\end{array}
$$

$6 \times 169 = C$
$1014 = C$

4. Check. We have an answer, 1014, that is much greater than the cost of any individual chair, which is reasonable. We can repeat our calculation. We can also check by estimating:

$6 \times 169 \approx 6 \times 170 \approx 1020 \approx 1014.$

The answer checks.

5. State. The total cost of 6 chairs is $1014.

> Do Exercise 6.

6. Total Cost of Gas Grills. What is the total cost of 14 gas grills, each with 520 sq in. of total cooking surface, if each one costs $398?

EXAMPLE 5 *Area of an Oriental Rug.* The dimensions of the oriental rug in the Fosters' front hallway are 42 in. by 66 in. What is the area of the rug?

1. Familiarize. We first make a drawing to visualize the situation. We let A = the area of the rug and use the formula for the area of a rectangle, A = length · width = $l \cdot w$. Since we usually consider length to be larger than width, we will let l = 66 in. and w = 42 in.

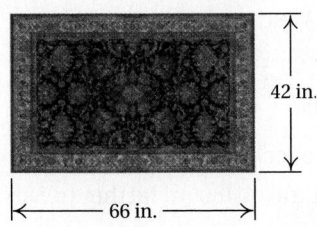

42 in.

66 in.

2. Translate. We substitute in the formula:

$A = l \cdot w = 66 \cdot 42.$

3. Solve. We carry out the multiplication.

$$
\begin{array}{r}
6\ 6 \\
\times\ 4\ 2 \\
\hline
1\ 3\ 2 \\
2\ 6\ 4\ 0 \\
\hline
2\ 7\ 7\ 2
\end{array}
$$

$A = 66 \cdot 42$
$A = 2772$

4. Check. We can repeat the calculation. We can also round and estimate:

$66 \times 42 \approx 70 \times 40 \approx 2800 \approx 2772.$

The answer checks.

5. State. The area of the rug is 2772 sq in.

> Do Exercise 7.

7. Bed Sheets. The dimensions of a flat sheet for a queen-size bed are 90 in. by 102 in. What is the area of the sheet?

Answers

6. $5572   **7.** 9180 sq in.

EXAMPLE 6 *Packages of Paper Towels.* A paper-products company produces 3304 rolls of paper towels. How many 12-roll packages can be filled? How many rolls will be left over?

1. **Familiarize.** We first make a drawing. We let n = the number of 12-roll packages that can be filled. The problem can be considered as repeated subtraction, taking successive sets of 12 rolls and putting them into n packages.

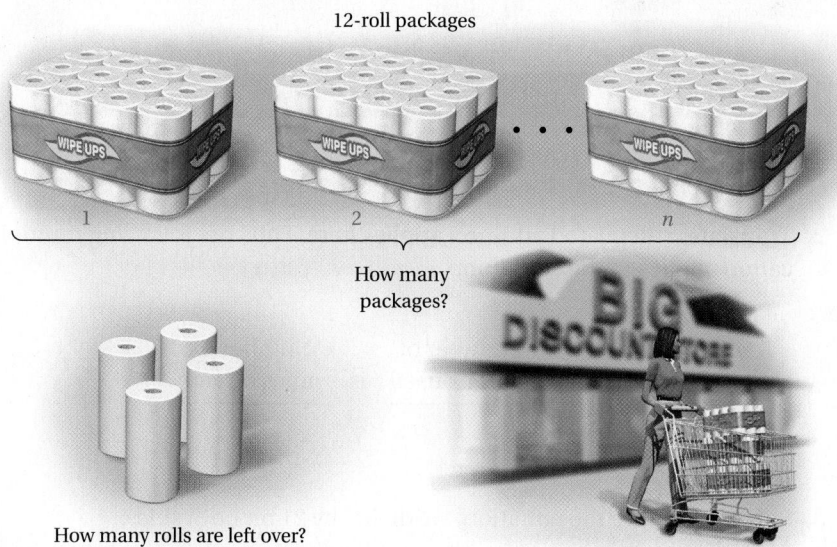

12-roll packages

How many packages?

How many rolls are left over?

2. **Translate.** We translate to an equation:

$$
\underbrace{3304}_{\substack{\text{Number} \\ \text{of} \\ \text{rolls}}} \underbrace{\div}_{\substack{\text{divided} \\ \text{by}}} \underbrace{12}_{\substack{\text{Number} \\ \text{in each} \\ \text{package}}} \underbrace{=}_{\text{is}} \underbrace{n.}_{\substack{\text{Number} \\ \text{of} \\ \text{packages}}}
$$

3. **Solve.** We solve the equation by carrying out the division.

```
        2 7 5
  1 2 ) 3 3 0 4
        2 4
        ─────
          9 0
          8 4
          ─────
            6 4          3304 ÷ 12 = n
            6 0
            ─────        275 R 4 = n
              4
```

4. **Check.** We can check by multiplying the number of packages by 12 and adding the remainder, 4:

$12 \cdot 275 = 3300,$

$3300 + 4 = 3304.$

5. **State.** Thus, 275 twelve-roll packages of paper towels can be filled. There will be 4 rolls left over.

Do Exercise 8.

8. **Packages of Paper Towels.** The paper-products company in Example 6 also produces 6-roll packages. How many 6-roll packages can be filled with 2269 rolls of paper towels? How many rolls will be left over?

Answer

8. 378 packages with 1 roll left over

EXAMPLE 7 *Automobile Mileage.* The 2009 Toyota Matrix gets 21 miles to the gallon (mpg) in city driving. How many gallons will it use in 3843 mi of city driving?

Source: Toyota

1. **Familiarize.** We first make a drawing. We let g = the number of gallons of gasoline used in 3843 mi of city driving.

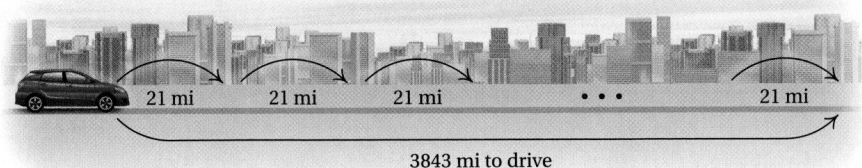

21 mi 21 mi 21 mi • • • 21 mi

3843 mi to drive

2. **Translate.** Repeated addition applies here. Thus the following multiplication applies to the situation.

Number of miles per gallon	times	Number of gallons used	is	Number of miles driven
↓	↓	↓	↓	↓
21	·	g	=	3843

3. **Solve.** To solve the equation, we divide by 21 on both sides.

$$21 \cdot g = 3843$$
$$\frac{21 \cdot g}{21} = \frac{3843}{21}$$
$$g = 183$$

```
        1 8 3
 2 1 ) 3 8 4 3
       2 1
       1 7 4
       1 6 8
           6 3
           6 3
             0
```

4. **Check.** To check, we multiply 183 by 21.

```
      1 8 3
   ×   2 1
      1 8 3
    3 6 6 0
    3 8 4 3
```

The answer checks.

5. **State.** The Toyota Matrix will use 183 gal of gasoline.

Do Exercise 9.

Multistep Problems

Sometimes we must use more than one operation to solve a problem, as in the following example.

EXAMPLE 8 *Weight Loss.* To lose one pound, you must burn about 3500 calories in excess of what you already burn doing your regular daily activities. The chart on the next page shows how long a person must engage in several types of exercise in order to burn 100 calories. For how long would a person have to run at a brisk pace in order to lose one pound?

9. Automobile Mileage. The 2009 Toyota Matrix gets 29 miles to the gallon (mpg) in highway driving. How many gallons will it use in 2291 mi of highway driving?

Source: Toyota

Answer
9. 79 gal

1. Familiarize. This is a multistep problem. We begin by visualizing the situation.

ONE POUND 3500 CALORIES			
100 cal 8 min	100 cal 8 min	...	100 cal 8 min

To burn 100 calories, you must:

- Run for 8 minutes at a brisk pace, or
- Swim for 2 minutes at a brisk pace, or
- Bicycle for 15 minutes at 9 mph, or
- Do aerobic exercises for 15 minutes, or
- Golf, walking, for 20 minutes, or
- Play tennis, singles, for 11 minutes

We will first find how many hundreds are in 3500. This will tell us how many times a person must run for 8 min in order to lose one pound. Then we will multiply to find the total number of minutes required for the weight loss.

We let x = the number of hundreds in 3500.

2. Translate. We translate to an equation. Repeated addition applies here, so we will multiply.

$$
\underbrace{100}_{\substack{100 \\ \text{calories}}} \quad \underbrace{\cdot}_{\text{times}} \quad \underbrace{x}_{\substack{\text{How} \\ \text{many} \\ \text{hundreds}}} \quad \underbrace{=}_{\text{is}} \quad \underbrace{3500}_{3500}
$$

3. Solve. We divide by 100 on both sides of the equation.

$$100 \cdot x = 3500$$
$$\frac{100 \cdot x}{100} = \frac{3500}{100}$$
$$x = 35$$

$$
\begin{array}{r}
3\,5 \\
100\,\overline{)\,3\,5\,0\,0} \\
\underline{3\,0\,0} \\
5\,0\,0 \\
\underline{5\,0\,0} \\
0
\end{array}
$$

We know that running for 8 min will burn 100 calories. This must be done 35 times in order to lose one pound. We let t = the time it takes to lose one pound. Thus we have the following.

$$t = 35 \times 8$$
$$t = 280$$

$$
\begin{array}{r}
3\,5 \\
\times\quad 8 \\
\hline
2\,8\,0
\end{array}
$$

4. Check. $280 \div 8 = 35$, so there are 35 8's in 280 min, and $35 \cdot 100 = 3500$, the number of calories that must be burned in order to lose one pound. The answer checks.

5. State. You must run for 280 min, or 4 hr 40 min, at a brisk pace in order to lose one pound.

Do Exercise 10.

10. Weight Loss. Use the information in Example 8 to determine how long an individual must swim at a brisk pace in order to lose one pound.

Answer

10. 70 min, or 1 hr 10 min

You will find it helpful to look for the words, phrases, and concepts in the table below as you familiarize yourself with applied problems. They will be useful when you translate the problems to equations.

KEYWORDS, PHRASES, AND CONCEPTS

ADDITION (+)	SUBTRACTION (−)	MULTIPLICATION (·)	DIVISION (÷)
add	subtract	multiply	divide
added to	subtracted from	multiplied by	divided by
sum	difference	product	quotient
total	minus	times	repeated subtraction
plus	less than	of	missing factor
more than	decreased by	repeated addition	finding equal quantities
increased by	take away	rectangular arrays	
	how much more		

The following tips will also be helpful in problem solving.

PROBLEM-SOLVING TIPS

1. Look for patterns when solving problems. Each time you study an example in the text, you may observe a pattern for problems found later in the exercise sets or in other practical situations.

2. When translating in mathematics, consider the dimensions of the variables and constants in the equation. The variables that represent length should all be in the same unit, those that represent money should all be in dollars or all in cents, and so on.

3. Make sure that units appear in the answer whenever appropriate and that you completely answer the original problem.

STUDY TIPS

SOLVING APPLIED PROBLEMS

Don't be discouraged if, at first, you find the exercises in this section to be more challenging than those in earlier sections or if you have had difficulty working applied problems in the past. Your skill will improve with each problem you solve. After you have done your homework for this section, you might want to work extra problems from the text or from the online tutorial that accompanies the text. As you gain experience solving applied problems, you will find yourself becoming comfortable with them.

Translating for Success

1. Brick-Mason Expense. A commercial contractor is building 30 two-unit condominiums in a retirement community. The brick-mason expense for each building is $10,860. What is the total cost of bricking the buildings?

2. Heights. Dean's sons are on the high school basketball team. Their heights are 73 in., 69 in., and 76 in. How much taller is the tallest son than the shortest son?

3. Account Balance. James has $423 in his checking account. Then he deposits $73 and uses his debit card for purchases of $76 and $69. How much is left in the account?

4. Purchasing Camcorder. A camcorder is on sale for $423. Jenny has only $69. How much more does she need to buy the camcorder?

5. Purchasing Coffee Makers. Sara purchases 8 coffee makers for the newly remodeled bed-and-breakfast hotel that she manages. If she pays $52 for each coffee maker, what is the total cost of her purchase?

The goal of these matching questions is to practice step (2), *Translate*, of the five-step problem-solving process. Translate each word problem to an equation and select a correct translation from equations A–O.

A. $8 \cdot 52 = n$

B. $69 \cdot n = 76$

C. $73 - 76 - 69 = n$

D. $423 + 73 - 76 - 69 = n$

E. $30 \cdot 10{,}860 = n$

F. $15 \cdot n = 195$

G. $69 + n = 423$

H. $n = 10{,}860 - 300$

I. $n = 423 \div 69$

J. $30 \cdot n = 10{,}860$

K. $15 \cdot 195 = n$

L. $n = 52 - 8$

M. $69 + n = 76$

N. $15 \div 195 = n$

O. $52 + n = 60$

Answers on page A-2

6. Hourly Rate. Miller Auto Repair charges $52 per hour for labor. Jackson Auto Care charges $60 per hour. How much more does Jackson charge than Miller?

7. College Band. A college band with 195 members marches in a 15-row formation in the homecoming halftime performance. How many members are in each row?

8. Shoe Purchase. A professional football team purchases 15 pairs of shoes at $195 a pair. What is the total cost of this purchase?

9. Loan Payment. Kendra's uncle loans her $10,860, interest free, to buy a car. The loan is to be paid off in 30 payments. How much is each payment?

10. College Enrollment. At the beginning of the fall term, the total enrollment in Lakeview Community College was 10,860. By the end of the first two weeks, 300 students had withdrawn. How many students were then enrolled?

 Solve.

Roller Coasters. The table below shows the lengths of the fastest roller coasters in the world. Use this information to do Exercises 1–4.

Fastest Roller Coasters

ROLLER COASTER	LENGTH (in feet)
Kingda Ka (128 mph) Six Flags Great Adventure, New Jersey	3118
Top Thrill Dragster (120 mph) Cedar Point, Ohio	2800
Dodonpa (107 mph) Fuji-Q Highland, Japan	3901
Steel Dragon 2000 (95 mph) Nagashima Spa Land, Japan	8133

SOURCE: ultimaterollercoaster.com

1. How much longer is Kingda Ka than Top Thrill Dragster?

2. How much longer is Steel Dragon 2000 than Kingda Ka?

3. The Steel Dragon 2000 is the longest roller coaster in the world. It is 683 ft longer than the second-longest roller coaster, The Ultimate, in Lightwater Valley, UK. How long is The Ultimate?

4. The longest roller coaster in the United States is Millennium Force, in Cedar Point, Ohio. It is 3795 ft longer than Top Thrill Dragster, in the same amusement park. How long is Millennium Force?

5. *Caffeine Content.* An 8-oz serving of Red Bull energy drink contains 76 milligrams of caffeine. An 8-oz serving of brewed coffee contains 19 more milligrams of caffeine than the energy drink. How many milligrams of caffeine does the 8-oz serving of coffee contain?

   Source: The Mayo Clinic

6. *Caffeine Content.* Hershey's 6-oz milk chocolate almond bar contains 25 milligrams of caffeine. A 20-oz bottle of Coca-Cola has 32 more milligrams of caffeine than the Hershey bar. How many milligrams of caffeine does the 20-oz bottle of Coca-Cola have?

   Source: *National Geographic,* "Caffeine," by T. R. Reid, January 2005

7. A carpenter drills 216 holes in a rectangular array in a pegboard. There are 12 holes in each row. How many rows are there?

8. Lou arranges 504 entries on a spreadsheet in a rectangular array that has 36 rows. How many entries are in each row?

Copyright © 2012 Pearson Education, Inc.

9. *TV Watching.* On average, people age 12 and older spent 1704 hr watching TV in 2008. This is 202 hr more than in 2000. Determine the number of hours people in this age group spent watching TV in 2000.

Source: U. S. Census Bureau

10. *Drilling Activity.* In 1988, there were 554 rotary rigs drilling for crude oil in the United States. This was 257 more rigs than were active in 2007. Find the number of active rotary oil rigs in 2007.

Source: Energy Information Administration

11. *Boundaries between Countries.* The boundary between mainland United States and Canada including the Great Lakes is 3987 mi long. The length of the boundary between the United States and Mexico is 1933 mi. How much longer is the Canadian border?

Source: U.S. Geological Survey

12. *Longest Rivers.* The longest river in the world is the Nile in Egypt at about 4135 mi. The longest river in the United States is the Missouri–Mississippi at about 3860 mi. How much longer is the Nile?

13. *Pixels.* A high-definition television (HDTV) screen consists of small rectangular dots called *pixels*. How many pixels are there on a screen that has 1080 rows with 1920 pixels in each row?

Pixel

14. *Crossword.* The *USA Today* crossword puzzle is a rectangle containing 15 rows with 15 squares in each row. How many squares does the puzzle have altogether?

15. *Associate's Degrees.* About 697,000 associate's degrees were earned in the United States in 2005. Of these, 429,000 were earned by women. How many men earned associate's degrees in 2005?

16. *Bachelor's Degrees.* About 613,000 bachelor's degrees were earned by men in the United States in 2005. This is 215,000 fewer than the number of bachelor's degrees earned by women the same year. How many bachelor's degrees were earned by women in 2005?

17. There are 24 hr in a day and 7 days in a week. How many hours are there in a week?

18. There are 60 min in an hour and 24 hr in a day. How many minutes are there in a day?

Housing Costs.   The graph below shows the average monthly rent for a one-bedroom apartment in several cities in June 2008. Use this graph to do Exercises 19–24.

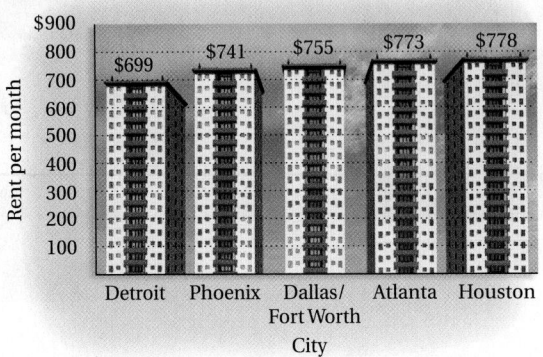

Average Rent for a One-Bedroom Apartment

SOURCE: Apartments.com

19. How much higher is the average monthly rent in Houston than in Dallas/Fort Worth?

20. How much lower is the average monthly rent in Phoenix than in Atlanta?

21. Phil, Scott, and Julio plan to rent a one-bedroom apartment in Detroit immediately after graduation, sharing the rent equally. What average monthly rent can each of them expect to pay?

22. Maria and her sister Theresa share a one-bedroom apartment in Houston, dividing the average monthly rent equally between them. How much does each pay?

23. On average, how much rent would a tenant pay for a one-bedroom apartment in Atlanta during a 12-month period?

24. On average, how much rent would a tenant pay for a one-bedroom apartment in Dallas/Fort Worth during a 6-month period?

25. *Colonial Population.*   Before the establishment of the U.S. Census in 1790, it was estimated that the Colonial population in 1780 was 2,780,400. This was an increase of 2,628,900 from the population in 1680. What was the Colonial population in 1680?

Source: *Time Almanac, 2005*

26. *Interstate Speed Limits.*   The speed limit for passenger cars on interstate highways in rural areas in Montana is 75 mph. This is 10 mph faster than the speed limit for trucks on the same roads. What is the speed limit for trucks?

Copyright © 2012 Pearson Education, Inc.

27. *Motorcycle Sales.* Motorcycle sales totaled 710,000 in the United States in 2000. Sales in 2006 exceeded this total by 480,000. How many motorcycles were sold in 2006?

Source: Motorcycle Industry Council

28. *Summer Olympics.* There were 43 events in the first modern Olympic games in Athens, Greece, in 1896. There were 259 more events in the 2008 Summer Olympics in Beijing, China. How many events were there in 2008?

Sources: *USA Today* research; beijing2008.cn

29. *Yard-Sale Profit.* Ruth made $312 at her yard sale and divided the money equally among her four grandchildren. How much did each child receive?

30. *Paper Measures.* A quire of paper consists of 25 sheets, and a ream of paper consists of 500 sheets. How many quires are in a ream?

31. *Parking Rates.* The most expensive parking in the United States occurs in midtown New York City, where the average rate is $585 per month. This is $545 per month more than in the city with the least expensive rate, Bakersfield, California. What is the average monthly parking rate in Bakersfield?

Source: Colliers International

32. *Trade Balance.* In 2006, foreign visitors spent $422,594,000,000 traveling in the United States, while Americans spent $342,845,000,000 traveling abroad. How much more was spent by visitors to the United States than by Americans traveling abroad?

Source: U. S. Census Bureau

33. *Refrigerator Purchase.* Gourmet Deli has a chain of 24 restaurants. It buys a commercial refrigerator for each store at a cost of $1019 each. Determine the total cost of the purchase.

34. *Microwave Purchase.* Bridgeway College is constructing new dorms, in which each room has a small kitchen. It buys 96 microwave ovens at $88 each. Determine the total cost of the purchase.

35. *"Seinfeld."* A local television station plans to air the 177 episodes of the long-running comedy series "Seinfeld." If the station airs 5 episodes per week, how many full weeks will pass before it must begin re-airing previously shown episodes? How many unaired episodes will be shown the following week before the previously aired episodes are rerun?

36. *"Everybody Loves Raymond."* The popular television comedy series "Everybody Loves Raymond" had 208 scripted episodes and 2 additional episodes consisting of clips from previous shows. A local television station plans to air the 208 scripted episodes, showing 5 episodes per week. How many full weeks will pass before it must begin re-airing episodes? How many unaired episodes will be shown the following week before the previously aired episodes are rerun?

37. *Automobile Mileage.* The 2008 Hyundai Tucson GLS gets 25 miles to the gallon (mpg) in highway driving. How many gallons will it use in 5900 mi of highway driving?
Source: Hyundai

38. *Automobile Mileage.* The 2008 Volkswagen Jetta (5 cylinder) gets 21 miles to the gallon (mpg) in city driving. How many gallons will it use in 3465 mi of city driving?
Source: Volkswagen of America, Inc.

39. *Crossword.* The *Los Angeles Times* crossword puzzle is a rectangle containing 441 squares arranged in 21 rows. How many columns does the puzzle have?

40. *Mailing Labels.* A box of mailing labels contains 750 labels on 25 sheets. How many labels are on each sheet?

41. *High School Court.* The standard basketball court used by high school players has dimensions of 50 ft by 84 ft.
  a) What is its area?
  b) What is its perimeter?

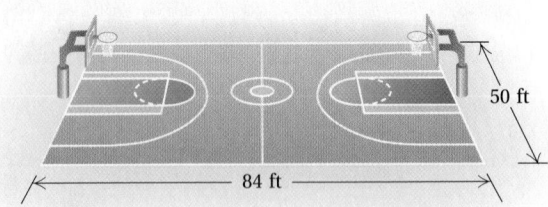

42. *College Court.* The standard basketball court used by college players has dimensions of 50 ft by 94 ft.
  a) What is its area?
  b) What is its perimeter?
  c) How much greater is the area of a college court than a high school court? (See Exercise 41.)

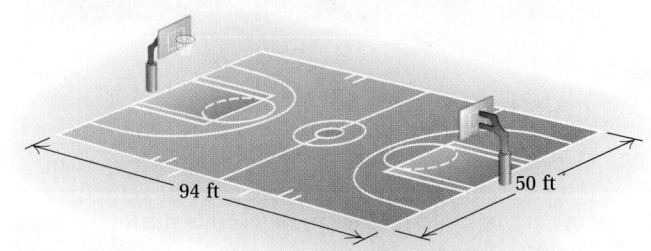

Copyright © 2012 Pearson Education, Inc.

43. *Loan Payments.* Dana borrows $5928 for a used car. The loan is to be paid off in 24 equal monthly payments. How much is each payment (excluding interest)?

44. *Home Improvement Loan.* The Van Reken family borrows $7824 to build a sunroom on the back of their home. The loan is to be paid off in equal monthly payments of $163 (excluding interest). How many months will it take to pay off the loan?

45. *Map Drawing.* A map has a scale of 215 mi to the inch. How far apart *in reality* are two cities that are 3 in. apart on the map? How far apart *on the map* are two cities that, in reality, are 1075 mi apart?

46. *Map Drawing.* A map has a scale of 288 mi to the inch. How far apart *on the map* are two cities that, in reality, are 2016 mi apart? How far apart *in reality* are two cities that are 8 in. apart on the map?

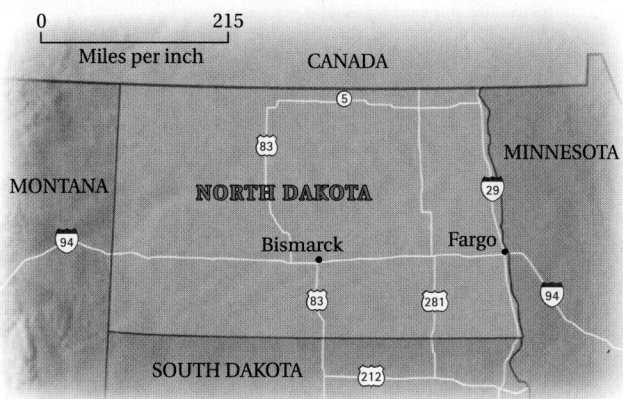

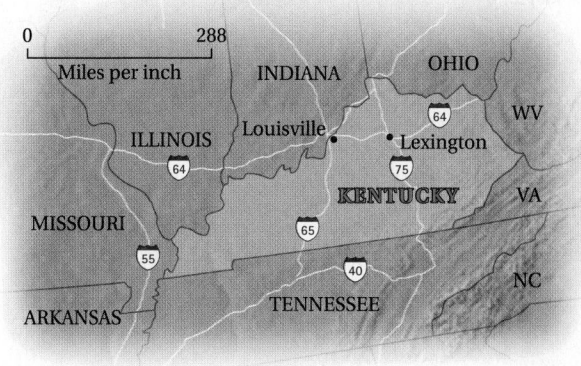

47. Copies of this book are usually shipped from the warehouse in cartons containing 24 books each. How many cartons are needed to ship 1344 books?

48. The H. J. Heinz Company ships 16-oz bottles of ketchup in cartons containing 12 bottles each. How many cartons are needed to ship 528 bottles of ketchup?

49. Elena buys 5 video games at $64 each and pays for them with $10 bills. How many $10 bills does it take?

50. Pedro buys 5 video games at $64 each and pays for them with $20 bills. How many $20 bills does it take?

51. The balance in Meg's bank account is $568. She uses her debit card for purchases of $46, $87, and $129. Then she deposits $94 in the account after returning a book. How much is left in her account?

52. The balance in Dylan's bank account is $749. He uses his debit card for purchases of $34 and $65. Then he makes a deposit of $123 from his paycheck. What is the new balance?

Refer to the information in Example 8 to do Exercises 53–56.

53. For how long must you do aerobic exercises in order to lose one pound?

54. For how long must you bicycle at 9 mph in order to lose one pound?

55. For how long must you play golf in order to lose one pound?

56. For how long must you play tennis singles in order to lose one pound?

57. *Seating Configuration.* The seats in the Boeing 737-500 airplanes in United Airlines' North American fleet are configured with 2 rows of 4 seats across in first class and 16 rows of 6 seats across in economy class. Determine the total seating capacity of the plane.
Source: United Airlines

Economy class: 16 rows of 6 seats   First class: 2 rows of 4 seats

58. *Seating Configuration.* The seats in the Airbus 320 airplanes in United Airlines' North American fleet are configured with 3 rows of 4 seats across in first class and 21 rows of 6 seats across in economy class. Determine the total seating capacity of the plane.
Source: United Airlines

Economy class: 21 rows of 6 seats   First class: 3 rows of 4 seats

59. *Bones in the Hands and Feet.* There are 27 bones in each human hand and 26 bones in each human foot. How many bones are there in all in the hands and feet?

60. An office for adjunct instructors at a community college has 6 bookshelves, each of which is 3 ft wide. The office is moved to a new location that has dimensions of 16 ft by 21 ft. Is it possible for the bookshelves to be put side by side on the 16-ft wall?

Skill Maintenance

Round 234,562 to the nearest: [1.3d]

61. Hundred.   **62.** Ten.   **63.** Thousand.

Estimate each sum or difference by rounding to the nearest thousand.   [1.3e]

64. 2783 + 4602 + 5797 + 8111   **65.** 28,430 − 11,977

66. 5800 − 2100   **67.** 2100 + 5800

Estimate each product by rounding to the nearest hundred.   [1.3e]

68. 787 · 363   **69.** 887 · 799   **70.** 10,362 · 4531

Synthesis

71. 📱 *Speed of Light.* Light travels about 186,000 miles per second (mi/sec) in a vacuum such as in outer space. In ice it travels about 142,000 mi/sec, and in glass it travels about 109,000 mi/sec. In 18 sec, how many more miles will light travel in a vacuum than in ice? than in glass?

72. Carney Community College has 1200 students. Each instructor teaches 4 classes and each student takes 5 classes. There are 30 students and 1 instructor in each classroom. How many instructors are there at Carney Community College?

Copyright © 2012 Pearson Education, Inc.

1.6 Exponential Notation and Order of Operations

(a) Writing Exponential Notation

Consider the product $3 \cdot 3 \cdot 3 \cdot 3$. Such products occur often enough that mathematicians have found it convenient to create a shorter notation, called **exponential notation**, for them. For example,

$\underbrace{3 \cdot 3 \cdot 3 \cdot 3}_{\text{4 factors}}$ is shortened to $3^{4} \leftarrow$ exponent

$\quad\quad\quad\quad\quad\quad\quad\quad\quad\quad\quad\quad\quad$ base

We read exponential notation as follows.

NOTATION	WORD DESCRIPTION
3^4	"three to the fourth power," or "the fourth power of three"
5^3	"five-cubed," or "the cube of five," or "five to the third power," or "the third power of five"
7^2	"seven squared," or "the square of seven," or "seven to the second power," or "the second power of seven"

The wording "seven squared" for 7^2 is derived from the fact that a square with side s has area A given by $A = s^2$.

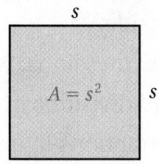

An expression like $3 \cdot 5^2$ is read "three times five squared," or "three times the square of five."

EXAMPLE 1 Write exponential notation for $10 \cdot 10 \cdot 10 \cdot 10 \cdot 10$.

Exponential notation is 10^5.   5 is the *exponent*.   10 is the *base*.

EXAMPLE 2 Write exponential notation for $2 \cdot 2 \cdot 2$.

Exponential notation is 2^3.

Do Exercises 1–4.

OBJECTIVES

(a) Write exponential notation for products such as $4 \cdot 4 \cdot 4$.

(b) Evaluate exponential notation.

(c) Simplify expressions using the rules for order of operations.

(d) Remove parentheses within parentheses.

Write exponential notation.

1. $5 \cdot 5 \cdot 5 \cdot 5$

2. $5 \cdot 5 \cdot 5 \cdot 5 \cdot 5 \cdot 5$

3. $10 \cdot 10$

4. $10 \cdot 10 \cdot 10 \cdot 10$

Answers

1. 5^4 2. 5^6 3. 10^2 4. 10^4

b Evaluating Exponential Notation

We evaluate exponential notation by rewriting it as a product and then computing the product.

EXAMPLE 3 Evaluate: 10^3.   ---------- *Caution!* -------

$$10^3 = 10 \cdot 10 \cdot 10 = 1000$$ 10^3 does not mean $10 \cdot 3$.

EXAMPLE 4 Evaluate: 5^4.

$$5^4 = 5 \cdot 5 \cdot 5 \cdot 5 = 625$$

Do Exercises 5–8.

Evaluate.

5. 10^4 **6.** 10^2

7. 8^3 **8.** 2^5

c Simplifying Expressions

Suppose we have a calculation like the following:

$$3 + 4 \cdot 8.$$

How do we find the answer? Do we add 3 to 4 and then multiply by 8, or do we multiply 4 by 8 and then add 3? In the first case, the answer is 56. In the second, the answer is 35. We agree to compute as in the second case:

$$3 + 4 \cdot 8 = 3 + 32 = 35.$$

Now consider the calculation

$$7 \cdot 14 - (12 + 18).$$

What do the parentheses mean? To deal with these questions, we must make some agreement regarding the order in which we perform operations. The rules are as follows.

RULES FOR ORDER OF OPERATIONS

1. Do all calculations within parentheses ( ), brackets [ ], or braces { } before operations outside.
2. Evaluate all exponential expressions.
3. Do all multiplications and divisions in order from left to right.
4. Do all additions and subtractions in order from left to right.

It is worth noting that these are the rules that computers and most scientific calculators use to do computations.

EXAMPLE 5 Simplify: $16 \div 8 \cdot 2$.

There are no parentheses or exponents, so we begin with the third step.

$$16 \div 8 \cdot 2 = 2 \cdot 2$$ Doing all multiplications and
$$= 4$$ divisions in order from left to right

Calculator Corner

Exponential Notation

Many calculators have a $\boxed{y^x}$ or $\boxed{\wedge}$ key for raising a base to a power. To find 16^3, for example, we press $\boxed{1}\ \boxed{6}\ \boxed{y^x}\ \boxed{3}\ \boxed{=}$ or $\boxed{1}\ \boxed{6}\ \boxed{\wedge}\ \boxed{3}\ \boxed{=}$. The result is 4096.

Exercises: Use a calculator to find each of the following.

1. 3^5

2. 5^6

3. 12^4

4. 2^{11}

Answers

5. 10,000   6. 100   7. 512   8. 32

EXAMPLE 6 Simplify: $7 \cdot 14 - (12 + 18)$.

$$7 \cdot 14 - (12 + 18) = 7 \cdot 14 - 30 \qquad \text{Carrying out operations inside parentheses}$$

$$= 98 - 30 \qquad \text{Doing all multiplications and divisions}$$

$$= 68 \qquad \text{Doing all additions and subtractions}$$

Do Exercises 9–12.

Simplify.

9. $93 - 14 \cdot 3$

10. $104 \div 4 + 4$

11. $25 \cdot 26 - (56 + 10)$

12. $75 \div 5 + (83 - 14)$

EXAMPLE 7 Simplify and compare: $23 - (10 - 9)$ and $(23 - 10) - 9$.

We have

$$23 - (10 - 9) = 23 - 1 = 22;$$
$$(23 - 10) - 9 = 13 - 9 = 4.$$

We can see that $23 - (10 - 9)$ and $(23 - 10) - 9$ represent different numbers. Thus subtraction is not associative.

Do Exercises 13 and 14.

Simplify and compare.

13. $64 \div (32 \div 2)$ and $(64 \div 32) \div 2$

14. $(28 + 13) + 11$ and $28 + (13 + 11)$

EXAMPLE 8 Simplify: $7 \cdot 2 - (12 + 0) \div 3 - (5 - 2)$.

$$7 \cdot 2 - (12 + 0) \div 3 - (5 - 2)$$

$$= 7 \cdot 2 - 12 \div 3 - 3 \qquad \text{Carrying out operations inside parentheses}$$

$$= 14 - 4 - 3 \qquad \text{Doing all multiplications and divisions in order from left to right}$$

$$= 10 - 3$$
$$= 7 \qquad \text{Doing all additions and subtractions in order from left to right}$$

Do Exercise 15.

15. Simplify:

$9 \times 4 - (20 + 4) \div 8 - (6 - 2)$.

EXAMPLE 9 Simplify: $15 \div 3 \cdot 2 \div (10 - 8)$.

$$15 \div 3 \cdot 2 \div (10 - 8)$$

$$= 15 \div 3 \cdot 2 \div 2 \qquad \text{Carrying out operations inside parentheses}$$

$$= 5 \cdot 2 \div 2$$
$$= 10 \div 2 \qquad \text{Doing all multiplications and divisions in order from left to right}$$
$$= 5$$

Do Exercises 16–18.

Simplify.

16. $5 \cdot 5 \cdot 5 + 26 \cdot 71 - (16 + 25 \cdot 3)$

17. $30 \div 5 \cdot 2 + 10 \cdot 20 + 8 \cdot 8 - 23$

18. $95 - 2 \cdot 2 \cdot 2 \cdot 5 \div (24 - 4)$

Answers

9. 51   **10.** 30   **11.** 584   **12.** 84   **13.** 4; 1
14. 52; 52   **15.** 29   **16.** 1880   **17.** 253
18. 93

EXAMPLE 10 Simplify: $4^2 \div (10 - 9 + 1)^3 \cdot 3 - 5$.

$$4^2 \div (10 - 9 + 1)^3 \cdot 3 - 5$$
$$= 4^2 \div (1 + 1)^3 \cdot 3 - 5 \qquad \text{Subtracting inside parentheses}$$
$$= 4^2 \div 2^3 \cdot 3 - 5 \qquad \text{Adding inside parentheses}$$
$$= 16 \div 8 \cdot 3 - 5 \qquad \text{Evaluating exponential expressions}$$
$$= 2 \cdot 3 - 5 \left.\vphantom{\begin{matrix}a\\b\end{matrix}}\right\} \quad \begin{matrix}\text{Doing all multiplications and}\\ \text{divisions in order from left to right}\end{matrix}$$
$$= 6 - 5$$
$$= 1 \qquad \text{Subtracting}$$

Simplify.

19. $5^3 + 26 \cdot 71 - (16 + 25 \cdot 3)$

20. $(1 + 3)^3 + 10 \cdot 20 + 8^2 - 23$

21. $81 - 3^2 \cdot 2 \div (12 - 9)$

Do Exercises 19–21.

EXAMPLE 11 Simplify: $2^9 \div 2^6 \cdot 2^3$.

$$2^9 \div 2^6 \cdot 2^3 = 512 \div 64 \cdot 8 \qquad \begin{matrix}\text{There are no parentheses. Evaluating}\\ \text{exponential expressions}\end{matrix}$$
$$= 8 \cdot 8 \left.\vphantom{\begin{matrix}a\\b\end{matrix}}\right\} \quad \begin{matrix}\text{Doing all multiplications and}\\ \text{divisions in order from left to right}\end{matrix}$$
$$= 64$$

22. Simplify: $2^3 \cdot 2^8 \div 2^9$.

Do Exercise 22.

Calculator Corner

Order of Operations To determine whether a calculator is programmed to follow the rules for order of operations, we can enter a simple calculation that requires using those rules. For example, we enter [3] [+] [4] [×] [2] [=]. If the result is 11, we know that the rules for order of operations have been followed. That is, the multiplication $4 \times 2 = 8$ was performed first and then 3 was added to produce a result of 11. If the result is 14, we know that the calculator performs operations as they are entered rather than following the rules for order of operations. That means, in this case, that 3 and 4 were added first to get 7 and then that sum was multiplied by 2 to produce the result of 14. For such calculators, we would have to enter the operations in the order in which we want them performed. In this case, we would press [4] [×] [2] [+] [3] [=].

Many calculators have parenthesis keys that can be used to enter an expression containing parentheses. To enter $5(4 + 3)$, for example, we press [5] [(] [4] [+] [3] [)] [=]. The result is 35.

Exercises: Simplify.

1. $84 - 5 \cdot 7$ **2.** $80 + 50 \div 10$

3. $3^2 + 9^2 \div 3$ **4.** $4^4 \div 64 - 4$

5. $15 \cdot 7 - (23 + 9)$ **6.** $(4 + 3)^2$

Answers

19. 1880   **20.** 305   **21.** 75   **22.** 4

Averages

In order to find the average of a set of numbers, we use addition and then division. For example, the average of 2, 3, 6, and 9 is found as follows.

The number of addends is 4.

$$\text{Average} = \frac{2 + 3 + 6 + 9}{4} = \frac{20}{4} = 5$$

Divide by 4.

The fraction bar acts as a pair of grouping symbols so

$$\frac{2 + 3 + 6 + 9}{4} \quad \text{is equivalent to} \quad (2 + 3 + 6 + 9) \div 4.$$

Thus we are using order of operations when we compute an average.

AVERAGE

The **average** of a set of numbers is the sum of the numbers divided by the number of addends.

EXAMPLE 12 *Average Height of Waterfalls.* The heights of the four highest waterfalls in the world are shown in the figure below. Determine the average height of the four falls.

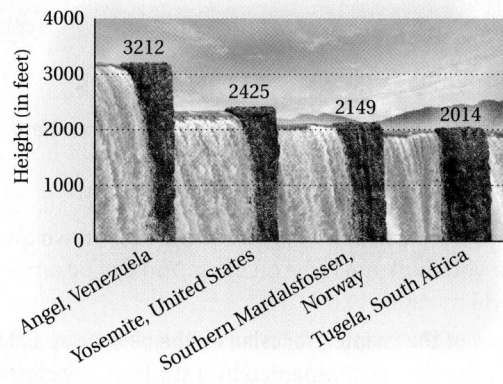

World's Highest Waterfalls

SOURCE: World Almanac

The average is given by

$$\frac{3212 + 2425 + 2149 + 2014}{4} = \frac{9800}{4} = 2450.$$

The average height of the world's four highest waterfalls is 2450 ft.

Do Exercise 23.

(d) Removing Parentheses within Parentheses

When parentheses occur within parentheses, we can make them different shapes, such as [ ] (also called "brackets") and { } (also called "braces"). All of these have the same meaning. When parentheses occur within parentheses, computations in the innermost ones are to be done first.

23. Average Number of Career Hits. The numbers of career hits of five Hall of Fame baseball players are given in the bar graph below. Find the average number of career hits of all five.

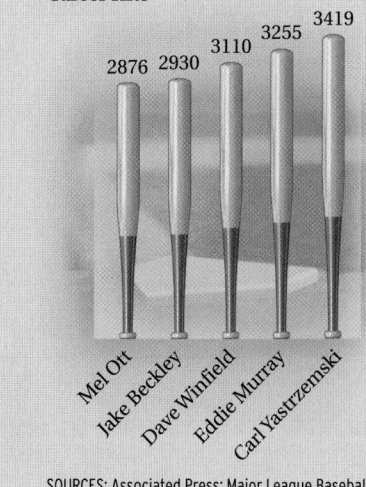

Career Hits

SOURCES: Associated Press; Major League Baseball

Answer

23. 3118 hits

EXAMPLE 13 Simplify: $[25 - (4 + 3) \cdot 3] \div (11 - 7)$.

$$[25 - (4 + 3) \cdot 3] \div (11 - 7)$$

$= [25 - 7 \cdot 3] \div (11 - 7)$ Doing the calculations in the innermost parentheses first

$= [25 - 21] \div (11 - 7)$ Doing the multiplication in the brackets

$= 4 \div 4$ Subtracting

$= 1$ Dividing

EXAMPLE 14 Simplify: $16 \div 2 + \{40 - [13 - (4 + 2)]\}$.

$$16 \div 2 + \{40 - [13 - (4 + 2)]\}$$

$= 16 \div 2 + \{40 - [13 - 6]\}$ Doing the calculations in the innermost parentheses first

$= 16 \div 2 + \{40 - 7\}$ Again, doing the calculations in the innermost brackets

$= 16 \div 2 + 33$ Subtracting inside the braces

$= 8 + 33$ Doing all multiplications and divisions in order from left to right

$= 41$ Adding

Do Exercises 24 and 25.

Simplify.

24. $9 \times 5 + \{6 \div [14 - (5 + 3)]\}$

25. $[18 - (2 + 7) \div 3] - (31 - 10 \times 2)$

STUDY TIPS

PREPARING FOR AND TAKING TESTS

You are probably ready to begin preparing for your first test. Here are some test-taking study tips.

- **Make up your own test questions as you study.** After you have done your homework over a particular objective, write one or two questions on your own that you think might be on a test. You will be amazed at the insight this will provide.

- **Do an overall review of the chapter, focusing on the objectives and the examples.** This should be accompanied by a study of any class notes you may have taken.

- **Do the exercises in the mid-chapter review and in the end-of-chapter review.** Check your answers at the back of the book. If you have trouble with an exercise, use the objective symbol as a guide to go back and do further study of that objective.

- **Take the chapter test at the end of the chapter.** Check the answers and use the objective symbols at the back of the book as a reference for review.

- **When taking a test, read each question carefully. Try to do all the questions the first time through, but pace yourself.** Answer all the questions, and mark those to recheck if you have time at the end. Very often, your first hunch will be correct.

- **Write your test in a neat and orderly manner.** Doing so will allow you to check your work easily and will also help your instructor follow the steps you took in answering the test questions.

Answers

24. 46   25. 4

1.6

Exercise Set

For Extra Help

MyMathLab

Math XL
PRACTICE

WATCH

DOWNLOAD

READ

REVIEW

a Write exponential notation.

1. $3 \cdot 3 \cdot 3 \cdot 3$

2. $2 \cdot 2 \cdot 2 \cdot 2 \cdot 2$

3. $5 \cdot 5$

4. $13 \cdot 13 \cdot 13$

5. $7 \cdot 7 \cdot 7 \cdot 7 \cdot 7$

6. $9 \cdot 9$

7. $10 \cdot 10 \cdot 10$

8. $1 \cdot 1 \cdot 1 \cdot 1$

b Evaluate.

9. 7^2

10. 5^3

11. 9^3

12. 8^2

13. 12^4

14. 10^5

15. 3^5

16. 2^6

c Simplify.

17. $12 + (6 + 4)$

18. $(12 + 6) + 18$

19. $52 - (40 - 8)$

20. $(52 - 40) - 8$

21. $1000 \div (100 \div 10)$

22. $(1000 \div 100) \div 10$

23. $(256 \div 64) \div 4$

24. $256 \div (64 \div 4)$

25. $(2 + 5)^2$

26. $2^2 + 5^2$

27. $(11 - 8)^2 - (18 - 16)^2$

28. $(32 - 27)^3 + (19 + 1)^3$

29. $16 \cdot 24 + 50$

30. $23 + 18 \cdot 20$

31. $83 - 7 \cdot 6$

32. $10 \cdot 7 - 4$

33. $10 \cdot 10 - 3 \cdot 4$

34. $90 - 5 \cdot 5 \cdot 2$

35. $4^3 \div 8 - 4$

36. $8^2 - 8 \cdot 2$

37. $17 \cdot 20 - (17 + 20)$

38. $1000 \div 25 - (15 + 5)$

39. $6 \cdot 10 - 4 \cdot 10$

40. $3 \cdot 8 + 5 \cdot 8$

41. $300 \div 5 + 10$

42. $144 \div 4 - 2$

43. $3 \cdot (2 + 8)^2 - 5 \cdot (4 - 3)^2$

44. $7 \cdot (10 - 3)^2 - 2 \cdot (3 + 1)^2$

45. $4^2 + 8^2 \div 2^2$

46. $6^2 - 3^4 \div 3^3$

47. $10^3 - 10 \cdot 6 - (4 + 5 \cdot 6)$

48. $7^2 + 20 \cdot 4 - (28 + 9 \cdot 2)$

49. $6 \cdot 11 - (7 + 3) \div 5 - (6 - 4)$

50. $8 \times 9 - (12 - 8) \div 4 - (10 - 7)$

51. $120 - 3^3 \cdot 4 \div (5 \cdot 6 - 6 \cdot 4)$

52. $80 - 2^4 \cdot 15 \div (7 \cdot 5 - 45 \div 3)$

53. $2^3 \cdot 2^8 \div 2^6$

54. $2^7 \div 2^5 \cdot 2^4 \div 2^2$

55. Find the average of $64, $97, and $121.

56. Find the average of four test grades of 86, 92, 80, and 78.

57. Find the average of 320, 128, 276, and 880.

58. Find the average of $1025, $775, $2062, $942, and $3721.

(d) Simplify.

59. $8 \times 13 + \{42 \div [18 - (6 + 5)]\}$

60. $72 \div 6 - \{2 \times [9 - (4 \times 2)]\}$

61. $[14 - (3 + 5) \div 2] - [18 \div (8 - 2)]$

62. $[92 \times (6 - 4) \div 8] + [7 \times (8 - 3)]$

Copyright © 2012 Pearson Education, Inc.

63. $(82 - 14) \times [(10 + 45 \div 5) - (6 \cdot 6 - 5 \cdot 5)]$

64. $(18 \div 2) \cdot \{[(9 \cdot 9 - 1) \div 2] - [5 \cdot 20 - (7 \cdot 9 - 2)]\}$

65. $4 \times \{(200 - 50 \div 5) - [(35 \div 7) \cdot (35 \div 7) - 4 \times 3]\}$

66. $15(23 - 4 \cdot 2)^3 \div (3 \cdot 25)$

67. $\{[18 - 2 \cdot 6] - [40 \div (17 - 9)]\} + \{48 - 13 \times 3 + [(50 - 7 \cdot 5) + 2]\}$

68. $(19 - 2^4)^5 - (141 \div 47)^2$

Skill Maintenance

Solve.   [1.4b]

69. $x + 341 = 793$

70. $4197 + x = 5032$

71. $7 \cdot x = 91$

72. $1554 = 42 \cdot y$

73. $3240 = y + 898$

74. $6000 = 1102 + t$

75. $25 \cdot t = 625$

76. $10,000 = 100 \cdot t$

Solve.   [1.5a]

77. *Colorado.*   The state of Colorado is roughly the shape of a rectangle that is 273 mi by 382 mi. What is its area?

78. On a long four-day trip, a family bought the following amounts of gasoline for their motor home:

23 gallons,   24 gallons,

26 gallons,   25 gallons.

How much gasoline did they buy in all?

Synthesis

Each of the answers in Exercises 79–81 is incorrect. First find the correct answer. Then place as many parentheses as needed in the expression in order to make the incorrect answer correct.

79. $1 + 5 \cdot 4 + 3 = 36$

80. $12 \div 4 + 2 \cdot 3 - 2 = 2$

81. $12 \div 4 + 2 \cdot 3 - 2 = 4$

82. Use one occurrence each of 1, 2, 3, 4, 5, 6, 7, 8, and 9 and any of the symbols $+$, $-$, $\cdot$, $\div$, and ( ) to represent 100.

1.7

Factorizations

OBJECTIVES

a Determine whether one number is a factor of another, and find the factors of a number.

b Find some multiples of a number, and determine whether a number is divisible by another.

c Given a number from 1 to 100, tell whether it is prime, composite, or neither.

d Find the prime factorization of a composite number.

SKILL TO REVIEW
Objective 1.3c: Divide whole numbers.

Divide.

1. $329 \div 8$

2. $23\overline{)1081}$

In this chapter, we begin our work with fractions and fraction notation. Certain skills make such work easier. For example, in order to simplify $\frac{12}{32}$, it is important that we be able to *factor* 12 and 32, as follows:

$$\frac{12}{32} = \frac{4 \cdot 3}{4 \cdot 8}.$$

Then we "remove" a factor of 1:

$$\frac{4 \cdot 3}{4 \cdot 8} = \frac{4}{4} \cdot \frac{3}{8} = 1 \cdot \frac{3}{8} = \frac{3}{8}.$$

Thus factoring is an important skill in working with fractions.

a Factors and Factorization

In Sections 1.7 and 1.8, we consider only the **natural numbers** 1, 2, 3, and so on.

Let's look at the product $3 \cdot 4 = 12$. We say that 3 and 4 are **factors** of 12. When we divide 12 by 3, we get a remainder of 0. We say that the divisor 3 is a **factor** of the dividend 12.

FACTOR

- In the product $a \cdot b$, a and b are called **factors**.
- If we divide Q by d and get a remainder of 0, then the divisor d is a **factor** of the dividend Q.

EXAMPLE 1 Determine by long division **(a)** whether 6 is a factor of 198 and **(b)** whether 15 is a factor of 198.

a)
```
      33
  6)198
    18
    ──
     18
     18
    ──
      0  ← Remainder is 0.
```
The remainder is 0, so 6 is a factor of 198.

b)
```
       13
  15)198
     15
    ──
     48
     45
    ──
      3  ← Not 0
```
The remainder is not 0, so 15 is not a factor of 198.

Do Margin Exercises 1 and 2.

Determine whether the second number is a factor of the first.

1. 72; 8   **2.** 2384; 28

Consider $12 = 3 \cdot 4$. We say that $3 \cdot 4$ is a **factorization** of 12. Similarly, $6 \cdot 2$, $12 \cdot 1$, $2 \cdot 2 \cdot 3$, and $1 \cdot 3 \cdot 4$ are also factorizations of 12. Since $a = a \cdot 1$, every number has a factorization, and every number has factors. For some numbers, the factors consist of only the number itself and 1. For example, the only factorization of 17 is $17 \cdot 1$, so the only factors of 17 are 17 and 1.

Answers

Skill to Review:
1. 41 R 1   2. 47

Margin Exercises:
1. Yes   2. No

EXAMPLE 2 Find all the factors of 70.

We find as many "two-factor" factorizations as we can. We check sequentially the numbers 1, 2, 3, and so on, to see if we can form any factorizations:

70

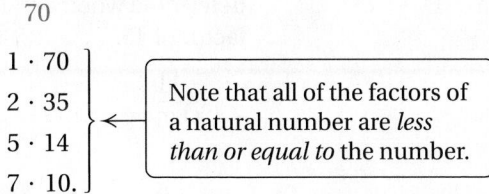

$$\left.\begin{array}{l} 1 \cdot 70 \\ 2 \cdot 35 \\ 5 \cdot 14 \\ 7 \cdot 10. \end{array}\right\}$$ Note that all of the factors of a natural number are *less than or equal to* the number.

Note that 3, 4, and 6 are not factors. If there are additional factors, they must be between 7 and 10. Since 8 and 9 are not factors, we are finished. The factors of 70 are 1, 2, 5, 7, 10, 14, 35, and 70.

Do Exercises 3-6.

Find all the factors of each number.

3. 10   **4.** 45

5. 62   **6.** 24

(b) Multiples and Divisibility

A **multiple** of a natural number is a product of that number and some natural number. For example, some multiples of 2 are

$$\left.\begin{array}{l} 2 \quad (\text{because } 2 = 1 \cdot 2); \\ 4 \quad (\text{because } 4 = 2 \cdot 2); \\ 6 \quad (\text{because } 6 = 3 \cdot 2); \\ 8 \quad (\text{because } 8 = 4 \cdot 2). \end{array}\right\}$$ Note that all but one of the multiples of a number are *larger* than the number.

We find multiples of 2 by counting by twos: 2, 4, 6, 8, and so on. We can find multiples of 3 by counting by threes: 3, 6, 9, 12, and so on.

EXAMPLE 3 Show that each of the numbers 8, 12, 20, and 36 is a multiple of 4.

$$8 = 2 \cdot 4 \qquad 12 = 3 \cdot 4 \qquad 20 = 5 \cdot 4 \qquad 36 = 9 \cdot 4$$

Do Exercises 7 and 8.

7. Show that each of the numbers 5, 45, and 100 is a multiple of 5.

8. Show that each of the numbers 10, 60, and 110 is a multiple of 10.

EXAMPLE 4 Multiply by 1, 2, 3, and so on, to find ten multiples of 7.

$1 \cdot 7 = 7$	$3 \cdot 7 = 21$	$5 \cdot 7 = 35$	$7 \cdot 7 = 49$	$9 \cdot 7 = 63$
$2 \cdot 7 = 14$	$4 \cdot 7 = 28$	$6 \cdot 7 = 42$	$8 \cdot 7 = 56$	$10 \cdot 7 = 70$

Do Exercise 9.

9. Multiply by 1, 2, 3, and so on, to find ten multiples of 5.

DIVISIBILITY

The number a is **divisible** by another number b if there exists a number c such that $a = b \cdot c$. The statements "a is **divisible** by b," "a is a **multiple** of b," and "b is a **factor** of a" all have the same meaning.

Thus, 27 is *divisible* by 3 because $27 = 3 \cdot 9$. We can also say that 27 is a *multiple* of 3, and 3 is a *factor* of 27.

Answers

3. 1, 2, 5, 10   **4.** 1, 3, 5, 9, 15, 45
5. 1, 2, 31, 62   **6.** 1, 2, 3, 4, 6, 8, 12, 24
7. $5 = 1 \cdot 5; 45 = 9 \cdot 5; 100 = 20 \cdot 5$
8. $10 = 1 \cdot 10; 60 = 6 \cdot 10; 110 = 11 \cdot 10$
9. 5, 10, 15, 20, 25, 30, 35, 40, 45, 50

EXAMPLE 5 Determine **(a)** whether 45 is divisible by 9 and **(b)** whether 45 is divisible by 4.

a) We divide 45 by 9 to determine whether 9 is a factor of 45.

$$\begin{array}{r} 5 \\ 9\overline{)45} \\ \underline{45} \\ 0 \end{array} \leftarrow \text{Remainder is 0.}$$

Because the remainder is 0, 45 is divisible by 9.

b) We divide 45 by 4 to determine whether 4 is a factor of 45.

$$\begin{array}{r} 11 \\ 4\overline{)45} \\ \underline{4} \\ 5 \\ \underline{4} \\ 1 \end{array} \leftarrow \text{Not 0}$$

Since the remainder is not 0, 45 is not divisible by 4.

10. Determine whether 16 is divisible by 2.

11. Determine whether 125 is divisible by 5.

12. Determine whether 125 is divisible by 6.

Do Exercises 10–12.

Calculator Corner

Divisibility and Factors We can use a calculator to determine whether one number is divisible by another number or whether one number is a factor of another number. For example, to determine whether 387 is divisible by 9, we press ▢3 ▢8 ▢7 ▢÷ ▢9 ▢=. The display is ▢43. Since 43 is a natural number, we know that 387 is a multiple of 9; that is, 387 = 43 · 9. Thus, 387 is divisible by 9, and 9 is a factor of 387.

Exercises: For each pair of numbers, determine whether the second number is a factor of the first number.

1. 502; 8

2. 651; 21

3. 3875; 25

4. 1047; 14

---

13. Tell whether each number is prime, composite, or neither.

1, 2, 6, 12, 13, 19, 41, 65, 73, 99

---

c **Prime and Composite Numbers**

> **PRIME AND COMPOSITE NUMBERS**
>
> - A natural number that has exactly two *different* factors, only itself and 1, is called a **prime number**.
> - The number 1 is *not* prime.
> - A natural number, other than 1, that is not prime is **composite**.

EXAMPLE 6 Determine whether the numbers 1, 2, 7, 8, 9, 11, 18, 27, 39, 43, 56, 59, and 77 are prime, composite, or neither.

The number 1 is not prime. It does not have *two* different factors.

The number 2 is prime. It has only the factors 2 and 1.

The numbers 7, 11, 43, and 59 are prime. Each has only two factors, itself and 1.

The number 8 is not prime. It has the factors 1, 2, 4, and 8 and is composite.

The numbers 9, 18, 27, 39, 56, and 77 are composite. Each has more than two factors.

Thus we have

Prime: 2, 7, 11, 43, 59;

Composite: 8, 9, 18, 27, 39, 56, 77;

Neither: 1.

The number 2 is the *only* even prime number. It is also the smallest prime number. The number 0 is neither prime nor composite, but 0 is *not* a natural number and thus is not considered here. We are considering only natural numbers.

Do Exercise 13.

Answers

10. Yes **11.** Yes **12.** No **13.** 2, 13, 19, 41, 73 are prime; 6, 12, 65, 99 are composite; 1 is neither.

The table at right lists the prime numbers from 2 to 97. There are more extensive tables, but these prime numbers will be the most helpful to you in this text.

A TABLE OF PRIME NUMBERS FROM 2 TO 97

2, 3, 5, 7, 11, 13, 17, 19, 23, 29, 31, 37, 41, 43, 47, 53, 59, 61, 67, 71, 73, 79, 83, 89, 97

(d) Prime Factorizations

When we factor a composite number into a product of primes, we find the **prime factorization** of the number. To do this, we consider the primes

2, 3, 5, 7, 11, 13, 17, 19, 23, and so on,

and determine whether a given number is divisible by the primes.

EXAMPLE 7 Find the prime factorization of 39.

a) We divide by the first prime, 2.

$$\begin{array}{r} 19 \\ 2\overline{)39} \\ \underline{2} \\ 19 \\ \underline{18} \\ 1 \end{array}$$

Because the remainder is not 0, 2 is not a factor of 39, and 39 is not divisible by 2.

b) We divide by the next prime, 3.

$$\begin{array}{r} 13 \quad R = 0 \\ 3\overline{)39} \end{array}$$

The remainder is 0, so we know that $39 = 3 \cdot 13$. Because 13 is a prime, we are finished. The prime factorization is

$$39 = 3 \cdot 13.$$

EXAMPLE 8 Find the prime factorization of 220.

a) We divide by the first prime, 2.

$$\begin{array}{r} 110 \quad R = 0 \\ 2\overline{)220} \end{array} \qquad 220 = 2 \cdot 110$$

b) Because 110 is composite, we continue to divide, starting with 2 again.

$$\begin{array}{r} 55 \quad R = 0 \\ 2\overline{)110} \end{array} \qquad 220 = 2 \cdot 2 \cdot 55$$

c) Since 55 is composite and is not divisible by 2 or 3, we divide by the next prime, 5.

$$\begin{array}{r} 11 \quad R = 0 \\ 5\overline{)55} \end{array} \qquad 220 = 2 \cdot 2 \cdot 5 \cdot 11$$

Because 11 is prime, we are finished. The prime factorization is

$$220 = 2 \cdot 2 \cdot 5 \cdot 11.$$

We abbreviate our procedure as follows.

$$
\begin{array}{r}
11 \\
5\overline{)55} \\
2\overline{)110} \\
2\overline{)220}
\end{array}
$$

$$220 = 2 \cdot 2 \cdot 5 \cdot 11$$

Because multiplication is commutative, a factorization such as $2 \cdot 2 \cdot 5 \cdot 11$ could also be expressed as $5 \cdot 2 \cdot 2 \cdot 11$ or $2 \cdot 5 \cdot 11 \cdot 2$ (or, in exponential notation, as $2^2 \cdot 5 \cdot 11$ or $11 \cdot 2^2 \cdot 5$), but the prime factors are the same in each case. For this reason, we agree that any of these is "the" prime factorization of 220.

> Every number has just one (unique) prime factorization.

-------------- *Caution!* --------------

Keep in mind the difference between finding all the factors of a number and finding the prime factorization. In Example 9, the prime factorization of 72 is $2 \cdot 2 \cdot 2 \cdot 3 \cdot 3$. The factors of 72 are 1, 2, 3, 4, 6, 8, 9, 12, 18, 24, 36, and 72.

EXAMPLE 9   Find the prime factorization of 72.

We can do divisions "up" as follows:

$$
\begin{array}{r}
3 \leftarrow \text{Prime quotient}\\
3\overline{)\ 9} \\
2\overline{)18} \\
2\overline{)36} \\
2\overline{)72} \leftarrow \text{Begin here}
\end{array}
$$

$$72 = 2 \cdot 2 \cdot 2 \cdot 3 \cdot 3$$

Another way to find the prime factorization of 72 uses a **factor tree** as follows. Begin by determining any factorization you can, and then continue factoring.

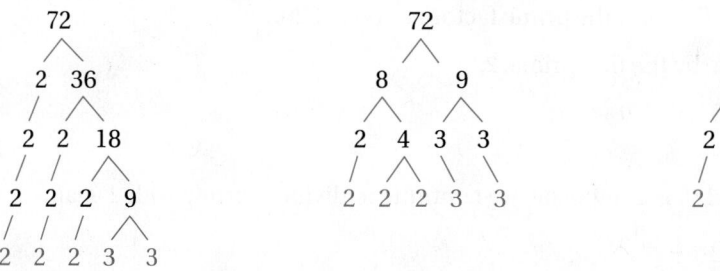

EXAMPLE 10   Find the prime factorization of 189.

We can use a string of successive divisions or a factor tree. Since 189 is not divisible by 2, we begin with 3.

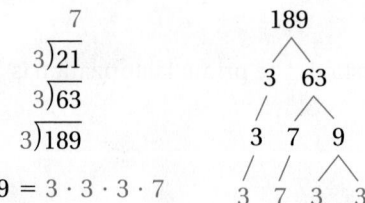

$$189 = 3 \cdot 3 \cdot 3 \cdot 7$$

Find the prime factorization of each number.

14. 6   **15.** 12

16. 45   **17.** 98

18. 126   **19.** 144

20. 1960   **21.** 1925

Do Exercises 14–21.

Answers

14. $2 \cdot 3$ **15.** $2 \cdot 2 \cdot 3$ **16.** $3 \cdot 3 \cdot 5$
17. $2 \cdot 7 \cdot 7$ **18.** $2 \cdot 3 \cdot 3 \cdot 7$
19. $2 \cdot 2 \cdot 2 \cdot 2 \cdot 3 \cdot 3$ **20.** $2 \cdot 2 \cdot 2 \cdot 5 \cdot 7 \cdot 7$
21. $5 \cdot 5 \cdot 7 \cdot 11$

a   Determine whether the second number is a factor of the first.

1. 52; 14   **2.** 52; 13   **3.** 625; 25   **4.** 680; 16

Find all the factors of each number.

5. 18   **6.** 16   **7.** 54   **8.** 48

9. 4   **10.** 9   **11.** 1   **12.** 13

13. 98   **14.** 100   **15.** 255   **16.** 120

b   Multiply by 1, 2, 3, and so on, to find ten multiples of each number.

17. 4   **18.** 11   **19.** 20   **20.** 50

21. 3   **22.** 5   **23.** 12   **24.** 13

25. 10   **26.** 6   **27.** 9   **28.** 14

29. Determine whether 26 is divisible by 6.   **30.** Determine whether 48 is divisible by 8.

31. Determine whether 1880 is divisible by 8.   **32.** Determine whether 4227 is divisible by 3.

33. Determine whether 256 is divisible by 16.   **34.** Determine whether 102 is divisible by 4.

35. Determine whether 4227 is divisible by 9.   **36.** Determine whether 200 is divisible by 25.

37. Determine whether 8650 is divisible by 16.   **38.** Determine whether 4143 is divisible by 7.

c   Determine whether each number is prime, composite, or neither.

39. 1   **40.** 2   **41.** 9   **42.** 19

43. 11   **44.** 27   **45.** 29   **46.** 49

Find the prime factorization of each number.

47. 8   **48.** 16   **49.** 14   **50.** 15   **51.** 42

52. 32   **53.** 25   **54.** 40   **55.** 50   **56.** 62

57. 169   **58.** 140   **59.** 100   **60.** 110   **61.** 35

62. 70   **63.** 72   **64.** 86   **65.** 77   **66.** 99

67. 2884   **68.** 484   **69.** 51   **70.** 91   **71.** 1200

72. 1800   **73.** 273   **74.** 675   **75.** 1122   **76.** 6435

Skill Maintenance

Multiply. [1.3a]

77. $2 \cdot 13$ **78.** $8 \cdot 32$ **79.** $17 \cdot 25$ **80.** $25 \cdot 168$

Divide. [1.3c]

81. $0 \div 22$ **82.** $22 \div 1$ **83.** $22 \div 22$ **84.** $66 \div 22$

Solve. [1.5a]

85. *Morel Mushrooms.* During the spring, Kate's Country Market sold 43 pounds of fresh morel mushrooms. The mushrooms sold for $22 a pound. Find the total amount Kate took in from the sale of the mushrooms.

86. Sandy can type 62 words per minute. How long will it take her to type 12,462 words?

Synthesis

87. *Factors and Sums.* The top number in each column of the table below can be factored as a product of two numbers whose sum is the bottom number in the column. For example, in the first column, 56 has been factored as $7 \cdot 8$, and $7 + 8 = 15$. Fill in the blank spaces in the table.

PRODUCT	56	63	36	72	140	96		168	110			
FACTOR	7									9	24	3
FACTOR	8						8	8		10	18	
SUM	15	16	20	38	24	20	14		21			24

Copyright © 2012 Pearson Education, Inc.

1.8 Divisibility

Suppose you are asked to find the simplest fraction notation for

$$\frac{117}{225}.$$

Since the numbers are quite large, you might feel that the task is difficult. However, both the numerator and the denominator are divisible by 9. If you knew this, you could factor and simplify quickly as follows:

$$\frac{117}{225} = \frac{9 \cdot 13}{9 \cdot 25} = \frac{9}{9} \cdot \frac{13}{25} = 1 \cdot \frac{13}{25} = \frac{13}{25}.$$

How did we know that both numbers have 9 as a factor? There is a simple test for determining this.

In this section, you learn quick ways to determine whether a number is divisible by 2, 3, 4, 5, 6, 8, 9, or 10. This will make simplifying fraction notation much easier.

a Rules for Divisibility

Divisibility by 2

You may already know the test for divisibility by 2.

> **BY 2**
>
> A number is **divisible by 2** (is *even*) if it has a ones digit of 0, 2, 4, 6, or 8 (that is, it has an even ones digit).

Let's see why this test works. Consider 354, which is

$$3 \text{ hundreds} + 5 \text{ tens} + 4.$$

Hundreds and tens are both multiples of 2. If the last digit is a multiple of 2, then the entire number is a multiple of 2.

EXAMPLES Determine whether each number is divisible by 2.

1. 355 is *not* divisible by 2; 5 is *not* even.
2. 4786 is divisible by 2; 6 is even.
3. 8990 is divisible by 2; 0 is even.
4. 4261 is *not* divisible by 2; 1 is *not* even.

Do Margin Exercises 1–4.

OBJECTIVE

a Determine whether a number is divisible by 2, 3, 4, 5, 6, 8, 9, or 10.

SKILL TO REVIEW
Objective 1.2a: Add whole numbers.

Add.

1. $9 + 8 + 2 + 1$
2. $7 + 3 + 0 + 2 + 6$

Determine whether each number is divisible by 2.

1. 84
2. 59
3. 998
4. 2225

Answers

Skill to Review:
1. 20   2. 18

Margin Exercises:
1. Yes   2. No   3. Yes   4. No

STUDY TIPS

FORMING A STUDY GROUP

Consider forming a study group with some of your fellow students. Exchange e-mail addresses, telephone numbers, and schedules so that you can coordinate study time for homework and tests.

Determine whether each number is divisible by 3.

5. 111   **6.** 1111

7. 309   **8.** 17,216

Determine whether each number is divisible by 6.

9. 420   **10.** 106

11. 321   **12.** 444

Answers

5. Yes   6. No   7. Yes   8. No   9. Yes
10. No   11. No   12. Yes

84   CHAPTER 1   Whole Numbers

Divisibility by 3

> **BY 3**
>
> A number is **divisible by 3** if the sum of its digits is divisible by 3.

Let's illustrate why the test for divisibility by 3 works. Consider 852; since $852 = 3 \cdot 284$, 852 is divisible by 3.

$$852 = 8 \cdot 100 + 5 \cdot 10 + 2 \cdot 1$$
$$= 8(99 + 1) + 5(9 + 1) + 2(1)$$
$$= 8 \cdot 99 + 8 \cdot 1 + 5 \cdot 9 + 5 \cdot 1 + 2 \cdot 1$$

Using the distributive law: $a(b + c) = a \cdot b + a \cdot c$

Since 99 and 9 are each a multiple of 3, we see that $8 \cdot 99$ and $5 \cdot 9$ are multiples of 3. This leaves $8 \cdot 1 + 5 \cdot 1 + 2 \cdot 1$, or $8 + 5 + 2$. If $8 + 5 + 2$, the sum of the digits, is divisible by 3, then 852 is divisible by 3.

EXAMPLES Determine whether each number is divisible by 3.

5. 18 $1 + 8 = 9$
6. 93 $9 + 3 = 12$
7. 201 $2 + 0 + 1 = 3$

Each is divisible by 3 because the sum of its digits is divisible by 3.

8. 256 $2 + 5 + 6 = 13$ The sum of the digits, 13, is *not* divisible by 3, so 256 is *not* divisible by 3.

Do Exercises 5–8.

Divisibility by 6

A number divisible by 6 is a multiple of 6. But $6 = 2 \cdot 3$, so the number is also a multiple of 2 and 3. Thus we have the following.

> **BY 6**
>
> A number is **divisible by 6** if its ones digit is 0, 2, 4, 6, or 8 (is even) and the sum of its digits is divisible by 3.

EXAMPLES Determine whether each number is divisible by 6.

9. 720

Because 720 is even, it is divisible by 2. Also, $7 + 2 + 0 = 9$, so 720 is divisible by 3. Thus, 720 is divisible by 6.

720          $7 + 2 + 0 = 9$
Even   Divisible by 3

10. 73

73 is *not* divisible by 6 because it is *not* even.

11. 256

Although 256 is even, it is *not* divisible by 6 because the sum of its digits, $2 + 5 + 6$, or 13, is *not* divisible by 3.

Do Exercises 9–12.

Divisibility by 9

The test for divisibility by 9 is similar to the test for divisibility by 3.

> **BY 9**
>
> A number is **divisible by 9** if the sum of its digits is divisible by 9.

EXAMPLES   Determine whether each number is divisible by 9.

12. 6984

Because $6 + 9 + 8 + 4 = 27$ and 27 is divisible by 9, 6984 is divisible by 9.

13. 322

Because $3 + 2 + 2 = 7$ and 7 is *not* divisible by 9, 322 is *not* divisible by 9.

Do Exercises 13–16.

> Determine whether each number is divisible by 9.
>
> **13.** 16   **14.** 117
>
> **15.** 930   **16.** 29,223

Divisibility by 10

> **BY 10**
>
> A number is **divisible by 10** if its ones digit is 0.

We know that this test works because the product of 10 and *any* number has a ones digit of 0.

EXAMPLES   Determine whether each number is divisible by 10.

14. 3440   is divisible by 10 because the ones digit is 0.

15. 3447   is *not* divisible by 10 because the ones digit is not 0.

Do Exercises 17–20.

> Determine whether each number is divisible by 10.
>
> **17.** 305   **18.** 847
>
> **19.** 300   **20.** 8760

Divisibility by 5

> **BY 5**
>
> A number is **divisible by 5** if its ones digit is 0 or 5.

EXAMPLES   Determine whether each number is divisible by 5.

16. 220   is divisible by 5 because the ones digit is 0.

17. 475   is divisible by 5 because the ones digit is 5.

18. 6514   is *not* divisible by 5 because the ones digit is neither 0 nor 5.

Do Exercises 21–24.

> Determine whether each number is divisible by 5.
>
> **21.** 5780   **22.** 3427
>
> **23.** 34,678   **24.** 7775

Let's see why the test for 5 works. Consider 7830:

$$7830 = 10 \cdot 783 = 5 \cdot 2 \cdot 783.$$

Since 7830 is divisible by 10 and 5 is a factor of 10, 7830 is divisible by 5.

Answers

13. No   14. Yes   15. No   16. Yes
17. No   18. No   19. Yes 20. Yes
21. Yes 22. No   23. No   24. Yes

Consider 6734:

$$6734 = 673 \text{ tens} + 4.$$

Tens are multiples of 5, so the only number that must be checked is the ones digit. If the last digit is a multiple of 5, then the entire number is. In this case, 4 is *not* a multiple of 5, so 6734 is *not* divisible by 5.

Divisibility by 4

The test for divisibility by 4 is similar to the test for divisibility by 2.

BY 4

A number is **divisible by 4** if the number named by its last *two* digits is divisible by 4.

EXAMPLES Determine whether the number is divisible by 4.

19. 8212   is divisible by 4 because 12 is divisible by 4.

20. 5216   is divisible by 4 because 16 is divisible by 4.

21. 8211   is *not* divisible by 4 because 11 is *not* divisible by 4.

22. 7538   is *not* divisible by 4 because 38 is *not* divisible by 4.

Do Exercises 25–28.

To see why the test for divisibility by 4 works, consider 516:

$$516 = 5 \text{ hundreds} + 16.$$

Hundreds are multiples of 4. If the number named by the last two digits is a multiple of 4, then the entire number is a multiple of 4.

Divisibility by 8

The test for divisibility by 8 is an extension of the tests for divisibility by 2 and 4.

BY 8

A number is **divisible by 8** if the number named by its last *three* digits is divisible by 8.

EXAMPLES Determine whether the number is divisible by 8.

23.   5648   is divisible by 8 because 648 is divisible by 8.

24. 96,088   is divisible by 8 because 88 is divisible by 8.

25.   7324   is *not* divisible by 8 because 324 is *not* divisible by 8.

26. 13,420   is *not* divisible by 8 because 420 is *not* divisible by 8.

Do Exercises 29–32.

A Note about Divisibility by 7

There are several tests for divisibility by 7, but all of them are more complicated than simply dividing by 7. So if you want to test for divisibility by 7, simply divide by 7, either by hand or using a calculator.

Determine whether each number is divisible by 4.

25. 216   **26.** 217

27. 5862   **28.** 23,524

Determine whether each number is divisible by 8.

29. 7564   **30.** 7864

31. 17,560   **32.** 25,716

Answers

25. Yes   26. No   27. No   28. Yes
29. No   30. Yes   31. Yes   32. No

a To answer Exercises 1–8, consider the following numbers.

46	300	85	256
224	36	711	8064
19	45,270	13,251	1867
555	4444	254,765	21,568

1. Which of the above are divisible by 2?

2. Which of the above are divisible by 3?

3. Which of the above are divisible by 4?

4. Which of the above are divisible by 5?

5. Which of the above are divisible by 6?

6. Which of the above are divisible by 8?

7. Which of the above are divisible by 9?

8. Which of the above are divisible by 10?

To answer Exercises 9–16, consider the following numbers.

56	200	75	35
324	42	812	402
784	501	2345	111,111
55,555	3009	2001	1005

9. Which of the above are divisible by 3?

10. Which of the above are divisible by 2?

11. Which of the above are divisible by 5?

12. Which of the above are divisible by 4?

13. Which of the above are divisible by 8?

14. Which of the above are divisible by 6?

15. Which of the above are divisible by 10?

16. Which of the above are divisible by 9?

To answer Exercises 17–24, consider the following numbers.

305	313,332	876	64,000
1101	7624	1110	9990
13,205	111,126	5128	126,111

17. Which of the above are divisible by 2?

18. Which of the above are divisible by 3?

19. Which of the above are divisible by 6?

20. Which of the above are divisible by 5?

21. Which of the above are divisible by 9?

22. Which of the above are divisible by 8?

23. Which of the above are divisible by 10?

24. Which of the above are divisible by 4?

Skill Maintenance

Solve. [1.4b]

25. $56 + x = 194$

26. $y + 124 = 263$

27. $3008 = x + 2134$

28. $18 \cdot t = 1008$

29. $24 \cdot m = 624$

30. $338 = a \cdot 26$

Divide. [1.3c]

31. $2106 \div 9$

32. $4\,5 \overline{)\,1\,8\,0,1\,3\,5}$

Solve. [1.5a]

33. Marty's automobile has a 5-speed transmission and gets 33 mpg in city driving. How many gallons of gas will it use to travel 1485 mi of city driving?

34. There are 60 min in 1 hr. How many minutes are there in 72 hr?

Synthesis

Find the prime factorization of each number. Use divisibility tests where applicable.

35. 7800

36. 2520

37. 2772

38. 1998

39. ▦ Fill in the missing digits of the number

$$95,\square\,\square\,8$$

so that it is divisible by 99.

40. A passenger in a taxicab asks for the driver's company number. The driver says abruptly, "Sure—you can have my number. Work it out: If you divide it by 2, 3, 4, 5, or 6, you will get a remainder of 1. If you divide it by 11, the remainder will be 0 and no driver has a company number that meets these requirements and is smaller than this one." Determine the number.

Copyright © 2012 Pearson Education, Inc.

1.9

Least Common Multiples

In Chapter 2, we will study addition and subtraction using fraction notation. Suppose we want to add $\frac{2}{3}$ and $\frac{1}{2}$. To do so, we rewrite the fractions with a common denominator. The number we choose for the common denominator is the least common multiple of the denominators, 6; $\frac{2}{3} + \frac{1}{2} = \frac{4}{6} + \frac{3}{6}$. Then we add the numerators and keep the common denominator. In order to do this, we must be able to find the **least common denominator (LCD)**, or **least common multiple (LCM)**, of the denominators.

a Finding Least Common Multiples

> ### LEAST COMMON MULTIPLE, LCM
>
> The **least common multiple**, or LCM, of two natural numbers is the smallest number that is a multiple of both numbers.

EXAMPLE 1 Find the LCM of 20 and 30.

First, we list some multiples of 20 by multiplying 20 by 1, 2, 3, and so on:

$20, 40, 60, 80, 100, 120, 140, 160, 180, 200, 220, 240, \ldots$.

Then we list some multiples of 30 by multiplying 30 by 1, 2, 3, and so on:

$30, 60, 90, 120, 150, 180, 210, 240, \ldots$.

Now we determine the smallest number *common* to both lists. The LCM of 20 and 30 is 60.

Do Margin Exercise 1.

Next, we develop three methods that are more efficient for finding LCMs. You may choose to learn only one method. (Consult with your instructor.) If you are going to study algebra, you should definitely learn method 2.

Method 1: Finding LCMs Using One List of Multiples

One method for finding LCMs uses *one* list of multiples. Let's consider finding the LCM of 9 and 12. The larger number, 12, is not a multiple of 9, so we check multiples of 12 until we find a number that is also a multiple of 9:

$1 \cdot 12 = 12$,   not a multiple of 9;

$2 \cdot 12 = 24$,   not a multiple of 9;

$3 \cdot 12 = 36$,   a multiple of 9: $4 \cdot 9 = 36$.

The LCM of 9 and 12 is 36.

OBJECTIVE

a Find the least common multiple, or LCM, of two or more numbers.

SKILL TO REVIEW
Objective 1.7b: Find some multiples of a number.

Multiply by 1, 2, 3, and so on, to find six multiples of each number.

1. 8   **2.** 25

1. Find the LCM of 9 and 15 by examining lists of multiples.

Answers

Skill to Review:
1. 8, 16, 24, 32, 40, 48
2. 25, 50, 75, 100, 125, 150

Margin Exercise:
1. 45

> *Method 1.* To find the LCM of a set of numbers using a list of multiples:
>
> a) Determine whether the largest number is a multiple of the others. If it is, it is the LCM. That is, if the largest number has the others as factors, the LCM is that number.
>
> b) If not, check multiples of the largest number until you get one that is a multiple of each of the others.

EXAMPLE 2 Find the LCM of 12 and 15.

a) 15 is not a multiple of 12.

b) Check multiples of 15:

$$1 \cdot 15 = 15,$$ Not a multiple of 12. When we divide 15 by 12, we get a nonzero remainder.

$$2 \cdot 15 = 30,$$ Not a multiple of 12

$$3 \cdot 15 = 45,$$ Not a multiple of 12

$$4 \cdot 15 = 60.$$ A multiple of 12: $5 \cdot 12 = 60$

The LCM $= 60$.

Do Exercise 2.

2. Find the LCM of 8 and 10 by examining lists of multiples.

EXAMPLE 3 Find the LCM of 8 and 32.

a) 32 is a multiple of $8 (4 \cdot 8 = 32)$, so the LCM $= 32$.

EXAMPLE 4 Find the LCM of 10, 20, and 50.

a) 50 is a multiple of 10 but not a multiple of 20.

b) Check multiples of 50:

$$1 \cdot 50 = 50,$$

$$2 \cdot 50 = 100.$$ A multiple of 10 and of 20: $10 \cdot 10 = 100$ and $5 \cdot 20 = 100$

The LCM $= 100$.

Do Exercises 3–6.

Find the LCM.

3. 10, 15 **4.** 6, 8

5. 5, 10 **6.** 20, 45, 80

Method 2: Finding LCMs Using Prime Factorizations

A second method for finding LCMs uses prime factorizations. Consider again 20 and 30. Their prime factorizations are $20 = 2 \cdot 2 \cdot 5$ and $30 = 2 \cdot 3 \cdot 5$. Let's look at these prime factorizations in order to find the LCM. Any multiple of 20 will have to have *two* 2's as factors and *one* 5 as a factor. Any multiple of 30 will need to have *one* 2, *one* 3, and *one* 5 as factors. The smallest number satisfying these conditions is

Two 2's, one 5; makes 20 a factor

$$2 \cdot 2 \cdot 3 \cdot 5.$$

One 2, one 3, one 5; makes 30 a factor

Answers

2. 40 **3.** 30 **4.** 24 **5.** 10 **6.** 720

Thus the LCM of 20 and 30 is $2 \cdot 2 \cdot 3 \cdot 5$, or 60. It has all the factors of 20 and all the factors of 30, but the factors are not repeated when they are common to both numbers.

Note that the greatest number of times that 2 occurs as a factor of either 20 or 30 is two, and the LCM has 2 as a factor twice. The greatest number of times that 3 occurs as a factor of either 20 or 30 is one, and the LCM has 3 as a factor once. The greatest number of times that 5 occurs as a factor of either 20 or 30 is one, and the LCM has 5 as a factor once.

STUDY TIPS

TUNE OUT DISTRACTIONS

Do you generally study in noisy places? If there is constant noise in your home, dorm, or other study area, consider finding a quiet place in the library—preferably a spot away from the main traffic areas so that distractions are kept to a minimum.

> *Method 2.* To find the LCM of a set of numbers using prime factorizations:
>
> a) Find the prime factorization of each number.
> b) Create a product of factors, using each factor the greatest number of times that it occurs in any one factorization.

EXAMPLE 5 Find the LCM of 6 and 8.

a) Find the prime factorization of each number.

$$6 = 2 \cdot 3, \qquad 8 = 2 \cdot 2 \cdot 2$$

b) Create a product by writing factors that appear in the factorizations of 6 and 8, using each the greatest number of times that it occurs in any one factorization.

Consider the factor 2. The greatest number of times that 2 occurs in any one factorization is three. We write 2 as a factor three times.

$$2 \cdot 2 \cdot 2 \cdot ?$$

Consider the factor 3. The greatest number of times that 3 occurs in any one factorization is one. We write 3 as a factor one time.

$$2 \cdot 2 \cdot 2 \cdot 3 \cdot ?$$

Since there are no other prime factors in either factorization, the

LCM is $2 \cdot 2 \cdot 2 \cdot 3$, or 24.

EXAMPLE 6 Find the LCM of 24 and 36.

a) Find the prime factorization of each number.

$$24 = 2 \cdot 2 \cdot 2 \cdot 3, \qquad 36 = 2 \cdot 2 \cdot 3 \cdot 3$$

b) Create a product by writing factors, using each the greatest number of times that it occurs in any one factorization.

Consider the factor 2. The greatest number of times that 2 occurs in any one factorization is three. We write 2 as a factor three times:

$$2 \cdot 2 \cdot 2 \cdot ?$$

Consider the factor 3. The greatest number of times that 3 occurs in any one factorization is two. We write 3 as a factor two times:

$$2 \cdot 2 \cdot 2 \cdot 3 \cdot 3 \cdot ?$$

Since there are no other prime factors in either factorization, the

LCM is $2 \cdot 2 \cdot 2 \cdot 3 \cdot 3$, or 72.

Do Exercises 7–9.

Use prime factorizations to find each LCM.

7. 8, 10

8. 18, 40

9. 32, 54

Answers

7. 40   **8.** 360   **9.** 864

EXAMPLE 7 Find the LCM of 81, 90, and 84.

a) Find the prime factorization of each number.

$$81 = 3 \cdot 3 \cdot 3 \cdot 3, \qquad 90 = 2 \cdot 3 \cdot 3 \cdot 5, \qquad 84 = 2 \cdot 2 \cdot 3 \cdot 7$$

b) Create a product by writing factors, using each the greatest number of times that it occurs in any one factorization.

Consider the factor 2. The greatest number of times that 2 occurs in any one factorization is two. We write 2 as a factor two times:

$$2 \cdot 2 \cdot ?$$

Consider the factor 3. The greatest number of times that 3 occurs in any one factorization is four. We write 3 as a factor four times:

$$2 \cdot 2 \cdot 3 \cdot 3 \cdot 3 \cdot 3 \cdot ?$$

Consider the factor 5. The greatest number of times that 5 occurs in any one factorization is one. We write 5 as a factor one time:

$$2 \cdot 2 \cdot 3 \cdot 3 \cdot 3 \cdot 3 \cdot 5 \cdot ?$$

Consider the factor 7. The greatest number of times that 7 occurs in any one factorization is one. We write 7 as a factor one time:

$$2 \cdot 2 \cdot 3 \cdot 3 \cdot 3 \cdot 3 \cdot 5 \cdot 7 \cdot ?$$

Since there are no other prime factors in any of the factorizations, the

LCM is $2 \cdot 2 \cdot 3 \cdot 3 \cdot 3 \cdot 3 \cdot 5 \cdot 7$, or 11,340.

10. Find the LCM of 24, 35, and 45.

Do Exercise 10.

EXAMPLE 8 Find the LCM of 8 and 9.

We find the prime factorization of each number.

$$8 = 2 \cdot 2 \cdot 2, \qquad 9 = 3 \cdot 3$$

Note that the two numbers, 8 and 9, have no common prime factor. When this is the case, the LCM is just the product of the two numbers. Thus the LCM is $2 \cdot 2 \cdot 2 \cdot 3 \cdot 3$, or $8 \cdot 9$, or 72.

Find the LCM.

11. 4, 9

12. 5, 6, 7

Do Exercises 11 and 12.

EXAMPLE 9 Find the LCM of 7 and 21.

We find the prime factorization of each number. Because 7 is prime, it has no prime factorization.

$$7 = 7, \qquad 21 = 3 \cdot 7$$

Note that 7 is a factor of 21. We stated earlier that if one number is a factor of another, the LCM is the larger of the numbers. Thus the LCM is $7 \cdot 3$, or 21.

Find the LCM.

13. 3, 18   **14.** 12, 24

Do Exercises 13 and 14.

Answers

10. 2520   **11.** 36   **12.** 210   **13.** 18
14. 24

a Find the LCM of each set of numbers.

1. 2, 4   **2.** 3, 15   **3.** 10, 25   **4.** 10, 15   **5.** 20, 40

6. 8, 12   **7.** 18, 27   **8.** 9, 11   **9.** 30, 50   **10.** 24, 36

11. 30, 40   **12.** 21, 27   **13.** 18, 24   **14.** 12, 18   **15.** 60, 70

16. 35, 45   **17.** 16, 36   **18.** 18, 20   **19.** 32, 36   **20.** 36, 48

21. 2, 3, 5   **22.** 3, 5, 7   **23.** 5, 18, 3   **24.** 6, 12, 18   **25.** 24, 36, 12

26. 8, 16, 22   **27.** 5, 12, 15   **28.** 12, 18, 40   **29.** 9, 12, 6   **30.** 8, 16, 12

31. 180, 100, 450, 60   **32.** 18, 30, 50, 48   **33.** 8, 48   **34.** 16, 32   **35.** 5, 50

36. 12, 72   **37.** 11, 13   **38.** 13, 14   **39.** 12, 35   **40.** 23, 25

41. 54, 63   **42.** 56, 72   **43.** 81, 90   **44.** 75, 100   **45.** 36, 54, 80

46. 22, 42, 51   **47.** 39, 91, 108, 26   **48.** 625, 75, 500, 25   **49.** 2000, 3000   **50.** 300, 4000

Applications of LCMs: Planet Orbits. Jupiter, Saturn, and Uranus all revolve around the sun. Jupiter takes 12 yr, Saturn 30 yr, and Uranus 84 yr to make a complete revolution. On a certain night, you look at Jupiter, Saturn, and Uranus and wonder how many years it will take before they have the same position again. (*Hint*: To find out, you find the LCM of 12, 30, and 84. It will be that number of years.)

Source: *The Handy Science Answer Book*

51. How often will Jupiter and Saturn appear in the same direction in the night sky as seen from the earth?

52. How often will Jupiter and Uranus appear in the same direction in the night sky as seen from the earth?

53. How often will Saturn and Uranus appear in the same direction in the night sky as seen from the earth?

54. How often will Jupiter, Saturn, and Uranus appear in the same direction in the night sky as seen from the earth?

Skill Maintenance

55. *Tornadoes.* The United States reports more tornadoes per year than any other country in the world. From January through May 2008, 1007 tornadoes were recorded. This was an increase of 348 tornadoes over the same time period in 2007. How many tornadoes occurred from January through May in 2007? [1.5a]

Sources: NOAA's National Weather Service; www.tornadoarchive.com/History.aspx

56. *Population of Africa.* In 2007, the population of Africa was about 564,000,000 greater than the population of South America. The population of Africa was approximately 940,000,000. What was the population of South America? [1.5a]

Sources: Population Division/International Programs Center; *The World Almanac* 2008

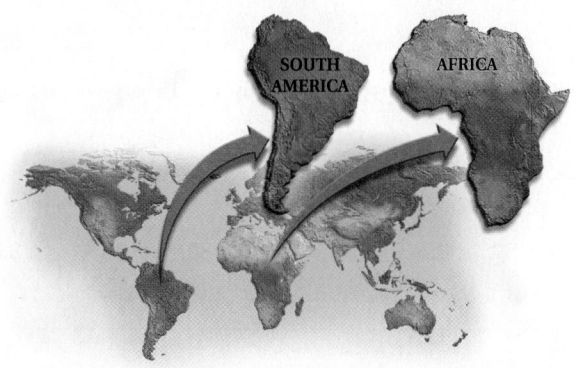

57. Divide: 663 ÷ 17. [1.3c]

58. Add: 23,456 + 5677 + 4002. [1.2a]

59. Multiply: 2118 × 3001. [1.3a]

60. Subtract: 80,004 − 2305. [1.2c]

Synthesis

61. A pencil company uses two sizes of boxes, 5 in. by 6 in. and 5 in. by 8 in. These boxes are packed in bigger cartons for shipping. Find the width and the length of the smallest carton that will accommodate boxes of either size without any room left over. (Each carton can contain only one type of box and all boxes must point in the same direction.)

62. Consider 8 and 12. Determine whether each of the following is the LCM of 8 and 12. Tell why or why not.
a) $2 \cdot 2 \cdot 3 \cdot 3$
b) $2 \cdot 2 \cdot 3$
c) $2 \cdot 3 \cdot 3$
d) $2 \cdot 2 \cdot 2 \cdot 3$

Copyright © 2012 Pearson Education, Inc.

Key Terms and Properties

digit, p. 2
periods, p. 2
place-value chart, p. 2
whole numbers, p. 3
natural numbers, p. 3
equation, p. 6
inequality, p. 6
sum, p. 11
addend, p. 11
additive identity, p. 11
perimeter, p. 13
minuend, p. 14
subtrahend, p. 14

difference, p. 14
factor, p. 20
product, p. 20
multiplicative identity, p. 21
dividend, p. 24
divisor, p. 24
quotient, p. 24
remainder, p. 27
rounding, p. 30
solution of an equation, p. 44
exponential notation, p. 67
base, p. 67
exponent, p. 67

average, p. 71
factor (noun), p. 76
factor (verb), p. 76
factorization, p. 76
multiple, p. 77
divisible, p. 77
prime number, p. 78
composite number, p. 78
prime factorization, p. 79
even number, p. 83
least common multiple, p. 89
least common denominator, p. 89

Concept Reinforcement

Determine whether each statement is true or false.

_____ 1. $a > b$ is true when a is to the right of b on the number line. [1.1d]

_____ 2. Any nonzero number divided by itself is 1. [1.3c]

_____ 3. For any whole number a, $a \div 0 = 0$. [1.3c]

_____ 4. Every equation is true. [1.4a]

_____ 5. The rules for order of operations tell us to multiply and divide before adding and subtracting. [1.6c]

_____ 6. The average of three numbers is the middle number. [1.6c]

_____ 7. The least common multiple of two numbers is always larger than or equal to the larger number. [1.9a]

Important Concepts

Objective 1.1a Give the meaning of digits in standard notation.

Example What does the digit 7 mean in 2,379,465?

    2,3 [7] 9,465

7 means 7 ten thousands.

Practice Exercise

1. What does the digit 2 mean in 432,079?

Objective 1.1d Use < or > for ☐ to write a true sentence in a situation like 6 ☐ 10.

Example Use < or > for ☐ to write a true sentence:
34 ☐ 29.
   Since 34 is to the right of 29 on the number line,
   34 > 29.

Practice Exercise

2. Use < or > for ☐ to write a true sentence:
   78 ☐ 81.

Objective 1.2a Add whole numbers.

Example Add: 7368 + 3547.

$$\begin{array}{r} {\scriptstyle 1\ 1} \\ 7\ 3\ 6\ 8 \\ +\ 3\ 5\ 4\ 7 \\ \hline 1\ 0{,}9\ 1\ 5 \end{array}$$

Practice Exercise

3. Add: 36,047 + 29,255.

Objective 1.2c Subtract whole numbers.

Example Subtract: 8045 − 2897.

$$\begin{array}{r} {\scriptstyle 7\ 9\ \overset{13}{\cancel{3}}\ 15} \\ \cancel{8}\ 0\ \cancel{4}\ \cancel{5} \\ -\ 2\ 8\ 9\ 7 \\ \hline 5\ 1\ 4\ 8 \end{array}$$

Practice Exercise

4. Subtract: 4805 − 1568.

Objective 1.3a Multiply whole numbers.

Example Multiply: 57 × 315.

$$\begin{array}{r} {\scriptstyle \ \ \ 2} \\ {\scriptstyle 1\ \ 3} \\ 3\ 1\ 5 \\ \times\ \ \ 5\ 7 \\ \hline 2\ 2\ 0\ 5 \leftarrow 315 \times 7 \\ 1\ 5\ 7\ 5\ 0 \leftarrow 315 \times 50 \\ \hline 1\ 7{,}9\ 5\ 5 \end{array}$$

Practice Exercise

5. Multiply: 329 × 684.

Objective 1.3c Divide whole numbers.

Example Divide: 6463 ÷ 26.

$$\begin{array}{r} 2\ 4\ 8 \\ 26\ )\overline{6\ 4\ 6\ 3} \\ \underline{5\ 2} \\ 1\ 2\ 6 \\ \underline{1\ 0\ 4} \\ 2\ 2\ 3 \\ \underline{2\ 0\ 8} \\ 1\ 5 \end{array}$$

The answer is 248 R 15.

Practice Exercise

6. Divide: 8519 ÷ 27.

Objective 1.3d Round to the nearest ten, hundred, or thousand.

Example Round 6471 to the nearest hundred.

6 4 **7** 1

↑

The digit 4 is in the hundreds place. We consider the next digit to the right. Since the digit, 7, is 5 or higher, we round 4 hundreds up to 5 hundreds. Then we change all digits to the right of the hundreds digit to zeros. The answer is 6500.

Practice Exercises

7. Round 36,468 to the nearest hundred.

Objective 1.3d (*continued*)

Example Round to the nearest thousand.

6 4 7 1
↑

The digit 6 is in the thousands place. We consider the next digit to the right. Since the digit, 4, is 4 or lower, we round 6 thousands down, meaning that 6 thousands stays as 6 thousands. Change all digits to the right of the thousands digit to zeros. The answer is 6000.

8. Round 36,468 to the nearest thousand.

Objective 1.4b Solve equations like $t + 28 = 54$, $28 \cdot x = 168$, and $98 \cdot 2 = y$.

Example Solve: $y + 12 = 27$.

$$y + 12 = 27$$
$$y + 12 - 12 = 27 - 12$$
$$y + 0 = 15$$
$$y = 15$$

The solution is 15.

Practice Exercise

9. Solve: $24 \cdot x = 864$.

Objective 1.6b Evaluate exponential notation.

Example Evaluate: 5^4.

$$5^4 = 5 \cdot 5 \cdot 5 \cdot 5 = 625$$

Practice Exercise

10. Evaluate: 6^3.

Objective 1.7a Find the factors of a number.

Example Find the factors of 84.

We find as many "two-factor" factorizations as we can.

$1 \cdot 84$ $4 \cdot 21$

$2 \cdot 42$ $6 \cdot 14$

$3 \cdot 28$ $7 \cdot 12$ ← Since 8, 9, 10, and 11 are not factors, we are finished.

The factors are 1, 2, 3, 4, 6, 7, 12, 14, 21, 28, 42, and 84.

Practice Exercise

11. Find the factors of 104.

Objective 1.7d Find the prime factorization of a composite number.

Example Find the prime factorization of 84.

To find the prime factorization, we can use either successive divisions or a factor tree.

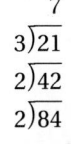

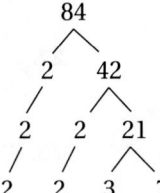

Thus, $84 = 2 \cdot 2 \cdot 3 \cdot 7$.

Practice Exercise

12. Find the prime factorization of 104.

Objective 1.9a Find the least common multiple, or LCM, of two or more numbers.

Example Find the LCM of 105 and 90.

$$105 = 3 \cdot 5 \cdot 7,$$
$$90 = 2 \cdot 3 \cdot 3 \cdot 5;$$
$$LCM = 2 \cdot 3 \cdot 3 \cdot 5 \cdot 7 = 630$$

Practice Exercise

13. Find the LCM of 52 and 78.

Review Exercises

The review exercises that follow are for practice. Answers are given at the back of the book. If you miss an exercise, restudy the objective indicated in red next to the exercise or on the direction line that precedes it.

1. What does the digit 8 mean in 4,678,952? [1.1a]

2. In 13,768,940, what digit tells the number of millions? [1.1a]

Write expanded notation. [1.1b]

3. 2793

4. 56,078

5. 4,007,101

Write a word name. [1.1c]

6. 67,819

7. 2,781,427

Write standard notation. [1.1c]

8. *Subway Ridership.* Ridership on the New York City Subway system totaled one billion, five hundred sixty-three million in 2007.

Source: Metropolitan Transit Authority

Use < or > for ☐ to write a true sentence. [1.1d]

9. 67 ☐ 56

10. 1 ☐ 23

Add. [1.2a]

11. 7304 + 6968

12. 27,609 + 38,415

13. 2703 + 4125 + 6004 + 8956

14.
$$\begin{array}{r} 9\,1,4\,2\,6 \\ +\quad 7,4\,9\,5 \\ \hline \end{array}$$

Subtract. [1.2c]

15. 8045 − 2897

16. 9001 − 7312

17. 6003 − 3729

18.
$$\begin{array}{r} 3\,7,4\,0\,5 \\ -\,1\,9,6\,4\,8 \\ \hline \end{array}$$

Multiply. [1.3a]

19. 17,000 · 300

20. 7846 · 800

21. 726 · 698

22. 587 · 47

23.
$$\begin{array}{r} 8\,3\,0\,5 \\ \times\quad 6\,4\,2 \\ \hline \end{array}$$

Divide. [1.3c]

24. 63 ÷ 5

25. 80 ÷ 16

26. 7) 6 3 9 4

27. 3073 ÷ 8

28. 6 0) 2 8 6

29. 4266 ÷ 79

30. 3 8) 1 7,1 7 6

31. 52,668 ÷ 12

Copyright © 2012 Pearson Education, Inc.

Round 345,759 to the nearest: [1.3d]

32. Hundred.   **33.** Ten.

34. Thousand.   **35.** Hundred thousand.

Estimate each sum, difference, or product by first rounding to the nearest hundred. Show your work. [1.3e]

36. $41,348 + 19,749$ **37.** $38,652 - 24,549$

38. $396 \cdot 748$

Solve. [1.4b]

39. $46 \cdot n = 368$ **40.** $47 + x = 92$

41. $1 \cdot y = 58$ **42.** $24 = x + 24$

43. Write exponential notation: $4 \cdot 4 \cdot 4$. [1.6a]

Evaluate. [1.6b]

44. 10^4 **45.** 6^2

Simplify. [1.6c, d]

46. $8 \cdot 6 + 17$

47. $10 \cdot 24 - (18 + 2) \div 4 - (9 - 7)$

48. $(80 \div 16) \times [(20 - 56 \div 8) + (8 \cdot 8 - 5 \cdot 5)]$

49. Find the average of 157, 170, and 168.

Solve. [1.5a]

50. *Computer Workstation.* Natasha has $196 and wants to buy a computer workstation for $698. How much more does she need?

51. Toni has $406 in her checking account. She is paid $78 for a part-time job and deposits that in her checking account. How much is then in her account?

52. *Lincoln-Head Pennies.* In 1909, the first Lincoln-head pennies were minted. Seventy-three years later, these pennies were first minted with a decreased copper content. In what year was the copper content reduced?

53. An apartment builder bought 13 gas stoves at $425 each and 13 refrigerators at $620 each. What was the total cost?

54. An apple farmer keeps bees in her orchard to help pollinate the apple blossoms. The bees from an average beehive can pollinate 30 surrounding trees during one growing season. A farmer has 420 trees. How many beehives does she need to pollinate all of them?
Source: Jordan Orchards, Westminster, PA

55. *Olympic Trampoline.* Shown below is an Olympic trampoline. Determine the area and the perimeter of the trampoline. [1.2b], [1.3b]
Source: International Trampoline Industry Association, Inc.

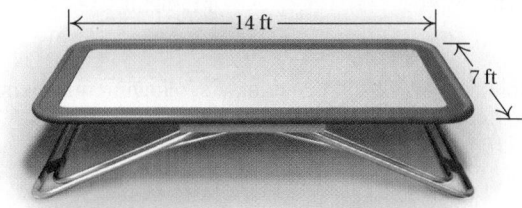

56. A chemist has 2753 mL of alcohol. How many 20-mL beakers can be filled? How much will be left over?

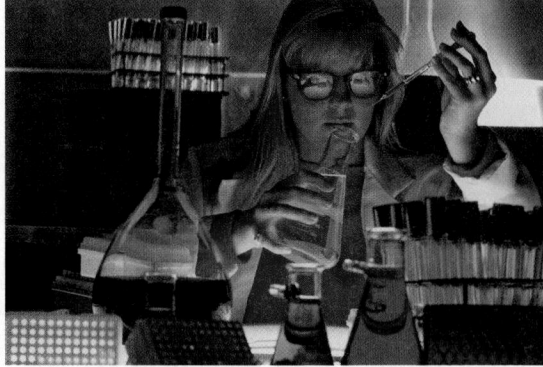

57. A family budgeted $7825 for food and clothing and $2860 for entertainment. The yearly income of the family was $38,283. How much of this income remained after these two allotments?

Find all the factors of each number. [1.7a]

58. 60 **59.** 176

60. Multiply by 1, 2, 3, and so on, to find ten multiples of 8. [1.7b]

61. Determine whether 924 is divisible by 11. [1.7b]

62. Determine whether 1800 is divisible by 16. [1.7b]

Determine whether each number is prime, composite, or neither. [1.7c]

63. 37 **64.** 1 **65.** 91

Find the prime factorization of each number. [1.7d]

66. 70 **67.** 30

68. 45 **69.** 150

70. 648 **71.** 5250

To do Exercises 72–79, consider the following numbers:

140	716	93	2802
95	2432	330	711
182	4344	255,555	
475	600	780	

Which of the above are divisible by the given number? [1.8a]

72. 3 **73.** 2

74. 4 **75.** 8

76. 5 **77.** 6

78. 9 **79.** 10

Find the LCM. [1.9a]

80. 12 and 18 **81.** 18 and 45

82. 3, 6, and 30 **83.** 26, 36, and 54

84. Simplify: $7 + (4 + 3)^2$. [1.6c]
 A. 32 **B.** 56
 C. 151 **D.** 196

85. Simplify: $7 + 4^2 + 3^2$. [1.6c]
 A. 32 **B.** 56
 C. 130 **D.** 196

86. Simplify: $[46 - (4 - 2) \cdot 5] \div 2 + 4$. [1.6d]
 A. 6 **B.** 20
 C. 114 **D.** 22

Synthesis

87. 🖩 Determine the missing digits a and b. [1.3c]

$$2\,b\,1\,)\overline{\,2\,3\,6{,}4\,2\,1\,}\quad\begin{smallmatrix}9\,a\,1\end{smallmatrix}$$

88. A prime number that remains a prime number when its digits are reversed is called a **palindrome prime**. For example, 17 is a palindrome prime because both 17 and 71 are primes. Which of the following numbers are palindrome primes? [1.7c]

13, 91, 16, 11, 15, 24, 29, 101, 201, 37

89. A mining company estimates that a crew must tunnel 2000 ft into a mountain to reach a deposit of copper ore. Each day, the crew tunnels about 500 ft. Each night, about 200 ft of loose rocks roll back into the tunnel. How many days will it take the mining company to reach the copper deposit? [1.5a]

Understanding Through Discussion and Writing

1. Use the number 9432 to explain why the test for divisibility by 9 works. [1.8a]

2. Explain a method for finding a composite number that contains exactly two factors other than itself and 1. [1.7c]

3. Write a problem for a classmate to solve. Design the problem so that the solution is "The driver still has 329 mi to travel." [1.5a]

4. Consider the expressions $9 - (4 \cdot 2)$ and $(3 \cdot 4)^2$. Are the parentheses necessary in each case? Explain. [1.6c]

Copyright © 2012 Pearson Education, Inc.

Test   For Extra Help

CHAPTER Test Prep VIDEOS

Step-by-step test solutions are found on the Chapter Test Prep Videos available via the Video Resources on DVD, in *MyMathLab* , and on You Tube (search "BittingerDevMath" and click on "Channels").

1. In the number 546,789, which digit tells the number of hundred thousands?

2. Write expanded notation: 8843.

3. Write a word name: 38,403,277.

Add.

4.   6 8 1 1
     + 3 1 7 8

5.   4 5,8 8 9
     + 1 7,9 0 2

6.   1 2 3 9
       8 4 3
       3 0 1
     +   7 8 2

7.   6 2 0 3
     + 4 3 1 2

Subtract.

8.   7 9 8 3
     − 4 3 5 3

9.   2 9 7 4
     − 1 9 3 5

10.   8 9 0 7
      − 2 0 5 9

11.   2 3,0 6 7
      − 1 7,8 9 2

Multiply.

12.   4 5 6 8
     ×   9

13.   8 8 7 6
     ×   6 0 0

14.   6 5
     × 3 7

15.   6 7 8
     × 7 8 8

Divide.

16. 15 ÷ 4

17. 420 ÷ 6

18. 8 9) 8 6 3 3

19. 4 4) 3 5,4 2 8

Solve.

20. *Calorie Content.* An 8-oz serving of whole milk contains 146 calories. This is 63 calories more than the number of calories in an 8-oz serving of skim milk. How many calories are in an 8-oz serving of skim milk?
Source: *American Journal of Clinical Nutrition*

21. A box contains 5000 staples. How many staplers can be filled from the box if each stapler holds 250 staples?

22. *Office Supplies.* Morgan manages the office of a small graphics firm. He buys 3 black inkjet cartridges at $15 each and 2 photo inkjet cartridges at $25 each. How much does the purchase cost?

23. *Pool Tables.* The Bradford™ pool table made by Brunswick Billiards comes in three sizes of playing area, 50 in. by 100 in., 44 in. by 88 in., and 38 in. by 76 in.
Source: Brunswick Billiards

a) Determine the perimeter and the playing area of each table.
b) By how much does the area of the largest table exceed the area of the smallest table?

Round 34,528 to the nearest:

24. Thousand.

25. Ten.

26. Hundred.

Estimate each sum, difference, or product by first rounding to the nearest hundred. Show your work.

27.
$$\begin{array}{r} 2\ 3{,}6\ 4\ 9 \\ +\ 5\ 4{,}7\ 4\ 6 \\ \hline \end{array}$$

28.
$$\begin{array}{r} 5\ 4{,}7\ 5\ 1 \\ -\ 2\ 3{,}6\ 4\ 9 \\ \hline \end{array}$$

29.
$$\begin{array}{r} 8\ 2\ 4 \\ \times\ 4\ 8\ 9 \\ \hline \end{array}$$

Solve.

30. $28 + x = 74$

31. $169 \div 13 = n$

32. $38 \cdot y = 532$

33. $381 = 0 + a$

34. Write exponential notation: $12 \cdot 12 \cdot 12 \cdot 12$.

Evaluate.

35. 7^3

36. 10^5

Use $<$ or $>$ for ☐ to write a true sentence.

37. $34 \ \square \ 17$

38. $117 \ \square \ 157$

Simplify.

39. $35 - 1 \cdot 28 \div 4 + 3$

40. $10^2 - 2^2 \div 2$

41. $(25 - 15) \div 5$

42. $2^4 + 24 \div 12$

43. $8 \times \{(20 - 11) \cdot [(12 + 48) \div 6 - (9 - 2)]\}$

Determine whether each number is prime, composite, or neither.

44. 41

45. 14

Find the prime factorization of the number.

46. 18

47. 60

48. Determine whether 1784 is divisible by 8.

49. Determine whether 784 is divisible by 9.

50. Determine whether 5552 is divisible by 5.

51. Determine whether 2322 is divisible by 6.

Find the LCM.

52. 16 and 12

53. 15, 40, and 50

54. Find the average of 97, 99, 87, and 89.

    A. 93   **B.** 124   **C.** 186   **D.** 372

Synthesis

55. An open cardboard container is 8 in. wide, 12 in. long, and 6 in. high. How many square inches of cardboard are used?

56. Use trials to find the single-digit number a for which
$$359 - 46 + a \div 3 \times 25 - 7^2 = 339.$$

Copyright © 2012 Pearson Education, Inc.

Fraction Notation

Real-World Application

Black bears typically have two cubs. In January 2007 in northern New Hampshire, a black bear sow gave birth to a litter of 5 cubs. This is so rare that Tom Sears, a wildlife photographer, spent 28 hr per week for six weeks watching for the perfect opportunity to photograph this family of six. At the time of this photo, an observer estimated that the cubs weighed $7\frac{1}{2}$ lb, 8 lb, $9\frac{1}{2}$ lb, $10\frac{5}{8}$ lb, and $11\frac{3}{4}$ lb. What was the average weight of the cubs?

Source: Andrew Timmins, New Hampshire Fish and Game Department, *Northcountry News*, Warren, NH; Tom Sears, photographer

This problem appears as Exercise 25 in Section 2.6.

2.1

Fraction Notation and Simplifying

OBJECTIVES

a Identify the numerator and the denominator of a fraction and write fraction notation for part of an object.

b Simplify fraction notation like n/n to 1, $0/n$ to 0, and $n/1$ to n.

c Multiply a fraction by a fraction, and multiply a fraction by a whole number.

d Multiply a number by 1 to find fraction notation with a specified denominator.

e Simplify fraction notation.

SKILL TO REVIEW
Objective 1.7d: Find the prime factorization of a composite number.

Find the prime factorization.
1. 84   **2.** 2250

For each fraction, identify the numerator and the denominator.

1. $\frac{3}{20}$ of people age 5 and older in Maryland speak a language other than English at home.
Source: 2006 American Community Survey

2. $\frac{19}{100}$ of the U.S. population in 2050 is projected to be foreign-born.
Source: Pew Research Center

The study of arithmetic begins with the set of whole numbers

0, 1, 2, 3, 4, 5, 6, 7, 8, 9, 10, 11, and so on.

But we also need to be able to use fractional parts of numbers such as halves, thirds, fourths, and so on. Here is an example.

The tread depth of an IRL Indy Car Series tire is $\frac{3}{32}$ in. Tires for a normal car have a tread depth of $\frac{10}{32}$ in. when new and are considered bald at $\frac{2}{32}$ in.
Sources: Indy500.com; *Consumer Reports*

a Fractions and the Real World

Numbers like those above are written in **fraction notation**. The top number is called the **numerator** and the bottom number is called the **denominator**.

EXAMPLE 1 Identify the numerator and the denominator.

$$\frac{7}{8} \quad \begin{array}{l} \leftarrow \text{Numerator} \\ \leftarrow \text{Denominator} \end{array}$$

Do Margin Exercises 1 and 2.

Let's look at various situations that involve fractions.

Fractions as a Partition of an Object Divided into Equal Parts

Consider a candy bar divided into 5 equal sections. If you eat 2 sections, you have eaten $\frac{2}{5}$ of the candy bar. The denominator 5 tells us the unit, $\frac{1}{5}$. The numerator 2 tells us the number of equal parts we are considering, 2.

EXAMPLE 2 What part is shaded?

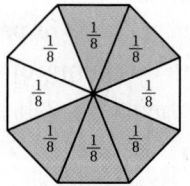

Answers

Skill to Review:
1. $2 \cdot 2 \cdot 3 \cdot 7$ **2.** $2 \cdot 3 \cdot 3 \cdot 5 \cdot 5 \cdot 5$

Margin Exercises:
1. Numerator: 3; denominator: 20
2. Numerator: 19; denominator: 100

There are 8 equal parts. This tells us the unit, $\frac{1}{8}$. The *denominator* is 8. We have 5 of the units shaded. This tells us the *numerator*, 5. Thus,

$\dfrac{5}{8}$ ← 5 units are shaded.
     ← The unit is $\frac{1}{8}$.

is shaded.

EXAMPLE 3 What part is shaded?

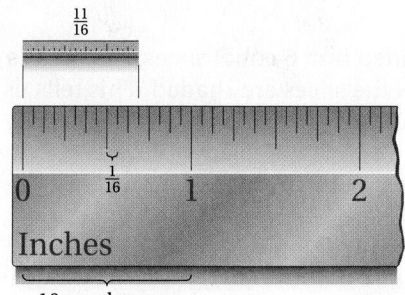

There are 18 equal parts. Thus the unit is $\frac{1}{18}$. The denominator is 18. We have 7 units shaded. This tells us the numerator, 7. Thus, $\frac{7}{18}$ is shaded.

Do Exercises 3–6.

The markings on a ruler use fractions.

EXAMPLE 4 What part of an inch is highlighted?

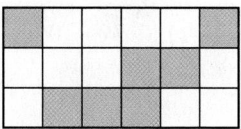

16 equal spaces

Each inch on the ruler shown above is divided into 16 equal parts. The highlighting extends to the 11th mark. Thus, $\frac{11}{16}$ of an inch is highlighted.

Do Exercise 7.

Fractions greater than or equal to 1, such as $\frac{24}{24}$, $\frac{10}{3}$, and $\frac{5}{4}$, correspond to situations like the following.

EXAMPLE 5 What part is shaded?

a)
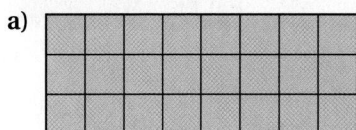

The rectangle is divided into 24 equal parts. Thus the unit is $\frac{1}{24}$. The denominator is 24. All 24 equal parts are shaded. This tells us that the numerator is 24. Thus, $\frac{24}{24}$ is shaded.

What part is shaded?

3.

4. 1 mile

5. 1 gallon

6.

7. What part of an inch is highlighted?

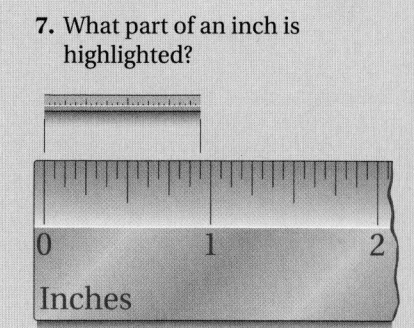

Answers

3. $\frac{5}{6}$ **4.** $\frac{1}{3}$ **5.** $\frac{3}{4}$ **6.** $\frac{8}{15}$ **7.** $\frac{15}{16}$

What part is shaded?

8.

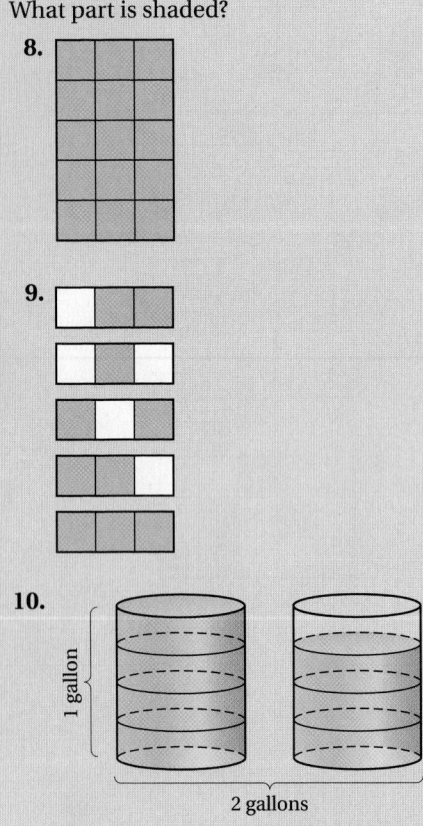

9.

10.

b)

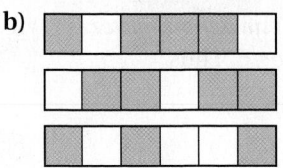

Each rectangle is divided into 6 parts. Thus the unit is $\frac{1}{6}$. The denominator is 6. We see that 11 of the equal units are shaded. This tells us that the numerator is 11. Thus, $\frac{11}{6}$ is shaded.

EXAMPLE 6 *Ice-Cream Roll-up Cake.* What part of an ice-cream roll-up cake is shaded?

3 ice cream roll-up cakes

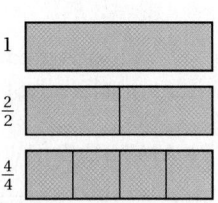

Each cake is divided into 6 equal slices. The unit is $\frac{1}{6}$. The *denominator* is 6. We see that 13 of the slices are shaded. This tells us that the *numerator* is 13. Thus, $\frac{13}{6}$ is shaded.

Do Exercises 8–10.

Fractions larger than or equal to 1, such as $\frac{13}{6}$ or $\frac{9}{9}$, are sometimes referred to as "improper" fractions. We will not use this terminology because notation such as $\frac{27}{8}$, $\frac{11}{3}$, and $\frac{4}{4}$ is quite "proper" and very common in algebra.

b Some Fraction Notation for Whole Numbers

Fraction Notation for 1

The number 1 corresponds to situations like those shown here. If we divide an object into n parts and take n of them, we get all of the object (1 whole object).

1

$\frac{2}{2}$

$\frac{4}{4}$

Answers

8. $\frac{15}{15}$ **9.** $\frac{10}{3}$ **10.** $\frac{7}{4}$

THE NUMBER 1 IN FRACTION NOTATION

$\dfrac{n}{n} = 1$,   for any whole number n that is not 0.

EXAMPLES   Simplify.

7. $\dfrac{5}{5} = 1$ **8.** $\dfrac{9}{9} = 1$ **9.** $\dfrac{23}{23} = 1$

Do Exercises 11–16.

Simplify.

11. $\dfrac{1}{1}$ **12.** $\dfrac{4}{4}$

13. $\dfrac{34}{34}$ **14.** $\dfrac{100}{100}$

15. $\dfrac{2347}{2347}$ **16.** $\dfrac{103}{103}$

Fraction Notation for 0

Consider the fraction $\frac{0}{4}$. This corresponds to dividing an object into 4 parts and taking none of them. We get 0.

THE NUMBER 0 IN FRACTION NOTATION

$\dfrac{0}{n} = 0$,   for any whole number n that is not 0.

EXAMPLES   Simplify.

10. $\dfrac{0}{1} = 0$ **11.** $\dfrac{0}{9} = 0$ **12.** $\dfrac{0}{23} = 0$

Fraction notation with a denominator of 0, such as $n/0$, is meaningless because we cannot speak of an object being divided into *zero* parts. See also the discussion of excluding division by 0 in Section 1.3.

A DENOMINATOR OF 0

$\dfrac{n}{0}$ is not defined for any whole number n.

Do Exercises 17–22.

Simplify, if possible.

17. $\dfrac{0}{1}$ **18.** $\dfrac{0}{8}$

19. $\dfrac{0}{107}$ **20.** $\dfrac{4-4}{567}$

21. $\dfrac{15}{0}$ **22.** $\dfrac{0}{3-3}$

Other Whole Numbers

Consider the fraction $\frac{4}{1}$. This corresponds to taking 4 objects and dividing each into 1 part. (In other words, we do not divide them.) We have 4 objects.

ANY WHOLE NUMBER IN FRACTION NOTATION

Any whole number divided by 1 is the whole number. That is,

$\dfrac{n}{1} = n$,   for any whole number n.

Answers

11. 1   **12.** 1   **13.** 1   **14.** 1   **15.** 1
16. 1   **17.** 0   **18.** 0   **19.** 0   **20.** 0
21. Not defined   **22.** Not defined

Simplify.

23. $\dfrac{8}{1}$ **24.** $\dfrac{10}{1}$

25. $\dfrac{346}{1}$ **26.** $\dfrac{24-1}{23-22}$

EXAMPLES Simplify.

13. $\dfrac{2}{1} = 2$ **14.** $\dfrac{9}{1} = 9$ **15.** $\dfrac{34}{1} = 34$

Do Exercises 23–26.

c Multiplication Using Fraction Notation

Let's visualize the product of two fractions. We consider the multiplication

$$\frac{3}{5} \cdot \frac{3}{4}.$$

This is equivalent to finding $\frac{3}{5}$ of $\frac{3}{4}$. We first consider an object and take $\frac{3}{4}$ of it. We divide the object into 4 equal parts using vertical lines and take 3 of them. That is shown by the shading below.

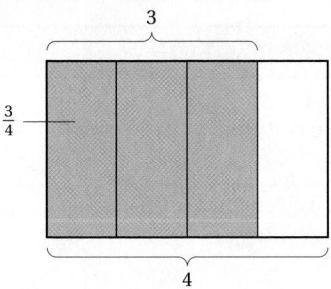

Next, we take $\frac{3}{5}$ of the shaded area. We divide it into 5 equal parts using horizontal lines and take 3 of them. That is shown by the darker shading below.

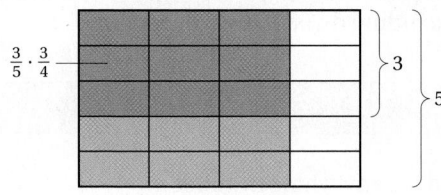

The entire object has now been divided into 20 parts, and we have shaded 9 of them twice. Thus we see that $\frac{3}{5}$ of $\frac{3}{4}$ is $\frac{9}{20}$, or

$$\frac{3}{5} \cdot \frac{3}{4} = \frac{9}{20}.$$

The figure above shows a rectangular array inside a rectangular array. The number of pieces in the entire array is $5 \cdot 4$ (the product of the denominators). The number of pieces shaded a second time is $3 \cdot 3$ (the product of the numerators). The product is represented by 9 pieces out of a set of 20, or $\frac{9}{20}$, which is the product of the numerators over the product of the denominators. This leads us to a statement of the procedure for multiplying a fraction by a fraction.

Do Exercise 27.

27. Draw a diagram like the one at right to show the multiplication $\dfrac{2}{3} \cdot \dfrac{4}{5}$.

Answers

23. 8   **24.** 10   **25.** 346   **26.** 23
27.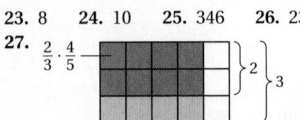

We find a product such as $\frac{9}{7} \cdot \frac{3}{4}$ as follows.

To multiply a fraction by a fraction,

a) multiply the numerators to get the new numerator, and

$$\frac{9}{7} \cdot \frac{3}{4} = \frac{9 \cdot 3}{7 \cdot 4} = \frac{27}{28}$$

b) multiply the denominators to get the new denominator.

EXAMPLES Multiply.

16. $\frac{5}{6} \times \frac{7}{4} = \frac{5 \times 7}{6 \times 4} = \frac{35}{24}$

Skip writing this step whenever you can.

17. $\frac{3}{5} \cdot \frac{7}{8} = \frac{3 \cdot 7}{5 \cdot 8} = \frac{21}{40}$

18. $\frac{5}{3} \cdot \frac{4}{3} = \frac{20}{9}$

19. $\frac{1}{4} \cdot \frac{1}{3} = \frac{1}{12}$

20. $5 \times \frac{3}{8} = \frac{5}{1} \times \frac{3}{8} = \frac{5 \times 3}{1 \times 8} = \frac{15}{8}$

Do Exercises 28–31.

Multiply.

28. $\frac{3}{8} \cdot \frac{5}{7}$ **29.** $\frac{4}{3} \times \frac{8}{5}$

30. $\frac{3}{10} \cdot \frac{1}{10}$ **31.** $7 \cdot \frac{2}{3}$

d Multiplying by 1

Recall the following:

$$1 = \frac{1}{1} = \frac{2}{2} = \frac{3}{3} = \frac{4}{4} = \frac{10}{10} = \frac{45}{45} = \frac{100}{100} = \frac{n}{n}.$$

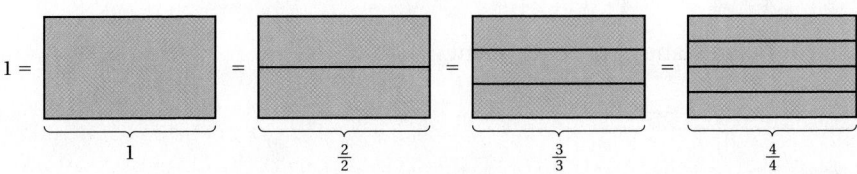

$$1 = \quad \underset{1}{} \quad = \quad \underset{\frac{2}{2}}{} \quad = \quad \underset{\frac{3}{3}}{} \quad = \quad \underset{\frac{4}{4}}{}$$

Any nonzero number divided by itself is 1. (See Section 1.3.)

Now recall the multiplicative identity from Section 1.3. For any whole number a, $1 \cdot a = a \cdot 1 = a$. This holds for fractions as well.

MULTIPLICATIVE IDENTITY FOR FRACTIONS

When we multiply a number by 1, we get the same number:

$$\frac{3}{5} = \frac{3}{5} \cdot 1 = \frac{3}{5} \cdot \frac{4}{4} = \frac{12}{20}.$$

Answers

28. $\frac{15}{56}$ **29.** $\frac{32}{15}$ **30.** $\frac{3}{100}$ **31.** $\frac{14}{3}$

Since $\frac{3}{5} = \frac{12}{20}$, we know that $\frac{3}{5}$ and $\frac{12}{20}$ are two names for the same number. We also say that $\frac{3}{5}$ and $\frac{12}{20}$ are **equivalent fractions**.

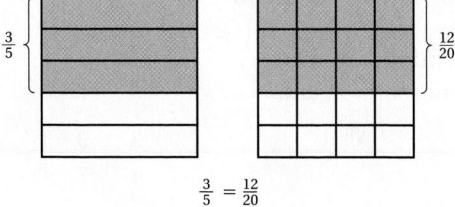

$$\frac{3}{5} = \frac{12}{20}$$

Do Exercises 32–35.

Suppose we want to find a name for $\frac{2}{3}$, but one that has a denominator of 9. We can multiply by 1 to find equivalent fractions. Since $9 = 3 \cdot 3$, we choose $\frac{3}{3}$ for 1 in order to get a denominator of 9:

$$\frac{2}{3} = \frac{2}{3} \cdot 1 = \frac{2}{3} \cdot \frac{3}{3} = \frac{2 \cdot 3}{3 \cdot 3} = \frac{6}{9}.$$

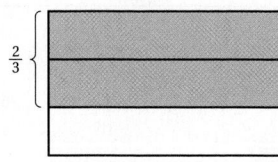 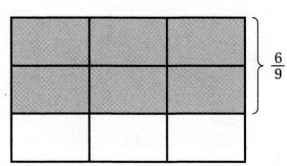

$$\frac{2}{3} = \frac{6}{9}$$

EXAMPLE 21 Find a name for $\frac{2}{5}$ with a denominator of 35.

Since $5 \cdot 7 = 35$, we multiply by $\frac{7}{7}$:

$$\frac{2}{5} = \frac{2}{5} \cdot \frac{7}{7} = \frac{2 \cdot 7}{5 \cdot 7} = \frac{14}{35}.$$

We say that $\frac{2}{5}$ and $\frac{14}{35}$ represent the same number. They are equivalent.

EXAMPLE 22 Find a name for $\frac{1}{4}$ with a denominator of 24.

Since $4 \cdot 6 = 24$, we multiply by $\frac{6}{6}$:

$$\frac{1}{4} = \frac{1}{4} \cdot \frac{6}{6} = \frac{1 \cdot 6}{4 \cdot 6} = \frac{6}{24}.$$

The numbers $\frac{1}{4}$ and $\frac{6}{24}$ are equivalent.

Do Exercises 36–39.

(e) Simplifying Fraction Notation

All of the following are names for three-fourths:

$$\frac{3}{4}, \frac{6}{8}, \frac{9}{12}, \frac{12}{16}, \frac{15}{20}.$$

We say that $\frac{3}{4}$ is **simplest** because it has the smallest numerator and the smallest denominator. That is, the numerator and the denominator have no common factor other than 1.

Multiply.

32. $\frac{1}{2} \cdot \frac{8}{8}$ **33.** $\frac{3}{5} \cdot \frac{10}{10}$

34. $\frac{13}{25} \cdot \frac{4}{4}$ **35.** $\frac{8}{3} \cdot \frac{25}{25}$

Find another name for each number, but with the denominator indicated. Use multiplying by 1.

36. $\frac{4}{3} = \frac{?}{9}$ **37.** $\frac{8}{7} = \frac{?}{49}$

38. $\frac{9}{10} = \frac{?}{100}$ **39.** $\frac{3}{15} = \frac{?}{45}$

Answers

32. $\frac{8}{16}$ **33.** $\frac{30}{50}$ **34.** $\frac{52}{100}$ **35.** $\frac{200}{75}$
36. $\frac{12}{9}$ **37.** $\frac{56}{49}$ **38.** $\frac{90}{100}$ **39.** $\frac{9}{45}$

To simplify, we reverse the process of multiplying by 1:

$$\frac{12}{18} = \frac{2 \cdot 6}{3 \cdot 6} \quad \begin{array}{l} \leftarrow \text{Factoring the numerator} \\ \leftarrow \text{Factoring the denominator} \end{array}$$

$$= \frac{2}{3} \cdot \frac{6}{6} \qquad \text{Factoring the fraction}$$

$$= \frac{2}{3} \cdot 1 \qquad \frac{6}{6} = 1$$

$$= \frac{2}{3}. \qquad \text{Removing a factor of 1: } \frac{2}{3} \cdot 1 = \frac{2}{3}$$

EXAMPLES Simplify.

23. $\dfrac{8}{20} = \dfrac{2 \cdot 4}{5 \cdot 4} = \dfrac{2}{5} \cdot \dfrac{4}{4} = \dfrac{2}{5}$

24. $\dfrac{2}{6} = \dfrac{1 \cdot 2}{3 \cdot 2} = \dfrac{1}{3} \cdot \dfrac{2}{2} = \dfrac{1}{3}$

> The number 1 allows for pairing of factors in the numerator and the denominator.

Do Exercises 40–43.

Simplify.

40. $\dfrac{2}{8}$ **41.** $\dfrac{24}{18}$

42. $\dfrac{10}{12}$ **43.** $\dfrac{15}{80}$

The use of prime factorizations can be helpful for simplifying when numerators and/or denominators are large numbers.

EXAMPLE 25 Simplify: $\dfrac{90}{84}$.

$$\frac{90}{84} = \frac{2 \cdot 3 \cdot 3 \cdot 5}{2 \cdot 2 \cdot 3 \cdot 7} \qquad \begin{array}{l} \text{Factoring the numerator and} \\ \text{the denominator into primes} \end{array}$$

$$= \frac{2 \cdot 3 \cdot 3 \cdot 5}{2 \cdot 3 \cdot 2 \cdot 7} \qquad \begin{array}{l} \text{Changing the order so that like primes} \\ \text{are above and below each other} \end{array}$$

$$= \frac{2}{2} \cdot \frac{3}{3} \cdot \frac{3 \cdot 5}{2 \cdot 7} \qquad \text{Factoring the fraction}$$

$$= 1 \cdot 1 \cdot \frac{3 \cdot 5}{2 \cdot 7}$$

$$= \frac{3 \cdot 5}{2 \cdot 7} \qquad \text{Removing factors of 1}$$

$$= \frac{15}{14}$$

The tests for divisibility (Section 1.8) are very helpful in simplifying fraction notation. We could have shortened the preceding example had we noted that 6 is a factor of both the numerator and the denominator. Then we have

$$\frac{90}{84} = \frac{6 \cdot 15}{6 \cdot 14} = \frac{6}{6} \cdot \frac{15}{14} = \frac{15}{14}.$$

STUDY TIPS

SKILL MAINTENANCE EXERCISES

It is never too soon to begin reviewing for the final examination. The Skill Maintenance exercises found in each exercise set review and reinforce skills taught in earlier sections. Include all of these exercises in your weekly preparation. Answers to *all* of the Skill Maintenance exercises, along with section references, appear at the back of the book.

Answers

40. $\dfrac{1}{4}$ **41.** $\dfrac{4}{3}$ **42.** $\dfrac{5}{6}$ **43.** $\dfrac{3}{16}$

Simplify.

44. $\dfrac{35}{40}$ **45.** $\dfrac{801}{702}$ **46.** $\dfrac{24}{21}$

47. $\dfrac{75}{300}$ **48.** $\dfrac{280}{960}$ **49.** $\dfrac{1332}{2880}$

50. Simplify each fraction in this circle graph.

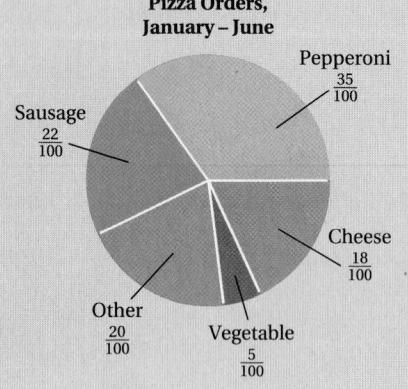

**Pizza Orders,
January – June**

Pepperoni $\frac{35}{100}$

Sausage $\frac{22}{100}$

Cheese $\frac{18}{100}$

Other $\frac{20}{100}$

Vegetable $\frac{5}{100}$

Calculator Corner

Simplifying Fraction Notation   Fraction calculators are equipped with a key, often labeled a^b/c, that allows for simplification with fraction notation. To simplify 208/256 with such a fraction calculator, the following keystrokes can be used.

$$\boxed{2}\ \boxed{0}\ \boxed{8}\ \boxed{a^b/c}$$
$$\boxed{2}\ \boxed{5}\ \boxed{6}\ \boxed{=}.$$

The display $\boxed{13\ \lrcorner\ 16.}$ represents simplified fraction notation $\frac{13}{16}$.

Exercises: Use a fraction calculator to simplify each of the following.

1. $\dfrac{84}{90}$ **2.** $\dfrac{35}{40}$

3. $\dfrac{690}{835}$ **4.** $\dfrac{42}{150}$

Answers

44. $\dfrac{7}{8}$ **45.** $\dfrac{89}{78}$ **46.** $\dfrac{8}{7}$ **47.** $\dfrac{1}{4}$ **48.** $\dfrac{7}{24}$

49. $\dfrac{37}{80}$ **50.** $\dfrac{22}{100} = \dfrac{11}{50}$; $\dfrac{35}{100} = \dfrac{7}{20}$; $\dfrac{18}{100} = \dfrac{9}{50}$;

$\dfrac{5}{100} = \dfrac{1}{20}$; $\dfrac{20}{100} = \dfrac{1}{5}$

EXAMPLE 26   Simplify: $\dfrac{603}{207}$.

At first glance this looks difficult. But note, using the test for divisibility by 9 (sum of digits is divisible by 9), that both the numerator and the denominator are divisible by 9. Thus we write both numbers with a factor of 9:

$$\frac{603}{207} = \frac{9 \cdot 67}{9 \cdot 23} = \frac{9}{9} \cdot \frac{67}{23} = \frac{67}{23}.$$

EXAMPLE 27   Simplify: $\dfrac{660}{1140}$.

Using the tests for divisibility, we have

$$\frac{660}{1140} = \frac{10 \cdot 66}{10 \cdot 114} = \frac{10}{10} \cdot \frac{66}{114} = \frac{66}{114}$$ Both 660 and 1140 are divisible by 10.

$$= \frac{6 \cdot 11}{6 \cdot 19} = \frac{6}{6} \cdot \frac{11}{19} = \frac{11}{19}.$$ Both 66 and 114 are divisible by 6.

Do Exercises 44–50.

Canceling

Canceling is a shortcut that you may have used for removing a factor of 1 when working with fraction notation. With *great* concern, we mention it as a possibility for speeding up your work. Canceling may be done only when removing common factors in numerators and denominators. Each such pair allows us to remove a factor of 1 in a fraction.

Our concern is that canceling be done with care and understanding. In effect, slashes are used to indicate factors of 1 that have been removed. For instance, Example 25 might have been done faster as follows:

$$\frac{90}{84} = \frac{2 \cdot 3 \cdot 3 \cdot 5}{2 \cdot 2 \cdot 3 \cdot 7}$$ Factoring the numerator and the denominator

$$= \frac{2 \cdot 3 \cdot 3 \cdot 5}{2 \cdot 2 \cdot 3 \cdot 7}$$ When a factor of 1 is noted, it is "canceled" as shown: $\dfrac{2}{2} \cdot \dfrac{3}{3} = 1$.

$$= \frac{3 \cdot 5}{2 \cdot 7} = \frac{15}{14}.$$

--------------------------------- *Caution!* ---------------------------------

The difficulty with canceling is that it is often applied incorrectly in situations like the following:

$$\frac{2+3}{2} = 3; \qquad \frac{4+1}{4+2} = \frac{1}{2}; \qquad \frac{15}{54} = \frac{1}{4}.$$

Wrong!   Wrong!   Wrong!

The correct answers are

$$\frac{2+3}{2} = \frac{5}{2}; \qquad \frac{4+1}{4+2} = \frac{5}{6}; \qquad \frac{15}{54} = \frac{3 \cdot 5}{3 \cdot 18} = \frac{3}{3} \cdot \frac{5}{18} = \frac{5}{18}.$$

In each situation, the number canceled was not a factor of 1. Factors are parts of products. For example, in $2 \cdot 3$, 2 and 3 are factors, but in $2 + 3$, 2 and 3 are *not* factors. Canceling may not be done when sums or differences are in numerators or denominators, as shown here. **If you cannot factor, you cannot cancel! If in doubt, do not cancel!**

2.1 Exercise Set

For Extra Help

 MyMathLab

 Math XL PRACTICE

 WATCH

 DOWNLOAD

 READ

 REVIEW

 Identify the numerator and the denominator.

1. $\frac{3}{4}$ 2. $\frac{9}{10}$ 3. $\frac{11}{2}$ 4. $\frac{18}{5}$ 5. $\frac{0}{7}$ 6. $\frac{1}{13}$

What part of each object or set of objects is shaded?

7.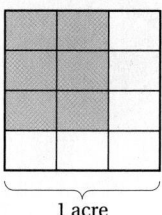
1 acre

8.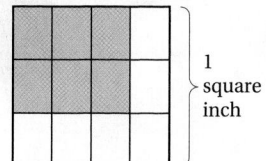
1 square inch

9.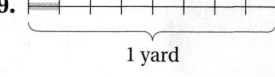
1 yard

10. 1 gold bar
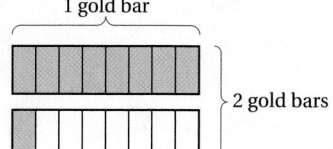
2 gold bars

11.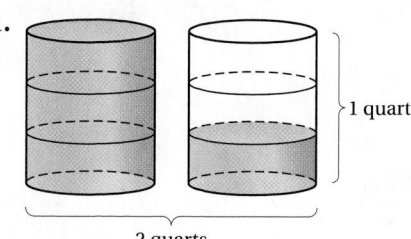
1 quart
2 quarts

12. 1 foot
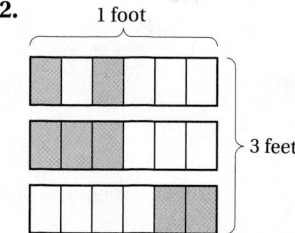
3 feet

What part of an inch is highlighted?

13.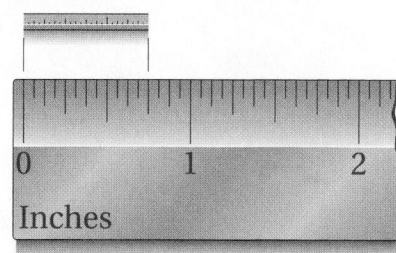

14.

15.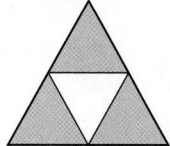

16.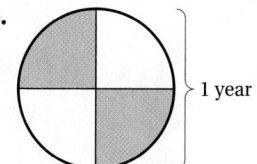
1 year

17.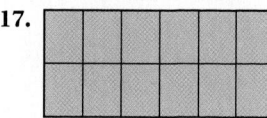

18.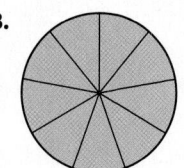

19.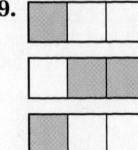

20.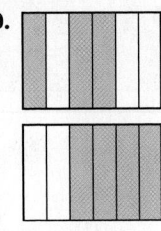

21. 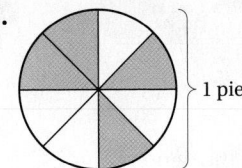 } 1 pie

22.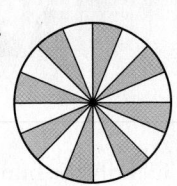

For each of Exercises 23–26, give fraction notation for the amount of gas (**a**) in the tank and (**b**) used from a full tank.

23.

24.

25.

26.

b Simplify.

27. $\dfrac{20}{20}$

28. $\dfrac{0}{16}$

29. $\dfrac{729}{0}$

30. $\dfrac{56}{56}$

31. $\dfrac{0}{238}$

32. $\dfrac{13}{10-10}$

33. $\dfrac{8-1}{9-8}$

34. $\dfrac{8}{8}$

35. $\dfrac{5}{6-6}$

36. $\dfrac{8-8}{1247}$

37. $\dfrac{3}{3}$

38. $\dfrac{1317}{0}$

39. $\dfrac{0}{8}$

40. $\dfrac{11-1}{10-9}$

c Multiply.

41. $\dfrac{2}{5} \cdot \dfrac{2}{3}$

42. $\dfrac{3}{4} \cdot \dfrac{3}{5}$

43. $10 \cdot \dfrac{7}{9}$

44. $9 \cdot \dfrac{5}{8}$

45. $\dfrac{7}{8} \cdot \dfrac{7}{8}$

46. $\dfrac{4}{5} \cdot \dfrac{4}{5}$

47. $\dfrac{2}{3} \times \dfrac{1}{5}$

48. $\dfrac{3}{5} \times \dfrac{1}{5}$

49. $\dfrac{8}{7} \cdot \dfrac{5}{3}$

50. $\dfrac{11}{2} \cdot \dfrac{9}{8}$

51. $\dfrac{2}{5} \cdot 3$

52. $\dfrac{3}{5} \cdot 4$

53. $\dfrac{1}{2} \cdot \dfrac{1}{3}$

54. $\dfrac{1}{6} \cdot \dfrac{1}{4}$

55. $17 \times \dfrac{5}{6}$

Copyright © 2012 Pearson Education, Inc.

56. $\frac{3}{7} \cdot 40$

57. $\frac{1}{10} \cdot \frac{7}{10}$

58. $\frac{3}{10} \cdot \frac{7}{100}$

59. $\frac{2}{5} \cdot 1$

60. $2 \cdot \frac{1}{3}$

61. $\frac{2}{3} \cdot \frac{7}{13}$

62. $\frac{3}{11} \cdot \frac{4}{5}$

63. $5 \times \frac{1}{8}$

64. $4 \times \frac{1}{5}$

65. $\frac{1}{4} \times \frac{1}{10}$

66. $\frac{21}{4} \cdot \frac{7}{5}$

67. $\frac{8}{3} \cdot \frac{20}{9}$

68. $\frac{1}{3} \times \frac{1}{10}$

69. $\frac{14}{15} \cdot \frac{13}{19}$

70. $\frac{12}{13} \cdot \frac{12}{13}$

(d) Find another name for the given number, but with the denominator indicated. Use multiplying by 1.

71. $\frac{5}{8} = \frac{?}{32}$

72. $\frac{1}{6} = \frac{?}{18}$

73. $\frac{7}{8} = \frac{?}{32}$

74. $\frac{5}{6} = \frac{?}{48}$

75. $\frac{17}{18} = \frac{?}{54}$

76. $\frac{11}{5} = \frac{?}{30}$

77. $\frac{7}{22} = \frac{?}{132}$

78. $\frac{3}{8} = \frac{?}{56}$

(e) Simplify.

79. $\frac{2}{4}$

80. $\frac{4}{8}$

81. $\frac{6}{8}$

82. $\frac{8}{12}$

83. $\frac{3}{15}$

84. $\frac{8}{10}$

85. $\frac{24}{8}$

86. $\frac{36}{9}$

87. $\frac{18}{24}$

88. $\frac{42}{48}$

89. $\frac{14}{16}$

90. $\frac{15}{25}$

91. $\frac{12}{10}$

92. $\frac{16}{14}$

93. $\frac{16}{48}$

94. $\frac{100}{20}$

95. $\frac{150}{25}$

96. $\frac{19}{76}$

97. $\frac{17}{51}$

98. $\frac{425}{525}$

99. $\frac{540}{810}$

100. $\frac{1000}{1080}$

101. $\frac{210}{2700}$

102. $\frac{300}{2250}$

Synthesis

What part of each object is shaded?

103.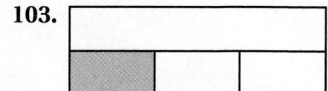

104.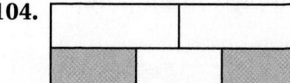

105.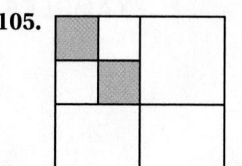

106.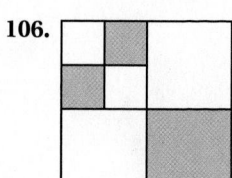

2.2 Multiplication and Division

OBJECTIVES

a Multiply and simplify using fraction notation.

b Find the reciprocal of a number.

c Divide and simplify using fraction notation.

d Solve equations of the type $a \cdot x = b$ and $x \cdot a = b$, where a and b may be fractions.

SKILL TO REVIEW
Objective 1.8a: Determine whether a number is divisible by 2, 3, 4, 5, 6, 8, 9, or 10.

Determine whether each number is divisible by 9.

1. 486   **2.** 129

a Multiplying and Simplifying Using Fraction Notation

It is often possible to simplify after we multiply. To make such simplifying easier, it is usually best not to carry out the products in the numerator and the denominator immediately, but to factor and simplify first. Consider the product

$$\frac{3}{8} \cdot \frac{4}{9}.$$

We proceed as follows:

$$\frac{3}{8} \cdot \frac{4}{9} = \frac{3 \cdot 4}{8 \cdot 9} \qquad \text{We write the products in the numerator and the denominator, but we do not carry them out.}$$

$$= \frac{3 \cdot 2 \cdot 2}{2 \cdot 2 \cdot 2 \cdot 3 \cdot 3} \qquad \text{Factoring the numerator and the denominator}$$

$$= \frac{3 \cdot 2 \cdot 2 \cdot 1}{2 \cdot 2 \cdot 2 \cdot 3 \cdot 3} \qquad \text{Using the identity property of 1 to insert the number 1 as a factor}$$

$$= \frac{3 \cdot 2 \cdot 2}{3 \cdot 2 \cdot 2} \cdot \frac{1}{2 \cdot 3} \qquad \text{Factoring the fraction}$$

$$= 1 \cdot \frac{1}{2 \cdot 3}$$

$$= \frac{1}{2 \cdot 3} \qquad \text{Removing a factor of 1}$$

$$= \frac{1}{6}.$$

The procedure could have been shortened had we noticed that 4 is a factor of the 8 in the denominator:

$$\frac{3}{8} \cdot \frac{4}{9} = \frac{3 \cdot 4}{8 \cdot 9} = \frac{3 \cdot 4}{4 \cdot 2 \cdot 3 \cdot 3} = \frac{3 \cdot 4}{3 \cdot 4} \cdot \frac{1}{2 \cdot 3} = 1 \cdot \frac{1}{2 \cdot 3} = \frac{1}{2 \cdot 3} = \frac{1}{6}.$$

STUDY TIPS

ASKING QUESTIONS

Don't be afraid to ask questions in class. Most instructors welcome this and encourage students to ask them. Other students probably have the same questions you do.

To multiply and simplify:

a) Write the products in the numerator and the denominator, but do not carry them out.

b) Factor the numerator and the denominator.

c) Factor the fraction to remove a factor of 1, if possible.

d) Carry out the remaining products.

EXAMPLES Multiply and simplify.

1. $\dfrac{2}{3} \cdot \dfrac{9}{4} = \dfrac{2 \cdot 9}{3 \cdot 4} = \dfrac{2 \cdot 3 \cdot 3}{3 \cdot 2 \cdot 2} = \dfrac{2 \cdot 3}{2 \cdot 3} \cdot \dfrac{3}{2} = 1 \cdot \dfrac{3}{2} = \dfrac{3}{2}$

2. $\dfrac{6}{7} \cdot \dfrac{5}{3} = \dfrac{6 \cdot 5}{7 \cdot 3} = \dfrac{3 \cdot 2 \cdot 5}{7 \cdot 3} = \dfrac{3}{3} \cdot \dfrac{2 \cdot 5}{7} = 1 \cdot \dfrac{2 \cdot 5}{7} = \dfrac{2 \cdot 5}{7} = \dfrac{10}{7}$

3. $40 \cdot \dfrac{7}{8} = \dfrac{40}{1} \cdot \dfrac{7}{8} = \dfrac{40 \cdot 7}{1 \cdot 8} = \dfrac{8 \cdot 5 \cdot 7}{1 \cdot 8} = \dfrac{8}{8} \cdot \dfrac{5 \cdot 7}{1} = 1 \cdot \dfrac{5 \cdot 7}{1} = \dfrac{5 \cdot 7}{1} = 35$

Answers
Skill to Review:
1. Yes   2. No

-------------------------------- *Caution!* --------------------------------

Canceling can be used as follows for these examples.

1. $\dfrac{2}{3} \cdot \dfrac{9}{4} = \dfrac{2 \cdot 9}{3 \cdot 4} = \dfrac{2 \cdot 3 \cdot 3}{3 \cdot 2 \cdot 2} = \dfrac{3}{2}$

Removing a factor of 1:
$\dfrac{2 \cdot 3}{2 \cdot 3} = 1$

2. $\dfrac{6}{7} \cdot \dfrac{5}{3} = \dfrac{6 \cdot 5}{7 \cdot 3} = \dfrac{3 \cdot 2 \cdot 5}{7 \cdot 3} = \dfrac{2 \cdot 5}{7} = \dfrac{10}{7}$

Removing a factor of 1:
$\dfrac{3}{3} = 1$

3. $40 \cdot \dfrac{7}{8} = \dfrac{40 \cdot 7}{1 \cdot 8} = \dfrac{8 \cdot 5 \cdot 7}{1 \cdot 8} = \dfrac{5 \cdot 7}{1} = 35$

Removing a factor of 1:
$\dfrac{8}{8} = 1$

Remember: if you can't factor, you can't cancel!

> Do Exercises 1–4.

> **Multiply and simplify.**
>
> **1.** $\dfrac{2}{3} \cdot \dfrac{7}{8}$ **2.** $\dfrac{4}{5} \cdot \dfrac{5}{12}$
>
> **3.** $16 \cdot \dfrac{3}{8}$ **4.** $\dfrac{5}{8} \cdot 4$

b Reciprocals

Look at these products:

$$8 \cdot \dfrac{1}{8} = \dfrac{8}{1} \cdot \dfrac{1}{8} = \dfrac{8 \cdot 1}{1 \cdot 8} = \dfrac{8}{8} = 1; \qquad \dfrac{2}{3} \cdot \dfrac{3}{2} = \dfrac{2 \cdot 3}{3 \cdot 2} = \dfrac{6}{6} = 1.$$

RECIPROCALS

If the product of two numbers is 1, we say that they are **reciprocals** of each other. To find the reciprocal of a fraction, interchange the numerator and the denominator.

Number: $\dfrac{3}{4}$ ⟶ Reciprocal: $\dfrac{4}{3}$

EXAMPLES Find the reciprocal.

4. The reciprocal of $\dfrac{4}{5}$ is $\dfrac{5}{4}$. $\dfrac{4}{5} \cdot \dfrac{5}{4} = \dfrac{20}{20} = 1$

5. The reciprocal of 24 is $\dfrac{1}{24}$. Think of 24 as $\dfrac{24}{1}$: $\dfrac{24}{1} \cdot \dfrac{1}{24} = \dfrac{24}{24} = 1.$

6. The reciprocal of $\dfrac{1}{3}$ is 3. $\dfrac{1}{3} \cdot 3 = \dfrac{1}{3} \cdot \dfrac{3}{1} = \dfrac{3}{3} = 1$

> **Find the reciprocal.**
>
> **5.** $\dfrac{2}{5}$ **6.** $\dfrac{10}{7}$
>
> **7.** 9 **8.** $\dfrac{1}{5}$

> Do Exercises 5–8.

Does 0 have a reciprocal? If it did, it would have to be a number x such that $0 \cdot x = 1$. But 0 times any number is 0. Thus we have the following.

0 HAS NO RECIPROCAL

The number 0, or $\dfrac{0}{n}$, has no reciprocal. $\left(\text{Recall that } \dfrac{n}{0} \text{ is not defined.}\right)$

Answers

1. $\dfrac{7}{12}$ **2.** $\dfrac{1}{3}$ **3.** 6 **4.** $\dfrac{5}{2}$

5. $\dfrac{5}{2}$ **6.** $\dfrac{7}{10}$ **7.** $\dfrac{1}{9}$ **8.** 5

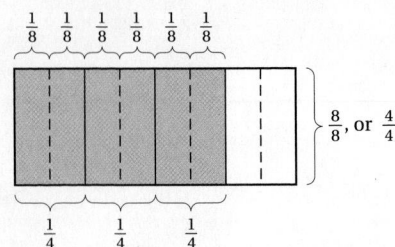

$$\frac{8}{8}, \text{ or } \frac{4}{4}$$

(c) Dividing Using Fraction Notation

Consider the division $\frac{3}{4} \div \frac{1}{8}$. We are asking how many $\frac{1}{8}$'s are in $\frac{3}{4}$. We can answer this by looking at the figure at left. We see that there are six $\frac{1}{8}$'s in $\frac{3}{4}$. Thus,

$$\frac{3}{4} \div \frac{1}{8} = 6.$$

We can check this by multiplying:

$$6 \cdot \frac{1}{8} = \frac{6}{1} \cdot \frac{1}{8} = \frac{6}{8} = \frac{2 \cdot 3}{2 \cdot 4} = \frac{2}{2} \cdot \frac{3}{4} = \frac{3}{4}.$$

Here is a faster way to do this division:

$$\frac{3}{4} \div \frac{1}{8} = \frac{3}{4} \cdot \frac{8}{1} = \frac{3 \cdot 8}{4 \cdot 1} = \frac{24}{4} = 6.$$ Multiplying by the reciprocal of the divisor

> To divide fractions, multiply the dividend by the reciprocal of the divisor:
>
> $$\frac{2}{5} \div \frac{3}{4} = \frac{2}{5} \cdot \frac{4}{3} = \frac{2 \cdot 4}{5 \cdot 3} = \frac{8}{15}.$$
>
> Multiply by the reciprocal of the divisor.

EXAMPLES Divide and simplify.

7. $\dfrac{5}{6} \div \dfrac{2}{3} = \dfrac{5}{6} \cdot \dfrac{3}{2} = \dfrac{5 \cdot 3}{6 \cdot 2} = \dfrac{5 \cdot 3}{3 \cdot 2 \cdot 2} = \dfrac{3}{3} \cdot \dfrac{5}{2 \cdot 2} = \dfrac{5}{2 \cdot 2} = \dfrac{5}{4}$

8. $\dfrac{7}{8} \div \dfrac{1}{16} = \dfrac{7}{8} \cdot \dfrac{16}{1} = \dfrac{7 \cdot 16}{8 \cdot 1} = \dfrac{7 \cdot 2 \cdot 8}{8 \cdot 1} = \dfrac{8}{8} \cdot \dfrac{7 \cdot 2}{1} = \dfrac{7 \cdot 2}{1} = 14$

9. $\dfrac{2}{5} \div 6 = \dfrac{2}{5} \cdot \dfrac{1}{6} = \dfrac{2 \cdot 1}{5 \cdot 6} = \dfrac{2 \cdot 1}{5 \cdot 2 \cdot 3} = \dfrac{2}{2} \cdot \dfrac{1}{5 \cdot 3} = \dfrac{1}{5 \cdot 3} = \dfrac{1}{15}$

-------------------------------- *Caution!* --------------------------------

Canceling can be used as follows for Examples 7–9.

7. $\dfrac{5}{6} \div \dfrac{2}{3} = \dfrac{5}{6} \cdot \dfrac{3}{2} = \dfrac{5 \cdot 3}{6 \cdot 2} = \dfrac{5 \cdot \cancel{3}}{\cancel{3} \cdot 2 \cdot 2} = \dfrac{5}{2 \cdot 2} = \dfrac{5}{4}$ Removing a factor of 1: $\frac{3}{3} = 1$

8. $\dfrac{7}{8} \div \dfrac{1}{16} = \dfrac{7}{8} \cdot \dfrac{16}{1} = \dfrac{7 \cdot 16}{8 \cdot 1} = \dfrac{7 \cdot 2 \cdot \cancel{8}}{\cancel{8} \cdot 1} = \dfrac{7 \cdot 2}{1} = 14$ Removing a factor of 1: $\frac{8}{8} = 1$

9. $\dfrac{2}{5} \div 6 = \dfrac{2}{5} \cdot \dfrac{1}{6} = \dfrac{2 \cdot 1}{5 \cdot 6} = \dfrac{\cancel{2} \cdot 1}{5 \cdot \cancel{2} \cdot 3} = \dfrac{1}{5 \cdot 3} = \dfrac{1}{15}$ Removing a factor of 1: $\frac{2}{2} = 1$

Remember: if you can't factor, you can't cancel!

Do Exercises 9–12.

Divide and simplify.

9. $\dfrac{6}{7} \div \dfrac{3}{4}$ **10.** $\dfrac{2}{3} \div \dfrac{1}{4}$

11. $\dfrac{4}{5} \div 8$ **12.** $60 \div \dfrac{3}{5}$

Answers

9. $\dfrac{8}{7}$ 10. $\dfrac{8}{3}$ 11. $\dfrac{1}{10}$ 12. 100

What is the explanation for multiplying by a reciprocal when dividing? Let's consider $\frac{2}{3} \div \frac{7}{5}$. We multiply by 1. The name for 1 that we will use is $(5/7)/(5/7)$; it comes from the reciprocal of $\frac{7}{5}$.

$$\frac{2}{3} \div \frac{7}{5} = \frac{\frac{2}{3}}{\frac{7}{5}} = \frac{\frac{2}{3}}{\frac{7}{5}} \cdot 1 = \frac{\frac{2}{3}}{\frac{7}{5}} \cdot \frac{\frac{5}{7}}{\frac{5}{7}} = \frac{\frac{2}{3} \cdot \frac{5}{7}}{\frac{7}{5} \cdot \frac{5}{7}} = \frac{\frac{2}{3} \cdot \frac{5}{7}}{1} = \frac{2}{3} \cdot \frac{5}{7} = \frac{10}{21}$$

Thus,

$$\frac{2}{3} \div \frac{7}{5} = \frac{2}{3} \cdot \frac{5}{7} = \frac{10}{21}.$$

Do Exercise 13.

13. Divide by multiplying by 1:

$$\frac{\frac{4}{5}}{\frac{6}{7}}$$

(d) Solving Equations

Now let's solve equations $a \cdot x = b$ and $x \cdot a = b$, where a and b may be fractions. We proceed as we did with equations involving whole numbers. We divide by a on both sides.

EXAMPLE 10 Solve: $\frac{4}{3} \cdot x = \frac{6}{7}$.

We have

$$\frac{4}{3} \cdot x = \frac{6}{7}$$

$$\frac{\frac{4}{3} \cdot x}{\frac{4}{3}} = \frac{\frac{6}{7}}{\frac{4}{3}} \qquad \text{Dividing by } \tfrac{4}{3} \text{ on both sides}$$

$$x = \frac{6}{7} \cdot \frac{3}{4} \qquad \text{Multiplying by the reciprocal}$$

$$= \frac{6 \cdot 3}{7 \cdot 4} = \frac{2 \cdot 3 \cdot 3}{7 \cdot 2 \cdot 2} = \frac{2}{2} \cdot \frac{3 \cdot 3}{7 \cdot 2} = \frac{3 \cdot 3}{7 \cdot 2} = \frac{9}{14}.$$

The solution is $\frac{9}{14}$.

EXAMPLE 11 Solve: $t \cdot \frac{4}{5} = 80$.

Dividing by $\frac{4}{5}$ on both sides, we get

$$t = 80 \div \frac{4}{5} = 80 \cdot \frac{5}{4} = \frac{80 \cdot 5}{4} = \frac{4 \cdot 20 \cdot 5}{4 \cdot 1} = \frac{4}{4} \cdot \frac{20 \cdot 5}{1}$$

$$= \frac{20 \cdot 5}{1} = 100.$$

The solution is 100.

Do Exercises 14 and 15.

Solve.

14. $\frac{5}{6} \cdot y = \frac{2}{3}$

15. $\frac{3}{4} \cdot n = 24$

Answers

13. $\frac{14}{15}$ **14.** $\frac{4}{5}$ **15.** 32

a Multiply and simplify.   Don't forget to simplify!

1. $\dfrac{7}{8} \cdot \dfrac{1}{7}$

2. $\dfrac{4}{9} \cdot \dfrac{1}{4}$

3. $\dfrac{1}{4} \cdot \dfrac{2}{3}$

4. $\dfrac{4}{6} \cdot \dfrac{1}{6}$

5. $\dfrac{12}{5} \cdot \dfrac{9}{8}$

6. $\dfrac{16}{15} \cdot \dfrac{5}{4}$

7. $9 \cdot \dfrac{1}{9}$

8. $4 \cdot \dfrac{1}{4}$

9. $\dfrac{7}{10} \cdot \dfrac{10}{7}$

10. $\dfrac{8}{9} \cdot \dfrac{9}{8}$

11. $\dfrac{7}{5} \cdot \dfrac{5}{7}$

12. $\dfrac{2}{11} \cdot \dfrac{11}{2}$

13. $\dfrac{1}{4} \cdot 8$

14. $\dfrac{1}{3} \cdot 18$

15. $24 \cdot \dfrac{1}{6}$

16. $16 \cdot \dfrac{1}{2}$

17. $12 \cdot \dfrac{3}{4}$

18. $18 \cdot \dfrac{5}{6}$

19. $\dfrac{3}{8} \cdot 24$

20. $\dfrac{2}{9} \cdot 36$

21. $35 \cdot \dfrac{3}{14}$

22. $15 \cdot \dfrac{1}{6}$

23. $240 \cdot \dfrac{1}{8}$

24. $150 \cdot \dfrac{1}{5}$

25. $\dfrac{4}{10} \cdot \dfrac{5}{10}$

26. $\dfrac{7}{10} \cdot \dfrac{34}{150}$

27. $\dfrac{8}{10} \cdot \dfrac{45}{100}$

28. $\dfrac{3}{10} \cdot \dfrac{8}{10}$

29. $\dfrac{11}{24} \cdot \dfrac{3}{5}$

30. $\dfrac{15}{22} \cdot \dfrac{4}{7}$

31. $\dfrac{10}{21} \cdot \dfrac{3}{4}$

32. $\dfrac{17}{18} \cdot \dfrac{3}{5}$

b Find the reciprocal of each number.

33. $\dfrac{5}{6}$

34. $\dfrac{7}{8}$

35. 6

36. 4

37. $\dfrac{1}{6}$

38. $\dfrac{1}{4}$

39. $\dfrac{10}{3}$

40. $\dfrac{17}{4}$

Copyright © 2012 Pearson Education, Inc.

Divide and simplify. | Don't forget to simplify!

41. $\dfrac{3}{5} \div \dfrac{3}{4}$

42. $\dfrac{2}{3} \div \dfrac{3}{4}$

43. $\dfrac{3}{5} \div \dfrac{9}{4}$

44. $\dfrac{6}{7} \div \dfrac{3}{5}$

45. $\dfrac{4}{3} \div \dfrac{1}{3}$

46. $\dfrac{10}{9} \div \dfrac{1}{3}$

47. $\dfrac{1}{3} \div \dfrac{1}{6}$

48. $\dfrac{1}{4} \div \dfrac{1}{5}$

49. $\dfrac{3}{8} \div 3$

50. $\dfrac{5}{6} \div 5$

51. $\dfrac{12}{7} \div 4$

52. $\dfrac{18}{5} \div 2$

53. $12 \div \dfrac{3}{2}$

54. $24 \div \dfrac{3}{8}$

55. $28 \div \dfrac{4}{5}$

56. $40 \div \dfrac{2}{3}$

57. $\dfrac{5}{8} \div \dfrac{5}{8}$

58. $\dfrac{2}{5} \div \dfrac{2}{5}$

59. $\dfrac{8}{15} \div \dfrac{4}{5}$

60. $\dfrac{6}{13} \div \dfrac{3}{26}$

61. $\dfrac{9}{5} \div \dfrac{4}{5}$

62. $\dfrac{5}{12} \div \dfrac{25}{36}$

63. $120 \div \dfrac{5}{6}$

64. $360 \div \dfrac{8}{7}$

d Solve.

65. $\dfrac{4}{5} \cdot x = 60$

66. $\dfrac{3}{2} \cdot t = 90$

67. $\dfrac{5}{3} \cdot y = \dfrac{10}{3}$

68. $\dfrac{4}{9} \cdot m = \dfrac{8}{3}$

69. $x \cdot \dfrac{25}{36} = \dfrac{5}{12}$

70. $p \cdot \dfrac{4}{5} = \dfrac{8}{15}$

71. $n \cdot \dfrac{8}{7} = 360$

72. $y \cdot \dfrac{5}{6} = 120$

Skill Maintenance

Divide. [1.3c]

73. $7140 \div 35$

74. $32{,}200 \div 46$

75. $9\,\overline{)\,2\,7{,}0\,0\,9}$

76. $3\,5\,\overline{)\,7\,1\,4\,8}$

What does the digit 8 mean in each number? [1.1a]

77. 4,678,952

78. 8,473,901

79. 7148

80. 23,803

Synthesis

81. If $\dfrac{1}{3}$ of a number is $\dfrac{1}{4}$, what is $\dfrac{1}{2}$ of the number?

82. $\left(\dfrac{5}{12} \div \dfrac{1}{6} \div \dfrac{3}{4} \right)^2$

OBJECTIVES

a Add using fraction notation.

b Subtract using fraction notation.

c Use < or > with fraction notation to write a true sentence.

d Solve equations of the type $x + a = b$ and $a + x = b$, where a and b may be fractions.

1. Find $\frac{1}{5} + \frac{3}{5}$.

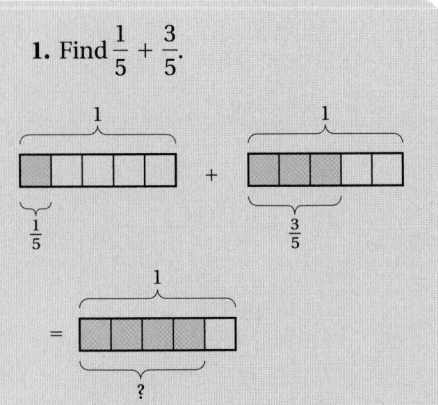

Add and simplify.

2. $\frac{5}{13} + \frac{9}{13}$

3. $\frac{1}{3} + \frac{2}{3}$

4. $\frac{5}{12} + \frac{1}{12}$

5. $\frac{9}{16} + \frac{3}{16}$

Answers

1. $\frac{4}{5}$ 2. $\frac{14}{13}$ 3. 1   4. $\frac{1}{2}$ 5. $\frac{3}{4}$

a Addition Using Fraction Notation

Like Denominators

Addition using fraction notation corresponds to combining or putting like things together, just as addition with whole numbers does. For example,

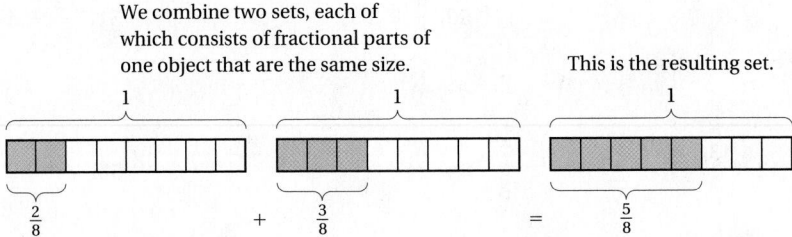

2 eighths + 3 eighths = 5 eighths,

or $\quad 2 \cdot \frac{1}{8} + 3 \cdot \frac{1}{8} = 5 \cdot \frac{1}{8},\quad$ or $\quad \frac{2}{8} + \frac{3}{8} = \frac{5}{8}.$

We see that to add when denominators are the same, we add the numerators and keep the denominator.

Do Exercise 1.

To add when denominators are the same,

a) add the numerators,

b) keep the denominator, and

c) simplify, if possible.

$$\frac{2}{6} + \frac{5}{6} = \frac{2 + 5}{6} = \frac{7}{6}$$

EXAMPLES Add and simplify.

1. $\frac{2}{4} + \frac{1}{4} = \frac{2 + 1}{4} = \frac{3}{4}\qquad$ No simplifying is possible.

2. $\frac{11}{6} + \frac{3}{6} = \frac{11 + 3}{6} = \frac{14}{6} = \frac{2 \cdot 7}{2 \cdot 3} = \frac{2}{2} \cdot \frac{7}{3} = 1 \cdot \frac{7}{3} = \frac{7}{3}\qquad$ Here we simplified.

3. $\frac{3}{12} + \frac{5}{12} = \frac{3 + 5}{12} = \frac{8}{12} = \frac{4 \cdot 2}{4 \cdot 3} = \frac{4}{4} \cdot \frac{2}{3} = 1 \cdot \frac{2}{3} = \frac{2}{3}$

Do Exercises 2-5.

Different Denominators

What do we do when denominators are different? We can find a common denominator by multiplying by 1. Consider adding $\frac{1}{6}$ and $\frac{3}{4}$. There are many common denominators that can be obtained. Let's look at two possibilities.

A. $\frac{1}{6} + \frac{3}{4} = \frac{1}{6} \cdot 1 + \frac{3}{4} \cdot 1$

$= \frac{1}{6} \cdot \frac{4}{4} + \frac{3}{4} \cdot \frac{6}{6}$

$= \frac{4}{24} + \frac{18}{24}$

$= \frac{22}{24}$

$= \frac{11}{12}$ Simplifying

B. $\frac{1}{6} + \frac{3}{4} = \frac{1}{6} \cdot 1 + \frac{3}{4} \cdot 1$

$= \frac{1}{6} \cdot \frac{2}{2} + \frac{3}{4} \cdot \frac{3}{3}$

$= \frac{2}{12} + \frac{9}{12}$

$= \frac{11}{12}$

STUDY TIPS

BEING A TUTOR

Try being a tutor for a fellow student. Your understanding and retention of concepts can be increased if you explain the material to someone else.

We had to simplify in (A) but not in (B). In (B), we used the least common multiple of the denominators, 12, as the common denominator. That number is called the **least common denominator**, or **LCD**. As we will see in Example 6, we may still need to simplify when using the LCD, but it is usually easier than when we use a larger common denominator.

To add when denominators are different:

a) Find the least common multiple of the denominators. That number is the least common denominator, LCD.

b) Multiply by 1, using an appropriate notation, n/n, to express each number in terms of the LCD.

c) Add the numerators, keeping the same denominator.

d) Simplify, if possible.

EXAMPLE 4 Add: $\frac{3}{4} + \frac{1}{8}$.

The LCD is 8.   4 is a factor of 8, so the LCM of 4 and 8 is 8.

$\frac{3}{4} + \frac{1}{8} = \frac{3}{4} \cdot 1 + \frac{1}{8}$ ← This fraction already has the LCD as its denominator.

$= \frac{3}{4} \cdot \frac{2}{2} + \frac{1}{8}$ *Think*: $4 \times \square = 8$. The answer is 2, so we multiply by 1, using $\frac{2}{2}$.

$= \frac{6}{8} + \frac{1}{8} = \frac{7}{8}$

EXAMPLE 5 Add: $\frac{1}{9} + \frac{5}{6}$.

The LCD is 18. $9 = 3 \cdot 3$ and $6 = 2 \cdot 3$, so the LCM of 9 and 6 is $2 \cdot 3 \cdot 3$, or 18.

$\frac{1}{9} + \frac{5}{6} = \frac{1}{9} \cdot 1 + \frac{5}{6} \cdot 1 = \frac{1}{9} \cdot \frac{2}{2} + \frac{5}{6} \cdot \frac{3}{3}$ *Think*: $6 \times \square = 18$. The answer is 3, so we multiply by 1 using $\frac{3}{3}$.

Think: $9 \times \square = 18$. The answer is 2, so we multiply by 1 using $\frac{2}{2}$.

$= \frac{2}{18} + \frac{15}{18} = \frac{17}{18}$

Add.

6. $\frac{2}{3} + \frac{1}{6}$

7. $\frac{3}{8} + \frac{5}{6}$

Do Exercises 6 and 7.

Answers

6. $\frac{5}{6}$ 7. $\frac{29}{24}$

EXAMPLE 6 Add: $\dfrac{5}{9} + \dfrac{11}{18}$.

The LCD is 18.   9 is a factor of 18, so the LCM is 18.

$$\dfrac{5}{9} + \dfrac{11}{18} = \dfrac{5}{9} \cdot \dfrac{2}{2} + \dfrac{11}{18} = \dfrac{10}{18} + \dfrac{11}{18}$$

$$\left.\begin{array}{l} = \dfrac{21}{18} = \dfrac{3 \cdot 7}{3 \cdot 6} = \dfrac{3}{3} \cdot \dfrac{7}{6} \\[2mm] = \dfrac{7}{6} \end{array}\right\} \quad \text{Simplifying}$$

8. Add: $\dfrac{1}{6} + \dfrac{7}{18}$.

Do Exercise 8.

EXAMPLE 7 Add: $\dfrac{1}{10} + \dfrac{3}{100} + \dfrac{7}{1000}$.

Since 10 and 100 are factors of 1000, the LCD is 1000. Then

$$\dfrac{1}{10} + \dfrac{3}{100} + \dfrac{7}{1000} = \dfrac{1}{10} \cdot \dfrac{100}{100} + \dfrac{3}{100} \cdot \dfrac{10}{10} + \dfrac{7}{1000}$$

$$= \dfrac{100}{1000} + \dfrac{30}{1000} + \dfrac{7}{1000} = \dfrac{137}{1000}.$$

9. Add: $\dfrac{4}{10} + \dfrac{1}{100} + \dfrac{3}{1000}$.

Do Exercise 9.

When denominators are large, we most often use the prime factorization of each denominator to find the LCD. This is shown in Example 8.

EXAMPLE 8 Add: $\dfrac{13}{70} + \dfrac{11}{21} + \dfrac{8}{15}$.

We have

$$\dfrac{13}{70} + \dfrac{11}{21} + \dfrac{8}{15} = \dfrac{13}{2 \cdot 5 \cdot 7} + \dfrac{11}{3 \cdot 7} + \dfrac{8}{3 \cdot 5}. \quad \text{Factoring denominators}$$

The LCD is $2 \cdot 3 \cdot 5 \cdot 7$, or 210. Then

$$\dfrac{13}{70} + \dfrac{11}{21} + \dfrac{8}{15} = \dfrac{13}{2 \cdot 5 \cdot 7} \cdot \dfrac{3}{3} + \dfrac{11}{3 \cdot 7} \cdot \dfrac{2 \cdot 5}{2 \cdot 5} + \dfrac{8}{3 \cdot 5} \cdot \dfrac{2 \cdot 7}{2 \cdot 7}$$

> The LCM of 70, 21, and 15 is $2 \cdot 3 \cdot 5 \cdot 7$. In each case, think of which factors are needed to get the LCD. Then multiply by 1 to obtain the LCD in each denominator.

Add.

10. $\dfrac{7}{10} + \dfrac{2}{21} + \dfrac{6}{7}$

11. $\dfrac{5}{18} + \dfrac{7}{24} + \dfrac{11}{36}$

$$= \dfrac{13 \cdot 3}{2 \cdot 5 \cdot 7 \cdot 3} + \dfrac{11 \cdot 2 \cdot 5}{3 \cdot 7 \cdot 2 \cdot 5} + \dfrac{8 \cdot 2 \cdot 7}{3 \cdot 5 \cdot 2 \cdot 7}$$

$$= \dfrac{39}{2 \cdot 3 \cdot 5 \cdot 7} + \dfrac{110}{2 \cdot 3 \cdot 5 \cdot 7} + \dfrac{112}{2 \cdot 3 \cdot 5 \cdot 7}$$

$$= \dfrac{261}{2 \cdot 3 \cdot 5 \cdot 7} = \dfrac{3 \cdot 3 \cdot 29}{2 \cdot 3 \cdot 5 \cdot 7} \quad \text{Factoring the numerator}$$

$$= \dfrac{3}{3} \cdot \dfrac{3 \cdot 29}{2 \cdot 5 \cdot 7} = \dfrac{3 \cdot 29}{2 \cdot 5 \cdot 7} = \dfrac{87}{70}.$$

Do Exercises 10 and 11.

Answers

8. $\dfrac{5}{9}$ **9.** $\dfrac{413}{1000}$ **10.** $\dfrac{347}{210}$ **11.** $\dfrac{7}{8}$

b Subtraction Using Fraction Notation

Like Denominators

Let's consider the difference $\frac{4}{8} - \frac{3}{8}$.

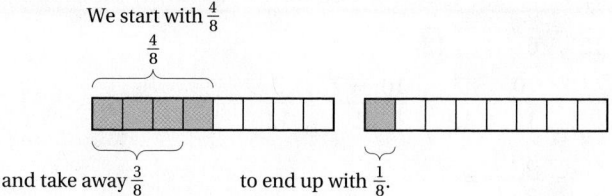

We start with $\frac{4}{8}$

$\frac{4}{8}$

and take away $\frac{3}{8}$ to end up with $\frac{1}{8}$.

We start with 4 eighths and take away 3 eighths:

$$4 \text{ eighths} - 3 \text{ eighths} = 1 \text{ eighth,}$$

or $4 \cdot \frac{1}{8} - 3 \cdot \frac{1}{8} = \frac{1}{8}$,   or $\frac{4}{8} - \frac{3}{8} = \frac{1}{8}$.

> To subtract when denominators are the same,
>
> **a)** subtract the numerators,
>
> **b)** keep the denominator, and $\quad \dfrac{7}{10} - \dfrac{4}{10} = \dfrac{7-4}{10} = \dfrac{3}{10}$
>
> **c)** simplify, if possible.

EXAMPLES Subtract and simplify.

9. $\dfrac{32}{12} - \dfrac{25}{12} = \dfrac{32 - 25}{12} = \dfrac{7}{12}$

10. $\dfrac{7}{10} - \dfrac{3}{10} = \dfrac{7-3}{10} = \dfrac{4}{10} = \dfrac{2 \cdot 2}{5 \cdot 2} = \dfrac{2}{5} \cdot \dfrac{2}{2} = \dfrac{2}{5} \cdot 1 = \dfrac{2}{5}$

11. $\dfrac{8}{9} - \dfrac{2}{9} = \dfrac{8-2}{9} = \dfrac{6}{9} = \dfrac{2 \cdot 3}{3 \cdot 3} = \dfrac{2}{3} \cdot \dfrac{3}{3} = \dfrac{2}{3} \cdot 1 = \dfrac{2}{3}$

Do Exercises 12–14.

Subtract and simplify.

12. $\dfrac{7}{8} - \dfrac{3}{8}$

13. $\dfrac{10}{16} - \dfrac{4}{16}$

14. $\dfrac{8}{10} - \dfrac{3}{10}$

Different Denominators

The procedure for subtraction with different denominators is similar to the procedure for addition.

> To subtract when denominators are different:
>
> **a)** Find the least common multiple of the denominators. That number is the least common denominator, LCD.
>
> **b)** Multiply by 1, using an appropriate notation, n/n, to express each number in terms of the LCD.
>
> **c)** Subtract the numerators, keeping the same denominator.
>
> **d)** Simplify, if possible.

Answers

12. $\frac{1}{2}$ 13. $\frac{3}{8}$ 14. $\frac{1}{2}$

EXAMPLE 12 Subtract: $\dfrac{5}{6} - \dfrac{7}{12}$.

Since 12 is a multiple of 6, the LCM of 6 and 12 is 12. The LCD is 12.

Think: $6 \times \square = 12$. The answer is 2, so we multiply by 1, using $\frac{2}{2}$.

$$\frac{5}{6} - \frac{7}{12} = \frac{5}{6} \cdot \frac{2}{2} - \frac{7}{12}$$

$$= \frac{10}{12} - \frac{7}{12} = \frac{10-7}{12} = \frac{3}{12}$$

$$= \frac{3 \cdot 1}{3 \cdot 4} = \frac{3}{3} \cdot \frac{1}{4} = \frac{1}{4}$$

Subtract.

15. $\dfrac{5}{6} - \dfrac{1}{9}$ **16.** $\dfrac{4}{5} - \dfrac{3}{10}$

Do Exercises 15 and 16.

EXAMPLE 13 Subtract: $\dfrac{17}{24} - \dfrac{4}{15}$.

We have

$$\frac{17}{24} - \frac{4}{15} = \frac{17}{2 \cdot 2 \cdot 2 \cdot 3} - \frac{4}{3 \cdot 5}. \qquad \text{Factoring denominators}$$

The LCD is $2 \cdot 2 \cdot 2 \cdot 3 \cdot 5$, or 120. Then

$$\frac{17}{24} - \frac{4}{15} = \frac{17}{2 \cdot 2 \cdot 2 \cdot 3} \cdot \frac{5}{5} - \frac{4}{3 \cdot 5} \cdot \frac{2 \cdot 2 \cdot 2}{2 \cdot 2 \cdot 2}$$

The LCM of 24 and 15 is $2 \cdot 2 \cdot 2 \cdot 3 \cdot 5$. In each case, we multiply by 1 to obtain the LCD.

$$= \frac{17 \cdot 5}{2 \cdot 2 \cdot 2 \cdot 3 \cdot 5} - \frac{4 \cdot 2 \cdot 2 \cdot 2}{3 \cdot 5 \cdot 2 \cdot 2 \cdot 2}$$

$$= \frac{85}{120} - \frac{32}{120} = \frac{53}{120}.$$

17. Subtract: $\dfrac{11}{28} - \dfrac{5}{16}$.

Do Exercise 17.

c Order

We see from this figure that $\frac{4}{5}$ is greater than $\frac{3}{5}$, and $\frac{3}{5}$ is less than $\frac{4}{5}$. That is, $\frac{4}{5} > \frac{3}{5}$, and $\frac{3}{5} < \frac{4}{5}$.

$\frac{4}{5}$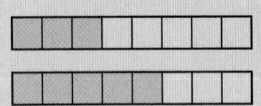

$\frac{3}{5}$

18. Use < or > for $\square$ to write a true sentence:

$$\frac{3}{8} \,\square\, \frac{5}{8}.$$

To determine which of two numbers is greater when there is a common denominator, compare the numerators:

$$\frac{4}{5}, \frac{3}{5}; \qquad 4 > 3; \qquad \frac{4}{5} > \frac{3}{5}.$$

19. Use < or > for $\square$ to write a true sentence:

$$\frac{7}{10} \,\square\, \frac{6}{10}.$$

Do Exercises 18 and 19.

Answers

15. $\dfrac{13}{18}$ 16. $\dfrac{1}{2}$ 17. $\dfrac{9}{112}$ 18. <   19. >

When denominators are different, we cannot compare numerators until we multiply by 1 to make the denominators the same.

EXAMPLE 14 Use $<$ or $>$ for $\square$ to write a true sentence:

$$\frac{2}{5} \square \frac{3}{4}.$$

The LCD is 20. We have

$$\frac{2}{5} \cdot \frac{4}{4} = \frac{8}{20}; \qquad \text{We multiply by 1 using } \frac{4}{4} \text{ to get the LCD.}$$

$$\frac{3}{4} \cdot \frac{5}{5} = \frac{15}{20}. \qquad \text{We multiply by 1 using } \frac{5}{5} \text{ to get the LCD.}$$

Now that the denominators are the same, 20, we can compare the numerators. Since $8 < 15$, it follows that $\frac{8}{20} < \frac{15}{20}$, so

$$\frac{2}{5} < \frac{3}{4}.$$

EXAMPLE 15 Use $<$ or $>$ for $\square$ to write a true sentence:

$$\frac{9}{10} \square \frac{89}{100}.$$

The LCD is 100. We write $\frac{9}{10}$ with a denominator of 100 to make the denominators the same.

$$\frac{9}{10} \cdot \frac{10}{10} = \frac{90}{100} \qquad \text{We multiply by } \frac{10}{10} \text{ to get the LCD.}$$

Since $90 > 89$, it follows that $\frac{90}{100} > \frac{89}{100}$, so

$$\frac{9}{10} > \frac{89}{100}.$$

Do Exercises 20–22.

Use $<$ or $>$ for $\square$ to write a true sentence:

20. $\frac{2}{3} \square \frac{5}{8}$

21. $\frac{3}{4} \square \frac{8}{12}$

22. $\frac{5}{6} \square \frac{7}{8}$

(d) Solving Equations

Now let's solve equations of the form $x + a = b$ or $a + x = b$, where a and b may be fractions. Proceeding as we have before, we subtract a on both sides of the equation.

EXAMPLE 16 Solve: $x + \frac{1}{4} = \frac{3}{5}$.

$$x + \frac{1}{4} - \frac{1}{4} = \frac{3}{5} - \frac{1}{4} \qquad \text{Subtracting } \frac{1}{4} \text{ on both sides}$$

$$x + 0 = \frac{3}{5} \cdot \frac{4}{4} - \frac{1}{4} \cdot \frac{5}{5} \qquad \text{The LCD is 20. We multiply by 1 to get the LCD.}$$

$$x = \frac{12}{20} - \frac{5}{20} = \frac{7}{20}$$

Do Exercises 23 and 24.

Solve.

23. $x + \frac{2}{3} = \frac{5}{6}$

24. $\frac{3}{5} + t = \frac{7}{8}$

Answers

20. $>$ **21.** $>$ **22.** $<$ **23.** $\frac{1}{6}$ **24.** $\frac{11}{40}$

a Add and simplify.

1. $\dfrac{7}{8} + \dfrac{1}{8}$

2. $\dfrac{2}{5} + \dfrac{3}{5}$

3. $\dfrac{1}{8} + \dfrac{5}{8}$

4. $\dfrac{3}{10} + \dfrac{3}{10}$

5. $\dfrac{2}{3} + \dfrac{5}{6}$

6. $\dfrac{5}{6} + \dfrac{1}{9}$

7. $\dfrac{1}{8} + \dfrac{1}{6}$

8. $\dfrac{1}{6} + \dfrac{3}{4}$

9. $\dfrac{4}{5} + \dfrac{7}{10}$

10. $\dfrac{3}{4} + \dfrac{1}{12}$

11. $\dfrac{5}{12} + \dfrac{3}{8}$

12. $\dfrac{7}{8} + \dfrac{1}{16}$

13. $\dfrac{3}{20} + \dfrac{3}{4}$

14. $\dfrac{2}{15} + \dfrac{2}{5}$

15. $\dfrac{5}{6} + \dfrac{7}{9}$

16. $\dfrac{5}{8} + \dfrac{5}{6}$

17. $\dfrac{3}{10} + \dfrac{1}{100}$

18. $\dfrac{9}{10} + \dfrac{3}{100}$

19. $\dfrac{5}{12} + \dfrac{4}{15}$

20. $\dfrac{3}{16} + \dfrac{1}{12}$

21. $\dfrac{9}{10} + \dfrac{99}{100}$

22. $\dfrac{3}{10} + \dfrac{27}{100}$

23. $\dfrac{7}{8} + \dfrac{0}{1}$

24. $\dfrac{0}{1} + \dfrac{5}{6}$

25. $\dfrac{3}{8} + \dfrac{1}{6}$

26. $\dfrac{5}{8} + \dfrac{1}{6}$

27. $\dfrac{5}{12} + \dfrac{7}{24}$

28. $\dfrac{1}{18} + \dfrac{7}{12}$

29. $\dfrac{3}{16} + \dfrac{5}{16} + \dfrac{4}{16}$

30. $\dfrac{3}{8} + \dfrac{1}{8} + \dfrac{2}{8}$

31. $\dfrac{8}{10} + \dfrac{7}{100} + \dfrac{4}{1000}$

32. $\dfrac{1}{10} + \dfrac{2}{100} + \dfrac{3}{1000}$

33. $\dfrac{3}{8} + \dfrac{5}{12} + \dfrac{8}{15}$

34. $\dfrac{1}{2} + \dfrac{3}{8} + \dfrac{1}{4}$

35. $\dfrac{15}{24} + \dfrac{7}{36} + \dfrac{91}{48}$

36. $\dfrac{5}{7} + \dfrac{25}{52} + \dfrac{7}{4}$

Copyright © 2012 Pearson Education, Inc.

b Subtract and simplify.

37. $\dfrac{5}{6} - \dfrac{1}{6}$ **38.** $\dfrac{5}{8} - \dfrac{3}{8}$ **39.** $\dfrac{11}{12} - \dfrac{2}{12}$ **40.** $\dfrac{17}{18} - \dfrac{11}{18}$ **41.** $\dfrac{3}{4} - \dfrac{1}{8}$ **42.** $\dfrac{2}{3} - \dfrac{1}{9}$

43. $\dfrac{1}{8} - \dfrac{1}{12}$ **44.** $\dfrac{1}{6} - \dfrac{1}{8}$ **45.** $\dfrac{4}{3} - \dfrac{5}{6}$ **46.** $\dfrac{7}{8} - \dfrac{1}{16}$ **47.** $\dfrac{3}{4} - \dfrac{3}{28}$ **48.** $\dfrac{2}{5} - \dfrac{2}{15}$

49. $\dfrac{3}{4} - \dfrac{3}{20}$ **50.** $\dfrac{5}{6} - \dfrac{1}{2}$ **51.** $\dfrac{3}{4} - \dfrac{1}{20}$ **52.** $\dfrac{3}{4} - \dfrac{4}{16}$ **53.** $\dfrac{5}{12} - \dfrac{2}{15}$ **54.** $\dfrac{9}{10} - \dfrac{11}{16}$

55. $\dfrac{6}{10} - \dfrac{7}{100}$ **56.** $\dfrac{9}{10} - \dfrac{3}{100}$ **57.** $\dfrac{7}{15} - \dfrac{3}{25}$ **58.** $\dfrac{18}{25} - \dfrac{4}{35}$ **59.** $\dfrac{99}{100} - \dfrac{9}{10}$ **60.** $\dfrac{78}{100} - \dfrac{11}{20}$

61. $\dfrac{2}{3} - \dfrac{1}{8}$ **62.** $\dfrac{3}{4} - \dfrac{1}{2}$ **63.** $\dfrac{3}{5} - \dfrac{1}{2}$ **64.** $\dfrac{5}{6} - \dfrac{2}{3}$ **65.** $\dfrac{5}{12} - \dfrac{3}{8}$ **66.** $\dfrac{7}{12} - \dfrac{2}{9}$

67. $\dfrac{7}{8} - \dfrac{1}{16}$ **68.** $\dfrac{5}{12} - \dfrac{5}{16}$ **69.** $\dfrac{17}{25} - \dfrac{4}{15}$ **70.** $\dfrac{11}{18} - \dfrac{7}{24}$ **71.** $\dfrac{23}{25} - \dfrac{112}{150}$ **72.** $\dfrac{89}{90} - \dfrac{53}{120}$

c Use < or > for $\square$ to write a true sentence.

73. $\dfrac{5}{8}\ \square\ \dfrac{6}{8}$ **74.** $\dfrac{7}{9}\ \square\ \dfrac{5}{9}$ **75.** $\dfrac{1}{3}\ \square\ \dfrac{1}{4}$ **76.** $\dfrac{1}{8}\ \square\ \dfrac{1}{6}$ **77.** $\dfrac{2}{3}\ \square\ \dfrac{5}{7}$

78. $\dfrac{3}{5}\ \square\ \dfrac{4}{7}$ **79.** $\dfrac{4}{5}\ \square\ \dfrac{5}{6}$ **80.** $\dfrac{3}{2}\ \square\ \dfrac{7}{5}$ **81.** $\dfrac{19}{20}\ \square\ \dfrac{4}{5}$ **82.** $\dfrac{5}{6}\ \square\ \dfrac{13}{16}$

83. $\dfrac{19}{20}\ \square\ \dfrac{9}{10}$ **84.** $\dfrac{3}{4}\ \square\ \dfrac{11}{15}$ **85.** $\dfrac{31}{21}\ \square\ \dfrac{41}{13}$ **86.** $\dfrac{12}{7}\ \square\ \dfrac{132}{49}$

(d) Solve.

87. $x + \dfrac{1}{30} = \dfrac{1}{10}$

88. $y + \dfrac{9}{12} = \dfrac{11}{12}$

89. $\dfrac{2}{3} + t = \dfrac{4}{5}$

90. $\dfrac{2}{3} + p = \dfrac{7}{8}$

91. $x + \dfrac{1}{3} = \dfrac{5}{6}$

92. $m + \dfrac{5}{6} = \dfrac{9}{10}$

Skill Maintenance

93. *Honey Production.* In 2007, 154,907,000 lb of honey were produced in the United States. The two states with the greatest honey production were North Dakota and California. North Dakota produced 25,900,000 lb of honey, and California produced 19,760,000 lb. How many more pounds of honey were produced in North Dakota than in California? [1.5a]

Source: www.cattlenetwork.com

94. *Crayons.* The Crayola 64 box of crayons with a built-in sharpener celebrated its 50th birthday in 2008. Since 1958, approximately 200 million Crayola 64 boxes have been sold. How many crayons in the 64 box have been sold altogether? [1.5a]

Source: Crayola LCC

Divide, if possible. If not possible, write "not defined." [1.3c], [2.1b]

95. $\dfrac{38}{38}$

96. $\dfrac{38}{0}$

97. $\dfrac{124}{0}$

98. $\dfrac{124}{31}$

Divide and simplify. [2.2c]

99. $\dfrac{3}{7} \div \dfrac{9}{4}$

100. $\dfrac{9}{10} \div \dfrac{3}{5}$

101. $7 \div \dfrac{1}{3}$

102. $\dfrac{1}{4} \div 8$

Synthesis

103. As part of a rehabilitation program, an athlete must swim and then walk a total of $\dfrac{9}{10}$ km each day. If one lap in the swimming pool is $\dfrac{3}{80}$ km, how far must the athlete walk after swimming 10 laps?

104. *Mountain Climbing.* A mountain climber, beginning at sea level, climbs $\dfrac{3}{5}$ km, descends $\dfrac{1}{4}$ km, climbs $\dfrac{1}{3}$ km, and then descends $\dfrac{1}{7}$ km. At what elevation does the climber finish?

Simplify. Use the rules for order of operations given in Section 1.6.

105. $\dfrac{7}{8} - \dfrac{1}{10} \times \dfrac{5}{6}$

106. $\dfrac{2}{5} + \dfrac{1}{6} \div 3$

107. $\left(\dfrac{2}{3}\right)^2 + \left(\dfrac{3}{4}\right)^2$

108. $5 \times \dfrac{3}{7} - \dfrac{1}{7} \times \dfrac{4}{5}$

Use <, >, or = for ☐ to write a true sentence.

109. 🖩 $\dfrac{37}{157} + \dfrac{19}{107}$ ☐ $\dfrac{6941}{16,799}$

110. 🖩 $\dfrac{12}{97} + \dfrac{67}{139}$ ☐ $\dfrac{8167}{13,289}$

Copyright © 2012 Pearson Education, Inc.

Mid-Chapter Review

Concept Reinforcement

Determine whether each statement is true or false.

_____ **1.** If $\dfrac{a}{b} > \dfrac{c}{b}, b \neq 0$, then $a > c$. [2.3c]

_____ **2.** The reciprocal of $\dfrac{d}{f}, f \neq 0$, is $-\dfrac{d}{f}$. [2.2a]

_____ **3.** For any whole number n that is not 0, $\dfrac{0}{n} < \dfrac{n}{n}$. [2.1b], [2.3c]

_____ **4.** To add fractions when denominators are the same, we keep the numerator and add the denominators. [2.3a]

Guided Solutions

Fill in each blank with the number that creates a correct statement or solution.

5. $\dfrac{25}{\square} = 1$ [2.1b]
6. $\dfrac{\square}{9} = 0$ [2.1b]
7. $\dfrac{8}{\square} = 8$ [2.1b]
8. $\dfrac{6}{13} = \dfrac{\square}{39}$ [2.1d]

Fill in each blank with the number that creates a correct solution.

9. Subtract: $\dfrac{11}{42} - \dfrac{3}{35}$. [2.3b]

$$\dfrac{11}{42} - \dfrac{3}{35} = \dfrac{11}{2 \cdot \square \cdot 7} - \dfrac{3}{\square \cdot 7} \qquad \text{Factoring the denominators}$$

$$= \dfrac{11}{2 \cdot \square \cdot 7} \cdot \left(\dfrac{\square}{\square}\right) - \dfrac{3}{\square \cdot 7} \cdot \left(\dfrac{\square \cdot \square}{\square \cdot \square}\right) \qquad \text{Multiplying by 1 to get the LCD}$$

$$= \dfrac{11 \cdot \square}{2 \cdot 3 \cdot 7 \cdot \square} - \dfrac{3 \cdot \square \cdot \square}{5 \cdot 7 \cdot \square \cdot \square} \qquad \text{Multiplying}$$

$$= \dfrac{\square}{2 \cdot 3 \cdot 5 \cdot 7} - \dfrac{\square}{2 \cdot 3 \cdot 5 \cdot 7} \qquad \text{Simplifying}$$

$$= \dfrac{\square - \square}{2 \cdot 3 \cdot 5 \cdot 7} = \dfrac{\square}{\square} \qquad \text{Subtracting and simplifying}$$

10. Solve: $x + \dfrac{1}{8} = \dfrac{2}{3}$. [2.3d]

$$x + \dfrac{1}{8} = \dfrac{2}{3}$$

$$x + \dfrac{1}{8} - \square = \dfrac{2}{3} - \square \qquad \text{Subtracting on both sides}$$

$$x + \square = \dfrac{2}{3} \cdot \dfrac{\square}{\square} - \dfrac{1}{8} \cdot \dfrac{\square}{\square} \qquad \text{Multiplying by 1 to get the LCD}$$

$$x = \dfrac{\square}{\square} - \dfrac{\square}{\square} \qquad \text{Simplifying and multiplying}$$

$$x = \dfrac{\square}{\square} \qquad \text{Subtracting}$$

Mixed Review

What part of each object or set of objects is shaded? [2.1a]

11.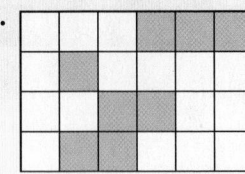

12.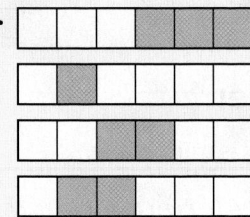

Simplify. [2.1b, e]

13. $\dfrac{24}{60}$

14. $\dfrac{220}{60}$

15. $\dfrac{17}{17}$

16. $\dfrac{0}{23}$

17. $\dfrac{14}{0}$

18. $\dfrac{7-7}{19-17}$

19. $\dfrac{54}{186}$

20. $\dfrac{36}{20}$

21. $\dfrac{75}{630}$

22. $\dfrac{315}{435}$

Calculate and simplify.

23. $\dfrac{1}{5} + \dfrac{7}{45}$ [2.3a]

24. $\dfrac{5}{6} + \dfrac{2}{3} + \dfrac{7}{12}$ [2.3a]

25. $\dfrac{6}{21} \div \dfrac{1}{7}$ [2.2c]

26. $\dfrac{5}{18} - \dfrac{1}{15}$ [2.3b]

27. $\dfrac{5}{11} \cdot 8$ [2.1c]

28. $\dfrac{1}{100} \div \dfrac{1}{10}$ [2.2c]

29. $\dfrac{3}{2} \cdot \dfrac{2}{3}$ [2.2a]

30. $\dfrac{8}{25} \cdot \dfrac{5}{6}$ [2.2a]

31. $\dfrac{19}{48} - \dfrac{11}{30}$ [2.3b]

32. $\dfrac{3}{7} + \dfrac{15}{17}$ [2.3a]

33. $80 \div \dfrac{4}{15}$ [2.2c]

34. $\dfrac{8}{65} - \dfrac{2}{35}$ [2.3b]

35. Solve: $\dfrac{2}{5} + x = \dfrac{9}{16}$. [2.3d]

36. Solve: $\dfrac{7}{2} \cdot y = \dfrac{49}{24}$. [2.2d]

37. Arrange in order from smallest to largest: $\dfrac{4}{9}, \dfrac{3}{10}, \dfrac{2}{7},$ and $\dfrac{1}{5}$.

[2.3c]

Understanding Through Discussion and Writing

38. Explain the role of multiplication when adding using fraction notation with different denominators. [2.3a]

39. A student made the following error:

$$\frac{8}{5} - \frac{8}{2} = \frac{8}{3}.$$

Find at least two ways to convince him of the mistake.
[2.3b]

40. Explain in your own words when it *is* possible to "cancel" and when it *is not* possible to "cancel." [2.1e]

41. Can fraction notation be simplified if the numerator and the denominator are two different prime numbers? Why or why not? [2.1e]

Copyright © 2012 Pearson Education, Inc.

2.4 Mixed Numerals

a Mixed Numerals

The following figure illustrates the use of a **mixed numeral**. The bolt shown is $2\frac{3}{8}$ in. long. The length is given as a whole-number part, 2, and a fractional part less than 1, $\frac{3}{8}$. We can also represent the measurement of the bolt with fraction notation as $\frac{19}{8}$, but the meaning or interpretation of such a symbol is less understandable or visual than that of mixed numeral notation.

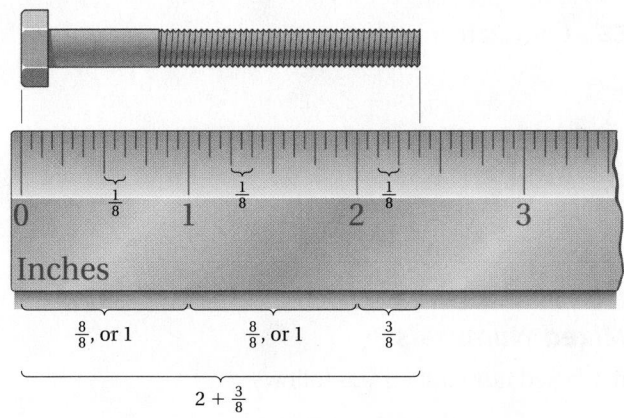

$\frac{8}{8}$, or 1 $\frac{8}{8}$, or 1 $\frac{3}{8}$

$2 + \frac{3}{8}$

A mixed numeral $2\frac{3}{8}$ represents a sum:

$$2\frac{3}{8} \quad \text{means} \quad 2 + \frac{3}{8}.$$

This is a whole number.   This is a fraction less than 1.

EXAMPLES Convert to a mixed numeral.

1. $7 + \frac{2}{5} = 7\frac{2}{5}$

2. $4 + \frac{3}{10} = 4\frac{3}{10}$

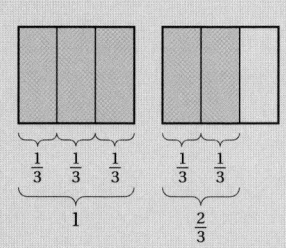

Do Exercises 1–3.

The notation $2\frac{3}{4}$ has a plus sign left out. To aid in understanding, we sometimes write the missing plus sign. This is especially helpful when we convert a mixed numeral to fraction notation.

EXAMPLES Convert to fraction notation.

3. $2\frac{3}{4} = 2 + \frac{3}{4}$ Inserting the missing plus sign

$\quad = \frac{2}{1} + \frac{3}{4}$ $2 = \frac{2}{1}$

$\quad = \frac{2}{1} \cdot \frac{4}{4} + \frac{3}{4}$ Finding a common denominator

$\quad = \frac{8}{4} + \frac{3}{4} = \frac{11}{4}$

OBJECTIVES

a Convert between mixed numerals and fraction notation.

b Add using mixed numerals.

c Subtract using mixed numerals.

d Multiply using mixed numerals.

e Divide using mixed numerals.

SKILL TO REVIEW
Objective 2.1e: Simplify fraction notation.

Simplify.

1. $\frac{18}{32}$ **2.** $\frac{78}{117}$

Convert to a mixed numeral.

1. $1 + \frac{2}{3} = \square\frac{\square}{\square}$

$\frac{1}{3}$ $\frac{1}{3}$ $\frac{1}{3}$ $\frac{1}{3}$ $\frac{1}{3}$

1    $\frac{2}{3}$

2. $2 + \frac{3}{4} = \square\frac{\square}{\square}$

3. $12 + \frac{2}{7}$

Answers

Skill to Review:

1. $\frac{9}{16}$ 2. $\frac{2}{3}$

Margin Exercises:

1. $1\frac{2}{3}$ 2. $2\frac{3}{4}$ 3. $12\frac{2}{7}$

Convert to fraction notation.

4. $4\frac{2}{5}$ **5.** $6\frac{1}{10}$

Convert to fraction notation. Use the faster method.

6. $4\frac{5}{6}$ **7.** $9\frac{1}{4}$

8. $20\frac{2}{3}$ **9.** $1\frac{9}{13}$

STUDY TIPS

WORKED-OUT SOLUTIONS

The *Student's Solutions Manual* is an excellent resource if you need additional help with an exercise in the exercise sets. It contains step-by-step solutions to the odd-numbered exercises in each exercise set.

4. $4\frac{3}{10} = 4 + \frac{3}{10} = \frac{4}{1} + \frac{3}{10} = \frac{4}{1} \cdot \frac{10}{10} + \frac{3}{10} = \frac{40}{10} + \frac{3}{10} = \frac{43}{10}$

Do Exercises 4 and 5.

> To convert from a mixed numeral to fraction notation:
>
> ⓐ Multiply the whole number by the denominator: $4 \cdot 10 = 40$.
> ⓑ Add the result to the numerator: $40 + 3 = 43$.
> ⓒ Keep the denominator.
>
> $4\frac{3}{10} = \frac{43}{10}$

EXAMPLES Convert to fraction notation.

5. $6\frac{2}{3} = \frac{20}{3}$ $6 \cdot 3 = 18, 18 + 2 = 20$

6. $8\frac{2}{9} = \frac{74}{9}$ $8 \cdot 9 = 72, 72 + 2 = 74$

Do Exercises 6-9.

Writing Mixed Numerals

We can find a mixed numeral for $\frac{5}{3}$ as follows:

$$\frac{5}{3} = \frac{3}{3} + \frac{2}{3} = 1 + \frac{2}{3} = 1\frac{2}{3}.$$

In terms of objects, we can think of $\frac{5}{3}$ as $\frac{3}{3}$, or 1, plus $\frac{2}{3}$, as shown below.

$$\frac{5}{3} = \quad \frac{3}{3}, \text{ or } 1 \quad + \quad \frac{2}{3}$$

Fraction symbols like $\frac{5}{3}$ also indicate division; $\frac{5}{3}$ means $5 \div 3$. Let's divide the numerator by the denominator.

$$\begin{array}{r} 1 \\ 3\overline{)5} \\ \underline{3} \\ 2 \end{array} \leftarrow 2 \div 3 = \frac{2}{3}$$

Thus, $\frac{5}{3} = 1\frac{2}{3}$.

> To convert from fraction notation to a mixed numeral, divide.
>
> $$\frac{13}{5} \qquad \begin{array}{r} 2 \\ 5\overline{)13} \\ \underline{10} \\ 3 \end{array} \qquad 2\frac{3}{5}$$
>
> The divisor — The quotient — The remainder

Answers

4. $\frac{22}{5}$ **5.** $\frac{61}{10}$ **6.** $\frac{29}{6}$ **7.** $\frac{37}{4}$

8. $\frac{62}{3}$ **9.** $\frac{22}{13}$

EXAMPLES Convert to a mixed numeral.

7. $\dfrac{69}{10}$

$$\begin{array}{r} 6 \\ 10\overline{)69} \\ 60 \\ \hline 9 \end{array}$$

$$\dfrac{69}{10} = 6\dfrac{9}{10}$$

8. $\dfrac{122}{8}$

$$\begin{array}{r} 15 \\ 8\overline{)122} \\ 8 \\ \hline 42 \\ 40 \\ \hline 2 \end{array}$$

$$\dfrac{122}{8} = 15\dfrac{2}{8} = 15\dfrac{1}{4}$$

Do Exercises 10–13.

Convert to a mixed numeral.

10. $\dfrac{7}{3}$ **11.** $\dfrac{11}{10}$

12. $\dfrac{110}{6}$ **13.** $\dfrac{229}{18}$

b Addition Using Mixed Numerals

To find the sum $1\frac{5}{8} + 3\frac{1}{8}$, we first add the fractions. Then we add the whole numbers.

$$\begin{array}{r} 1\dfrac{5}{8} = \\ + 3\dfrac{1}{8} = \\ \hline \dfrac{6}{8} \end{array} \qquad \begin{array}{r} 1\dfrac{5}{8} \\ + 3\dfrac{1}{8} \\ \hline 4\dfrac{6}{8} = 4\dfrac{3}{4} \end{array}$$

Simplifying: $\dfrac{6}{8} = \dfrac{3}{4}$

Add the fractions.   Add the whole numbers.

Sometimes we must write the fractional parts with a common denominator before we can add.

EXAMPLE 9 Add: $5\frac{2}{3} + 3\frac{5}{6}$. Write a mixed numeral for the answer.

The LCD is 6.

$$\begin{array}{rl} 5\dfrac{2}{3} \cdot \dfrac{2}{2} = & 5\dfrac{4}{6} \\ + 3\dfrac{5}{6} = & + 3\dfrac{5}{6} \\ \hline & 8\dfrac{9}{6} = 8 + \dfrac{9}{6} \\ & \qquad = 8 + 1\dfrac{1}{2} \\ & \qquad = 9\dfrac{1}{2} \end{array}$$

Writing $\frac{9}{6}$ as a mixed numeral, $1\frac{1}{2}$

Do Exercises 14 and 15.

Add.

14. $\begin{array}{r} 2\dfrac{3}{10} \\ + 5\dfrac{1}{10} \\ \hline \end{array}$ **15.** $\begin{array}{r} 8\dfrac{2}{5} \\ + 3\dfrac{7}{10} \\ \hline \end{array}$

Answers

10. $2\frac{1}{3}$ **11.** $1\frac{1}{10}$ **12.** $18\frac{1}{3}$ **13.** $12\frac{13}{18}$
14. $7\frac{2}{5}$ **15.** $12\frac{1}{10}$

EXAMPLE 10 Add: $10\frac{5}{6} + 7\frac{3}{8}$.

The LCD is 24.

$$10\ \frac{5}{6} \cdot \frac{4}{4} = 10\frac{20}{24}$$

$$+\ 7\ \frac{3}{8} \cdot \frac{3}{3} = +\ 7\frac{9}{24}$$

$$17\frac{29}{24} = 17 + \frac{29}{24}$$

$$= 17 + 1\frac{5}{24} \qquad \text{Writing } \tfrac{29}{24} \text{ as a mixed}$$
$$\phantom{= 17 + 1\frac{5}{24}} \qquad \text{numeral, } 1\tfrac{5}{24}$$

$$= 18\frac{5}{24}$$

Do Exercise 16.

(c) Subtraction Using Mixed Numerals

Subtraction is a lot like addition; we subtract the fractions and then the whole numbers.

EXAMPLE 11 Subtract: $7\frac{3}{4} - 2\frac{1}{4}$.

$$7\ \frac{3}{4} = \qquad 7\ \frac{3}{4}$$
$$-\ 2\ \frac{1}{4} = \qquad -\ 2\ \frac{1}{4}$$
$$\frac{2}{4} \qquad\qquad \frac{2}{4} = 5\frac{1}{2}$$

↑ Subtract the fractions.   ↑ Subtract the whole numbers.   ↑ Simplifying

EXAMPLE 12 Subtract: $9\frac{4}{5} - 3\frac{1}{2}$.

The LCD is 10.

$$9\ \frac{4}{5} \cdot \frac{2}{2} = \qquad 9\frac{8}{10}$$
$$-\ 3\ \frac{1}{2} \cdot \frac{5}{5} = -\ 3\frac{5}{10}$$
$$6\frac{3}{10}$$

Do Exercises 17 and 18.

EXAMPLE 13 Subtract: $7\frac{1}{6} - 2\frac{1}{4}$.

The LCD is 12.

$$7\ \frac{1}{6} \cdot \frac{2}{2} = \quad 7\frac{2}{12}$$
$$-\ 2\ \frac{1}{4} \cdot \frac{3}{3} = -\ 2\frac{3}{12}$$

We cannot subtract $\frac{3}{12}$ from $\frac{2}{12}$.
← We borrow 1, or $\frac{12}{12}$, from 7:
$7\frac{2}{12} = 6 + 1 + \frac{2}{12} = 6 + \frac{12}{12} + \frac{2}{12} = 6\frac{14}{12}$.

We can write this as

$$7\frac{2}{12} = \quad 6\frac{14}{12}$$
$$-\ 2\frac{3}{12} = -\ 2\frac{3}{12}$$
$$4\frac{11}{12}.$$

Do Exercise 19.

16. Add.

$$9\frac{3}{4}$$
$$+\ 3\frac{5}{6}$$

Subtract.

17. $\quad 10\frac{7}{8}$
$$-\ 9\frac{3}{8}$$

18. $\quad 8\frac{2}{3}$
$$-\ 5\frac{1}{2}$$

19. Subtract.

$$8\frac{1}{9}$$
$$-\ 4\frac{5}{6}$$

Answers

16. $13\frac{7}{12}$ **17.** $1\frac{1}{2}$ **18.** $3\frac{1}{6}$ **19.** $3\frac{5}{18}$

EXAMPLE 14 Subtract: $12 - 9\frac{3}{8}$.

$$
\begin{array}{r}
12 \;\; = \;\; 11\dfrac{8}{8} \\[4pt]
-\; 9\dfrac{3}{8} \;=\; -\; 9\dfrac{3}{8} \\[2pt]
\hline
2\dfrac{5}{8}
\end{array}
\qquad 12 = 11 + 1 = 11 + \dfrac{8}{8} = 11\dfrac{8}{8}
$$

Do Exercise 20.

Do Exercise 20.

20. Subtract.

$$
\begin{array}{r}
5 \\
-\; 1\dfrac{1}{3} \\
\end{array}
$$

(d) Multiplication Using Mixed Numerals

Carrying out addition and subtraction with mixed numerals is usually easier if the numbers are left as mixed numerals. With multiplication and division, however, it is easier to convert the numbers to fraction notation first.

> **MULTIPLICATION USING MIXED NUMERALS**
>
> To multiply using mixed numerals, first convert to fraction notation and multiply. Then convert the answer to a mixed numeral, if appropriate.

EXAMPLE 15 Multiply: $6 \cdot 2\frac{1}{2}$.

$$
6 \cdot 2\frac{1}{2} = \frac{6}{1} \cdot \frac{5}{2} = \frac{6 \cdot 5}{1 \cdot 2} = \frac{2 \cdot 3 \cdot 5}{2 \cdot 1} = \frac{2}{2} \cdot \frac{3 \cdot 5}{1} = 1 \cdot \frac{3 \cdot 5}{1} = 15
$$

Converting the numbers to fraction notation first makes it easier to carry out the multiplication.

EXAMPLE 16 Multiply: $3\frac{1}{2} \cdot \frac{3}{4}$.

$$
3\frac{1}{2} \cdot \frac{3}{4} = \frac{7}{2} \cdot \frac{3}{4} = \frac{21}{8} = 2\frac{5}{8}
$$

Here we write fraction notation.

Do Exercises 21 and 22.

Do Exercises 21 and 22.

Multiply.

21. $6 \cdot 3\frac{1}{3}$ **22.** $2\frac{1}{2} \cdot \frac{3}{4}$

EXAMPLE 17 Multiply: $8 \cdot 4\frac{2}{3}$.

$$
8 \cdot 4\frac{2}{3} = \frac{8}{1} \cdot \frac{14}{3} = \frac{112}{3} = 37\frac{1}{3}
$$

Answers

20. $3\frac{2}{3}$ **21.** 20 **22.** $1\frac{7}{8}$

Multiply.

23. $2 \cdot 6\frac{2}{5}$

24. $3\frac{1}{3} \cdot 2\frac{1}{2}$

EXAMPLE 18 Multiply: $2\frac{1}{4} \cdot 3\frac{2}{5}$.

$$2\frac{1}{4} \cdot 3\frac{2}{5} = \frac{9}{4} \cdot \frac{17}{5} = \frac{153}{20} = 7\frac{13}{20}$$

----------- *Caution!* -----------

$2\frac{1}{4} \cdot 3\frac{2}{5} \neq 6\frac{2}{20}$. A common error is to multiply the whole numbers and then the fractions. This does not give the correct answer, $7\frac{13}{20}$, which is found by converting to fraction notation first.

Do Exercises 23 and 24.

(e) Division Using Mixed Numerals

The division $1\frac{1}{2} \div \frac{1}{6}$ is shown at left. *Think*: "How many $\frac{1}{6}$'s are in $1\frac{1}{2}$?" We see that the answer is 9.

When we divide using mixed numerals, we convert to fraction notation first.

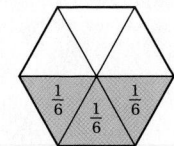

$$1\frac{1}{2} \div \frac{1}{6} = \frac{3}{2} \div \frac{1}{6} = \frac{3}{2} \cdot \frac{6}{1}$$

$$= \frac{3 \cdot 6}{2 \cdot 1} = \frac{3 \cdot 3 \cdot 2}{2 \cdot 1} = \frac{3 \cdot 3}{1} \cdot \frac{2}{2} = \frac{3 \cdot 3}{1} \cdot 1 = 9$$

> **DIVISION USING MIXED NUMERALS**
>
> To divide using mixed numerals, first write fraction notation and divide. Then convert the answer to a mixed numeral, if appropriate.

EXAMPLE 19 Divide: $32 \div 3\frac{1}{5}$.

$$32 \div 3\frac{1}{5} = \frac{32}{1} \div \frac{16}{5} \quad \text{Writing fraction notation}$$

$$= \frac{32}{1} \cdot \frac{5}{16} = \frac{32 \cdot 5}{1 \cdot 16} = \frac{2 \cdot 16 \cdot 5}{1 \cdot 16} = \frac{16}{16} \cdot \frac{2 \cdot 5}{1} = 1 \cdot \frac{2 \cdot 5}{1} = 10$$

Remember to multiply by the reciprocal.

25. Divide: $84 \div 5\frac{1}{4}$.

Do Exercise 25.

EXAMPLE 20 Divide: $35 \div 4\frac{1}{3}$.

$$35 \div 4\frac{1}{3} = \frac{35}{1} \div \frac{13}{3} = \frac{35}{1} \cdot \frac{3}{13} = \frac{105}{13} = 8\frac{1}{13}$$

Do Exercise 26.

26. Divide: $26 \div 3\frac{1}{2}$.

EXAMPLE 21 Divide: $2\frac{1}{3} \div 1\frac{3}{4}$.

$$2\frac{1}{3} \div 1\frac{3}{4} = \frac{7}{3} \div \frac{7}{4} = \frac{7}{3} \cdot \frac{4}{7} = \frac{7 \cdot 4}{3 \cdot 7} = \frac{7}{7} \cdot \frac{4}{3} = 1 \cdot \frac{4}{3} = \frac{4}{3} = 1\frac{1}{3}$$

Divide.

27. $2\frac{1}{4} \div 1\frac{1}{5}$

28. $1\frac{3}{4} \div 2\frac{1}{2}$

EXAMPLE 22 Divide: $1\frac{3}{5} \div 3\frac{1}{3}$.

$$1\frac{3}{5} \div 3\frac{1}{3} = \frac{8}{5} \div \frac{10}{3} = \frac{8}{5} \cdot \frac{3}{10} = \frac{8 \cdot 3}{5 \cdot 10} = \frac{2 \cdot 4 \cdot 3}{5 \cdot 2 \cdot 5} = \frac{2}{2} \cdot \frac{4 \cdot 3}{5 \cdot 5} = \frac{12}{25}$$

Answers

23. $12\frac{4}{5}$ **24.** $8\frac{1}{3}$ **25.** 16   **26.** $7\frac{3}{7}$

27. $1\frac{7}{8}$ **28.** $\frac{7}{10}$

Do Exercises 27 and 28.

138   CHAPTER 2   Fraction Notation

Exercise Set

a   Solve.

1. *Greenhouse Dimensions.* A community college horti-culture department builds a greenhouse that measures $32\frac{1}{2}$ ft $\times$ $20\frac{5}{6}$ ft $\times$ $11\frac{3}{4}$ ft. Convert $32\frac{1}{2}$, $20\frac{5}{6}$, and $11\frac{3}{4}$ to fraction notation.

2. A quilt design requires three different fabrics. The quilter determines that she needs $\frac{17}{4}$ yd of a dominant fabric, $\frac{10}{3}$ yd of a contrasting fabric, and $\frac{9}{8}$ yd of a border fabric. Convert $\frac{17}{4}$, $\frac{10}{3}$, and $\frac{9}{8}$ to mixed numerals.

$11\frac{3}{4}$ ft

$32\frac{1}{2}$ ft

$20\frac{5}{6}$ ft

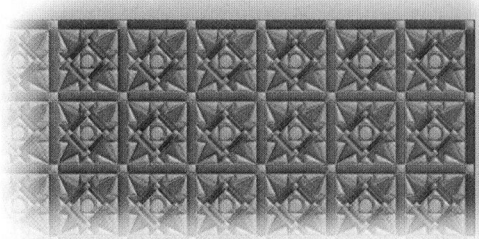

Convert to fraction notation.

3. $1\frac{5}{8}$ **4.** $30\frac{4}{5}$ **5.** $12\frac{3}{4}$ **6.** $5\frac{7}{10}$ **7.** $2\frac{3}{100}$ **8.** $33\frac{1}{3}$

Convert to a mixed numeral.

9. $\frac{27}{6}$ **10.** $\frac{50}{8}$ **11.** $\frac{53}{7}$ **12.** $\frac{39}{8}$ **13.** $\frac{57}{10}$ **14.** $\frac{223}{4}$

b   Add. Write a mixed numeral for the answer.

15. $\begin{array}{r} 20 \\ + \ 8\frac{3}{4} \\ \hline \end{array}$

16. $\begin{array}{r} 37 \\ + \ 18\frac{2}{3} \\ \hline \end{array}$

17. $1\frac{1}{4} + 1\frac{2}{3}$

18. $4\frac{1}{3} + 5\frac{2}{9}$

19. $\begin{array}{r} 8\frac{3}{4} \\ + \ 5\frac{5}{6} \\ \hline \end{array}$

20. $\begin{array}{r} 4\frac{3}{8} \\ + \ 6\frac{5}{12} \\ \hline \end{array}$

21. $\begin{array}{r} 3\frac{2}{5} \\ + \ 8\frac{7}{10} \\ \hline \end{array}$

22. $\begin{array}{r} 5\frac{1}{2} \\ + \ 3\frac{7}{10} \\ \hline \end{array}$

23. $5\dfrac{3}{8}$
$+\ 10\dfrac{5}{6}$

24. $\dfrac{5}{8}$
$+\ 1\dfrac{5}{6}$

25. $12\dfrac{4}{5}$
$+\ 8\dfrac{7}{10}$

26. $15\dfrac{5}{8}$
$+\ 11\dfrac{3}{4}$

27. $14\dfrac{5}{8}$
$+\ 13\dfrac{1}{4}$

28. $16\dfrac{1}{4}$
$+\ 15\dfrac{7}{8}$

29. $7\dfrac{1}{8}$
$9\dfrac{2}{3}$
$+\ 10\dfrac{3}{4}$

30. $45\dfrac{2}{3}$
$31\dfrac{3}{5}$
$+\ 12\dfrac{1}{4}$

c Subtract. Write a mixed numeral for the answer.

31. $4\dfrac{1}{5}$
$-\ 2\dfrac{3}{5}$

32. $5\dfrac{1}{8}$
$-\ 2\dfrac{3}{8}$

33. $6\dfrac{3}{5} - 2\dfrac{1}{2}$

34. $7\dfrac{2}{3} - 6\dfrac{1}{2}$

35. $34\dfrac{1}{3}$
$-\ 12\dfrac{5}{8}$

36. $23\dfrac{5}{16}$
$-\ 16\dfrac{3}{4}$

37. 21
$-\ 8\dfrac{3}{4}$

38. 42
$-\ 3\dfrac{7}{8}$

39. 34
$-\ 18\dfrac{5}{8}$

40. 23
$-\ 19\dfrac{3}{4}$

41. $21\dfrac{1}{6}$
$-\ 13\dfrac{3}{4}$

42. $42\dfrac{1}{10}$
$-\ 23\dfrac{7}{12}$

43. $14\dfrac{1}{8}$
$-\ \dfrac{3}{4}$

44. $28\dfrac{1}{6}$
$-\ 5$

45. $25\dfrac{1}{9}$
$-\ 13\dfrac{5}{6}$

46. $23\dfrac{5}{16}$
$-\ 14\dfrac{7}{12}$

d Multiply. Write a mixed numeral for the answer.

47. $8 \cdot 2\dfrac{5}{6}$

48. $5 \cdot 3\dfrac{3}{4}$

49. $3\dfrac{5}{8} \cdot \dfrac{2}{3}$

50. $6\dfrac{2}{3} \cdot \dfrac{1}{4}$

Copyright © 2012 Pearson Education, Inc.

51. $3\dfrac{1}{2} \cdot 2\dfrac{1}{3}$

52. $4\dfrac{1}{5} \cdot 5\dfrac{1}{4}$

53. $3\dfrac{2}{5} \cdot 2\dfrac{7}{8}$

54. $2\dfrac{3}{10} \cdot 4\dfrac{2}{5}$

55. $4\dfrac{7}{10} \cdot 5\dfrac{3}{10}$

56. $6\dfrac{3}{10} \cdot 5\dfrac{7}{10}$

57. $20\dfrac{1}{2} \cdot 10\dfrac{1}{5} \cdot 4\dfrac{2}{3}$

58. $21\dfrac{1}{3} \cdot 11\dfrac{1}{3} \cdot 3\dfrac{5}{8}$

e   Divide. Write a mixed numeral for the answer.

59. $20 \div 3\dfrac{1}{5}$

60. $18 \div 2\dfrac{1}{4}$

61. $8\dfrac{2}{5} \div 7$

62. $3\dfrac{3}{8} \div 3$

63. $4\dfrac{3}{4} \div 1\dfrac{1}{3}$

64. $5\dfrac{4}{5} \div 2\dfrac{1}{2}$

65. $1\dfrac{7}{8} \div 1\dfrac{2}{3}$

66. $4\dfrac{3}{8} \div 2\dfrac{5}{6}$

67. $5\dfrac{1}{10} \div 4\dfrac{3}{10}$

68. $4\dfrac{1}{10} \div 2\dfrac{1}{10}$

69. $20\dfrac{1}{4} \div 90$

70. $12\dfrac{1}{2} \div 50$

Skill Maintenance

71. Round to the nearest hundred: 45,765.   [1.3d]

72. Round to the nearest ten: 45,765.   [1.3d]

Determine whether the first number is divisible by the second.   [1.8a]

73. 9993 by 3

74. 9993 by 9

75. 2345 by 9

76. 2345 by 5

77. 2335 by 10

78. 7764 by 6

79. 18,888 by 8

80. 18,888 by 4

Synthesis

Simplify.

81. $8 \div \dfrac{1}{2} + \dfrac{3}{4} + \left(5 - \dfrac{5}{8}\right)^2$

82. $\left(\dfrac{5}{9} - \dfrac{1}{4}\right) \times 12 + \left(4 - \dfrac{3}{4}\right)^2$

83. $4\dfrac{1}{2} \div 2\dfrac{1}{2} + 8 - 4 \div \dfrac{1}{2}$

2.5

Applications and Problem Solving

OBJECTIVE

a Solve applied problems involving addition, subtraction, multiplication, and division using fraction notation and mixed numerals.

We solve applied problems using fraction notation and mixed numerals in the same way that we do when using whole numbers. The five steps for problem solving on p. 50 should be reviewed.

Many problems that can be solved by multiplying fractions can be thought of in terms of rectangular arrays.

EXAMPLE 1 A real estate developer owns a plot of land and plans to use $\frac{4}{5}$ of the plot for a small strip mall and parking lot. Of this, $\frac{2}{3}$ will be needed for the parking lot. What part of the plot will be used for parking?

1. **Familiarize.** We first make a drawing to help familiarize ourselves with the problem. The land may not be rectangular, but we can think of it as a rectangle. The strip mall, including the parking lot, uses $\frac{4}{5}$ of the plot. We shade $\frac{4}{5}$ as shown on the left below. The parking lot alone uses $\frac{2}{3}$ of the part we just shaded. We shade that as shown on the right below.

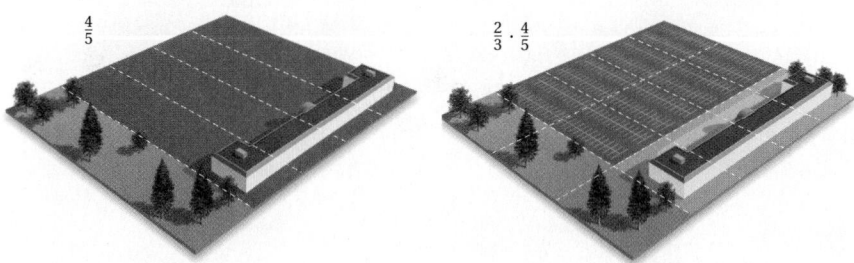

2. **Translate.** We let n = the part of the plot that is used for parking. We are taking "two-thirds of four-fifths." Recall from Section 1.5 that the word "of" corresponds to multiplication. Thus the following multiplication sentence corresponds to the situation:

$$\frac{2}{3} \cdot \frac{4}{5} = n.$$

3. **Solve.** The number sentence tells us what to do. We multiply:

$$\frac{2}{3} \cdot \frac{4}{5} = \frac{2 \cdot 4}{3 \cdot 5} = \frac{8}{15}.$$

Thus, $\frac{8}{15} = n$.

4. **Check.** We can do a partial check by noting that the answer is a fraction less than 1, which we expect since the developer is using only part of the original plot of land. Thus, $\frac{8}{15}$ is a reasonable answer. We can also check this in the figure above, where we see that 8 of 15 parts represent the parking lot.

5. **State.** The parking lot takes up $\frac{8}{15}$ of the plot of land.

> Do Exercise 1.

1. A resort hotel uses $\frac{3}{4}$ of its extra land for recreational purposes. Of that, $\frac{1}{2}$ is used for swimming pools. What part of the land is used for swimming pools?

Answer

1. $\frac{3}{8}$

EXAMPLE 2 *Area of a Cornfield.* The length of a rectangular cornfield is $\frac{15}{16}$ mi. The width is $\frac{5}{8}$ mi. What is the area of the cornfield?

1. **Familiarize.** Recall that area is length times width. We let A = the area of the cornfield.

2. **Translate.** Then we translate:

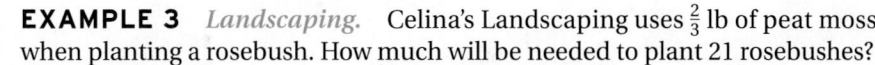

$$A = \frac{15}{16} \times \frac{5}{8}.$$

3. **Solve.** The sentence tells us what to do. We multiply:

$$A = \frac{15}{16} \cdot \frac{5}{8} = \frac{15 \cdot 5}{16 \cdot 8} = \frac{75}{128}.$$

4. **Check.** We check by repeating the calculation. This is left to the student.

5. **State.** The area is $\frac{75}{128}$ square mile (mi^2).

> Do Exercise 2.

EXAMPLE 3 *Landscaping.* Celina's Landscaping uses $\frac{2}{3}$ lb of peat moss when planting a rosebush. How much will be needed to plant 21 rosebushes?

1. **Familiarize.** We first make a drawing or at least visualize the situation. We let n = the number of pounds of peat moss needed.

21 rosebushes

$\frac{2}{3}$ pound of peat moss for each rosebush

2. **Translate.** The problem translates to the following equation:

$$n = 21 \cdot \frac{2}{3}.$$

3. **Solve.** To solve the equation, we carry out the multiplication:

$$n = 21 \cdot \frac{2}{3} = \frac{21}{1} \cdot \frac{2}{3} = \frac{21 \cdot 2}{1 \cdot 3} \qquad \text{Multiplying}$$

$$= \frac{3 \cdot 7 \cdot 2}{1 \cdot 3} = \frac{3}{3} \cdot \frac{7 \cdot 2}{1} = 14.$$

4. **Check.** We check by repeating the calculation. (This is left to the student.) We can also ask if the answer seems reasonable. We are putting less than a pound of peat moss on each bush, so the answer should be less than 21. Since 14 is less than 21, we have a partial check. The number 14 checks.

5. **State.** Celina's Landscaping will need 14 lb of peat moss to plant 21 rosebushes.

> Do Exercise 3.

2. Area of a Ceramic Tile. The length of a rectangular ceramic tile on an inlaid ceramic counter is $\frac{4}{9}$ ft. The width is $\frac{2}{9}$ ft. What is the area of one tile?

3. Truffles. Chocolate Delight sells $\frac{4}{5}$-lb boxes of truffles. How many pounds of truffles will be needed to fill 85 boxes?

Answers

2. $\frac{8}{81}$ ft^2 **3.** 68 lb

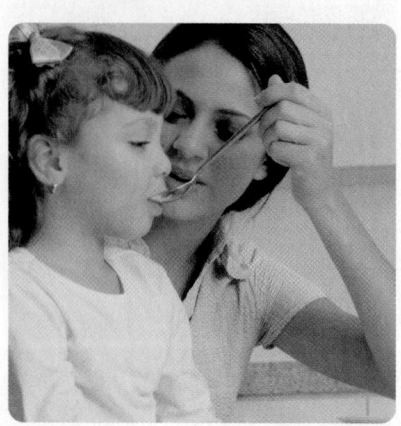

EXAMPLE 4 *Doses of an Antibiotic.* How many doses, each containing $\frac{15}{4}$ milliliters (mL), can be obtained from a bottle of a children's antibiotic that contains 60 mL?

1. **Familiarize.** We are asking the question "How many $\frac{15}{4}$'s are in 60?" Repeated addition will apply here. We make a drawing. We let $n =$ the number of doses in all.

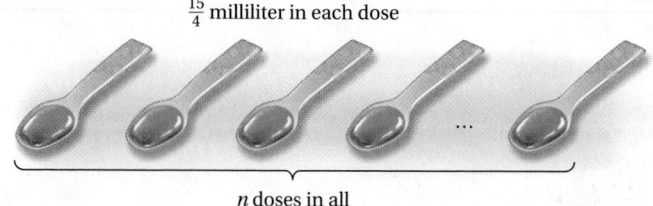

$\frac{15}{4}$ milliliter in each dose

n doses in all

2. **Translate.** The equation that corresponds to the situation is

$$n = 60 \div \frac{15}{4}.$$

3. **Solve.** We solve the equation by carrying out the division:

$$n = 60 \div \frac{15}{4} = 60 \cdot \frac{4}{15} = \frac{60}{1} \cdot \frac{4}{15}$$

$$= \frac{60 \cdot 4}{1 \cdot 15} = \frac{4 \cdot 15 \cdot 4}{1 \cdot 15} = \frac{15}{15} \cdot \frac{4 \cdot 4}{1}$$

$$= 1 \cdot 16 = 16.$$

4. **Check.** We check by multiplying the number of doses by the size of the dose: $16 \cdot \frac{15}{4} = 60$. The answer checks.

5. **State.** There are 16 doses in a 60-mL bottle of the antibiotic.

Do Exercise 4.

4. Each loop in a spring uses $\frac{21}{8}$ in. of wire. How many loops can be made from 210 in. of wire?

EXAMPLE 5 *Brick Walkway.* Logan's Landscape specializes in brick and stone walkways. After they complete 63 ft of a brick walkway between two buildings on campus, $\frac{7}{8}$ of the walkway is complete. What is the total length of this walkway?

1. **Familiarize.** We ask: "63 ft is $\frac{7}{8}$ of what length?" We make a drawing or at least visualize the problem. We let $w =$ the length of the walkway.

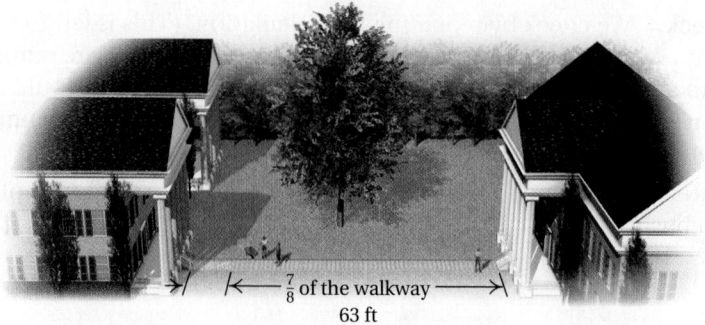

$\frac{7}{8}$ of the walkway
63 ft

Answer
4. 80 loops

2. Translate. We translate to an equation:

$$
\underbrace{\text{Fraction completed}}_{\dfrac{7}{8}} \quad \underbrace{\text{of}}_{\cdot} \quad \underbrace{\substack{\text{Total}\\ \text{length}\\ \text{of walkway}}}_{w} \quad \underbrace{\text{is}}_{=} \quad \underbrace{\substack{\text{Amount}\\ \text{already}\\ \text{completed}}}_{63.}
$$

3. Solve. We divide by $\frac{7}{8}$ on both sides and carry out the division:

$$
w = 63 \div \frac{7}{8} = \frac{63}{1} \cdot \frac{8}{7} = \frac{63 \cdot 8}{1 \cdot 7} = \frac{7 \cdot 9 \cdot 8}{1 \cdot 7} = \frac{7}{7} \cdot \frac{9 \cdot 8}{1} = 72.
$$

4. Check. We determine whether $\frac{7}{8}$ of 72 is 63:

$$
\frac{7}{8} \cdot 72 = \frac{7 \cdot 72}{8 \cdot 1} = \frac{7 \cdot 8 \cdot 9}{8 \cdot 1} = \frac{8}{8} \cdot \frac{7 \cdot 9}{1} = 63.
$$

The answer, 72, checks.

5. State. The total length of the walkway is 72 ft.

Do Exercise 5.

EXAMPLE 6 *Subflooring.* A contractor requires his subcontractors to use two layers of subflooring under a ceramic tile floor. First, the subcontractors install a $\frac{3}{4}$-in. layer of oriented strand board (OSB). Then a $\frac{1}{2}$-in. sheet of cement board is mortared to the OSB. The mortar is $\frac{1}{8}$-in. thick. What is the total thickness of the two installed subfloors?

1. Familiarize. We first make a drawing. We let $T =$ the total thickness of the subfloors.

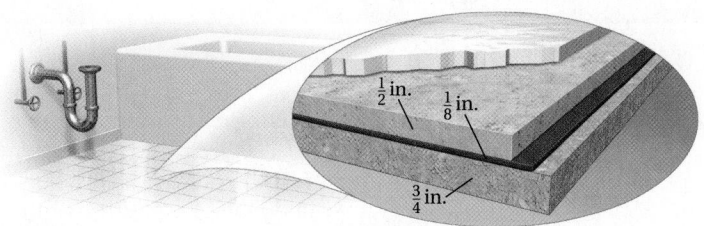

2. Translate. The problem can be translated to an equation as follows.

$$
\underbrace{\text{OSB}}_{\dfrac{3}{4}} \quad \underbrace{\text{plus}}_{+} \quad \underbrace{\text{Mortar}}_{\dfrac{1}{8}} \quad \underbrace{\text{plus}}_{+} \quad \underbrace{\substack{\text{Cement}\\ \text{board}}}_{\dfrac{1}{2}} \quad \underbrace{\text{is}}_{=} \quad \underbrace{\substack{\text{Total}\\ \text{thickness}}}_{T}
$$

5. Sales Trip. John Penna sells soybean seeds to seed companies. After he had driven 210 mi, $\frac{5}{6}$ of his sales trip was completed. How long was the total trip?

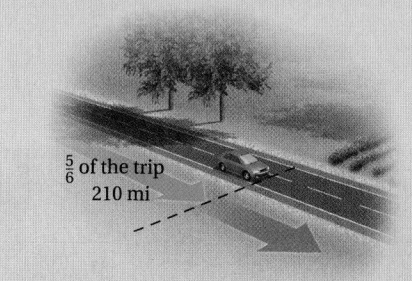

$\frac{5}{6}$ of the trip
210 mi

STUDY TIPS

STUDY RESOURCES

The new mathematical skills and concepts presented in class will be most easily learned if you begin your homework assignment as soon as possible after the lecture, while it is fresh in your mind. Then if you have difficulty with any of the exercises, you have time to access supplementary resources such as the *Student's Solutions Manual.*

Answer

5. 252 mi

6. Fruit Salad. A caterer prepares a mixed berry salad with $\frac{7}{8}$ qt of strawberries, $\frac{3}{4}$ qt of raspberries, and $\frac{5}{16}$ qt of blueberries. What is the total amount of berries in the salad?

7. Fraction of the Moon Illuminated. At midnight on April 18, 2008 (Eastern Daylight Time), $\frac{19}{20}$ of the moon appeared illuminated. By April 27, 2008, the illuminated part had decreased to $\frac{16}{25}$. How much less of the moon appeared illuminated on April 27 than on April 18?

Source: Astronomical Applications Department, U.S. Naval Observatory, Washington DC 20392

---

3. **Solve.** To solve the equation, we carry out the addition. The LCM of the denominators is 8 because 2 and 4 are factors of 8. We multiply by 1 in order to obtain the LCD:

$$T = \frac{3}{4} + \frac{1}{8} + \frac{1}{2} = \frac{3}{4} \cdot \frac{2}{2} + \frac{1}{8} + \frac{1}{2} \cdot \frac{4}{4} = \frac{6}{8} + \frac{1}{8} + \frac{4}{8} = \frac{11}{8}.$$

4. **Check.** We check by repeating the calculation. We also note that the sum should be larger than any of the individual measurements, which it is. This tells us that the answer is reasonable.

5. **State.** The total thickness of the installed subfloors is $\frac{11}{8}$ in.

Do Exercise 6.

EXAMPLE 7 *Fraction of the Moon Illuminated.* From anywhere on Earth, the moon appears to be a circular disk. At midnight on July 11, 2008 (Eastern Daylight Time), $\frac{3}{5}$ of the moon appeared illuminated. By July 22, 2008, the illuminated portion had increased to $\frac{17}{20}$. How much more of the moon appeared illuminated on July 22 than on July 11?

Source: Astronomical Applications Department, U.S. Naval Observatory, Washington DC 20392

1. **Familiarize.** We let m = the additional part of the moon that appeared illuminated.

2. **Translate.** We translate to an equation:

Amount illuminated on July 11, 2008	plus	Additional amount illuminated	is	Amount illuminated on July 22, 2008
↓	↓	↓	↓	↓
$\frac{3}{5}$	$+$	m	$=$	$\frac{17}{20}.$

3. **Solve.** To solve the equation, we subtract $\frac{3}{5}$ on both sides:

$$\frac{3}{5} + m = \frac{17}{20}$$

$$\frac{3}{5} + m - \frac{3}{5} = \frac{17}{20} - \frac{3}{5} \qquad \text{Subtracting } \frac{3}{5} \text{ on both sides}$$

$$m + 0 = \frac{17}{20} - \frac{3}{5} \cdot \frac{4}{4} \qquad \text{The LCD is 20. We multiply by 1 to obtain the LCD.}$$

$$m = \frac{17}{20} - \frac{12}{20} = \frac{5}{20} = \frac{5 \cdot 1}{5 \cdot 4} = \frac{5}{5} \cdot \frac{1}{4} = \frac{1}{4}.$$

4. **Check.** To check, we add:

$$\frac{3}{5} + \frac{1}{4} = \frac{3}{5} \cdot \frac{4}{4} + \frac{1}{4} \cdot \frac{5}{5} = \frac{12}{20} + \frac{5}{20} = \frac{17}{20}.$$

5. **State.** On July 22, $\frac{1}{4}$ more of the moon was illuminated than on July 11.

Do Exercise 7.

Answers

6. $\frac{31}{16}$ qt   7. $\frac{31}{100}$

EXAMPLE 8 *Widening a Driveway.* Sherry and Woody are widening their existing $17\frac{1}{4}$-ft driveway by adding $5\frac{9}{10}$ ft on one side. What is the width of the new driveway?

1. **Familiarize.** We let w = the width of the new driveway.

2. **Translate.** We translate as follows:

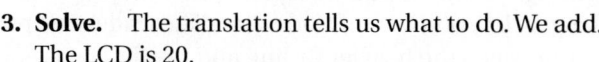

$$\underbrace{17\frac{1}{4}}_{\text{Width of existing driveway}} + \underbrace{5\frac{9}{10}}_{\text{Width of addition}} = \underbrace{w}_{\text{Width of new driveway}}.$$

3. **Solve.** The translation tells us what to do. We add. The LCD is 20.

$$17\frac{1}{4} = \quad 17\frac{1}{4} \cdot \frac{5}{5} = \quad 17\frac{5}{20}$$

$$+ 5\frac{9}{10} = +\; 5\frac{9}{10} \cdot \frac{2}{2} = +\; 5\frac{18}{20}$$

$$\overline{\qquad\qquad 22\frac{23}{20} = 23\frac{3}{20}}$$

Thus, $w = 23\frac{3}{20}$.

4. **Check.** We check by repeating the calculation. We also note that the answer is larger than either of the widths, which means that the answer is reasonable.

5. **State.** The width of the new driveway is $23\frac{3}{20}$ ft.

Do Exercise 8.

EXAMPLE 9 *Communication Cable.* Perfection Cable has two crews who install Internet communication cable. Crew A can install $38\frac{1}{8}$ ft per hour. Crew B can install $31\frac{2}{3}$ ft per hour. How many fewer feet can Crew B install per hour than Crew A?

1. **Familiarize.** The phrase "how many fewer" indicates subtraction. We let c = the difference in the numbers of feet per hour.

2. **Translate.** We translate as follows:

$$\underbrace{38\frac{1}{8}}_{\substack{\text{Crew A:}\\ \text{ft/hr}}} - \underbrace{31\frac{2}{3}}_{\substack{\text{Crew B:}\\ \text{ft/hr}}} = \underbrace{c}_{\substack{\text{Difference in}\\ \text{ft/hr}}}.$$

3. **Solve.** To solve the equation, we carry out the subtraction. The LCD = 24.

$$38\frac{1}{8} = \quad 38\frac{1}{8} \cdot \frac{3}{3} = \quad 38\frac{3}{24} = \quad 37\frac{27}{24}$$

$$- 31\frac{2}{3} = -31\frac{2}{3} \cdot \frac{8}{8} = -31\frac{16}{24} = -31\frac{16}{24}$$

$$\overline{\qquad\qquad\qquad 6\frac{11}{24}}$$

Thus, $c = 6\frac{11}{24}$.

8. Travel Distance. On a two-day business trip, Paul drove $213\frac{7}{10}$ mi the first day and $107\frac{5}{8}$ mi the second day. What was the total distance that Paul drove?

STUDY TIPS

TIME MANAGEMENT

Keep on Schedule. Your course syllabus provides a plan for the semester's schedule. Use a write-on calendar, daily planner, laptop computer, or personal digital assistant to outline your time for the semester. Be sure to note deadlines involving projects and exams so that you can begin a task early, breaking it down into small segments that can be accomplished easily.

Answer

8. $321\frac{13}{40}$ mi

9. Nail Length. A 30d nail is $4\frac{1}{2}$ in. long. A 5d nail is $1\frac{3}{4}$ in. long. How much longer is the 30d nail than the 5d nail? (The "d" stands for "penny," which was used years ago in England to specify the number of pennies needed to buy 100 nails. Today, "penny" is used only to indicate the length of the nail.)

Source: *Pocket Ref,* 2nd ed., by Thomas J. Glover, p. 280, Sequoia Publishing, Inc., Littleton, CO

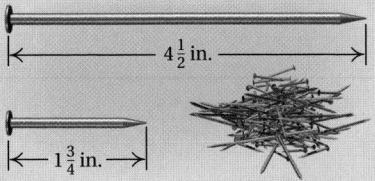

4. Check. To check, we add the difference, $6\frac{11}{24}$, to Crew B's rate:

$$31\frac{2}{3} + 6\frac{11}{24} = 31\frac{16}{24} + 6\frac{11}{24}$$

$$= 37\frac{27}{24} = 38\frac{3}{24} = 38\frac{1}{8}.$$

This checks.

5. State. Crew B installs $6\frac{11}{24}$ fewer feet of cable per hour than Crew A.

> Do Exercise 9.

EXAMPLE 10 *Fly Fishing.* Henry is putting together a fly fishing line and uses $58\frac{5}{8}$ ft of slow-sinking fly line and $8\frac{3}{4}$ ft of leader line. The leader line provides a low visibility link between the heavier fly line and the fly. He uses $\frac{3}{8}$ ft of the slow-sinking fly line to connect the two lines. The knot used to connect the fly to the leader line uses $\frac{1}{6}$ ft of the leader line. How long is the finished fly fishing line?

1. Familiarize. Let's make a drawing to organize the given information. We let l = the length of the finished fly fishing line, in feet.

Slow-sinking line: $58\frac{5}{8}$ ft

$\frac{3}{8}$ ft for connecting lines

Fly

Leader line: $8\frac{3}{4}$ ft

$\frac{1}{6}$ ft for the knot

2. Translate. From the drawing, we see that the length l is the sum of the lengths of the two lines, $58\frac{5}{8}$ ft and $8\frac{3}{4}$ ft, minus the sum of the lengths, $\frac{3}{8}$ ft and $\frac{1}{6}$ ft, needed for connecting the lines and attaching the fly with a knot. Thus we have

$$l = \left(58\frac{5}{8} + 8\frac{3}{4}\right) - \left(\frac{3}{8} + \frac{1}{6}\right).$$

3. Solve. This is a three-step problem.

a) We first add the two lengths $58\frac{5}{8}$ and $8\frac{3}{4}$.

$$58\frac{5}{8} = 58\frac{5}{8}$$

$$+ 8\frac{3}{4} = + 8\frac{6}{8}$$

$$66\frac{11}{8} = 67\frac{3}{8}$$

Answer

9. $2\frac{3}{4}$ in.

b) Next, we add the two lengths $\frac{3}{8}$ and $\frac{1}{6}$.

$$\frac{3}{8} + \frac{1}{6} = \frac{3}{8} \cdot \frac{3}{3} + \frac{1}{6} \cdot \frac{4}{4} = \frac{9}{24} + \frac{4}{24} = \frac{13}{24}$$

c) Finally, we subtract $\frac{13}{24}$ from $67\frac{3}{8}$.

$$
\begin{array}{rcrcr}
67\dfrac{3}{8} = & & 67\dfrac{9}{24} = & & 66\dfrac{33}{24} \\[2ex]
-\dfrac{13}{24} = & & -\dfrac{13}{24} = & & -\dfrac{13}{24} \\[2ex]
\hline
& & & & 66\dfrac{20}{24} = 66\dfrac{5}{6}
\end{array}
$$

Thus, $l = 66\frac{5}{6}$.

4. Check. We can check by adding the finished length to the lengths needed for the connection and the knot:

$$66\frac{5}{6} + \frac{3}{8} + \frac{1}{6} = \left(66\frac{5}{6} + \frac{1}{6}\right) + \frac{3}{8} = 67 + \frac{3}{8} = 67\frac{3}{8}.$$

This is the sum of the given lengths.

5. State. The finished length of the fly line is $66\frac{5}{6}$ ft.

> Do Exercise 10.

10. Liquid Fertilizer. There is $283\frac{5}{8}$ gal of liquid fertilizer in a fertilizer application tank. After applying $178\frac{2}{3}$ gal to a soybean field, the farmer requests that Braden's Farm Supply deliver an additional 250 gal. How many gallons of fertilizer are in the tank after the delivery?

EXAMPLE 11 *Average Speed in Indianapolis 500.* Arie Luyendyk won the Indianapolis 500 in 1990 with the highest average speed of about 186 mph. This record high through 2008 is about $2\frac{12}{25}$ times the average speed of the first winner, Ray Harroun, in 1911. What was the average speed in the first Indianapolis 500?

Source: Indianapolis Motor Speedway

1. Familiarize. We ask the question "186 is $2\frac{12}{25}$ times what number?" We let s = the average speed in 1911. Then the average speed in 1990 was $2\frac{12}{25} \cdot s$.

2. Translate. The problem can be translated to an equation as follows:

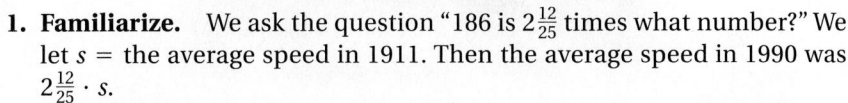

Average speed in 1990	is	$2\frac{12}{25}$	times	Average speed in 1911
186	=	$2\frac{12}{25}$	$\cdot$	$s.$

Answer

10. $354\frac{23}{24}$ gal

3. Solve. To solve the equation, we divide on both sides.

$$186 = \frac{62}{25} \cdot s \qquad \text{Converting } 2\frac{12}{25} \text{ to fraction notation}$$

$$\frac{186}{\frac{62}{25}} = \frac{\frac{62}{25} \cdot s}{\frac{62}{25}} \qquad \text{Dividing by } \frac{62}{25} \text{ on both sides}$$

$$\frac{186}{\frac{62}{25}} = s \qquad \text{Factoring and removing a factor of 1:} \\ (62/25)/(62/25) = 1$$

$$186 \cdot \frac{25}{62} = s \qquad \text{Multiplying by the reciprocal}$$

$$75 = s \qquad \text{Simplifying: } 186 \cdot \frac{25}{62} = \frac{3 \cdot 62 \cdot 25}{1 \cdot 62} = 75$$

4. Check. If the average speed in 1911 was about 75 mph, we find the average speed in 1990 by multiplying 75 by $2\frac{12}{25}$:

$$2\frac{12}{25} \cdot 75 = \frac{62}{25} \cdot 75 = \frac{62 \cdot 75}{25 \cdot 1} = \frac{62 \cdot 25 \cdot 3}{25 \cdot 1} = 62 \cdot 3 = 186.$$

The answer checks.

5. State. The average speed in the first Indianapolis 500 was about 75 mph.

Solve.

11. Kyle's pickup truck travels on an interstate highway at 65 mph for $3\frac{1}{2}$ hr. How far does it travel?

12. Holly's minivan travels 302 mi on $15\frac{1}{10}$ gal of gas. How many miles per gallon did it get?

> Do Exercises 11 and 12.

EXAMPLE 12 *Koi Pond.* Colleen designed a koi fish pond for her backyard. Using the dimensions shown in the diagram below, determine the area of Colleen's backyard before the pond was constructed and the area of the yard remaining after the pond was completed.

Sources: en.wikipedia.org; pondliner.com

The brightly colored koi originated in Japan in the 18th century. The hobby of keeping koi increased greatly after the plastic bag was available for safe shipping.

$15\frac{3}{4}$ yd $27\frac{1}{3}$ yd

$11\frac{1}{2}$ yd

$40\frac{2}{3}$ yd

1. Familiarize. From the diagram, we know that the dimensions of the backyard are $40\frac{2}{3}$ yd by $27\frac{1}{3}$ yd and the dimensions of the pond are $15\frac{3}{4}$ yd by $11\frac{1}{2}$ yd. We let $B =$ the area of the yard before the construction, $P =$ the area of the pond, and $R =$ the area of the yard that remains after the pond is complete.

Answers

11. $227\frac{1}{2}$ mi   **12.** 20 mpg

2. Translate. This is a multistep problem. To find R, the area of the yard remaining, we first find B, the area of the yard before construction, and P, the area of the pond. Then R is the area of the yard B minus the area of the pond P:

$$R = B - P.$$

We find each area using the formula for the area of a rectangle, $A = l \times w$.

3. Solve. We carry out the calculations as follows:

$$B = \text{length} \times \text{width} \qquad P = \text{length} \times \text{width}$$

$$= 40\frac{2}{3} \cdot 27\frac{1}{3} \qquad\qquad = 15\frac{3}{4} \cdot 11\frac{1}{2}$$

$$= \frac{122}{3} \cdot \frac{82}{3} \qquad\qquad = \frac{63}{4} \cdot \frac{23}{2}$$

$$= \frac{10{,}004}{9} = 1111\frac{5}{9} \text{ sq yd}; \qquad = \frac{1449}{8} = 181\frac{1}{8} \text{ sq yd}.$$

Then

$$R = B - P$$

$$= 1111\frac{5}{9} - 181\frac{1}{8}$$

$$= 1111\frac{40}{72} - 181\frac{9}{72}$$

$$= 930\frac{31}{72} \text{ sq yd}.$$

4. Check. We can perform a check by repeating the calculations or we can round the measurements to the nearest yard and estimate a solution.

$$B \approx 41 \times 27 \approx 1107;$$
$$P \approx 16 \times 12 \approx 192;$$
$$R \approx 1107 - 192 \approx 915 \text{ sq yd}$$

Since 915 sq yd is close to $930\frac{31}{72}$ sq yd, the answer seems reasonable.

5. State. The area of the yard before construction of the pond was $1111\frac{5}{9}$ sq yd. The area of the yard remaining after the pond was completed was $930\frac{31}{72}$ sq yd.

> Do Exercise 13.

STUDY TIPS

LEARNING RESOURCES ON CAMPUS

Your college or university probably has resources to support your learning.

1. There may be a learning lab or tutoring center for drop-in tutoring.

2. There many be group tutoring sessions for this specific course.

3. The math department may have a bulletin board or network for locating private tutors.

4. Visit your instructor during office hours if you need additional help. Also, many instructors welcome e-mails from students with questions.

---

13. A room measures $22\frac{1}{2}$ ft by $15\frac{1}{2}$ ft. A 9-ft by 12-ft rug is placed in the center of the room. How much floor area is not covered by the rug?

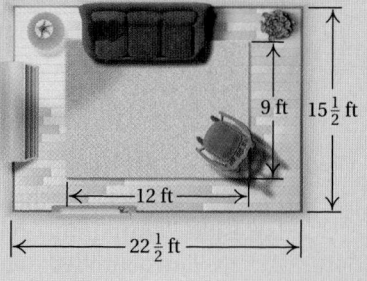

Answer

13. $240\frac{3}{4}$ ft^2

Translating for Success

1. *Raffle Tickets.* At the Happy Hollow Camp Fall Festival, Rico and Becca, together, spent $270 on raffle tickets that sell for $\$\frac{9}{20}$ each. How many tickets did they buy?

2. *Irrigation Pipe.* Jed uses two pipes, one of which measures $5\frac{1}{3}$ ft, to repair the irrigation system in the Buxtons' lawn. The total length of the two pipes is $8\frac{7}{12}$ ft. How long is the other pipe?

3. *Vacation Days.* Together, Helmut and Claire have 36 vacation days a year. Helmut has 22 vacation days per year. How many does Claire have?

4. *Enrollment in Japanese Classes.* Last year at the Lakeside Community College, 225 students enrolled in basic mathematics. This number is $4\frac{1}{2}$ times as many as the number who enrolled in Japanese. How many enrolled in Japanese?

5. *Bicycling.* Cole rode his bicycle $5\frac{1}{3}$ mi on Saturday and $8\frac{7}{12}$ mi on Sunday. How far did he ride on the weekend?

The goal of these matching questions is to practice step (2), *Translate*, of the five-step problem-solving process. Translate each word problem to an equation and select a correct translation from equations A–O.

A. $13\frac{11}{12} = x + 5\frac{1}{3}$

B. $\frac{3}{4} \cdot x = 1\frac{2}{3}$

C. $\frac{20}{9} \cdot 270 = x$

D. $225 = 4\frac{1}{2} \cdot x$

E. $98 \div 2\frac{1}{3} = x$

F. $22 + x = 36$

G. $x = 4\frac{1}{2} \cdot 225$

H. $x = 5\frac{1}{3} + 8\frac{7}{12}$

I. $22 \cdot x = 36$

J. $x = \frac{3}{4} \cdot 1\frac{2}{3}$

K. $5\frac{1}{3} + x = 8\frac{7}{12}$

L. $\frac{9}{20} \cdot 270 = x$

M. $1\frac{2}{3} + \frac{3}{4} = x$

N. $98 - 2\frac{1}{3} = x$

O. $\frac{9}{20} \cdot x = 270$

Answers on page A-4

---

6. *Deli Order.* For a promotional open house for contractors last year, the Bayside Builders Association ordered 225 turkey sandwiches. Due to increased registrations this year, $4\frac{1}{2}$ times as many sandwiches are needed. How many sandwiches are ordered?

7. *Dog Ownership.* In Sam's community, $\frac{9}{20}$ of the households own at least one dog. There are 270 households. How many own dogs?

8. *Magic Tricks.* Samantha has 98 ft of rope and needs to cut it into $2\frac{1}{3}$-ft pieces to be used in a magic trick. How many pieces can be cut from the rope?

9. *Painting.* Laura needs $1\frac{2}{3}$ gal of paint to paint the ceiling of the exercise room and $\frac{3}{4}$ gal of the same paint for the bathroom. How much paint does Laura need?

10. *Chocolate Fudge Bars.* A recipe for chocolate fudge bars that serves 16 includes $1\frac{2}{3}$ cups of sugar. How much sugar is needed for $\frac{3}{4}$ of this recipe?

2.5 | Exercise Set

For Extra Help

MyMathLab

Math XL
PRACTICE

WATCH

DOWNLOAD

READ

REVIEW

a Solve.

1. *Extension Cords.* An electrical supplier sells rolls of SJO 14-3 cable to a company that makes extension cords. It takes $\frac{7}{3}$ ft of cable to make each cord. How many extension cords can be made with a roll of cable containing 2240 ft of cable?

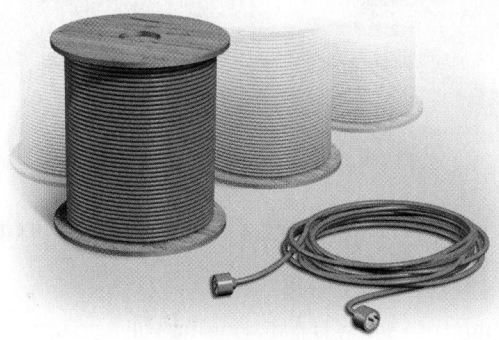

2. *Serving of Cheesecake.* At the Cheesecake Factory, a piece of cheesecake is $\frac{1}{12}$ of a cheesecake. How much of the cheesecake is $\frac{1}{2}$ piece?
Source: The Cheesecake Factory

3. A pair of basketball shorts requires $\frac{3}{4}$ yd of nylon. How many pairs of shorts can be made from 24 yd of nylon?

4. How many $\frac{2}{3}$-cup cereal bowls can be filled from 10 cups of cornflakes?

5. *Household Budgets.* A family has an annual income of $42,000. Of this, $\frac{1}{5}$ is spent for food, $\frac{1}{4}$ for housing, $\frac{1}{10}$ for clothing, $\frac{1}{14}$ for savings, $\frac{1}{5}$ for taxes, and the rest for other expenses. How much is spent for each?

6. *Household Budgets.* A family has an annual income of $28,140. Of this, $\frac{1}{5}$ is spent for food, $\frac{1}{4}$ for housing, $\frac{1}{10}$ for clothing, $\frac{1}{14}$ for savings, $\frac{1}{5}$ for taxes, and the rest for other expenses. How much is spent for each?

Family Income

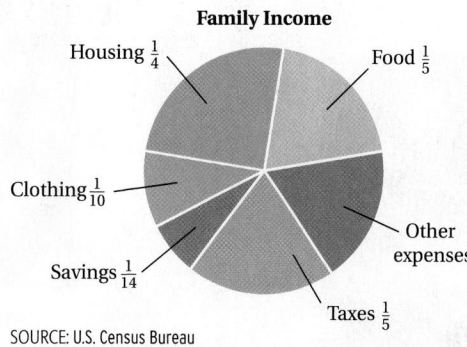

Housing $\frac{1}{4}$

Food $\frac{1}{5}$

Clothing $\frac{1}{10}$

Savings $\frac{1}{14}$

Other expenses

Taxes $\frac{1}{5}$

SOURCE: U.S. Census Bureau

7. For a research paper, Kaitlyn spent $\frac{3}{4}$ hr searching the Internet on google.com and $\frac{1}{3}$ hr on chacha.com. How many more hours did she spend on google.com than on chacha.com?

8. As part of a fitness program, Deb swims $\frac{1}{2}$ mi every day. One day she had already swum $\frac{1}{5}$ mi. How much farther should Deb swim?

9. *Riding a Segway®.* Tate rode a Segway® Personal Transporter $\frac{5}{6}$ mi to the library, then $\frac{3}{4}$ mi to class, and then $\frac{3}{2}$ mi to his part-time job. How far did he ride his Segway®?

10. *Caffeine.* To cut back on their caffeine intake, Michelle and Gerry mix caffeinated and decaffeinated coffee beans before grinding for a customized mix. They mix $\frac{3}{16}$ lb of decaffeinated beans with $\frac{5}{8}$ lb of caffeinated beans. What is the total amount of coffee beans in the mixture?

The *pitch* of a screw is the distance between its threads. With each complete rotation, the screw goes in or out a distance equal to its pitch. Use this information to do Exercises 11 and 12.

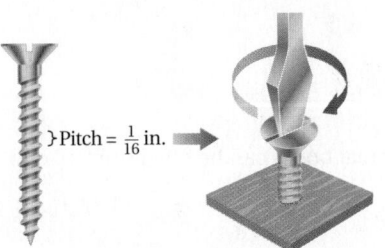

}Pitch = $\frac{1}{16}$ in.

Each rotation moves the screw in or out $\frac{1}{16}$ in.

11. The pitch of a screw is $\frac{1}{16}$ in. How far will it go into a piece of oak when it is turned 10 complete rotations clockwise?

12. The pitch of a screw is $\frac{3}{32}$ in. How many complete rotations are necessary to drive the screw $\frac{3}{4}$ in. into a piece of pine wood?

13. *Level of Education and Median Income.* The median yearly income of someone with an associate's degree is approximately $\frac{2}{3}$ of the median income of someone with a bachelor's degree. If the median income for those with bachelor's degrees is $72,420, what is the median income of those with associate's degrees?

Source: U.S. Census Bureau

14. *Map Scaling.* On a map, 1 in. represents 240 mi. What distance does $\frac{2}{3}$ in. represent?

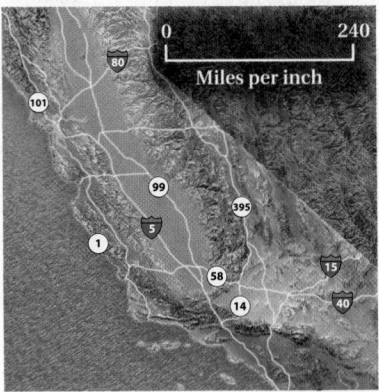

15. *Temperature.* Fahrenheit temperature can be obtained from Celsius (Centigrade) temperature by multiplying by $1\frac{4}{5}$ and adding 32°. What Fahrenheit temperature corresponds to a Celsius temperature of 20°?

16. *Servings of Tuna.* A serving of fish steak (cross section) is generally $\frac{1}{2}$ lb. How many servings can be prepared from a cleaned $18\frac{3}{4}$-lb tuna?

Copyright © 2012 Pearson Education, Inc.

17. *Iced Brownies.* The campus culinary arts department is preparing brownies for the international student reception. Students in the catering program iced the $\frac{11}{16}$-in. $\left(\frac{11''}{16}\right)$ butterscotch brownies with a $\frac{5}{32}$-in. $\left(\frac{5''}{32}\right)$ layer of icing. What is the thickness of the iced brownie?

18. A baker has a dispenser containing $\frac{15}{16}$ cup of icing and puts $\frac{1}{12}$ cup on a cinnamon roll. How much icing remains in the dispenser?

19. A tile $\frac{5}{8}$ in. thick is glued to a board $\frac{7}{8}$ in. thick. The glue is $\frac{3}{32}$ in. thick. How thick is the result?

20. A baker used $\frac{1}{2}$ lb of flour for rolls, $\frac{1}{4}$ lb for donuts, and $\frac{1}{3}$ lb for cookies. How much flour was used?

21. *Weight of Water.* The weight of water is $62\frac{1}{2}$ lb per cubic foot. What is the weight of $5\frac{1}{2}$ cubic feet of water?

22. *Temperature.* Fahrenheit temperature can be obtained from Celsius (Centigrade) temperature by multiplying by $1\frac{4}{5}$ and adding 32°. What Fahrenheit temperature corresponds to the Celsius temperature of boiling water, 100°?

23. From a $\frac{4}{5}$-lb wheel of cheese, a $\frac{1}{4}$-lb piece was served. How much cheese remained on the wheel?

24. For a community project, an earth science class volunteered one hour per day for three days to join the state highway beautification project. The students collected trash along a $\frac{4}{5}$-mi stretch of highway the first day, $\frac{5}{8}$ mi the second day, and $\frac{1}{2}$ mi the third day. How many miles along the highway did they clean?

25. *Stone Bench.* Baytown Village Stone Creations is making a custom stone bench as shown below. The recommended height for the bench is 18 in. The depth of the stone bench is $3\frac{3}{8}$ in. Each of the two supporting legs is made up of three stacked stones. Two of the stones measure $3\frac{1}{2}$ in. and $5\frac{1}{4}$ in. How much must the third stone measure?

18 in. $3\frac{3}{8}$ in. $3\frac{1}{2}$ in. $5\frac{1}{4}$ in.   ?

26. *Carpentry.* When cutting wood with a saw, a carpenter must take into account the thickness of the saw blade. Suppose that from a piece of wood 36 in. long, a carpenter cuts a $15\frac{3}{4}$-in. length with a saw blade that is $\frac{1}{8}$ in. thick. How long is the piece that remains?

27. Kim Park is a computer technician. One day, she drove $180\frac{7}{10}$ mi away from Los Angeles for a service call. The next day, she drove $85\frac{1}{2}$ mi back toward Los Angeles for another service call. How far was she then from Los Angeles?

28. *Upholstery Fabric.* Executive Car Care sells 45-in. upholstery fabric for car restoration. Art buys $9\frac{1}{4}$ yd and $10\frac{5}{6}$ yd for two car projects. How many yards did Art buy?

29. *Planting Flowers.* A landscaper planted $4\frac{1}{2}$ flats of impatiens, $6\frac{2}{3}$ flats of snapdragons, and $3\frac{3}{8}$ flats of phlox. How many flats did she plant altogether?

30. A plumber uses two pipes, each of length $51\frac{5}{16}$ in., and one pipe of length $34\frac{3}{4}$ in. in the installation of a shower. How much pipe was used in all?

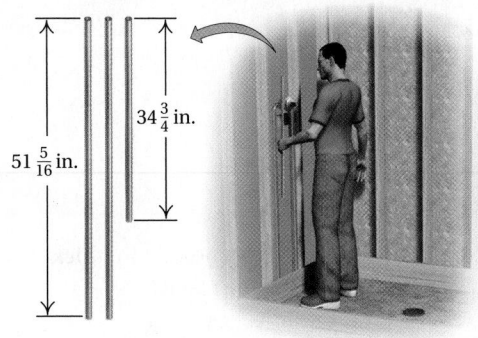

$34\frac{3}{4}$ in.

$51\frac{5}{16}$ in.

31. At a party, three friends, Ashley, Cole, and Lauren, shared a big tub of popcorn. Within 30 min, the tub was empty. Ashley ate $\frac{7}{12}$ of the tub while Lauren ate only $\frac{1}{6}$ of the tub. How much did Cole eat?

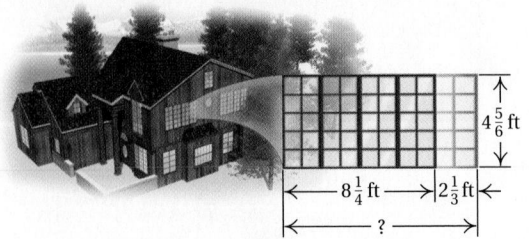

32. An estate was left to four children. One received $\frac{1}{4}$ of the estate, the second $\frac{1}{16}$, and the third $\frac{3}{8}$. How much did the fourth receive?

33. *Window Dimensions.* The Sanchez family is replacing a window in their lake house. The original window measures $4\frac{5}{6}$ ft $\times$ $8\frac{1}{4}$ ft. The new window is $2\frac{1}{3}$ ft wider. What are the dimensions of the new window?

$4\frac{5}{6}$ ft

$8\frac{1}{4}$ ft $2\frac{1}{3}$ ft

?

34. *Painting.* A painter used $1\frac{3}{4}$ gal of paint for the Garcias' living room and $1\frac{1}{3}$ gal for their family room. How much paint was used in all?

Copyright © 2012 Pearson Education, Inc.

35. Jovan has an $\frac{11}{10}$-lb mixture of cashews and peanuts that includes $\frac{3}{5}$ lb of cashews. How many pounds of peanuts are in the mixture?

36. *Cutco Cutlery.* The Essentials 5-piece set sold by Cutco contains three knives: $7\frac{5}{8}$" Petite Chef, $6\frac{3}{4}$" Petite Carver, and $2\frac{3}{4}$" Paring Knife. How much larger is the blade of the Petite Chef than that of the Petite Carver? than that of the Paring Knife?

Source: Cutco Cutlery Corporation, Fall 2008

37. Creative Glass sells a framed beveled mirror as shown below. Its dimensions are $30\frac{1}{2}$" wide by $36\frac{5}{8}$" high. What is the perimeter of (total distance around) the framed mirror?

$36\frac{5}{8}$ in.

$30\frac{1}{2}$ in.

38. *Winterizing a Swimming Pool.* To winterize their swimming pool, the Jablonskis are draining the water into a nearby field. The distance to the field is $103\frac{1}{2}$ ft. Because their only hose measures $62\frac{3}{4}$ ft, they need to buy an additional hose. How long must the new hose be?

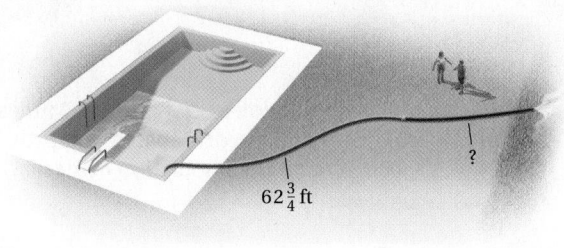

$62\frac{3}{4}$ ft

39. *Interior Design.* Sue worked $10\frac{1}{2}$ hr over a three-day period on an interior design project. If she worked $2\frac{1}{2}$ hr on the first day and $4\frac{1}{5}$ hr on the second, how many hours did Sue work on the third day?

40. *Painting.* Geri had $3\frac{1}{2}$ gal of paint. It took $2\frac{3}{4}$ gal to paint the family room. She estimated that it would take $2\frac{1}{4}$ gal to paint the living room. How much more paint did Geri need?

41. Find the perimeter (distance around).

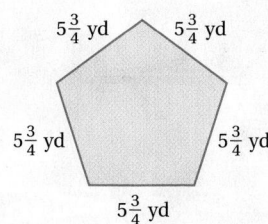

$5\frac{3}{4}$ yd $5\frac{3}{4}$ yd

$5\frac{3}{4}$ yd $5\frac{3}{4}$ yd

$5\frac{3}{4}$ yd

42. Find the length d.

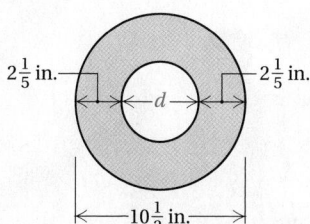

$2\frac{1}{5}$ in. d $2\frac{1}{5}$ in.

$10\frac{1}{2}$ in.

43. For a family barbecue, Cayla bought packages of hamburger weighing $1\frac{2}{3}$ lb and $5\frac{3}{4}$ lb. What was the total weight of the meat?

44. Nicholas is $73\frac{2}{3}$ in. tall and his daughter, Kendra, is $71\frac{5}{16}$ in. tall. How much shorter is Kendra?

45. *Weight of Water.*   The weight of water is $62\frac{1}{2}$ lb per cubic foot. How many cubic feet would be occupied by 25,000 lb of water?

46. *Spreading Grass Seed.*   Emily seeds lawns for Sam's Superior Lawn Care. When she walks at a rapid pace, the wheel on the broadcast spreader completes $150\frac{2}{3}$ revolutions per minute. How many revolutions does the wheel complete in 15 min?

47. *Population.*   The population of Alabama is $6\frac{4}{5}$ times that of Alaska. The population of Alabama is approximately 4,700,000. What is the population of Alaska?
Source: U.S. Census Bureau

48. *Population.*   The population of Iowa is $2\frac{1}{3}$ times the population of Hawaii. The population of Hawaii is approximately 1,300,000. What is the population of Iowa?
Source: U.S. Census Bureau

49. A car traveled 213 mi on $14\frac{2}{10}$ gal of gas. How many miles per gallon did it get?

50. *Half of a Recipe.*   A caterer is following a salad dressing recipe that calls for $1\frac{7}{8}$ cups of mayonnaise and $1\frac{1}{6}$ cups of sugar. How much mayonnaise and sugar will he need if he prepares $\frac{1}{2}$ of the amount of salad dressing?

51. *Sewing from a Pattern.*   Suppose you want to make a formal dress with jacket in size 8. Using 45-in. fabric, you need $1\frac{3}{8}$ yd for the dress, $\frac{5}{8}$ yd of contrasting fabric for the band at the bottom, and $3\frac{3}{8}$ yd for the jacket. How many yards of 45-in. fabric are needed to make the outfit?

52. *Weight of Water.*   The weight of water is $8\frac{1}{3}$ lb per gallon. Harry rolls his lawn with an 800-lb capacity roller. Express the water capacity of the roller in gallons.

53. *Construction.*   A rectangular lot has dimensions of $302\frac{1}{2}$ ft by $205\frac{1}{4}$ ft. A building with dimensions of 100 ft by $25\frac{1}{2}$ ft is built on the lot. How much area is left over?

54. Alyse bought $\frac{1}{3}$ lb of orange pekoe tea and $\frac{1}{2}$ lb of English cinnamon tea. How many pounds of tea did she buy?

Copyright © 2012 Pearson Education, Inc.

55. *Population.* The population of India is about $3\frac{3}{4}$ times the population of the United States. In 2007, the population of India was approximately 1,130,100,000. What was the population of the United States in 2007?

Source: Population Division/International Programs Center, U.S. Census Bureau, U.S. Dept. of Commerce

56. *Population.* The population of Cleveland is about $1\frac{1}{3}$ times the population of Cincinnati. In 2007, the population of Cincinnati was approximately 332,400. What was the population of Cleveland in 2007?

Source: U.S. Census Bureau

57. A bucket had 12 L of water in it when it was $\frac{3}{4}$ full. How much could it hold when full?

58. A tank had 20 L of gasoline in it when it was $\frac{4}{5}$ full. How much could it hold when full?

59. Find the area of the shaded region.

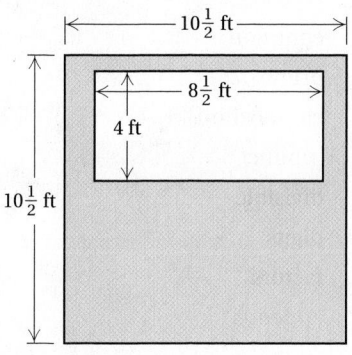

60. Find the perimeter.

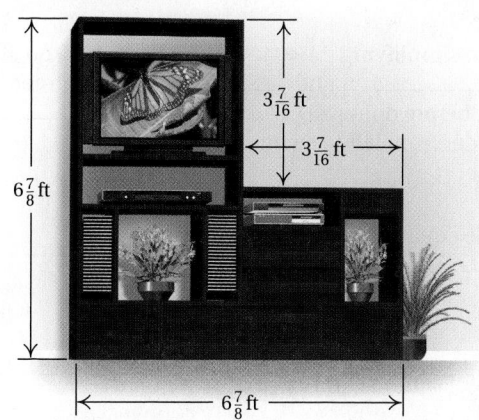

61. *Concrete Mix.* A cubic meter of concrete mix contains 420 kg of cement, 150 kg of stone, and 120 kg of sand. What is the total weight of a cubic meter of the mix? What part is cement? stone? sand? Add these fractional amounts. What is the result?

62. *Punch Recipe.* A recipe for strawberry punch calls for $\frac{1}{5}$ qt of ginger ale and $\frac{3}{5}$ qt of strawberry soda. How much liquid is needed? If the recipe is doubled, how much liquid is needed? If the recipe is halved, how much liquid is needed?

63. *Mural.* Cecilia hired an artist to paint a mural on the wall in her twin sons' bedroom. The dimensions of the mural are $6\frac{2}{3}$ ft by $9\frac{3}{8}$ ft. What is the area of the mural?

64. *Aeronautics.* Most space shuttles orbit the earth once every $1\frac{1}{2}$ hr. How many orbits are made every 24 hr?

65. Sidewalk. A sidewalk alongside a garden at the conservatory is to be $14\frac{2}{5}$ yd long. Rectangular stone tiles that are each $1\frac{1}{8}$ yd long are used to form the sidewalk. How many tiles are used?

66. Benny uses $\frac{2}{5}$ gram (g) of toothpaste each time he brushes his teeth. If Benny buys a 30-g tube, how many times will he be able to brush his teeth?

Skill Maintenance

In each of Exercises 67–74, fill in the blank with the correct term from the given list. Some of the choices may not be used and some may be used more than once.

67. In the equation $420 \div 60 = 7$, 60 is the _____, 7 the _____, and 420 the _____. [1.3c]

68. When denominators are the same, we say that fractions have a _____ denominator. [2.3a]

69. The numbers 91, 95, and 111 are examples of _____ numbers. [1.7c]

70. The number 22,223,133 is _____ by 9 because the sum of its digits is _____ by 9. [1.8a]

71. When simplifying $24 \div 4 + 4 \times 12 - 6 \div 2$, do all _____ and _____ in order from left to right before doing all _____ and _____ in order from left to right. [1.6c]

72. In the equation $2 + 3 = 5$, 2 and 3 are called _____. [1.2a]

73. In the expression $\frac{c}{d}$, we call c the _____. [2.1a]

74. The number 0 has no _____. [2.2b]

identity
reciprocal
divisor
dividend
quotient
additions
subtractions
multiplications
divisions
numerator
denominator
equal
common
prime
composite
product
divisible
digits
factors
addends

Synthesis

75. A guitarist's band is booked for Friday and Saturday nights at a local club. The guitarist is part of a trio on Friday and part of a quintet on Saturday. Thus the guitarist is paid one-third of one-half the weekend's pay for Friday and one-fifth of one-half the weekend's pay for Saturday. What fractional part of the band's pay did the guitarist receive for the weekend's work? If the band was paid $1200, how much did the guitarist receive?

76. A post for a pier is 29 ft long. Half of the post extends above the water's surface and $8\frac{3}{4}$ ft of the post is buried in mud. How deep is the water at that point?

77. College Profile. Of students entering a college, $\frac{7}{8}$ have completed high school and $\frac{2}{3}$ are older than 20. If $\frac{1}{7}$ of all students are left-handed, what fraction of students entering the college are left-handed high school graduates over the age of 20?

Copyright © 2012 Pearson Education, Inc.

2.6 Order of Operations; Estimation

a Order of Operations; Fraction Notation and Mixed Numerals

The rules for order of operations that we use with whole numbers (see Section 1.6) apply when we are simplifying expressions involving fraction notation and mixed numerals. For review, these rules are listed below.

> **RULES FOR ORDER OF OPERATIONS**
> 1. Do all calculations within parentheses before operations outside.
> 2. Evaluate all exponential expressions.
> 3. Do all multiplications and divisions in order from left to right.
> 4. Do all additions and subtractions in order from left to right.

EXAMPLE 1 Simplify: $\frac{1}{6} + \frac{2}{3} \div \frac{1}{2} \cdot \frac{5}{8}$.

$$\frac{1}{6} + \frac{2}{3} \div \frac{1}{2} \cdot \frac{5}{8} = \frac{1}{6} + \frac{2}{3} \cdot \frac{2}{1} \cdot \frac{5}{8}$$

Doing the division first by multiplying by the reciprocal of $\frac{1}{2}$

$$= \frac{1}{6} + \frac{2 \cdot 2 \cdot 5}{3 \cdot 1 \cdot 8}$$

Doing the multiplications in order from left to right

$$= \frac{1}{6} + \frac{2 \cdot 2 \cdot 5}{3 \cdot 1 \cdot 2 \cdot 2 \cdot 2}$$

Factoring in order to simplify

$$= \frac{1}{6} + \frac{5}{6}$$

Removing a factor of 1: $\frac{2 \cdot 2}{2 \cdot 2} = 1$; simplifying

$$= \frac{6}{6} = 1$$

Adding and simplifying

Do Margin Exercises 1 and 2.

EXAMPLE 2 Simplify: $\frac{2}{3} \cdot 24 - 11\frac{1}{2}$.

$$\frac{2}{3} \cdot 24 - 11\frac{1}{2} = \frac{2 \cdot 24}{3 \cdot 1} - 11\frac{1}{2}$$

Doing the multiplication first

$$= \frac{2 \cdot 3 \cdot 8}{3 \cdot 1} - 11\frac{1}{2}$$

Factoring the fraction

$$= 2 \cdot 8 - 11\frac{1}{2}$$

Removing a factor of 1: $\frac{3}{3} = 1$

$$= 16 - 11\frac{1}{2}$$

Completing the multiplication

$$= 4\frac{1}{2}, \text{ or } \frac{9}{2}$$

Doing the subtraction

Do Exercise 3.

OBJECTIVES

a Simplify expressions using the rules for order of operations.

b Estimate with fraction notation and mixed numerals.

SKILL TO REVIEW
Objective 1.6c: Simplify expressions using the rules for order of operations.

Simplify.
1. $22 - 3 \cdot 4$
2. $6(4 + 1)^2 - 3^4 \div 3$

Simplify.

1. $\frac{2}{5} \cdot \frac{5}{8} + \frac{1}{4}$

2. $\frac{1}{3} \cdot \frac{3}{4} \div \frac{5}{8} - \frac{1}{10}$

3. Simplify: $\frac{3}{4} \cdot 16 + 8\frac{2}{3}$.

Answers

Skill to Review:
1. 10 **2.** 123

Margin Exercises:
1. $\frac{1}{2}$ **2.** $\frac{3}{10}$ **3.** $20\frac{2}{3}$, or $\frac{62}{3}$

EXAMPLE 3 *Harvesting Walnut Trees.* A woodland owner decided to harvest five walnut trees in order to improve the growing conditions of the remaining trees. The logs she sold measured $7\frac{5}{8}$ ft, $8\frac{1}{4}$ ft, $8\frac{3}{4}$ ft, $9\frac{1}{8}$ ft, and $10\frac{1}{2}$ ft. What is the average length of the logs?

Recall that to compute an average, we add the numbers and then divide the sum by the number of addends. (See Section 1.6.) We have

$$\frac{7\frac{5}{8} + 8\frac{1}{4} + 8\frac{3}{4} + 9\frac{1}{8} + 10\frac{1}{2}}{5} = \frac{7\frac{5}{8} + 8\frac{2}{8} + 8\frac{6}{8} + 9\frac{1}{8} + 10\frac{4}{8}}{5}$$

$$= \frac{42\frac{18}{8}}{5} = \frac{42\frac{9}{4}}{5} = \frac{\frac{177}{4}}{5} \qquad \begin{array}{l}\text{Adding,}\\ \text{simplifying, and}\\ \text{converting}\\ \text{to fraction notation}\end{array}$$

$$= \frac{177}{4} \cdot \frac{1}{5} \qquad \begin{array}{l}\text{Multiplying}\\ \text{by the reciprocal}\end{array}$$

$$= \frac{177}{20}, \text{ or } 8\frac{17}{20}.$$

The average length of the logs is $8\frac{17}{20}$ ft.

Do Exercises 4–6.

4. Rachel has triplets. Their birth weights are $3\frac{1}{2}$ lb, $2\frac{3}{4}$ lb, and $3\frac{1}{8}$ lb. What is the average weight of her babies?

5. Find the average of
$$\frac{1}{2}, \frac{1}{3}, \text{ and } \frac{5}{6}.$$

6. Find the average of $\frac{3}{4}$ and $\frac{4}{5}$.

EXAMPLE 4 Simplify: $\left(\frac{7}{8} - \frac{1}{3}\right) \times 48 + \left(13 + \frac{4}{5}\right)^2.$

$$\left(\frac{7}{8} - \frac{1}{3}\right) \times 48 + \left(13 + \frac{4}{5}\right)^2$$

$$= \left(\frac{7}{8} \cdot \frac{3}{3} - \frac{1}{3} \cdot \frac{8}{8}\right) \times 48 + \left(13 \cdot \frac{5}{5} + \frac{4}{5}\right)^2 \qquad \begin{array}{l}\text{Carrying out operations}\\ \text{inside parentheses first.}\\ \text{To do so, we first multiply}\\ \text{by 1 to obtain the LCD.}\end{array}$$

$$= \left(\frac{21}{24} - \frac{8}{24}\right) \times 48 + \left(\frac{65}{5} + \frac{4}{5}\right)^2$$

$$= \frac{13}{24} \times 48 + \left(\frac{69}{5}\right)^2 \qquad \text{Completing the operations within parentheses}$$

$$= \frac{13}{24} \times 48 + \frac{4761}{25} \qquad \text{Evaluating the exponential expression next}$$

$$= 26 + \frac{4761}{25} \qquad \text{Doing the multiplication}$$

$$= 26 + 190\frac{11}{25} \qquad \text{Converting to a mixed numeral}$$

$$= 216\frac{11}{25}, \text{ or } \frac{5411}{25} \qquad \text{Adding}$$

Answers can be given using either fraction notation or mixed numerals.

Do Exercise 7.

7. Simplify:
$$\left(\frac{2}{3} + \frac{3}{4}\right) \div 2\frac{1}{3} - \left(\frac{1}{2}\right)^3.$$

Answers

4. $3\frac{1}{8}$ lb **5.** $\frac{5}{9}$ **6.** $\frac{31}{40}$ **7.** $\frac{27}{56}$

Estimation with Fraction Notation and Mixed Numerals

We now estimate with fraction notation and mixed numerals.

EXAMPLES Estimate each of the following as 0, $\frac{1}{2}$, or 1.

5. $\dfrac{2}{17}$

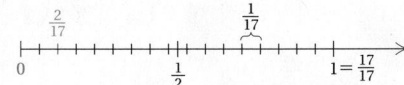

A fraction is close to 0 when the numerator is small in comparison to the denominator. Thus, 0 is an estimate for $\frac{2}{17}$ because 2 is small in comparison to 17. Thus, $\frac{2}{17} \approx 0$.

6. $\dfrac{11}{23}$

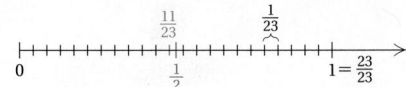

A fraction is close to $\frac{1}{2}$ when the denominator is about twice the numerator. Thus, $\frac{1}{2}$ is an estimate for $\frac{11}{23}$ because $2 \cdot 11 = 22$ and 22 is close to 23. Thus, $\frac{11}{23} \approx \frac{1}{2}$.

7. $\dfrac{37}{38}$

A fraction is close to 1 when the numerator is nearly equal to the denominator. Thus, 1 is an estimate for $\frac{37}{38}$ because 37 is nearly equal to 38. Thus, $\frac{37}{38} \approx 1$.

8. $\dfrac{43}{41}$

As in the preceding example, the numerator 43 is nearly equal to the denominator 41. Thus, $\frac{43}{41} \approx 1$.

> Do Exercises 8–11.

EXAMPLE 9 Estimate $16\frac{8}{9} + 11\frac{2}{13} - 4\frac{22}{43}$ by estimating each mixed numeral as a whole number or as a mixed numeral where the fractional part is $\frac{1}{2}$.

We estimate each fraction as 0, $\frac{1}{2}$, or 1. Then we calculate:

$$16\frac{8}{9} + 11\frac{2}{13} - 4\frac{22}{43} \approx 17 + 11 - 4\frac{1}{2}$$

$$= 28 - 4\frac{1}{2}$$

$$= 23\frac{1}{2}.$$

> Do Exercises 12–14.

Estimate each of the following as 0, $\frac{1}{2}$, or 1.

8. $\dfrac{3}{59}$ **9.** $\dfrac{61}{59}$

10. $\dfrac{29}{59}$ **11.** $\dfrac{57}{59}$

Estimate each of the following by estimating each mixed numeral as a whole number or as a mixed numeral where the fractional part is $\frac{1}{2}$ and each fraction as 0, $\frac{1}{2}$, or 1.

12. $5\dfrac{9}{10} + 26\dfrac{1}{2} - 10\dfrac{3}{29}$

13. $10\dfrac{7}{8} \cdot \left(25\dfrac{11}{13} - 14\dfrac{1}{9} \right)$

14. $\left(10\dfrac{4}{5} + 7\dfrac{5}{9} \right) \div \dfrac{17}{30}$

Answers

8. 0 **9.** 1 **10.** $\frac{1}{2}$ **11.** 1
12. $22\frac{1}{2}$ **13.** 132 **14.** 37

a Simplify.

1. $\dfrac{5}{8} \div \dfrac{1}{4} - \dfrac{2}{3} \cdot \dfrac{4}{5}$

2. $\dfrac{4}{7} \cdot \dfrac{7}{15} + \dfrac{2}{3} \div 8$

3. $\dfrac{3}{4} - \dfrac{2}{3} \cdot \left(\dfrac{1}{2} + \dfrac{2}{5}\right)$

4. $\dfrac{3}{4} \div \dfrac{1}{2} \cdot \left(\dfrac{8}{9} - \dfrac{2}{3}\right)$

5. $28\dfrac{1}{8} - 5\dfrac{1}{4} + 3\dfrac{1}{2}$

6. $10\dfrac{3}{5} - 4\dfrac{1}{10} - 1\dfrac{1}{2}$

7. $\dfrac{7}{8} \div \dfrac{1}{2} \cdot \dfrac{1}{4}$

8. $\dfrac{7}{10} \cdot \dfrac{4}{5} \div \dfrac{2}{3}$

9. $\left(\dfrac{2}{3}\right)^2 - \dfrac{1}{3} \cdot 1\dfrac{1}{4}$

10. $\left(\dfrac{3}{4}\right)^2 + 3\dfrac{1}{2} \div 1\dfrac{1}{4}$

11. $\dfrac{1}{2} - \left(\dfrac{1}{2}\right)^2 + \left(\dfrac{1}{2}\right)^3$

12. $1 + \dfrac{1}{4} + \left(\dfrac{1}{4}\right)^2 - \left(\dfrac{1}{4}\right)^3$

13. $\left(\dfrac{2}{3} + \dfrac{3}{4}\right) \div \left(\dfrac{5}{6} - \dfrac{1}{3}\right)$

14. $\left(\dfrac{3}{5} - \dfrac{1}{2}\right) \div \left(\dfrac{3}{4} - \dfrac{3}{10}\right)$

15. $\left(\dfrac{1}{2} + \dfrac{1}{3}\right)^2 \cdot 144 - \dfrac{5}{8} \div 10\dfrac{1}{2}$

16. $\left(3\dfrac{1}{2} - 2\dfrac{1}{3}\right)^2 + 6 \cdot 2\dfrac{1}{2} \div 32$

17. Find the average of $\dfrac{2}{3}$ and $\dfrac{7}{8}$.

18. Find the average of $\dfrac{1}{4}$ and $\dfrac{1}{5}$.

19. Find the average of $\dfrac{1}{6}, \dfrac{1}{8}$, and $\dfrac{3}{4}$.

20. Find the average of $\dfrac{4}{5}, \dfrac{1}{2}$, and $\dfrac{1}{10}$.

21. Find the average of $3\dfrac{1}{2}$ and $9\dfrac{3}{8}$.

22. Find the average of $10\dfrac{2}{3}$ and $24\dfrac{5}{6}$.

Copyright © 2012 Pearson Education, Inc.

23. *Hiking the Appalachian Trail.* Ellen camped and hiked for three consecutive days along a section of the Appalachian Trail. The distances she hiked on the three days were $15\frac{5}{32}$ mi, $20\frac{3}{16}$ mi, and $12\frac{7}{8}$ mi. Find the average of these distances.

24. *Vertical Leaps.* Eight-year-old Zachary registered vertical leaps of $12\frac{3}{4}$ in., $13\frac{3}{4}$ in., $13\frac{1}{2}$ in., and 14 in. Find his average vertical leap.

25. *Black Bear Cubs.* Black bears typically have two cubs. In January 2007 in northern New Hampshire, a black bear sow gave birth to a litter of 5 cubs. This is so rare that Tom Sears, a wildlife photographer, spent 28 hr per week for six weeks watching for the perfect opportunity to photograph this family of six. At the time of this photo, an observer estimated that the cubs weighed $7\frac{1}{2}$ lb, 8 lb, $9\frac{1}{2}$ lb, $10\frac{5}{8}$ lb, and $11\frac{3}{4}$ lb. What was the average weight of the cubs?

Source: Andrew Timmins, New Hampshire Fish and Game Department, *Northcountry News*, Warren, NH; Tom Sears, photographer

26. *Acceleration.* The results of a *Road & Track* road acceleration test for five cars are given in the graph below. The test measures the time in seconds required to go from 0 mph to 60 mph. What was the average time?

Acceleration: 0 mph to 60 mph

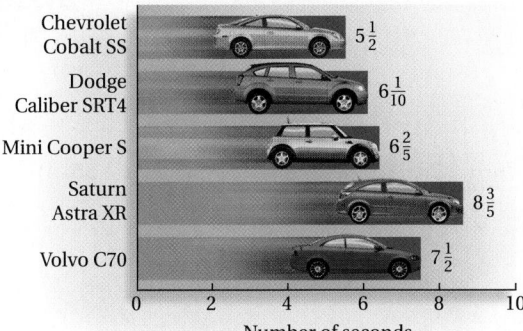

SOURCE: *Road & Track*, October 2008, pp.156–157

b Estimate each of the following as 0, $\frac{1}{2}$, or 1.

27. $\dfrac{2}{47}$ **28.** $\dfrac{5}{12}$ **29.** $\dfrac{7}{8}$ **30.** $\dfrac{1}{13}$ **31.** $\dfrac{6}{11}$ **32.** $\dfrac{11}{13}$

33. $\dfrac{7}{15}$ **34.** $\dfrac{1}{16}$ **35.** $\dfrac{7}{100}$ **36.** $\dfrac{5}{9}$ **37.** $\dfrac{19}{20}$ **38.** $\dfrac{4}{5}$

Estimate each of the following by estimating each mixed numeral as a whole number or as a mixed numeral where the fractional part is $\frac{1}{2}$ and by estimating each fraction as 0, $\frac{1}{2}$, or 1.

39. $2\dfrac{7}{8}$ **40.** $1\dfrac{1}{3}$ **41.** $12\dfrac{5}{6}$

42. $26\dfrac{6}{13}$ **43.** $\dfrac{4}{5} + \dfrac{7}{8}$ **44.** $\dfrac{1}{12} \cdot \dfrac{7}{15}$

45. $\dfrac{3}{8} + \dfrac{7}{13} + \dfrac{5}{9}$

46. $\dfrac{8}{9} + \dfrac{4}{5} + \dfrac{11}{12}$

47. $\dfrac{43}{100} + \dfrac{1}{10} - \dfrac{11}{1000}$

48. $\dfrac{23}{24} + \dfrac{37}{39} + \dfrac{51}{50}$

49. $7\dfrac{29}{60} + 10\dfrac{12}{13} \cdot 24\dfrac{2}{17}$

50. $5\dfrac{13}{14} - 1\dfrac{5}{8} + 1\dfrac{23}{28} \cdot 6\dfrac{35}{74}$

51. $24 \div 7\dfrac{8}{9}$

52. $43\dfrac{16}{17} \div 11\dfrac{2}{13}$

53. $76\dfrac{3}{14} + 23\dfrac{19}{20}$

54. $76\dfrac{13}{14} \cdot 23\dfrac{17}{20}$

55. $16\dfrac{1}{5} \div 2\dfrac{1}{11} + 25\dfrac{9}{10} - 4\dfrac{11}{23}$

56. $96\dfrac{2}{13} \div 5\dfrac{19}{20} + 3\dfrac{1}{7} \cdot 5\dfrac{18}{21}$

Skill Maintenance

Divide and simplify. [2.2c]

57. $\dfrac{4}{5} \div \dfrac{3}{10}$

58. $\dfrac{3}{10} \div \dfrac{4}{5}$

59. Classify the given numbers as prime, composite, or neither.
$1, 5, 7, 9, 14, 23, 43$ [1.7c]

60. Divide: $7865 \div 132$. [1.3c]

Solve.

61. *Luncheon Servings.* Ian purchased 6 lb of cold cuts for a luncheon. If he has allowed $\frac{3}{8}$ lb per person, how many people did he invite to the luncheon? [2.5a]

62. *Cholesterol.* A 3-oz serving of crabmeat contains 85 milligrams (mg) of cholesterol. A 3-oz serving of shrimp contains 128 mg of cholesterol. How much more cholesterol is in the shrimp? [1.5a]

Synthesis

63. ▦ In the sum below, *a* and *b* are digits. Find *a* and *b*.
$$\dfrac{a}{17} + \dfrac{1b}{23} = \dfrac{35a}{391}$$

64. ▦ Consider only the numbers 3, 4, 5, and 6. Assume each can be placed in a blank in the following.
$$\square + \dfrac{\square}{\square} \cdot \square = \,?$$
What placement of the numbers in the blanks yields the largest sum?

65. ▦ Consider only the numbers 2, 3, 4, and 5. Assume each is placed in a blank in the following.
$$\dfrac{\square}{\square} + \dfrac{\square}{\square} = \,?$$
What placement of the numbers in the blanks yields the largest sum?

66. ▦ Use a calculator to arrange the following in order from smallest to largest.
$$\dfrac{3}{4}, \dfrac{17}{21}, \dfrac{13}{15}, \dfrac{7}{9}, \dfrac{15}{17}, \dfrac{13}{12}, \dfrac{19}{22}$$

Copyright © 2012 Pearson Education, Inc.

Key Terms

fraction notation, p. 104   denominator, p. 104   mixed numeral, p. 133
numerator, p. 104   equivalent fractions, p. 110

Concept Reinforcement

Determine whether each statement is true or false.

_____ **1.** The mixed numeral $5\frac{2}{3}$ can be represented by the sum $5 \cdot \frac{3}{3} + \frac{2}{3}$.   [2.4a]

_____ **2.** All mixed numerals represent numbers larger than 1.   [2.4a]

_____ **3.** If $\frac{a}{b} < 1$, then $a > b$.   [2.6b]

_____ **4.** The product of any two mixed numerals is greater than 1.   [2.4d]

_____ **5.** The fraction $\frac{13}{9}$ is larger than the fraction $\frac{11}{6}$.   [2.3c]

Important Concepts

Objective 2.1b   Simplify fraction notation like n/n to 1, $0/n$ to 0, and $n/1$ to n.

Example   Simplify $\frac{6}{6}, \frac{0}{6}$, and $\frac{6}{1}$.

$$\frac{6}{6} = 1, \qquad \frac{0}{6} = 0, \qquad \frac{6}{1} = 6$$

Practice Exercise

1. Simplify $\frac{0}{18}, \frac{18}{18}$, and $\frac{18}{1}$.

Objective 2.1d   Multiply a number by 1 to find fraction notation with a specified denominator.

Example   Find a name for $\frac{2}{7}$ with a denominator of 63.

$$\frac{2}{7} = \frac{2}{7} \cdot \frac{9}{9} = \frac{2 \cdot 9}{7 \cdot 9} = \frac{18}{63} \qquad \text{Since } 7 \cdot 9 = 63,$$
$$\text{we multiply by } \frac{9}{9}.$$

Practice Exercise

2. Find a name for $\frac{7}{12}$ with a denominator of 96.

Objective 2.1e   Simplify fraction notation.

Example   Simplify: $\frac{315}{1650}$.

Using the test for divisibility by 5, we see that both the numerator and the denominator are divisible by 5:

$$\frac{315}{1650} = \frac{5 \cdot 63}{5 \cdot 330} = \frac{5}{5} \cdot \frac{63}{330} = 1 \cdot \frac{63}{330}$$
$$= \frac{63}{330} = \frac{3 \cdot 21}{3 \cdot 110} = \frac{3}{3} \cdot \frac{21}{110} = 1 \cdot \frac{21}{110} = \frac{21}{110}.$$

Practice Exercise

3. Simplify: $\frac{100}{280}$.

Objective 2.2a Multiply and simplify using fraction notation.

Example Multiply and simplify: $\dfrac{7}{16} \cdot \dfrac{40}{49}$.

$$\dfrac{7}{16} \cdot \dfrac{40}{49} = \dfrac{7 \cdot 40}{16 \cdot 49} = \dfrac{7 \cdot 2 \cdot 2 \cdot 2 \cdot 5}{2 \cdot 2 \cdot 2 \cdot 2 \cdot 7 \cdot 7}$$

$$= \dfrac{2 \cdot 2 \cdot 2 \cdot 7}{2 \cdot 2 \cdot 2 \cdot 7} \cdot \dfrac{5}{2 \cdot 7} = 1 \cdot \dfrac{5}{14} = \dfrac{5}{14}$$

Practice Exercise

4. Multiply and simplify: $\dfrac{80}{3} \cdot \dfrac{21}{72}$.

Objective 2.2c Divide and simplify using fraction notation.

Example Divide and simplify: $\dfrac{9}{20} \div \dfrac{18}{25}$.

$$\dfrac{9}{20} \div \dfrac{18}{25} = \dfrac{9}{20} \cdot \dfrac{25}{18} = \dfrac{9 \cdot 25}{20 \cdot 18} = \dfrac{3 \cdot 3 \cdot 5 \cdot 5}{2 \cdot 2 \cdot 5 \cdot 2 \cdot 3 \cdot 3}$$

$$= \dfrac{3 \cdot 3 \cdot 5}{3 \cdot 3 \cdot 5} \cdot \dfrac{5}{2 \cdot 2 \cdot 2} = 1 \cdot \dfrac{5}{8} = \dfrac{5}{8}$$

Practice Exercise

5. Divide and simplify: $\dfrac{9}{4} \div \dfrac{45}{14}$.

Objective 2.3a Add using fraction notation.

Example Add: $\dfrac{5}{24} + \dfrac{7}{45}$.

$$\dfrac{5}{24} + \dfrac{7}{45} = \dfrac{5}{2 \cdot 2 \cdot 2 \cdot 3} + \dfrac{7}{3 \cdot 3 \cdot 5}$$

$$= \dfrac{5}{2 \cdot 2 \cdot 2 \cdot 3} \cdot \dfrac{3 \cdot 5}{3 \cdot 5} + \dfrac{7}{3 \cdot 3 \cdot 5} \cdot \dfrac{2 \cdot 2 \cdot 2}{2 \cdot 2 \cdot 2}$$

$$= \dfrac{75}{360} + \dfrac{56}{360} = \dfrac{131}{360}$$

Practice Exercise

6. Add: $\dfrac{19}{60} + \dfrac{11}{36}$.

Objective 2.3b Subtract using fraction notation.

Example Subtract: $\dfrac{7}{12} - \dfrac{11}{60}$.

$$\dfrac{7}{12} - \dfrac{11}{60} = \dfrac{7}{12} \cdot \dfrac{5}{5} - \dfrac{11}{60} = \dfrac{35}{60} - \dfrac{11}{60}$$

$$= \dfrac{35 - 11}{60} = \dfrac{24}{60} = \dfrac{2 \cdot \cancel{12}}{5 \cdot \cancel{12}} = \dfrac{2}{5}$$

Practice Exercise

7. Subtract: $\dfrac{29}{35} - \dfrac{5}{7}$.

Objective 2.3c Use $<$ or $>$ with fraction notation to write a true sentence.

Example Use $<$ or $>$ for $\square$ to write a true sentence:

$$\dfrac{5}{12} \; \square \; \dfrac{9}{16}.$$

The LCD $= 48$. Thus we have

$$\dfrac{5}{12} \cdot \dfrac{4}{4} \; \square \; \dfrac{9}{16} \cdot \dfrac{3}{3}, \quad \text{or} \quad \dfrac{20}{48} \; \square \; \dfrac{27}{48}.$$

Since $20 < 27$, $\dfrac{20}{48} < \dfrac{27}{48}$ and thus $\dfrac{5}{12} < \dfrac{9}{16}$.

Practice Exercise

8. Use $<$ or $>$ for $\square$ to write a true sentence:

$$\dfrac{3}{13} \; \square \; \dfrac{5}{12}.$$

Objective 2.3d   Solve equations of the type $x + a = b$ and $a + x = b$, where a and b may be fractions.

Example   Solve: $x + \dfrac{1}{6} = \dfrac{5}{8}$.

$$x + \dfrac{1}{6} = \dfrac{5}{8}$$

$$x + \dfrac{1}{6} - \dfrac{1}{6} = \dfrac{5}{8} - \dfrac{1}{6}$$

$$x = \dfrac{5}{8} \cdot \dfrac{3}{3} - \dfrac{1}{6} \cdot \dfrac{4}{4}$$

$$x = \dfrac{15}{24} - \dfrac{4}{24} = \dfrac{11}{24}$$

Practice Exercise

9. Solve: $\dfrac{2}{9} + x = \dfrac{9}{11}$.

Objective 2.4a   Convert between mixed numerals and fraction notation.

Example   Convert $2\dfrac{5}{13}$ to fraction notation: $2\dfrac{5}{13} = \dfrac{31}{13}$.

Example   Convert $\dfrac{40}{9}$ to a mixed numeral: $\dfrac{40}{9} = 4\dfrac{4}{9}$.

Practice Exercises

10. Convert $8\dfrac{2}{3}$ to fraction notation.

11. Convert $\dfrac{47}{6}$ to a mixed numeral.

Objective 2.4c   Subtract using mixed numerals.

Example   Subtract: $3\dfrac{3}{8} - 1\dfrac{4}{5}$.

$$3\dfrac{3}{8} = \quad 3\dfrac{15}{40} \quad = \quad 2\dfrac{55}{40}$$

$$-1\dfrac{4}{5} = -1\dfrac{32}{40} \quad = -1\dfrac{32}{40}$$

$$1\dfrac{23}{40}$$

Practice Exercise

12. Subtract: $10\dfrac{5}{7} - 2\dfrac{3}{4}$.

Objective 2.4d   Multiply using mixed numerals.

Example   Multiply: $7\dfrac{1}{4} \cdot 5\dfrac{3}{10}$. Write a mixed numeral for the answer.

$$7\dfrac{1}{4} \cdot 5\dfrac{3}{10} = \dfrac{29}{4} \cdot \dfrac{53}{10} = \dfrac{1537}{40} = 38\dfrac{17}{40}$$

Practice Exercise

13. Multiply: $4\dfrac{1}{5} \cdot 3\dfrac{7}{15}$.

Objective 2.4e   Divide using mixed numerals.

Example   Divide: $5\dfrac{1}{8} \div 2\dfrac{1}{16}$. Write a mixed numeral for the answer.

$$5\dfrac{1}{8} \div 2\dfrac{1}{16} = \dfrac{41}{8} \div \dfrac{33}{16} = \dfrac{41}{8} \cdot \dfrac{16}{33} = \dfrac{82}{33} = 2\dfrac{16}{33}$$

Practice Exercise

14. Divide: $9\dfrac{5}{12} \div 3\dfrac{1}{6}$.

Objective 2.5a Solve applied problems involving division of fractions.

Example A rental car had 18 gal of gasoline when its gas tank was $\frac{6}{7}$ full. How much could the tank hold when full?

The equation that corresponds to the situation is

$$\frac{6}{7} \cdot g = 18.$$

We divide by $\frac{6}{7}$ on both sides and carry out the division:

$$g = 18 \div \frac{6}{7} = \frac{18}{1} \cdot \frac{7}{6} = \frac{18 \cdot 7}{1 \cdot 6}$$

$$= \frac{3 \cdot 6 \cdot 7}{1 \cdot 6} = \frac{6}{6} \cdot \frac{3 \cdot 7}{1} = 1 \cdot \frac{21}{1} = 21.$$

The rental car can hold 21 gal of gasoline.

Practice Exercise

15. A flower vase has $\frac{7}{4}$ cups of water in it when it is $\frac{3}{4}$ full. How much can it hold when full?

Objective 2.6a Simplify expressions using the rules for order of operations.

Example Simplify: $\left(\frac{4}{5}\right)^2 - \frac{1}{5} \cdot 2\frac{1}{8}$.

$$\left(\frac{4}{5}\right)^2 - \frac{1}{5} \cdot 2\frac{1}{8} = \frac{16}{25} - \frac{1}{5} \cdot \frac{17}{8}$$

$$= \frac{16}{25} - \frac{17}{40} = \frac{16}{25} \cdot \frac{8}{8} - \frac{17}{40} \cdot \frac{5}{5}$$

$$= \frac{128}{200} - \frac{85}{200} = \frac{43}{200}$$

Practice Exercise

16. Simplify: $\frac{3}{2} \cdot 1\frac{1}{3} \div \left(\frac{2}{3}\right)^2$.

Objective 2.6b Estimate with fraction notation and mixed numerals.

Example Estimate

$$3\frac{2}{5} + \frac{7}{10} + 6\frac{5}{9}$$

by estimating each mixed numeral as a whole number or as a mixed numeral where the fractional part is $\frac{1}{2}$ and by estimating each fraction as 0, $\frac{1}{2}$, or 1.

$$3\frac{2}{5} + \frac{7}{10} + 6\frac{5}{9} \approx 3\frac{1}{2} + \frac{1}{2} + 6\frac{1}{2} = 10\frac{1}{2}$$

Practice Exercise

17. Estimate

$$1\frac{19}{20} + 3\frac{1}{8} - \frac{8}{17}$$

by estimating each mixed numeral as a whole number or as a mixed numeral where the fractional part is $\frac{1}{2}$ and by estimating each fraction as 0, $\frac{1}{2}$, or 1.

Review Exercises

1. Identify the numerator and the denominator of $\frac{2}{7}$.
[2.1a]

What part of each object is shaded? [2.1a]

2.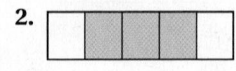

3.

Simplify. [2.1b, e]

4. $\frac{12}{30}$

5. $\frac{7}{28}$

6. $\frac{23}{23}$

7. $\frac{9}{27}$

8. $\frac{88}{184}$

9. $\frac{18}{0}$

10. $\frac{0}{25}$

11. $\frac{1170}{1200}$

12. $\frac{18}{1}$

13. $\frac{48}{8}$

14. $\frac{140}{490}$

15. $\frac{288}{2025}$

Copyright © 2012 Pearson Education, Inc.

16. Simplify the fractions on this circle graph, if possible. [2.1e]

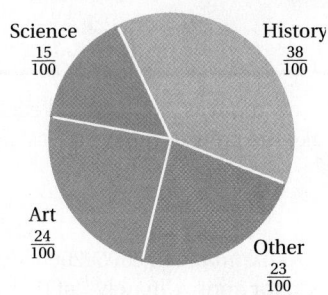

Museums in the United States

Science $\frac{15}{100}$

History $\frac{38}{100}$

Art $\frac{24}{100}$

Other $\frac{23}{100}$

Multiply and simplify. [2.2a]

17. $4 \cdot \frac{3}{8}$

18. $\frac{7}{3} \cdot 24$

19. $9 \cdot \frac{5}{18}$

20. $\frac{6}{5} \cdot 20$

21. $\frac{3}{4} \cdot \frac{8}{9}$

22. $\frac{5}{7} \cdot \frac{1}{10}$

23. $\frac{3}{7} \cdot \frac{14}{9}$

24. $\frac{1}{4} \cdot \frac{2}{11}$

25. $\frac{4}{25} \cdot \frac{15}{16}$

26. $\frac{11}{3} \cdot \frac{30}{77}$

Find the reciprocal. [2.2b]

27. $\frac{4}{5}$

28. 3

29. $\frac{1}{9}$

30. $\frac{47}{36}$

Divide and simplify. [2.2c]

31. $6 \div \frac{4}{3}$

32. $\frac{5}{9} \div \frac{5}{18}$

33. $\frac{1}{6} \div \frac{1}{11}$

34. $\frac{3}{14} \div \frac{6}{7}$

35. $\frac{1}{4} \div \frac{1}{9}$

36. $180 \div \frac{3}{5}$

37. $\frac{23}{25} \div \frac{23}{25}$

38. $\frac{2}{3} \div \frac{3}{2}$

Add and simplify. [2.3a]

39. $\frac{6}{5} + \frac{3}{8}$

40. $\frac{5}{16} + \frac{1}{12}$

41. $\frac{6}{5} + \frac{11}{15} + \frac{3}{20}$

42. $\frac{1}{1000} + \frac{19}{100} + \frac{7}{10}$

Subtract and simplify. [2.3b]

43. $\frac{5}{9} - \frac{2}{9}$

44. $\frac{7}{8} - \frac{3}{4}$

45. $\frac{11}{27} - \frac{2}{9}$

46. $\frac{5}{6} - \frac{2}{9}$

Use < or > for $\square$ to write a true sentence. [2.3c]

47. $\frac{4}{7} \,\square\, \frac{5}{9}$

48. $\frac{8}{9} \,\square\, \frac{11}{13}$

49. $\frac{2}{15} \,\square\, \frac{3}{13}$

50. $\frac{1}{94} \,\square\, \frac{1}{95}$

Solve.

51. $\frac{5}{4} \cdot t = \frac{3}{8}$ [2.2d]

52. $x \cdot \frac{2}{3} = 160$ [2.2d]

53. $x + \frac{2}{5} = \frac{7}{8}$ [2.3d]

54. $\frac{1}{2} + y = \frac{9}{10}$ [2.3d]

Convert to fraction notation. [2.4a]

55. $7\frac{1}{2}$

56. $8\frac{3}{8}$

57. $4\frac{1}{3}$

58. $10\frac{5}{7}$

Convert to a mixed numeral. [2.4a]

59. $\dfrac{7}{3}$ **60.** $\dfrac{27}{4}$

61. $\dfrac{63}{5}$ **62.** $\dfrac{7}{2}$

Add. Write a mixed numeral for the answer where appropriate. [2.4b]

63. $5\dfrac{3}{5}$
  $+\,4\dfrac{4}{5}$

64. $8\dfrac{1}{3}$
  $+\,3\dfrac{2}{5}$

65. $5\dfrac{5}{6}$
  $+\,4\dfrac{5}{6}$

66. $2\dfrac{3}{4}$
  $+\,5\dfrac{1}{2}$

Subtract. Write a mixed numeral for the answer where appropriate. [2.4c]

67. 12
  $-\,4\dfrac{2}{9}$

68. $9\dfrac{3}{5}$
  $-\,4\dfrac{13}{15}$

69. $10\dfrac{1}{4}$
  $-\,6\dfrac{1}{10}$

70. 24
  $-\,10\dfrac{5}{8}$

Multiply. Write a mixed numeral for the answer where appropriate. [2.4d]

71. $6 \cdot 2\dfrac{2}{3}$ **72.** $5\dfrac{1}{4} \cdot \dfrac{2}{3}$

73. $2\dfrac{1}{5} \cdot 1\dfrac{1}{10}$ **74.** $2\dfrac{2}{5} \cdot 2\dfrac{1}{2}$

Divide. Write a mixed numeral for the answer where appropriate. [2.4e]

75. $27 \div 2\dfrac{1}{4}$ **76.** $2\dfrac{2}{5} \div 1\dfrac{7}{10}$

77. $3\dfrac{1}{4} \div 26$ **78.** $4\dfrac{1}{5} \div 4\dfrac{2}{3}$

Solve. [2.5a]

79. A road crew repaves $\dfrac{1}{12}$ mi of road each day. How long will it take the crew to repave a $\dfrac{3}{4}$-mi stretch of road?

80. *Cotton Production.* In 2005–2006, the United States accounted for approximately $\dfrac{1}{5}$ of the world production of cotton. The total world cotton production was about 114,000,000 metric tons. How much cotton did the United States produce?

Sources: U.S. Department of Agriculture; Foreign Agricultural Service; *World Agricultural Production*, June 2007

81. *Sewing.* Gloria wants to make a dress and a jacket. She needs $1\dfrac{5}{8}$ yd of 60-in. fabric for the dress and $2\dfrac{5}{8}$ yd for the jacket. How many yards in all does Gloria need to make the outfit?

82. What is the sum of the areas in the figure below?

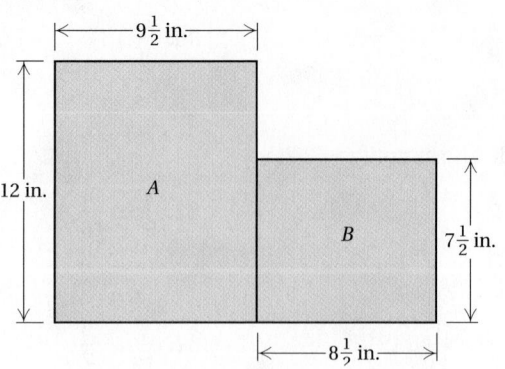

Copyright © 2012 Pearson Education, Inc.

83. In the figure in Exercise 82, how much larger is the area of rectangle *A* than the area of rectangle *B*?

84. *Carpentry.* A board $\frac{9}{10}$ in. thick is glued to a board $\frac{4}{5}$ in. thick. The glue is $\frac{3}{100}$ in. thick. How thick is the result?

85. *Turkey Servings.* Turkey contains $1\frac{1}{3}$ servings per pound. How many pounds are needed for 32 servings?

86. After driving 600 km, the Armstrong family has completed $\frac{3}{5}$ of their vacation. How long is the total trip?

87. *Building a Ziggurat.* The dimensions of all of the square bricks that King Nebuchadnezzar used over 2500 yr ago to build ziggurats were $13\frac{1}{4}$ in. $\times$ $13\frac{1}{4}$ in. $\times$ $3\frac{1}{4}$ in. What is the perimeter and the area of the $13\frac{1}{4}$ in. $\times$ $13\frac{1}{4}$ in. side? of the $13\frac{1}{4}$ in. $\times$ $3\frac{1}{4}$ in. side?
Source: www.eartharchitecture.org

88. Molly is making a pepper steak recipe that calls for $\frac{2}{3}$ cup of green bell peppers. How much would be needed to make $\frac{1}{2}$ recipe? 3 recipes?

89. Bernardo earns \$105 for working a full day. How much does he receive for working $\frac{1}{7}$ of a day?

90. A book bag requires $\frac{4}{5}$ yd of fabric. How many bags can be made from 48 yd?

91. *Painting a Border.* Katie hired an artist to paint a decorative border around the top of her son's bedroom. The artist charges \$20 per foot. The room measures $11\frac{3}{4}$ ft $\times$ $9\frac{1}{2}$ ft. What is Katie's cost for the project?

$9\frac{1}{2}$ ft

$11\frac{3}{4}$ ft

92. *Cake Recipe.* A wedding-cake recipe requires 12 cups of shortening. Being calorie-conscious, the wedding couple decides to reduce the shortening by $3\frac{5}{8}$ cups and replace it with prune purée. How many cups of shortening are used in their new recipe?

93. *Humane Society's Pie Sale.* Green River's Humane Society recently hosted its annual pie and ice cream social. Each of the 83 pies donated was cut into 6 pieces. At the end of the evening, 382 pieces of pie had been sold. How many pies were sold? How many were left over? Express your answers in mixed numerals.

Simplify each expression using the rules for order of operations. [2.6a]

94. $\frac{1}{8} \div \frac{1}{4} + \frac{1}{2}$

95. $\frac{4}{5} - \frac{1}{2} \cdot \left(1 + \frac{1}{4}\right)$

96. $20\frac{3}{4} - 1\frac{1}{2} \times 12 + \left(\frac{1}{2}\right)^2$

97. Find the average of $\frac{1}{2}, \frac{1}{4}, \frac{1}{3}$, and $\frac{1}{5}$. [2.6a]

Estimate each of the following as 0, $\frac{1}{2}$, or 1. [2.6b]

98. $\frac{29}{59}$ **99.** $\frac{2}{59}$ **100.** $\frac{61}{59}$

Estimate by estimating each mixed numeral as a whole number or as a mixed numeral where the fractional part is $\frac{1}{2}$ and by estimating each fraction as 0, $\frac{1}{2}$, or 1. [2.6b]

101. $6\frac{7}{8}$ **102.** $10\frac{2}{17}$

103. $\frac{11}{12} \cdot 5\frac{6}{13}$ **104.** $\frac{1}{15} \cdot \frac{2}{3}$

105. $\frac{6}{11} + \frac{5}{6} + \frac{31}{29}$

106. $32\frac{14}{15} + 27\frac{6}{7} - 4\frac{25}{28} \cdot 6\frac{37}{76}$

107. Simplify: $\frac{1}{4} + \frac{2}{5} \div 5^2$. [2.6a]

  A. $\frac{133}{500}$ **B.** $\frac{3}{500}$

  C. $\frac{117}{500}$ **D.** $\frac{5}{2}$

108. Multiply and simplify: $\frac{15}{26} \cdot \frac{13}{90}$. [2.2a]

  A. $\frac{195}{234}$ **B.** $\frac{1}{12}$

  C. $\frac{3}{36}$ **D.** $\frac{13}{156}$

109. Solve: $x + \frac{2}{3} = 5$. [2.3d]

  A. $\frac{15}{2}$ **B.** $5\frac{2}{3}$

  C. $\frac{10}{3}$ **D.** $4\frac{1}{3}$

110. Solve: $\frac{2}{13} \cdot x = \frac{1}{2}$. [2.2d]

  A. $\frac{1}{13}$ **B.** 13

  C. $\frac{4}{13}$ **D.** $\frac{13}{4}$

Synthesis

111. ▦ In the division below, find a and b. [2.2c]

$$\frac{19}{24} \div \frac{a}{b} = \frac{187,853}{268,224}$$

112. Place the numbers 3, 4, 5, and 6 in the boxes in order to make a true equation: [2.4b]

$$\frac{\square}{\square} + \frac{\square}{\square} = 3\frac{1}{4}.$$

Understanding Through Discussion and Writing

1. Is the sum of two mixed numerals always a mixed numeral? Why or why not? [2.4b]

2. A student incorrectly insists that $\frac{2}{5} \div \frac{3}{4}$ is $\frac{15}{8}$. What mistake is he probably making? [2.4e]

3. A student claims that "taking $\frac{1}{2}$ of a number is the same as dividing by $\frac{1}{2}$." Explain the error in this reasoning. [2.2c]

4. A student insists that $3\frac{2}{5} \cdot 1\frac{3}{7} = 3\frac{6}{35}$. What mistake is he making and how should he have proceeded? [2.4d]

5. Without performing the division, explain why $5 \div \frac{1}{7}$ is a greater number than $5 \div \frac{2}{3}$. [2.3c], [2.4e]

6. If a fraction's numerator and denominator have no factors (other than 1) in common, can the fraction be simplified? Why or why not? [2.1e]

Copyright © 2012 Pearson Education, Inc.

Test

For Extra Help

CHAPTER
Test Prep
VIDEOS

Step-by-step test solutions are found on the Chapter Test Prep Videos available via the Video Resources on DVD, in *MyMathLab*, and on You Tube (search "BittingerDevMath" and click on "Channels").

1. What part is shaded?

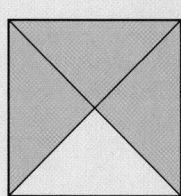

2. Use < or > for ☐ to write a true sentence:

$$\frac{6}{7} \ \square \ \frac{21}{25}.$$

Simplify.

3. $\dfrac{26}{1}$

4. $\dfrac{12}{12}$

5. $\dfrac{9}{0}$

6. $\dfrac{0}{16}$

7. $\dfrac{72}{108}$

Multiply and simplify.

8. $\dfrac{4}{3} \cdot 24$

9. $5 \cdot \dfrac{3}{10}$

10. $\dfrac{2}{3} \cdot \dfrac{15}{4}$

11. $\dfrac{22}{15} \cdot \dfrac{5}{33}$

Find the reciprocal.

12. $\dfrac{5}{8}$

13. $\dfrac{1}{4}$

14. 18

Divide and simplify.

15. $\dfrac{1}{5} \div \dfrac{1}{8}$

16. $12 \div \dfrac{2}{3}$

17. $\dfrac{24}{5} \div \dfrac{28}{15}$

Add and simplify.

18. $\dfrac{1}{2} + \dfrac{5}{2}$

19. $\dfrac{7}{8} + \dfrac{2}{3}$

20. $\dfrac{7}{10} + \dfrac{19}{100} + \dfrac{31}{1000}$

Subtract and simplify.

21. $\dfrac{5}{6} - \dfrac{3}{6}$

22. $\dfrac{5}{6} - \dfrac{3}{4}$

23. $\dfrac{17}{24} - \dfrac{1}{15}$

Solve.

24. $\dfrac{1}{4} + y = 4$

25. $t \cdot \dfrac{2}{5} = \dfrac{7}{10}$

26. Convert to a mixed numeral: $\dfrac{9}{2}$.

27. Convert to fraction notation: $9\dfrac{7}{8}$.

Add, subtract, multiply, or divide. Write a mixed numeral for the answer in Exercises 28–31.

28.
$$6\frac{2}{5}$$
$$+\ 7\frac{4}{5}$$

29.
$$10\frac{1}{6}$$
$$-\ 5\frac{7}{8}$$

30. $6\frac{3}{4} \cdot \frac{2}{3}$

31. $2\frac{1}{3} \div 1\frac{1}{6}$

32. *Carpentry.* The following diagram shows a middle drawer support guide for a cabinet drawer. Find each of the following.

  a) The short length a across the top
  b) The length b across the bottom

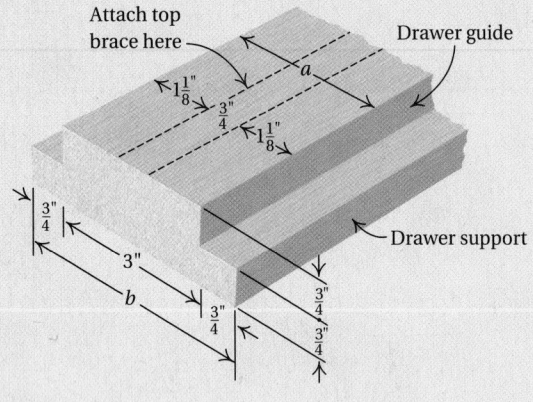

Attach top brace here

Drawer guide

$1\frac{1}{8}"$

$\frac{3}{4}"$

$1\frac{1}{8}"$

a

$\frac{3}{4}"$

$3"$

b

$\frac{3}{4}"$

Drawer support

$\frac{3}{4}"$

$\frac{3}{4}"$

33. *Book Order.* An order of books for a math course weighs 220 lb. Each book weighs $2\frac{3}{4}$ lb. How many books are in the order?

34. A thermos of iced tea held 3 qt of tea when it was $\frac{3}{5}$ full. How much tea could it hold when full?

35. *Carpentry.* In carpentry, some pieces of plywood that are called "$\frac{3}{4}$-inch" plywood are actually $\frac{11}{16}$ in. thick. How much thinner is such a piece than its name indicates?

36. Simplify: $1\frac{1}{2} - \frac{1}{2}\left(\frac{1}{2} \div \frac{1}{4}\right) + \left(\frac{1}{2}\right)^2$.

Estimate each of the following as 0, $\frac{1}{2}$, or 1.

37. $\frac{3}{82}$

38. $\frac{93}{91}$

Estimate each of the following by estimating each mixed numeral as a whole number or as a mixed numeral where the fractional part is $\frac{1}{2}$ and by estimating each fraction as 0, $\frac{1}{2}$, or 1.

39. $256 \div 15\frac{19}{21}$

40. $43\frac{15}{31} \cdot 27\frac{5}{6} - 9\frac{15}{28} + 6\frac{5}{76}$

41. A rectangular window measures $\frac{7}{5}$ m long by $\frac{4}{5}$ m wide. What is its area?

A. $\frac{28}{5}$ m^2

B. $\frac{28}{25}$ m^2

C. $\frac{11}{10}$ m^2

D. $\frac{11}{5}$ m^2

Synthesis

42. Simplify: $\left(\frac{3}{8}\right)^2 \div \frac{6}{7} \cdot \frac{2}{9} \div 5$.

43. Rebecca walks 17 laps at her health club. Trent walks 17 laps at his health club. If the track at Rebecca's health club is $\frac{1}{7}$ mi long, and the track at Trent's is $\frac{1}{8}$ mi long, who walks farther? How much farther?

Copyright © 2012 Pearson Education, Inc.

Decimal Notation

Real-World Application

Camping in national parks has declined steadily in recent years. The numbers of overnight camping stays in Park Service campgrounds in the National Park System from 2002 to 2006 were 5.8 million, 5.7 million, 5.4 million, 5.2 million, and 5.0 million, respectively. Find the average number of stays per year during this period.

Source: U.S. National Park Service

This problem appears as Exercise 77 in Section 3.4.

OBJECTIVES

a Given decimal notation, write a word name.

b Convert between decimal notation and fraction notation.

c Given a pair of numbers in decimal notation, tell which is larger.

d Round decimal notation to the nearest thousandth, hundredth, tenth, one, ten, hundred, or thousand.

SKILL TO REVIEW
Objective 1.3d: Round to the nearest ten, hundred, or thousand.

Round 4735 to the nearest:

1. Ten.   **2.** Hundred.

The set of **arithmetic numbers**, or **nonnegative rational numbers**, consists of the whole numbers 0, 1, 2, 3, 4, 5, 6, 7, 8, 9, 10, and so on, and fractions like $\frac{1}{2}, \frac{2}{3}, \frac{7}{8}, \frac{17}{10}$, and so on. Note that we can write the whole numbers using fraction notation. For example, 3 can be written as $\frac{3}{1}$. We studied the use of fraction notation for arithmetic numbers in Chapter 2.

In Chapter 3, we will study the use of *decimal notation*. The word *decimal* comes from the Latin word *decima*, meaning a tenth part. Although we are using different notation, we are still considering the nonnegative rational numbers. Using decimal notation, we can write 0.875 for $\frac{7}{8}$, for example, or 48.97 for $48\frac{97}{100}$.

a Decimal Notation and Word Names

One model of the Magellan GPS navigation system sells for $249.98. The dot in $249.98 is called a **decimal point**. Since $0.98, or 98¢, is $\frac{98}{100}$ of a dollar, it follows that

$$\$249.98 = 249 + \frac{98}{100} \text{ dollars.}$$

Also, since $0.98, or 98¢, has the same value as

9 dimes + 8 cents

and 1 dime is $\frac{1}{10}$ of a dollar and 1 cent is $\frac{1}{100}$ of a dollar, we can write

$$249.98 = 2 \cdot 100 + 4 \cdot 10 + 9 \cdot 1 + 9 \cdot \frac{1}{10} + 8 \cdot \frac{1}{100}.$$

This is an extension of the expanded notation for whole numbers that we used in Chapter 1. The place values are 100, 10, 1, $\frac{1}{10}$, $\frac{1}{100}$, and so on. We can see this on a **place-value chart**. The value of each place is $\frac{1}{10}$ as large as that of the one to its left.

Let's consider decimal notation using a place-value chart to represent 26.2922 min, the men's 10,000-meter run record held by Kenenisa Bekele from Ethiopia.

PLACE-VALUE CHART							
Hundreds	Tens	Ones	Tenths	Hundredths	Thousandths	Ten-Thousandths	Hundred-Thousandths
100	10	1	$\frac{1}{10}$	$\frac{1}{100}$	$\frac{1}{1000}$	$\frac{1}{10,000}$	$\frac{1}{100,000}$
	2	6 . 2	9	2	2		

Answers

Skill to Review:
1. 4740   2. 4700

The decimal notation 26.2922 means

$$20 + 6 + \frac{2}{10} + \frac{9}{100} + \frac{2}{1000} + \frac{2}{10{,}000}, \quad \text{or} \quad 26\frac{2922}{10{,}000}.$$

We read both 26.2922 and $26\frac{2922}{10{,}000}$ as

"Twenty-six *and* two thousand, nine hundred twenty-two ten-thousandths."

We can also read 26.2922 as

"Two six *point* two nine two two," or "twenty-six *point* two nine two two."

To write a word name from decimal notation,

a) write a word name for the whole number (the number named to the left of the decimal point),

397.685 $\longrightarrow$ Three hundred ninety-seven

b) write the word "and" for the decimal point, and

397.685 Three hundred ninety-seven and

c) write a word name for the number named to the right of the decimal point, followed by the place value of the last digit.

397.685 Three hundred ninety-seven and six hundred eighty-five *thousandths*

STUDY TIPS

QUIZ-TEST FOLLOW-UP

You may have just completed a chapter quiz or test. Immediately after doing so, write out a step-by-step solution of each question that you missed. Visit your instructor or tutor for help with problems that are still giving you trouble. When the week of the final examination arrives, you will be glad to have the excellent study guide these corrected tests provide.

EXAMPLE 1 *Birth Rate.* There were 14.3 births per 1000 Americans in a recent year. Write a word name for 14.3.

Source: U.S. Centers for Disease Control and Prevention

Fourteen and three tenths

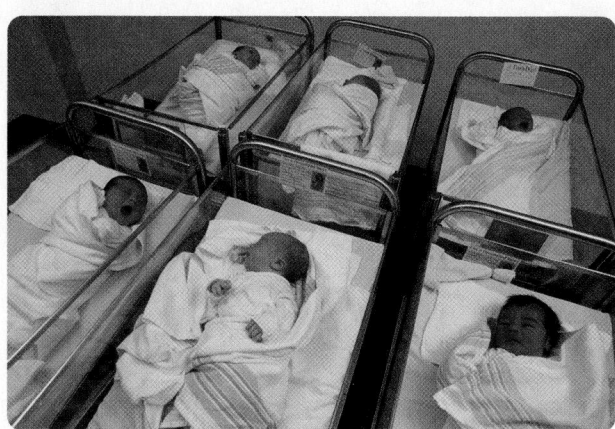

EXAMPLE 2 Write a word name for 410.87.

Four hundred ten and eighty-seven hundredths

Do Exercises 1–5.

1. Life Expectancy. The life expectancy at birth in the United States is projected to be 79.2 yr in 2015. Write a word name for 79.2.

Source: U.S. Census Bureau

2. Olympic Swimming. American swimmer Michael Phelps won eight gold medals in the 2008 Summer Olympics, including one for the 200-m freestyle, which he won in the world record time of 1.716 min. Write a word name for 1.716.

Source: beijing2008.cn

Write a word name for each number.

3. 245.89

4. 34.0064

5. 31,079.756

EXAMPLE 3 *Indianapolis 500.* In the 2009 Indianapolis 500-mile race, winner Helio Castroneves had a 1.9819-second margin of victory over second-place finisher Dan Wheldon. Write a word name for 1.9819.

Source: Indianapolis Motor Speedway, historian Donald Davidson

One and nine thousand, eight hundred nineteen ten-thousandths

EXAMPLE 4 Write a word name for 1788.045.

One thousand, seven hundred eighty-eight and forty-five thousandths

Do Exercises 1–5.

b Converting Between Decimal Notation and Fraction Notation

Given decimal notation, we can convert to fraction notation as follows:

$$9.875 = 9 + \frac{8}{10} + \frac{7}{100} + \frac{5}{1000}$$

$$= 9 \cdot \frac{1000}{1000} + \frac{8}{10} \cdot \frac{100}{100} + \frac{7}{100} \cdot \frac{10}{10} + \frac{5}{1000}$$

$$= \frac{9000}{1000} + \frac{800}{1000} + \frac{70}{1000} + \frac{5}{1000} = \frac{9875}{1000}.$$

Decimal notation ⎯⎯⎯ Fraction notation

9.875 $\frac{9875}{1000}$

3 decimal places   3 zeros

Answers

1. Seventy-nine and two tenths
2. One and seven hundred sixteen thousandths
3. Two hundred forty-five and eighty-nine hundredths
4. Thirty-four and sixty-four ten-thousandths
5. Thirty-one thousand, seventy-nine and seven hundred fifty-six thousandths

To convert from decimal to fraction notation,

a) count the number of decimal places,   4.98

                                                  2 places

b) move the decimal point that many places to the right, and   4.98.   Move 2 places.

c) write the answer over a denominator with a 1 followed by that number of zeros. $\dfrac{498}{100}$ 2 zeros

EXAMPLE 5   Write fraction notation for 0.876. Do not simplify.

0.876   0.876. $0.876 = \dfrac{876}{1000}$

                  3 places   3 zeros

For a number like 0.876, we generally write a 0 before the decimal point to draw attention to the presence of the decimal point.

EXAMPLE 6   Write fraction notation for 56.23. Do not simplify.

56.23   56.23. $56.23 = \dfrac{5623}{100}$

                  2 places   2 zeros

EXAMPLE 7   Write fraction notation for 1.5018. Do not simplify.

1.5018   1.5018. $1.5018 = \dfrac{15{,}018}{10{,}000}$

                  4 places   4 zeros

> Do Exercises 6–9.

> Write fraction notation.
>
> **6.** 0.896   **7.** 23.78
>
> **8.** 5.6789   **9.** 1.9

If fraction notation has a denominator that is a power of ten, such as 10, 100, 1000, and so on, we convert to decimal notation by reversing the procedure that we used before.

To convert from fraction notation to decimal notation when the denominator is 10, 100, 1000, and so on,

a) count the number of zeros, and   *denominator* $\dfrac{8679}{1000}$

                                              3 zeros

b) move the decimal point that number of places to the left. Leave off the denominator.   *numerator*   8.679.   Move 3 places.

                                         $\dfrac{8679}{1000} = 8.679$

EXAMPLE 8 Write decimal notation for $\frac{47}{10}$.

$$\frac{47}{10} \qquad 4.7. \qquad \frac{47}{10} = 4.7$$

1 zero   1 place

EXAMPLE 9 Write decimal notation for $\frac{123,067}{10,000}$.

$$\frac{123,067}{10,000} \qquad 12.3067. \qquad \frac{123,067}{10,000} = 12.3067$$

4 zeros   4 places

EXAMPLE 10 Write decimal notation for $\frac{13}{1000}$.

$$\frac{13}{1000} \qquad 0.013. \qquad \frac{13}{1000} = 0.013$$

3 zeros   3 places

EXAMPLE 11 Write decimal notation for $\frac{570}{100,000}$.

$$\frac{570}{100,000} \qquad 0.00570. \qquad \frac{570}{100,000} = 0.0057$$

5 zeros   5 places

Note that when we write decimal notation, it is not necessary to include the 0 that follows the 7.

Do Exercises 10–15.

When denominators are numbers other than 10, 100, and so on, we will use another method for conversion. It will be considered in Section 3.5.

If a mixed numeral has a fractional part with a denominator that is a power of ten, such as 10, 100, or 1000, and so on, we first write the mixed numeral as a sum of a whole number and a fraction. Then we convert to decimal notation.

EXAMPLE 12 Write decimal notation for $23\frac{59}{100}$.

$$23\frac{59}{100} = 23 + \frac{59}{100} = 23 \text{ and } \frac{59}{100} = 23.59$$

EXAMPLE 13 Write decimal notation for $772\frac{129}{10,000}$.

$$772\frac{129}{10,000} = 772 + \frac{129}{10,000} = 772 \text{ and } \frac{129}{10,000} = 772.0129$$

Do Exercises 16–18.

Write decimal notation.

10. $\frac{743}{100}$ **11.** $\frac{406}{1000}$

12. $\frac{67,089}{10,000}$ **13.** $\frac{9}{10}$

14. $\frac{57}{1000}$ **15.** $\frac{830}{10,000}$

Write decimal notation.

16. $4\frac{3}{10}$

17. $283\frac{71}{100}$

18. $456\frac{13}{1000}$

Answers

10. 7.43   **11.** 0.406   **12.** 6.7089
13. 0.9   **14.** 0.057   **15.** 0.083   **16.** 4.3
17. 283.71   **18.** 456.013

c) Order

To understand how to compare numbers in decimal notation, consider 0.85 and 0.9. First note that $0.9 = 0.90$ because $\frac{9}{10} = \frac{90}{100}$. Then $0.85 = \frac{85}{100}$ and $0.90 = \frac{90}{100}$. Since $\frac{85}{100} < \frac{90}{100}$, it follows that $0.85 < 0.90$. This leads us to a quick way to compare two numbers in decimal notation.

> **COMPARING NUMBERS IN DECIMAL NOTATION**
>
> To compare two numbers in decimal notation, start at the left and compare corresponding digits moving from left to right. If two digits differ, the number with the larger digit is the larger of the two numbers. To ease the comparison, extra zeros can be written to the right of the last decimal place.

EXAMPLE 14 Which of 2.109 and 2.1 is larger?

Think.

2.109   2.109
2.1   →   2.100

Same   └─Different; 9 > 0

Thus, 2.109 is larger than 2.1. That is, 2.109 > 2.1.

EXAMPLE 15 Which of 0.09 and 0.108 is larger?

Think.

0.09   0.090
0.108   →   0.108

Same   └─ Different; 1 > 0

Thus, 0.108 is larger than 0.09. That is, 0.108 > 0.09.

Do Exercises 19–24.

Which number is larger?

19. 2.04, 2.039

20. 0.06, 0.008

21. 0.5, 0.58

22. 1, 0.9999

23. 0.8989, 0.09898

24. 21.006, 21.05

d) Rounding

Rounding is done as for whole numbers. To understand, we first consider an example using the number line. It might help to review Section 1.3d, e.

EXAMPLE 16 Round 0.37 to the nearest tenth.

Here is part of a number line.

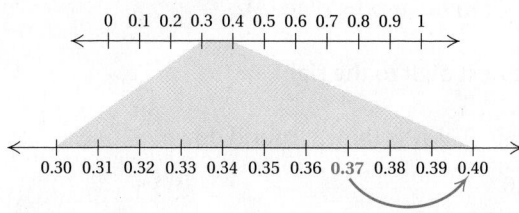

We see that 0.37 is closer to 0.40 than to 0.30. Thus, 0.37 rounded to the nearest tenth is 0.4.

Answers

19. 2.04   **20.** 0.06   **21.** 0.58   **22.** 1
23. 0.8989   **24.** 21.05

ROUNDING DECIMAL NOTATION

To round to a certain place:

a) Locate the digit in that place.

b) Consider the next digit to the right.

c) If the digit to the right is 5 or higher, round up. If the digit to the right is 4 or lower, round down.

EXAMPLE 17 Round 3872.2459 to the nearest tenth.

a) Locate the digit in the tenths place, 2.

   3 8 7 2.2 4 5 9
          ↑

b) Consider the next digit to the right, 4.

   3 8 7 2.2 4 5 9
            ↑

c) Since that digit, 4, is 4 or lower, round down.

   3 8 7 2.2 ← this is the answer.

------ *Caution!* ------

3872.3 is not a correct answer to Example 17. It is *incorrect* to round from the ten-thousandths digit over to the tenths digit, as follows:

3872.246 → 3872.25 → 3872.3.

EXAMPLE 18 Round 3872.2459 to the nearest thousandth, hundredth, tenth, one, ten, hundred, and thousand.

Thousandth:	3872.246	Ten:	3870
Hundredth:	3872.25	Hundred:	3900
Tenth:	3872.2	Thousand:	4000
One:	3872		

EXAMPLE 19 Round 14.8973 to the nearest hundredth.

a) Locate the digit in the hundredths place, 9.   1 4.8 9 7 3
                                                               ↑

b) Consider the next digit to the right, 7.   1 4.8 9 7 3
                                                             ↑

c) Since that digit, 7, is 5 or higher, round up. When we make the hundredths digit a 10, we carry 1 to the tenths place.

The answer is 14.90. Note that the 0 in 14.90 indicates that the answer is correct to the nearest hundredth.

EXAMPLE 20 Round 0.008 to the nearest tenth.

a) Locate the digit in the tenths place, 0.   0.0 0 8
                                                         ↑

b) Consider the next digit to the right, 0.   0.0 0 8
                                                             ↑

c) Since that digit, 0, is less than 5, round down.

The answer is 0.0.

Do Exercises 25–43.

Round to the nearest tenth.

25. 2.76   **26.** 13.85

27. 234.448   **28.** 7.009

Round to the nearest hundredth.

29. 0.636   **30.** 7.834

31. 34.675   **32.** 0.025

Round to the nearest thousandth.

33. 0.9434   **34.** 8.0038

35. 43.1119   **36.** 37.4005

Round 7459.3548 to the nearest:

37. Thousandth.

38. Hundredth.

39. Tenth.   **40.** One.

41. Ten. (*Caution:* "Tens" are not "tenths.")

42. Hundred.   **43.** Thousand.

Answers

25. 2.8 **26.** 13.9 **27.** 234.4 **28.** 7.0
29. 0.64 **30.** 7.83 **31.** 34.68 **32.** 0.03
33. 0.943 **34.** 8.004 **35.** 43.112
36. 37.401 **37.** 7459.355 **38.** 7459.35
39. 7459.4 **40.** 7459 **41.** 7460
42. 7500 **43.** 7000

a   Write a word name for the number in each sentence.

1. *Stock Price.* Google's stock was priced at $486.34 per share.
Source: New York Stock Exchange

2. *Soft-Drink Consumption.* The average American consumed 51.5 gal of carbonated soft drinks in a recent year.
Source: U.S. Department of Agriculture

3. *Currency Conversion.* One Chinese yuan was worth about $0.146 in U.S. currency recently.
Source: Interactive Data

4. *Currency Conversion.* One U.S. dollar was worth 0.6714 euros recently.
Source: Interactive Data

5. *Game System.* The Nintendo Wii game system sold for $249.89 recently.
Source: Best Buy

6. *Cell-Phone Plan.* The Sprint Talk/Message cell-phone plan with unlimited anytime minutes was priced at $89.99 per month recently.
Source: Sprint

7. One gallon of paint is equal to 3.785 L of paint.

8. *Water Weight.* One gallon of water weighs 8.35 lb.

Write a word name.

9. 27.1245

10. 34.891

b   Write fraction notation. Do not simplify.

11. 8.3

12. 203.6

13. 3.56

14. 0.17

15. 20.003　　　**16.** 1.509　　　**17.** 1.0008　　　**18.** 2.0114

19. 37.2　　　**20.** 4567.2　　　**21.** 0.00013　　　**22.** 6.14057

Write decimal notation.

23. $\dfrac{8}{10}$　　　**24.** $\dfrac{51}{10}$　　　**25.** $\dfrac{3798}{1000}$　　　**26.** $\dfrac{780}{1000}$

27. $\dfrac{889}{100}$　　　**28.** $\dfrac{92}{100}$　　　**29.** $\dfrac{19}{100,000}$　　　**30.** $\dfrac{56,788}{100,000}$

31. $\dfrac{78}{10,000}$　　　**32.** $\dfrac{13,463}{10,000}$　　　**33.** $\dfrac{376,193}{1,000,000}$　　　**34.** $\dfrac{8,953,074}{1,000,000}$

35. $2\dfrac{8}{10}$　　　**36.** $9243\dfrac{1}{10}$　　　**37.** $3\dfrac{98}{1000}$　　　**38.** $4\dfrac{67}{1000}$

39. $99\dfrac{44}{100}$　　　**40.** $67\dfrac{83}{100}$　　　**41.** $2\dfrac{1739}{10,000}$　　　**42.** $2256\dfrac{3059}{10,000}$

c Which number is larger?

43. 0.06, 0.58　　　**44.** 0.008, 0.8　　　**45.** 0.905, 0.91　　　**46.** 42.06, 42.1

47. 0.0009, 0.001　　　**48.** 7.067, 7.054　　　**49.** 234.07, 235.07　　　**50.** 0.99999, 1

51. 0.004, $\dfrac{4}{100}$　　　**52.** $\dfrac{73}{10}$, 0.73　　　**53.** 0.432, 0.4325　　　**54.** 0.8437, 0.84384

d Round to the nearest tenth.

55. 0.11　　　**56.** 0.85　　　**57.** 0.49　　　**58.** 0.5394

59. 2.7449　　　**60.** 4.78　　　**61.** 123.65　　　**62.** 36.049

Round to the nearest hundredth.

63. 0.893　　　**64.** 0.675　　　**65.** 0.6666　　　**66.** 6.524

67. 0.995　　　**68.** 207.9976　　　**69.** 0.094　　　**70.** 11.4246

Copyright © 2012 Pearson Education, Inc.

Round to the nearest thousandth.

71. 0.3246

72. 0.6666

73. 17.0014

74. 123.4562

75. 10.1011

76. 0.1161

77. 9.9989

78. 67.100602

Round 809.5732 to the nearest:

79. Hundred.

80. Tenth.

81. Thousandth.

82. Hundredth.

83. One.

84. Ten.

Round 34.54389 to the nearest:

85. Ten-thousandth.

86. Thousandth.

87. Hundredth.

88. Tenth.

89. One.

90. Ten.

Skill Maintenance

91. Subtract and simplify: $24 - 17\frac{2}{5}$. [2.4c]

92. Find the LCM of 18, 27, and 54. [1.9a]

Round 6172 to the nearest: [1.3d]

93. Ten.

94. Hundred.

95. Thousand.

Find the prime factorization. [1.7d]

96. 2000

97. 1530

98. 2002

99. 4312

Synthesis

100. Arrange the following numbers in order from smallest to largest.

0.99, 0.099, 1, 0.9999, 0.89999, 1.00009, 0.909, 0.9889

101. Arrange the following numbers in order from smallest to largest.

2.1, 2.109, 2.108, 2.018, 2.0119, 2.0302, 2.000001

Truncating. There are other methods of rounding decimal notation. To round using **truncating**, we drop off all decimal places past the rounding place, which is the same as changing all digits to the right to zeros. For example, rounding 6.78093456285102 to the ninth decimal place, using truncating, gives us 6.780934562. Use truncating to round each of the following to the fifth decimal place—that is, the hundred-thousandth place.

102. 6.78346623

103. 6.783465902

104. 99.999999999

105. 0.030303030303

3.2

Addition and Subtraction

OBJECTIVES

a Add using decimal notation.

b Subtract using decimal notation.

c Solve equations of the type $x + a = b$ and $a + x = b$, where a and b may be in decimal notation.

d Balance a checkbook.

a Addition

Adding with decimal notation is similar to adding whole numbers. First, we line up the decimal points so that we can add corresponding place-value digits. Then we add digits from the right. For example, we add the thousandths, then the hundredths, and so on, carrying if necessary. If desired, we can write extra zeros to the right of the decimal point so that the number of places is the same in all of the addends.

EXAMPLE 1 Add: 56.314 + 17.78.

$$\begin{array}{r} 5\ 6\ .\ 3\ 1\ 4 \\ +\ 1\ 7\ .\ 7\ 8\ 0 \\ \hline \end{array}$$

Lining up the decimal points in order to add

Writing an extra zero to the right of the decimal point

$$\begin{array}{r} 5\ 6\ .\ 3\ 1\ 4 \\ +\ 1\ 7\ .\ 7\ 8\ 0 \\ \hline 4 \end{array}$$

Adding thousandths

$$\begin{array}{r} 5\ 6\ .\ 3\ 1\ 4 \\ +\ 1\ 7\ .\ 7\ 8\ 0 \\ \hline 9\ 4 \end{array}$$

Adding hundredths

$$\begin{array}{r} \overset{1}{5}\ 6\ .\ 3\ 1\ 4 \\ +\ 1\ 7\ .\ 7\ 8\ 0 \\ \hline .\ 0\ 9\ 4 \end{array}$$

Adding tenths
We get 10 tenths = 1 one + 0 tenths, so we carry the 1 to the ones column. Writing a decimal point in the answer.

$$\begin{array}{r} \overset{1}{5}\ \overset{1}{6}\ .\ 3\ 1\ 4 \\ +\ 1\ 7\ .\ 7\ 8\ 0 \\ \hline 4\ .\ 0\ 9\ 4 \end{array}$$

Adding ones
We get 14 ones = 1 ten + 4 ones, so we carry the 1 to the tens column.

$$\begin{array}{r} \overset{1}{5}\ \overset{1}{6}\ .\ 3\ 1\ 4 \\ +\ 1\ 7\ .\ 7\ 8\ 0 \\ \hline 7\ 4\ .\ 0\ 9\ 4 \end{array}$$

Adding tens

Do Margin Exercises 1 and 2.

EXAMPLE 2 Add: 3.42 + 0.237 + 14.1.

$$\begin{array}{r} 3.4\ 2\ 0 \\ 0.2\ 3\ 7 \\ +\ 1\ 4.1\ 0\ 0 \\ \hline 1\ 7.7\ 5\ 7 \end{array}$$

Lining up the decimal points and writing extra zeros

Adding

Do Exercises 3–5.

SKILLS TO REVIEW

Objective 1.2a: Add whole numbers.
Objective 1.2c: Subtract whole numbers.

Add or subtract.

1. $\begin{array}{r} 3\ 8\ 7 \\ +\ 2\ 5\ 4 \\ \hline \end{array}$

2. $\begin{array}{r} 4\ 0\ 2\ 3 \\ -\ 1\ 6\ 6\ 7 \\ \hline \end{array}$

Add.

1. $\begin{array}{r} 0.8\ 4\ 7 \\ +\ 1\ 0.0\ 7 \\ \hline \end{array}$

2. $\begin{array}{r} 2.1 \\ 0.7\ 3 \\ +\ 3\ 1.3\ 6\ 8 \\ \hline \end{array}$

Add.

3. 0.02 + 4.3 + 0.649

4. 0.12 + 3.006 + 0.4357

5. 0.4591 + 0.2374 + 8.70894

Answers

Skills to Review:
1. 641 **2.** 2356

Margin Exercises:
1. 10.917 **2.** 34.198 **3.** 4.969
4. 3.5617 **5.** 9.40544

Now we consider the addition $3456 + 19.347$. Keep in mind that any whole number has an "unwritten" decimal point at the right that can be followed by zeros. For example, 3456 can also be written 3456.000. When adding, we can always write in the decimal point and extra zeros if desired.

EXAMPLE 3 Add: $3456 + 19.347$.

$$
\begin{array}{r}
\overset{1}{3\,4\,5\,6}.0\,0\,0 \\
+\quad\ \ 1\,9.3\,4\,7 \\
\hline
3\,4\,7\,5.3\,4\,7
\end{array}
$$
Writing in the decimal point and extra zeros
Lining up the decimal points
Adding

Do Exercises 6 and 7.

Add.

6. $789 + 123.67$

7. $45.78 + 2467 + 1.993$

b Subtraction

Subtracting with decimal notation is similar to subtracting whole numbers. First, we line up the decimal points so that we can subtract corresponding place-value digits. Then we subtract digits from the right. For example, we subtract the thousandths, then the hundredths, the tenths, and so on, borrowing if necessary.

EXAMPLE 4 Subtract: $56.314 - 17.78$.

$$
\begin{array}{r}
5\,6.3\,1\,4 \\
-\,1\,7.7\,8\,0 \\
\end{array}
$$
Lining up the decimal points in order to subtract
Writing an extra 0

$$
\begin{array}{r}
5\,6.3\,1\,4 \\
-\,1\,7.7\,8\,0 \\
\hline
4
\end{array}
$$
Subtracting thousandths

$$
\begin{array}{r}
\overset{2\ \ 11}{5\,6.3\,\cancel{1}\,4} \\
-\,1\,7.7\,8\,0 \\
\hline
3\,4
\end{array}
$$
Borrowing tenths to subtract hundredths

Subtracting hundredths

$$
\begin{array}{r}
\overset{5\ \ \ 2\ 11}{5\,6.3\,\cancel{1}\,4} \\
-\,1\,7.7\,8\,0 \\
\hline
.5\,3\,4
\end{array}
$$
Borrowing ones to subtract tenths

Subtracting tenths; writing a decimal point

$$
\begin{array}{r}
\overset{15\ 12}{\underset{4\ \ 5\ \ 2\ 11}{\cancel{5}\,\cancel{6}.3\,\cancel{1}\,4}} \\
-\,1\,7.7\,8\,0 \\
\hline
8.5\,3\,4
\end{array}
$$
Borrowing tens to subtract ones

Subtracting ones

$$
\begin{array}{r}
\overset{15\ 12}{\underset{4\ \ 5\ \ 2\ 11}{\cancel{5}\,\cancel{6}.3\,\cancel{1}\,4}} \\
-\,1\,7.7\,8\,0 \\
\hline
3\,8.5\,3\,4
\end{array}
$$
Subtracting tens

Check by adding:
$$
\begin{array}{r}
\overset{1\ \ 1\ 1}{3\,8.5\,3\,4} \\
+\,1\,7.7\,8\,0 \\
\hline
5\,6.3\,1\,4
\end{array}
$$

The answer checks because this is the top number in the subtraction.

Do Exercises 8 and 9.

Subtract.

8. $37.428 - 26.674$

9. $\begin{array}{r} 0.3\,4\,7 \\ -\,0.0\,0\,8 \end{array}$

Answers

6. 912.67 **7.** 2514.773 **8.** 10.754
9. 0.339

EXAMPLE 5 Subtract: 13.07 − 9.205.

$$
\begin{array}{r}
\overset{12}{\cancel{2}}\ ^{10}\ ^{6}\ ^{10} \\
\cancel{1}\ 3.\cancel{0}\ \cancel{7}\ \cancel{0} \\
-\quad 9.2\ 0\ 5 \\
\hline
3.8\ 6\ 5
\end{array}
$$
  Writing an extra zero

Subtracting

EXAMPLE 6 Subtract: 23.08 − 5.0053.

$$
\begin{array}{r}
^{1}\ ^{13}\quad\ ^{7}\ ^{9}\ ^{10} \\
2\ \cancel{3}.0\ \cancel{8}\ \cancel{0}\ \cancel{0} \\
-\quad 5.0\ 0\ 5\ 3 \\
\hline
1\ 8.0\ 7\ 4\ 7
\end{array}
$$
  Writing two extra zeros

Subtracting

Check by adding:

$$
\begin{array}{r}
^{1}\qquad\ ^{1}\ ^{1} \\
1\ 8.0\ 7\ 4\ 7 \\
+\quad 5.0\ 0\ 5\ 3 \\
\hline
2\ 3.0\ 8\ 0\ 0
\end{array}
$$

Do Exercises 10–12.

Subtract.

10. 1.2345 − 0.7

11. 0.9564 − 0.4392

12. 7.37 − 0.00008

When subtraction involves a whole number, again keep in mind that there is an "unwritten" decimal point that can be written in if desired. Extra zeros can also be written in to the right of the decimal point.

EXAMPLE 7 Subtract: 456 − 2.467.

$$
\begin{array}{r}
^{5}\ ^{9}\ ^{9}\ ^{10} \\
4\ 5\ \cancel{6}.\cancel{0}\ \cancel{0}\ \cancel{0} \\
-\quad 2.4\ 6\ 7 \\
\hline
4\ 5\ 3.5\ 3\ 3
\end{array}
$$
  Writing in the decimal point and extra zeros

Subtracting

Do Exercises 13 and 14.

Subtract.

13. 1277 − 82.78

14. 5 − 0.0089

Calculator Corner

Addition and Subtraction with Decimal Notation To use a calculator to add and subtract with decimal notation, we use the $\boxed{\cdot}$, $\boxed{+}$, $\boxed{-}$, and $\boxed{=}$ keys. To find 47.046 − 28.193, for example, we press $\boxed{4}$ $\boxed{7}$ $\boxed{\cdot}$ $\boxed{0}$ $\boxed{4}$ $\boxed{6}$ $\boxed{-}$ $\boxed{2}$ $\boxed{8}$ $\boxed{\cdot}$ $\boxed{1}$ $\boxed{9}$ $\boxed{3}$ $\boxed{=}$. The display reads $\boxed{18.853}$, so 47.046 − 28.193 = 18.853.

Exercises:

Use a calculator to add.

1. 274.159
   + 43.486

2. 19.805
   + 486.748

3. 1.7 + 14.56 + 0.89

4. 3.4 + 45 + 0.68

Use a calculator to subtract.

5. 9.2
   − 4.8

6. 52.34
   − 18.51

7. 489 − 34.26

8. 6.09 − 5.1

Answers

10. 0.5345   **11.** 0.5172   **12.** 7.36992
13. 1194.22   **14.** 4.9911

(c) Solving Equations

Now let's solve equations $x + a = b$ and $a + x = b$, where a and b may be in decimal notation. Proceeding as we have before, we subtract a on both sides.

EXAMPLE 8 Solve: $x + 28.89 = 74.567$.

We have

$$x + 28.89 - 28.89 = 74.567 - 28.89 \qquad \text{Subtracting 28.89 on both sides}$$
$$x = 45.677.$$

$$
\begin{array}{r}
{\scriptstyle 6\ \ \overset{13}{3}\ \overset{14}{4}\ 16} \\
7\ 4.5\ 6\ 7 \\
-\ 2\ 8.8\ 9\ 0 \\
\hline
4\ 5.6\ 7\ 7
\end{array}
$$

The solution is 45.677.

EXAMPLE 9 Solve: $0.8879 + y = 9.0026$.

We have

$$0.8879 + y - 0.8879 = 9.0026 - 0.8879 \qquad \text{Subtracting 0.8879 on both sides}$$
$$y = 8.1147.$$

$$
\begin{array}{r}
{\scriptstyle 8\ 9\ 9\ \overset{11}{1}\ 16} \\
9.0\ 0\ 2\ 6 \\
-\ 0.8\ 8\ 7\ 9 \\
\hline
8.1\ 1\ 4\ 7
\end{array}
$$

The solution is 8.1147.

Do Exercises 15 and 16.

EXAMPLE 10 Solve: $120 + x = 4380.6$.

We have

$$120 + x - 120 = 4380.6 - 120 \qquad \text{Subtracting 120 on both sides}$$
$$x = 4260.6.$$

$$
\begin{array}{r}
4\ 3\ 8\ 0.6 \\
-\ 1\ 2\ 0.0 \\
\hline
4\ 2\ 6\ 0.6
\end{array}
$$

The solution is 4260.6.

Do Exercise 17.

Solve.

15. $x + 17.78 = 56.314$

16. $8.906 + t = 23.07$

17. Solve: $241 + y = 2374.5$.

(d) Balancing a Checkbook

Let's use addition and subtraction with decimals to balance a checkbook.

EXAMPLE 11 Find the errors, if any, in the balances in this checkbook.

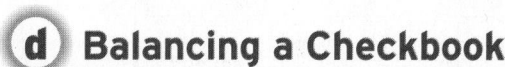

20		RECORD ALL CHARGES OR CREDITS THAT AFFECT YOUR ACCOUNT						
DATE	CHECK NUMBER	TRANSACTION DESCRIPTION	✓ T	(−) PAYMENT/ DEBIT	(+ OR −) OTHER	(+) DEPOSIT/ CREDIT	BALANCE FORWARD	
							8767	73
8/16	432	Burch Laundry		23 56			8744	16
8/19	433	Rogers Bakery		20 49			8764	65
8/20		Deposit				85 00	8848	65
8/21	434	Galaxy Video		48 60			8801	05
8/22	435	Benson's Garage		267 95			8533	09

Answers

15. 38.534   **16.** 14.164   **17.** 2133.5

18. Find the errors, if any, in this checkbook.

DATE	CHECK NUMBER	TRANSACTION DESCRIPTION	√T	(−) PAYMENT/ DEBIT	(+ OR −) OTHER	(+) DEPOSIT/ CREDIT	BALANCE FORWARD
							3078 92
12/1	888	H.H. Gregg Appliances		340 69			2738 23
12/3	889	Marie Callendar's Pies		78 54			2659 66
12/5		Deposit <Paycheck>				230 80	2890 46
12/6	890	Chili's Restaurant		13 17			2877 32
12/8	891	Stonecreek Golf Course		48 00			2829 32
12/8		Deposit <Molly>				39 58	2868 90
12/10	892	Frontier Trading Post		102 87			2766 83
12/14	893	Goody's Music		48 59			2697 45
12/15	894	Salvation Army		100 00			2497 45

There are two ways to determine whether there are errors. We assume that the amount $8767.73 in the "Balance forward" column is correct. If we can determine that the ending balance is correct, we have some assurance that the checkbook is correct. But two errors could offset each other to give us that balance.

METHOD 1

a) We add the debits: $23.56 + 20.49 + 48.60 + 267.95 = 360.60$.

b) We add the deposits/credits. In this case, there is only one deposit, 85.00.

c) We add the total of the deposits to the balance brought forward:

$$8767.73 + 85.00 = 8852.73.$$

d) We subtract the total of the debits: $8852.73 - 360.60 = 8492.13$.

The result should be the ending balance, 8533.09. We see that $8492.13 \neq 8533.09$. Since the numbers are not equal, we proceed to method 2.

METHOD 2 We successively add or subtract deposit/credits and debits, and check the result in the "Balance forward" column.

$$8767.73 - 23.56 = 8744.17.$$

We have found our first error. The subtraction was incorrect. We correct it and continue, using 8744.17 as the corrected balance forward:

$$8744.17 - 20.49 = 8723.68.$$

It looks as though 20.49 was added instead of subtracted. Actually, we would have to correct this line even if it had been subtracted, because the error of 1¢ in the first step has been carried through successive calculations. We correct that balance line and continue, using 8723.68 as the balance and adding the deposit 85.00:

$$8723.68 + 85.00 = 8808.68.$$

We make the correction and continue subtracting the last two debits:

$$8808.68 - 48.60 = 8760.08.$$

Then

$$8760.08 - 267.95 = 8492.13.$$

The corrected checkbook is below.

20		RECORD ALL CHARGES OR CREDITS THAT AFFECT YOUR ACCOUNT						
DATE	CHECK NUMBER	TRANSACTION DESCRIPTION	√T	(−) PAYMENT/ DEBIT	(+ OR −) OTHER	(+) DEPOSIT/ CREDIT	BALANCE FORWARD	
							8767 73	
8/16	432	Burch Laundry		23 56			8744 16	→ 8744.17
8/19	433	Rogers Bakery		20 49			8764 65	→ 8723.68
8/20		Deposit				85 00	8848 65	→ 8808.68
8/21	434	Galaxy Video		48 60			8801 05	→ 8760.08
8/22	435	Benson's Garage		267 95			8533 09	→ 8492.13

Answer

18. The "Balance forward" column should read:
$3078.92
2738.23
2659.67
2890.47
2877.33
2829.33
2868.91
2766.04
2697.45
2597.45

Do Exercise 18.

There are other ways in which errors can be made in checkbooks, such as forgetting to record a transaction or writing the amounts incorrectly, but we will not consider those here.

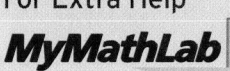
a Add.

1.
```
  3 1 6.2 5
+   1 8.1 2
```

2.
```
  6 4 1.8 0 3
+   1 4.9 3 5
```

3.
```
  6 5 9.4 0 3
+ 9 1 6.8 1 2
```

4.
```
  4 2 0 3.2 8
+       3.3 9
```

5.
```
      9.1 0 4
+ 1 2 3.4 5 6
```

6.
```
  8 1.0 0 8
+   3.4 0 9
```

7. 20.0124 + 30.0124

8. 0.687 + 0.9

9. 39 + 1.007

10. 2.3 + 0.729 + 23

11.
```
      4 7.8
    2 1 9.8 5 2
      4 3.5 9
+   6 6 6.7 1 3
```

12.
```
        1 3.7 2
          9.1 1 2
    6 5 4 2.7 9 0 8
+       2 3.9 0 1
```

13. 0.34 + 3.5 + 0.127 + 768

14. 17 + 3.24 + 0.256 + 0.3689

15. 99.6001 + 7285.18 + 500.042 + 870

16. 65.987 + 9.4703 + 6744.02 + 1.0003 + 200.895

b  Subtract.

17.
```
  5 1.3 1
−   2.2 9
```

18.
```
  4 4.3 4 5
−   3.1 0 5
```

19.
```
  9 2.3 4 1
−   6.4 2
```

20.
```
  9 7.0 1
−   3.1 5
```

21.
```
  2.5
− 0.0 0 2 5
```

22.
```
  3 9.0
−   0.2 8
```

23.
```
  3.4
− 0.0 0 3
```

24.
```
  2.8
− 2.0 8
```

25. 28.2 − 19.35

26. 100.16 − 0.118

27. 34.07 − 30.7

28. 36.2 − 16.28

29. $8.45 - 7.405$

30. $3.801 - 2.81$

31. $6.003 - 2.3$

32. $9.087 - 8.807$

33. $1 - 0.0098$

34. $2 - 1.0908$

35. $100 - 0.34$

36. $624 - 18.79$

37. $7.48 - 2.6$

38. $18.4 - 5.92$

39. $3 - 2.006$

40. $263.7 - 102.08$

41. $19 - 1.198$

42. $2548.98 - 2.007$

43. $65 - 13.87$

44. $45 - 0.999$

45.
$$\begin{array}{r} 3\,2.7\,9\,7\,8 \\ -\quad 0.0\,5\,9\,2 \\ \hline \end{array}$$

46.
$$\begin{array}{r} 0.4\,9\,6\,3\,4 \\ -\,0.1\,2\,6\,7\,8 \\ \hline \end{array}$$

47.
$$\begin{array}{r} 6.0\,7 \\ -\,2.0\,0\,7\,8 \\ \hline \end{array}$$

48.
$$\begin{array}{r} 1.0 \\ -\,0.9\,9\,9\,9 \\ \hline \end{array}$$

c Solve.

49. $x + 17.5 = 29.15$

50. $t + 50.7 = 54.07$

51. $17.95 + p = 402.63$

52. $w + 1.3004 = 47.8$

53. $13,083.3 = x + 12,500.33$

54. $100.23 = 67.8 + z$

55. $x + 2349 = 17,684.3$

56. $1830.4 + t = 23,067$

Copyright © 2012 Pearson Education, Inc.

(d) Find the errors, if any, in each checkbook.

57.

		RECORD ALL CHARGES OR CREDITS THAT AFFECT YOUR ACCOUNT					
20___							
DATE	CHECK NUMBER	TRANSACTION DESCRIPTION	√ T	(−) PAYMENT/ DEBIT	(+ OR −) OTHER	(+) DEPOSIT/ CREDIT	BALANCE FORWARD
							9704 56
8/8	342	Bill Rydman		27 44			9677 12
8/9		Deposit				1000 00	10,677 12
8/12	343	Chuck Taylor		123 95			10,553 17
8/14	344	Jennifer Crum		124 02			10,677 19
8/22	345	Neon Johnny's Pizza		12 43			10,664 76
8/24		Deposit				2500 00	13,164 76
8/29	346	Border's Bookstore		137 78			13,302 54
9/2		Deposit				18 88	13,283 66
9/3	347	Fireman's Fund		2800 00			10,483 66

58.

		RECORD ALL CHARGES OR CREDITS THAT AFFECT YOUR ACCOUNT					
20___							
DATE	CHECK NUMBER	TRANSACTION DESCRIPTION	√ T	(−) PAYMENT/ DEBIT	(+ OR −) OTHER	(+) DEPOSIT/ CREDIT	BALANCE FORWARD
							1876 43
4/1	500	Bart Kaufman		500 12			1376 31
4/3	501	Jim Lawler		28 56			1347 75
4/3		Deposit				10,000 00	11,347 75
4/3	502	Victoria Montoya		464 00			10,883 75
4/3		Deposit				2500 00	8383 75
4/4	503	Art's Garage		1600 00			6783 75
4/8	504	Golf Galaxy		1349 98			5433 77
4/12	505	Don Mitchell Pro Shops		658 97			4774 80
4/13		Deposit				900 00	5674 80
4/15	506	Kroger		185 58			5479 22

Skill Maintenance

59. Round 34,567 to the nearest thousand.   [1.3d]

60. Round 34,496 to the nearest thousand.   [1.3d]

Subtract.

61. $\dfrac{13}{24} - \dfrac{3}{8}$ [2.3b]

62. $\dfrac{8}{9} - \dfrac{2}{15}$ [2.3b]

63. $8805 - 2639$ [1.2c]

64. $8005 - 2639$ [1.2c]

Solve.

65. A serving of filleted fish is generally considered to be about $\frac{1}{3}$ lb. How many servings can be prepared from $5\frac{1}{2}$ lb of flounder fillet?   [2.5a]

66. A photocopier technician drove $125\frac{7}{10}$ mi away from Scottsdale for a repair call. The next day he drove $65\frac{1}{2}$ mi back toward Scottsdale for another service call. How far was the technician from Scottsdale?   [2.5a]

Synthesis

67. A student presses the wrong button when using a calculator and adds 235.7 instead of subtracting it. The incorrect answer is 817.2. What is the correct answer?

3.3

Multiplication

OBJECTIVES

a Multiply using decimal notation.

b Convert from notation like 45.7 million to standard notation, and convert between dollars and cents.

SKILL TO REVIEW

Objective 1.3a: Multiply whole numbers.

Multiply.

1. $\begin{array}{r} 4\ 2 \\ \times\ 6\ 3 \\ \hline \end{array}$ 2. $\begin{array}{r} 7\ 1\ 6 \\ \times\ \ \ 5\ 8 \\ \hline \end{array}$

STUDY TIPS

HAVE A POSITIVE ATTITUDE

You can choose to improve your attitude and raise the academic goals that you have set for yourself. Projecting a positive attitude toward your study of mathematics and expecting a positive outcome can make it easier for you to learn and to perform well in this course.

a Multiplication

Let's find the product

$$2.3 \times 1.12.$$

To understand how we find such a product, we first convert each factor to fraction notation. Next, we multiply the numerators and then divide by the product of the denominators.

$$2.3 \times 1.12 = \frac{23}{10} \times \frac{112}{100} = \frac{23 \times 112}{10 \times 100} = \frac{2576}{1000} = 2.576$$

Note the number of decimal places.

$$\begin{array}{r} 1.1\ 2 \\ \times\ \ \ 2.3 \\ \hline 2.5\ 7\ 6 \end{array} \quad \begin{array}{l} (2\ \text{decimal places}) \\ (1\ \text{decimal place}) \\ (3\ \text{decimal places}) \end{array}$$

Now consider

$$0.011 \times 15.0002 = \frac{11}{1000} \times \frac{150{,}002}{10{,}000} = \frac{1{,}650{,}022}{10{,}000{,}000} = 0.1650022.$$

Note the number of decimal places.

$$\begin{array}{r} 1\ 5.0\ 0\ 0\ 2 \\ \times\ \ \ \ \ \ \ 0.0\ 1\ 1 \\ \hline 0.1\ 6\ 5\ 0\ 0\ 2\ 2 \end{array} \quad \begin{array}{l} (4\ \text{decimal places}) \\ (3\ \text{decimal places}) \\ (7\ \text{decimal places}) \end{array}$$

To multiply using decimals:

a) Ignore the decimal points and multiply as though both factors were whole numbers.

b) Then place the decimal point in the result. The number of decimal places in the product is the sum of the numbers of places in the factors. (Count places from the right.)

0.8×0.43

$$\begin{array}{r} \overset{2}{0.4}\ 3 \\ \times\ \ \ 0.8 \\ \hline 3\ 4\ 4 \end{array} \quad \begin{array}{l} \text{Ignore the decimal} \\ \text{points for now.} \end{array}$$

$$\begin{array}{r} 0.4\ 3 \\ \times\ \ \ 0.8 \\ \hline 0.3\ 4\ 4 \end{array} \quad \begin{array}{l} (2\ \text{decimal places}) \\ (1\ \text{decimal place}) \\ (3\ \text{decimal places}) \end{array}$$

EXAMPLE 1 Multiply: 8.3×74.6.

a) We ignore the decimal points and multiply as though factors were whole numbers.

$$\begin{array}{r} 7\ 4.6 \\ \times\ \ \ \ 8.3 \\ \hline 2\ 2\ 3\ 8 \\ 5\ 9\ 6\ 8\ 0 \\ \hline 6\ 1\ 9\ 1\ 8 \end{array}$$

Answers

Skill to Review:

1. 2646   2. 41,528

b) We place the decimal point in the result. The number of decimal places in the product is the sum of the numbers of places in the factors, $1 + 1$, or 2.

$$
\begin{array}{r}
7\ 4\ .6 \qquad \text{(1 decimal place)} \\
\times \qquad 8.3 \qquad \text{(1 decimal place)} \\
\hline
2\ 2\ 3\ 8 \\
5\ 9\ 6\ 8\ 0 \\
\hline
6\ 1\ 9\ .1\ 8 \qquad \text{(2 decimal places)}
\end{array}
$$

Do Exercise 1.

EXAMPLE 2 Multiply: 0.0032×2148.

$$
\begin{array}{r}
2\ 1\ 4\ 8 \qquad \text{(0 decimal places)} \\
\times\ 0.0\ 0\ 3\ 2 \qquad \text{(4 decimal places)} \\
\hline
4\ 2\ 9\ 6 \\
6\ 4\ 4\ 4\ 0 \\
\hline
6.8\ 7\ 3\ 6 \qquad \text{(4 decimal places)}
\end{array}
$$

EXAMPLE 3 Multiply: 0.14×0.867.

$$
\begin{array}{r}
0.8\ 6\ 7 \qquad \text{(3 decimal places)} \\
\times \qquad 0.1\ 4 \qquad \text{(2 decimal places)} \\
\hline
3\ 4\ 6\ 8 \\
8\ 6\ 7\ 0 \\
\hline
0.1\ 2\ 1\ 3\ 8 \qquad \text{(5 decimal places)}
\end{array}
$$

Do Exercises 2 and 3.

1. Multiply.

$$
\begin{array}{r}
8\ 5.4 \\
\times \qquad 6.2 \\
\hline
\end{array}
$$

Multiply.

2.
$$
\begin{array}{r}
1\ 2\ 3\ 4 \\
\times\ 0.0\ 0\ 4\ 1 \\
\hline
\end{array}
$$

3.
$$
\begin{array}{r}
4\ 2.6\ 5 \\
\times\ 0.8\ 0\ 4 \\
\hline
\end{array}
$$

Multiplying by 0.1, 0.01, 0.001, and So On

Now let's consider some special kinds of products. The first involves multiplying by a tenth, hundredth, thousandth, ten-thousandth, and so on. Let's look at those products.

$$0.1 \times 38 = \frac{1}{10} \times 38 = \frac{38}{10} = 3.8$$

$$0.01 \times 38 = \frac{1}{100} \times 38 = \frac{38}{100} = 0.38$$

$$0.001 \times 38 = \frac{1}{1000} \times 38 = \frac{38}{1000} = 0.038$$

$$0.0001 \times 38 = \frac{1}{10,000} \times 38 = \frac{38}{10,000} = 0.0038$$

Note in each case that the product is *smaller* than 38. That is, the decimal point in each product is farther to the left than the unwritten decimal point in 38.

Answers

1. 529.48   **2.** 5.0594   **3.** 34.2906

To multiply any number by 0.1, 0.01, 0.001, and so on,

a) count the number of decimal places in the tenth, hundredth, or thousandth, and so on, and

0.001×34.45678

→ 3 places

b) move the decimal point in the other number that many places to the left.

$0.001 \times 34.45678 = 0.034.45678$

Move 3 places to the left.

$0.001 \times 34.45678 = 0.03445678$

EXAMPLES Multiply.

4. $0.1 \times 14.605 = 1.4605$ $1.4.605$

5. $0.01 \times 14.605 = 0.14605$

6. $0.001 \times 14.605 = 0.014605$ We write an extra zero.

7. $0.0001 \times 14.605 = 0.0014605$ We write two extra zeros.

Do Exercises 4–7.

Multiply.

4. 0.1×3.48

5. 0.01×3.48

6. 0.001×3.48

7. 0.0001×3.48

Multiplying by 10, 100, 1000, and So On

Next, let's consider multiplying by 10, 100, 1000, and so on. Let's look at those products.

$$10 \times 97.34 = 973.4$$
$$100 \times 97.34 = 9734$$
$$1000 \times 97.34 = 97,340$$

Note in each case that the product is *larger* than 97.34. That is, the decimal point in each product is farther to the right than the decimal point in 97.34.

To multiply any number by 10, 100, 1000, and so on,

a) count the number of zeros, and

1000×34.45678

→ 3 zeros

b) move the decimal point in the other number that many places to the right.

$1000 \times 34.45678 = 34.456.78$

Move 3 places to the right.

$1000 \times 34.45678 = 34,456.78$

Multiply.

8. 10×3.48

9. 100×3.48

10. 1000×3.48

11. $10,000 \times 3.48$

EXAMPLES Multiply.

8. $10 \times 14.605 = 146.05$ $14.6.05$

9. $100 \times 14.605 = 1460.5$

10. $1000 \times 14.605 = 14,605$

11. $10,000 \times 14.605 = 146,050$ $14.6050.$ We write an extra zero.

Do Exercises 8–11.

Answers

4. 0.348   **5.** 0.0348   **6.** 0.00348
7. 0.000348   **8.** 34.8   **9.** 348
10. 3480   **11.** 34,800

b Naming Large Numbers; Money Conversion

Naming Large Numbers

We often see notation like the following in newspapers and magazines and on television and the Internet.

- U.S. venture-capital firms invested $2.6 billion in alternative-energy startup enterprises during the first three quarters of 2007.
  Source: National Venture Capital Association

- Each day about 39.7 billion person-to-person e-mails, 17.1 billion automated e-mails, and 40.5 billion pieces of spam are sent worldwide.
  Source: IDC

- The largest building in the world is the Pentagon, which has 3.7 million square feet of floor space.

To understand such notation, consider the information in the following table.

NAMING LARGE NUMBERS

1 hundred = 100 = $10 \cdot 10 = 10^2$
→ 2 zeros

1 thousand = 1000 = $10 \cdot 10 \cdot 10 = 10^3$
→ 3 zeros

1 million = 1,000,000 = $10 \cdot 10 \cdot 10 \cdot 10 \cdot 10 \cdot 10 = 10^6$
→ 6 zeros

1 billion = 1,000,000,000 = 10^9
→ 9 zeros

1 trillion = 1,000,000,000,000 = 10^{12}
→ 12 zeros

Calculator Corner

Multiplication with Decimal Notation To use a calculator to multiply with decimal notation, we use the $\boxed{\cdot}$, $\boxed{\times}$, and $\boxed{=}$ keys. To find 4.78×0.34, for example, we press $\boxed{4}$ $\boxed{\cdot}$ $\boxed{7}$ $\boxed{8}$ $\boxed{\times}$ $\boxed{\cdot}$ $\boxed{3}$ $\boxed{4}$ $\boxed{=}$. The display reads $\boxed{1.6252}$, so $4.78 \times 0.34 = 1.6252$.

Exercises: Use a calculator to multiply.

1. $\begin{array}{r} 5.4 \\ \times \quad 9 \\ \hline \end{array}$

2. $\begin{array}{r} 415 \\ \times \ 16.7 \\ \hline \end{array}$

3. $\begin{array}{r} 17.63 \\ \times \quad 8.1 \\ \hline \end{array}$

4. 0.04×12.69

5. 586.4×13.5

6. 4.003×5.1

To convert a large number to standard notation, we proceed as follows.

EXAMPLE 12 Losses due to identity fraud totaled $49.3 billion in 2007. Convert 49.3 billion to standard notation.

Source: Javelin Strategy & Research

$$49.3 \text{ billion} = 49.3 \times 1 \text{ billion}$$
$$= 49.3 \times 1,\underline{000,000,000}$$

→ 9 zeros

$$= 49,300,000,000 \quad \text{Moving the decimal point 9 places to the right}$$

Do Exercises 12 and 13.

Money Conversion

Converting from dollars to cents is like multiplying by 100. To see why, consider $19.43.

$$\$19.43 = 19.43 \times \$1 \qquad \text{We think of } \$19.43 \text{ as } 19.43 \times 1 \text{ dollar, or } 19.43 \times \$1.$$
$$= 19.43 \times 100\cent \qquad \text{Substituting } 100\cent \text{ for } \$1: \ \$1 = 100\cent$$
$$= 1943\cent \qquad \text{Multiplying}$$

> **DOLLARS TO CENTS**
>
> To convert from dollars to cents, move the decimal point two places to the right and change the $ sign in front to a ¢ sign at the end.

EXAMPLES Convert from dollars to cents.

13. $189.64 = 18,964¢

14. $0.75 = 75¢

Do Exercises 14 and 15.

Converting from cents to dollars is like multiplying by 0.01. To see why, consider 65¢.

$$65\cent = 65 \times 1\cent \qquad \text{We think of } 65\cent \text{ as } 65 \times 1 \text{ cent, or } 65 \times 1\cent.$$
$$= 65 \times \$0.01 \qquad \text{Substituting } \$0.01 \text{ for } 1\cent: \ 1\cent = \$0.01$$
$$= \$0.65 \qquad \text{Multiplying}$$

> **CENTS TO DOLLARS**
>
> To convert from cents to dollars, move the decimal point two places to the left and change the ¢ sign at the end to a $ sign in front.

EXAMPLES Convert from cents to dollars.

15. 395¢ = $3.95

16. 8503¢ = $85.03

Do Exercises 16 and 17.

Convert the number in each sentence to standard notation.

12. The largest building in the world is the Pentagon, which has 3.7 million square feet of floor space.

13. Each day about 39.7 billion personal e-mails are sent.

Convert from dollars to cents.

14. $15.69

15. $0.17

Convert from cents to dollars.

16. 35¢

17. 577¢

Answers

12. 3,700,000 **13.** 39,700,000,000
14. 1569¢ **15.** 17¢ **16.** $0.35 **17.** $5.77

a Multiply.

1. 8.6
    × 7

2. 5.7
    × 0.8

3. 0.8 4
    ×   8

4. 9.4
    × 0.6

5.   6.3
    × 0.0 4

6.   9.8
    × 0.0 8

7.   8 7
    × 0.0 0 6

8. 1 8.4
    × 0.0 7

9. 10 × 23.76

10. 100 × 3.8798

11. 1000 × 583.686852

12. 0.34 × 1000

13. 7.8 × 100

14. 0.00238 × 10

15. 0.1 × 89.23

16. 0.01 × 789.235

17. 0.001 × 97.68

18. 8976.23 × 0.001

19. 78.2 × 0.01

20. 0.0235 × 0.1

21. 3 2.6
    ×   1 6

22. 9.2 8
    ×   8.6

23. 0.9 8 4
    ×   3.3

24. 8.4 8 9
    ×   7.4

25. 3 7 4
    ×   2.4

26. 8 6 5
    × 1.0 8

27. 7 4 9
    × 0.4 3

28. 9 7 8
    × 2 0.5

29. 0.8 7
    ×   6 4

30. 7.2 5
    ×   6 0

31. 4 6.5 0
    ×   7 5

32. 8.2 4
    × 7 0 3

33.
$$\begin{array}{r} 8\ 1.7 \\ \times\ 0.6\ 1\ 2 \\ \hline \end{array}$$

34.
$$\begin{array}{r} 3\ 1.8\ 2 \\ \times\ \ 7.1\ 5 \\ \hline \end{array}$$

35.
$$\begin{array}{r} 1\ 0.1\ 0\ 5 \\ \times\ 1\ 1.3\ 2\ 4 \\ \hline \end{array}$$

36.
$$\begin{array}{r} 1\ 5\ 1.2 \\ \times\ 4.5\ 5\ 5 \\ \hline \end{array}$$

37.
$$\begin{array}{r} 1\ 2.3 \\ \times\ 1.0\ 8 \\ \hline \end{array}$$

38.
$$\begin{array}{r} 7.8\ 2 \\ \times\ 0.0\ 2\ 4 \\ \hline \end{array}$$

39.
$$\begin{array}{r} 3\ 2.4 \\ \times\ \ 2.8 \\ \hline \end{array}$$

40.
$$\begin{array}{r} 8.0\ 9 \\ \times\ 0.0\ 0\ 7\ 5 \\ \hline \end{array}$$

41.
$$\begin{array}{r} 0.0\ 0\ 3\ 4\ 2 \\ \times\ \ 0.8\ 4 \\ \hline \end{array}$$

42.
$$\begin{array}{r} 2.0\ 0\ 5\ 6 \\ \times\ \ 3.8 \\ \hline \end{array}$$

43.
$$\begin{array}{r} 0.3\ 4\ 7 \\ \times\ \ 2.0\ 9 \\ \hline \end{array}$$

44.
$$\begin{array}{r} 2.5\ 3\ 2 \\ \times\ 1.0\ 6\ 7 \\ \hline \end{array}$$

45.
$$\begin{array}{r} 3.0\ 0\ 5 \\ \times\ 0.6\ 2\ 3 \\ \hline \end{array}$$

46.
$$\begin{array}{r} 1\ 6.3\ 4 \\ \times\ 0.0\ 0\ 0\ 5\ 1\ 2 \\ \hline \end{array}$$

47. 1000×45.678

48. 0.001×45.678

b   Convert from dollars to cents.

49. $28.88

50. $67.43

51. $0.66

52. $1.78

Convert from cents to dollars.

53. 34¢

54. 95¢

55. 3445¢

56. 933¢

Copyright © 2012 Pearson Education, Inc.

57. *Back-to-School Spending.* It is estimated that the amount spent on back-to-school supplies by college students and their families was $47.3 billion in 2007. Convert 47.3 billion to standard notation.

Source: National Retail Federation

58. *Cell-Phone Ads.* Global spending on advertisements appearing on cell phones is projected to be $16.2 billion in 2011. Convert 16.2 billion to standard notation.

Source: eMarketer

59. *Identity Fraud.* About 9.3 million adults were victims of identity fraud in the United States in 2007. Convert 9.3 million to standard notation.

Source: Javelin Strategy & Research

60. *Low-Cost Laptops.* It is estimated that 9.2 million low-cost laptop computers will be shipped worldwide in 2012. Convert 9.2 million to standard notation.

Source: IDC

61. *DVD Sales.* Spending on DVDs totaled $23.4 billion in 2007. Convert 23.4 billion to standard notation.

Source: The Digital Entertainment Group

62. *Text Messages.* In June 2007, 28.9 billion text messages were sent in the United States. Convert 28.9 billion to standard notation.

Source: CTIA

Skill Maintenance

Calculate.

63. $2\frac{1}{3} \cdot 4\frac{4}{5}$ [2.4d]

64. $2\frac{1}{3} \div 4\frac{4}{5}$ [2.4e]

65. $4\frac{4}{5} - 2\frac{1}{3}$ [2.4c]

66. $4\frac{4}{5} + 2\frac{1}{3}$ [2.4b]

Divide. [1.3c]

67. $2\,4\,\overline{)\,8\,2\,0\,8}$

68. $4\,\overline{)\,3\,4\,8}$

69. $7\,\overline{)\,3\,1,9\,6\,2}$

70. $1\,8\,\overline{)\,2\,2,6\,2\,6}$

71. $4\,0\,\overline{)\,3\,4\,8\,0}$

72. $1\,7\,\overline{)\,2\,0,0\,0\,6}$

Synthesis

Consider the following names for large numbers in addition to those already discussed in this section:

$$1 \text{ quadrillion} = 1{,}000{,}000{,}000{,}000{,}000 = 10^{15};$$
$$1 \text{ quintillion} = 1{,}000{,}000{,}000{,}000{,}000{,}000 = 10^{18};$$
$$1 \text{ sextillion} = 1{,}000{,}000{,}000{,}000{,}000{,}000{,}000 = 10^{21};$$
$$1 \text{ septillion} = 1{,}000{,}000{,}000{,}000{,}000{,}000{,}000{,}000 = 10^{24}.$$

Find each of the following. Express the answer with a name that is a power of 10.

73. (1 trillion) · (1 billion)

74. (1 million) · (1 billion)

75. (1 trillion) · (1 trillion)

76. Is a billion millions the same as a million billions? Explain.

3.4 Division

OBJECTIVES

a Divide using decimal notation.

b Solve equations of the type $a \cdot x = b$, where a and b may be in decimal notation.

c Simplify expressions using the rules for order of operations.

SKILL TO REVIEW

Objective 1.3c: Divide whole numbers.

Divide.

1. $5 \overline{)\ 2\ 4\ 5}$

2. $2\ 3 \overline{)\ 1\ 9\ 7\ 8}$

a Division

Whole-Number Divisors

We use the following method when we divide a decimal quantity by a whole number.

> To divide by a whole number,
>
> a) place the decimal point directly above the decimal point in the dividend, and
>
> b) divide as though dividing whole numbers.

$$\begin{array}{r} 0.8\ 4 \leftarrow \text{Quotient} \\ \text{Divisor} \rightarrow 7\ \overline{)\ 5.8\ 8} \leftarrow \text{Dividend} \\ 5\ 6 \\ \hline 2\ 8 \\ 2\ 8 \\ \hline 0 \leftarrow \text{Remainder} \end{array}$$

EXAMPLE 1 Divide: $379.2 \div 8$.

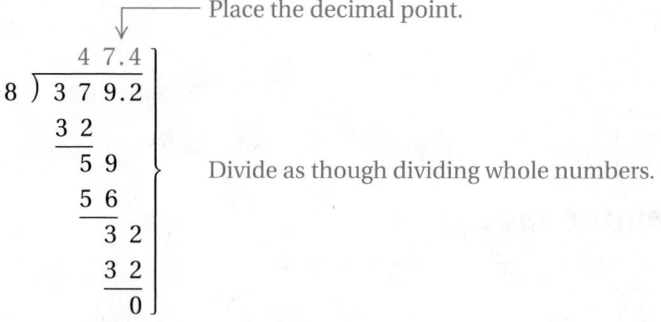

Place the decimal point.

$$\begin{array}{r} 4\ 7.4 \\ 8\ \overline{)\ 3\ 7\ 9.2} \\ 3\ 2 \\ \hline 5\ 9 \\ 5\ 6 \\ \hline 3\ 2 \\ 3\ 2 \\ \hline 0 \end{array}$$

Divide as though dividing whole numbers.

EXAMPLE 2 Divide: $82.08 \div 24$.

Place the decimal point.

$$\begin{array}{r} 3.4\ 2 \\ 2\ 4\ \overline{)\ 8\ 2.0\ 8} \\ 7\ 2 \\ \hline 1\ 0\ 0 \\ 9\ 6 \\ \hline 4\ 8 \\ 4\ 8 \\ \hline 0 \end{array}$$

Divide as though dividing whole numbers.

Do Margin Exercises 1–3.

Divide.

1. $9 \overline{)\ 5.4}$

2. $1\ 5 \overline{)\ 2\ 2.5}$

3. $8\ 2 \overline{)\ 3\ 8.5\ 4}$

Answers

Skill to Review:

1. 49   2. 86

Margin Exercises:

1. 0.6   2. 1.5   3. 0.47

We can think of a whole-number dividend as having a decimal point at the end with as many 0's as we wish after the decimal point. For example, 12 = 12. = 12.0 = 12.00 = 12.000, and so on. We can also add 0's after the last digit in the decimal portion of a number: 3.6 = 3.60 = 3.600, and so on.

EXAMPLE 3 Divide: 30 ÷ 8.

```
       3.
   8 ) 3 0.
       2 4
       ───
         6
```
Place the decimal point and divide to find how many ones.

```
       3.
   8 ) 3 0.0
       2 4 ↓
       ───
       6 0
```
Write an extra zero.

```
       3.7
   8 ) 3 0.0
       2 4
       ───
       6 0
       5 6
       ───
         4
```
Divide to find how many tenths.

```
       3.7
   8 ) 3 0.0 0
       2 4
       ───
       6 0
       5 6 ↓
       ───
         4 0
```
Write another zero.

```
       3.7 5
   8 ) 3 0.0 0
       2 4
       ───
       6 0
       5 6
       ───
         4 0
         4 0
         ───
           0
```
Divide to find how many hundredths.

Check:
```
         6 4
       3.7 5
   ×       8
   ─────────
   3 0 0.0 0
```

EXAMPLE 4 Divide: 4.5 ÷ 25.

```
       0.1 8
  2 5 ) 4.5 0
        2 5
        ───
        2 0 0
        2 0 0
        ─────
            0
```

Check:
```
       0.1 8
   ×    2 5
   ─────────
         9 0
       3 6 0
   ─────────
       4.5 0
```

Do Exercises 4–6.

Calculator Corner

Division with Decimal Notation To use a calculator to divide with decimal notation, we use the ▢, ÷, and = keys. To find 237.12 ÷ 5.2, for example, we press ② ③ ⑦ · ① ② ÷ ⑤ · ② = . The display reads [45.6], so 237.12 ÷ 5.2 = 45.6.

Exercises: Use a calculator to divide.
1. 12.4)177.32
2. 49)125.44
3. 1.6 ÷ 25
4. 518.472 ÷ 6.84

Divide.
4. 2 5) 8

5. 4) 1 5

6. 8 6) 2 1.5

Answers
4. 0.32 **5.** 3.75 **6.** 0.25

Divisors That Are Not Whole Numbers

Consider the division

$$0.24 \overline{)\ 8.2\ 0\ 8}$$

We write the division as $\dfrac{8.208}{0.24}$. Then we multiply by 1 to change to a whole-number divisor:

The division $0.24\overline{)8.208}$ is the same as $24\overline{)820.8}$.

$$\frac{8.208}{0.24} = \frac{8.208}{0.24} \times \frac{100}{100} = \frac{820.8}{24}.$$

The divisor is now a whole number.

To divide when the divisor is not a whole number,

a) move the decimal point (multiply by 10, 100, and so on) to make the divisor a whole number;

$$0.2\ 4 \overline{)\ 8.2\ 0\ 8}$$
Move 2 places to the right.

b) move the decimal point in the dividend the same number of places (multiply the same way); and

$$0.2\ 4 \overline{)\ 8.2\ 0\ 8}$$
Move 2 places to the right.

c) place the decimal point directly above the new decimal point in the dividend and divide as though dividing whole numbers.

$$
\begin{array}{r}
3\ 4.2 \\
0.2\ 4 \overline{)\ 8.2\ 0_{\wedge}8} \\
7\ 2 \\
\hline
1\ 0\ 0 \\
9\ 6 \\
\hline
4\ 8 \\
4\ 8 \\
\hline
0
\end{array}
$$

(The new decimal point in the dividend is indicated by a caret.)

EXAMPLE 5 Divide: $5.848 \div 8.6$.

$$8.6 \overline{)\ 5.8\ 4\ 8}$$

Multiply the divisor by 10. (Move the decimal point 1 place.) Multiply the same way in the dividend. (Move 1 place.)

$$
\begin{array}{r}
0.6\ 8 \\
8.6 \overline{)\ 5.8_{\wedge}4\ 8} \\
5\ 1\ 6 \\
\hline
6\ 8\ 8 \\
6\ 8\ 8 \\
\hline
0
\end{array}
$$

Place a decimal point above the new decimal point and then divide.

Note: $\dfrac{5.848}{8.6} = \dfrac{5.848}{8.6} \cdot \dfrac{10}{10} = \dfrac{58.48}{86}.$

Do Exercises 7–9.

7. a) Complete.

$$\frac{3.75}{0.25} = \frac{3.75}{0.25} \times \frac{100}{100}$$

$$= \frac{(\quad)}{25}$$

b) Divide.

$$0.2\ 5 \overline{)\ 3.7\ 5}$$

Divide.

8. $0.8\ 3 \overline{)\ 4.0\ 6\ 7}$

9. $3.5 \overline{)\ 4\ 4.8}$

Answers

7. (a) 375; **(b)** 15   **8.** 4.9   **9.** 12.8

EXAMPLE 6 Divide: $12 \div 0.64$.

$$0.64 \overline{\smash{)}\ 1\ 2.}$$

Place a decimal point at the end of the whole number.

$$0.64 \overline{\smash{)}\ 1\ 2.0\ 0}$$

Multiply the divisor by 100. (Move the decimal point 2 places.) Multiply the same way in the dividend. (Move 2 places after adding extra zeros.)

$$
\begin{array}{r}
1\ 8.7\ 5 \\
0.64 \overline{\smash{)}\ 1\ 2.0\ 0_{\wedge}0\ 0} \\
\underline{6\ 4} \\
5\ 6\ 0 \\
\underline{5\ 1\ 2} \\
4\ 8\ 0 \\
\underline{4\ 4\ 8} \\
3\ 2\ 0 \\
\underline{3\ 2\ 0} \\
0
\end{array}
$$

Place a decimal point above the new decimal point and then divide.

Do Exercise 10.

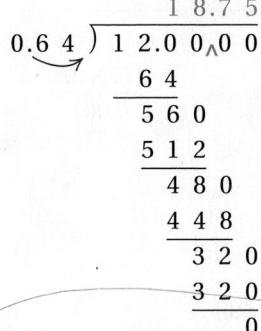

10. Divide.

$$1.6 \overline{\smash{)}\ 2\ 5}$$

Dividing by 10, 100, 1000, and So On

It is often helpful to be able to divide quickly by a ten, hundred, or thousand, or by a tenth, hundredth, or thousandth. Each procedure we use is based on multiplying by 1. Consider the following example:

$$\frac{23.789}{1000} = \frac{23.789}{1000} \cdot \frac{1000}{1000} = \frac{23{,}789}{1{,}000{,}000} = 0.023789.$$

We are dividing by a number greater than 1: The result is *smaller* than 23.789.

To divide by 10, 100, 1000, and so on,

a) count the number of zeros in the divisor, and

$$\frac{713.49}{100}$$

↳ 2 zeros

b) write the quotient by moving the decimal point in the dividend that number of places to the left.

$$\frac{713.49}{100}, \qquad 7.13.49, \qquad \frac{713.49}{100} = 7.1349$$

2 places to the left

EXAMPLE 7 Divide: $\dfrac{0.0104}{10}$.

$$\frac{0.0104}{10}, \qquad 0.0.0104, \qquad \frac{0.0104}{10} = 0.00104$$

1 zero   1 place to the left

Answer

10. 15.625

Dividing by 0.1, 0.01, 0.001, and So On

Now consider the following example:

$$\frac{23.789}{0.01} = \frac{23.789}{0.01} \cdot \frac{100}{100} = \frac{2378.9}{1} = 2378.9.$$

We are dividing by a number less than 1: The result is *larger* than 23.789. We use the following procedure.

> To divide by 0.1, 0.01, 0.001, and so on,
>
> a) count the number of decimal places in the divisor, and
>
> $$\frac{713.49}{0.001}$$
>
> $\longrightarrow$ 3 places
>
> b) write the quotient by moving the decimal point in the dividend that number of places to the right.
>
> $$\frac{713.49}{0.001},\qquad 713.490.\qquad \frac{713.49}{0.001} = 713{,}490$$
>
> 3 places to the right to change 0.001 to 1

Divide.

11. $\dfrac{0.1278}{0.01}$ 12. $\dfrac{0.1278}{100}$

13. $\dfrac{98.47}{1000}$ 14. $\dfrac{6.7832}{0.1}$

EXAMPLE 8 Divide: $\dfrac{23.738}{0.001}$.

$$\frac{23.738}{0.001},\qquad 23.738.\qquad \frac{23.738}{0.001} = 23{,}738$$

3 places   3 places to the right

Do Exercises 11–14.

(b) Solving Equations

Now let's solve equations of the type $a \cdot x = b$, where a and b may be in decimal notation. Proceeding as before, we divide by a on both sides.

EXAMPLE 9 Solve: $8 \cdot x = 27.2$.

We have

$$\frac{8 \cdot x}{8} = \frac{27.2}{8} \qquad \text{Dividing by 8 on both sides}$$

$$x = 3.4.$$

$$
\begin{array}{r}
3.4 \\
8\overline{)27.2} \\
2\,4 \\
\hline
3\,2 \\
3\,2 \\
\hline
0
\end{array}
$$

The solution is 3.4.

Answers

11. 12.78   12. 0.001278   13. 0.09847
14. 67.832

EXAMPLE 10 Solve: $2.9 \cdot t = 0.14616$.

We have

$$\frac{2.9 \cdot t}{2.9} = \frac{0.14616}{2.9} \quad \text{Dividing by 2.9 on both sides}$$

$$t = 0.0504.$$

$$\begin{array}{r} 0.0\ 5\ 0\ 4 \\ 2.9\ \overline{)\ 0.1_{\wedge}4\ 6\ 1\ 6} \\ \underline{1\ 4\ 5} \\ 1\ 1\ 6 \\ \underline{1\ 1\ 6} \\ 0 \end{array}$$

The solution is 0.0504.

Do Exercises 15 and 16.

Solve.

15. $100 \cdot x = 78.314$

16. $0.25 \cdot y = 276.4$

(c) Order of Operations: Decimal Notation

The same rules for order of operations used with whole numbers and fraction notation apply when simplifying expressions with decimal notation.

> **RULES FOR ORDER OF OPERATIONS**
>
>   1. Do all calculations within grouping symbols before operations outside.
>   2. Evaluate all exponential expressions.
>   3. Do all multiplications and divisions in order from left to right.
>   4. Do all additions and subtractions in order from left to right.

EXAMPLE 11 Simplify: $2.56 \times 25.6 \div 25{,}600 \times 256$.

There are no exponents or parentheses, so we multiply and divide from left to right:

$$\begin{aligned} 2.56 \times 25.6 \div 25{,}600 \times 256 &= 65.536 \div 25{,}600 \times 256 \\ &= 0.00256 \times 256 \\ &= 0.65536. \end{aligned}$$

Doing all multiplications and divisions in order from left to right

EXAMPLE 12 Simplify: $(5 - 0.06) \div 2 + 3.42 \times 0.1$.

$$\begin{aligned} (5 - 0.06) \div 2 + 3.42 \times 0.1 &= 4.94 \div 2 + 3.42 \times 0.1 \end{aligned}$$

Carrying out the operation inside parentheses

$$\begin{aligned} &= 2.47 + 0.342 \\ &= 2.812 \end{aligned}$$

Doing all multiplications and divisions in order from left to right

Answers

15. 0.78314   16. 1105.6

EXAMPLE 13 Simplify: $10^2 \times \{[(3 - 0.24) \div 2.4] - (0.21 - 0.092)\}$.

$10^2 \times \{[(3 - 0.24) \div 2.4] - (0.21 - 0.092)\}$

$= 10^2 \times \{[2.76 \div 2.4] - 0.118\}$ Doing the calculations in the innermost parentheses first

$= 10^2 \times \{1.15 - 0.118\}$ Again, doing the calculations in the innermost grouping symbols

$= 10^2 \times 1.032$ Subtracting inside the grouping symbols

$= 100 \times 1.032$ Evaluating the exponential expression

$= 103.2$

Do Exercises 17–19.

Do Exercise 20.

Simplify.

17. $625 \div 62.5 \times 25 \div 6250$

18. $0.25 \cdot (1 + 0.08) - 0.0274$

19. $20^2 - 3.4^2 +$
$\{2.5[20(9.2 - 5.6)] + 5(10 - 5)\}$

STUDY TIPS

HOMEWORK TIPS

Prepare for your homework assignment by reading the explanations of concepts and by following the step-by-step solutions of examples in the text. The time that you spend preparing will save valuable time when you do your assignment.

EXAMPLE 14 *Mountains in Peru.* The figure below shows a range of very high mountains in Peru, together with their altitudes, given both in feet and in meters. Find the average height of these mountains, in feet.

Source: *National Geographic*, July 1968, p. 130

Nev. Sara Sara, 18,060 ft 5,505 m
Nev. Coropuna, 21,079 ft 6,425 m
Nevado Ampato, 20,700 ft 6,309 m
Nev. Chachani, 19,931 ft 6,075 m
Volcan Misti, 19,101 ft 5,822 m
Nev. Pichu Pichu, 18,600 ft 5,669 m
Arequipa
Pacific Ocean
Peru
South America
Area enlarged
Scale varies in this perspective.
SOURCE: WOOD RONASVILLE HARLIN INC/NGS Image Collection

20. Mountains in Peru. Refer to the figure in Example 14. Find the average height of the mountains, in meters.

The **average** of a set of numbers is the sum of the numbers divided by the number of addends. (See Section 1.6c.) We find the sum of the heights divided by the number of addends, 6:

$$\frac{18,060 + 21,079 + 20,700 + 19,931 + 19,101 + 18,600}{6} = \frac{117,471}{6} = 19,578.5.$$

Thus the average height of these mountains is 19,578.5 ft.

Answers

17. 0.04   **18.** 0.2426   **19.** 593.44
20. 5967.5 m

a Divide.

1. $2 \overline{)5.98}$

2. $5 \overline{)18}$

3. $4 \overline{)95.12}$

4. $8 \overline{)25.92}$

5. $12 \overline{)89.76}$

6. $23 \overline{)25.07}$

7. $33 \overline{)237.6}$

8. $54 \overline{)448.2}$

9. $9.144 \div 8$

10. $4.5 \div 9$

11. $12.123 \div 3$

12. $12.4 \div 4$

13. $0.06 \overline{)3.36}$

14. $0.04 \overline{)1.68}$

15. $0.12 \overline{)8.4}$

16. $0.36 \overline{)2.88}$

17. $3.4 \overline{)68}$

18. $0.25 \overline{)5}$

19. $15 \overline{)6}$

20. $12 \overline{)1.8}$

21. $36 \overline{)14.76}$

22. $52 \overline{)119.6}$

23. $3.2 \overline{)27.2}$

24. $8.5 \overline{)27.2}$

25. $4.2 \overline{)39.06}$

26. $4.8 \overline{)0.1104}$

27. $8 \overline{)5}$

28. $8 \overline{)3}$

29. $0.47 \overline{)0.1222}$

30. $1.08 \overline{)0.54}$

31. $4.8 \overline{)75}$

32. $0.2\,8\,\overline{)\,6\,3}$ **33.** $0.0\,3\,2\,\overline{)\,0.0\,7\,4\,8\,8}$ **34.** $0.0\,1\,7\,\overline{)\,1.5\,8\,1}$

35. $8\,2\,\overline{)\,3\,8.5\,4}$ **36.** $3\,4\,\overline{)\,0.1\,4\,6\,2}$ **37.** $\dfrac{213.4567}{1000}$ **38.** $\dfrac{769.3265}{1000}$

39. $\dfrac{23.59}{10}$ **40.** $\dfrac{83.57}{10}$ **41.** $\dfrac{426.487}{100}$ **42.** $\dfrac{591.348}{100}$

43. $\dfrac{16.94}{0.1}$ **44.** $\dfrac{100.7604}{0.1}$ **45.** $\dfrac{1.0237}{0.001}$ **46.** $\dfrac{3.4029}{0.001}$

47. $\dfrac{42.561}{0.01}$ **48.** $\dfrac{98.473}{0.01}$

b) Solve.

49. $4.2 \cdot x = 39.06$ **50.** $36 \cdot y = 14.76$ **51.** $1000 \cdot y = 9.0678$

52. $789.23 = 0.25 \cdot q$ **53.** $1048.8 = 23 \cdot t$ **54.** $28.2 \cdot x = 423$

c) Simplify.

55. $14 \times (82.6 + 67.9)$ **56.** $(26.2 - 14.8) \times 12$

57. $0.003 + 3.03 \div 0.01$ **58.** $9.94 + 4.26 \div (6.02 - 4.6) - 0.9$

Copyright © 2012 Pearson Education, Inc.

59. $42 \times (10.6 + 0.024)$

60. $(18.6 - 4.9) \times 13$

61. $4.2 \times 5.7 + 0.7 \div 3.5$

62. $123.3 - 4.24 \times 1.01$

63. $9.0072 + 0.04 \div 0.1^2$

64. $12 \div 0.03 - 12 \times 0.03^2$

65. $(8 - 0.04)^2 \div 4 + 8.7 \times 0.4$

66. $(5 - 2.5)^2 \div 100 + 0.1 \times 6.5$

67. $86.7 + 4.22 \times (9.6 - 0.03)^2$

68. $2.48 \div (1 - 0.504) + 24.3 - 11 \times 2$

69. $4 \div 0.4 + 0.1 \times 5 - 0.1^2$

70. $6 \times 0.9 + 0.1 \div 4 - 0.2^3$

71. $5.5^2 \times [(6 - 4.2) \div 0.06 + 0.12]$

72. $12^2 \div (12 + 2.4) - [(2 - 1.6) \div 0.8]$

73. $200 \times \{[(4 - 0.25) \div 2.5] - (4.5 - 4.025)\}$

74. $0.03 \times \{1 \times 50.2 - [(8 - 7.5) \div 0.05]\}$

75. Find the average of $1276.59, $1350.49, $1123.78, and $1402.58.

76. Find the average weight of two wrestlers who weigh 308 lb and 296.4 lb.

77. *Camping in National Parks.* Camping in national parks has declined steadily in recent years. The graph below shows the numbers of overnight camping stays in Park Service campgrounds in the National Park System from 2002 to 2006. Find the average number of stays per year during this period.

Camping in Park Service Campgrounds

SOURCE: U.S. National Park Service

78. *Unclaimed Prizes.* Each year millions of lottery prize dollars go unclaimed. The table below shows the five states with the most unclaimed prize money for a recent year. Find the average amount that went unclaimed in these states.

STATE	UNCLAIMED PRIZES (in millions)
New York	$73.6
Texas	58.9
Florida	48.4
Ohio	33.4
California	29.4

SOURCE: Individual state lotteries

Skill Maintenance

Simplify. [2.1e]

79. $\dfrac{36}{42}$

80. $\dfrac{56}{64}$

81. $\dfrac{38}{146}$

82. $\dfrac{92}{124}$

Find the prime factorization. [1.7d]

83. 684

84. 162

85. 2007

86. 2005

87. Add: $10\frac{1}{2} + 4\frac{5}{8}$. [2.4b]

88. Subtract: $10\frac{1}{2} - 4\frac{5}{8}$. [2.4c]

Synthesis

Simplify.

89. ▦ $9.0534 - 2.041^2 \times 0.731 \div 1.043^2$

90. ▦ $23.042(7 - 4.037 \times 1.46 - 0.932^2)$

In Exercises 91–94, find the missing value.

91. $439.57 \times 0.01 \div 1000 \times \square = 4.3957$

92. $5.2738 \div 0.01 \times 1000 \div \square = 52.738$

93. $0.0329 \div 0.001 \times 10^4 \div \square = 3290$

94. $0.0047 \times 0.01 \div 10^4 \times \square = 4.7$

Copyright © 2012 Pearson Education, Inc.

Mid-Chapter Review

Concept Reinforcement

Determine whether each statement is true or false.

_____ **1.** In the number 308.00567, the digit 6 names the tens place.   [3.1a]

_____ **2.** When writing a word name for decimal notation, we write the word "and" for the decimal point.   [3.1a]

_____ **3.** To multiply any number by 10, 100, 1000, and so on, count the number of zeros and move the decimal point that many places to the right.   [3.3a]

Guided Solutions

Fill in each blank with the number that creates a correct statement or solution.

4. Solve: $y + 12.8 = 23.35$.   [3.2c]

$$y + 12.8 = 23.35$$
$$y + 12.8 - \square = 23.35 - \square \qquad \text{Subtracting 12.8 on both sides}$$
$$y + \square = \square \qquad \text{Carrying out the subtraction}$$
$$y = \square$$

5. Simplify: $5.6 + 4.3 \times (6.5 - 0.25)^2$.   [3.4c]

$$5.6 + 4.3 \times (6.5 - 0.25)^2 = 5.6 + 4.3 \times (\square)^2 \qquad \text{Carrying out the operation inside parentheses}$$
$$= 5.6 + 4.3 \times \square \qquad \text{Evaluating the exponential expression}$$
$$= 5.6 + \square \qquad \text{Multiplying}$$
$$= \square \qquad \text{Adding}$$

Mixed Review

6. Usain Bolt of Jamaica set a world record of 9.69 sec in the men's 100-m race at the 2008 Summer Olympics. Write a word name for 9.69.   [3.1a]

Source: beijing2008.cn

7. After removing coins from their pockets at security checkpoints in U.S. airports, travelers forgot to reclaim coins totaling about $1.05 million from 2005 to 2007. Convert 1.05 million to standard notation.   [3.3b]

Source: Transportation Security Administration

Write fraction notation.   [3.1b]

8. 4.53

9. 0.287

Which number is larger?   [3.1c]

10. 0.07, 0.13

11. 5.2, 5.09

Write decimal notation.   [3.1b]

12. $\dfrac{7}{10}$

13. $\dfrac{639}{100}$

14. $35\dfrac{67}{100}$

15. $8\dfrac{2}{1000}$

Round 28.4615 to the nearest: [3.1d]

16. Thousandth.

17. Hundredth.

18. Tenth.

19. One

Add. [3.2a]

20.
```
  4 7.6 3 8
+    2.4 5 7
```

21.
```
    1 5.6
  2 3 4.7 2 9
      3.0 8
+ 9 6 1.4 5 3
```

22. $4.5 + 0.728$

23. $16 + 0.34 + 1.9$

Subtract. [3.2b]

24.
```
  3 2 1.5 7
-     4 9.3 8
```

25.
```
  5.6
- 0.0 0 7
```

26. $34.3 - 18.75$

27. $49.07 - 9.7$

Multiply. [3.3a]

28.
```
    4.6
×   0.9
```

29.
```
   1 5.3
×    6.0 7
```

30. 100×81.236

31. 0.1×29.37

Divide. [3.4a]

32. $20.24 \div 4$

33. $21.76 \div 6.8$

34. $76.34 \div 0.1$

35. $914.036 \div 1000$

36. Convert $20.45 to cents. [3.3b]

37. Convert 147¢ to dollars. [3.3b]

38. Solve: $46.3 + x = 59$. [3.2c]

39. Solve: $42.84 = 5.1 \cdot y$. [3.4b]

Simplify. [3.4c]

40. $6.594 + 0.5318 \div 0.01$

41. $7.3 \times 4.6 - 0.8 \div 3.2$

Understanding Through Discussion and Writing

42. A fellow student rounds 236.448 to the nearest one and gets 237. Explain the possible error. [3.1d]

43. Explain the error in the following: [3.2b]
Subtract.
$$73.089 - 5.0061 = 2.3028$$

44. Explain why $10 \div 0.2 = 100 \div 2$. [3.4a]

45. Kayla made these two computational mistakes:
$$0.247 \div 0.1 = 0.0247; \quad 0.247 \div 10 = 2.47.$$
In each case, how could you convince her that a mistake has been made? [3.4a]

Copyright © 2012 Pearson Education, Inc.

3.5 Converting from Fraction Notation to Decimal Notation

a Fraction Notation to Decimal Notation

When a denominator has no prime factors other than 2's and 5's, we can find decimal notation by multiplying by 1. We multiply to get a denominator that is a power of ten, like 10, 100, or 1000.

EXAMPLE 1 Find decimal notation for $\frac{3}{5}$.

$$\frac{3}{5} = \frac{3}{5} \cdot \frac{2}{2} = \frac{6}{10} = 0.6$$

$5 \cdot 2 = 10$, so we use $\frac{2}{2}$ for 1 to get a denominator of 10.

EXAMPLE 2 Find decimal notation for $\frac{7}{20}$.

$$\frac{7}{20} = \frac{7}{20} \cdot \frac{5}{5} = \frac{35}{100} = 0.35$$

$20 \cdot 5 = 100$, so we use $\frac{5}{5}$ for 1 to get a denominator of 100.

EXAMPLE 3 Find decimal notation for $\frac{87}{25}$.

$$\frac{87}{25} = \frac{87}{25} \cdot \frac{4}{4} = \frac{348}{100} = 3.48$$

$25 \cdot 4 = 100$, so we use $\frac{4}{4}$ for 1 to get a denominator of 100.

EXAMPLE 4 Find decimal notation for $\frac{9}{40}$.

$$\frac{9}{40} = \frac{9}{40} \cdot \frac{25}{25} = \frac{225}{1000} = 0.225$$

$40 \cdot 25 = 1000$, so we use $\frac{25}{25}$ for 1 to get a denominator of 1000.

> Do Margin Exercises 1–4.

We can always divide to find decimal notation.

EXAMPLE 5 Find decimal notation for $\frac{3}{5}$.

$$\frac{3}{5} = 3 \div 5 \qquad \begin{array}{r} 0.6 \\ 5\overline{)3.0} \\ \underline{3\ 0} \\ 0 \end{array} \qquad \frac{3}{5} = 0.6$$

EXAMPLE 6 Find decimal notation for $\frac{7}{8}$.

$$\frac{7}{8} = 7 \div 8 \qquad \begin{array}{r} 0.8\ 7\ 5 \\ 8\overline{)7.0\ 0\ 0} \\ \underline{6\ 4} \\ 6\ 0 \\ \underline{5\ 6} \\ 4\ 0 \\ \underline{4\ 0} \\ 0 \end{array} \qquad \frac{7}{8} = 0.875$$

> Do Exercises 5 and 6.

OBJECTIVES

a Convert from fraction notation to decimal notation.

b Round numbers named by repeating decimals in problem solving.

c Calculate using fraction notation and decimal notation together.

SKILL TO REVIEW
Objective 3.4a: Divide using decimal notation.

Divide.

1. $3 \div 4$ 2. $25 \div 8$

Find decimal notation. Use multiplying by 1.

1. $\frac{4}{5}$ 2. $\frac{9}{20}$

3. $\frac{11}{40}$ 4. $\frac{33}{25}$

Find decimal notation.

5. $\frac{2}{5}$ 6. $\frac{3}{8}$

Answers

Skill to Review:
1. 0.75   **2.** 3.125

Margin Exercises:
1. 0.8   **2.** 0.45   **3.** 0.275
4. 1.32   **5.** 0.4   **6.** 0.375

<table><thead><tr><th></th></tr></thead><tbody><tr><td></td></tr></tbody></table>

STUDY TIPS

MAKING POSITIVE CHOICES

Making these choices will contribute to your success in this course.

- Choose to make a strong commitment to learning.
- Choose to place the primary responsibility for learning on yourself.
- Choose to allocate the proper amount of time to learn.

In Examples 5 and 6, the division *terminated,* meaning that eventually we got a remainder of 0. A **terminating decimal** occurs when the denominator has only 2's or 5's, or both, as factors, as in $\frac{17}{25}$, $\frac{5}{8}$, or $\frac{83}{100}$. This assumes that the fraction notation has been simplified.

Consider a different situation:

$$\frac{5}{6}, \quad \text{or} \quad \frac{5}{2 \cdot 3}.$$

Since 6 has a 3 as a factor, the division will not terminate. Although we can still use division to get decimal notation, the answer will be a **repeating decimal**, as follows.

EXAMPLE 7 Find decimal notation for $\frac{5}{6}$.

$$\frac{5}{6} = 5 \div 6 \qquad \begin{array}{r} 0.8\,3\,3 \\ 6\overline{)5.0\,0\,0} \\ \underline{4\,8} \\ 2\,0 \\ \underline{1\,8} \\ 2\,0 \\ \underline{1\,8} \\ 2 \end{array}$$

Since 2 keeps reappearing as a remainder, the digits repeat and will continue to do so; therefore,

$$\frac{5}{6} = 0.83333\ldots.$$

The red dots indicate an endless sequence of digits in the quotient. When there is a repeating pattern, the dots are often replaced by a bar to indicate the repeating part—in this case, only the 3:

$$\frac{5}{6} = 0.8\overline{3}.$$

Do Exercises 7 and 8.

Find decimal notation.

7. $\frac{1}{6}$ **8.** $\frac{2}{3}$

EXAMPLE 8 Find decimal notation for $\frac{4}{11}$.

$$\frac{4}{11} = 4 \div 11 \qquad \begin{array}{r} 0.3\,6\,3\,6 \\ 11\overline{)4.0\,0\,0\,0} \\ \underline{3\,3} \\ 7\,0 \\ \underline{6\,6} \\ 4\,0 \\ \underline{3\,3} \\ 7\,0 \\ \underline{6\,6} \\ 4 \end{array}$$

Since 7 and 4 keep repeating as remainders, the sequence of digits "36" repeats in the quotient, and

$$\frac{4}{11} = 0.363636\ldots, \quad \text{or} \quad 0.\overline{36}.$$

Do Exercises 9 and 10.

Find decimal notation.

9. $\frac{5}{11}$ **10.** $\frac{12}{11}$

Answers

7. $0.1\overline{6}$ **8.** $0.\overline{6}$ **9.** $0.\overline{45}$ **10.** $1.\overline{09}$

EXAMPLE 9 Find decimal notation for $\frac{5}{7}$.

$$
\begin{array}{r}
0.7\ 1\ 4\ 2\ 8\ 5 \\
7\overline{)\ 5.0\ 0\ 0\ 0\ 0\ 0} \\
\underline{4\ 9} \\
1\ 0 \\
\underline{7} \\
3\ 0 \\
\underline{2\ 8} \\
2\ 0 \\
\underline{1\ 4} \\
6\ 0 \\
\underline{5\ 6} \\
4\ 0 \\
\underline{3\ 5} \\
5
\end{array}
$$

Since 5 appears again as a remainder, the sequence of digits "714285" repeats in the quotient, and

$$\frac{5}{7} = 0.714285714285\ldots, \quad \text{or} \quad 0.\overline{714285}.$$

The length of a repeating part can be very long—too long to find on a calculator. An example is $\frac{5}{97}$, which has a repeating part of 96 digits.

> Do Exercise 11.

11. Find decimal notation for $\frac{3}{7}$.

b Rounding in Problem Solving

In applied problems, repeating decimals are rounded to get approximate answers. To round a repeating decimal, we can extend the decimal notation at least one place past the rounding digit, and then round as before.

EXAMPLES Round each of the following to the nearest tenth, hundredth, and thousandth.

	Nearest tenth	*Nearest hundredth*	*Nearest thousandth*
10. $0.8\overline{3} = 0.83333\ldots$	0.8	0.83	0.833
11. $0.\overline{09} = 0.090909\ldots$	0.1	0.09	0.091
12. $0.\overline{714285} = 0.714285714285\ldots$	0.7	0.71	0.714

> Do Exercises 12–14.

Round each to the nearest tenth, hundredth, and thousandth.

12. $0.\overline{6}$

13. $0.\overline{80}$

14. $6.\overline{245}$

Converting Ratios to Decimal Notation

When solving applied problems, we often convert ratios to decimal notation.

EXAMPLE 13 *Gas Mileage.* A car travels 457 mi on 16.4 gal of gasoline. The ratio of number of miles driven to amount of gasoline used is *gas mileage*. Find the gas mileage and convert the ratio to decimal notation rounded to the nearest tenth.

$$\frac{\text{Miles driven}}{\text{Gasoline used}} = \frac{457}{16.4} \approx 27.86 \quad \text{Dividing to 2 decimal places}$$

$$\approx 27.9 \quad \text{Rounding to 1 decimal place}$$

The gas mileage is 27.9 miles to the gallon.

Answers

11. $0.\overline{428571}$ **12.** 0.7; 0.67; 0.667
13. 0.8; 0.81; 0.808 **14.** 6.2; 6.25; 6.245

15. Coin Tossing. A coin is tossed 51 times. It lands heads 26 times. Find the ratio of heads to tosses and convert it to decimal notation rounded to the nearest thousandth. (This is also the experimental probability of getting heads.)

16. Gas Mileage. A car travels 380 mi on 15.7 gal of gasoline. Find the gasoline mileage and convert the ratio to decimal notation rounded to the nearest tenth.

EXAMPLE 14 *Wildfires.*
A severe thunderstorm system that moved through northern and central California on June 20, 2008, produced over 6000 lightning strikes. This sparked 2096 wildfires that burned about 1,200,000 acres. Find the ratio of the number of acres burned to the number of fires and convert it to decimal notation rounded to the nearest thousandth.

Source: California Department of Forestry and Fire Prevention

We have

$$\frac{\text{Acres burned}}{\text{Number of fires}} = \frac{1,200,000 \text{ acres}}{2096 \text{ fires}}$$
$$\approx 572.51908.$$

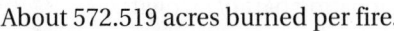

About 572.519 acres burned per fire.

Do Exercises 15 and 16.

Averages

When finding an average, we may at times need to round an answer.

EXAMPLE 15 *Peer-to-Peer Loans.* Peer-to-peer lending, in which individuals make loans to other individuals via the Internet, is beginning to soar. The graph below shows the amounts of peer-to-peer loans made from 2005 to 2010. Find the average amount loaned per year during this period. Round to the nearest thousandth.

Peer-to-Peer Loans

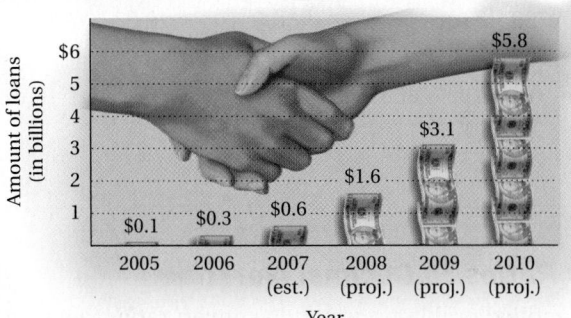

SOURCE: Celent

17. Peer-to-Peer Loans. Refer to the data on peer-to-peer loans in Example 15. Find the average amount loaned per year from 2007 to 2009. Round to the nearest thousandth.

We add the amounts of the loans and divide by the number of addends, 6. The average is

$$\frac{0.1 + 0.3 + 0.6 + 1.6 + 3.1 + 5.8}{6} = \frac{11.5}{6} = 1.91\overline{6} \approx 1.917.$$

Peer-to-peer loans made from 2005 to 2010 averaged a total of about $1.917 billion per year.

Do Exercise 17.

Answers

15. 0.510   **16.** 24.2 miles per gallon
17. About $1.767 billion

(c) Calculations with Fraction Notation and Decimal Notation Together

In certain kinds of calculations, fraction notation and decimal notation might occur together. In such cases, there are at least three ways in which we might proceed.

EXAMPLE 16 Calculate: $\frac{2}{3} \times 0.576$.

METHOD 1: One way to do this calculation is to convert the fraction notation to decimal notation so that both numbers are in decimal notation. Since $\frac{2}{3}$ converts to repeating decimal notation, it is first rounded to some chosen decimal place. We choose three decimal places because 0.576 has three decimal places. Then, using decimal notation, we multiply.

$$\frac{2}{3} \times 0.576 = 0.\overline{6} \times 0.576 \approx 0.667 \times 0.576 = 0.384192$$

METHOD 2: A second way to do this calculation is to convert the decimal notation to fraction notation so that both numbers are in fraction notation. The answer can be left in fraction notation and simplified, or we can convert to decimal notation and round, if appropriate.

$$\frac{2}{3} \times 0.576 = \frac{2}{3} \cdot \frac{576}{1000} = \frac{2 \cdot 576}{3 \cdot 1000}$$

$$= \frac{2 \cdot 2 \cdot 2 \cdot 2 \cdot 2 \cdot 2 \cdot 3 \cdot 3}{2 \cdot 2 \cdot 2 \cdot 3 \cdot 5 \cdot 5 \cdot 5}$$

$$= \frac{2 \cdot 2 \cdot 2 \cdot 3}{2 \cdot 2 \cdot 2 \cdot 3} \cdot \frac{2 \cdot 2 \cdot 2 \cdot 2 \cdot 3}{5 \cdot 5 \cdot 5}$$

$$= 1 \cdot \frac{2 \cdot 2 \cdot 2 \cdot 2 \cdot 3}{5 \cdot 5 \cdot 5}$$

$$= \frac{2 \cdot 2 \cdot 2 \cdot 2 \cdot 3}{5 \cdot 5 \cdot 5} = \frac{48}{125}, \text{ or } 0.384$$

METHOD 3: A third way to do this calculation is to treat 0.576 as $\frac{0.576}{1}$. Then we multiply 0.576 by 2, and divide the result by 3.

$$\frac{2}{3} \times 0.576 = \frac{2}{3} \times \frac{0.576}{1} = \frac{2 \times 0.576}{3} = \frac{1.152}{3} = 0.384$$

Note that we get an exact answer with methods 2 and 3, but method 1 gives an approximation since we rounded decimal notation for $\frac{2}{3}$.

Do Exercise 18.

EXAMPLE 17 Calculate: $\frac{2}{3} \times 0.576 + 3.287 \div \frac{4}{5}$.

We use the rules for order of operations, doing first the multiplication and then the division. Then we add.

$$\frac{2}{3} \times 0.576 + 3.287 \div \frac{4}{5} = 0.384 + 3.287 \cdot \frac{5}{4}$$

Method 3:
$\frac{2}{3} \times \frac{0.576}{1} = 0.384;$
$\frac{3.287}{1} \times \frac{5}{4} = 4.10875$

$$= 0.384 + 4.10875$$

$$= 4.49275$$

Do Exercises 19 and 20.

18. Calculate: $\frac{5}{6} \times 0.864$.

Calculate.

19. $\frac{1}{3} \times 0.384 + \frac{5}{8} \times 0.6784$

20. $\frac{5}{6} \times 0.864 + 14.3 \div \frac{8}{5}$

Answers
18. 0.72   19. 0.552   20. 9.6575

3.5
Exercise Set

For Extra Help

MyMathLab

Math XL
PRACTICE

WATCH

DOWNLOAD

READ

REVIEW

a Find decimal notation.

1. $\dfrac{23}{100}$ **2.** $\dfrac{9}{100}$ **3.** $\dfrac{3}{5}$ **4.** $\dfrac{19}{20}$ **5.** $\dfrac{13}{40}$ **6.** $\dfrac{3}{16}$

7. $\dfrac{1}{5}$ **8.** $\dfrac{4}{5}$ **9.** $\dfrac{17}{20}$ **10.** $\dfrac{11}{20}$ **11.** $\dfrac{3}{8}$ **12.** $\dfrac{7}{8}$

13. $\dfrac{39}{40}$ **14.** $\dfrac{31}{40}$ **15.** $\dfrac{13}{25}$ **16.** $\dfrac{61}{125}$ **17.** $\dfrac{2502}{125}$ **18.** $\dfrac{181}{200}$

19. $\dfrac{1}{4}$ **20.** $\dfrac{1}{2}$ **21.** $\dfrac{29}{25}$ **22.** $\dfrac{37}{25}$ **23.** $\dfrac{19}{16}$ **24.** $\dfrac{5}{8}$

25. $\dfrac{4}{15}$ **26.** $\dfrac{7}{9}$ **27.** $\dfrac{1}{3}$ **28.** $\dfrac{1}{9}$ **29.** $\dfrac{4}{3}$ **30.** $\dfrac{8}{9}$

31. $\dfrac{7}{6}$ **32.** $\dfrac{7}{11}$ **33.** $\dfrac{4}{7}$ **34.** $\dfrac{14}{11}$ **35.** $\dfrac{11}{12}$ **36.** $\dfrac{5}{12}$

b

37.–47. *Odds.* Round each answer of the odd-numbered Exercises 25–35 to the nearest tenth, hundredth, and thousandth.

38.–48. *Evens.* Round each answer of the even-numbered Exercises 26–36 to the nearest tenth, hundredth, and thousandth.

Round each to the nearest tenth, hundredth, and thousandth.

49. $0.1\overline{8}$ **50.** $0.8\overline{3}$ **51.** $0.2\overline{7}$ **52.** $3.5\overline{4}$

Copyright © 2012 Pearson Education, Inc.

53. For this set of people, what is the ratio, in decimal notation rounded to the nearest thousandth, where appropriate, of:

   a) women to the total number of people?
   b) women to men?
   c) men to the total number of people?
   d) men to women?

54. For this set of pennies and quarters, what is the ratio, in decimal notation rounded to the nearest thousandth, where appropriate, of:

   a) pennies to quarters?
   b) quarters to pennies?
   c) pennies to total number of coins?
   d) total number of coins to pennies?

Gas Mileage.   In each of Exercises 55–58, find the gas mileage rounded to the nearest tenth.

55. 285 mi; 18 gal

56. 396 mi; 17 gal

57. 324.8 mi; 18.2 gal

58. 264.8 mi; 12.7 gal

59. *Windy Cities.*   Although nicknamed the Windy City, Chicago is not the windiest city in the United States. Listed in the table below are the six windiest cities and their average wind speeds. Find the average of these wind speeds and round your answer to the nearest tenth.

Source: *The Handy Geography Answer Book*

CITY	AVERAGE WIND SPEED (in miles per hour)
Mt. Washington, NH	35.3
Boston, MA	12.5
Honolulu, HI	11.3
Dallas, TX	10.7
Kansas City, MO	10.7
Chicago, IL	10.4

60. *Areas of the New England States.*   The table below lists the areas of the New England states. Find the average area and round your answer to the nearest tenth.

Source: *The New York Times Almanac*

STATE	TOTAL AREA (in square miles)
Maine	33,265
New Hampshire	9,279
Vermont	9,614
Massachusetts	8,284
Connecticut	5,018
Rhode Island	1,211

Stock Prices. At one time, stock prices were given using mixed numerals involving halves, fourths, eighths, and so on. The Securities and Exchange Commission now mandates the use of decimal notation. Thus a price of 23\frac{13}{16}$ is expressed in decimal notation, rounded to the nearest hundredth, as $23.81. Complete the following table.

	STOCK	PRICE PER SHARE	DECIMAL NOTATION	ROUNDED TO NEAREST HUNDREDTH
61.	General Electric	29\frac{9}{16}$		
62.	Intel	24\frac{7}{16}$		
63.	Microsoft	27\frac{7}{8}$		
64.	Home Depot	27\frac{1}{8}$		
65.	Verisign	32\frac{31}{64}$		
66.	Hewlett Packard	45\frac{53}{64}$		

SOURCE: New York Stock Exchange

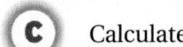 Calculate.

67. $\frac{7}{8} \times 12.64$

68. $\frac{4}{5} \times 384.8$

69. $2\frac{3}{4} + 5.65$

70. $4\frac{4}{5} + 3.25$

71. $\frac{47}{9} \times 79.95$

72. $\frac{7}{11} \times 2.7873$

73. $\frac{1}{2} - 0.5$

74. $3\frac{1}{8} - 2.75$

75. $4.875 - 2\frac{1}{16}$

76. $55\frac{3}{5} - 12.22$

77. $\frac{5}{6} \times 0.0765 + \frac{5}{4} \times 0.1124$

78. $\frac{3}{5} \times 6384.1 - \frac{3}{8} \times 156.56$

79. $\frac{4}{5} \times 384.8 + 24.8 \div \frac{8}{3}$

80. $102.4 \div \frac{2}{5} - 12 \times \frac{5}{6}$

Copyright © 2012 Pearson Education, Inc.

81. $\frac{7}{8} \times 0.86 - 0.76 \times \frac{3}{4}$

82. $17.95 \div \frac{5}{8} + \frac{3}{4} \times 16.2$

83. $3.375 \times 5\frac{1}{3}$

84. $2.5 \times 3\frac{5}{8}$

85. $6.84 \div 2\frac{1}{2}$

86. $8\frac{1}{2} \div 2.125$

Skill Maintenance

Multiply.   [2.4d]

87. $9 \cdot 2\frac{1}{3}$

88. $10\frac{1}{2} \cdot 22\frac{3}{4}$

Divide.   [2.4e]

89. $84 \div 8\frac{2}{5}$

90. $8\frac{3}{5} \div 10\frac{2}{5}$

Add.   [2.4b]

91. $17\frac{5}{6} + 32\frac{3}{8}$

92. $14\frac{3}{5} + 16\frac{1}{10}$

Subtract.   [2.4c]

93. $16\frac{1}{10} - 14\frac{3}{5}$

94. $32\frac{3}{8} - 17\frac{5}{6}$

Solve.   [2.5a]

95. A recipe for bread calls for $\frac{2}{3}$ cup of water, $\frac{1}{4}$ cup of milk, and $\frac{1}{8}$ cup of oil. How many cups of liquid ingredients does the recipe call for?

96. A board $\frac{7}{10}$ in. thick is glued to a board $\frac{3}{5}$ in. thick. The glue is $\frac{3}{100}$ in. thick. How thick is the result?

Synthesis

⊞ Find decimal notation.

97. $\frac{1}{7}$

98. $\frac{2}{7}$

99. $\frac{3}{7}$

100. $\frac{4}{7}$

101. $\frac{5}{7}$

102. ⊞ From the pattern of Exercises 97–101, guess the decimal notation for $\frac{6}{7}$. Check on your calculator.

⊞ Find decimal notation.

103. $\frac{1}{9}$

104. $\frac{1}{99}$

105. $\frac{1}{999}$

106. ⊞ From the pattern of Exercises 103–105, guess the decimal notation for $\frac{1}{9999}$. Check on your calculator.

3.6

Estimating

SKILL TO REVIEW

Objective 1.3e: Estimate sums, differences, products, and quotients by rounding.

Estimate by first rounding to the nearest ten.

1.	4 6 7	2.	5 4
	− 2 8 4		× 2 9

a Estimating Sums, Differences, Products, and Quotients

Estimating has many uses. It can be done before a problem is even attempted in order to get an idea of the answer. It can be done afterward as a check, even when we are using a calculator. In many situations, an estimate is all we need. We usually estimate by rounding the numbers so that there are one or two nonzero digits, depending on how accurate we want our estimate. Consider the following prices for Examples 1–3.

$289.95

8.2 Megapixel Digital Camera

19" Flat-Panel HDTV

Four Burner Gas Grill

$139.97

$449.99

EXAMPLE 1 Estimate by rounding to the nearest ten the total cost of one grill and one TV.

We are estimating the sum

$289.95 + $449.99 = Total cost.

The estimate found by rounding the addends to the nearest ten is

$290 + $450 = $740.   (Estimated total cost)

Do Margin Exercise 1.

1. Estimate by rounding to the nearest ten the total cost of one grill and one camera. Which of the following is an appropriate estimate?

a) $43   b) $400
c) $410   d) $430

EXAMPLE 2 About how much more does the TV cost than the camera? Estimate by rounding to the nearest ten.

We are estimating the difference

$449.99 − $139.97 = Price difference.

The estimate, found by rounding the minuend and the subtrahend to the nearest ten, is

$450 − $140 = $310.   (Estimated price difference)

Do Exercise 2.

2. About how much more does the TV cost than the grill? Estimate by rounding to the nearest ten. Which of the following is an appropriate estimate?

a) $100   b) $150
c) $160   d) $300

Answers

Skill to Review:
1. 190   2. 1500

Margin Exercises:
1. (d)   2. (c)

EXAMPLE 3 Estimate the total cost of 4 cameras.

We are estimating the product

$$4 \times \$139.97 = \text{Total cost}.$$

The estimate is found by rounding 139.97 to the nearest ten:

$$4 \times \$140 = \$560.$$

Do Exercise 3.

EXAMPLE 4 About how many Blu-ray discs at $29.99 each can be purchased for $154?

We estimate the quotient

$$\$154 \div \$29.99.$$

Since we want a whole-number estimate, we choose our rounding appropriately. Rounding $29.99 to the nearest one, we get $30. Since $154 is close to $150, which is a multiple of 30, we estimate

$$\$150 \div \$30,$$

so the answer is 5.

Do Exercise 4.

EXAMPLE 5 Estimate: 4.8×52. Do not find the actual product. Which of the following is an appropriate estimate?

a) 25   b) 250   c) 2500   d) 360

We round 4.8 to the nearest one and 52 to the nearest ten:

$$5 \times 50 = 250. \quad \text{(Estimated product)}$$

Thus an approximate estimate is (b).

Other estimates that we might have used in Example 5 are

$$5 \times 52 = 260 \quad \text{or} \quad 4.8 \times 50 = 240.$$

The estimate in Example 5, $5 \times 50 = 250$, is the easiest to do because the factors have the fewest nonzero digits. You could probably do it mentally. In general, we try to round so that a computation has as few nonzero digits as possible while still keeping the estimated value close to the original value.

Do Exercises 5–10.

---

3. Estimate the total cost of 6 TVs. Which of the following is an appropriate estimate?

a) $450   b) $2700

c) $4500   d) $27,000

4. About how many Blu-ray discs can be purchased for $485? Choose an appropriate estimate from the following.

a) 16   b) 21

c) 25   d) 30

Estimate each product. Do not find the actual product. Which of the following is an appropriate estimate?

5. 2.4×8

a) 16   b) 34

c) 125   d) 5

6. 24×0.6

a) 200   b) 5

c) 110   d) 20

7. 0.86×0.432

a) 0.04   b) 0.4

c) 1.1   d) 4

8. 0.82×0.1

a) 800   b) 8

c) 0.08   d) 80

9. 0.12×18.248

a) 180   b) 1.8

c) 0.018   d) 18

10. 24.234×5.2

a) 200   b) 120

c) 12.5   d) 234

Answers

3. (b)   4. (a)   5. (a)   6. (d)   7. (b)
8. (c)   9. (b)   10. (b)

EXAMPLE 6 Estimate: $82.08 \div 24$. Which of the following is an appropriate estimate?

a) 400   b) 16   c) 40   d) 4

This is about $80 \div 20$, so the answer is about 4. Thus an appropriate estimate is (d).

EXAMPLE 7 Estimate: $94.18 \div 3.2$. Which of the following is an appropriate estimate?

a) 30   b) 300   c) 3   d) 60

This is about $90 \div 3$, so the answer is about 30. Thus an appropriate estimate is (a).

EXAMPLE 8 Estimate: $0.0156 \div 1.3$. Which of the following is an appropriate estimate?

a) 0.2   b) 0.002   c) 0.02   d) 20

This is about $0.02 \div 1$, so the answer is about 0.02. Thus an appropriate estimate is (c).

> Do Exercises 11–13.

In some cases, it is easier to estimate a quotient directly rather than by rounding the divisor and the dividend.

EXAMPLE 9 Estimate: $0.0074 \div 0.23$. Which of the following is an appropriate estimate?

a) 0.3   b) 0.03   c) 300   d) 3

We estimate 3 for a quotient. We check by multiplying.

$$0.23 \times 3 = 0.69$$

We make the estimate smaller. We estimate 0.3 and check by multiplying.

$$0.23 \times 0.3 = 0.069$$

We make the estimate smaller. We estimate 0.03 and check by multiplying.

$$0.23 \times 0.03 = 0.0069$$

This is about 0.0074, so the quotient is about 0.03. Thus an appropriate estimate is (b).

> Do Exercise 14.

Estimate each quotient. Which of the following is an appropriate estimate?

11. $59.78 \div 29.1$

     a) 200   b) 20

     c) 2   d) 0.2

12. $82.08 \div 2.4$

     a) 40   b) 4.0

     c) 400   d) 0.4

13. $0.1768 \div 0.08$

     a) 8   b) 10

     c) 2   d) 20

14. Estimate: $0.0069 \div 0.15$. Which of the following is an appropriate estimate?

     a) 0.5   b) 50

     c) 0.05   d) 0.004

Answers

11. (c)   12. (a)   13. (c)   14. (c)

a Consider the following prices for Exercises 1–8. Estimate the sums, differences, products, or quotients involved in these problems. Indicate which of the choices is an appropriate estimate.

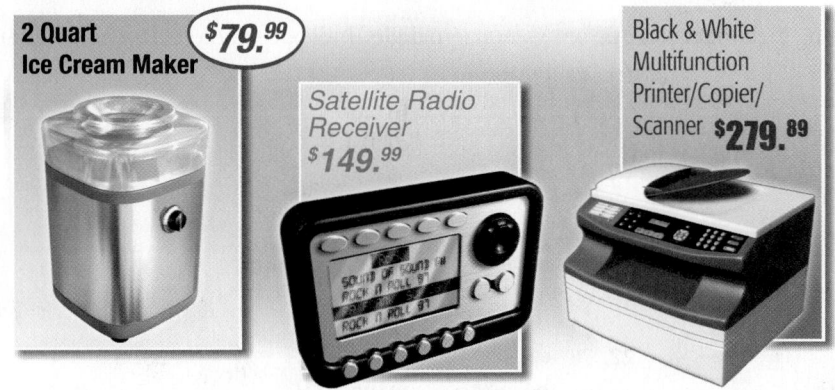

2 Quart Ice Cream Maker $79.⁹⁹

Satellite Radio Receiver $149.⁹⁹

Black & White Multifunction Printer/Copier/Scanner $279.⁸⁹

1. Estimate the total cost of one printer and one satellite radio.
   a) $43   **b)** $4300   **c)** $360   **d)** $430

2. Estimate the total cost of one satellite radio and one ice cream maker.
   a) $230   **b)** $23   **c)** $2300   **d)** $400

3. About how much more does the printer cost than the satellite radio?
   a) $1300   **b)** $200   **c)** $130   **d)** $13

4. About how much more does the satellite radio cost than the ice cream maker?
   a) $7000   **b)** $70   **c)** $130   **d)** $700

5. Estimate the total cost of 6 ice cream makers.
   a) $480   **b)** $48   **c)** $240   **d)** $4800

6. Estimate the total cost of 4 printers.
   a) $1200   **b)** $1120   **c)** $11,200   **d)** $600

7. About how many ice cream makers can be purchased for $830?
   a) 120   **b)** 100   **c)** 10   **d)** 1000

8. About how many printers can be purchased for $5627?
   a) 200   **b)** 20   **c)** 1800   **d)** 2000

Estimate by rounding as directed.

9. $0.02 + 1.31 + 0.34$;
   nearest tenth

10. $0.88 + 2.07 + 1.54$;
   nearest one

11. $6.03 + 0.007 + 0.214$;
   nearest one

12. $1.11 + 8.888 + 99.94$;
   nearest one

13. $52.367 + 1.307 + 7.324$;
   nearest one

14. $12.9882 + 1.2115$;
   nearest tenth

15. $2.678 - 0.445$;
nearest tenth

16. $12.9882 - 1.0115$;
nearest one

17. $198.67432 - 24.5007$;
nearest ten

Estimate. Choose a rounding digit that gives one or two nonzero digits. Indicate which of the choices is an appropriate estimate.

18. $234.12321 - 200.3223$
   a) 600   **b)** 60
   c) 300   **d)** 30

19. 49×7.89
   a) 400   **b)** 40
   c) 4   **d)** 0.4

20. 7.4×8.9
   a) 95   **b)** 63
   c) 124   **d)** 6

21. 98.4×0.083
   a) 80   **b)** 12
   c) 8   **d)** 0.8

22. 78×5.3
   a) 400   **b)** 800
   c) 40   **d)** 8

23. $3.6 \div 4$
   a) 10   **b)** 1
   c) 0.1   **d)** 0.01

24. $0.0713 \div 1.94$
   a) 3.5   **b)** 0.35
   c) 0.035 **d)** 35

25. $74.68 \div 24.7$
   a) 9   **b)** 3
   c) 12   **d)** 120

26. $914 \div 0.921$
   a) 10   **b)** 100
   c) 1000   **d)** 1

27. *Fence Posts.* A zoo plans to construct a fence around its proposed animals of the Great Plains exhibit. The perimeter of the area to be fenced is 1760 ft. Estimate the number of wooden fence posts needed if the posts are placed 8.625 ft apart.

28. *Ticketmaster.* Recently, Ticketmaster stock sold for $22.25 per share. Estimate how many shares can be purchased for $4400.

Copyright © 2012 Pearson Education, Inc.

29. *Day-Care Supplies.* Helen wants to buy 12 boxes of crayons at $1.89 per box for the day care center that she runs. Estimate the total cost of the crayons.

30. *Batteries.* Oscar buys 6 packages of AAA batteries at $5.29 per package. Estimate the total cost of the purchase.

Skill Maintenance

In each of Exercises 31–38, fill in the blank with the correct term from the given list. Some of the choices may not be used and some may be used more than once.

31. The decimal $0.57\overline{3}$ is an example of a(n) _____ decimal. [3.5a]

32. The least common _____ of two natural numbers is the smallest number that is a multiple of both. [1.9a]

33. In the product $10 \cdot \frac{3}{4}$, 10 and $\frac{3}{4}$ are _____. [1.7a]

34. A _____ of an equation is a replacement for the variable that makes the equation true. [1.4a]

35. The number 1 is the _____ identity. [1.3a]

36. The product of 6 and $\frac{1}{6}$ is 1; we say that 6 and $\frac{1}{6}$ are _____ of each other. [2.2b]

37. The least common _____ of two or more fractions is the least common _____ of their denominators. [2.3a]

38. The number 3728 is _____ by 4 if the number named by the last two digits is _____ by 4. [1.8a]

additive

multiplicative

numerator

denominator

reciprocals

factors

solution

divisible

terminating

repeating

multiple

factor

Synthesis

The following were done on a calculator. Estimate to determine whether the decimal point was placed correctly.

39. $178.9462 \times 61.78 = 11{,}055.29624$

40. $14{,}973.35 \div 298.75 = 501.2$

41. $19.7236 - 1.4738 \times 4.1097 = 1.366672414$

42. $28.46901 \div 4.9187 - 2.5081 = 3.279813473$

43. ▦ Use one of $+$, $-$, $\times$, and $\div$ in each blank to make a true sentence.

    a) $(0.37 \ \square \ 18.78) \ \square \ 2^{13} = 156{,}876.8$

    b) $2.56 \ \square \ 6.4 \ \square \ 51.2 \ \square \ 17.4 = 312.84$

Applications and Problem Solving

a Solving Applied Problems

Solving applied problems with decimals is like solving applied problems with whole numbers. We translate first to an equation that corresponds to the situation. Then we solve the equation.

EXAMPLE 1 *Canals.* The Panama Canal in Panama is 50.7 mi long. The Suez Canal in Egypt is 119.9 mi long. How much longer is the Suez Canal?

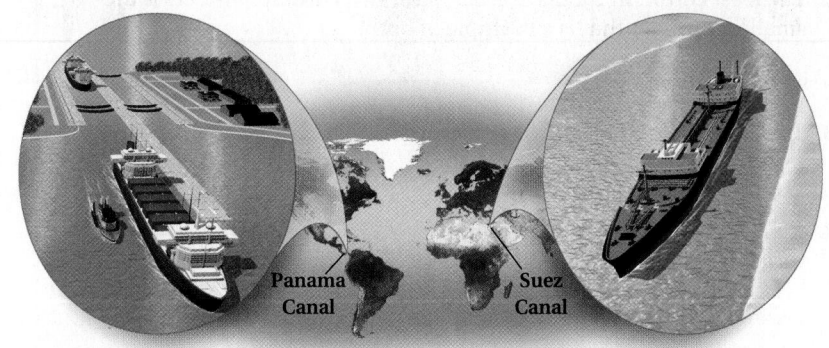

Panama Canal   Suez Canal

1. **Familiarize.** We let l = the distance in miles that the length of the longer canal differs from the length of the shorter canal.

2. **Translate.** We translate as follows, using the given information:

Length of Panama Canal, the shorter canal	plus	Additional length	is	Length of Suez Canal, the longer canal
↓	↓	↓	↓	↓
50.7 mi	+	l	=	119.9 mi.

3. **Solve.** We solve the equation by subtracting 50.7 mi on both sides:

$$50.7 + l = 119.9$$
$$50.7 + l - 50.7 = 119.9 - 50.7$$
$$l = 69.2.$$

4. **Check.** We can check by adding.

$$\begin{array}{r} 5\ 0.7 \\ +\ \ 6\ 9.2 \\ \hline 1\ 1\ 9.9 \end{array}$$

The answer checks.

5. **State.** The Suez Canal is 69.2 mi longer than the Panama Canal.

Do Exercise 1.

1. Debit-Card Transactions.
Debit-card transactions in 2000 totaled 9.8 billion. The number of transactions projected to be made in 2010 is 42.5 billion. How many more debit-card transactions are expected in 2010 than in 2000?

Source: *The Nilson Report*

Answer

1. 32.7 billion transactions

EXAMPLE 2 *Meat and Seafood Consumption.* In a recent year, the average American consumed about 62.8 lb of beef, 47.3 lb of pork and lamb, 73.6 lb of poultry, and 16.1 lb of seafood. Find the total amount of meat and seafood consumed by the average American per year.

Meat and Seafood Consumption

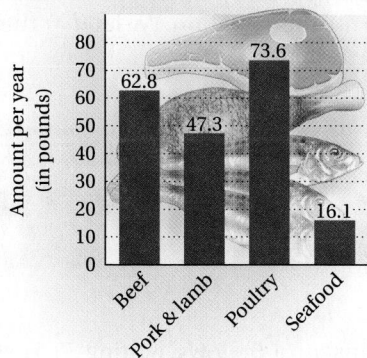

SOURCE: U.S. Department of Agriculture

1. **Familiarize.** The figure above helps us visualize the situation. We let t = the total amount of meat and seafood consumed by the average American per year.

2. **Translate.** We are combining amounts. We translate to an equation that does this.

Beef	plus	Pork and lamb	plus	Poultry	plus	Seafood	is	Total
↓	↓	↓	↓	↓	↓	↓	↓	↓
62.8	+	47.3	+	73.6	+	16.1	=	t

3. **Solve.** To solve, we carry out the addition.

$$
\begin{array}{r}
\overset{1}{6}\,\overset{1}{2}.8 \\
4\,7.3 \\
7\,3.6 \\
+\;\;1\,6.1 \\
\hline
1\,9\,9.8
\end{array}
$$

Thus, $t = 199.8$.

4. **Check.** We can check by repeating our addition. We can also see whether our answer is reasonable by first noting that it is indeed larger than any of the numbers being added. We can also do a check by rounding and estimating:

$$62.8 + 47.3 + 73.6 + 16.1 \approx 60 + 50 + 70 + 20$$
$$\approx 200 \approx 199.8.$$

If we had gotten an answer like 19.98 or 1998, then the estimate, 200, would have told us that we had made a mistake, such as not lining up the decimal points.

5. **State.** The average American consumes about 199.8 lb of meat and seafood per year.

Do Exercise 2.

2. Amount of Medication. Over a 24-hr period, a patient received injections of 2.8 mL, 1.35 mL, 2.0 mL, and 1.88 mL of a medication. What was the total amount of medication received?

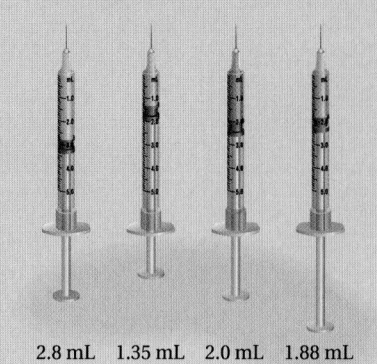

2.8 mL   1.35 mL   2.0 mL   1.88 mL

Answer

2. 8.03 mL

EXAMPLE 3 *IRS Driving Allowance.* The Internal Revenue Service allowed a tax deduction of 58.5¢ per mile driven for business purposes in the last six months of 2008. What deduction, in dollars, would be allowed for driving 9143 mi during this time period?

Source: Internal Revenue Service

1. **Familiarize.** We first make a drawing or at least visualize the situation. Repeated addition fits this situation. We let $d =$ the deduction, in dollars, allowed for driving 9143 mi.

9143 mi

2. **Translate.** We translate as follows, writing 58.5¢ as $0.585:

Deduction for each mile	times	Number of miles driven	is	Total deduction
↓	↓	↓	↓	↓
$0.585	×	9143	=	d.

3. **Solve.** To solve the equation, we carry out the multiplication.

$$
\begin{array}{r}
9\ 1\ 4\ 3 \\
\times\ 0.5\ 8\ 5 \\
\hline
4\ 5\ 7\ 1\ 5 \\
7\ 3\ 1\ 4\ 4\ 0 \\
4\ 5\ 7\ 1\ 5\ 0\ 0 \\
\hline
5\ 3\ 4\ 8.6\ 5\ 5
\end{array}
$$

Thus, $d = 5348.655 \approx 5348.66$.

4. **Check.** We can obtain a partial check by rounding and estimating:

$$9143 \times 0.585 \approx 9000 \times 0.6 \approx 5400 \approx 5348.66.$$

5. **State.** The total allowable deduction would be $5348.66.

Do Exercise 3.

3. Printing Costs. At Kwik Copy, the cost of copying is 11 cents per page. How much, in dollars, would it cost to make 466 copies?

EXAMPLE 4 *Loan Payments.* A car loan of $7382.52 is to be paid off in 36 equal monthly payments. How much is each payment?

1. **Familiarize.** We first make a drawing. We let $n =$ the amount of each payment.

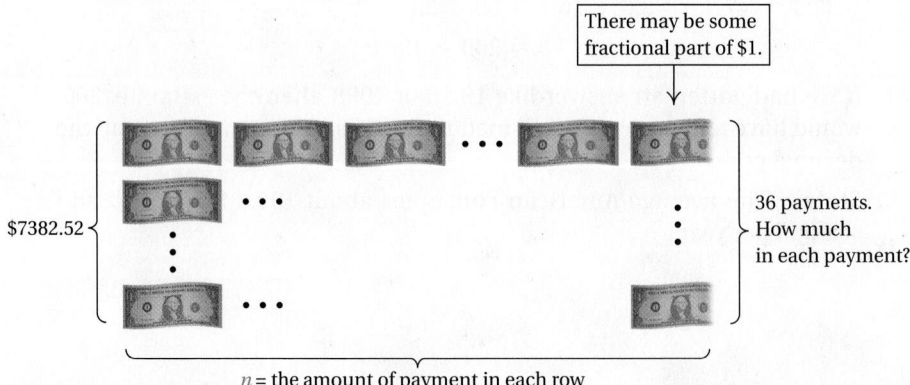

There may be some fractional part of $1.

$7382.52

36 payments. How much in each payment?

$n =$ the amount of payment in each row

Answer

3. $51.26

2. **Translate.** The problem can be translated to the following equation, thinking that

(Total loan) ÷ (Number of payments) = Amount of each payment

$$\$7382.52 \div 36 = n.$$

3. **Solve.** To solve the equation, we carry out the division.

```
          2 0 5.0 7
  3 6 ) 7 3 8 2.5 2
         7 2
         ‾‾‾
         1 8 2
         1 8 0
         ‾‾‾‾‾
             2 5 2
             2 5 2
             ‾‾‾‾‾
                 0
```

Thus, $n = 205.07$.

4. **Check.** A partial check can be obtained by estimating the quotient: $\$7382.56 \div 36 \approx 8000 \div 40 \approx 200 \approx 205.07$. The estimate checks.

5. **State.** Each payment is $205.07.

Do Exercise 4.

4. Loan Payments. A loan of $4425 is to be paid off in 12 equal monthly payments. How much is each payment?

EXAMPLE 5 *Travel Poster.* Sam is decorating his dorm room with travel posters. The dimensions of each poster are 27.4 in. by 19.3 in. Find the area of a poster.

1. **Familiarize.** We first make a drawing. We let A = the area.

27.4 in.

19.3 in.

2. **Translate.** We use the formula $A = l \cdot w$ and substitute:

$$A = l \cdot w$$
$$A = 27.4 \times 19.3.$$

Answer
4. $368.75

5. Index Cards. A standard-size index card measures 12.7 cm by 7.6 cm. What is its area?

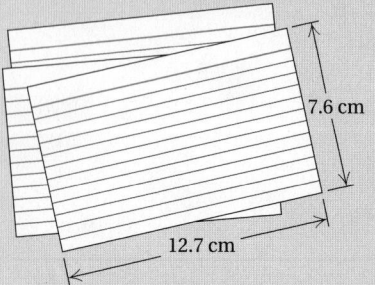

7.6 cm

12.7 cm

3. Solve. We solve by carrying out the multiplication.

$$
\begin{array}{r}
2\,7.4 \\
\times\ 1\,9.3 \\
\hline
8\,2\,2 \\
2\,4\,6\,6\,0 \\
2\,7\,4\,0\,0 \\
\hline
5\,2\,8.8\,2
\end{array}
$$

Thus, $A = 528.82$.

4. Check. We obtain a partial check by estimating the product:

$$A = 27.4 \times 19.3 \approx 25 \times 20 \approx 500.$$

This estimate is close to 528.82, so the answer is probably correct.

5. State. The area of the travel poster is 528.82 in².

Do Exercise 5.

EXAMPLE 6 *Digital Camera Purchase.* Dawson Real Estate spent $10,399.74 on 26 Nikon Coolpix 10.1 megapixel digital cameras, so that its agents could place photos of properties on the firm's Web site. How much did each camera cost?

1. Familiarize. We let c = the cost of each camera.

2. Translate. We translate as follows:

Cost of each camera	is	Total cost of purchase	divided by	Number of cameras purchased
↓	↓	↓	↓	↓
c	=	$10,399.74	÷	26.

3. Solve. To solve, we carry out the division.

$$
\begin{array}{r}
3\,9\,9.9\,9 \\
26\,\overline{)\,1\,0,3\,9\,9.7\,4} \\
7\,8 \\
\hline
2\,5\,9 \\
2\,3\,4 \\
\hline
2\,5\,9 \\
2\,3\,4 \\
\hline
2\,5\,7 \\
2\,3\,4 \\
\hline
2\,3\,4 \\
2\,3\,4 \\
\hline
0
\end{array}
$$

4. Check. We check by estimating

$$10,399.74 \div 26 \approx 10,000 \div 25 = 400.$$

Since 400 is close to 399.99, the answer is probably correct.

5. State. The cost of each camera was $399.99.

Do Exercise 6.

6. One pound of lean boneless ham contains 4.5 servings. It costs $7.99 per pound. What is the cost per serving? Round to the nearest cent.

Answers

5. 96.52 cm²   **6.** $1.78

Multistep Problems

EXAMPLE 7 *Gas Mileage.* Ava filled her gas tank and noted that the odometer read 67,507.8. After the next filling, the odometer read 68,006.1. It took 16.5 gal to fill the tank. How many miles per gallon did Ava get?

1. Familiarize. We first make a drawing.

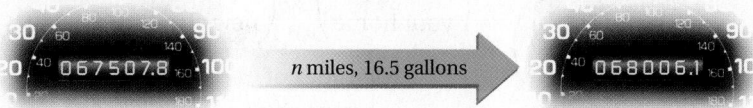

n miles, 16.5 gallons

This is a two-step problem. First, we find the number of miles that have been driven between fillups. We let *n* = the number of miles driven.

2., 3. Translate and **Solve.** We translate and solve as follows:

First odometer reading	plus	Number of miles driven	is	Second odometer reading
↓	↓	↓	↓	↓
67,507.8	+	*n*	=	68,006.1.

To solve the equation, we subtract 67,507.8 on both sides:

$$n = 68,006.1 - 67,507.8$$
$$= 498.3.$$

$$
\begin{array}{r}
6\,8{,}0\,0\,6.1 \\
-\ 6\,7{,}5\,0\,7.8 \\
\hline
4\,9\,8.3
\end{array}
$$

Next, we divide the total number of miles driven by the number of gallons. This gives us *m* = the number of miles per gallon—that is, the mileage. The division that corresponds to the situation is

$$498.3 \div 16.5 = m.$$

To find the number *m*, we divide.

$$
\begin{array}{r}
3\,0.2 \\
1\,6.5\,)\overline{4\,9\,8.3{\scriptstyle\wedge}0} \\
4\,9\,5 \\
\hline
3\,3\,0 \\
3\,3\,0 \\
\hline
0
\end{array}
$$

Thus, *m* = 30.2.

4. Check. To check, we first multiply the number of miles per gallon times the number of gallons to find the number of miles driven:

$$16.5 \times 30.2 = 498.3.$$

Then we add 498.3 to 67,507.8 to find the new odometer reading:

$$67,507.8 + 498.3 = 68,006.1.$$

The mileage 30.2 checks.

5. State. Ava got 30.2 miles per gallon.

Do Exercise 7.

STUDY TIPS

FIVE STEPS FOR PROBLEM SOLVING

Are you using the five steps for problem solving that were developed in Section 1.5?

1. **Familiarize** yourself with the situation.
   a) Carefully read and reread until you understand what you are being asked to find.
   b) Draw a diagram or see if there is a formula that applies.
   c) Assign a letter, or *variable*, to the unknown.

2. **Translate** the problem to an equation using the letter or variable.

3. **Solve** the equation.

4. **Check** the answer in the original wording of the problem.

5. **State** the answer to the problem clearly with appropriate units.

7. Gas Mileage. John filled his gas tank and noted that the odometer read 38,320.8. After the next filling, the odometer read 38,735.5. It took 14.5 gal to fill the tank. How many miles per gallon did John get?

Answer

7. 28.6 mpg

FOR SALE

EXAMPLE 8 *Home-Cost Comparison.* Suppose you own a home like the one shown here and it is valued at $225,000 in Tulsa, Oklahoma. What would it cost to buy a similar home in Boston, Massachusetts? To find out, we can use an index table prepared by Coldwell Banker Real Estate Corporation. (For a complete index table, contact your local representative.) We use the following formula:

$$\begin{pmatrix} \text{Cost of your} \\ \text{home in new city} \end{pmatrix} = \dfrac{\begin{pmatrix} \text{Value of} \\ \text{your home} \end{pmatrix} \times \begin{pmatrix} \text{Index of} \\ \text{new city} \end{pmatrix}}{\begin{pmatrix} \text{Index of} \\ \text{your city} \end{pmatrix}}.$$

Find the cost of your Tulsa home in Boston.

STATE	CITY	INDEX	STATE	CITY	INDEX
Massachusetts	Boston	327	Texas	Dallas	72
Illinois	Chicago	173	Oklahoma	Tulsa	36
California	Palo Alto	397	Florida	Miami	151
	Sacramento	90		Orlando	96
	San Diego	147		Key West	220
Alaska	Juneau	110	Colorado	Boulder	146
Kentucky	Louisville	56	North Carolina	Charlotte	61

SOURCE: Coldwell Banker Real Estate Corporation

1. **Familiarize.** We let C = the cost of the home in Boston. We use the table and look up the indexes of Tulsa and the new city, Boston. We see that Tulsa's index is 36 and Boston's index is 327.

2. **Translate.** Using the formula, we translate to the following equation:

$$C = \frac{\$225{,}000 \times 327}{36}.$$

3. **Solve.** To solve, we carry out the computations using the rules for order of operations. (See Section 3.4.)

$$C = \frac{\$225{,}000 \times 327}{36}$$

$$= \frac{\$73{,}575{,}000}{36} \qquad \text{Carrying out the multiplication first}$$

$$= \$2{,}043{,}750 \qquad \text{Carrying out the division}$$

On a calculator, the computation could be done in one step.

4. **Check.** We can repeat our computations.

5. **State.** A home that sells for $225,000 in Tulsa would cost about $2,043,750 in Boston.

Do Exercises 8 and 9.

Refer to the table in Example 8 to answer Exercises 8 and 9. Round to the nearest dollar.

8. **Home-Cost Comparison.** Suppose your home in Charlotte is valued at $180,000. What would it cost to buy a similar home in Chicago?

9. **Home-Cost Comparison.** Suppose your home in Boulder is valued at $315,000. What would it cost to buy a similar home in Louisville?

Answers

8. $510,492   9. $120,822

Translating
for Success

1. *Gas Mileage.* Art filled his SUV's gas tank and noted that the odometer read 38,271.8. At the next filling, the odometer read 38,677.92. It took 28.4 gal to fill the tank. How many miles per gallon did the SUV get?

2. *Dimensions of a Parking Lot.* Seals' parking lot is a rectangle that measures 85.2 ft by 52.3 ft. What is the area of the parking lot?

3. *Game Snacks.* Three students pay $18.40 for snacks at a football game. What is each person's share?

4. *Electrical Wiring.* An electrician needs 1314 ft of wiring cut into $2\frac{1}{2}$-ft pieces. How many pieces will she have?

5. *College Tuition.* Wayne needs $4638 for the fall semester's tuition. On the day of registration, he has only $3092. How much does he need to borrow?

The goal of these matching questions is to practice step (2), *Translate,* of the five-step problem-solving process. Translate each word problem to an equation and select a correct translation from equations A–O.

A. $2\frac{1}{2} \cdot n = 1314$

B. $18.4 \times 3.87 = n$

C. $n = 85.2 \times 52.3$

D. $1314.28 - 437 = n$

E. $3 \times 18.40 = n$

F. $2\frac{1}{2} \cdot 1314 = n$

G. $3092 + n = 4638$

H. $18.4 \cdot n = 3.87$

I. $\dfrac{406.12}{28.4} = n$

J. $52.3 \cdot n = 85.2$

K. $n = 1314.28 + 437$

L. $52.3 + n = 85.2$

M. $3092 + 4638 = n$

N. $3 \cdot n = 18.40$

O. $85.2 + 52.3 = n$

Answers on page A-5

6. *Cost of Gasoline.* What is the cost, in dollars, of 18.4 gal of gasoline at $3.87 per gallon?

7. *Savings Account Balance.* Margaret has $1314.28 in her savings account. Before using her debit card to buy an office chair, she transferred $437 to her checking account. How much was left in her savings account?

8. *Acres Planted.* This season Sam planted 85.2 acres of corn and 52.3 acres of soybeans. Find the total number of acres that he planted.

9. *Amount Inherited.* Tara inherited $2\frac{1}{2}$ times as much as her cousin. Her cousin received $1314. How much did Tara receive?

10. *Travel Funds.* The athletic department needs travel funds of $4638 for the tennis team and $3092 for the golf team. What is the total amount needed for travel?

3.7 Exercise Set

For Extra Help

MyMathLab

Math XL
PRACTICE

WATCH

DOWNLOAD

READ

REVIEW

a   Solve.

Hurricane Damage.   The amount of damage caused by the five most costly Atlantic hurricanes in the United States is shown in the table below. Use this table to do Exercises 1 and 2.

Most Costly Hurricanes

RANK	HURRICANE	YEAR	COST IN 2007 DOLLARS (in billions)
1	Katrina	2005	$81.2
2	Andrew	1992	38.1
3	Wilma	2005	30.4
4	Ivan	2004	18.1
5	Charley	2004	16.2

SOURCE: National Hurricane Center

1. How much more costly was Hurricane Katrina than Hurricane Andrew?

2. What was the total cost of the two hurricanes that occurred in 2005?

Top American Sky Routes.   The figure below shows the numbers of airline passengers carried on the top five sky routes in the United States from December 2006 to November 2007. Note that these routes go in both directions. Use this figure to do Exercises 3 and 4.

Top American Sky Routes

New York City–Chicago	3.47
Washington–Chicago	2.82
Atlanta–Orlando	2.77
Los Angeles–Chicago	2.71
Atlanta–New York City	2.69

Number of passengers (in millions)

SOURCE: U.S. Bureau of Transportation Statistics

3. What is the total number of passengers carried on the top two routes?

4. How many more passengers were carried on the New York City–Chicago route than on the Los Angeles–Chicago route?

5. *Record Movie Openings.*   The movie *The Dark Knight* took in $155.34 million on its first weekend. This topped the previous high opening weekend revenue set by *Spider-Man 3* by $4.24 million. How much did *Spider-Man 3* take in on its opening weekend?
Source: Associated Press

6. *Counterfeit Money.*   The amount of counterfeit money passed in the United States is on the rise. About $62.0 million was passed in 2006. This amount was $22.8 million more than entered circulation in 1999. How much counterfeit money was passed in 1999?
Source: U.S. Secret Service

Copyright © 2012 Pearson Education, Inc.

7. *Cost of Bottled Water.* The cost of a year's supply of a popular brand of bottled water, based on the recommended consumption of 64 oz per day, at the supermarket price of $3.99 for a six-pack of half-liter bottles is $918.82. This is $918.31 more than the cost of drinking the same amount of tap water for a year. What is the cost of drinking tap water for a year?

Source: American Water Works Association

8. *Bottled Water Consumption.* The annual consumption of bottled water in the United States was 27.6 gal per person in 2006. This was an increase of 26 gal per person over the amount consumed in 1976. What was the annual consumption of bottled water in 1976?

Source: Beverage Marketing Corporation

9. *Body Temperature.* Normal body temperature is 98.6°F. During an illness, a patient's temperature rose 4.2°. What was the new temperature?

10. *Gasoline Cost.* What is the cost, in dollars, of 12.6 gal of gasoline at $3.79 per gallon? Round the answer to the nearest cent.

11. *Lottery Winnings.* The largest lotto jackpot ever won in California totaled $193,000,000 and was shared equally by 3 winners. How much was each winner's share? Round to the nearest cent.

Source: California State Lottery

12. *Lunch Costs.* A group of 4 students pays $47.84 for lunch and splits the cost equally. What is each person's share?

13. *Stamp.* Find the area and the perimeter of the stamp shown here.

2.5 cm

3.25 cm

14. *Pole Vault Pit.* Find the area and the perimeter of the landing area of the pole vault pit shown here.

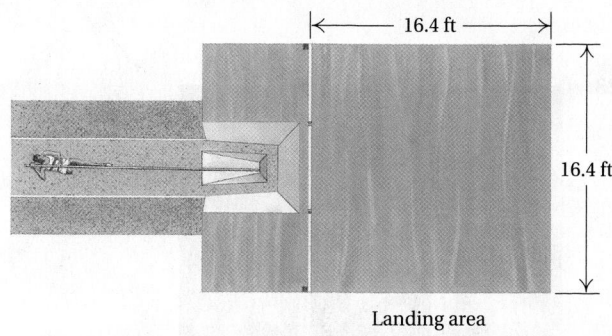

16.4 ft

16.4 ft

Landing area

15. *Odometer Reading.* The Binford family's odometer reads 22,456.8 at the beginning of a trip. The family's online driving directions tell them that they will be driving 234.7 mi. What will the odometer read at the end of the trip?

16. *Miles Driven.* Petra bought gasoline when the odometer read 14,296.3. At the next gasoline purchase, the odometer read 14,515.8. How many miles had been driven?

17. *Gas Mileage.* Peggy filled her van's gas tank and noted that the odometer read 26,342.8. After the next filling, the odometer read 26,736.7. It took 19.5 gal to fill the tank. How many miles per gallon did the van get?

18. *Gas Mileage.* Henry filled his Honda's gas tank and noted that the odometer read 18,943.2. After the next filling, the odometer read 19,306.2. It took 13.2 gal to fill the tank. How many miles per gallon did the car get?

19. *Chemistry.* The water in a filled tank weighs 748.45 lb. One cubic foot of water weighs 62.5 lb. How many cubic feet of water does the tank hold?

20. *Highway Routes.* You can drive from home to work using either of two routes:

> *Route A*: Via interstate highway, 7.6 mi, with a speed limit of 65 mph.

> *Route B*: Via a country road, 5.6 mi, with a speed limit of 50 mph.

Assuming you drive at the posted speed limit, which route takes less time? (Use the formula *Distance* = *Speed* × *Time*.)

Find the perimeter of each figure.

21.
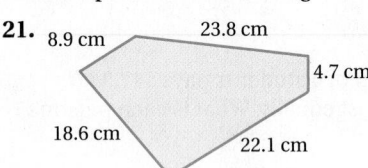
8.9 cm 23.8 cm 4.7 cm 18.6 cm 22.1 cm

22.
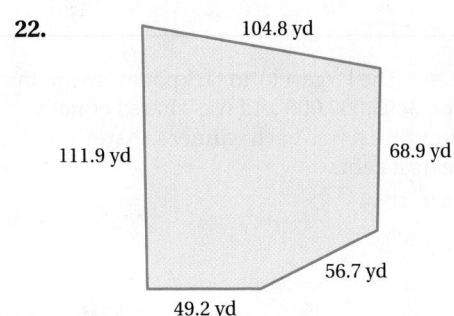
104.8 yd 111.9 yd 68.9 yd 56.7 yd 49.2 yd

23.

2.5 cm 2.25 cm

24.
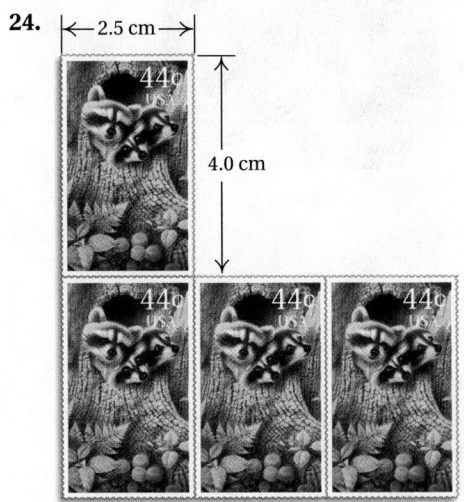
2.5 cm 4.0 cm

25. Andrew bought a DVD of the movie *Horton Hears a Who* for his nephew for $23.99 plus $1.68 sales tax. He paid for it with a $50 bill. How much change did he receive?

26. Claire bought a copy of the book *Make Way for Ducklings* for her daughter for $16.95 plus $0.85 sales tax. She paid for it with a $20 bill. How much change did she receive?

Copyright © 2012 Pearson Education, Inc.

Find the length *d* in each figure.

27.

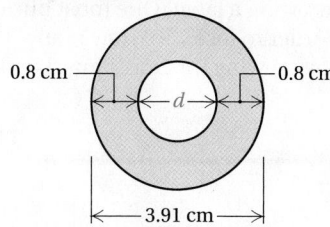

0.8 cm — — 0.8 cm

d

← 3.91 cm →

28.

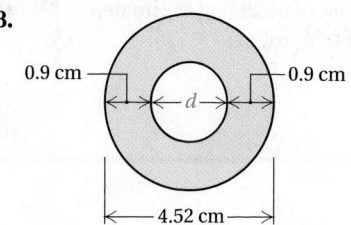

0.9 cm — — 0.9 cm

d

← 4.52 cm →

29. *Calories Burned Mowing.*   A person weighing 150 lb burns 7.3 calories per minute while mowing a lawn with a power lawnmower. How many calories would be burned in 2 hr of mowing?

Source: *The Handy Science Answer Book*

30. Lot A measures 250.1 ft by 302.7 ft. Lot B measures 389.4 ft by 566.2 ft. What is the total area of the two lots?

31. Holly had $1123.56 in her checking account. She used her debit card to make purchases of $23.82, $507.88, and $98.32. She then deposited a bonus check of $678.20. How much was in her account after these changes?

32. Natalie had $185.00 to spend for fall clothes: $44.95 was spent on shoes, $71.95 for a jacket, and $55.35 for pants. How much was left?

33. A rectangular yard is 20 ft by 15 ft. The yard is covered with grass except for an 8.5-ft-square flower garden. How much grass is in the yard?

34. Rita earns a gross paycheck (before deductions) of $495.72. Her deductions are $59.60 for federal income tax, $29.00 for FICA, and $29.00 for medical insurance. What is her take-home paycheck?

35. *Batting Average.*   Chipper Jones of the Atlanta Braves won the 2008 National League batting title with 160 hits in 439 times at bat. What part of his at-bats were hits? Give decimal notation rounded to the nearest thousandth. (This is a *batting average*.)

Source: Major League Baseball

36. *Batting Average.*   Joe Mauer of the Minnesota Twins won the 2008 American League batting title with 176 hits in 536 times at bat. What part of his at-bats were hits? Give decimal notation rounded to the nearest thousandth.

Source: Major League Baseball

37. *Field Dimensions.*   The dimensions of a World Cup soccer field are 114.9 yd by 74.4 yd. The dimensions of a standard football field are 120 yd by 53.3 yd. How much greater is the area of a World Cup soccer field?

World Cup Soccer Field

Football Field

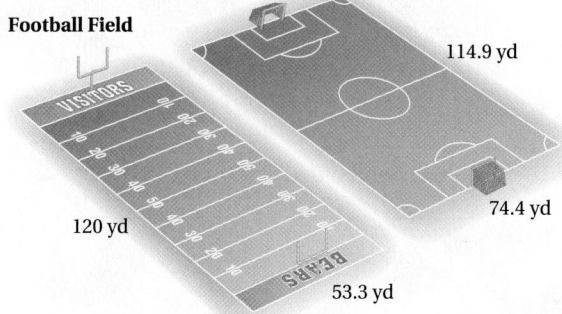

114.9 yd

120 yd

74.4 yd

53.3 yd

38. *Loan Payment.*   In order to make money on loans, financial institutions are paid back more money than they loan. Suppose you borrow $120,000 to buy a house and agree to make monthly payments of $880.52 for 30 yr. How much do you pay back altogether? How much more do you pay back than the amount of the loan?

39. *Egg Costs.* A restaurant owner bought 20 dozen eggs for $25.80. Find the cost of each egg to the nearest tenth of a cent (thousandth of a dollar).

40. *Weight Loss.* A person weighing 170 lb burns 8.6 calories per minute while mowing a lawn. One must burn about 3500 calories in order to lose 1 lb. How many pounds would be lost by mowing for 2 hr? Round to the nearest tenth.

41. *Construction Pay.* A construction worker is paid $18.50 per hour for the first 40 hr of work, and time and a half, or $27.75 per hour, for any overtime exceeding 40 hr per week. One week she works 46 hr. How much is her pay?

42. *Summer Work.* Zachary worked 53 hr during a week one summer. He earned $7.50 per hour for the first 40 hr and $11.25 per hour for overtime (hours exceeding 40). How much did Zachary earn during the week?

43. *Projected World Population.* Using the information in the bar graph below, determine the average population of the world for the years 1950 through 2050. Round to the nearest thousandth of a billion.

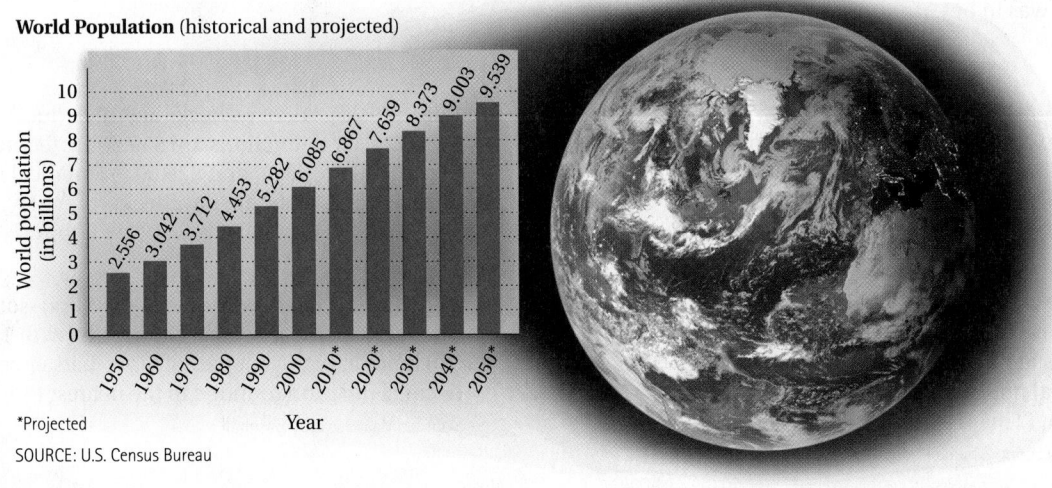

World Population (historical and projected)

2.556 3.042 3.712 4.453 5.282 6.085 6.867 7.659 8.373 9.003 9.539

1950 1960 1970 1980 1990 2000 2010* 2020* 2030* 2040* 2050*

World population (in billions)

Year

*Projected

SOURCE: U.S. Census Bureau

44. *Number of Volunteers.* The table at right lists the number of Americans in various age groups who do volunteer work. What is the average number of volunteers in all the age groups shown?

AGE	NUMBER OF VOLUNTEERS (in millions)
16–24 yr	8.044
25–34 yr	9.096
35–44 yr	13.308
45–54 yr	13.415
55–64 yr	8.819
65 yr and older	8.518

SOURCE: U.S. Census Bureau

Copyright © 2012 Pearson Education, Inc.

45. *Body Temperature.* Normal body temperature is 98.6°F. A baby's bath water should be 100°F. How many degrees above normal body temperature is this?

46. *Body Temperature.* Normal body temperature is 98.6°F. The lowest temperature at which a patient has survived is 69°F. How many degrees below normal is this?

Home-Cost Comparison. Use the table and the formula in Example 8 to do Exercises 47–54. In each of the following cases, find the value of the house in the new location. Round to the nearest dollar.

Source: Coldwell Banker Real Estate Corporation

	VALUE	PRESENT LOCATION	NEW LOCATION	NEW VALUE
47.	$125,000	Dallas	Miami	
48.	$180,000	San Diego	Key West	
49.	$96,000	Juneau	Orlando	
50.	$300,000	Palo Alto	Dallas	
51.	$240,000	Louisville	Boston	
52.	$160,000	Charlotte	Sacramento	
53.	$140,000	Chicago	Tulsa	
54.	$99,000	Boulder	Orlando	

55. *Cell-Phone Plan.* In 2008, at&t offered an individual cell-phone plan with 450 anytime minutes for a monthly access fee of $39.99. Minutes in excess of 450 were charged at the rate of $0.45 per minute. In June, Leila used her cell phone for 479 min. What was she charged?
Source: at&t

56. *Cell-Phone Plan.* In 2008, at&t offered an individual cell-phone plan with 900 anytime minutes per month for a monthly access fee of $59.99. Minutes in excess of 900 were charged at the rate of $0.40 per minute. One month Jeff used his cell phone for 946 min. What was the charge?
Source: at&t

IRS Driving Allowance. The Internal Revenue Service allowed a tax deduction of 50.5¢ per mile driven for business purposes from January 1, 2008, through June 30, 2008. In response to increasing gas prices, this deduction was increased to 58.5¢ per mile driven from July 1, 2008, through December 31, 2008. Use this information for Exercises 57 and 58.
Source: Internal Revenue Service

57. Sheila drove 3156 mi for business purposes between January 1, 2008, and June 30, 2008. She drove an additional 3678 mi between July 1, 2008, and December 31, 2008. What deduction, in dollars, was she allowed to take?

58. Manolo drove 1250 mi for business purposes between January 1, 2008, and June 30, 2008. He drove an additional 1872 mi between July 1, 2008, and December 31, 2008. What deduction, in dollars, was he allowed to take?

59. *Property Taxes.* The Brunners own a house with an assessed value of $165,500. For every $1000 of assessed value, they pay $8.50 in property taxes each year. How much do they pay in property taxes each year?

60. *Property Taxes.* The Colavitos own a house with an assessed value of $184,500. For every $1000 of assessed value, they pay $7.68 in property taxes each year. How much do they pay in property taxes each year?

Skill Maintenance

Add.

61. $4569 + 1766$ [1.2a]

62. $\dfrac{2}{3} + \dfrac{5}{8}$ [2.3a]

63. $4\dfrac{1}{3} + 2\dfrac{1}{2}$ [2.4b]

64. $\dfrac{5}{6} + \dfrac{7}{10}$ [2.3a]

Subtract.

65. $\dfrac{2}{3} - \dfrac{5}{8}$ [2.3b]

66. $4569 - 1766$ [1.2c]

67. $\dfrac{5}{6} - \dfrac{7}{10}$ [2.3b]

68. $4\dfrac{1}{3} - 2\dfrac{1}{2}$ [2.4c]

Simplify. [2.1e]

69. $\dfrac{3225}{6275}$

70. $\dfrac{125}{400}$

71. $\dfrac{325}{625}$

72. $\dfrac{625}{475}$

Solve.

73. If a water wheel made 469 revolutions at a rate of $16\dfrac{3}{4}$ revolutions per minute, for how long did it rotate? [2.5a]

74. If a bicycle wheel made 480 revolutions at a rate of $66\dfrac{2}{3}$ revolutions per minute, for how long did it rotate? [2.5a]

75. *Calories in Pie.* A piece of pecan pie $\left(\dfrac{1}{8}\text{ of a 9-in. pie}\right)$ has 502 calories. A piece of pumpkin pie has 316 calories. How many more calories does a piece of pecan pie have than a piece of pumpkin pie? [1.5a]

76. *Calories in Turkey.* Dark meat turkey contains 187 calories per 3.5-oz serving. White meat turkey contains 157 calories per 3.5-oz serving. How many more calories per 3.5-oz serving does the dark turkey meat contain than the white turkey meat? [1.5a]

Synthesis

77. Suppose you buy a half-dozen packs of basketball cards with a dozen cards in each pack. The cost is twelve dozen cents for each half-dozen cards. How much do you pay for the cards?

Copyright © 2012 Pearson Education, Inc.

Summary and Review

Key Terms

arithmetic numbers, p. 178   terminating decimal, p. 218   repeating decimal, p. 218

Concept Reinforcement

Determine whether each statement is true or false.

_____   **1.** One thousand billion is one trillion.   [3.3b]

_____   **2.** The number of decimal places in the product of two numbers is the product of the numbers of places in the factors.   [3.3a]

_____   **3.** When we divide a number by 0.1, 0.01, 0.001, and so on, the quotient is larger than the divisor.   [3.4a]

_____   **4.** For a fraction with a factor other than 2 or 5 in its denominator, decimal notation terminates.   [3.5a]

_____   **5.** An estimate found by rounding to the nearest ten is usually more accurate than one found by rounding to the nearest hundred.   [3.6a]

Important Concepts

Objective 3.1b   Convert between decimal notation and fraction notation.

Example   Write fraction notation for 5.347.

$$5.347 \qquad 5.347. \qquad \frac{5347}{1000}$$

3 decimal places   Move 3 places to the right.   3 zeros

$$5.347 = \frac{5347}{1000}$$

Practice Exercise

1. Write fraction notation for 50.93.

Example   Write decimal notation for $\frac{29}{1000}$.

$$\frac{29}{1000} \qquad 0.029.$$

3 zeros   Move 3 places to the left.

$$\frac{29}{1000} = 0.029$$

Practice Exercise

2. Write decimal notation for $\frac{817}{10}$.

Example   Write decimal notation for $4\frac{63}{100}$.

$$4\frac{63}{100} = 4 + \frac{63}{100} = 4 \text{ and } \frac{63}{100} = 4.63$$

Practice Exercise

3. Write decimal notation for $42\frac{159}{1000}$.

Objective 3.1d Round decimal notation to the nearest thousandth, hundredth, tenth, one, ten, hundred, or thousand.

Example Round 19.7625 to the nearest hundredth.

Locate the digit in the hundredths place, 6. Consider the next digit to the right, 2. Since that digit, 2, is 4 or lower, round down.

19.7625
↓
19.76

Practice Exercise

4. Round 153.346 to the nearest hundredth.

Objective 3.2a Add using decimal notation.

Example Add: 14.26 + 63.589.

$$\begin{array}{r} \overset{1}{1\,4.2\,6\,0} \\ +\ 6\,3.5\,8\,9 \\ \hline 7\,7.8\,4\,9 \end{array}$$ Writing an extra zero

Practice Exercise

5. Add: 5.54 + 33.071.

Objective 3.2b Subtract using decimal notation.

Example Subtract: 67.345 − 24.28.

$$\begin{array}{r} 6\,7.3\,\overset{2\ 14}{\cancel{4}}\,5 \\ -\ 2\,4.2\,8\,0 \\ \hline 4\,3.0\,6\,5 \end{array}$$ Writing an extra zero

Practice Exercise

6. Subtract: 221.04 − 13.192.

Objective 3.3a Multiply using decimal notation.

Example Multiply: 1.8 × 0.04.

$$\begin{array}{r} 1.8 \\ \times\ 0.0\,4 \\ \hline 0.0\,7\,2 \end{array}$$

(1 decimal place)
(2 decimal places)
(3 decimal places)

Example Multiply: 0.001 × 87.1.

0.001 × 87.1   0.087.1

3 decimal places   Move 3 places to the left.
                     We write an extra zero.

0.001 × 87.1 = 0.0871

Example Multiply: 63.4 × 100.

63.4 × 100   63.40.

2 zeros   Move 2 places to the right.
                    We write an extra zero.

63.4 × 100 = 6340

Practice Exercise

7. Multiply: 5.46 × 3.5.

Practice Exercise

8. Multiply: 17.6 × 0.01.

Practice Exercise

9. Multiply: 1000 × 60.437.

Objective 3.4a Divide using decimal notation.

Example Divide: $21.35 \div 6.1$.

$$
\begin{array}{r}
3.5 \\
6.1\overline{)2\ 1.3\!\wedge\!5} \\
\underline{1\ 8\ 3} \\
3\ 0\ 5 \\
\underline{3\ 0\ 5} \\
0
\end{array}
$$

Practice Exercise

10. Divide: $26.64 \div 3.6$.

Example Divide: $\dfrac{16.7}{1000}$.

$$\dfrac{16.7}{1000} \qquad 0.016.7$$

3 zeros   Move 3 places to the left.

$$\dfrac{16.7}{1000} = 0.0167$$

Practice Exercise

11. Divide: $\dfrac{4.7}{100}$.

Example Divide: $\dfrac{42.93}{0.001}$.

$$\dfrac{42.93}{0.001} \qquad 42.930.$$

3 decimal places   Move 3 places to the right.

$$\dfrac{42.93}{0.001} = 42{,}930$$

Practice Exercise

12. Divide: $\dfrac{156.9}{0.01}$.

Review Exercises

Convert the number in each sentence to standard notation. [3.3b]

1. Russia has the largest total area of any country in the world, at 6.59 million square miles.

2. Americans eat more than 3.1 billion lb of chocolate each year.
Source: Chocolate Manufacturers' Association

Write a word name.   [3.1a]

3. 3.47

4. 0.031

5. 27.0001

6. 0.9

Write fraction notation.   [3.1b]

7. 0.09

8. 4.561

9. 0.089

10. 3.0227

Write decimal notation.   [3.1b]

11. $\dfrac{34}{1000}$

12. $\dfrac{42{,}603}{10{,}000}$

13. $27\dfrac{91}{100}$

14. $867\dfrac{6}{1000}$

Which number is larger?   [3.1c]

15. 0.034, 0.0185

16. 0.91, 0.19

17. 0.741, 0.6943

18. 1.038, 1.041

Round 17.4287 to the nearest: [3.1d]

19. Tenth.

20. Hundredth.

21. Thousandth.

22. One.

Add. [3.2a]

23.
```
      2.0 4 8
     6 5.3 7 1
   + 5 0 7.1
```

24.
```
     0.6
     0.0 0 4
     0.0 7
   + 0.0 0 9 8
```

25. $219.3 + 2.8 + 7$

26. $0.41 + 4.1 + 41 + 0.041$

Subtract. [3.2b]

27.
```
    3 0.0
  − 0.7 9 0 8
```

28.
```
    8 4 5.0 8
  −   5 4.7 9
```

29. $37.645 − 8.497$

30. $70.8 − 0.0109$

Multiply. [3.3a]

31.
```
      4 8
  × 0.2 7
```

32.
```
    0.1 7 4
  ×   0.8 3
```

33. 100×0.043

34. 0.001×24.68

Divide. [3.4a]

35. $8\overline{)6\ 0}$

36. $5\ 2\overline{)2\ 3.4}$

37. $2.6\overline{)1\ 1\ 7.5\ 2}$

38. $2.1\ 4\overline{)2.1\ 8\ 7\ 0\ 8}$

39. $\dfrac{276.3}{1000}$

40. $\dfrac{13.892}{0.01}$

Solve. [3.2c], [3.4b]

41. $x + 51.748 = 548.0275$

42. $3 \cdot x = 20.85$

43. $10 \cdot y = 425.4$

44. $0.0089 + y = 5$

Solve. [3.7a]

45. Stacia earned $620.80 working as a coronary intensive-care nurse during a 40-hr week. What is her hourly wage?

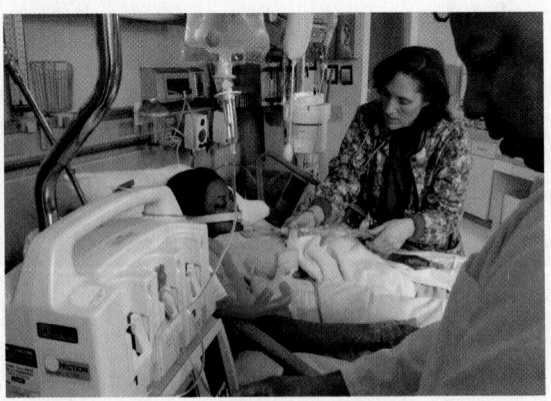

46. *Nutrition.* The average person eats 688.6 lb of fruits and vegetables in a year. What is the average consumption in one day? (Use 1 year = 365 days.) Round to the nearest tenth of a pound.
Source: U.S. Department of Agriculture

47. Derek had $1034.46 in his checking account. He used his debit card to buy a Wii game system for $249.99. How much was left in his account?

48. *Cell-Phone Plan.* In 2008, at&t offered its FamilyTalk cell-phone plan with 2 lines and 700 anytime minutes for a monthly access fee of $69.99. Minutes in excess of 700 were charged at the rate of $0.45 per minute. One month, Mr. and Mrs. Wu used their cell phones for 925 min. What was the charge?
Source: at&t

49. *Gas Mileage.* Ellie wants to estimate the gas mileage of her car. At 36,057.1 mi, she fills the tank with 10.7 gal. At 36,217.6 mi, she fills the tank with 11.1 gal. Find the mileage per gallon. Round to the nearest tenth.

50. *Seafood Consumption.* The graph below shows the annual consumption, in pounds, of seafood per person in the United States in recent years.

a) Find the total consumption per person for the seven years.

b) Find the average consumption per person for the years shown, rounded to the nearest tenth.

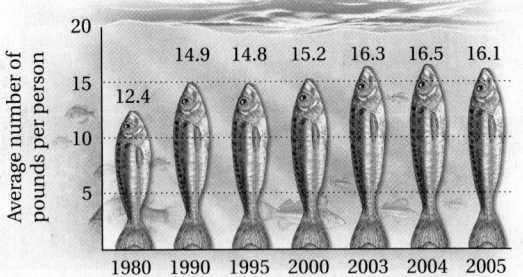

Seafood Consumption

SOURCE: U.S. Department of Agriculture

Copyright © 2012 Pearson Education, Inc.

Estimate each of the following. [3.6a]

51. The product 7.82×34.487 by rounding to the nearest one

52. The difference $219.875 - 4.478$ by rounding to the nearest one

53. The sum $\$45.78 + \$78.99$ by rounding to the nearest one

Find decimal notation. Use multiplying by 1. [3.5a]

54. $\dfrac{13}{25}$ **55.** $\dfrac{9}{20}$ **56.** $\dfrac{11}{4}$

Find decimal notation. Use division. [3.5a]

57. $\dfrac{13}{4}$ **58.** $\dfrac{7}{6}$ **59.** $\dfrac{17}{11}$

Round the answer to Exercise 59 to the nearest: [3.5b]

60. Tenth. **61.** Hundredth. **62.** Thousandth.

Convert from cents to dollars. [3.3b]

63. 8273¢ **64.** 487¢

Convert from dollars to cents. [3.3b]

65. $24.93 **66.** $9.86

Calculate. [3.4c], [3.5c]

67. $(8 - 1.23) \div 4 + 5.6 \times 0.02$

68. $(1 + 0.07)^2 + 10^3 \div 10^2$
$+ [4(10.1 - 5.6) + 8(11.3 - 7.8)]$

69. $\dfrac{3}{4} \times 20.85$

70. Divide: $\dfrac{346.295}{0.001}$. [3.4a]

   A. 0.346295   **B.** 3.46295
   C. 34,629.5   **D.** 346,295

71. Estimate the quotient $82.304 \div 17.287$ by rounding to the nearest ten. [3.6a]

   A. 0.4   **B.** 4
   C. 40   **D.** 400

Synthesis

72. ▦ In each of the following, use one of $+$, $-$, $\times$, and $\div$ in each blank to make a true sentence. [3.4c]

   a) $2.56 \ \square \ 6.4 \ \square \ 51.2 \ \square \ 17.4 \ \square \ 89.7 = 72.62$
   b) $(11.12 \ \square \ 0.29) \ \square \ 3^4 = 877.23$

73. Use the fact that $\frac{1}{3} = 0.\overline{3}$ to find repeating decimal notation for 1. Explain how you got your answer. [3.5a]

Understanding Through Discussion and Writing

1. Describe in your own words a procedure for converting from decimal notation to fraction notation. [3.1b]

2. A student insists that $346.708 \times 0.1 = 3467.08$. How could you convince him that a mistake had been made without checking on a calculator? [3.3a]

3. When is long division *not* the fastest way to convert from fraction notation to decimal notation? [3.5a]

4. Consider finding decimal notation for $\frac{44}{125}$. Discuss as many ways as you can for finding such notation and give the answer. [3.5a]

Test For Extra Help

Step-by-step test solutions are found on the Chapter Test Prep Videos available via the Video Resources on DVD, in *MyMathLab* , and on You Tube (search "BittingerDevMath" and click on "Channels").

Convert the number in each sentence to standard notation.

1. The United States issued 18.4 million passports in 2007, an all-time high, due in part to new rules requiring a passport for travel to Canada and Mexico.
Source: Associated Press

2. An ethanol boom helped to deliver a corn crop of a record 13.1 billion bushels in 2007.
Source: U.S. Department of Agriculture

Write a word name.

3. 2.34

4. 105.0005

Write fraction notation

5. 0.91

6. 2.769

Write decimal notation.

7. $\dfrac{74}{1000}$

8. $\dfrac{37,047}{10,000}$

9. $756\dfrac{9}{100}$

10. $91\dfrac{703}{1000}$

Which number is larger?

11. 0.07, 0.162

12. 0.078, 0.06

13. 0.09, 0.9

Round 5.6783 to the nearest:

14. One.

15. Hundredth.

16. Thousandth.

17. Tenth.

Calculate

18.
```
   0.7
   0.0 8
   0.0 0 9
 + 0.0 0 1 2
```

19. $102.4 + 6.1 + 78$

20. $0.93 + 9.3 + 93 + 930$

21.
```
   5 2.6 7 8
 -    4.3 2 1
```

22.
```
   2 0.0
 -    0.9 0 9 9
```

23. $234.6788 - 81.7854$

24.
```
   0.1 2 5
 ×    0.2 4
```

25. 0.001×213.45

26. 1000×73.962

27. $4\overline{)19}$

Copyright © 2012 Pearson Education, Inc.

28. $3.3\overline{)100.32}$

29. $82\overline{)15.58}$

30. $\dfrac{346.89}{1000}$

31. $\dfrac{346.89}{0.01}$

Solve.

32. $4.8 \cdot y = 404.448$

33. $x + 0.018 = 9$

34. *Cell-Phone Plan.* In 2008, at&t offered its FamilyTalk cell-phone plan with 2 lines and 1400 anytime minutes for a monthly access fee of \$89.99. Minutes in excess of 1400 were charged at the rate of \$0.40 per minute. One month, Mr. and Mrs. Tews used their cell phones for 1510 min. What was the charge?
Source: at&t

35. *Gas Mileage.* Tina wants to estimate the gas mileage in her economy car. At 76,843 mi, she fills the tank with 14.3 gal of gasoline. At 77,310 mi, she fills the tank with 16.5 gal of gasoline. Find the mileage per gallon. Round to the nearest tenth.

36. *Checking Account Balance.* Nicholas has a balance of \$820 in his checking account before making purchases of \$123.89, \$56.68, and \$46.98 with his debit card. What was the balance after the purchases had been made?

37. The office manager for the Drake, Smith, and Hartner law firm buys 7 cases of copy paper at \$41.99 per case. What is the total cost?

38. *Busiest Airports.* The graph below shows the numbers of passengers in 2007 who traveled through the country's busiest airports. Find the average total number of passengers through these airports.

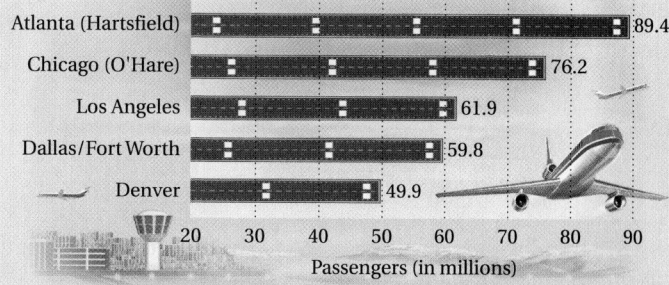

Busiest Airports in the United States

Atlanta (Hartsfield) 89.4
Chicago (O'Hare) 76.2
Los Angeles 61.9
Dallas/Fort Worth 59.8
Denver 49.9

Passengers (in millions)

SOURCE: Airports Council International

Estimate each of the following.

39. The product 8.91×22.457 by rounding to the nearest one

40. The quotient $78.2209 \div 16.09$ by rounding to the nearest ten

Find decimal notation. Use multiplying by 1.

41. $\frac{7}{20}$ **42.** $\frac{22}{25}$ **43.** $\frac{21}{4}$

Find decimal notation. Use division.

44. $\frac{3}{4}$ **45.** $\frac{11}{9}$ **46.** $\frac{15}{7}$

Round the answer to Exercise 46 to the nearest:

47. Tenth. **48.** Hundredth. **49.** Thousandth.

Calculate.

50. $256 \div 3.2 \div 2 - 1.56 + 78.325 \times 0.02$

51. $(1 - 0.08)^2 + 6[5(12.1 - 8.7) + 10(14.3 - 9.6)]$

52. $\frac{7}{8} \times 345.6$

53. Convert from cents to dollars: $949¢$.

  A. $0.949¢$ **B.** $\$9.49$ **C.** $\$94.90$ **D.** $\$949$

Synthesis

54. The Silver's Health Club charges a $79 membership fee and $42.50 a month. Allise has a coupon that will allow her to join the club for $299 for six months. How much will Allise save if she uses the coupon?

55. ▦ Arrange from smallest to largest.

$\frac{2}{3}, \frac{15}{19}, \frac{11}{13}, \frac{5}{7}, \frac{13}{15}, \frac{17}{20}$

Copyright © 2012 Pearson Education, Inc.

Percent Notation

Real-World Application

The Dow Jones Industrial Average (DJIA) plunged from 11,143 to 10,365 on September 29, 2008. This was the largest one-day drop in its history. What was the percent of decrease?

Sources: Nightly Business Reports, September 29, 2008; DJIA

This problem appears as Example 3 in Section 4.6.

4.1

Ratio and Proportion

OBJECTIVES

a Find fraction notation for ratios.

b Give the ratio of two different measures as a rate.

c Determine whether two pairs of numbers are proportional.

d Solve proportions.

e Solve applied problems involving proportions.

SKILL TO REVIEW

Objective 2.1e: Simplify fraction notation.

Simplify.

1. $\dfrac{16}{64}$ 2. $\dfrac{40}{24}$

1. Find the ratio of 5 to 11.

2. Find the ratio of 57.3 to 86.1.

3. Find the ratio of $6\dfrac{3}{4}$ to $7\dfrac{2}{5}$.

a Ratios

> **RATIO**
>
> A **ratio** is the quotient of two quantities.

In the 2007–2008 regular basketball season, the Boston Celtics scored a total of 8245 points and allowed their opponents a total of 7404 points. The *ratio* of points scored to points allowed is given by the fraction notation

$\dfrac{8245}{7404}$ ← Points scored
← Points allowed   or by the colon notation   8245 : 7404.

We read both forms of notation as "the ratio of 8245 to 7404."

> **RATIO NOTATION**
>
> The **ratio** of a to b is given by the fraction notation $\dfrac{a}{b}$, where a is the numerator and b is the denominator, or by the colon notation $a : b$.

EXAMPLE 1 Find the ratio of 31.4 to 100.

The ratio is $\dfrac{31.4}{100}$, or 31.4 : 100.

Do Margin Exercises 1–3.

In most of our work, we will use fraction notation for ratios.

EXAMPLE 2 *Record Rainfall.* The greatest rainfall ever recorded in the United States during a 12-month period was 739 in. in Kukui, Maui, Hawaii, from December 1981 to December 1982. What is the ratio of amount of rainfall, in inches, to time, in months? of time, in months, to amount of rainfall, in inches?

Source: *Time Almanac*

The ratio of amount of rainfall, in inches, to time, in months, is

$\dfrac{739}{12}$. ← Rainfall
← Time

The ratio of time, in months, to amount of rainfall, in inches, is

$\dfrac{12}{739}$. ← Time
← Rainfall

Answers

Skill to Review:

1. $\dfrac{1}{4}$ 2. $\dfrac{5}{3}$

Margin Exercises:

1. $\dfrac{5}{11}$, or 5 : 11   2. $\dfrac{57.3}{86.1}$, or 57.3 : 86.1

3. $\dfrac{6\frac{3}{4}}{7\frac{2}{5}}$, or $6\frac{3}{4} : 7\frac{2}{5}$

EXAMPLE 3 Refer to the triangle below.

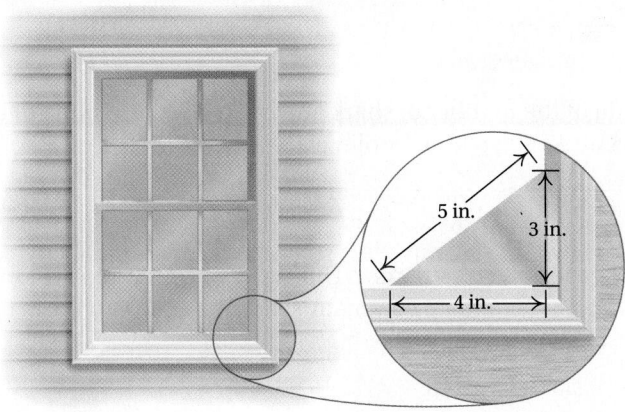

a) What is the ratio of the length of the longest side to the length of the shortest side?

$\dfrac{5}{3}$ ← Longest side
← Shortest side

b) What is the ratio of the length of the shortest side to the length of the longest side?

$\dfrac{3}{5}$ ← Shortest side
← Longest side

Do Exercises 4-6.

EXAMPLE 4 *Shark Attacks.* Of the 71 shark attacks recorded worldwide in 2007, 50 occurred in U.S. waters. The bar graph below shows the breakdown by state.

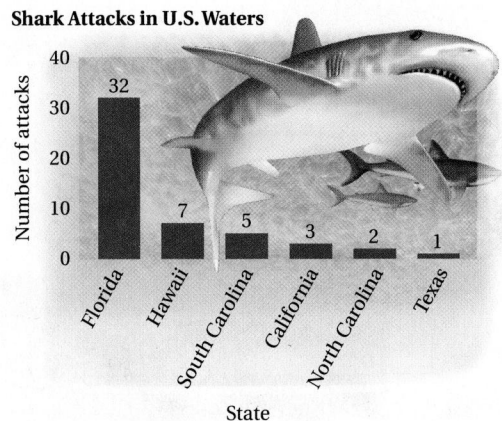

Shark Attacks in U.S. Waters

SOURCE: University of Florida

a) What is the ratio of the number of shark attacks in U.S. waters to the number of shark attacks worldwide?

b) What is the ratio of the number of shark attacks in North Carolina to the number of shark attacks in South Carolina?

c) What is the ratio of the number of shark attacks in Florida to the total number of shark attacks in the other five states?

4. Record Snowfall. The greatest snowfall recorded in North America during a 24-hr period was 76 in. in Silver Lake, Colorado, on April 14–15, 1921. What is the ratio of amount of snowfall, in inches, to time, in hours?
Source: U.S. Army Corps of Engineers

5. Frozen Fruit Drinks.
A Berries & Kreme Chiller from Krispy Kreme contains 960 calories, while Smoothie King's MangoFest drink contains 258 calories. What is the ratio of the number of calories in the Krispy Kreme drink to the number of calories in the Smoothie King drink? of the number of calories in the Smoothie King drink to the number of calories in the Krispy Kreme drink?
Source: Physicians Committee for Responsible Medicine

6. In the triangle below, what is the ratio of the length of the shortest side to the length of the longest side?

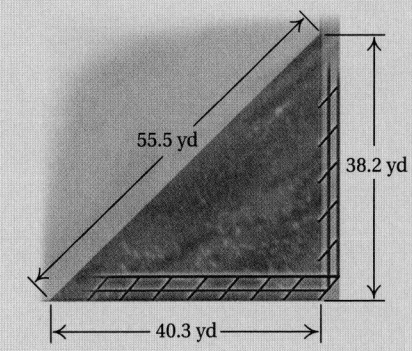

55.5 yd

38.2 yd

40.3 yd

Answers

4. $\dfrac{76}{24}$ **5.** $\dfrac{960}{258}; \dfrac{258}{960}$ **6.** $\dfrac{38.2}{55.5}$

7. Soap Box Derby. Of the 538 participants in the 2008 All-American Soap Box Derby, 296 were boys and 242 were girls. What was the ratio of girls to boys? of boys to girls? of boys to total number of participants?

Source: All-American Soap Box Derby

a) The ratio of the number of shark attacks in U.S. waters to the number of shark attacks worldwide is

$$\frac{50}{71}. \quad \begin{matrix} \leftarrow \text{ Attacks in U.S. waters} \\ \leftarrow \text{ Attacks worldwide} \end{matrix}$$

b) The ratio of the number of shark attacks in North Carolina to the number of shark attacks in South Carolina is

$$\frac{2}{5}. \quad \begin{matrix} \leftarrow \text{ Attacks in North Carolina} \\ \leftarrow \text{ Attacks in South Carolina} \end{matrix}$$

c) Of the 50 shark attacks in U.S. waters, 32 occurred in Florida. We subtract to determine how many shark attacks took place in the other five states. We have

$$50 - 32 = 18.$$

Thus the ratio of the number of shark attacks in Florida to the number of shark attacks in the other five states is

$$\frac{32}{18}. \quad \begin{matrix} \leftarrow \text{ Attacks in Florida} \\ \leftarrow \text{ Attacks in other five states} \end{matrix}$$

Do Exercise 7.

EXAMPLE 5 Find the ratio of 2.4 to 10. Then simplify to find two other numbers in the same ratio.

We first write the ratio in fraction notation. Next, we multiply by 1 to clear the decimal from the numerator. Then we simplify.

$$\frac{2.4}{10} = \frac{2.4}{10} \cdot \frac{10}{10} = \frac{24}{100} = \frac{4 \cdot 6}{4 \cdot 25} = \frac{4}{4} \cdot \frac{6}{25} = \frac{6}{25}$$

Thus the ratio of 6 to 25 is the same as the ratio of 2.4 to 10.

8. Find the ratio of 3.6 to 12. Then simplify to find two other numbers in the same ratio.

9. Find the ratio of 1.2 to 1.5. Then simplify to find two other numbers in the same ratio.

Do Exercises 8 and 9.

EXAMPLE 6 An HDTV screen that measures 46 in. diagonally has a width of 40 in. and a height of $22\frac{1}{2}$ in. Find the ratio of width to height and simplify.

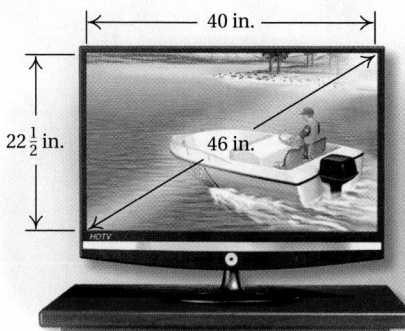

10. An HDTV screen that measures 44 in. diagonally has a width of 38.4 in. and a height of 21.6 in. Find the ratio of height to width and simplify.

The ratio is $\dfrac{40}{22\frac{1}{2}} = \dfrac{40}{22.5} = \dfrac{40}{22.5} \cdot \dfrac{10}{10} = \dfrac{400}{225} = \dfrac{25 \cdot 16}{25 \cdot 9} = \dfrac{25}{25} \cdot \dfrac{16}{9} = \dfrac{16}{9}.$

Thus we can say that the ratio of width to height is 16 to 9, which can also be expressed as 16 : 9.

Do Exercise 10.

Answers

7. $\frac{242}{296}; \frac{296}{242}; \frac{296}{538}$ 8. 3.6 is to 12 as 3 is to 10.

9. 1.2 is to 1.5 as 4 is to 5. 10. $\frac{9}{16}$, or 9:16

b Rates

A 2008 Kia Sportage EX can travel 414 mi on 18 gal of gasoline. Let's consider the ratio of miles to gallons:

Source: Kia Motors America, Inc.

$$\frac{414 \text{ mi}}{18 \text{ gal}} = \frac{414}{18} \frac{\text{miles}}{\text{gallon}} = \frac{23}{1} \frac{\text{miles}}{\text{gallon}}$$

$$= 23 \text{ miles per gallon} = 23 \text{ mpg}.$$

"per" means "division," or "for each."

The ratio

$$\frac{414 \text{ mi}}{18 \text{ gal}}, \quad \text{or} \quad \frac{414}{18} \frac{\text{mi}}{\text{gal}}, \quad \text{or } 23 \text{ mpg},$$

is called a **rate**.

RATE

When a ratio is used to compare two different kinds of measure, we call it a **rate**.

Suppose David says his car travels 392.4 mi on 16.8 gal of gasoline. Is the mpg (mileage) of his car better than that of the Kia Sportage above? To determine this, it helps to convert the ratio to decimal notation and perhaps round. Then we have

$$\frac{392.4 \text{ miles}}{16.8 \text{ gallons}} = \frac{392.4}{16.8} \text{ mpg} \approx 23.357 \text{ mpg}.$$

Since $23.357 > 23$, David's car gets better mileage than the Kia Sportage does.

EXAMPLE 7 It takes 60 oz of grass seed to seed 3000 sq ft of lawn. What is the rate in ounces per square foot?

$$\frac{60 \text{ oz}}{3000 \text{ sq ft}} = \frac{1}{50} \frac{\text{oz}}{\text{sq ft}}, \quad \text{or} \quad 0.02 \frac{\text{oz}}{\text{sq ft}}$$

EXAMPLE 8 Martina bought 5 lb of organic russet potatoes for $4.99. What was the rate in cents per pound?

$$\frac{\$4.99}{5 \text{ lb}} = \frac{499 \text{ cents}}{5 \text{ lb}} = 99.8\text{¢/lb}$$

EXAMPLE 9 A pharmacy student employed as a pharmacist's assistant earned $3930 for working 3 months one summer. What was the rate of pay per month?

The rate of pay is the ratio of money earned to length of time worked, or

$$\frac{\$3930}{3 \text{ mo}} = 1310 \frac{\text{dollars}}{\text{month}}, \quad \text{or} \quad \$1310 \text{ per month}.$$

Do Exercises 11–15.

A ratio of distance traveled to time is called *speed*. What is the rate, or speed, in miles per hour?

11. 45 mi, 9 hr

12. 120 mi, 10 hr

What is the rate, or speed, in feet per second?

13. 2200 ft, 2 sec

14. 52 ft, 13 sec

15. Babe Ruth. In his baseball career, Babe Ruth had 1330 strikeouts and 714 home runs. What was his home-run to strikeout rate?

Source: Major League Baseball

Answers

11. 5 mi/hr, or 5 mph **12.** 12 mi/hr, or 12 mph **13.** 1100 ft/sec **14.** 4 ft/sec
15. $\frac{714}{1330}$ home runs per strikeout ≈ 0.537 home run per strikeout

c Proportions

Suppose we want to compare $\frac{3}{6}$ and $\frac{2}{4}$. First, we find a common denominator. To do this, we multiply each fraction by 1, using the denominator of the other fraction to form the symbol for 1. We multiply $\frac{3}{6}$ by $\frac{4}{4}$ and $\frac{2}{4}$ by $\frac{6}{6}$:

$$\frac{3}{6} = \frac{3}{6} \cdot \frac{4}{4} = \frac{3 \cdot 4}{6 \cdot 4} = \frac{12}{24}; \qquad \text{Multiplying by } \frac{4}{4}$$

$$\frac{2}{4} = \frac{2}{4} \cdot \frac{6}{6} = \frac{2 \cdot 6}{4 \cdot 6} = \frac{12}{24}. \qquad \text{Multiplying by } \frac{6}{6}$$

Once we have a common denominator, 24, we compare the numerators. And since these numerators are both 12, the fractions are equal.

Note in the preceding that if

$$\frac{3}{6} = \frac{2}{4}, \quad \text{then} \quad 3 \cdot 4 = 6 \cdot 2.$$

This tells us that we need to check only the products $3 \cdot 4$ and $6 \cdot 2$ to compare the fractions.

STUDY TIPS

AVOID DISTRACTIONS

Don't allow yourself to be distracted from your studies by electronic "time robbers" such as video games, the Internet, and television. Be disciplined and *study first*. Then reward yourself with a leisure activity if there is enough time in your day.

A TEST FOR EQUALITY

We multiply these two numbers: $3 \cdot 4$.

We multiply these two numbers: $6 \cdot 2$.

$$\frac{3}{6} \,\square\, \frac{2}{4}$$

We call $3 \cdot 4$ and $6 \cdot 2$ **cross products**. Since the cross products are the same—that is, $3 \cdot 4 = 6 \cdot 2$—we know that

$$\frac{3}{6} = \frac{2}{4}.$$

When two pairs of numbers, such as 3, 6 and 2, 4, have the same ratio, we say that they are **proportional**. The equation

$$\frac{3}{6} = \frac{2}{4}$$

states that the pairs 3, 6 and 2, 4 are proportional. Such an equation is called a **proportion**. We sometimes read $\frac{3}{6} = \frac{2}{4}$ as "3 is to 6 as 2 is to 4."

EXAMPLE 10 Determine whether 1, 2 and 3, 6 are proportional.

We can use cross products:

$$1 \cdot 6 = 6 \qquad \overset{?}{\frac{1}{2} = \frac{3}{6}} \qquad 2 \cdot 3 = 6.$$

Since the cross products are the same, $6 = 6$, we know that $\frac{1}{2} = \frac{3}{6}$, so the numbers are proportional.

EXAMPLE 11 Determine whether 2, 5 and 4, 7 are proportional.

We can use cross products:

$$2 \cdot 7 = 14 \quad \frac{2}{5} \overset{?}{=} \frac{4}{7} \quad 5 \cdot 4 = 20.$$

Since the cross products are not the same, $14 \neq 20$, we know that $\frac{2}{5} \neq \frac{4}{7}$, so the numbers are not proportional.

Do Exercises 16–18.

Determine whether the two pairs of numbers are proportional.

16. 3, 4 and 6, 8

17. 1, 4 and 10, 39

18. 1, 2 and 20, 39

d Solving Proportions

Let's now look at solving proportions. Consider the proportion

$$\frac{x}{3} = \frac{4}{6}.$$

One way to solve a proportion is to use cross products. Then we can divide on both sides to get the variable alone:

$$\frac{x}{3} = \frac{4}{6}$$

$$x \cdot 6 = 3 \cdot 4 \qquad \text{Equating cross products (finding cross products and setting them equal)}$$

$$\frac{x \cdot 6}{6} = \frac{3 \cdot 4}{6} \qquad \text{Dividing by 6 on both sides}$$

$$x = \frac{3 \cdot 4}{6} = \frac{12}{6} = 2.$$

We can check that 2 is the solution by replacing x with 2 and finding cross products:

$$2 \cdot 6 = 12 \quad \frac{2}{3} \overset{?}{=} \frac{4}{6} \quad 3 \cdot 4 = 12.$$

Since the cross products are the same, it follows that $\frac{2}{3} = \frac{4}{6}$. Thus the pairs of numbers 2, 3 and 4, 6 are proportional, and 2 is the solution of the equation.

> **SOLVING PROPORTIONS**
>
> To solve $\dfrac{x}{a} = \dfrac{c}{d}$, equate *cross products* and divide on both sides to get x alone.

Do Exercise 19.

STUDY TIPS

LEARN FROM YOUR MISTAKES

When your instructor returns a graded homework assignment, quiz, or test, take time to review it and understand the mistakes that you made. Be sure to ask your instructor for help if you can't see what your mistakes are. We often learn much more from our mistakes than from the things we do correctly.

19. Solve: $\dfrac{x}{63} = \dfrac{2}{9}$.

Answers

16. Yes **17.** No **18.** No **19.** 14

EXAMPLE 12 Solve: $\dfrac{x}{7} = \dfrac{5}{3}$. Write a mixed numeral for the answer.

We have

$$\dfrac{x}{7} = \dfrac{5}{3}$$

$$x \cdot 3 = 7 \cdot 5 \qquad \text{Equating cross products}$$

$$\dfrac{x \cdot 3}{3} = \dfrac{7 \cdot 5}{3} \qquad \text{Dividing by 3}$$

$$x = \dfrac{7 \cdot 5}{3} = \dfrac{35}{3}, \text{or } 11\tfrac{2}{3}.$$

The solution is $11\tfrac{2}{3}$.

20. Solve: $\dfrac{x}{9} = \dfrac{5}{4}$. Write a mixed numeral for the answer.

> Do Exercise 20.

EXAMPLE 13 Solve: $\dfrac{7.7}{15.4} = \dfrac{y}{2.2}$.

We have

$$\dfrac{7.7}{15.4} = \dfrac{y}{2.2}$$

$$7.7 \times 2.2 = 15.4 \times y \qquad \text{Equating cross products}$$

$$\dfrac{7.7 \times 2.2}{15.4} = \dfrac{15.4 \times y}{15.4} \qquad \text{Dividing by 15.4}$$

$$\dfrac{7.7 \times 2.2}{15.4} = y$$

$$\dfrac{16.94}{15.4} = y \qquad \text{Multiplying}$$

$$1.1 = y. \qquad \text{Dividing:}$$

$$
\begin{array}{r}
1.1 \\
15.4 \overline{)16.9\,4} \\
\underline{15\,4} \\
15\,4 \\
\underline{15\,4} \\
0
\end{array}
$$

The solution is 1.1.

EXAMPLE 14 Solve: $\dfrac{8}{x} = \dfrac{5}{3}$. Write decimal notation for the answer.

We have

$$\dfrac{8}{x} = \dfrac{5}{3}$$

$$8 \cdot 3 = x \cdot 5 \qquad \text{Equating cross products}$$

$$\dfrac{8 \cdot 3}{5} = x \qquad \text{Dividing by 5}$$

$$\dfrac{24}{5} = x \qquad \text{Multiplying}$$

$$4.8 = x. \qquad \text{Simplifying}$$

The solution is 4.8.

21. Solve: $\dfrac{21}{5} = \dfrac{n}{2.5}$.

22. Solve: $\dfrac{6}{x} = \dfrac{25}{11}$. Write decimal notation for the answer.

> Do Exercises 21 and 22.

Answers

20. $11\tfrac{1}{4}$ **21.** 10.5   **22.** 2.64

EXAMPLE 15 Solve: $\dfrac{3.4}{4.93} = \dfrac{10}{n}$.

$$\frac{3.4}{4.93} = \frac{10}{n}$$

$3.4 \times n = 4.93 \times 10$ Equating cross products

$\dfrac{3.4 \times n}{3.4} = \dfrac{4.93 \times 10}{3.4}$ Dividing by 3.4

$n = \dfrac{4.93 \times 10}{3.4}$

$n = \dfrac{49.3}{3.4}$ Multiplying

$n = 14.5.$ Dividing

The solution is 14.5.

Do Exercise 23.

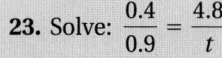

23. Solve: $\dfrac{0.4}{0.9} = \dfrac{4.8}{t}$.

(e) Applications and Problem Solving

Proportions have applications in such diverse fields as business, chemistry, health sciences, and home economics, as well as in many areas of daily life. Proportions are useful in making predictions.

EXAMPLE 16 *Predicting Total Distance.* Donna drives her delivery van 800 mi in 3 days. At this rate, how far will she drive in 15 days?

1. **Familiarize.** We let d = the distance traveled in 15 days.

2. **Translate.** We translate to a proportion. We make each side the ratio of distance to time, with distance in the numerator and time in the denominator.

$$\begin{array}{c} \text{Distance in 15 days} \to \\ \text{Time} \to \end{array} \dfrac{d}{15} = \dfrac{800}{3} \begin{array}{c} \leftarrow \text{Distance in 3 days} \\ \leftarrow \text{Time} \end{array}$$

It may help to verbalize the proportion above as "the unknown distance d is to 15 days as the known distance 800 mi is to 3 days."

3. **Solve.** Next, we solve the proportion:

$3 \cdot d = 15 \cdot 800$ Equating cross products

$\dfrac{3 \cdot d}{3} = \dfrac{15 \cdot 800}{3}$ Dividing by 3 on both sides

$d = \dfrac{15 \cdot 800}{3}$

$d = 4000.$ Multiplying and dividing

4. **Check.** We substitute into the proportion and check cross products:

$$\frac{4000}{15} = \frac{800}{3};$$

$4000 \cdot 3 = 12{,}000; \qquad 15 \cdot 800 = 12{,}000.$

The cross products are the same.

5. **State.** Donna will drive 4000 mi in 15 days.

Do Exercise 24.

24. Burning Calories. The readout on Mary's treadmill indicates that she burns 108 calories when she walks for 24 min. How many calories will she burn if she walks at the same rate for 30 min?

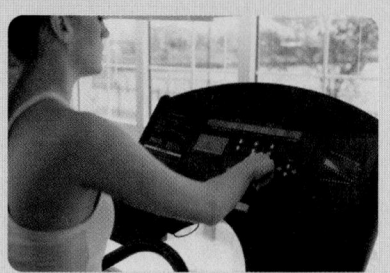

Answers

23. 10.8   **24.** 135 calories

EXAMPLE 17 *Recommended Dosage.* To control a fever, a doctor suggests that a child who weighs 28 kg be given 320 mg of a liquid pain reliever. If the dosage is proportional to the child's weight, how much of the medication is recommended for a child who weighs 35 kg?

STUDY TIPS

RELYING ON THE ANSWER SECTION

Don't begin solving a homework problem by working backward from the answer in the answer section at the back of the text. If you are having trouble getting the correct answer to an exercise, you might need to reread the section preceding the exercise set, paying particular attention to the example that corresponds to the type of exercise you are doing, and/or work more slowly and carefully. Keep in mind that when you take quizzes and tests you have no answer section to rely on.

1. **Familiarize.** We let t = the number of milligrams of the liquid pain reliever.

2. **Translate.** We translate to a proportion, keeping the amount of medication in the numerators.

$$\text{Medication suggested} \rightarrow \frac{320}{28} = \frac{t}{35} \leftarrow \text{Medication suggested}$$
$$\text{Child's weight} \rightarrow \phantom{\frac{320}{28}} \phantom{\frac{t}{35}} \leftarrow \text{Child's weight}$$

3. **Solve.** Next, we solve the proportion:

$$320 \cdot 35 = 28 \cdot t \qquad \text{Equating cross products}$$

$$\frac{320 \cdot 35}{28} = \frac{28 \cdot t}{28} \qquad \text{Dividing by 28 on both sides}$$

$$\frac{320 \cdot 35}{28} = t$$

$$400 = t. \qquad \text{Multiplying and dividing}$$

4. **Check.** We substitute into the proportion and check cross products:

$$\frac{320}{28} = \frac{400}{35};$$

$$320 \cdot 35 = 11{,}200; \qquad 28 \cdot 400 = 11{,}200.$$

The cross products are the same.

5. **State.** The dosage for a child who weighs 35 kg is 400 mg.

> Do Exercise 25.

25. Determining Paint Needs.
Lowell and Chris run a summer painting company to pay for their college expenses. They can paint 1600 ft^2 of clapboard with 4 gal of paint. How much paint would be needed for a building with 6000 ft^2 of clapboard?

EXAMPLE 18 *Purchasing Tickets.* Carey bought 8 tickets to an international food festival for $52. How many tickets could she purchase with $90?

1. **Familiarize.** We let n = the number of tickets that can be purchased with $90.

2. **Translate.** We translate to a proportion, keeping the number of tickets in the numerators.

$$\text{Tickets} \rightarrow \frac{8}{52} = \frac{n}{90} \leftarrow \text{Tickets}$$
$$\text{Cost} \rightarrow \phantom{\frac{8}{52}} \phantom{\frac{n}{90}} \leftarrow \text{Cost}$$

Answer
25. 15 gal

3. Solve. Next, we solve the proportion:

$52 \cdot n = 8 \cdot 90$ Equating cross products

$\dfrac{52 \cdot n}{52} = \dfrac{8 \cdot 90}{52}$ Dividing by 52 on both sides

$n = \dfrac{8 \cdot 90}{52}$

$n \approx 13.8.$ Multiplying and dividing

Because it is impossible to buy a fractional part of a ticket, we must round our answer *down* to 13.

4. Check. As a check, we use a different approach: We find the cost per ticket and then divide $90 by that price. Since $52 \div 8 = 6.50$ and $90 \div 6.50 \approx 13.8$, we have a check.

5. State. Carey could purchase 13 tickets with $90.

Do Exercise 26.

26. Purchasing Shirts. If 2 shirts can be bought for $47, how many shirts can be bought with $200?

EXAMPLE 19 *Construction Plans.* Architects make blueprints of projects to be constructed. These are scale drawings in which lengths are in proportion to actual sizes. The Hennesseys are adding a rectangular deck to their house. The architectural blueprints are rendered such that $\frac{3}{4}$ in. on the drawing is actually 2.25 ft on the deck. The width of the deck on the drawing is 4.3 in. How wide is the deck in reality?

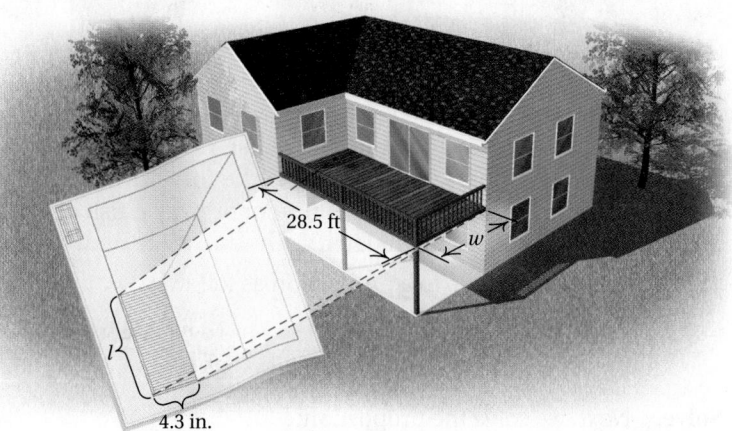

28.5 ft

w

l

4.3 in.

1. Familiarize. We let $w =$ the width of the deck.

2. Translate. Then we translate to a proportion, using 0.75 for $\frac{3}{4}$ in.

Measure on drawing $\rightarrow \dfrac{0.75}{2.25} = \dfrac{4.3}{w} \leftarrow$ Width on drawing
Measure on deck $\rightarrow$ $\phantom{\dfrac{0.75}{2.25}}$ $\leftarrow$ Width on deck

3. Solve. Next, we solve the proportion:

$0.75 \times w = 2.25 \times 4.3$ Equating cross products

$\dfrac{0.75 \times w}{0.75} = \dfrac{2.25 \times 4.3}{0.75}$ Dividing by 0.75 on both sides

$w = \dfrac{2.25 \times 4.3}{0.75}$

$w = 12.9.$

Answer

26. 8 shirts

4. Check. We substitute into the proportion and check cross products:

$$\frac{0.75}{2.25} = \frac{4.3}{12.9};$$

$$0.75 \times 12.9 = 9.675; \qquad 2.25 \times 4.3 = 9.675.$$

The cross products are the same.

5. State. The width of the deck is 12.9 ft.

Do Exercise 27.

27. Construction Plans. In Example 19, the length of the actual deck is 28.5 ft. What is the length of the deck on the blueprints?

EXAMPLE 20 *Estimating a Wildlife Population.* To determine the number of fish in a lake, a conservationist catches 225 fish, tags them, and throws them back into the lake. Later, 108 fish are caught, and it is found that 15 of them are tagged. Estimate how many fish are in the lake.

1. Familiarize. We let $F =$ the number of fish in the lake. We assume that the ratio of the number of tagged fish to the total number of fish in the lake is the same as the ratio of the number of tagged fish caught later to the total number of fish caught later.

2. Translate. We translate to a proportion as follows:

Fish tagged originally $\rightarrow \dfrac{225}{F} = \dfrac{15}{108}. \begin{array}{l} \leftarrow \text{Tagged fish caught later} \\ \leftarrow \text{Fish caught later} \end{array}$
Fish in lake $\rightarrow$

3. Solve. Next, we solve the proportion:

$$225 \cdot 108 = F \cdot 15 \qquad \text{Equating cross products}$$

$$\frac{225 \cdot 108}{15} = \frac{F \cdot 15}{15} \qquad \text{Dividing by 15 on both sides}$$

$$\frac{225 \cdot 108}{15} = F$$

$$1620 = F. \qquad \text{Multiplying and dividing}$$

28. Estimating a Deer Population. To determine the number of deer in a forest, a conservationist catches 153 deer, tags them, and releases them. Later, 62 deer are caught, and it is found that 18 of them are tagged. Estimate how many deer are in the forest.

4. Check. We substitute into the proportion and check cross products:

$$\frac{225}{1620} = \frac{15}{108};$$

$$225 \cdot 108 = 24{,}300; \qquad 1620 \cdot 15 = 24{,}300.$$

The cross products are the same.

5. State. We estimate that there are 1620 fish in the lake.

Do Exercise 28.

Answers

27. 9.5 in.   **28.** 527 deer

4.1 **Exercise Set**

For Extra Help

MyMathLab

Math XL
PRACTICE

WATCH

DOWNLOAD

READ

REVIEW

a   Find fraction notation for each ratio. You need not simplify.

1. 178 to 572

2. 3 to 2

3. $8\frac{3}{4}$ to $9\frac{5}{6}$

4. 456.2 to 333.1

5. *Space Plane.*   It is estimated that it will take 4 hr to fly from London to Sydney on the beyond-the-atmosphere space plane being developed in Europe. This 10,600-mi trip currently takes about 21 hr. What is the ratio of the time of the current trip to the time of the trip on the space plane? of the time of the trip on the space plane to the time of the current trip?

Source: EADS Atrium

6. *Population Estimates.*   It is estimated that, of every 1000 people in the United States in 2050, 118 will be age 75 and older. What is the ratio of all people to those age 75 and older? of those age 75 and older to all people?

Source: U.S. Census Bureau

Find the ratio of the first number to the second and simplify.

7. 4 to 6

8. 28 to 36

9. 2.8 to 3.6

10. 5.6 to 10

11. In this rectangle, find the ratios of length to width and of width to length.

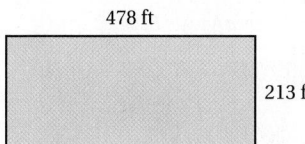

478 ft

213 ft

12. In this right triangle, find the ratios of shortest length to longest length and of longest length to shortest length.

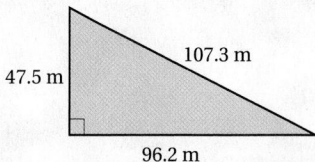

107.3 m

47.5 m

96.2 m

b   In Exercises 1–4, find each rate, or speed, as a ratio of distance to time. Round to the nearest hundredth where appropriate.

13. 120 km, 3 hr

14. 18 mi, 9 hr

15. 217 mi, 29 sec

16. 443 m, 48 sec

17. *Mazda A3—Highway Driving.* A 2008 Mazda A3 will travel 624 mi on 19.5 gal of gasoline in highway driving. What is the rate in miles per gallon?

Source: Ford Motor Company

18. *Chevrolet Cobalt LS—Highway Driving.* A 2008 Chevrolet Cobalt LS will travel 486 mi on 13.5 gal of gasoline in highway driving. What is the rate in miles per gallon?

Source: Chevrolet

19. *Population Density of Monaco.* Monaco is a tiny country on the Mediterranean coast of France. It has an area of 0.75 square mile and a population of 32,796 people. What is the rate of number of people per square mile? The rate per square mile is called the *population density.* Monaco has the highest population density of any country in the world.

Source: *The World Factbook*

20. *Rebounds per Game.* Dwight Howard of the Orlando Magic got 1161 rebounds in 82 games during the 2007–2008 basketball season. What was the rate in rebounds per game?

Source: National Basketball Association

21. *Speed of Light.* Light travels 186,000 mi in 1 sec. What is its rate, or speed, in miles per second?

Source: *The Handy Science Answer Book*

22. *Speed of Sound.* Sound travels 1100 ft in 1 sec. What is its rate, or speed, in feet per second?

Source: *The Handy Science Answer Book*

23. *Lawn Watering.* Watering a lawn adequately requires 623 gal of water for every 1000 ft². What is the rate in gallons per square foot?

24. A car is driven 200 km on 40 L of gasoline. What is the rate in kilometers per liter?

25. Impulses in nerve fibers travel 310 km in 2.5 hr. What is the rate, or speed, in kilometers per hour?

26. *Elephant Heart Rate.* The heart of an elephant, at rest, will beat an average of 1500 beats in 60 min. What is the rate in beats per minute?

Source: *The Handy Science Answer Book*

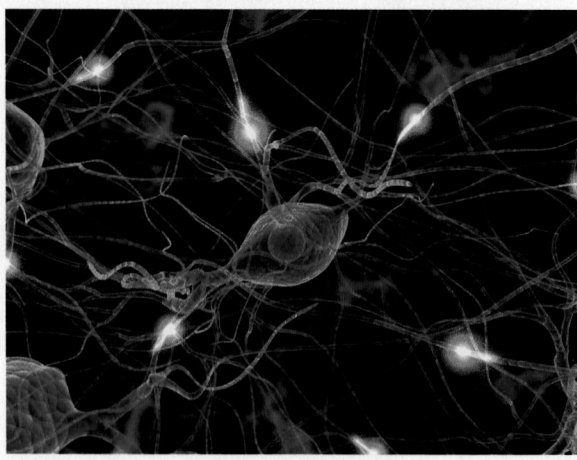

Copyright © 2012 Pearson Education, Inc.

c Determine whether the two pairs of numbers are proportional.

27. 5, 6 and 7, 9

28. 7, 5 and 6, 4

29. 1, 2 and 10, 20

30. 7, 3 and 21, 9

31. 2.4, 3.6 and 1.8, 2.7

32. 4.5, 3.8 and 6.7, 5.2

33. $5\frac{1}{3}, 8\frac{1}{4}$ and $2\frac{1}{5}, 9\frac{1}{2}$

34. $2\frac{1}{3}, 3\frac{1}{2}$ and 14, 21

d Solve.

35. $\dfrac{x}{8} = \dfrac{9}{6}$

36. $\dfrac{8}{10} = \dfrac{n}{5}$

37. $\dfrac{2}{5} = \dfrac{8}{n}$

38. $\dfrac{10}{6} = \dfrac{5}{x}$

39. $\dfrac{16}{12} = \dfrac{24}{x}$

40. $\dfrac{8}{12} = \dfrac{20}{x}$

41. $\dfrac{12}{9} = \dfrac{x}{7}$

42. $\dfrac{x}{20} = \dfrac{16}{15}$

43. $\dfrac{1.2}{4} = \dfrac{x}{9}$

44. $\dfrac{x}{11} = \dfrac{7.1}{2}$

45. $\dfrac{8}{2.4} = \dfrac{6}{y}$

46. $\dfrac{3}{y} = \dfrac{5}{4.5}$

47. $\dfrac{y}{\frac{3}{5}} = \dfrac{\frac{7}{12}}{\frac{14}{15}}$

48. $\dfrac{\frac{5}{8}}{\frac{5}{4}} = \dfrac{y}{\frac{3}{2}}$

49. $\dfrac{x}{1\frac{3}{5}} = \dfrac{2}{15}$

50. $\dfrac{1}{7} = \dfrac{x}{4\frac{1}{2}}$

51. $\dfrac{0.5}{n} = \dfrac{2.5}{3.5}$

52. $\dfrac{6.3}{0.9} = \dfrac{0.7}{n}$

53. $\dfrac{\frac{1}{5}}{\frac{1}{10}} = \dfrac{\frac{1}{10}}{x}$

54. $\dfrac{\frac{1}{4}}{\frac{1}{2}} = \dfrac{\frac{1}{2}}{x}$

e Solve.

55. *Quality Control.* A quality-control inspector examined 100 lightbulbs and found 7 of them to be defective. At this rate, how many defective bulbs will there be in a lot of 2500?

56. *Sugaring.* When 20 gal of maple sap are boiled down, the result is $\frac{1}{2}$ gal of maple syrup. How much sap is needed to produce 9 gal of syrup?

Source: University of Maine

57. *Estimating a Deer Population.* To determine the number of deer in a game preserve, a forest ranger catches 318 deer, tags them, and releases them. Later, 168 deer are caught, and it is found that 56 of them are tagged. Estimate how many deer are in the game preserve.

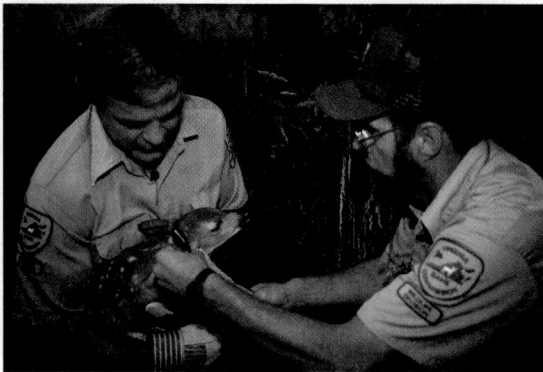

58. *Hits.* After playing 145 games in the 2008 Major League Baseball season, Ichiro Suzuki of the Seattle Mariners had 191 hits.

  a) At this rate, how many games would it take him to get 200 hits?

  b) At this rate, how many hits would Suzuki get in the 162-game baseball season?

Source: Major League Baseball

59. *Metallurgy.* In a metal alloy, the ratio of zinc to copper is 3 to 13. If there are 520 lb of copper, how many pounds of zinc are there?

60. *Snow to Water.* Under typical conditions, $1\frac{1}{2}$ ft of snow will melt to 2 in. of water. To how many inches of water will $5\frac{1}{2}$ ft of snow melt?

61. *Grass-Seed Coverage.* It takes 60 oz of grass seed to seed 3000 ft^2 of lawn. At this rate, how much would be needed for 5000 ft^2 of lawn?

62. *Coffee Production.* Coffee beans from 18 trees are required to produce enough coffee each year for a person who drinks 2 cups of coffee per day. Jared brews 15 cups of coffee each day for himself and his coworkers. How many coffee trees are required for this?

63. *Overweight Americans.* A recent study determined that of every 100 Americans, 66 are overweight or obese. It is estimated that the U.S. population will be about 322 million in 2015. At the given rate, how many Americans would be considered overweight or obese in 2015?

Source: U.S. Centers for Disease Control and Prevention

64. *Prevalence of Diabetes.* A recent study determined that of every 1000 Americans in the 65- to 74-year age group, 185 have been diagnosed with diabetes. It is estimated that there will be about 26.6 million Americans in this age group in 2015. At the given rate, how many in this age group will be diagnosed with diabetes in 2015?

Source: U.S. Centers for Disease Control and Prevention

65. *Gas Mileage.* A 2008 Ford Mustang GT Convertible will travel 341 mi on 15.5 gal of gasoline in highway driving.

  a) How many gallons of gasoline will it take to drive 2690 mi from Boston to Phoenix?

  b) How far can the car be driven on 140 gal of gasoline?

Source: Ford Motor Company

66. *Class Size.* A college advertises that its student-to-faculty ratio is 14 to 1. If 56 students register for Introductory Spanish, how many sections of the course would you expect to see offered?

Copyright © 2012 Pearson Education, Inc.

67. *Cap'n Crunch's Peanut Butter Crunch® Cereal.* The nutritional chart on the side of a box of Quaker Cap'n Crunch's Peanut Butter Crunch® Cereal states that there are 110 calories in a $\frac{3}{4}$-cup serving. How many calories are there in 6 cups of the cereal?

Nutrition Facts

Serving Size 3/4 Cup (27g)

Amount Per Serving	Cereal Alone	with 1/2 Cup Vitamin A&D Fortified Skim Milk
Calories	110	150
Calories from Fat	25	25
	% Daily Value	
Total Fat 2.5g	4%	4%
Saturated Fat 1g	5%	6%
Trans Fat 0g		
Polyunsaturated Fat 0.5g		
Monounsaturated Fat 1g		
Cholesterol 0mg	0%	1%
Sodium 200mg	8%	10%
Potassium 65mg	2%	7%
Total Carbohydrate 21g	7%	9%
Dietary Fiber 1g	3%	3%
Sugars 9g		
Other Carbohydrate 11g		
Protein 2g		

68. *Currency Exchange.* On 12 September 2008, 1 U.S. dollar was worth about 10.5859 Mexican pesos.

a) How much would 150 U.S. dollars be worth in Mexican pesos?

b) While traveling in Mexico, Jake bought a watch that cost 3600 Mexican pesos. How much did it cost in U.S. dollars?

69. *Map Scaling.* On a road atlas map, 1 in. represents 16.6 mi. If two cities are 3.5 in. apart on the map, how far apart are they in reality?

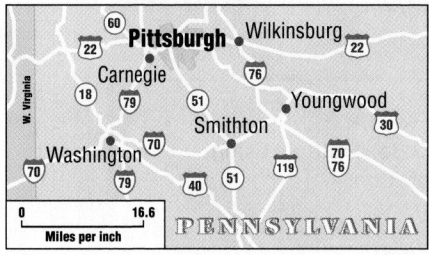

70. *Waterproofing.* Bonnie can waterproof 450 ft² of decking with 2 gal of sealant. How many gallons should Bonnie buy for a 1200-ft² deck?

71. *Painting.* Helen can paint 950 ft² with 2 gal of paint. How many 1-gal cans does she need in order to paint a 30,000-ft² wall?

72. *Bicycling.* Roy bicycled 234 mi in 14 days. At this rate, how far would Roy bicycle in 42 days?

Skill Maintenance

Solve.

73. *Drive-in Movie Theaters.* The number of outdoor movie theaters has declined steadily since the 1950s. In 2007, there were 405 drive-in theaters. This is 3658 fewer than in 1958. How many drive-in movie theaters were there in 1958? [1.5a]

Source: Drive-Ins.com

74. *Shifting Music Sales.* Sales of individual digital music tracks outpaced sales of albums by 176.9 million in the first quarter of 2008. During that quarter, 104.5 million albums were sold. How many individual tracks were sold during the same time period? [3.7a]

Source: Nielsen SoundScan

Synthesis

75. 🖩 *Real-Estate Values.* According to Coldwell Banker Real Estate Corporation, a home selling for $189,000 in Austin, Texas, would sell for $437,850 in Denver, Colorado. How much would a $350,000 home in Denver sell for in Austin? Round to the nearest $1000.

Source: Coldwell Banker Real Estate Corporation

76. *Baseball Statistics.* Cy Young, one of the greatest baseball pitchers of all time, gave up an average of 2.63 earned runs every 9 innings. Young pitched 7356 innings, more than anyone else in the history of baseball. How many earned runs did he give up?

4.2

Percent Notation

OBJECTIVES

a Write three kinds of notation for a percent.

b Convert between percent notation and decimal notation.

SKILL TO REVIEW

Objective 3.3a: Multiply using decimal notation.

Multiply.

1. 68.3×0.01

2. 3013×2.4

a Understanding Percent Notation

Of all the surface area of the earth, 70% is covered by water. What does this mean? It means that of every 100 square miles of the earth's surface area, 70 square miles are covered by water. Thus, 70% is a ratio of 70 to 100, or $\frac{70}{100}$.

Source: *The Handy Geography Answer Book*

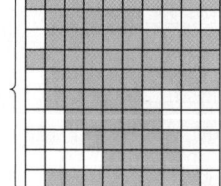

70 of 100 squares are shaded.

70% or $\frac{70}{100}$ or 0.70 of the large square is shaded.

Percent notation is used extensively in our everyday lives. Here are some examples.

25.2% of the adult population in Washington, D.C., has a graduate degree.

Almost 22% of the glass that is produced is recycled.

A blood alcohol level of 0.08% is the standard used by most states as the legal limit for drunk driving.

71% of people in the United States use the Internet; 17% of people in China use the Internet.

In California, 42.5% of people age 5 and older speak a language other than English at home. In Kansas, the percentage is 10.3%.

Percent notation is often represented using a circle graph, or pie chart, to show how the parts of a quantity are related. For example, the circle graph at left illustrates the percentage of people in the United States with each of the four blood types.

Blood Types in the United States

Type AB 4%
Type B 10%
Type A 42%
Type O 44%

SOURCE: bloodcenter.stanford.edu/about_blood/blood_types.html

PERCENT NOTATION
The notation **n%** means "*n* per hundred."

Answers

Skill to Review:

1. 0.683   **2.** 7231.2

This definition leads us to the following equivalent ways of defining percent notation.

> **NOTATION FOR *n*%**
>
> **Percent notation, *n*%,** can be expressed using:
>
> ratio $\longrightarrow n\% =$ the ratio of n to $100 = \dfrac{n}{100}$,
>
> fraction notation $\longrightarrow n\% = n \times \dfrac{1}{100}$, or
>
> decimal notation $\longrightarrow n\% = n \times 0.01$.

At the airport in Oslo, Norway, 64% of all passengers arrive and leave using trains and buses. At the airport in San Francisco, the percentage is 23%.
SOURCE: Transportation Research Board

EXAMPLE 1 Write three kinds of notation for 35%.

Using ratio: $35\% = \dfrac{35}{100}$ A ratio of 35 to 100

Using fraction notation: $35\% = 35 \times \dfrac{1}{100}$ Replacing % with $\times \dfrac{1}{100}$

Using decimal notation: $35\% = 35 \times 0.01$ Replacing % with $\times 0.01$

EXAMPLE 2 Write three kinds of notation for 67.8%.

Using ratio: $67.8\% = \dfrac{67.8}{100}$ A ratio of 67.8 to 100

Using fraction notation: $67.8\% = 67.8 \times \dfrac{1}{100}$ Replacing % with $\times \dfrac{1}{100}$

Using decimal notation: $67.8\% = 67.8 \times 0.01$ Replacing % with $\times 0.01$

Do Exercises 1–4.

Write three kinds of notation as in Examples 1 and 2.

1. 70%   **2.** 23.4%

3. 100%   **4.** 0.6%

b Converting Between Percent Notation and Decimal Notation

Consider 78%. To convert to decimal notation, we can think of percent notation as a ratio and write

$$78\% = \frac{78}{100} \qquad \text{Using the definition of percent as a ratio}$$
$$= 0.78. \qquad \text{Dividing}$$

Similarly,

$$4.9\% = \frac{4.9}{100} \qquad \text{Using the definition of percent as a ratio}$$
$$= 0.049. \qquad \text{Dividing}$$

We could also convert 78% to decimal notation by replacing "%" with "$\times 0.01$" and write

$$78\% = 78 \times 0.01 \qquad \text{Replacing % with } \times 0.01$$
$$= 0.78. \qquad \text{Multiplying}$$

Answers

1. $\dfrac{70}{100}$; $70 \times \dfrac{1}{100}$; 70×0.01

2. $\dfrac{23.4}{100}$; $23.4 \times \dfrac{1}{100}$; 23.4×0.01

3. $\dfrac{100}{100}$; $100 \times \dfrac{1}{100}$; 100×0.01

4. $\dfrac{0.6}{100}$; $0.6 \times \dfrac{1}{100}$; 0.6×0.01

Calculator Corner

Converting from Percent Notation to Decimal Notation Many calculators have a % key that can be used to convert from percent notation to decimal notation. This is often the second operation associated with a particular key and is accessed by first pressing a 2nd or SHIFT key. To convert 57.6% to decimal notation, for example, you might press 5 7 · 6 2nd % or 5 7 · 6 SHIFT % . The display would read 0.576 , so 57.6% = 0.576.

Exercises: Use a calculator to find decimal notation.

1. 14%   2. 0.069%
3. 43.8%   4. 125%

Similarly,

$$4.9\% = 4.9 \times 0.01 \qquad \text{Replacing \% with } \times 0.01$$
$$= 0.049. \qquad \text{Multiplying}$$

Dividing by 100 amounts to moving the decimal point two places to the left, which is the same as multiplying by 0.01. This leads us to a quick way to convert from percent notation to decimal notation: We drop the percent symbol and move the decimal point two places to the left.

To convert from percent notation to decimal notation,	36.5%
a) replace the percent symbol % with $\times 0.01$, and	36.5×0.01
b) multiply by 0.01, which means move the decimal point two places to the left.	0.36.5 Move 2 places to the left.
	36.5% = 0.365

EXAMPLE 3 Find decimal notation for 99.44%.

a) Replace the percent symbol with $\times 0.01$. 99.44×0.01

b) Move the decimal point two places to the left.   0.99.44

Thus, 99.44% = 0.9944.

EXAMPLE 4 The interest rate on a $2\frac{1}{2}$-year certificate of deposit is $6\frac{3}{8}$%. Find decimal notation for $6\frac{3}{8}$%.

a) Convert $6\frac{3}{8}$ to decimal notation and replace the percent symbol with $\times 0.01$. $6\frac{3}{8}\%$ 6.375×0.01

b) Move the decimal point two places to the left.   0.06.375

Thus, $6\frac{3}{8}\% = 0.06375$.

Do Exercises 5–8.

To convert 0.38 to percent notation, we can first write fraction notation, as follows:

$$0.38 = \frac{38}{100} \qquad \text{Converting to fraction notation}$$
$$= 38\%. \qquad \text{Using the definition of percent as a ratio}$$

Note that $100\% = 100 \times 0.01 = 1$. Thus to convert 0.38 to percent notation, we can multiply by 1, using 100% as a symbol for 1.

$$0.38 = 0.38 \times 1$$
$$= 0.38 \times 100\%$$
$$= 0.38 \times 100 \times 0.01 \qquad \text{Replacing 100\% with } 100 \times 0.01$$
$$= (0.38 \times 100) \times 0.01 \qquad \text{Using the associative law of multiplication}$$
$$= 38 \times 0.01$$
$$= 38\% \qquad \text{Replacing } \times 0.01 \text{ with \%}$$

Find decimal notation.

5. 34%   6. 78.9%

Find decimal notation for the percent notation in each sentence.

7. **Working Online.** Of all American adults who use the Internet, 42% have gone online to work from home.
   Sources: U.S. Bureau of Labor Statistics; Nielsen Home Technology Report

8. **Blood Alcohol Level.** A blood alcohol level of 0.08% is the standard used by most states as the legal limit for drunk driving.

Answers

5. 0.34   6. 0.789
7. 0.42   8. 0.0008

Even more quickly, since $0.38 = 0.38 \times 100\%$, we can simply multiply 0.38 by 100 and write the % symbol.

To convert from decimal notation to percent notation, we multiply by 100%. That is, we move the decimal point two places to the right and write a percent symbol.

It is thought that the Roman emperor Augustus began percent notation by taxing goods sold at a rate of $\frac{1}{100}$. In time, the symbol "%" evolved by interchanging the parts of the symbol "100" to "0/0" and then to "%."

To convert from decimal notation to percent notation, multiply by 100%. That is,

$$0.675 = 0.675 \times 100\%$$

a) move the decimal point two places to the right, and

   0.67.5   Move 2 places to the right.

b) write a % symbol.

   67.5%

$$0.675 = 67.5\%$$

EXAMPLE 5 Find percent notation for 1.27.

a) Move the decimal point two places to the right.   1.27.

b) Write a % symbol.   127%

Thus, $1.27 = 127\%$.

EXAMPLE 6 Of the time that people declare as sick leave, 0.21 is actually used for family issues. Find percent notation for 0.21.
Source: CCH Inc.

a) Move the decimal point two places to the right.   0.21.

b) Write a % symbol.   21%

Thus, $0.21 = 21\%$.

EXAMPLE 7 Find percent notation for 5.6.

a) Move the decimal point two places to the right, adding an extra zero.   5.60.

b) Write a % symbol.   560%

Thus, $5.6 = 560\%$.

EXAMPLE 8 Of those who play golf, 0.149 play 8–24 rounds per year. Find percent notation for 0.149.
Source: U.S. Golf Association

a) Move the decimal point two places to the right.   0.14.9

b) Write a % symbol.   14.9%

Thus, $0.149 = 14.9\%$.

Do Exercises 9–14.

Find percent notation.

9. 0.24   **10.** 3.47

11. 1   **12.** 0.05

Find percent notation for the decimal notation in each sentence.

13. Women in Congress. In 2008, 0.16 of the members of the United States Congress were women.
Source: Center for American Women and Politics at Rutgers University

14. Soccer. For Americans in the 18–24 age group, 0.311 have played soccer; for the 12–17 age group, 0.396 have played.
Source: ESPN Sports Poll, a service of TNS Sport

Answers

9. 24%   **10.** 347%   **11.** 100%   **12.** 5%
13. 16%   **14.** 31.1%; 39.6%

4.2 **Exercise Set**

For Extra Help

MyMathLab

Math XL
PRACTICE

WATCH

DOWNLOAD

READ

REVIEW

a Write three kinds of notation as in Examples 1 and 2 on p. 273.

1. 90%

2. 58.7%

3. 12.5%

4. 130%

b Find decimal notation.

5. 67%

6. 17%

7. 45.6%

8. 76.3%

9. 59.01%

10. 30.02%

11. 10%

12. 80%

13. 1%

14. 100%

15. 200%

16. 300%

17. 0.1%

18. 0.4%

19. 0.09%

20. 0.12%

21. 0.18%

22. 5.5%

23. 23.19%

24. 87.99%

25. $14\frac{7}{8}\%$

26. $93\frac{1}{8}\%$

27. $56\frac{1}{2}\%$

28. $61\frac{3}{4}\%$

Find decimal notation for the percent notation(s) in each sentence.

29. *Video Games.* According to a recent survey, 97% of the 12–17 age group play video games.

Sources: Pew Survey; *Time*, September 29, 2008

30. *Female Astronauts.* Of the 466 astronauts who have flown in space, 10.52% are female.

Source: *Encyclopedia Astronautica*

Copyright © 2012 Pearson Education, Inc.

31. *Fuel Efficiency.* Speeding up by only 5 mph on the highway cuts fuel efficiency by approximately 7% to 8%.

Source: *Wall Street Journal*, "Pain Relief," by A. J. Miranda, September 15, 2008

32. *Foreign-Born Population.* In 2008, the U.S. foreign-born population was 12.6%, the highest since 1920.

Source: U.S. Census Bureau

33. *High School Sports.* During the 2007–2008 academic year, 54.8% of all high school students were involved in high school sports.

Source: National Federation of State High School Associations

34. *Eating Out.* On a given day, 58% of all Americans eat meals and snacks away from home.

Source: U.S. Department of Agriculture

Find percent notation.

35. 0.47   **36.** 0.87   **37.** 0.03   **38.** 0.01   **39.** 8.7

40. 4   **41.** 0.334   **42.** 0.889   **43.** 0.75   **44.** 0.99

45. 0.4   **46.** 0.5   **47.** 0.006   **48.** 0.008   **49.** 0.017

50. 0.024   **51.** 0.2718   **52.** 0.8911   **53.** 0.0239   **54.** 0.00073

Find percent notation for the decimal notation(s) in each sentence.

55. *Wasting Food.* Americans waste an estimated 0.27 of the food available for consumption. The waste occurs in restaurants, supermarkets, cafeterias, and household kitchens.

Source: *New York Times*, "One Country's Table Scraps, Another Country's Meal," by Andrew Martin, May 18, 2008

56. *Recycling Newspapers.* Over 0.73 of all newspapers are recycled.

Source: Newspaper Association of America

57. *Age 65 and Older.* In Alaska, 0.057 of the residents are age 65 and older. In Florida, 0.176 are age 65 and older.

Source: U.S. Census Bureau

58. *Dining Together.* In 2008, 0.2 of families dined together every evening. This rate declined from 0.59 in 1987.

Source: Online polls at USATODAY.com

59. *Cancer Survival.* In 2005, the estimated 10-yr survival rate was 0.906 for children diagnosed with non-Hodgkin's lymphoma (NHL) and 0.88 for those diagnosed with acute lymphoblastic leukemia (ALL).

Source: *Journal of the National Cancer Institute*, news release, September 8, 2008

60. *Postsecondary Degrees.* In 2007, 0.296 of those 25 to 29 years old in the United States had attained a bachelor's degree or higher.

Source: National Center for Education Statistics, U.S. Department of Commerce, U.S. Census Bureau, Current Population Survey, March Supplement 1971–2007

Find decimal notation for each percent notation in the graph.

61.

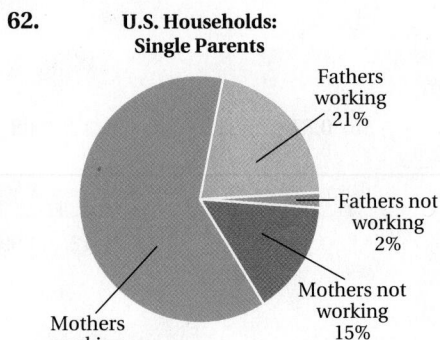

**U.S. Households:
Married with Children**

Only husband works 30%

Only wife works 4%

Neither works 2%

Both parents work 64%

SOURCE: U.S. Census Bureau;
U.S. Bureau of Labor Statistics

62.

**U.S. Households:
Single Parents**

Fathers working 21%

Fathers not working 2%

Mothers not working 15%

Mothers working 62%

SOURCE: U.S. Census Bureau;
U.S. Bureau of Labor Statistics

Skill Maintenance

Convert to a mixed numeral.   [2.4a]

63. $\dfrac{100}{3}$

64. $\dfrac{75}{2}$

65. $\dfrac{75}{8}$

66. $\dfrac{297}{16}$

67. $\dfrac{567}{98}$

68. $\dfrac{2345}{21}$

Convert to decimal notation.   [3.5a]

69. $\dfrac{2}{3}$

70. $\dfrac{1}{3}$

71. $\dfrac{5}{6}$

72. $\dfrac{17}{12}$

73. $\dfrac{8}{3}$

74. $\dfrac{15}{16}$

Synthesis

Find percent notation. (*Hint*: Multiply by a form of 1 and obtain a denominator of 100.)

75. $\dfrac{1}{2}$

76. $\dfrac{3}{4}$

77. $\dfrac{7}{10}$

78. $\dfrac{2}{5}$

Find percent notation for each shaded area.

79.

80.

Copyright © 2012 Pearson Education, Inc.

4.3 Percent Notation and Fraction Notation

a Convert from Fraction Notation to Percent Notation

Consider the fraction notation $\frac{7}{8}$. To convert to percent notation, we use two skills that we already have. We first find decimal notation by dividing: $7 \div 8$.

$$
\begin{array}{r}
0.8\ 7\ 5 \\
8\overline{)7.0\ 0\ 0} \\
6\ 4 \\
\hline
6\ 0 \\
5\ 6 \\
\hline
4\ 0 \\
4\ 0 \\
\hline
0
\end{array}
\qquad \frac{7}{8} = 0.875
$$

Then we convert the decimal notation to percent notation. We move the decimal point two places to the right

$$0.8\ 7.5$$

and write a % symbol:

$$\frac{7}{8} = 87.5\%, \text{ or } 87\tfrac{1}{2}\%. \qquad 0.5 = \tfrac{1}{2}$$

To convert from fraction notation to percent notation,

$\frac{3}{5}$ Fraction notation

a) find decimal notation by division, and

$$
\begin{array}{r}
0.6 \\
5\overline{)3.0} \\
3\ 0 \\
\hline
0
\end{array}
$$

b) convert the decimal notation to percent notation.

$0.6 = 0.60 = 60\%$ Percent notation

$\frac{3}{5} = 60\%$

EXAMPLE 1 Find percent notation for $\frac{9}{16}$.

a) We first find decimal notation by division.

$$
\begin{array}{r}
0.5\ 6\ 2\ 5 \\
1\ 6\overline{)9.0\ 0\ 0\ 0} \\
8\ 0 \\
\hline
1\ 0\ 0 \\
9\ 6 \\
\hline
4\ 0 \\
3\ 2 \\
\hline
8\ 0 \\
8\ 0 \\
\hline
0
\end{array}
\qquad \frac{9}{16} = 0.5625
$$

OBJECTIVES

a Convert from fraction notation to percent notation.

b Convert from percent notation to fraction notation.

SKILL TO REVIEW
Objective 3.5a: Convert from fraction notation to decimal notation.

Find decimal notation.

1. $\frac{11}{16}$ 2. $\frac{5}{9}$

Calculator Corner

Converting from Fraction Notation to Percent Notation A calculator can be used to convert from fraction notation to percent notation. We simply perform the division on the calculator and then use the percent key. To convert $\frac{17}{40}$ to percent notation, for example, we press

$\boxed{1}\ \boxed{7}\ \boxed{\div}\ \boxed{4}\ \boxed{0}\ \boxed{\text{2nd}}\ \boxed{\%}$, or

$\boxed{1}\ \boxed{7}\ \boxed{\div}\ \boxed{4}\ \boxed{0}\ \boxed{\text{SHIFT}}\ \boxed{\%}$.

The display reads $\boxed{\quad 42.5 \quad}$, so $\frac{17}{40} = 42.5\%$.

Exercises: Use a calculator to find percent notation. Round to the nearest hundredth of a percent.

1. $\frac{13}{25}$ 2. $\frac{5}{13}$

3. $\frac{43}{39}$ 4. $\frac{12}{7}$

5. $\frac{217}{364}$ 6. $\frac{2378}{8401}$

Answers

Skill to Review:
1. 0.6875 2. $0.\overline{5}$

b) Next, we convert the decimal notation to percent notation. We move the decimal point two places to the right and write a % symbol.

0.56.25
⤴

$$\frac{9}{16} = 56.25\%, \text{ or } 56\frac{1}{4}\% \qquad 0.25 = \frac{1}{4}$$

Don't forget the % symbol.

Do Exercises 1 and 2.

Fractions named by repeating decimals also can be converted to percent notation.

EXAMPLE 2 *Without Health Insurance.* Approximately $\frac{1}{6}$ of all people in the United States are without health insurance. Find percent notation for $\frac{1}{6}$.

Source: U.S. Census Bureau, *Current Population Survey*, March 2003

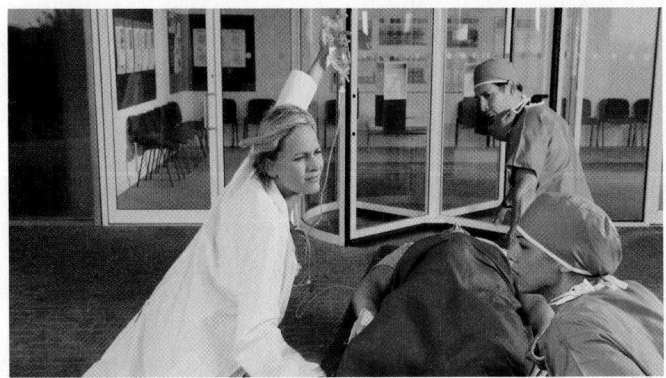

a) Find decimal notation by division.

```
      0.1 6 6
6 ) 1.0 0 0
      6
      ───
      4 0
      3 6
      ───
        4 0
        3 6
        ───
          4
```

We get a repeating decimal: $0.16\overline{6}$.

b) Convert the answer to percent notation.

0.16.$\overline{6}$
⤴

$$\frac{1}{6} = 16.\overline{6}\%, \text{ or } 16\frac{2}{3}\% \qquad 0.\overline{6} = \frac{2}{3}$$

Do Exercises 3 and 4.

Find percent notation.

1. $\frac{1}{4}$ **2.** $\frac{5}{8}$

3. Water is the single most abundant chemical in the body. The human body is about $\frac{2}{3}$ water. Find percent notation for $\frac{2}{3}$.

4. Find percent notation: $\frac{5}{6}$.

Answers

1. 25%   **2.** 62.5%, or $62\frac{1}{2}\%$

3. $66.\overline{6}\%$, or $66\frac{2}{3}\%$

4. $83.\overline{3}\%$, or $83\frac{1}{3}\%$

In some cases, division is not the fastest way to convert. The following are some optional ways in which conversion might be done.

EXAMPLE 3 Find percent notation for $\frac{69}{100}$.

We use the definition of percent as a ratio.

$$\frac{69}{100} = 69\%$$

EXAMPLE 4 Find percent notation for $\frac{17}{20}$.

We want to multiply by 1 to get 100 in the denominator. We think of what we must multiply 20 by in order to get 100. That number is 5, so we multiply by 1 using $\frac{5}{5}$.

$$\frac{17}{20} \cdot \frac{5}{5} = \frac{85}{100} = 85\%$$

Note that this shortcut works only when the denominator is a factor of 100.

EXAMPLE 5 Find percent notation for $\frac{18}{25}$.

$$\frac{18}{25} = \frac{18}{25} \cdot \frac{4}{4} = \frac{72}{100} = 72\%$$

Do Exercises 5–8.

Find percent notation.

5. $\frac{57}{100}$

6. $\frac{19}{25}$

7. $\frac{7}{10}$

8. $\frac{1}{4}$

(b) Converting from Percent Notation to Fraction Notation

To convert from percent notation to fraction notation,	30%	Percent notation
a) use the definition of percent as a ratio, and	$\frac{30}{100}$	
b) simplify, if possible.	$\frac{3}{10}$	Fraction notation

EXAMPLE 6 Find fraction notation for 75%.

$$75\% = \frac{75}{100} \qquad \text{Using the definition of percent}$$

$$= \frac{3 \cdot 25}{4 \cdot 25} = \frac{3}{4} \cdot \frac{25}{25} \Bigg\} \quad \text{Simplifying}$$

$$= \frac{3}{4}$$

Answers

5. 57%   6. 76%   7. 70%
8. 25%

STUDY TIPS

MEMORIZING

Memorizing is a very helpful tool in the study of mathematics. Don't underestimate its power as you memorize the table of decimal, fraction, and percent notation below and on the inside back cover.

EXAMPLE 7 Find fraction notation for 62.5%.

$$62.5\% = \frac{62.5}{100} \qquad \text{Using the definition of percent}$$

$$= \frac{62.5}{100} \times \frac{10}{10} \qquad \text{Multiplying by 1 to eliminate the decimal point in the numerator}$$

$$= \frac{625}{1000}$$

$$= \frac{5 \cdot 125}{8 \cdot 125} = \frac{5}{8} \cdot \frac{125}{125} \left.\begin{array}{c} \\ \\ \end{array}\right\} \text{Simplifying}$$

$$= \frac{5}{8}$$

EXAMPLE 8 Find fraction notation for $16\frac{2}{3}\%$.

$$16\frac{2}{3}\% = \frac{50}{3}\% \qquad \text{Converting from the mixed numeral to fraction notation}$$

$$= \frac{50}{3} \times \frac{1}{100} \qquad \text{Using the definition of percent}$$

$$= \frac{50 \cdot 1}{3 \cdot 50 \cdot 2} = \frac{1}{3 \cdot 2} \cdot \frac{50}{50} \left.\begin{array}{c} \\ \\ \end{array}\right\} \text{Simplifying}$$

$$= \frac{1}{6}$$

Do Exercises 9–12.

Find fraction notation.

9. 60%   **10.** 3.25%

11. $66\frac{2}{3}\%$ **12.** $12\frac{1}{2}\%$

The table below lists fraction, decimal, and percent equivalents used so often that it would speed up your work if you memorized them. For example, $\frac{1}{3} = 0.\overline{3}$, so we say that the **decimal equivalent** of $\frac{1}{3}$ is $0.\overline{3}$, or that $0.\overline{3}$ has the **fraction equivalent** $\frac{1}{3}$. This table also appears on the inside back cover.

FRACTION, DECIMAL, AND PERCENT EQUIVALENTS

FRACTION NOTATION	$\frac{1}{10}$	$\frac{1}{8}$	$\frac{1}{6}$	$\frac{1}{5}$	$\frac{1}{4}$	$\frac{3}{10}$	$\frac{1}{3}$	$\frac{3}{8}$	$\frac{2}{5}$	$\frac{1}{2}$	$\frac{3}{5}$	$\frac{5}{8}$	$\frac{2}{3}$	$\frac{7}{10}$	$\frac{3}{4}$	$\frac{4}{5}$	$\frac{5}{6}$	$\frac{7}{8}$	$\frac{9}{10}$	$\frac{1}{1}$
DECIMAL NOTATION	0.1	0.125	$0.16\overline{6}$	0.2	0.25	0.3	$0.33\overline{3}$	0.375	0.4	0.5	0.6	0.625	$0.66\overline{6}$	0.7	0.75	0.8	$0.83\overline{3}$	0.875	0.9	1
PERCENT NOTATION	10%	12.5%, or $12\frac{1}{2}\%$	$16.\overline{6}\%$, or $16\frac{2}{3}\%$	20%	25%	30%	$33.\overline{3}\%$, or $33\frac{1}{3}\%$	37.5%, or $37\frac{1}{2}\%$	40%	50%	60%	62.5%, or $62\frac{1}{2}\%$	$66.\overline{6}\%$, or $66\frac{2}{3}\%$	70%	75%	80%	$83.\overline{3}\%$, or $83\frac{1}{3}\%$	87.5%, or $87\frac{1}{2}\%$	90%	100%

EXAMPLE 9 Find fraction notation for $16.\overline{6}\%$.

We can use the table above or recall that $16.\overline{6}\% = 16\frac{2}{3}\% = \frac{1}{6}$. We can also recall from our work with repeating decimals in Chapter 3 that $0.\overline{6} = \frac{2}{3}$. Then we have $16.\overline{6}\% = 16\frac{2}{3}\%$ and can proceed as in Example 8.

Do Exercises 13 and 14.

Find fraction notation.

13. $33.\overline{3}\%$ **14.** $83.\overline{3}\%$

Answers

9. $\frac{3}{5}$ **10.** $\frac{13}{400}$ **11.** $\frac{2}{3}$

12. $\frac{1}{8}$ **13.** $\frac{1}{3}$ **14.** $\frac{5}{6}$

4.3 Exercise Set

For Extra Help

MyMathLab

Math XL
PRACTICE

WATCH

DOWNLOAD

READ

REVIEW

a Find percent notation.

1. $\dfrac{41}{100}$

2. $\dfrac{36}{100}$

3. $\dfrac{5}{100}$

4. $\dfrac{1}{100}$

5. $\dfrac{2}{10}$

6. $\dfrac{7}{10}$

7. $\dfrac{3}{10}$

8. $\dfrac{9}{10}$

9. $\dfrac{1}{2}$

10. $\dfrac{3}{4}$

11. $\dfrac{7}{8}$

12. $\dfrac{1}{8}$

13. $\dfrac{4}{5}$

14. $\dfrac{2}{5}$

15. $\dfrac{2}{3}$

16. $\dfrac{1}{3}$

17. $\dfrac{1}{6}$

18. $\dfrac{5}{6}$

19. $\dfrac{3}{16}$

20. $\dfrac{11}{16}$

21. $\dfrac{13}{16}$

22. $\dfrac{7}{16}$

23. $\dfrac{4}{25}$

24. $\dfrac{17}{25}$

25. $\dfrac{1}{20}$

26. $\dfrac{31}{50}$

27. $\dfrac{17}{50}$

28. $\dfrac{3}{20}$

Find percent notation for the fraction notation in each sentence.

29. *Heart Transplants.* In the United States in 2006, $\frac{2}{25}$ of the organ transplants were heart transplants and $\frac{59}{100}$ were kidney transplants.
Source: 2007 OPTN/SRTR Annual Report, Table 1.7

30. *Car Colors.* The four most popular colors for 2006 compact/sports cars were silver, gray, black, and red. Of all cars in this category, $\frac{9}{50}$ were silver, $\frac{3}{20}$ gray, $\frac{3}{20}$ black, and $\frac{3}{20}$ red.
Sources: Ward's Automotive Group; DuPont Automotive Products

In Exercises 31–36, write percent notation for the fractions in the pie chart below.

How Food Dollars Are Spent

Dairy $\frac{3}{25}$

Beverages (nonalcoholic) $\frac{3}{25}$

Sugar $\frac{1}{25}$

Cereal and baked goods $\frac{13}{100}$

Fats and oils $\frac{3}{100}$

Fruits and vegetables $\frac{3}{20}$

Other $\frac{9}{50}$

Meat, poultry, and fish $\frac{11}{50}$

Eggs $\frac{1}{50}$

SOURCES: U.S. Bureau of Labor Statistics; Consumer Price Index; *The Hoosier Farmer*, Summer 2008

31. $\dfrac{11}{50}$

32. $\dfrac{9}{50}$

33. $\dfrac{3}{25}$

34. $\dfrac{1}{25}$

35. $\dfrac{3}{20}$

36. $\dfrac{13}{100}$

b   Find fraction notation. Simplify.

37. 85%

38. 55%

39. 62.5%

40. 12.5%

41. $33\frac{1}{3}$%

42. $83\frac{1}{3}$%

43. $16.\overline{6}$%

44. $66.\overline{6}$%

45. 7.25%

46. 4.85%

47. 0.8%

48. 0.2%

49. $25\frac{3}{8}$%

50. $48\frac{7}{8}$%

51. $78\frac{2}{9}$%

52. $16\frac{5}{9}$%

53. $64\frac{7}{11}$%

54. $73\frac{3}{11}$%

55. 150%

56. 110%

57. 0.0325%

58. 0.419%

59. $33.\overline{3}$%

60. $83.\overline{3}$%

In Exercises 61–66, find fraction notation for the percent notations in the table below.

**U.S. POPULATION BY SELECTED
AGE CATEGORIES (Data have been
rounded to the nearest percent.)**

AGE CATEGORY	PERCENT OF POPULATION
5–17 years	18%
18–24 years	10
15–44 years	42
18 years and older	75
65 years and older	12
75 years and older	6

SOURCES: U.S. Census Bureau; 2006 American Community Survey

61. 6%

62. 18%

63. 12%

64. 42%

65. 75%

66. 10%

Copyright © 2012 Pearson Education, Inc.

Find fraction notation for the percent notation in each sentence.

67. A $\frac{3}{4}$-cup serving of Post Selects Great Grains cereal with $\frac{1}{2}$ cup fat-free milk satisfies 15% of the minimum daily requirement for calcium.
Source: Kraft Foods Global, Inc.

68. A 1.8-oz serving of Frosted Mini-Wheats®, Blueberry Muffin, with $\frac{1}{2}$ cup fat-free milk satisfies 35% of the minimum daily requirement for Vitamin B_{12}.
Source: Kellogg, Inc.

69. In 2006, 20.9% of Americans age 18 and older smoked cigarettes.
Sources: *Washington Post,* March 9, 2006; U.S. Centers for Disease Control and Prevention

70. In 2006, 14.9% of the adults age 18 and older in California smoked cigarettes.
Sources: U.S. Centers for Disease Control and Prevention; *AARP Magazine,* March 2008

Complete each table.

71.

FRACTION NOTATION	DECIMAL NOTATION	PERCENT NOTATION
$\frac{1}{8}$		12.5%, or $12\frac{1}{2}$%
$\frac{1}{6}$		
		20%
	0.25	
		33.$\overline{3}$%, or $33\frac{1}{3}$%
		37.5%, or $37\frac{1}{2}$%
		40%
$\frac{1}{2}$		

72.

FRACTION NOTATION	DECIMAL NOTATION	PERCENT NOTATION
$\frac{3}{5}$		
	0.625	
$\frac{2}{3}$		
	0.75	75%
$\frac{4}{5}$		
$\frac{5}{6}$		83.$\overline{3}$%, or $83\frac{1}{3}$%
$\frac{7}{8}$		87.5%, or $87\frac{1}{2}$%
		100%

73.

FRACTION NOTATION	DECIMAL NOTATION	PERCENT NOTATION
	0.5	
$\frac{1}{3}$		
		25%
		16.$\overline{6}$%, or $16\frac{2}{3}$%
	0.125	
$\frac{3}{4}$		
	0.8$\overline{3}$	
$\frac{3}{8}$		

74.

FRACTION NOTATION	DECIMAL NOTATION	PERCENT NOTATION
		40%
		62.5%, or $62\frac{1}{2}$%
	0.875	
$\frac{1}{1}$		
	0.6	
	0.$\overline{6}$	
$\frac{1}{5}$		

Skill Maintenance

Solve.

75. $13 \cdot x = 910$ [1.4b]

76. $15 \cdot y = 75$ [1.4b]

77. $0.05 \times b = 20$ [3.4b]

78. $3 = 0.16 \times b$ [3.4b]

79. $\dfrac{24}{37} = \dfrac{15}{x}$ [4.1d]

80. $\dfrac{17}{18} = \dfrac{x}{27}$ [4.1d]

81. $\dfrac{9}{10} = \dfrac{x}{5}$ [4.1d]

82. $\dfrac{7}{x} = \dfrac{4}{5}$ [4.1d]

Convert to a mixed numeral.   [2.4a]

83. $\dfrac{100}{3}$

84. $\dfrac{75}{2}$

85. $\dfrac{250}{3}$

86. $\dfrac{123}{6}$

87. $\dfrac{345}{8}$

88. $\dfrac{373}{6}$

89. $\dfrac{75}{4}$

90. $\dfrac{67}{9}$

Convert from a mixed numeral to fraction notation.   [2.4a]

91. $1\dfrac{1}{17}$

92. $20\dfrac{9}{10}$

93. $101\dfrac{1}{2}$

94. $32\dfrac{3}{8}$

Synthesis

Write percent notation.

95. $\dfrac{41}{369}$

96. $\dfrac{54}{999}$

97. $2.5\overline{74631}$

98. $3.2\overline{93847}$

Write decimal notation.

99. $\dfrac{14}{9}\%$

100. $\dfrac{19}{12}\%$

101. $\dfrac{729}{7}\%$

102. $\dfrac{637}{6}\%$

103. Arrange the following numbers from smallest to largest.

$$16\dfrac{1}{6}\%, \ 1.6, \ \dfrac{1}{6}\%, \ \dfrac{1}{2}, \ 0.2, \ 1.6\%, \ 1\dfrac{1}{6}\%, \ 0.5\%, \ \dfrac{2}{7}\%, \ 0.\overline{54}$$

Copyright © 2012 Pearson Education, Inc.

4.4 Solving Percent Problems Using Percent Equations

a   Translating to Equations

To solve a problem involving percents, it is helpful to translate first to an equation. To distinguish the method discussed in this section from that of Section 4.5, we will call these *percent equations*.

KEY WORDS IN PERCENT TRANSLATIONS

"**Of**" translates to "·", or "×".   "**Is**" translates to "=".

"**What**" translates to any letter.   "**%**" translates to "× $\frac{1}{100}$" or "× 0.01".

EXAMPLES   Translate each of the following.

1. 23%   of   5   is   what?
  ↓   ↓   ↓   ↓   ↓
  23%   ·   5   = a This is a *percent equation*.

2. What   is   11%   of   49?
   ↓   ↓   ↓   ↓   ↓
   a =   11%   ·   49   Any letter can be used.

Do Margin Exercises 1 and 2.

EXAMPLES   Translate each of the following.

3. 3   is   10%   of   what?
  ↓   ↓   ↓   ↓   ↓
  3   =   10%   · b

4. 45%   of   what   is   23?
   ↓   ↓   ↓   ↓   ↓
   45%   × b =   23

Do Exercises 3 and 4.

EXAMPLES   Translate each of the following.

5. 10   is   what percent   of   20?
   ↓   ↓   ↓   ↓   ↓
   10   = p ×   20

6. What percent   of   50   is   7?
        ↓   ↓   ↓   ↓   ↓
        p ·   50   =   7

Do Exercises 5 and 6.

OBJECTIVES

a Translate percent problems to percent equations.

b Solve basic percent problems.

SKILL TO REVIEW
Objective 3.4b: Solve equations of the type $a \cdot x = b$, where a and b may be in decimal notation.

Solve.

1. $0.05 \cdot x = 830$

2. $8 \cdot y = 40.648$

Translate to an equation. Do not solve.

1. 12% of 50 is what?

2. What is 40% of 60?

Translate to an equation. Do not solve.

3. 45 is 20% of what?

4. 120% of what is 60?

Translate to an equation. Do not solve.

5. 16 is what percent of 40?

6. What percent of 84 is 10.5?

Answers

Skill to Review:
1. 16,600   **2.** 5.081

Margin Exercises:
1. 12% × 50 = a **2.** a = 40% × 60
3. 45 = 20% × b **4.** 120% × b = 60
5. 16 = p × 40   **6.** p × 84 = 10.5

Each year, Americans spend about $40 billion on pets; approximately 23.9% of that amount is spent on veterinary care. What is spent per year on veterinary care? (See Example 7.)

SOURCE: American Pet Products Manufacturers Association

b Solving Percent Problems

In solving percent problems, we use the *Translate* and *Solve* steps in the problem-solving strategy used throughout this text.

Percent problems are actually of three different types. Although the method we present does *not* require that you be able to identify which type you are solving, it is helpful to know them. Each of the three types of percent problems depends on which of the three pieces of information is missing.

1. **Finding the *amount* (the result of taking the percent)**

   Example: What is 25% of 60?

   Translation: a = 25% · 60

2. **Finding the *base* (the number you are taking the percent of)**

   Example: 15 is 25% of what?

   Translation: 15 = 25% · b

3. **Finding the *percent number* (the percent itself)**

   Example: 15 is what percent of 60?

   Translation: 15 = p · 60

Finding the Amount

EXAMPLE 7   What is 23.9% of $40,000,000,000?

Translate: $a = 23.9\% \times 40,000,000,000$.

Solve: The letter is by itself. To solve the equation, we just convert 23.9% to decimal notation and multiply:

$$a = 23.9\% \times 40,000,000,000$$
$$a = 0.239 \times 40,000,000,000 = 9,560,000,000.$$

Thus, $9,560,000,000 is 23.9% of $40,000,000,000. The answer is $9,560,000,000.

Do Exercise 7.

7. Solve:

What is 12% of $50?

EXAMPLE 8   120% of 42 is what?

Translate: $120\% \times 42 = a$.

Solve: The letter is by itself. To solve the equation, we carry out the calculation:

$$a = 120\% \times 42$$
$$a = 1.2 \times 42 \qquad 120\% = 1.2$$
$$a = 50.4.$$

Thus, 120% of 42 is 50.4. The answer is 50.4.

Do Exercise 8.

8. Solve:

64% of 55 is what?

Answers

7. $6   **8.** 35.20

Finding the Base

EXAMPLE 9 5% of what is 20?

Translate: 5% × b = 20.

Solve: This time the letter is *not* by itself. To solve the equation, we divide by 5% on both sides:

$$\frac{5\% \times b}{5\%} = \frac{20}{5\%} \qquad \text{Dividing by 5\% on both sides}$$

$$b = \frac{20}{0.05} \qquad 5\% = 0.05$$

$$b = 400.$$

Thus, 5% of 400 is 20. The answer is 400.

EXAMPLE 10 $3 is 16% of what?

Translate:
$$
\begin{array}{ccccc}
\$3 & \text{is} & 16\% & \text{of} & \text{what?} \\
\downarrow & \downarrow & \downarrow & \downarrow & \downarrow \\
3 & = & 16\% & \times & b
\end{array}
$$

Solve: To solve the equation, we divide by 16% on both sides:

$$\frac{3}{16\%} = \frac{16\% \times b}{16\%} \qquad \text{Dividing by 16\% on both sides}$$

$$\frac{3}{0.16} = b \qquad 16\% = 0.16$$

$$18.75 = b.$$

Thus, $3 is 16% of $18.75. The answer is $18.75.

> Do Exercises 9 and 10.

Finding the Percent Number

In solving these problems, you *must* remember to convert to percent notation after you have solved the equation.

EXAMPLE 11 2100 is what percent of 30,000?

Translate:
$$
\begin{array}{ccccc}
2100 & \text{is} & \text{what percent} & \text{of} & 30{,}000? \\
\downarrow & \downarrow & \downarrow & \downarrow & \downarrow \\
2100 & = & p & \times & 30{,}000
\end{array}
$$

Solve: To solve the equation, we divide by 30,000 on both sides and convert the result to percent notation:

$$p \times 30{,}000 = 2100$$

$$\frac{p \times 30{,}000}{30{,}000} = \frac{2100}{30{,}000} \qquad \text{Dividing by 30,000 on both sides}$$

$$p = 0.07 \qquad \text{Converting to decimal notation}$$

$$p = 7\%. \qquad \text{Converting to percent notation}$$

Thus, 2100 is 7% of 30,000. The answer is 7%.

In a survey of a group of people, it was found that 5%, or 20 people, chose strawberry as their favorite ice cream flavor. How many people were surveyed? (See Example 9.)
SOURCE: International Ice Cream Association

Solve.

9. 20% of what is 45?

10. $60 is 120% of what?

In 2007, there were about 30,000 earthquakes worldwide. Of this number, 2100 earthquakes had magnitudes greater than 5.0. What percent of the 30,000 earthquakes had magnitudes greater than 5.0? (See Example 11.)
SOURCE: National Earthquake Information Center, U.S. Geological Survey

Answers
9. 225 **10.** $50

EXAMPLE 12 What percent of $50 is $16?

Translate: $\underbrace{\text{What percent}}_{p}$ $\underset{\times}{\text{of}}$ $\underset{50}{\$50}$ $\underset{=}{\text{is}}$ $\underset{16}{\$16?}$

Solve: To solve the equation, we divide by 50 on both sides and convert the answer to percent notation:

$$\frac{p \times 50}{50} = \frac{16}{50} \qquad \text{Dividing by 50 on both sides}$$

$$p = \frac{16}{50}$$

$$p = 0.32$$

$$p = 32\%. \qquad \text{Converting to percent notation}$$

Thus, 32% of $50 is $16. The answer is 32%.

Do Exercises 11 and 12.

Solve:

11. 16 is what percent of 40?

12. What percent of $84 is $10.50?

------- *Caution!* -------

When a question asks "what percent?", be sure to give the answer in percent notation.

Calculator Corner

Using Percents in Computations   Many calculators have a % key that can be used in computations. (See the Calculator Corner on page 274.) For example, to find 11% of 49, we press 1 1 2nd % × 4 9 =, or 4 9 × 1 1 SHIFT % . The display reads [5.39], so 11% of 49 is 5.39.

In Example 9, we perform the computation 20/5%. To use the % key in this computation, we press 2 0 ÷ 5 2nd % =, or 2 0 ÷ 5 SHIFT % . The result is 400.

We can also use the % key to find the percent number in a problem. In Example 11, for instance, we answer the question "2100 is what percent of 30,000?" On a calculator, we press 2 1 0 0 ÷ 3 0 0 0 0 2nd % =, or 2 1 0 0 ÷ 3 0 0 0 0 SHIFT % . The result is 7, so 2100 is 7% of 30,000.

Exercises: Use a calculator to find each of the following.

1. What is 12.6% of $40?

2. 0.04% of 28 is what?

3. 8% of what is 36?

4. $45 is 4.5% of what?

5. 23 is what percent of 920?

6. What percent of $442 is $53.04?

Answers

11. 40%   **12.** 12.5%

290   CHAPTER 4   Percent Notation

a   Translate to an equation. Do not solve.

1. What is 32% of 78?

2. 98% of 57 is what?

3. 89 is what percent of 99?

4. What percent of 25 is 8?

5. 13 is 25% of what?

6. 21.4% of what is 20?

b   Translate to an equation and solve.

7. What is 85% of 276?

8. What is 74% of 53?

9. 150% of 30 is what?

10. 100% of 13 is what?

11. What is 6% of $300?

12. What is 4% of $45?

13. 3.8% of 50 is what?

14. $33\frac{1}{3}$% of 480 is what?
$\left(Hint: 33\frac{1}{3}\% = \frac{1}{3}.\right)$

15. $39 is what percent of $50?

16. $16 is what percent of $90?

17. 20 is what percent of 10?

18. 60 is what percent of 20?

19. What percent of $300 is $150?

20. What percent of $50 is $40?

21. What percent of 80 is 100?

22. What percent of 60 is 15?

23. 20 is 50% of what?

24. 57 is 20% of what?

25. 40% of what is $16?

26. 100% of what is $74?

27. 56.32 is 64% of what?

28. 71.04 is 96% of what?

29. 70% of what is 14?

30. 70% of what is 35?

31. What is $62\frac{1}{2}$% of 10?

32. What is $35\frac{1}{4}$% of 1200?

33. What is 8.3% of $10,200?

34. What is 9.2% of $5600?

35. 2.5% of what is 30.4?

36. 8.2% of what is 328?

Skill Maintenance

Write fraction notation.   [3.1b]

37. 0.09

38. 1.79

39. 0.875

40. 0.125

41. 0.9375

42. 0.6875

Write decimal notation.   [3.1b]

43. $\dfrac{89}{100}$

44. $\dfrac{7}{100}$

45. $\dfrac{3}{10}$

46. $\dfrac{17}{1000}$

Synthesis

Solve.

47. What is 7.75% of $10,880?
Estimate _____
Calculate _____

48. 50,951.775 is what percent of 78,995?
Estimate _____
Calculate _____

49. $2496 is 24% of what amount?
Estimate _____
Calculate _____

50. What is 38.2% of $52,345.79?
Estimate _____
Calculate _____

51. 40% of $18\frac{3}{4}$% of $25,000 is what?

Copyright © 2012 Pearson Education, Inc.

4.5

Solving Percent Problems Using Proportions*

(a) Translating to Proportions

A percent is a ratio of some number to 100. For example, 46% is the ratio $\frac{46}{100}$. The numbers 67,620,000 and 147,000,000 have the same ratio as 46 and 100.

$$\frac{46}{100} = \frac{67,620,000}{147,000,000}$$

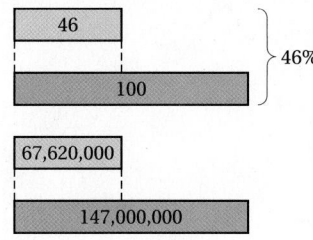

To solve a percent problem using a proportion, we translate as follows:

$$\text{Number} \to \frac{N}{100} = \frac{a}{b} \begin{array}{l} \leftarrow \text{Amount} \\ \leftarrow \text{Base} \end{array}$$
$$100 \to$$

> You might find it helpful to read this as "part is to whole as part is to whole."

For example, 60% of 25 is 15 translates to

$$\frac{60}{100} = \frac{15}{25} \begin{array}{l} \leftarrow \text{Amount} \\ \leftarrow \text{Base} \end{array}$$

A clue in translating is that the base, b, corresponds to 100 and usually follows the wording "percent of." Also, $N\%$ always translates to $N/100$. Another aid in translating is to make a comparison drawing. To do this, we start with the percent side and list 0% at the top and 100% near the bottom. Then we estimate where the specified percent—in this case, 60%—is located. The corresponding quantities are then filled in. The base—in this case, 25—always corresponds to 100%, and the amount—in this case, 15—corresponds to the specified percent.

Percents	Quantities	Percents	Quantities	Percents	Quantities
0%	0	0%	0	0%	0
		60%		60%	15
100%		100%		100%	25

The proportion can then be read easily from the drawing: $\frac{60}{100} = \frac{15}{25}$.

---

*Note: This section presents an alternative method for solving basic percent problems. You can use either equations or proportions to solve percent problems, but you might prefer one method over the other, or your instructor may direct you to use one method over the other.

OBJECTIVES

(a) Translate percent problems to proportions.

(b) Solve basic percent problems.

SKILL TO REVIEW
Objective 4.1d: Solve proportions.

Solve.

1. $\dfrac{3}{100} = \dfrac{27}{b}$

2. $\dfrac{4.3}{20} = \dfrac{N}{100}$

In the United States, 46% of the labor force is women. In 2007, there were approximately 147,000,000 people in the labor force. This means that about 67,620,000 were women.

SOURCES: U.S. Department of Labor; U.S. Bureau of Labor Statistics

Answers

Skill to Review:
1. 900   2. 21.5

EXAMPLE 1 Translate to a proportion.

23% of 5 is what?

$$\frac{23}{100} = \frac{a}{5}$$

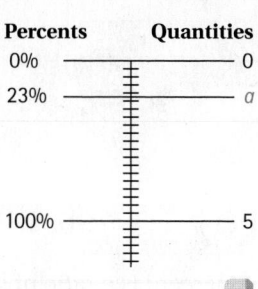

EXAMPLE 2 Translate to a proportion.

What is 124% of 49?

$$\frac{124}{100} = \frac{a}{49}$$

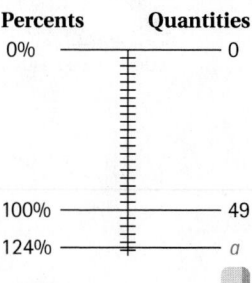

Do Exercises 1–3.

Translate to a proportion. Do not solve.

1. 12% of 50 is what?

2. What is 40% of 60?

3. 130% of 72 is what?

EXAMPLE 3 Translate to a proportion.

3 is 10% of what?

$$\frac{10}{100} = \frac{3}{b}$$

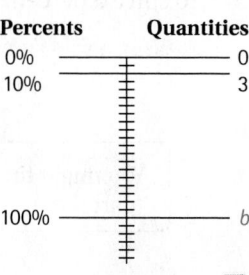

EXAMPLE 4 Translate to a proportion.

45% of what is 23?

$$\frac{45}{100} = \frac{23}{b}$$

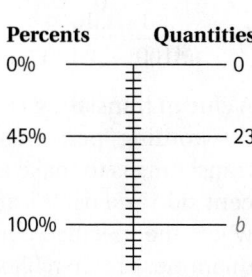

Do Exercises 4 and 5.

Translate to a proportion. Do not solve.

4. 45 is 20% of what?

5. 120% of what is 60?

EXAMPLE 5 Translate to a proportion.

10 is what percent of 20?

$$\frac{N}{100} = \frac{10}{20}$$

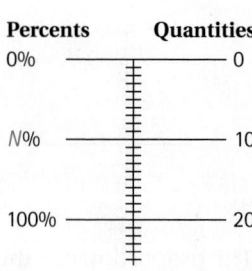

Answers

1. $\frac{12}{100} = \frac{a}{50}$ 2. $\frac{40}{100} = \frac{a}{60}$ 3. $\frac{130}{100} = \frac{a}{72}$

4. $\frac{20}{100} = \frac{45}{b}$ 5. $\frac{120}{100} = \frac{60}{b}$

EXAMPLE 6 Translate to a proportion.

What percent of 50 is 7?

$$\frac{N}{100} = \frac{7}{50}$$

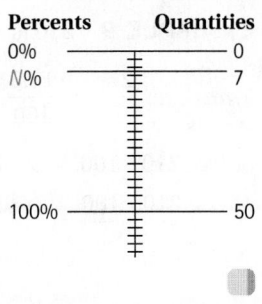

Do Exercises 6 and 7.

Translate to a proportion. Do not solve.

6. 16 is what percent of 40?

7. What percent of 84 is 10.5?

b Solving Percent Problems

After a percent problem has been translated to a proportion, we solve as in Section 4.1d.

EXAMPLE 7 5% of what is $20?

Translate: $\dfrac{5}{100} = \dfrac{20}{b}$

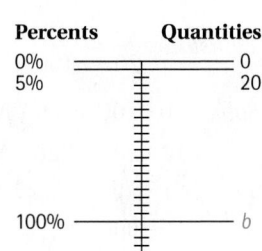

Solve: $5 \cdot b = 100 \cdot 20$ Equating cross products

$\dfrac{5 \cdot b}{5} = \dfrac{100 \cdot 20}{5}$ Dividing by 5

$b = \dfrac{2000}{5}$

$b = 400$ Simplifying

Thus, 5% of $400 is $20. The answer is $400.

Do Exercise 8.

8. Solve:

20% of what is $45?

EXAMPLE 8 120% of 42 is what?

Translate: $\dfrac{120}{100} = \dfrac{a}{42}$

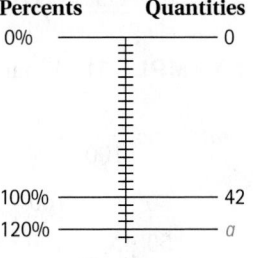

Solve: $120 \cdot 42 = 100 \cdot a$ Equating cross products

$\dfrac{120 \cdot 42}{100} = \dfrac{100 \cdot a}{100}$ Dividing by 100

$\dfrac{5040}{100} = a$

$50.4 = a$ Simplifying

Thus, 120% of 42 is 50.4. The answer is 50.4.

Do Exercises 9 and 10.

Solve.

9. 64% of 55 is what?

10. What is 12% of 50?

Answers

6. $\dfrac{N}{100} = \dfrac{16}{40}$ **7.** $\dfrac{N}{100} = \dfrac{10.5}{84}$ **8.** $225

9. 35.2 **10.** 6

EXAMPLE 9 210 is $10\frac{1}{2}$% of what?

Translate: $\dfrac{210}{b} = \dfrac{10.5}{100}$ $\qquad 10\frac{1}{2}\% = 10.5\%$

Solve: $210 \cdot 100 = b \cdot 10.5$ $\qquad$ Equating cross products

$\dfrac{210 \cdot 100}{10.5} = \dfrac{b \cdot 10.5}{10.5}$ $\qquad$ Dividing by 10.5

$\dfrac{21{,}000}{10.5} = b$ $\qquad$ Multiplying and simplifying

$2000 = b$ $\qquad$ Dividing

Thus, 210 is $10\frac{1}{2}$% of 2000. The answer is 2000.

Do Exercise 11.

11. Solve:

60 is 120% of what?

EXAMPLE 10 $10 is what percent of $20?

Translate: $\dfrac{10}{20} = \dfrac{N}{100}$

Solve: $10 \cdot 100 = 20 \cdot N$ $\qquad$ Equating cross products

$\dfrac{10 \cdot 100}{20} = \dfrac{20 \cdot N}{20}$ $\qquad$ Dividing by 20

$\dfrac{1000}{20} = N$ $\qquad$ Multiplying and simplifying

$50 = N$ $\qquad$ Dividing

Note when solving percent problems using proportions that N is a percent and need not be converted.

Thus, $10 is 50% of $20. The answer is 50%.

Do Exercise 12.

12. Solve:

$12 is what percent of $40?

EXAMPLE 11 What percent of 50 is 16?

Translate: $\dfrac{N}{100} = \dfrac{16}{50}$

Solve: $50 \cdot N = 100 \cdot 16$ $\qquad$ Equating cross products

$\dfrac{50 \cdot N}{50} = \dfrac{100 \cdot 16}{50}$ $\qquad$ Dividing by 50

$N = \dfrac{1600}{50}$ $\qquad$ Multiplying and simplifying

$N = 32$ $\qquad$ Dividing

Thus, 32% of 50 is 16. The answer is 32%.

Do Exercise 13.

13. Solve:

What percent of 84 is 10.5?

Answers

11. 50 **12.** 30% **13.** 12.5%

a Translate to a proportion. Do not solve.

1. What is 37% of 74?

2. 66% of 74 is what?

3. 4.3 is what percent of 5.9?

4. What percent of 6.8 is 5.3?

5. 14 is 25% of what?

6. 133% of what is 40?

b Translate to a proportion and solve.

7. What is 76% of 90?

8. What is 32% of 70?

9. 70% of 660 is what?

10. 80% of 920 is what?

11. What is 4% of 1000?

12. What is 6% of 2000?

13. 4.8% of 60 is what?

14. 63.1% of 80 is what?

15. $24 is what percent of $96?

16. $14 is what percent of $70?

17. 102 is what percent of 100?

18. 103 is what percent of 100?

19. What percent of $480 is $120?

20. What percent of $80 is $60?

21. What percent of 160 is 150?

22. What percent of 33 is 11?

23. $18 is 25% of what?

24. $75 is 20% of what?

25. 60% of what is 54?

26. 80% of what is 96?

27. 65.12 is 74% of what?

28. 63.7 is 65% of what?

29. 80% of what is 16?

30. 80% of what is 10?

31. What is $62\frac{1}{2}$% of 40?

32. What is $43\frac{1}{4}$% of 2600?

33. What is 9.4% of $8300?

34. What is 8.7% of $76,000?

35. 80.8 is $40\frac{2}{5}$% of what?

36. 66.3 is $10\frac{1}{5}$% of what?

Skill Maintenance

Solve. [4.1d]

37. $\dfrac{x}{188} = \dfrac{2}{47}$

38. $\dfrac{15}{x} = \dfrac{3}{800}$

39. $\dfrac{4}{7} = \dfrac{x}{14}$

40. $\dfrac{612}{t} = \dfrac{72}{244}$

41. $\dfrac{5000}{t} = \dfrac{3000}{60}$

42. $\dfrac{75}{100} = \dfrac{n}{20}$

43. $\dfrac{x}{1.2} = \dfrac{36.2}{5.4}$

44. $\dfrac{y}{1\frac{1}{2}} = \dfrac{2\frac{3}{4}}{22}$

Solve.

45. A recipe for muffins calls for $\frac{1}{2}$ qt of buttermilk, $\frac{1}{3}$ qt of skim milk, and $\frac{1}{16}$ qt of oil. How many quarts of liquid ingredients does the recipe call for? [2.5a]

46. The Ferristown School District purchased $\frac{3}{4}$ ton (T) of clay. If the clay is to be shared equally among the district's 6 art departments, how much will each art department receive? [2.5a]

Synthesis

Solve.

47. 🖩 What is 8.85% of $12,640?

Estimate _____

Calculate _____

48. 🖩 78.8% of what is 9809.024?

Estimate _____

Calculate _____

Copyright © 2012 Pearson Education, Inc.

Mid-Chapter Review

Concept Reinforcement

Determine whether each statement is true or false.

_____ **1.** If $\dfrac{x}{t} = \dfrac{y}{s}$, then $xy = ts$. [4.1d]

_____ **2.** When converting decimal notation to percent notation, move the decimal point two places to the right and write a percent symbol. [4.2b]

_____ **3.** The symbol % is equivalent to $\times\ 0.10$. [4.2a]

_____ **4.** Of the numbers $\frac{1}{10}$, 1%, 0.1%, 10%, and $\frac{1}{100}$, the smallest number is 0.1%. [4.2b], [4.3a, b]

Guided Solutions

Fill in each blank with the number that creates a correct statement or solution. [4.2b], [4.3a, b]

5. $\dfrac{1}{2}\% = \dfrac{1}{2} \cdot \dfrac{1}{\square} = \dfrac{1}{\square}$

6. $\dfrac{80}{1000} = \dfrac{\square}{100} = \square\ \%$

7. $5.5\% = \dfrac{\square}{100} = \dfrac{\square}{1000} = \dfrac{11}{\square}$

8. $0.375 = \dfrac{\square}{1000} = \dfrac{\square}{100} = \square\ \%$

9. Solve: 15 is what percent of 80? [4.4b]

$15 = p \times \square$ Translating

$\dfrac{15}{\square} = \dfrac{p \times \square}{\square}$ Dividing on both sides

$\dfrac{15}{\square} = p$ Simplifying

$\square = p$ Dividing

$\square\% = p$ Converting to percent notation

10. Solve: $\dfrac{x}{4} = \dfrac{3}{6}$. [4.1d]

$\dfrac{x}{4} = \dfrac{3}{6}$

$x \cdot \square = \square \cdot 3$ Equating cross products

$\dfrac{x \cdot 6}{\square} = \dfrac{4 \cdot 3}{\square}$ Dividing on both sides

$x = \square$ Simplifying

Mixed Review

Find the ratio of the first number to the second and simplify. [4.1a]

11. 25 to 75

12. 2.4 to 8.4

Find each rate, or speed, as a ratio of distance to time. Round to the nearest hundredth where appropriate. [4.1b]

13. 146 km, 3 hr

14. 243 mi, 4 hr

Solve. [4.1d]

15. $\dfrac{x}{24} = \dfrac{30}{18}$

16. $\dfrac{12}{y} = \dfrac{20}{15}$

17. $\dfrac{0.24}{0.02} = \dfrac{y}{0.36}$

18. $\dfrac{\frac{1}{4}}{x} = \dfrac{\frac{1}{8}}{\frac{1}{4}}$

19. Martha bought 12 oz of deli honey ham for $5.99. What is the unit price in cents per ounce? [4.1e]

20. Jerome bought an 18-oz jar of grape jelly for $2.09. What is the unit price in cents per ounce? [4.1e]

Find decimal notation. [4.2b]

21. 28%

22. 0.15%

23. $5\frac{3}{8}$%

24. 240%

Find percent notation. [4.2b], [4.3a]

25. 0.71

26. $\frac{9}{100}$

27. 0.3891

28. $\frac{3}{16}$

29. 0.005

30. $\frac{37}{50}$

31. 6

32. $\frac{5}{6}$

Find fraction notation. Simplify. [4.3b]

33. 85%

34. 0.048%

35. $22\frac{3}{4}$%

36. $16.\overline{6}$%

Write percent notation for the shaded area. [4.3a]

37.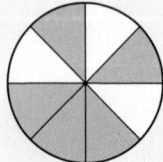

38.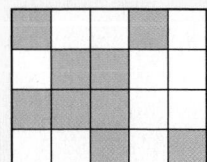

Solve. [4.4b], [4.5b]

39. 25% of what is 14.5?

40. 220 is what percent of 1320?

41. What is 3.2% of 80,000?

42. $17.50 is 35% of what?

43. Arrange the following numbers from smallest to largest. [4.2b], [4.3a, b]

$\frac{1}{2}$%, 5%, 0.275, $\frac{13}{100}$, 1%, 0.1%, 0.05%, $\frac{3}{10}$, $\frac{7}{20}$, 10%

44. Solve: $102,000 is what percent of $3.6 million? [4.4b], [4.5b]

A. $2.8\overline{3}$ million

B. $2\frac{5}{6}$%

C. $0.028\overline{3}$%

D. $28.\overline{3}$

Understanding Through Discussion and Writing

45. Is it always best to convert from fraction notation to percent notation by first finding decimal notation? Why or why not? [4.3a]

46. Suppose we know that 40% of 92 is 36.8. What is a quick way to find 4% of 92? 400% of 92? Explain. [4.4b]

47. Instead of equating cross products, a student solves $\frac{x}{7} = \frac{5}{3}$ by multiplying on both sides by the least common denominator, 21. Is his approach a good one? Why or why not? [4.1d]

48. What do the following have in common? Explain. [4.2b], [4.3a, b]

$\frac{23}{16}$, $1\frac{875}{2000}$, 1.4375, $\frac{207}{144}$, $1\frac{7}{16}$, 143.75%, $1\frac{4375}{10,000}$

Copyright © 2012 Pearson Education, Inc.

4.6

Applications of Percent

(a) Applied Problems Involving Percent

Applied problems involving percent are not always stated in a manner easily translated to an equation. In such cases, it is helpful to rephrase the problem before translating. Sometimes it also helps to make a drawing.

EXAMPLE 1 *Extinction of Mammals.* According to a study conducted for the International Union for the Conservation of Nature (IUCN), the world's mammals are in danger of an extinction crisis. Of the 5487 species of mammals on Earth, 1141 are on the IUCN Red List of Threatened Species. Six of those mammals are shown below. What percent of all mammals are threatened with extinction?

Sources: Environment News Service, October 6, 2008; IUCN

OBJECTIVES

(a) Solve applied problems involving percent.

(b) Solve applied problems involving percent of increase or percent of decrease.

SKILL TO REVIEW
Objective 3.4a: Divide using decimal notation.

Divide.
1. $345 \div 57.5$
2. $111.87 \div 9.9$

Top row, left to right: Tasmanian devils, Père David's deer, African elephant. *Bottom row, left to right:* Iberian lynx, black-footed ferret, giant panda.

1. **Familiarize.** The question asks for a percent of the world's mammals that are in danger of extinction. We note that 5487 is approximately 5500 and 1141 is approximately 1100. Since 1100 is $\frac{1100}{5500}$, or $\frac{1}{5}$, or 20% of 5500, our answer is close to 20%. We let $p =$ the percent of mammals that are in danger of extinction.

2. **Translate.** There are two ways in which we can translate this problem.

Percent equation (see Section 4.4):

1141	is	what percent	of	5487?
↓	↓	↓	↓	↓
1141	=	p	·	5487

Proportion (see Section 4.5):

$$\frac{N}{100} = \frac{1141}{5487}$$

For proportions, $N\% = p$.

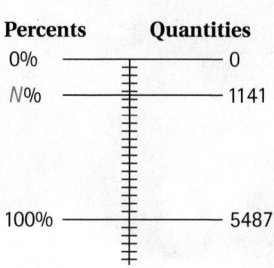

Percents	Quantities
0%	0
N%	1141
100%	5487

Answers
Skill to Review:
1. 6   **2.** 11.3

3. Solve. We now have two ways in which to solve this problem.

Percent equation (see Section 4.4):

$$1141 = p \cdot 5487$$

$$\frac{1141}{5487} = \frac{p \cdot 5487}{5487} \qquad \text{Dividing by 5487 on both sides}$$

$$\frac{1141}{5487} = p$$

$$0.208 \approx p \qquad \text{Finding decimal notation and rounding to the nearest thousandth}$$

$$20.8\% \approx p \qquad \text{Remember to find percent notation.}$$

Note here that the solution, p, includes the % symbol.

Proportion (see Section 4.5):

$$\frac{N}{100} = \frac{1141}{5487}$$

$$N \cdot 5487 = 100 \cdot 1141 \qquad \text{Equating cross products}$$

$$\frac{N \cdot 5487}{5487} = \frac{114{,}100}{5487} \qquad \text{Dividing by 5487 on both sides}$$

$$N = \frac{114{,}100}{5487}$$

$$N = 20.8 \qquad \text{Dividing and rounding to the nearest tenth}$$

We use the solution of the proportion to express the answer to the problem as 20.8%. Note that in the proportion method, $N\% = p$.

4. Check. To check, we note that the answer 20.8% is close to 20%, as estimated in the *Familiarize* step.

5. State. About 20.8% of the world's mammals are threatened with extinction.

| Do Exercise 1. |

EXAMPLE 2 *Transportation to Work.* In the United States, there are about 147,000,000 workers 16 years and older. Approximately 77% drive to work alone. How many workers drive to work alone?

Transportation to Work in the United States

Taxi 0.1%
Motorcycle 0.2%
Bicycle 0.4%
Other means 0.9%
Walk 2.5%
Work from home 3.6%
Public transportation 4.7%
Carpool 10.7%
Drive alone 76.9%

SOURCES: U.S. Census Bureau; American Community Survey

---

1. Presidential Assassinations in Office. Of the 43 different U.S. presidents, 4 have been assassinated in office. These were James A. Garfield, William McKinley, Abraham Lincoln, and John F. Kennedy. What percent have been assassinated in office?

Answer

1. About 9.3%

1. **Familiarize.** We can simplify the pie chart shown on the preceding page to help familiarize ourselves with the problem. We let $a =$ the total number of workers who drive to work alone.

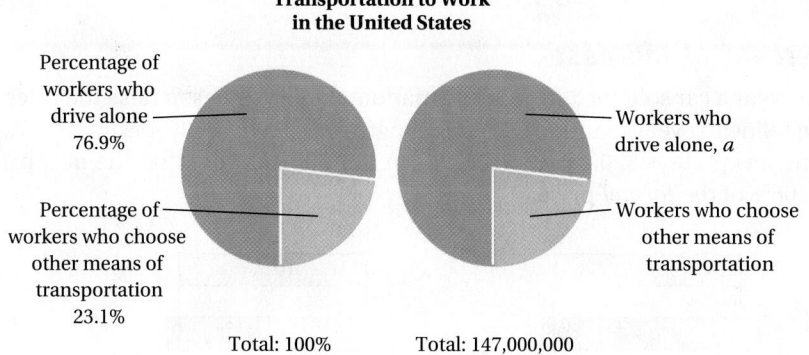

Transportation to Work in the United States

Percentage of workers who drive alone 76.9%

Workers who drive alone, a

Percentage of workers who choose other means of transportation 23.1%

Workers who choose other means of transportation

Total: 100%   Total: 147,000,000

2. **Translate.** There are two ways in which we can translate this problem.

Percent equation:

What number   is   76.9%   of   147,000,000?

a $=$ 76.9% $\cdot$ 147,000,000

Proportion:

$$\frac{76.9}{100} = \frac{a}{147,000,000}$$

3. **Solve.** We now have two ways in which to solve this problem.

Percent equation:

$a = 76.9\% \cdot 147,000,000$

We convert 76.9% to decimal notation and multiply:

$a = 0.769 \times 147,000,000 = 113,043,000.$

Proportion:

$$\frac{76.9}{100} = \frac{a}{147,000,000}$$

$76.9 \times 147,000,000 = 100 \cdot a$ Equating cross products

$$\frac{76.9 \cdot 147,000,000}{100} = \frac{100 \cdot a}{100}$$ Dividing by 100

$$\frac{11,304,300,000}{100} = a$$

$113,043,000 = a$ Simplifying

4. **Check.** To check, we can repeat the calculations. We can also do a partial check by estimating. Since 76.9% is about 80%, or $\frac{4}{5}$, and $\frac{4}{5}$ of 147,000,000 is 117,600,000 and 117,600,000 is close to 113,043,000, our answer is reasonable.

5. **State.** The number of workers who drive to work alone is 113,043,000.

Do Exercise 2.

STUDY TIPS

MAKING APPLICATIONS REAL

Newspapers and magazines are full of mathematical applications. Some of the easiest ones to find in the area of Basic College Mathematics are about percent. Find such an application and share it with your class. As you obtain more skills in mathematics, you will find yourself observing the world from a different perspective, seeing mathematics everywhere. Math courses become more interesting when we connect the concepts to the real world.

2. **Transportation to Work.** There are about 147,000,000 workers 16 years or older in the United States. Approximately 10.7% carpool to work. How many workers carpool to work?
Sources: U.S. Census Bureau; American Community Survey

Answer

2. 15,729,000 workers

b Percent of Increase or Decrease

Percent is often used to state increase or decrease. Let's consider an example of each, using the price of a car as the original number.

Percent of Increase

One year a car sold for $20,455. The manufacturer decides to raise the price of the following year's model by 6%. The increase is 0.06 × $20,455, or $1227.30. The new price is $20,455 + $1227.30, or $21,682.30. Note that the new price is 106% of the *former* price.

New price: $21,682.30

Increase ↑

Former price: $20,455

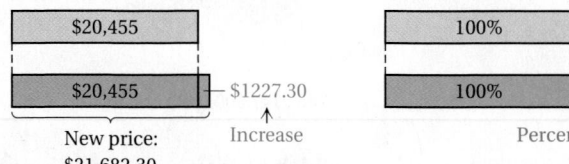

The increase, $1227.30, is 6% of the *former* price, $20,455. The *percent of increase* is 6%.

Percent of Decrease

Abigail buys the car listed above for $20,455. After one year, the car depreciates in value by 25%. The decrease is 0.25 × $20,455, or $5113.75. This lowers the value of the car to $20,455 − $5113.75, or $15,341.25. Note that the new value is 75% of the original price. If Abigail decides to sell the car after one year, $15,341.25 might be the most she could expect to get for it.

Original price: $20,455

Decrease ↓

New value: $15,341.25

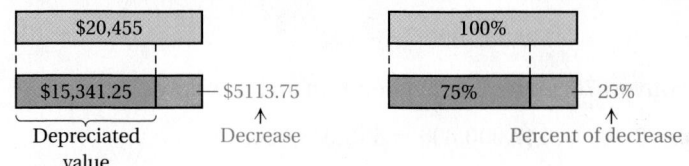

The decrease, $5113.75, is 25% of the *original* price, $20,455. The *percent of decrease* is 25%.

Do Exercises 3 and 4.

When a quantity is decreased by a certain percent, we say that we have **percent of decrease**.

EXAMPLE 3 *Dow Jones Industrial Average.* The Dow Jones Industrial Average (DJIA) plunged from 11,143 to 10,365 on September 29, 2008. This was the largest one-day drop in its history. What was the percent of decrease?
Sources: *Nightly Business Reports*, September 29, 2008; DJIA

---

3. Percent of Increase. The price of a car is $36,875. The price is increased by 4%.

a) How much is the increase?

b) What is the new price?

4. Percent of Decrease. The value of a car is $36,875. The car depreciates in value by 25% after one year.

a) How much is the decrease?

b) What is the depreciated value of the car?

Answers

3. (a) $1475; (b) $38,350
4. (a) $9218.75; (b) $27,656.25

1. **Familiarize.** We first determine the amount of decrease and then make a drawing.

$$\begin{array}{r} 11{,}143 \\ -10{,}365 \\ \hline 778 \end{array}$$ Opening average
Closing average
Decrease

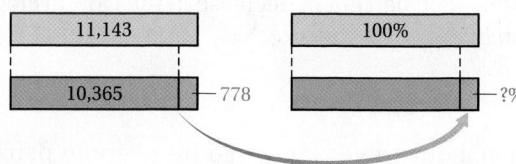

We are asking this question: The decrease is what percent of the opening average? We let $p =$ the percent of decrease.

2. **Translate.** There are two ways in which we can translate this problem.

Percent equation:

$$\underbrace{778}_{} \ \underbrace{\text{is}}_{} \ \underbrace{\text{what percent}}_{} \ \underbrace{\text{of}}_{} \ \underbrace{11{,}143?}_{}$$
$$778 \ = \qquad p \qquad \times \quad 11{,}143$$

Proportion:

$$\frac{N}{100} = \frac{778}{11{,}143}$$

For proportions, $N\% = p$.

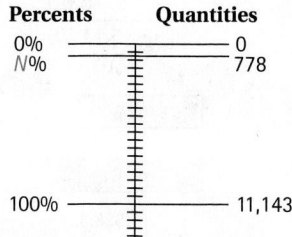

Percents	Quantities
0%	0
N%	778
100%	11,143

3. **Solve.** We have two ways in which to solve this problem.

Percent equation:

$$778 = p \times 11{,}143$$

$$\frac{778}{11{,}143} = \frac{p \times 11{,}143}{11{,}143} \qquad \text{Dividing by 11,143 on both sides}$$

$$\frac{778}{11{,}143} = p$$

$$0.07 \approx p$$

$$7\% \approx p \qquad \text{Converting to percent notation}$$

Proportion:

$$\frac{N}{100} = \frac{778}{11{,}143}$$

$$11{,}143 \times N = 100 \times 778 \qquad \text{Equating cross products}$$

$$\frac{11{,}143 \times N}{11{,}143} = \frac{100 \times 778}{11{,}143} \qquad \text{Dividing by 11,143 on both sides}$$

$$N = \frac{77{,}800}{11{,}143}$$

$$N \approx 7$$

We use the solution of the proportion to express the answer to the problem as 7%.

5. Volume of Mail. The volume of U.S. mail decreased from about 213,138 million pieces of mail in 2006 to 212,234 million pieces in 2007. What was the percent of decrease?

Source: U.S. Postal Service

4. Check. To check, we note that, with a 7% decrease, the closing Dow average should be 93% of the opening average. Since

$$93\% \times 11{,}143 = 0.93 \times 11{,}143 \approx 10{,}363,$$

and 10,363 is close to 10,365, our answer checks. (Remember that we rounded to get 7%.)

5. State. The percent of decrease in the Dow average was approximately 7%.

> Do Exercise 5.

When a quantity is increased by a certain percent, we say we have **percent of increase**.

EXAMPLE 4 *Costs for Moviegoers.* The average cost of movie tickets for a family of four was $16.56 in 1993. The cost rose to $28.32 in 2008. What was the percent of increase in the cost for a family of four to attend a movie?

Source: Motion Picture Association of America

1. Familiarize. We first determine the increase in the cost and then make a drawing.

$$
\begin{array}{rl}
\$28.32 & \text{Cost in 2008} \\
-\quad 16.56 & \text{Cost in 1993} \\
\hline
\$11.76 & \text{Increase}
\end{array}
$$

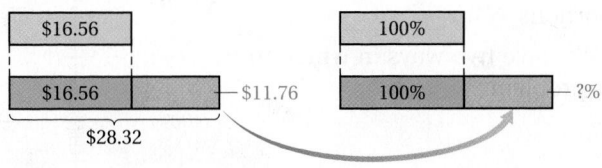

We are asking this question: The increase is what percent of the *original* cost? We let p = the percent of increase.

2. Translate. There are two ways in which we can translate this problem.

Percent equation:

$$
\begin{array}{ccccc}
11.76 & \text{is} & \text{what percent} & \text{of} & 16.56? \\
\downarrow & \downarrow & \downarrow & \downarrow & \downarrow \\
11.76 & = & p & \cdot & 16.56
\end{array}
$$

Proportion:

$$\frac{N}{100} = \frac{11.76}{16.56}$$

For proportions, $N\% = p$.

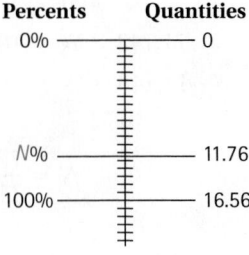

Percents	Quantities
0%	0
$N\%$	11.76
100%	16.56

3. Solve. We have two ways in which to solve this problem.

Percent equation:

$$11.76 = p \times 16.56$$

$$\frac{11.76}{16.56} = \frac{p \times 16.56}{16.56} \qquad \text{Dividing by 16.56 on both sides}$$

$$\frac{11.76}{16.56} = p$$

$$0.71 \approx p$$

$$71\% \approx p \qquad \text{Converting to percent notation}$$

Proportion:

$$\frac{N}{100} = \frac{11.76}{16.56}$$

$$16.56 \times N = 100 \times 11.76 \qquad \text{Equating cross products}$$

$$\frac{16.56 \times N}{16.56} = \frac{100 \times 11.76}{16.56} \qquad \text{Dividing by 16.56 on both sides}$$

$$N = \frac{1176}{16.56}$$

$$N \approx 71$$

We use the solution of the proportion to express the answer to the problem as 71%.

4. Check. To check, we take 71% of 16.56:

$$71\% \times 16.56 = 0.71 \times 16.56 = 11.7576.$$

The approximation 11.7576 is close enough to 11.76 to be an excellent check. (Remember that we rounded to get 71%.)

5. State. The percent of increase in the cost for a family of four to attend a movie is 71%.

Do Exercise 6.

6. Shipping Costs. The total cost of shipping a 40-ft container from Shanghai to New York rose from $5100 in 2005 to $8350 in 2008. Find the percent of increase.
Source: CIBC World Markets, IMF

Answer

6. About 64%

Translating for Success

1. **Distance Walked.** After knee replacement, Alex walked $\frac{1}{8}$ mi each morning and $\frac{1}{5}$ mi each afternoon. How much farther did he walk in the afternoon?

2. **Stock Prices.** A stock sold for $5 per share on Monday and only $2.125 per share on Friday. What was the percent of decrease from Monday to Friday?

3. **SAT Score.** After attending a class titled *Improving Your SAT Scores*, Jacob raised his total score from 884 to 1040. What was the percent of increase?

4. **Change in Population.** The population of a small farming community decreased from 1040 to 884. What was the percent of decrease?

5. **Lawn Mowing.** During the summer, brothers Steve and Rob earned money for college by mowing lawns. The largest lawn that they mowed was $2\frac{1}{8}$ acres. Steve can mow $\frac{1}{5}$ acre per hour, and Rob can mow only $\frac{1}{8}$ acre per hour. Working together, how many acres did they mow per hour?

The goal of these matching questions is to practice step (2), *Translate*, of the five-step problem-solving process. Translate each word problem to an equation and select a correct translation from equations A–O.

A. $x + \dfrac{1}{5} = \dfrac{1}{8}$

B. $250 = x \cdot 1040$

C. $884 = x \cdot 1040$

D. $\dfrac{250}{16.25} = \dfrac{1000}{x}$

E. $156 = x \cdot 1040$

F. $16.25 = 250 \cdot x$

G. $\dfrac{1}{5} + \dfrac{1}{8} = x$

H. $2\dfrac{1}{8} = x \cdot 5$

I. $5 = 2.875 \cdot x$

J. $\dfrac{1}{8} + x = \dfrac{1}{5}$

K. $1040 = x \cdot 884$

L. $\dfrac{250}{16.25} = \dfrac{x}{1000}$

M. $2.875 = x \cdot 5$

N. $x \cdot 884 = 156$

O. $x = 16.25 \cdot 250$

Answers on page A-7

6. **Land Sale.** Cole sold $2\frac{1}{8}$ acres from the 5 acres he inherited from his uncle. What percent did he sell?

7. **Travel Expenses.** A magazine photographer is reimbursed 16.25¢ per mile for business travel up to 1000 mi per week. In a recent week, he traveled 250 mi. What was the total reimbursement for travel?

8. **Trip Expenses.** The total expenses for Claire's recent business trip were $1040. She put $884 on her credit card and paid the balance in cash. What percent did she place on her credit card?

9. **Cost of Copies.** During the first summer session at a community college, the campus copy center advertised 250 copies for $16.25. At this rate, what is the cost of 1000 copies?

10. **Cost of Insurance.** Following a raise in the cost of health insurance, 250 of a company's 1040 employees dropped their health coverage. What percent of the employees canceled their insurance?

a Solve.

1. *Foreign Students.* In the 2006–2007 school year, of the 15 million college students in the United States, 583,000 were from foreign countries. Approximately 10.70% of the foreign students were from South Korea and 6.05% were from Japan. How many foreign students were from South Korea? from Japan?
Source: Institute of International Education

2. *Mississippi River.* The Mississippi River, which extends from its source, at Lake Itasca in Minnesota, to the Gulf of Mexico, is 2348 mi long. Approximately 77% of the river is navigable. How many miles of the river are navigable?
Source: National Oceanic and Atmospheric Administration

Mississippi River

3. A person earns $43,200 one year and receives an 8% raise in salary. What is the new salary?

4. A person earns $28,600 one year and receives a 5% raise in salary. What is the new salary?

5. *Test Results.* On a test, Juan got 85%, or 119, of the items correct. How many items were on the test?

6. *Test Results.* On a test, Maj Ling got 86%, or 81.7, of the items correct. (There was partial credit on some items.) How many items were on the test?

7. *Farmland.* In Kansas, 47,000,000 acres are farmland. About 5% of all the farm acreage in the United States is in Kansas. What is the total number of acres of farmland in the United States?
Sources: U.S. Department of Agriculture; National Agricultural Statistics Service

8. *World Population.* World population is increasing by 1.2% each year. In 2008, it was 6.68 billion. What will the population be in 2015?
Sources: U.S. Census Bureau; International Data Base

9. *Car Depreciation.* A car generally depreciates 25% of its original value in the first year. A car is worth $27,300 after the first year. What was its original cost?

10. *Car Depreciation.* Given normal use, an American-made car will depreciate 25% of its original cost the first year and 14% of its remaining value in the second year. What is the value of a car at the end of the second year if its original cost was $36,400? $28,400? $26,800?

11. *Test Results.* On a test of 80 items, Pedro got 93% correct. (There was partial credit on some items.) How many items did he get correct? incorrect?

12. *Test Results.* On a test of 40 items, Christina got 91% correct. (There was partial credit on some items.) How many items did she get correct? incorrect?

13. *Under 15 Years Old.* In Egypt, 32.6% of the population is under 15 years old. In the United States, 20.4% of the population is under 15. The population of Egypt is 75,449,000, and the population of the United States is 305,468,000. How many are under 15 years old in Egypt? in the United States?

Sources: U.S. Census Bureau; International Data Base

14. *Age 65 and Older.* In Egypt, 4.5% of the population is age 65 and older. In the United States, 12.5% of the population is age 65 and older. The population of Egypt is 75,449,000, and the population of the United States is 305,468,000. How many are age 65 and older in Egypt? in the United States?

Sources: U.S. Census Bureau; International Data Base

15. *Transplant Waiting List.* The total number of patients waiting for transplants as of September 27, 2007, was 96,749. Of this number, 16,737 were waiting for a liver transplant. What percent were waiting for a liver transplant?

Source: United Network for Organ Sharing

16. *Doctors' Salaries.* In 2007, the starting salary for a neurologist was approximately 64.5% of that of an anesthesiologist. The beginning salary for an anesthesiologist was $275,000. What was the beginning salary for a neurologist?

Source: *Journal of the American Medical Association*

17. *Tipping.* For a party of 8 or more, some restaurants add an 18% tip to the bill. What is the total amount charged for a party of 10 if the cost of the meal, without tip, is $195?

18. *Tipping.* Diners frequently add a 15% tip when charging a meal to a credit card. What is the total amount charged if the cost of the meal, without tip, is $18? $34? $49?

Copyright © 2012 Pearson Education, Inc.

19. *Fast-Food Cooks.* The United States has 392,850 full-time farmers. This number is about 64.2% of the number of fast-food cooks. How many fast-food cooks are there in the United States?
Source: U.S. Department of Agriculture

20. *Spending in Restaurants.* Americans spent $364 billion in grocery stores in 2007. This amount is about $93\frac{1}{3}$% of the amount spent in restaurants. How much was spent in restaurants?
Source: U.S. Department of Agriculture

21. A lab technician has 540 mL of a solution of alcohol and water; 8% is alcohol. How many milliliters are alcohol? water?

22. A lab technician has 680 mL of a solution of water and acid; 3% is acid. How many milliliters are acid? water?

23. *U.S. Armed Forces.* There were 1,385,000 people in the United States in active military service in 2006. The numbers in the four armed services are listed in the table below. What percent of the total does each branch represent? Round the answers to the nearest tenth of a percent.

U.S. ARMED FORCES: 2006

TOTAL	1,385,000*
AIR FORCE	349,000
ARMY	505,000
NAVY	350,000
MARINES	180,000

*Includes National Guard, Reserve, and retired regular personnel on extended or continuous active duty. Excludes Coast Guard.

SOURCES: U.S. Department of Defense; U.S. Census Bureau

24. *Living Veterans.* There were 23,977,000 living veterans in the United States in 2006. Numbers in selected age groups are listed in the table below. What percent of the total does each age group represent? Round the answers to the nearest tenth of a percent.

LIVING VETERANS BY AGE: 2006

TOTAL	23,977,000
UNDER 35 YEARS OLD	1,949,000
35–44 YEARS OLD	2,901,000
45–54 YEARS OLD	3,846,000
55–64 YEARS OLD	6,081,000
65 YEARS OLD AND OLDER	9,200,000

SOURCES: U.S. Department of Defense; U.S. Census Bureau

b Solve.

25. *Mortgage Payment Increase.* A monthly mortgage payment increases from $840 to $882. What is the percent of increase?

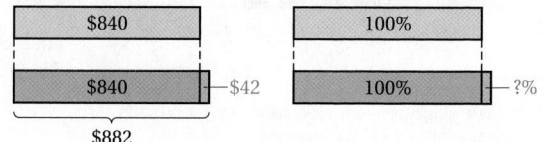

26. *Savings Increase.* The amount in a savings account increased from $200 to $216. What was the percent of increase?

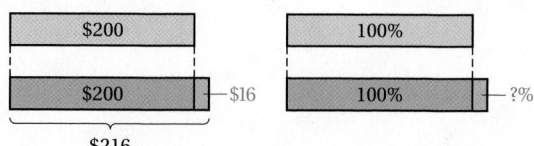

27. A person on a diet goes from a weight of 160 lb to a weight of 136 lb. What is the percent of decrease?

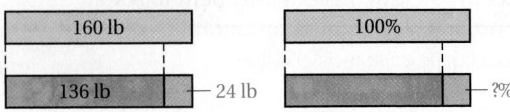

28. During a sale, a dress decreased in price from $90 to $72. What was the percent of decrease?

29. *Insulation.* A 15" roll of unfaced fiberglass insulation has a retail price of $23.43. For two weeks, it is on sale for $15.31. What is the percent of decrease?

30. *Set of Weights.* A 300-lb weight set retails for $199.95. For its grand opening, a sporting goods store reduced the price to $154.95. What is the percent of decrease?

31. *Mass Transit.* From April through June of 2008, people took 2.8 billion rides on public transit in the United States. The ridership was up from 2.1 billion rides in 1998. What is the percent of increase?

Source: American Public Transportation Association

32. *Miles of Railroad Track.* The greatest combined length of U.S.-owned operating railroad track was 254,037 mi in 1916, when industrial activity increased during World War I. The total length has decreased ever since. By 2006, the number of miles of track had decreased to 140,490 mi. What is the percent of decrease from 1916 to 2006?

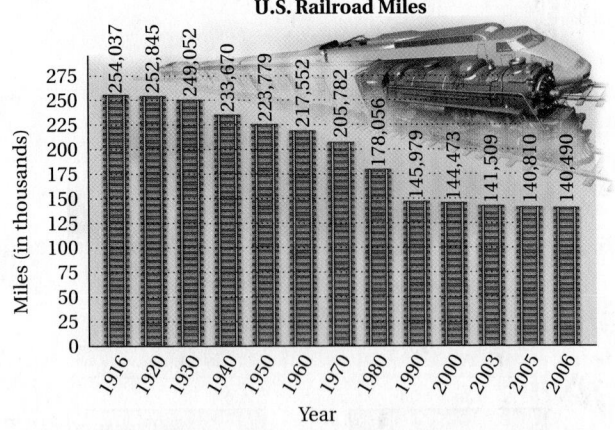

U.S. Railroad Miles

NOTE: The lengths exclude yard tracks, sidings, and parallel tracks.
SOURCE: Association of American Railroads

Copyright © 2012 Pearson Education, Inc.

33. *Overdraft Fees.* Consumers are paying record amounts of fees for overdrawing their bank accounts. In 2007, banks, thrifts, and credit unions collected $45.6 billion in overdraft fees, which is $15.1 billion more than in 2001. What is the percent of increase?

Source: Moebs Services

34. *Credit-Card Debt.* In 2007, the average credit-card debt per household in the United States was $9840. In 1990, the average credit-card debt was $2966. What is the percent of increase?

Sources: CardWeb.com; *USA TODAY*

35. *Immigrant Applications.* From January through June of 2008, 46,866 immigrants applied for citizenship each month. During this same period in 2007, 114,469 immigrants applied each month. What is the percent of decrease?

Source: U.S. Citizenship and Immigration Services (USCIS)

36. *Pharmacists.* It is projected that there will be 296,000 people employed as pharmacists in 2016. In 2006, 243,000 members of the labor force were pharmacists. What is the percent of increase?

Source: EarnMyDegree.com

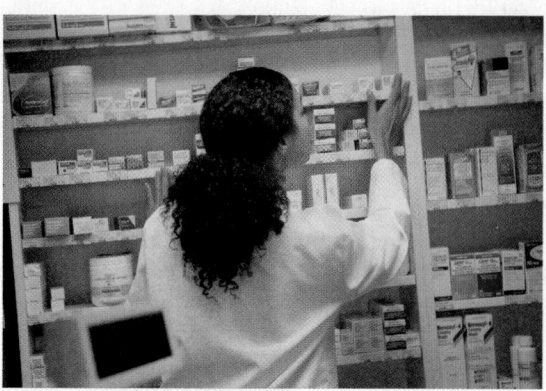

37. *Patents Issued.* The U.S. Patent and Trademark Office (USPTO) issued a total of 157,284 utility patents in 2007. This number of patents is down from 173,794 in 2006. What is the percent of decrease?

Source: IFI Patent Intelligence

38. *Highway Fatalities.* In 2007, there were 41,059 highway fatalities, which was 1649 fewer deaths than in 2006. What is the percent of decrease?

Source: National Highway Traffic Safety Administration

39. *Two-by-Four.* A cross-section of a standard or nominal "two-by-four" board actually measures $1\frac{1}{2}$ in. by $3\frac{1}{2}$ in. The rough board is 2 in. by 4 in. but is planed and dried to the finished size. What percent of the wood is removed in planing and drying?

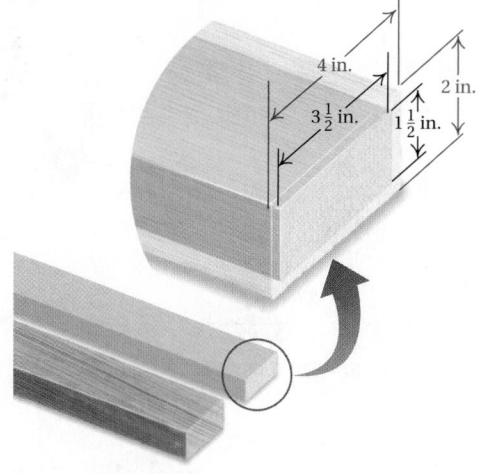

40. *Strike Zone.* In baseball, the *strike zone* is normally a 17-in. by 30-in. rectangle. Some batters give the pitcher an advantage by swinging at pitches thrown out of the strike zone. By what percent is the area of the strike zone increased if a 2-in. border is added to the outside?

Source: Major League Baseball

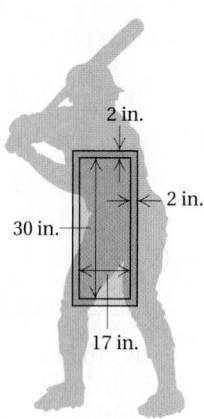

Population Increase. The table below provides data showing how the populations of various states increased from 2000 to 2006. Complete the table by filling in the missing numbers. Round percents to the nearest tenth of a percent.

	STATE	POPULATION IN 2000	POPULATION IN 2006	CHANGE	PERCENT CHANGE
41.	Vermont	608,827	623,908		
42.	Wisconsin	5,363,675		192,831	
43.	Arizona		6,166,318	1,035,686	
44.	Virginia		7,642,884	564,369	
45.	Idaho	1,293,953		172,512	
46.	Georgia	8,186,453	9,363,941		

SOURCE: U.S. Census Bureau

47. *Decrease in Population.* Between 2000 and 2006, the population of North Dakota decreased from 642,200 to 635,867. What was the percent of decrease?

Sources: U.S. Census Bureau; U.S. Department of Commerce

48. *Decrease in Population.* Between 2000 and 2006, the population of Louisiana decreased from 4,468,976 to 4,287,768. What was the percent of decrease?

Sources: U.S. Census Bureau; U.S. Department of Commerce

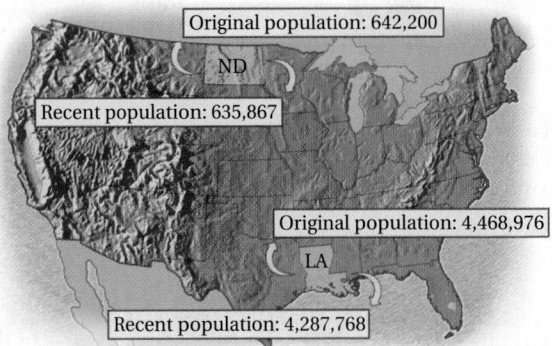

Skill Maintenance

Convert to decimal notation. [3.1b], [3.5a]

49. $\dfrac{25}{11}$

50. $\dfrac{11}{25}$

51. $\dfrac{27}{8}$

52. $\dfrac{43}{9}$

53. $\dfrac{23}{25}$

54. $\dfrac{20}{24}$

55. $\dfrac{14}{32}$

56. $\dfrac{2317}{1000}$

57. $\dfrac{34,809}{10,000}$

58. $\dfrac{27}{40}$

Synthesis

59. A coupon allows a couple to have dinner and then have $10 subtracted from the bill. Before subtracting $10, however, the restaurant adds a tip of 20%. If the couple is presented with a bill for $40.40, how much would the dinner (without tip) have cost without the coupon?

60. If p is 120% of q, then q is what percent of p?

Copyright © 2012 Pearson Education, Inc.

4.7

Sales Tax, Commission, and Discount

a) Sales Tax

Sales tax computations represent a special type of percent of increase problem. The sales tax rate in Pennsylvania is 6%. This means that the tax is 6% of the purchase price. Suppose the purchase price of a guitar is $839.95. The sales tax is then 6% of $839.95, or 0.06 × $839.95, or $50.397, or about $50.40.

OBJECTIVES

a) Solve applied problems involving sales tax and percent.

b) Solve applied problems involving commission and percent.

c) Solve applied problems involving discount and percent.

PENNSYLVANIA

$839.95 + 6% sales tax

BILL:

Purchase price	= $839.95
Sales tax (6% of $839.95)	= + 50.40
Total price	$890.35

The total that you pay is the purchase price plus the sales tax:

$839.95 + $50.40,   or $890.35.

SALES TAX

Sales tax = Sales tax rate × Purchase price

Total price = Purchase price + Sales tax

EXAMPLE 1 *Wisconsin Sales Tax.*   The sales tax rate in Wisconsin is 5%. How much tax is charged on the purchase of 3 gal of paint at $42.99 each? What is the total price?

a) We first find the cost of the paint. It is

3 × $42.99 = $128.97.

b) The sales tax on items costing $128.97 is

$$\underbrace{\text{Sales tax rate}}_{5\%} \times \underbrace{\text{Purchase price}}_{\$128.97},$$

or 0.05 × 128.97, or 6.4485. Thus the tax is $6.45 (rounded to the nearest cent).

$42.99 each plus 5% sales tax

TRUE BLUE

WISCONSIN

c) The total price is given by the purchase price plus the sales tax:

$128.97 + $6.45,   or $135.42.

To check, note that the total price is the purchase price plus 5% of the purchase price. Thus the total price is 105% of the purchase price. Since 1.05 × 128.97 ≈ 135.42, we have a check. The sales tax is $6.45, and the total price is $135.42.

Do Exercises 1 and 2.

1. **Texas Sales Tax.** The sales tax rate in Texas is 6.25%. In Texas, how much tax is charged on the purchase of an ultrasound toothbrush that sells for $139.95? What is the total price?

2. **Wyoming Sales Tax.** Samantha buys 7 copies of *The Last Lecture* by Randy Pausch with Jeffrey Zaslow for $14.95 each. The sales tax rate in Wyoming is 4%. In Wyoming, how much sales tax will be charged? What is the total price?

EXAMPLE 2 The sales tax on the purchase of this GPS navigator, which costs $799, is $55.93. What is the sales tax rate?

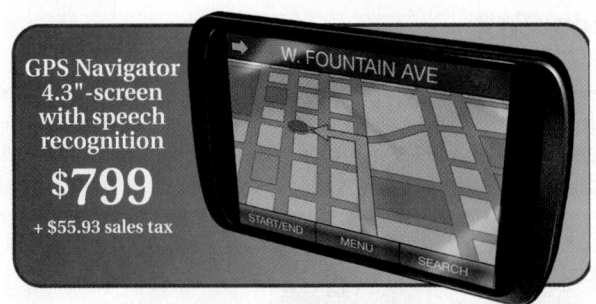

GPS Navigator 4.3"-screen with speech recognition
$799
+ $55.93 sales tax

We rephrase and translate as follows:

Rephrase: Sales tax   is   what percent   of   purchase price?

Translate: 55.93   =   r   ×   799.

To solve the equation, we divide by 799 on both sides:

$$\frac{55.93}{799} = \frac{r \times 799}{799}$$

$$\frac{55.93}{799} = r$$

$$0.07 = r$$

$$7\% = r.$$

The sales tax rate is 7%.

Do Exercise 3.

3. The sales tax on the purchase of a set of holiday dishes that costs $449 is $26.94. What is the sales tax rate?

Price: ?
$12.74 tax @ 8%

EXAMPLE 3 The sales tax on the purchase of a stone-top firepit is $12.74 and the sales tax rate is 8%. Find the purchase price (the price before taxes are added).

We rephrase and translate as follows:

Rephrase: Sales tax   is   8%   of   what?

Translate: 12.74   =   8%   ×   b,   or

12.74 = 0.08 × b.

To solve, we divide by 0.08 on both sides:

$$\frac{12.74}{0.08} = \frac{0.08 \times b}{0.08}$$

$$\frac{12.74}{0.08} = b$$

$$159.25 = b.$$

The purchase price is $159. 25.

4. The sales tax on the purchase of a pair of designer jeans is $4.84 and the sales tax rate is 5.5%. Find the purchase price (the price before taxes are added).

Do Exercise 4.

Answers

1. $8.75; $148.70   2. $4.19; $108.84
3. 6%   4. $88

b Commission

When you work for a **salary**, you receive the same amount of money each week or month. When you work for a **commission**, you are paid a percentage of the total sales for which you are responsible.

COMMISSION

Commission = Commission rate × Sales

EXAMPLE 4 *Appliance Sales.* A salesperson's commission rate is 3%. What is the commission from the sale of $8300 worth of appliances?

$$Commission = Commission\ rate \times Sales$$
$$C = 3\% \times 8300$$
$$C = 0.03 \times 8300$$
$$C = 249$$

The commission is $249.

Do Exercise 5.

EXAMPLE 5 *Earth-Moving Equipment Sales.* Gavin earns a commission of $20,800 selling $320,000 worth of earth-moving equipment. What is the commission rate?

$$Commission = Commission\ rate \times Sales$$
$$20,800 = r \times 320,000$$

STUDY TIPS

PACE YOURSELF

Most instructors agree that it is better for a student to study for one hour four days in a week than to study once a week for four hours. Of course, the total weekly study time will vary from student to student. It is common to expect an average of two hours of homework for each hour of class time.

5. Hailey's commission rate is 15%. What is the commission from the sale of $9260 worth of exercise equipment?

Answer

5. $1389

To solve this equation, we divide by 320,000 on both sides:

$$\frac{20,800}{320,000} = \frac{r \times 320,000}{320,000}$$

$$0.065 = r$$

$$6.5\% = r.$$

The commission rate is 6.5%.

6. William earns a commission of $2040 selling $17,000 worth of concert tickets. What is the commission rate?

Do Exercise 6.

EXAMPLE 6 *Cruise Vacations.* Mia's commission rate is 5.6%. She received a commission of $2457 on cruise vacation packages that she sold in November. How many dollars worth of cruise vacations did she sell?

$$Commission = Commission\ rate \times Sales$$
$$2457 = 5.6\% \times S, \quad or$$
$$2457 = 0.056 \times S$$

To solve this equation, we divide by 0.056 on both sides:

$$\frac{2457}{0.056} = \frac{0.056 \times S}{0.056}$$

$$\frac{2457}{0.056} = S$$

$$43,875 = S.$$

Mia sold $43,875 worth of cruise vacation packages.

7. Dylan's commission rate is 7.5%. He receives a commission of $2970 from the sale of winter ski passes. How many dollars worth of ski passes did he sell?

Do Exercise 7.

c Discount

Suppose that the regular price of a rug is $60, and the rug is on sale at 25% off. Since 25% of $60 is $15, the sale price is $60 − $15, or $45. We call $60 the **original**, or **marked**, **price**, 25% the **rate of discount**, $15 the **discount**, and $45 the **sale price**. Note that discount problems are a type of percent of decrease problem.

DISCOUNT AND SALE PRICE

Discount = Rate of discount × Original price
Sale price = Original price − Discount

Answers

6. 12%   7. $39,600

EXAMPLE 7 A leather sofa marked $2379 is on sale at $33\frac{1}{3}$% off. What is the discount? the sale price?

Leather sofa
$2379 original price
Save $33\frac{1}{3}$%

a) *Discount* = *Rate of discount* × *Original price*

$$D = 33\frac{1}{3}\% \times 2379$$

$$D = \frac{1}{3} \times 2379$$

$$D = \frac{2379}{3} = 793$$

b) *Sale price* = *Original price* − *Discount*

$$S = 2379 - 793$$

$$S = 1586$$

The discount is $793, and the sale price is $1586.

Do Exercise 8.

EXAMPLE 8 The price of a snowblower is marked down from $950 to $779. What is the rate of discount?

We first find the discount by subtracting the sale price from the original price:

$$950 - 779 = 171.$$

The discount is $171.

Next, we use the equation for discount:

Discount = *Rate of discount* × *Original price*

$$171 = r \times 950.$$

To solve, we divide by 950 on both sides:

$$\frac{171}{950} = \frac{r \times 950}{950}$$

$$\frac{171}{950} = r$$

$$0.18 = r$$

$$18\% = r.$$

The discount rate is 18%.

> To check, note that an 18% discount rate means that 82% of the original price is paid:
>
> $$0.82 \times \$950 = \$779.$$

Do Exercise 9.

8. A computer marked $660 is on sale at $16\frac{2}{3}$% off. What is the discount? the sale price?

9. The price of a winter coat is reduced from $75 to $60. Find the rate of discount.

Answers

8. $110; $550   **9.** 20%

 Solve.

1. *Wyoming Sales Tax.* The sales tax rate in Wyoming is 4%. How much sales tax would be charged on a fireplace screen with doors that costs $239?

2. *Kansas Sales Tax.* The sales tax rate in Kansas is 5.3%. How much sales tax would be charged on a fireplace screen with doors that costs $239?

3. *Ohio Sales Tax.* The sales tax rate in Ohio is 5.5%. How much sales tax would be charged on a dog jacket that sells for $29.50?

4. *New Mexico Sales Tax.* The sales tax rate in New Mexico is 5%. How much sales tax would be charged on a pair of sunglasses that sells for $129.95?

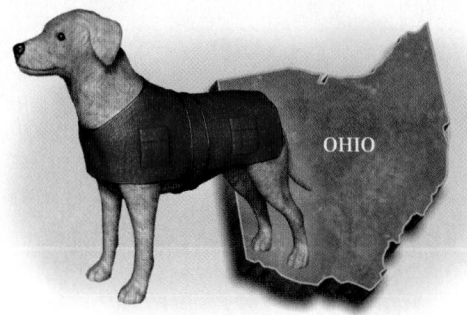

OHIO

NEW MEXICO

5. *California Sales Tax.* The sales tax rate in California is 7.25%. How much sales tax is charged on a purchase of 4 travel contour foam pillows at $39.95 each? What is the total price?

6. *Illinois Sales Tax.* The sales tax rate in Illinois is 6.25%. How much sales tax is charged on a purchase of 3 wet–dry vacs at $60.99 each? What is the total price?

7. The sales tax is $30 on the purchase of a diamond ring that sells for $750. What is the sales tax rate?

8. The sales tax is $48 on the purchase of a dining room set that sells for $960. What is the sales tax rate?

9. The sales tax on the purchase of a new fishing boat is $112 and the sales tax rate is 2%. What is the purchase price (the price before tax is added)?

10. The sales tax on the purchase of a used car is $100 and the sales tax rate is 5%. What is the purchase price?

11. The sales tax rate in New York City, New York, is 4.375% for the city and 4% for the state. Find the total amount paid for 6 boxes of chocolates at $17.95 each.

12. The sales tax rate in Nashville, Tennessee, is 2.25% for Davidson County and 7% for the state. Find the total amount paid for 2 ladders at $39 each.

Copyright © 2012 Pearson Education, Inc.

13. The sales tax rate in Seattle, Washington, is 2.5% for King County and 6.5% for the state. Find the total amount paid for 3 ceiling fans at $84.49 each.

14. The sales tax rate in Miami, Florida, is 1% for Dade County and 6% for the state. Find the total amount paid for 2 tires at $49.95 each.

15. The sales tax rate in Atlanta, Georgia, is 1% for the city, 3% for Fulton County, and 4% for the state. Find the total amount paid for 6 basketballs at $29.95 each.

16. The sales tax rate in Dallas, Texas, is 1% for the city, 1% for Dallas County, and 6.25% for the state. Find the total amount paid for 5 shrubs at $19.95 each.

 Solve.

17. Jose's commission rate is 21%. What is the commission from the sale of $12,500 worth of windows?

18. Jasmine's commission rate is 6%. What is the commission from the sale of $45,000 worth of lawn irrigation systems?

19. Olivia earns $408 selling $3400 worth of shoes. What is the commission rate?

20. Mitchell earns $120 selling $2400 worth of television sets. What is the commission rate?

21. *Clothing Consignment Commission.* A clothing consignment shop's commission rate is 40%. The shop receives a commission of $552. How many dollars worth of clothing were sold?

22. *Real Estate Commission.* A real estate agent's commission rate is 7%. She receives a commission of $12,950 from the sale of a home. How much did the home sell for?

23. David earns $1147.50 selling $7650 worth of car parts. What is the commission rate?

24. Isabella earns $280.80 selling $2340 worth of tee shirts. What is the commission rate?

25. Sabrina's commission is increased according to how much she sells. She receives a commission of 4% for the first $1000 of sales and 7% for the amount over $1000. What is the total commission on sales of $5500?

26. Miguel's commission is increased according to how much he sells. He receives a commission of 5% for the first $2000 of sales and 8% for the amount over $2000. What is the total commission on sales of $6200?

c Complete the table below by filling in the missing numbers.

	MARKED PRICE	RATE OF DISCOUNT	DISCOUNT	SALE PRICE
27.	$300	10%		
28.	$2000	40%		
29.		10%	$12.50	
30.		15%	$65.70	
31.	$600		$240	
32.	$12,800		$1920	

33. Find the discount and the rate of discount for the pinball machine in this ad.

34. Find the marked price and the rate of discount for the digital photo frame in this ad.

Skill Maintenance

Find decimal notation. [3.5a]

35. $\frac{5}{9}$ **36.** $\frac{23}{11}$ **37.** $\frac{11}{12}$ **38.** $\frac{13}{7}$ **39.** $\frac{15}{7}$ **40.** $\frac{19}{12}$

Convert to standard notation. [3.3b]

41. 4.03 trillion   **42.** 5.8 million   **43.** 42.7 million   **44.** 6.09 trillion

Synthesis

45. 🖩 John receives a 10% commission on the first $5000 in sales and 15% on all sales beyond $5000. If John receives a commission of $2405, how much did he sell? Use a calculator and trial and error if you wish.

46. Tee shirts are being sold at the mall for $5 each, or 3 for $10. If you buy three tee shirts, what is the rate of discount?

Copyright © 2012 Pearson Education, Inc.

Key Terms and Formulas

ratio, p. 256
rate, p. 259
cross products, p. 260
proportional, p. 260
percent notation, $n\%$, p. 273
percent of decrease, p. 304
percent of increase, p. 306
purchase price, p. 315

sales tax, p. 315
total price, p. 315
commission, p. 317
original price, p. 318
marked price, p. 318
rate of discount, p. 318
discount, p. 318

sale price, p. 318
principal, p. 323
interest rate, p. 323
simple interest, p. 323
compound interest, p. 324
compounded annually, p. 324
compounded semi-annually, p. 325

Commission = Commission rate × Sales

Discount = Rate of discount × Original price

Sale price = Original price − Discount

Simple Interest: $\quad I = P \cdot r \cdot t$

Compound Interest: $\quad A = P \cdot \left(1 + \dfrac{r}{n}\right)^{n \cdot t}$

Concept Reinforcement

Determine whether each statement is true or false.

_____ **1.** When we simplify a ratio like $\frac{8}{12}$, we find two other numbers in the same ratio.   [4.1a]

_____ **2.** The proportion $\dfrac{a}{b} = \dfrac{c}{d}$ can also be written as $\dfrac{c}{a} = \dfrac{d}{b}$.   [4.1d]

_____ **3.** A fixed principal invested for 4 years will earn more interest when interest is compounded quarterly than when interest is compounded semiannually.   [4.8b]

_____ **4.** Of the numbers 0.5%, $\dfrac{5}{1000}\%$, $\dfrac{1}{2}\%$, $\dfrac{1}{5}$, and $0.\overline{1}$, the largest number is $0.\overline{1}$.   [4.2b], [4.3a, b]

_____ **5.** If principal A equals principal B and principal A is invested for 2 years at 4%, compounded quarterly, while principal B is invested for 4 years at 2%, compounded semiannually, the interest earned from each investment is the same.   [4.8b]

Important Concepts

Objective 4.1a   Find fraction notation for ratios.

Example   Find the ratio of 7 to 18.

Write a fraction with a numerator of 7 and a denominator of 18: $\dfrac{7}{18}$.

Practice Exercise

1. Find the ratio of 17 to 3.

Objective 4.1b   Give the ratio of two different measures as a rate.

Example   A driver travels 156 mi on 6.5 gal of gas. What is the rate in miles per gallon?

$$\frac{156 \text{ mi}}{6.5 \text{ gal}} = \frac{156}{6.5}\frac{\text{mi}}{\text{gal}} = 24 \frac{\text{mi}}{\text{gal}}, \text{ or } 24 \text{ mpg}$$

Practice Exercise

2. A student earned $120 for working 16 hr. What was the rate of pay per hour?

Objective 4.1c Determine whether two pairs of numbers are proportional.

Example Determine whether 3, 4 and 7, 9 are proportional.

We have

$$3 \cdot 9 = 27 \qquad \frac{3}{4} \overset{?}{=} \frac{7}{9} \qquad 4 \cdot 7 = 28.$$

Since the cross products are not the same ($27 \neq 28$), $\frac{3}{4} \neq \frac{7}{9}$ and the numbers are not proportional.

Practice Exercise

3. Determine whether 7, 9 and 21, 27 are proportional.

Objective 4.1d Solve proportions.

Example Solve: $\frac{3}{4} = \frac{y}{7}$.

$$\frac{3}{4} = \frac{y}{7}$$

$$3 \cdot 7 = 4 \cdot y \qquad \text{Equating cross products}$$

$$\frac{3 \cdot 7}{4} = \frac{4 \cdot y}{4} \qquad \text{Dividing by 4 on both sides}$$

$$\frac{21}{4} = y$$

The solution is $\frac{21}{4}$.

Practice Exercise

4. Solve: $\frac{9}{x} = \frac{8}{3}$.

Objective 4.1e Solve applied problems involving proportions.

Example Martina bought 3 tickets to a campus theater production for $16.50. How much would 8 tickets cost?

We translate to a proportion.

$$\begin{array}{l} \textit{Tickets} \longrightarrow \\ \textit{Cost} \longrightarrow \end{array} \frac{3}{16.50} = \frac{8}{c} \begin{array}{l} \longleftarrow \textit{Tickets} \\ \longleftarrow \textit{Cost} \end{array}$$

$$3 \cdot c = 16.50 \cdot 8 \qquad \text{Equating cross products}$$

$$c = \frac{16.50 \cdot 8}{3}$$

$$c = 44$$

Eight tickets would cost $44.

Practice Exercise

5. On a map, $\frac{1}{2}$ in. represents 50 mi. If two cities are $1\frac{3}{4}$ in. apart on the map, how far apart are they in reality?

Objective 4.2b Convert between percent notation and decimal notation.

Example Find decimal notation for $12\frac{3}{4}\%$.

$$12\frac{3}{4}\% = 12.75 \times 0.01$$

$$= 0.1275$$

Practice Exercise

6. Find decimal notation for $62\frac{5}{8}\%$.

Objective 4.3a Convert from fraction notation to percent notation.

Example Find percent notation for $\frac{5}{12}$.

$$
\begin{array}{r}
0.4\ 1\ 6 \\
1\ 2\ )\overline{5.0\ 0\ 0} \\
\underline{4\ 8} \\
2\ 0 \\
\underline{1\ 2} \\
8\ 0 \\
\underline{7\ 2} \\
8
\end{array}
\qquad \frac{5}{12} = 0.41\overline{6} = 41.\overline{6}\%, \text{ or } 41\frac{2}{3}\%
$$

Practice Exercise

7. Find percent notation for $\frac{7}{11}$.

Objective 4.3b Convert from percent notation to fraction notation.

Example Find fraction notation for 9.5%.

$$9.5\% = \frac{9.5}{100} = \frac{95}{1000} = \frac{5 \cdot 19}{5 \cdot 200} = \frac{5}{5} \cdot \frac{19}{200} = \frac{19}{200}$$

Practice Exercise

8. Find fraction notation for 6.8%.

Objective 4.4b Solve basic percent problems.

Example 165 is what percent of 3300?

$$165 = p \cdot 3300 \qquad \text{Translating to a percent equation}$$

$$\frac{165}{3300} = p \qquad \text{Dividing by 3300 on both sides}$$

$$0.05 = p$$

$$5\% = p$$

Thus, 165 is 5% of 3300.

Practice Exercise

9. 12 is what percent of 288?

Objective 4.5b Solve basic percent problems.

Example 18% of what is 1296?

$$\frac{18}{100} = \frac{1296}{b} \qquad \text{Translating to a proportion}$$

$$18 \cdot b = 100 \cdot 1296 \qquad \text{Equating cross products}$$

$$b = 7200 \qquad \text{Dividing by 18 on both sides}$$

Thus, 18% of 7200 is 1296.

Practice Exercise

10. 3% of what is 300?

Objective 4.6b Solve applied problems involving percent of increase or percent of decrease.

Example The total cost for 16 basic grocery items in the second quarter of 2008 averaged $46.67 nationally. The total cost of these 16 items in the second quarter of 2007 averaged $42.95. What was the percent of increase?

Source: American Farm Bureau Federation

Practice Exercise

11. In Indiana, the cost for 16 basic grocery items increased from $40.07 in the second quarter of 2007 to $46.20 in the second quarter of 2008. What was the percent of increase from 2007 to 2008?

Objective 4.6b (continued)

We first determine the amount of increase: $46.67 − $42.95 = $3.72. Then we translate to a percent equation or a proportion and solve.

Rewording: $3.72 is what percent of $42.95?

Percent Equation: *Proportion:*

$$3.72 = p \cdot 42.95 \qquad \frac{N}{100} = \frac{3.72}{42.95}$$

$$\frac{3.72}{42.95} = \frac{p \cdot 42.95}{42.95} \qquad 42.95N = 100 \cdot 3.72$$

$$\frac{3.72}{42.95} = p \qquad \frac{42.95N}{42.95} = \frac{100 \cdot 3.72}{42.95}$$

$$0.087 \approx p \qquad N = \frac{372}{42.95}$$

$$8.7\% \approx p \qquad N \approx 8.7$$

The percent of increase was 8.7%.

Objective 4.7a   Solve applied problems involving sales tax and percent.

Example   The sales tax is $34.23 on the purchase of a flat-screen high-definition television that costs $489. What is the sales tax rate?

     Rephrase: Sales tax is what percent of purchase price?

     Translate: $34.23 = r \times 489$

     Solve: $\dfrac{34.23}{489} = \dfrac{r \times 489}{489}$

$$\frac{34.23}{489} = r$$

$$0.07 = r$$

$$7\% = r$$

The sales tax rate is 7%.

Practice Exercise

12. The sales tax is $1102.20 on the purchase of a new car that costs $18,370. What is the sales tax rate?

Objective 4.7b   Solve applied problems involving commission and percent.

Example   A real estate agent's commission rate is $6\frac{1}{2}\%$. She received a commission of $17,160 on the sale of a home. For how much did the home sell?

     Rephrase: Commission is $6\frac{1}{2}\%$ of what selling price?

     Translate: $17{,}160 = 6\frac{1}{2}\% \times S$

     Solve: $17{,}160 = 0.065 \times S$

$$\frac{17{,}160}{0.065} = \frac{0.065 \times S}{0.065}$$

$$264{,}000 = S$$

The home sold for $264,000.

Practice Exercise

13. A real estate agent's commission rate is 7%. He received a commission of $12,950 on the sale of a home. For how much did the home sell?

Review Exercises

Write fraction notation for each ratio. Do not simplify. [4.1a]

1. 47 to 84

2. 46 to 1.27

3. 83 to 100

4. 0.72 to 197

5. At Preston Seafood Market, 12,480 lb of tuna and 16,640 lb of salmon were sold one year. [4.1a]

a) Write fraction notation for the ratio of tuna sold to salmon sold.

b) Write fraction notation for the ratio of salmon sold to the total number of pounds of both kinds of fish sold.

Find the ratio of the first number to the second number and simplify. [4.1a]

6. 9 to 12

7. 3.6 to 6.4

8. *Gas Mileage.* The Chrysler PT Cruiser will travel 377 mi on 14.5 gal of gasoline in highway driving. What is the rate in miles per gallon? [4.1b]
Source: Chrysler Motor Corporation

9. *Flywheel Revolutions.* A certain flywheel makes 472,500 revolutions in 75 min. What is the rate of spin in revolutions per minute? [4.1b]

10. A lawn requires 319 gal of water for every 500 ft². What is the rate in gallons per square foot? [4.1b]

Determine whether the two pairs of numbers are proportional. [4.1c]

11. 9, 15 and 36, 60

12. 24, 37 and 40, 46.25

Copyright © 2012 Pearson Education, Inc.

Solve. [4.1d]

13. $\dfrac{8}{9} = \dfrac{x}{36}$

14. $\dfrac{6}{x} = \dfrac{48}{56}$

15. $\dfrac{120}{\frac{3}{7}} = \dfrac{7}{x}$

16. $\dfrac{4.5}{120} = \dfrac{0.9}{x}$

Solve. [4.1e]

17. *Quality Control.* A factory manufacturing computer circuits found 3 defective circuits in a lot of 65 circuits. At this rate, how many defective circuits can be expected in a lot of 585 circuits?

18. *Exchanging Money.* On 16 September 2008, 1 U.S. dollar was worth about 1.068 Canadian dollars.

    a) How much would 250 U.S. dollars be worth in Canada?

    b) While traveling in Canada, Jamal saw a sweatshirt that cost 50 Canadian dollars. How much would it cost in U.S. dollars?

19. A train travels 448 mi in 7 hr. At this rate, how far will it travel in 13 hr?

20. Fifteen acres of land is required to produce 54 bushels of tomatoes. At this rate, how many acres are required to produce 97.2 bushels of tomatoes?

21. *Trash Production.* A study shows that 5 people generate 23 lb of trash each day. The population of Austin, Texas, is 743,074. How many pounds of trash are produced in Austin in one day?

Sources: U.S. Environmental Protection Agency; U.S. Census Bureau

22. *Snow to Water.* Under typical conditions, $1\frac{1}{2}$ ft of snow will melt to 2 in. of water. To how many inches of water will $4\frac{1}{2}$ ft of snow melt?

23. *Lawyers in Chicago.* In Illinois, there are about 4.8 lawyers for every 1000 people. The population of Chicago is 2,842,518. How many lawyers would you expect there to be in Chicago?

Sources: American Bar Association; U.S. Census Bureau

Find decimal notation for the percent notations in each sentence. [4.2b]

24. In the 2006–2007 school year, about 4% of the 15 million college students in the United States were foreign students. Approximately 14.4% of the foreign students were from India.

Source: Institute of International Education

25. Poland is 62.1% urban; Sweden is 84.2% urban.

Source: *The World Almanac,* 2008

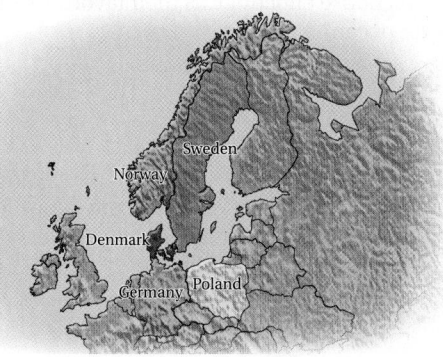

Find percent notation. [4.2b]

26. 1.7

27. 0.065

Find percent notation. [4.3a]

28. $\dfrac{3}{8}$

29. $\dfrac{1}{3}$

Find fraction notation. [4.3b]

30. 24%

31. 6.3%

Translate to a percent equation. Then solve. [4.4a, b]

32. 30.6 is what percent of 90?

33. 63 is 84% of what?

34. What is $38\frac{1}{2}$% of 168?

Translate to a proportion. Then solve. [4.5a, b]

35. 24 percent of what is 16.8?

36. 42 is what percent of 30?

37. What is 10.5% of 84?

Solve. [4.6a, b]

38. *Favorite Ice Creams.* According to a survey, 8.9% of those interviewed chose chocolate as their favorite ice cream flavor and 4.2% chose butter pecan. At this rate, of the 2000 students in a freshman class, how many would choose chocolate as their favorite ice cream? butter pecan?

Source: International Ice Cream Association

39. *Prescriptions.* Of the 305 million people in the United States, 140.3 million take at least one type of prescription drug per day. What percent take at least one type of prescription drug per day?

Source: William N. Kelly, *Pharmacy: What It Is and How It Works*, 2nd ed., CRC Press Pharmaceutical Education, 2006

40. *Water Output.* The average person expels 200 mL of water per day by sweating. This is 8% of the total output of water from the body. How much is the total output of water?

Source: Elaine N. Marieb, *Essentials of Human Anatomy and Physiology*, 6th ed. Boston: Addison Wesley Longman, Inc., 2000

41. *Test Scores.* After Sheila got a 75 on a math test, she was allowed to go to the math lab and take a retest. She increased her score to 84. What was the percent of increase?

42. *Test Scores.* James got an 80 on a math test. By taking a retest in the math lab, he increased his score by 15%. What was his new score?

Solve. [4.7a, b, c]

43. A state charges a meals tax of $7\frac{1}{2}$%. What is the meals tax charged on a dinner party costing $320?

44. In a certain state, a sales tax of $453.60 is collected on the purchase of a used car for $7560. What is the sales tax rate?

45. Kim earns $753.50 selling $6850 worth of televisions. What is the commission rate?

46. An air conditioner has a marked price of $350. It is placed on sale at 12% off. What are the discount and the sale price?

47. The price of a fax machine is marked down from $305 to $262.30. What is the rate of discount?

48. An insurance salesperson receives a 7% commission. If $42,000 worth of life insurance is sold, what is the commission?

49. What is the rate of discount of this stepladder?

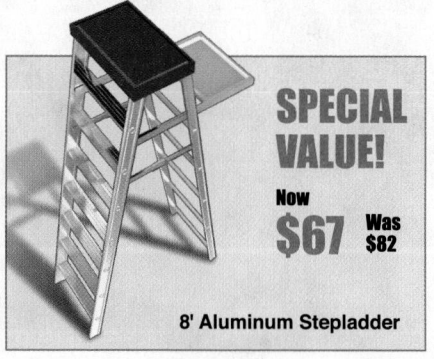

SPECIAL VALUE!

Now **$67**   Was **$82**

8' Aluminum Stepladder

Copyright © 2012 Pearson Education, Inc.

Solve. [4.8a, b, c]

50. What is the simple interest on $1800 at 6% for $\frac{1}{3}$ year?

51. The Dress Shack borrows $24,000 at 10% simple interest for 60 days. Find **(a)** the amount of interest due and **(b)** the total amount that must be paid after 60 days.

52. The Armstrongs invest $7500 in an investment account paying an annual interest rate of 4%, compounded monthly. How much is in the account after 3 months?

53. Find the amount in an investment account if $8000 is invested at 9%, compounded annually, for 2 years.

54. *Credit Cards.* At the end of her junior year of college, Kasha has a balance of $6428.74 on a credit card with an annual percentage rate (APR) of 18.7%. She decides not to make additional purchases with this card until she has paid off the balance.

a) Many credit cards require a minimum payment of 2% of the balance. At this rate, what is Kasha's minimum payment on a balance of $6428.74? Round the answer to the nearest dollar.

b) Find the amount of interest and the amount applied to reduce the principal in the minimum payment found in part (a).

c) If Kasha had transferred her balance to a card with an APR of 13.2%, how much of her payment would be interest and how much would be applied to reduce the principal?

d) Compare the amounts for 13.2% from part (c) with the amounts for 18.7% from part (b).

55. If 3 dozen eggs cost $5.04, how much will 5 dozen eggs cost? [4.1e]

A. $6.72 **B.** $6.96
C. $8.40 **D.** $10.08

56. Find the amount in a money market account if $10,500 is invested at 6%, compounded semiannually, for $1\frac{1}{2}$ years. [4.8b]

A. $11,139.45 **B.** $12,505.67
C. $11,473.63 **D.** $10,976.03

Synthesis

57. A worker receives raises of 3%, 6%, and then 9%. By what percent has the original salary increased? [4.6a]

58. Shine-and-Glo Painters uses 2 gal of finishing paint for every 3 gal of primer. Each gallon of finishing paint covers 450 ft^2. If a surface of 4950 ft^2 needs both primer and finishing paint, how many gallons of each should be purchased? [4.1e]

Understanding Through Discussion and Writing

1. Which is the better deal for a consumer and why: a discount of 40% or a discount of 20% followed by another of 22%? [4.7c]

2. If you were a college president, which would you prefer: a low or high faculty-to-student ratio? Why? [4.1a]

3. Ollie buys a microwave oven during a 10%-off sale. The sale price that Ollie paid was $162. To find the original price, Ollie calculates 10% of $162 and adds that to $162. Is this correct? Why or why not? [4.7c]

4. Which is better for a wage earner, and why: a 10% raise followed by a 5% raise a year later, or a 5% raise followed by a 10% raise a year later? [4.6a]

5. You take 40% of 50% of a number. What percent of the number could you take to obtain the same result making only one multiplication? Explain your answer. [4.6a]

6. A firm must choose between borrowing $5000 at 10% for 30 days and borrowing $10,000 at 8% for 60 days. Give arguments in favor of and against each option. [4.8a]

CHAPTER

4

Test

For Extra Help

CHAPTER
Test Prep
VIDEOS

Step-by-step test solutions are found on the Chapter Test Prep Videos available via the Video Resources on DVD, in *MyMathLab*, and on You Tube (search "BittingerDevMath" and click on "Channels").

Write fraction notation for each ratio. Do not simplify.

1. 85 to 97

2. 0.34 to 124

Find the ratio of the first number to the second number and simplify.

3. 18 to 20

4. 0.75 to 0.96

5. *Ham Servings.* A 12-lb shankless ham contains 16 servings. What is the rate in servings per pound?

6. *Gas Mileage.* The 2008 Chevrolet Malibu LTZ will travel 464 mi on 14.5 gal of gasoline in highway driving. What is the rate in miles per gallon?

Source: General Motors Corporation

Determine whether the two pairs of numbers are proportional.

7. 7, 8 and 63, 72

8. 1.3, 3.4 and 5.6, 15.2

Solve.

9. $\dfrac{68}{y} = \dfrac{17}{25}$

10. $\dfrac{150}{2.5} = \dfrac{x}{6}$

Solve.

11. *Map Scaling.* On a map, 3 in. represents 225 mi. If two cities are 7 in. apart on the map, how far are they apart in reality?

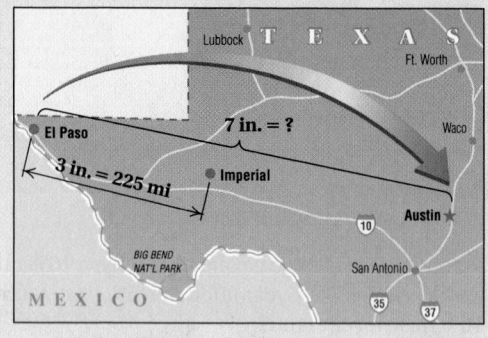

12. *Exchanging Money.* On 18 September 2008, 1 U.S. dollar was worth about 7.781 Hong Kong dollars.

a) How much would 450 U.S. dollars be worth in Hong Kong dollars?

b) While traveling in Hong Kong, Mitchell saw a DVD player that cost 795 Hong Kong dollars. How much would it cost in U.S. dollars?

13. *Thanksgiving Dinner.* A traditional turkey dinner for 8 people cost about $33.81 in a recent year. How much would it cost to serve a turkey dinner for 14 people?

Source: American Farm Bureau Federation

14. *Time Loss.* A watch loses 2 min in 10 hr. At this rate, how much will it lose in 24 hr?

Copyright © 2012 Pearson Education, Inc.

15. *Land-Line Phone Service.* About 14.7% of U.S. households were projected to cut land-line phone service in 2009. Find decimal notation for 14.7%.

Source: Yankee Group 2006, *USA TODAY*, January 15, 2007

16. *Gravity.* The gravity of Mars is 0.38 as strong as Earth's. Find percent notation for 0.38.

Source: www.marsinstitute.info/epo/mermarsfacts.html

17. Find percent notation for $\frac{11}{8}$.

18. Find fraction notation for 65%.

19. Translate to a percent equation. Then solve.

What is 40% of 55?

20. Translate to a proportion. Then solve.

What percent of 80 is 65?

Solve.

21. *Organ Transplants.* In 2006, there were 28,291 organ transplants in the United States. The pie chart below shows the percentages for the main transplants. How many kidney transplants were there in 2006? liver transplants? heart transplants?

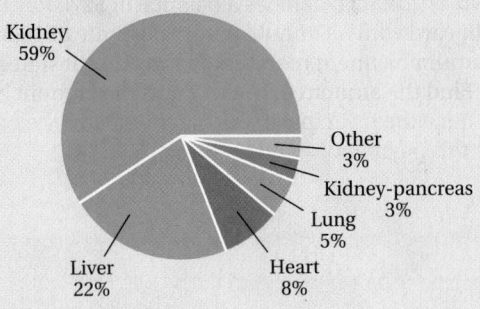

Organ Transplants in the United States, 2006

Kidney 59%
Other 3%
Kidney-pancreas 3%
Lung 5%
Liver 22%
Heart 8%

SOURCE: 2007 OPTN/SRTR Annual Report, Table 1.7; United Network for Organ Sharing

22. *Batting Average.* Garrett Atkins, third baseman for the Colorado Rockies, got 175 hits during the 2008 baseball season. This was about 28.64% of his at-bats. How many at-bats did he have?

Source: Major League Baseball

23. *Foreign Adoptions.* The number of foreign children adopted by Americans declined from 20,679 in 2006 to 19,292 in 2007. Find the percent of decrease.

Source: U.S. State Department, *USA TODAY*, August 13, 2008

24. There are about 6,603,000,000 people living in the world today, and approximately 4,002,000,000 live in Asia. What percent of people live in Asia?

Source: Population Division/International Programs Center, U.S. Census Bureau, U.S. Dept. of Commerce

25. *Oklahoma Sales Tax.* The sales tax rate in Oklahoma is 4.5%. How much tax is charged on a purchase of $560? What is the total price?

26. Noah's commission rate is 15%. What is the commission from the sale of $4200 worth of merchandise?

27. The marked price of a DVD player is $200 and the item is on sale at 20% off. What are the discount and the sale price?

28. What is the simple interest on a principal of $120 at the interest rate of 7.1% for 1 year?

29. A city orchestra invests $5200 at 6% simple interest. How much is in the account after $\frac{1}{2}$ year?

30. Find the amount in an account if $1000 is invested at $5\frac{3}{8}$% compounded annually, for 2 years.

31. *Job Opportunities.* The table below lists job opportunities in 2006 and projected increases for 2016. Complete the table by filling in the missing numbers.

OCCUPATION	TOTAL EMPLOYMENT IN 2006	PROJECTED EMPLOYMENT IN 2016	CHANGE	PERCENT OF INCREASE
Dental assistant	280,000	362,000	82,000	29.3%
Plumber	705,000		52,000	
Veterinary assistant	71,000	100,000		
Motorcycle repair technician		24,000	3000	
Fitness professional		298,000		26.8%

SOURCE: EarnMyDegree.com

32. The Suarez family invests $10,000 at an annual interest rate of 4.9%, compounded monthly. How much is in the account after 3 years?

33. Find the discount and the discount rate of the television in this ad.

19" LCD HDTV

$299⁹⁹

was $349⁹⁹

34. *Credit Cards.* Jayden has a balance of $2704.27 on a credit card with an annual percentage rate of 16.3%. The minimum payment required on the current statement is $54. Find the amount of interest and the amount applied to reduce the principal in this payment and the balance after this payment.

35. 0.75% of what number is 300?

   A. 2.25   **B.** 40,000   **C.** 400   **D.** 225

36. Lucita walks $4\frac{1}{2}$ mi in $1\frac{1}{2}$ hr. What is her rate in miles per hour?

   A. $\frac{1}{3}$ mph   **B.** $1\frac{1}{2}$ mph

   C. 3 mph   **D.** $4\frac{1}{2}$ mph

Synthesis

37. By selling a home without using a realtor, Juan and Marie can avoid paying a 7.5% commission. They receive an offer of $180,000 from a potential buyer. In order to give a comparable offer, for what price would a realtor need to sell the house? Round to the nearest hundred.

38. Karen's commission rate is 16%. She invests her commission from the sale of $15,000 worth of merchandise at an interest rate of 12%, compounded quarterly. How much is Karen's investment worth after 6 months?

Copyright © 2012 Pearson Education, Inc.

Geometry

Real-World Application

Malaria is the leading cause of death among children in Africa. Bed nets prevent malaria transmission by creating a protective barrier against mosquitoes at night. In November 2006, the United Nations Foundation, the United Methodist Church, and the National Basketball Association launched the Nothing But Nets campaign to distribute mosquito netting in Africa. Two years later, 2,194,124 insecticide-treated bed nets had been sent to seven African countries. A medium-sized net measures approximately 9.843 ft by 8.2025 ft. A large-sized net measures approximately 13.124 ft by 8.2025 ft. Find the area of each net. How much larger is the area of the larger net than that of the medium net?

Source: www.nothingbutnets.net

This problem appears as Exercise 10 in Section 6.3.

6.1 Basic Geometric Figures

OBJECTIVES

a Draw and name segments, rays, and lines. Also, identify endpoints, if they exist.

b Name an angle in five different ways, and given an angle, measure it with a protractor.

c Classify an angle as right, straight, acute, or obtuse.

d Identify perpendicular lines.

e Classify a triangle as equilateral, isosceles, or scalene and as right, obtuse, or acute. Given a polygon of twelve, ten, or fewer sides, classify it as a dodecagon, a decagon, and so on.

f Given a polygon of n sides, find the sum of its angle measures using the formula $(n - 2) \cdot 180°$.

In geometry we study sets of points. A **geometric figure** (or *figure*) is simply a set of points. Thus a figure can be a set with one point, a set with two points, or sets that look like those below.

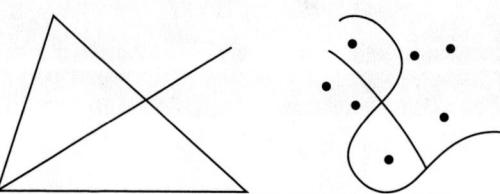

a Segments, Rays, and Lines

A **segment** is a geometric figure consisting of two points, called *endpoints*, and all points between them. The segment whose endpoints are A and B is shown below. It can be named $\overline{AB}$ or $\overline{BA}$.

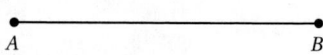

Do Exercise 1.

We get an idea of a geometric figure called a ray by thinking of a ray of light. A **ray** consists of a segment, say $\overline{AB}$, and all points X such that B is between A and X, that is, $\overline{AB}$ and all points "beyond" B.

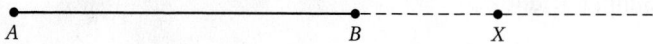

A ray is usually drawn as shown below. It has just one endpoint. The arrow indicates that it extends forever in one direction.

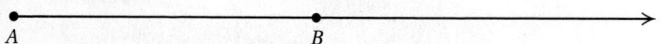

A ray is named $\overrightarrow{AB}$, where B is some point on the ray other than A. The endpoint is always listed first. Thus rays $\overrightarrow{AB}$ and $\overrightarrow{BA}$ are different.

Do Exercises 2–5.

Two rays such as $\overrightarrow{PQ}$ and $\overrightarrow{QP}$ make up what is known as a **line**. A line can be named with a smaller letter m, as shown below, or it can be named by two points P and Q on the line as $\overleftrightarrow{PQ}$.

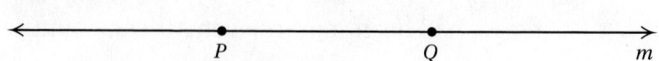

---

1. **a)** Draw a segment.

   b) Label its endpoints E and F.

   c) Name this segment in two ways.

2. Draw two points P and Q.

3. Draw $\overline{PQ}$.

4. Draw $\overrightarrow{PQ}$. What is its endpoint?

5. Use a colored pencil to draw $\overrightarrow{QR}$. What is its endpoint?

Answers

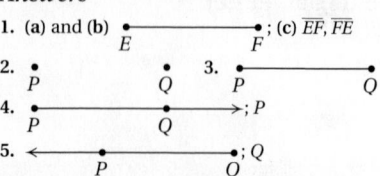

1. (a) and (b) •————————• ; (c) $\overline{EF}$, $\overline{FE}$
           E F
2. •   •   3. •————————•
   P Q P Q
4. •————•——→ ; P
   P Q
5. ←————•——• ; Q
       P Q

Lines in the same plane are called **coplanar**. Coplanar lines that do not intersect are called **parallel**. For example, lines *l* and *m* below are *parallel* ($l \parallel m$).

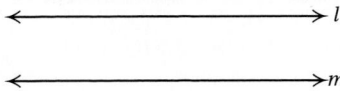

The figure below shows two lines that cross. Their *intersection* is *D*. They are also called **intersecting lines**.

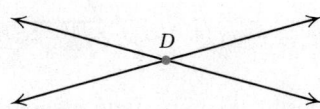

b) Measuring Angles

We see a real-world application of *angles* of various types in the different back postures of the bicycle riders illustrated below.

Style of Biking Determines Cycling Posture

Road	Mountain	Comfort
About 180° flat	About 45°	About 90°

Riders prefer a more aerodynamic flat-back position.

Riders prefer a semi-upright position to help lift the front wheel over obstacles.

Riders prefer an upright position that lessens stress on the lower back and neck.

SOURCE: USA TODAY research

An **angle** is a set of points consisting of two **rays**, or half-lines, with a common endpoint. The endpoint is called the **vertex** of the angle. The rays are called the **sides** of the angle.

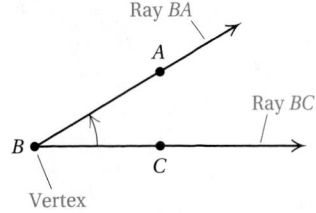

The angle above can be named

angle *ABC*,   angle *CBA*,   ∠*ABC*,   ∠*CBA*,   or   ∠*B*.

Note that the name of the vertex is either in the middle or, if no confusion results, listed by itself.

6. Draw two points *R* and *S*.

7. Draw $\overline{RS}$. What are its endpoints?

8. Draw $\overrightarrow{RS}$. What is its endpoint?

9. Draw $\overrightarrow{SR}$. What is its endpoint?

10. Draw $\overleftrightarrow{RS}$. What are its endpoints?

11. Name this line in seven different ways.

Answers

6. $\quad \bullet \atop R \qquad\qquad \bullet \atop S$

7. $\bullet \!\!-\!\!-\!\!-\!\!\bullet \atop R \qquad\qquad S$; *R* and *S*

8. ; *R*

9. ; *S*

10. ;

no endpoints   **11.** $\overleftrightarrow{RS}$, $\overleftrightarrow{SR}$, $\overleftrightarrow{RT}$, $\overleftrightarrow{TR}$, $\overleftrightarrow{ST}$, $\overleftrightarrow{TS}$, *n*

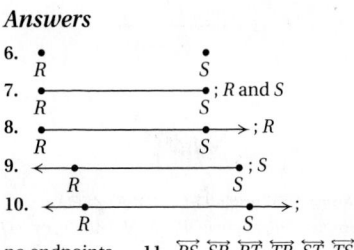

Name the angle in five different ways.

12.

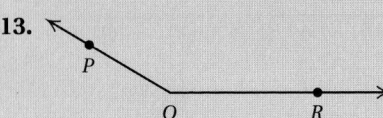

13.

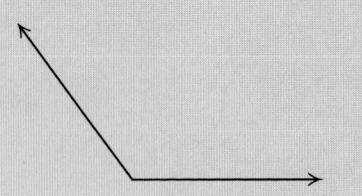

Do Exercises 12 and 13.

Measuring angles is similar to measuring segments. To measure angles, we start with some arbitrary angle and assign to it a measure of 1. We call it a *unit angle*. Suppose that ∠U, shown below, is a unit angle. Let's measure ∠DEF. If we made 3 copies of ∠U, they would "fill up" ∠DEF. Thus the measure of ∠DEF would be 3.

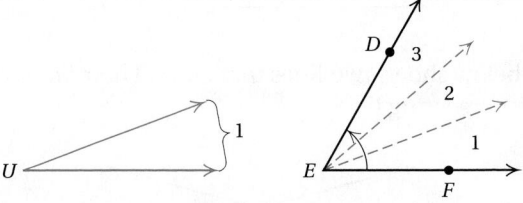

The unit most commonly used for angle measure is the degree. Below is such a unit. Its measure is 1 degree, or 1°.

A 1° angle:

Here are some other angles with their degree measures.

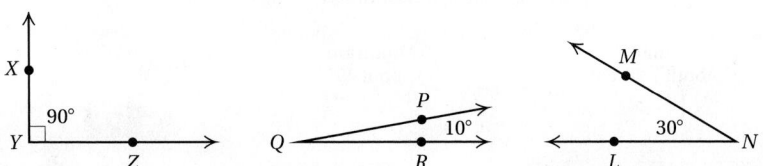

To indicate the *measure* of ∠XYZ, we write m ∠XYZ = 90°. The symbol ⌐ is sometimes drawn on a figure to indicate a 90° angle.

A device called a **protractor** is used to measure angles. Protractors have two scales. To measure an angle like ∠Q below, we place the protractor's ▲ at the vertex and line up one of the angle's sides at 0°. Then we check where the angle's other side crosses the scale. In the figure below, 0° is on the inside scale, so we check where the angle's other side crosses the inside scale. We see that m ∠Q = 145°. The notation m ∠Q is read "the measure of angle Q."

STUDY TIPS

KEY TERMS

The terms introduced in this chapter are listed with page references at the beginning of the Summary and Review at the end of this chapter. As part of your review for a quiz or a chapter test, review this list. It is helpful to write out the definitions of the terms that are new to you.

14. Use a protractor to measure this angle.

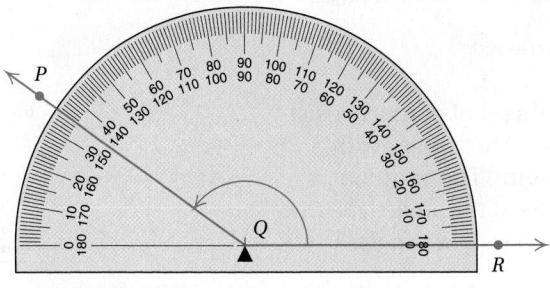

Do Exercise 14.

Answers

12. Angle *DEF*, angle *FED*, ∠*DEF*, ∠*FED*, or ∠*E*
13. Angle *PQR*, angle *RQP*, ∠*PQR*, ∠*RQP*, or ∠*Q*
14. 127°

Let's find the measure of ∠ABC. This time we will use the 0° on the outside scale. We see that $m \angle ABC = 42°$.

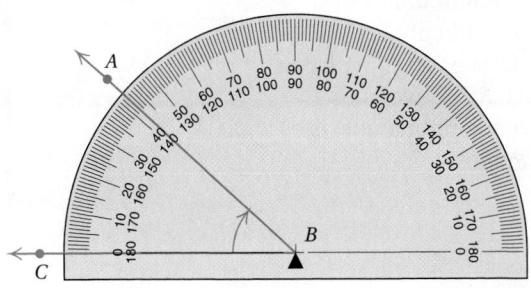

Do Exercise 15.

c Classifying Angles

The following are ways in which we classify angles.

TYPES OF ANGLES

Right angle: An angle whose measure is 90°.

Straight angle: An angle whose measure is 180°.

Acute angle: An angle whose measure is greater than 0° and less than 90°.

Obtuse angle: An angle whose measure is greater than 90° and less than 180°.

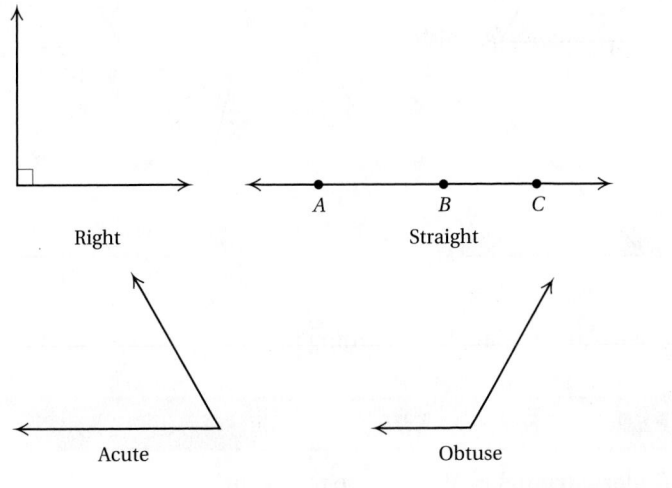

Do Exercises 16–19.

15. Use a protractor to measure this angle.

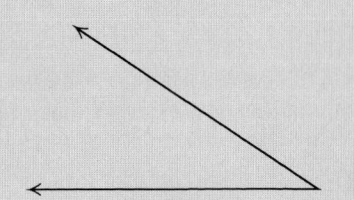

Classify each angle as right, straight, acute, or obtuse. Use a protractor if necessary.

16.

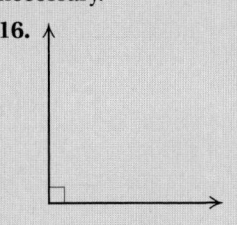

17.

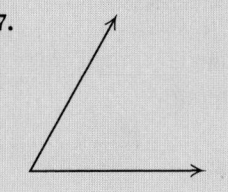

18.

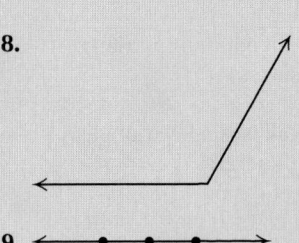

19.

Answers

15. 33°   **16.** Right   **17.** Acute
18. Obtuse   **19.** Straight

Determine whether the pair of lines is perpendicular. Use a protractor.

20.

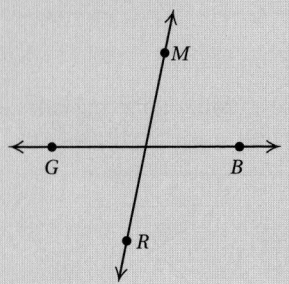

21.

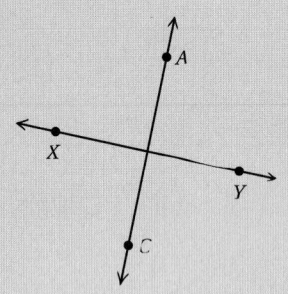

d) Perpendicular Lines

Two lines are **perpendicular** if they intersect to form a right angle.

To say that $\overleftrightarrow{AB}$ is perpendicular to $\overleftrightarrow{RS}$, we write $\overleftrightarrow{AB} \perp \overleftrightarrow{RS}$. If two lines intersect to form one right angle, they form four right angles.

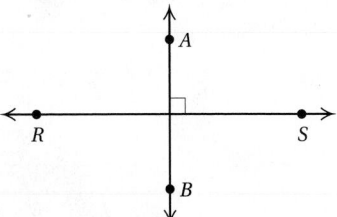

Do Exercises 20 and 21.

e) Polygons

The figures below are examples of **polygons**.

A **triangle** is a polygon made up of three segments, or sides. Consider these triangles. The triangle with vertices A, B, and C can be named $\triangle ABC$.

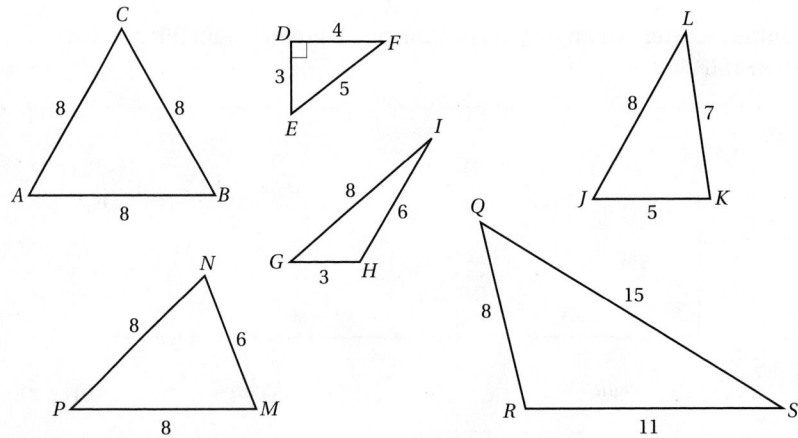

We can classify triangles according to sides and according to angles.

22. Which triangles at right are:
  a) equilateral?
  b) isosceles?
  c) scalene?

23. Are all equilateral triangles isosceles?

24. Are all isosceles triangles equilateral?

25. Which triangles at right are:
  a) right triangles?
  b) obtuse triangles?
  c) acute triangles?

TYPES OF TRIANGLES

Equilateral triangle: All sides are the same length.
Isosceles triangle: Two or more sides are the same length.
Scalene triangle: All sides are of different lengths.
Right triangle: One angle is a right angle.
Obtuse triangle: One angle is an obtuse angle.
Acute triangle: All three angles are acute.

Do Exercises 22–25.

Answers

20. Not perpendicular   **21.** Perpendicular
22. (a) $\triangle ABC$; (b) $\triangle ABC$, $\triangle MPN$; (c) $\triangle DEF$, $\triangle GHI$, $\triangle JKL$, $\triangle QRS$ **23.** Yes   **24.** No
25. (a) $\triangle DEF$; (b) $\triangle GHI$, $\triangle QRS$; (c) $\triangle ABC$, $\triangle MPN$, $\triangle JKL$

We can further classify polygons as follows.

NUMBER OF SIDES	POLYGON	NUMBER OF SIDES	POLYGON
4	Quadrilateral	8	Octagon
5	Pentagon	9	Nonagon
6	Hexagon	10	Decagon
7	Heptagon	12	Dodecagon

Do Exercises 26–31.

(f) Sum of the Angle Measures of a Polygon

The sum of the angle measures of a triangle is 180°. To see this, note that we can think of cutting apart a triangle as shown on the left below. If we reassemble the pieces, we see that a straight angle is formed.

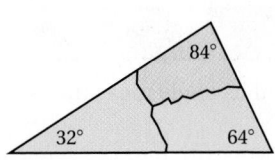 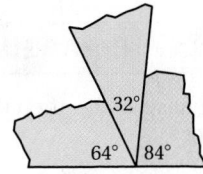

$64° + 32° + 84° = 180°$

SUM OF THE ANGLE MEASURES OF A TRIANGLE

In any $\triangle ABC$, the sum of the measures of the angles is 180°:

$$m\angle A + m\angle B + m\angle C = 180°.$$

Do Exercise 32.

If we know the measures of two angles of a triangle, we can calculate the measure of the third angle.

EXAMPLE 1 Find the missing angle measure.

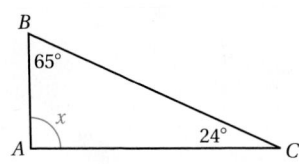

$$m\angle A + m\angle B + m\angle C = 180°$$
$$x + 65° + 24° = 180°$$
$$x + 89° = 180°$$
$$x = 180° - 89°$$
$$x = 91°$$

Thus, $m\angle A = 91°$.

Classify the polygon by name.
26.
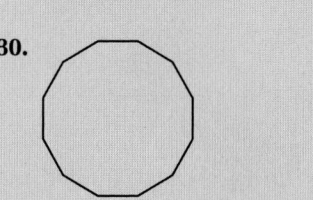

27.

28.

29.

30.

31.
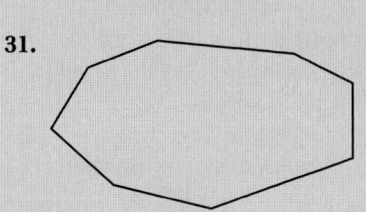

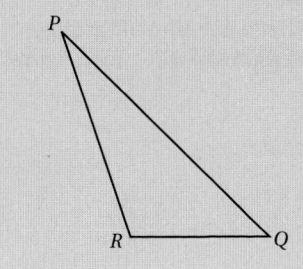

32. Find $m\angle P + m\angle Q + m\angle R$.

Answers

26. Quadrilateral 27. Hexagon
28. Triangle 29. Quadrilateral
30. Dodecagon 31. Octagon 32. 180°

33. Find the missing angle measure.

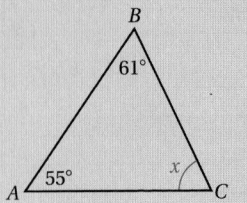

34. Consider a five-sided figure:

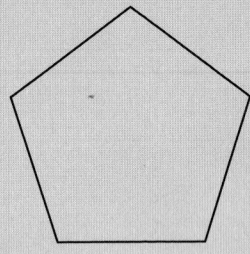

Complete.

a) The figure can be divided into _____ triangles.

b) The sum of the angle measures of each triangle is _____.

c) The sum of the angle measures of the polygon is _____ · 180°, or _____.

35. What is the sum of the angle measures of an octagon?

36. What is the sum of the angle measures of a 25-sided figure?

Do Exercise 33.

Now let's use this idea to find the sum of the measures of the angles of a polygon of n sides. First let's consider a four-sided figure:

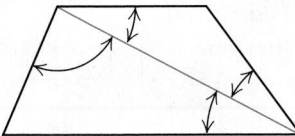

We can divide the figure into two triangles. The sum of the angle measures of each triangle is 180°. We have two triangles, so the sum of the angle measures of the figure is 2 · 180°, or 360°.

Do Exercise 34.

If a polygon has n sides, it can be divided into $n - 2$ triangles, each having 180° as the sum of its angle measures. Thus the sum of the angle measures of the polygon is $(n - 2) \cdot 180°$.

SUM OF ANGLE MEASURES

If a polygon has n sides, then the sum of its angle measures is $(n - 2) \cdot 180°$.

EXAMPLE 2 What is the sum of the angle measures of a hexagon?

A hexagon has 6 sides. We use the formula $(n - 2) \cdot 180°$:

$$(n - 2) \cdot 180° = (6 - 2) \cdot 180°$$
$$= 4 \cdot 180°$$
$$= 720°.$$

Do Exercises 35 and 36.

Answers

33. 64°   **34.** (a) 3; (b) 180°; (c) 3, 540°
35. 1080°   **36.** 4140°

a

1. Draw the segment whose endpoints are *G* and *H*. Name the segment in two ways.

> •
> *G*   •
>   *H*

2. Draw the segment whose endpoints are *C* and *D*. Name the segment in two ways.

> •
> *C*   •
>   *D*

3. Draw the ray with endpoint *Q*. Name the ray.

> •
> *Q*   •
>   *D*

4. Draw the ray with endpoint *D*. Name the ray.

> •
> *Q*   •
>   *D*

Name the line in seven different ways.

5.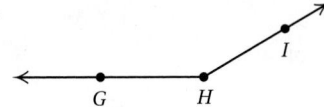

6.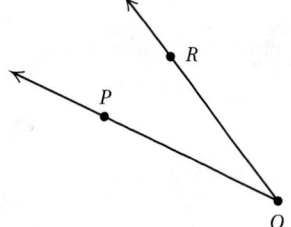

b   Name each angle in five different ways.

7.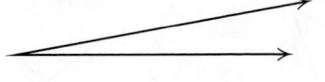

8.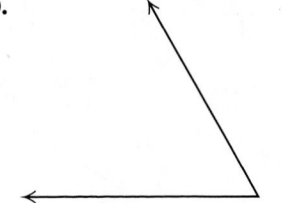

Use a protractor to measure each angle.

9.   **10.**   **11.**

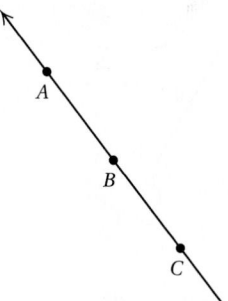

12.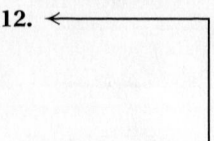

13.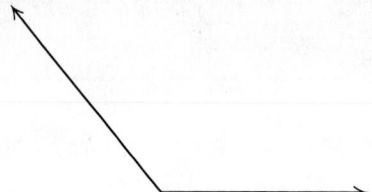

14.

 c

15.–22. Classify each of the angles in Exercises 7–14 as right, straight, acute, or obtuse.

23.–26. Classify each of the angles in Margin Exercises 12–15 as right, straight, acute, or obtuse.

d Determine whether the pair of lines is perpendicular. Use a protractor.

27.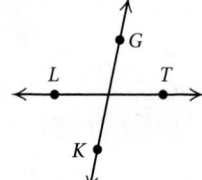

28.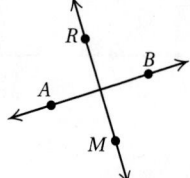

29.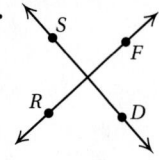

30.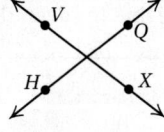

e Classify the triangle as equilateral, isosceles, or scalene. Then classify it as right, obtuse, or acute.

31.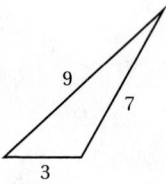

32.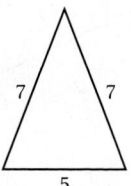

33.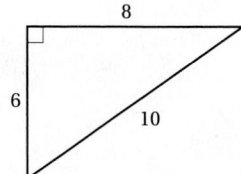

34.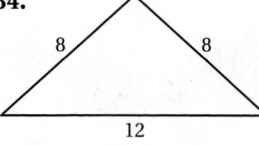

35.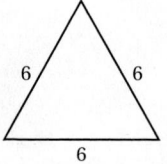

36.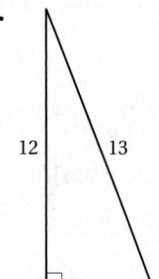

37.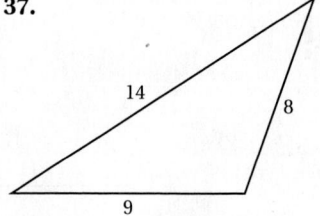

38.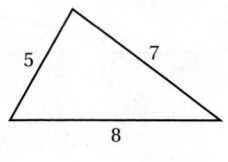

Copyright © 2012 Pearson Education, Inc.

Classify the polygon by name.

39.

40.

41.

42.

43.

44.

45.

46.

47.

48.

f Find the sum of the angle measures of each of the following.

49. A decagon

50. A quadrilateral

51. A heptagon

52. A nonagon

53. A 14-sided polygon

54. A 17-sided polygon

55. A 20-sided polygon

56. A 32-sided polygon

Find the missing angle measure.

57.
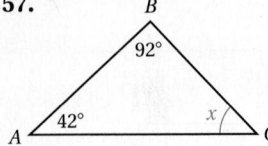

58.
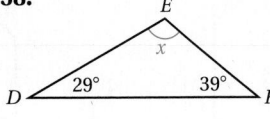

59.
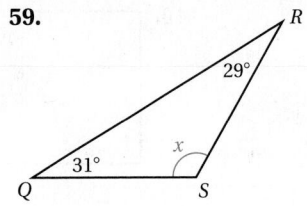

60.
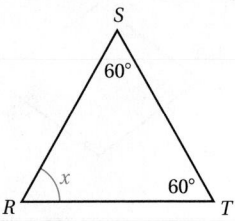

61. In $\triangle RST$, $m(\angle S) = 58°$ and $m(\angle T) = 79°$. Find $m(\angle R)$.

62. In $\triangle KNP$, $m(\angle K) = 137°$ and $m(\angle P) = 12°$. Find $m(\angle N)$.

Skill Maintenance

Find the simple interest. [4.8a]

	PRINCIPAL	RATE OF INTEREST	TIME	SIMPLE INTEREST
63.	$2000	8%	1 year	
64.	$750	6%	$\frac{1}{2}$ year	
65.	$4000	7.4%	$\frac{1}{2}$ year	
66.	$200,000	6.7%	$\frac{1}{12}$ year	

Interest is compounded semiannually. Find the amount in the account after the given length of time. Round to the nearest cent. [4.8b]

	PRINCIPAL	RATE OF INTEREST	TIME	AMOUNT IN THE ACCOUNT
67.	$25,000	6%	5 years	
68.	$150,000	$6\frac{7}{8}$%	15 years	
69.	$150,000	7.4%	20 years	
70.	$160,000	7.4%	20 years	

Synthesis

71. Find $m \angle ACB$, $m \angle CAB$, $m \angle EBC$, $m \angle EBA$, $m \angle AEB$, and $m \angle ADB$ in the rectangle shown below.

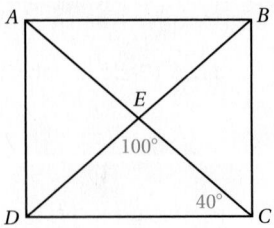

72. 🖩 In the figure, $m\angle 2 = 42.17°$ and $m\angle 3 = 81.9°$. Find $m\angle 1$, $m\angle 4$, $m\angle 5$, and $m\angle 6$.

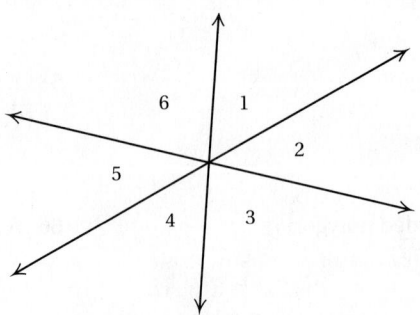

Copyright © 2012 Pearson Education, Inc.

6.2 Perimeter

a Finding Perimeters

OBJECTIVES

a Find the perimeter of a polygon.

b Solve applied problems involving perimeter.

PERIMETER OF A POLYGON

A **polygon** is a closed geometric figure with three or more sides. The **perimeter of a polygon** is the distance around it, or the sum of the lengths of its sides.

EXAMPLE 1 Find the perimeter of this polygon.

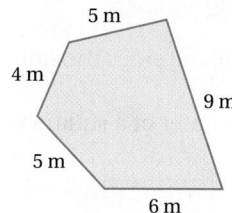

We add the lengths of the sides. Since all units are the same, we add the numbers, keeping meters (m) as the unit.

Perimeter = 6 m + 5 m + 4 m + 5 m + 9 m
         = (6 + 5 + 4 + 5 + 9) m
         = 29 m

Do Margin Exercises 1 and 2.

A **rectangle** is a polygon with four sides and four 90° angles, like the one shown in Example 2.

EXAMPLE 2 Find the perimeter of a rectangle that is 3 cm by 4 cm. The symbol ⌐ in the corner indicates 90°.

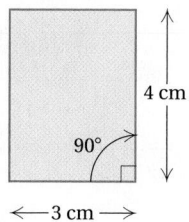

Perimeter = 3 cm + 4 cm + 3 cm + 4 cm
         = (3 + 4 + 3 + 4) cm
         = 14 cm

Do Exercise 3.

SKILL TO REVIEW
Objective 2.4d: Multiply using mixed numerals.

Multiply.

1. $2 \times 8\frac{1}{3}$ **2.** $4 \times 6\frac{2}{5}$

Find the perimeter of each polygon.
1.

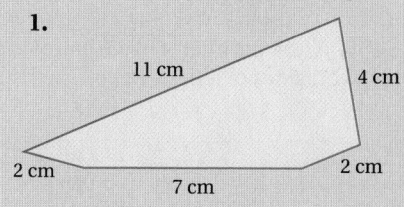

2.

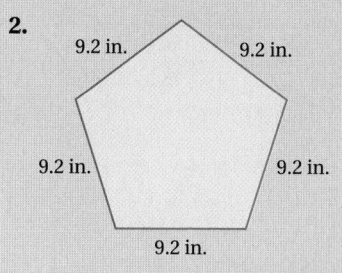

3. Find the perimeter of a rectangle that is 2 cm by 4 cm.

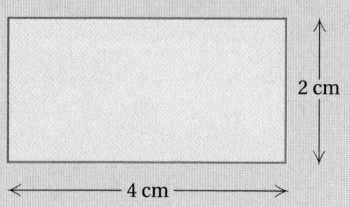

Answers

Skill to Review:
1. $\frac{50}{3}$, or $16\frac{2}{3}$ **2.** $\frac{128}{5}$, or $25\frac{3}{5}$

Margin Exercises:
1. 26 cm   **2.** 46 in.   **3.** 12 cm

PERIMETER OF A RECTANGLE

The **perimeter of a rectangle** is twice the sum of the length and the width, or 2 times the length plus 2 times the width:

$$P = 2 \cdot (l + w), \quad \text{or} \quad P = 2 \cdot l + 2 \cdot w.$$

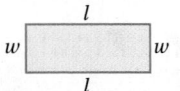

EXAMPLE 3 Find the perimeter of a rectangle that is 7.8 ft by 4.3 ft.

$$P = 2 \cdot (l + w)$$
$$= 2 \cdot (7.8 \text{ ft} + 4.3 \text{ ft})$$
$$= 2 \cdot (12.1 \text{ ft})$$
$$= 24.2 \text{ ft}$$

4. Find the perimeter of a rectangle that is 5.25 yd by 3.5 yd.

5. Find the perimeter of a rectangle that is $8\frac{1}{4}$ in. by $5\frac{2}{3}$ in.

Do Exercises 4 and 5.

A **square** is a rectangle with all sides the same length.

EXAMPLE 4 Find the perimeter of a square whose sides are 9 mm long.

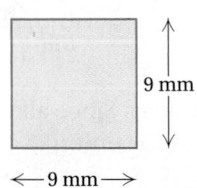

$$P = 9 \text{ mm} + 9 \text{ mm} + 9 \text{ mm} + 9 \text{ mm}$$
$$= (9 + 9 + 9 + 9) \text{ mm}$$
$$= 36 \text{ mm}$$

6. Find the perimeter of a square with sides of length 10 km.

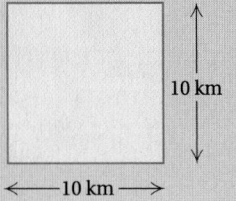

Do Exercise 6.

PERIMETER OF A SQUARE

The **perimeter of a square** is four times the length of a side:

$$P = 4 \cdot s.$$

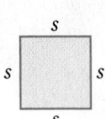

Answers

4. 17.5 yd   **5.** $27\frac{5}{6}$ in.   **6.** 40 km

EXAMPLE 5 Find the perimeter of a square whose sides are $20\frac{1}{8}$ in. long.

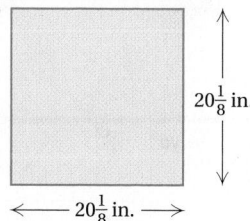

$20\frac{1}{8}$ in.

$\longleftarrow 20\frac{1}{8}$ in. $\longrightarrow$

$$P = 4 \cdot s = 4 \cdot 20\frac{1}{8} \text{ in.}$$

$$= 4 \cdot \frac{161}{8} \text{ in.} = \frac{4 \cdot 161}{4 \cdot 2} \text{ in.}$$

$$= \frac{4}{4} \cdot \frac{161}{2} \text{ in.} = 80\frac{1}{2} \text{ in.}$$

7. Find the perimeter of a square with sides of length $5\frac{1}{4}$ yd.

8. Find the perimeter of a square with sides of length 7.8 km.

Do Exercises 7 and 8.

b Solving Applied Problems

EXAMPLE 6 Jaci is adding crown molding to the top edge of each wall in her rectangular dining room, which measures 14 ft by 12 ft. How many feet of trim will be needed? If the crown molding sells for $2.25 per foot, what will the trim cost?

1. **Familiarize.** We make a drawing and let P = the perimeter.

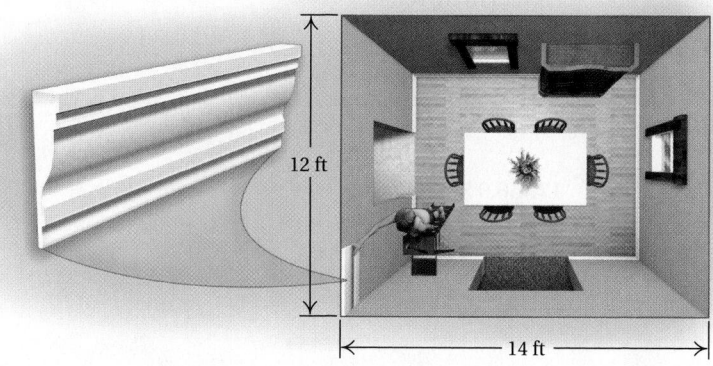

12 ft

14 ft

2. **Translate.** The perimeter of the room is given by

$$P = 2 \cdot (l + w) = 2 \cdot (14 \text{ ft} + 12 \text{ ft}).$$

3. **Solve.** We calculate the perimeter as follows:

$$P = 2 \cdot (14 \text{ ft} + 12 \text{ ft}) = 2 \cdot (26 \text{ ft}) = 52 \text{ ft}.$$

Then we multiply by $2.25 to find the cost of the crown molding:

$$\text{Cost} = \$2.25 \times \text{Perimeter} = \$2.25 \times 52 \text{ ft} = \$117.$$

4. **Check.** The check is left to the student.

5. **State.** The 52 ft of crown molding that is needed will cost $117.

Do Exercise 9.

9. A fence is to be built around a vegetable garden that measures 20 ft by 15 ft. How many feet of fence will be needed? If fencing sells for $2.95 per foot, what will the fencing cost?

Answers
7. 21 yd   **8.** 31.2 km   **9.** 70 ft; $206.50

6.2 **Exercise Set**

For Extra Help

*Math*XL
PRACTICE
WATCH
DOWNLOAD
READ
REVIEW

a Find the perimeter of each polygon.

1.

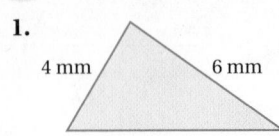

4 mm   6 mm
7 mm

2.

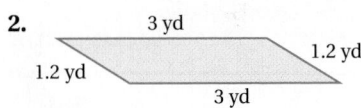

3 yd
1.2 yd
1.2 yd
3 yd

3.

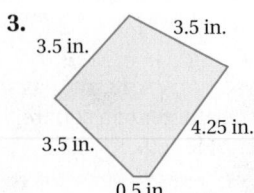

3.5 in.   3.5 in.
3.5 in.   4.25 in.
3.5 in.
0.5 in.

4.

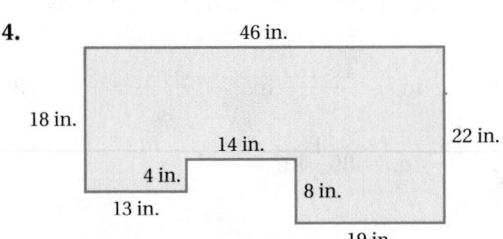

46 in.
18 in.
14 in.   22 in.
4 in.
13 in.   8 in.
19 in.

5.

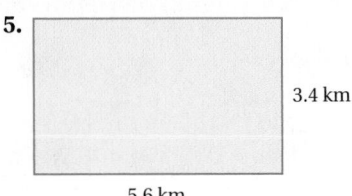

3.4 km
5.6 km

6.

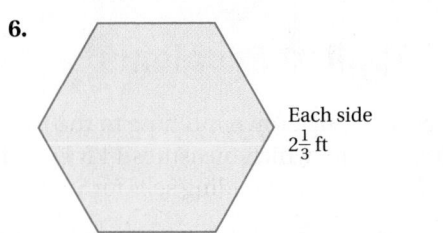

Each side
$2\frac{1}{3}$ ft

Find the perimeter of each rectangle.

7. 5 ft by 10 ft

8. 2.5 m by 100 m

9. $3\frac{1}{2}$ yd by $4\frac{1}{2}$ yd

10. 34.67 cm by 4.9 cm

Find the perimeter of each square.

11. 22 ft on a side

12. 56.9 km on a side

13. 45.5 mm on a side

14. $3\frac{1}{8}$ yd on a side

b Solve.

15. Most billiard tables are twice as long as they are wide. What is the perimeter of a billiard table that measures 4.5 ft by 9 ft?

16. A security fence is to be built around a 173-m by 240-m rectangular lot. What is the perimeter of the lot? If 5-ft-high galvanized fence wire costs $7.29 per meter, what will the fencing cost?

Copyright © 2012 Pearson Education, Inc.

17. A piece of flooring tile is a square with sides of length 30.5 cm. What is the perimeter of a piece of tile?

18. A rectangular posterboard is 61.8 cm by 87.9 cm. What is the perimeter of the board?

19. A rectangular glass backboard for a basketball goal measures 2 ft 8 in. by 4 ft 6 in. What is the perimeter of the backboard? (*Hint:* Convert 2 ft 8 in. to 32 in. and 4 ft 6 in. to 54 in.)

20. A standard license plate measures 12 in. by 6 in. What is the perimeter of the license plate?

21. A rain gutter is to be installed around the office building shown in the figure.

   a) Find the perimeter of the office building.
   b) If the gutter costs $4.59 per foot, what is the total cost of the gutter?

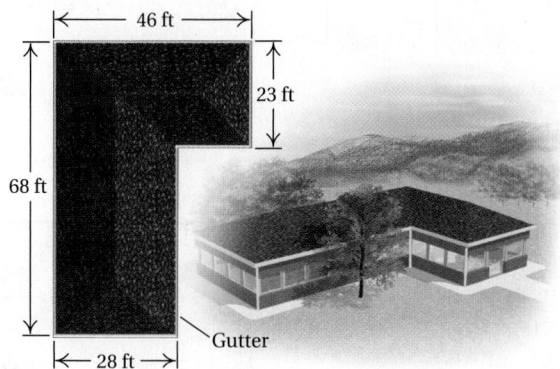

22. A carpenter is to build a fence around a 9-m by 12-m garden.

   a) The posts are 3 m apart. How many posts will be needed?
   b) The posts cost $8.65 each. How much will the posts cost?
   c) The fence will surround all but 3 m of the garden, which will be a gate. How long will the fence be?
   d) The fence costs $3.85 per meter. What will the cost of the fence be?
   e) The gate costs $69.95. What is the total cost of the materials?

Skill Maintenance

23. Find the simple interest on $600 at 6.4% for $\frac{1}{2}$ year.   [4.8a]

24. Find the simple interest on $600 at 8% for 2 years.   [4.8a]

Evaluate.   [1.6b]

25. 10^3

26. 11^3

27. 15^2

28. 22^2

29. 7^2

30. 4^3

Solve.

31. *Sales Tax.* In a certain state, a sales tax of $878 is collected on the purchase of a car for $17,560. What is the sales tax rate?   [4.7a]

32. *Commission Rate.* Rich earns $1854.60 selling $16,860 worth of cell phones. What is the commission rate?   [4.7b]

Synthesis

33. If it takes 18 in. to make the bow, how much ribbon is needed for the entire package shown here?

34. Find the perimeter, in feet, of the figure.

78 in.

5.5 yd

6.3

Area

OBJECTIVES

a Find the area of a rectangle and a square.

b Find the area of a parallelogram, a triangle, and a trapezoid.

c Solve applied problems involving areas of rectangles, squares, parallelograms, triangles, and trapezoids.

(a) Rectangles and Squares

A polygon and its interior form a plane region. We can find the area of a *rectangular region*, or *rectangle*, by filling it in with square units. Two such units, a *square inch* and a *square centimeter*, are shown below.

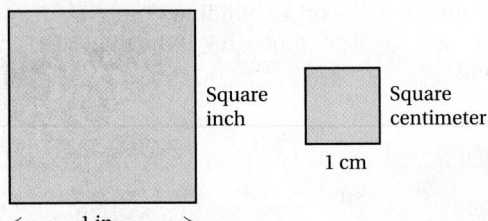

Square inch

Square centimeter

1 cm

SKILL TO REVIEW

Objective 3.5c: Calculate using fraction notation and decimal notation together.

Calculate.

1. $\frac{1}{2} \times 16.243$ **2.** $0.5 \times \frac{3}{8}$

EXAMPLE 1 What is the area of this region?

We have a rectangular array. Since the region is filled with 12 square centimeters, its area is 12 square centimeters (sq cm), or 12 cm². The number of units is 3 × 4, or 12.

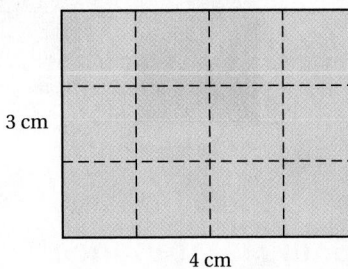

3 cm

4 cm

Do Margin Exercise 1.

---

1. What is the area of this region? Count the number of square centimeters.

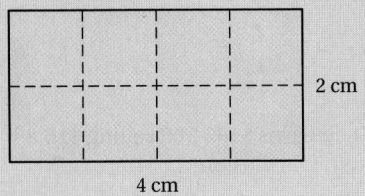

2 cm

4 cm

> **AREA OF A RECTANGLE**
>
> The **area of a rectangle** is the product of the length *l* and the width *w*:
>
> $A = l \cdot w$.
>
>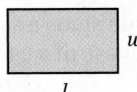
>
> *w*
>
> *l*

---

2. Find the area of a rectangle that is 7 km by 8 km.

3. Find the area of a rectangle that is $5\frac{1}{4}$ yd by $3\frac{1}{2}$ yd.

EXAMPLE 2 Find the area of a rectangle that is 7 yd by 4 yd.

We have

$A = l \cdot w = 7\,\text{yd} \cdot 4\,\text{yd}$

$= 7 \cdot 4 \cdot \text{yd} \cdot \text{yd} = 28\,\text{yd}^2.$

We think of yd · yd as (yd)² and denote it yd². Thus we read "28 yd²" as "28 square yards."

Do Exercises 2 and 3.

Answers

Skill to Review:

1. 8.1215   **2.** 0.1875, or $\frac{3}{16}$

Margin Exercises:

1. 8 cm²   **2.** 56 km²   **3.** $18\frac{3}{8}$ yd²

EXAMPLE 3 Find the area of a square with sides of length 9 mm.

$$A = (9 \text{ mm}) \cdot (9 \text{ mm})$$
$$= 9 \cdot 9 \cdot \text{mm} \cdot \text{mm}$$
$$= 81 \text{ mm}^2$$

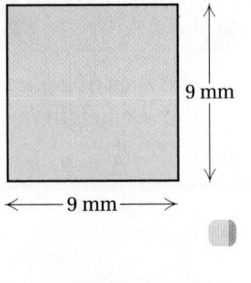

9 mm

9 mm

Do Exercise 4.

4. Find the area of a square with sides of length 12 km.

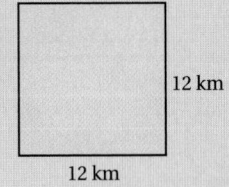

12 km

12 km

AREA OF A SQUARE

The **area of a square** is the square of the length of a side:

$$A = s \cdot s, \quad \text{or} \quad A = s^2.$$

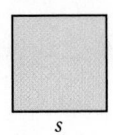

s

s

EXAMPLE 4 Find the area of a square with sides of length 20.3 m.

$$A = s \cdot s = 20.3 \text{ m} \times 20.3 \text{ m} = 20.3 \times 20.3 \times \text{m} \times \text{m} = 412.09 \text{ m}^2$$

Do Exercises 5 and 6.

5. Find the area of a square with sides of length 10.9 m.

6. Find the area of a square with sides of length $3\frac{1}{2}$ yd.

(b) Finding Other Areas

Parallelograms

A **parallelogram** is a four-sided figure with two pairs of parallel sides, as shown below.

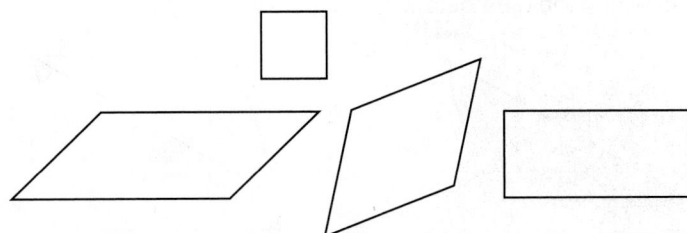

To find the area of a parallelogram, consider the one below.

If we cut off a piece and move it to the other end, we get a rectangle.

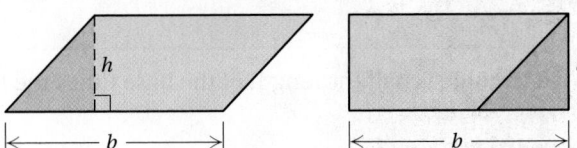

h h

b b

We can find the area by multiplying the length b, called a **base**, by h, called the **height**.

STUDY TIPS

STUDYING THE DRAWINGS

When you study a section of a mathematics text, read it slowly, observing all the details of the corresponding drawings that are discussed in the paragraphs. This tip applies especially to this chapter because geometry, by its nature, is quite visual.

Answers

4. 144 km^2 **5.** 118.81 m^2 **6.** $12\frac{1}{4}$ yd^2

AREA OF A PARALLELOGRAM

The **area of a parallelogram** is the product of the length of the base b and the height h:

$$A = b \cdot h.$$

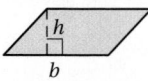

EXAMPLE 5 Find the area of this parallelogram.

$A = b \cdot h$
$\quad = 7\,\text{km} \cdot 5\,\text{km}$
$\quad = 35\,\text{km}^2$

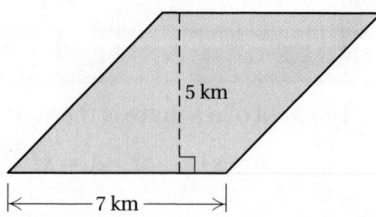

Find the area.

7.

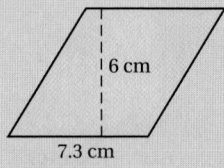

6 cm

7.3 cm

8.

5.5 km

2.25 km

EXAMPLE 6 Find the area of this parallelogram.

$A = b \cdot h$
$\quad = 1.2\,\text{m} \times 6\,\text{m}$
$\quad = 7.2\,\text{m}^2$

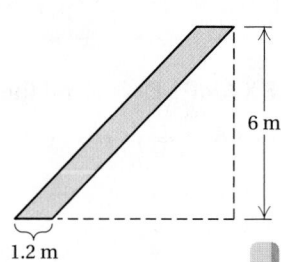

6 m

1.2 m

Do Exercises 7 and 8.

Triangles

A **triangle** is a polygon with three sides. To find the area of a triangle like the one shown on the left below, think of cutting out another just like it and placing it as shown on the right below.

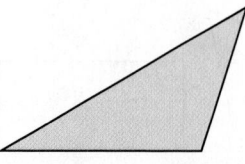

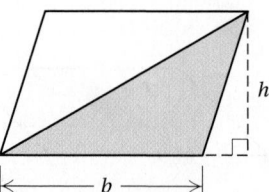

The resulting figure is a parallelogram whose area is

$$b \cdot h.$$

The triangle we began with has half the area of the parallelogram, or

$$\frac{1}{2} \cdot b \cdot h.$$

AREA OF A TRIANGLE

The **area of a triangle** is half the length of the base times the height:

$$A = \frac{1}{2} \cdot b \cdot h.$$

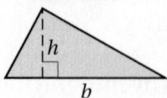

Answers
7. $43.8\,\text{cm}^2$ **8.** $12.375\,\text{km}^2$

EXAMPLE 7 Find the area of this triangle.

$$A = \frac{1}{2} \cdot b \cdot h$$

$$= \frac{1}{2} \cdot 9 \, m \cdot 6 \, m$$

$$= \frac{9 \cdot 6}{2} \, m^2$$

$$= 27 \, m^2$$

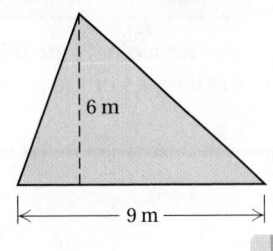

EXAMPLE 8 Find the area of this triangle.

$$A = \frac{1}{2} \cdot b \cdot h$$

$$= \frac{1}{2} \times 6.25 \, cm \times 5.5 \, cm$$

$$= 0.5 \times 6.25 \times 5.5 \, cm^2$$

$$= 17.1875 \, cm^2$$

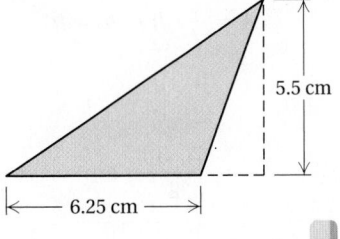

Do Exercises 9 and 10.

Find the area.

9.

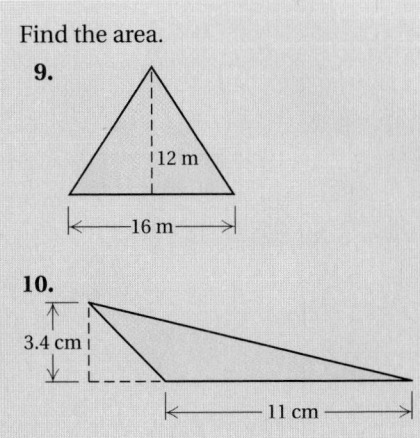

10.

Trapezoids

A **trapezoid** is a polygon with four sides, two of which, the **bases**, are parallel to each other.

To find the area of a trapezoid, think of cutting out another just like it.

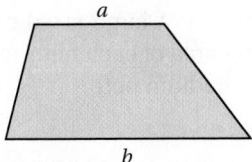

Then place the second one like this.

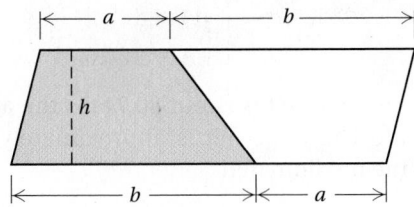

The resulting figure is a parallelogram whose area is

$$h \cdot (a + b). \quad \text{The base is } a + b.$$

The trapezoid we began with has half the area of the parallelogram, or

$$\frac{1}{2} \cdot h \cdot (a + b).$$

Answers
9. 96 m² 10. 18.7 cm²

Find the area.

11.

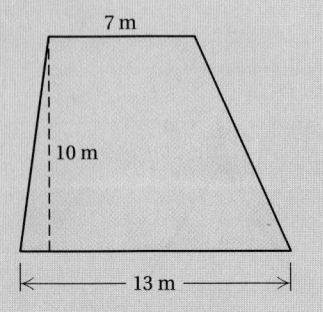

7 m

10 m

13 m

12.

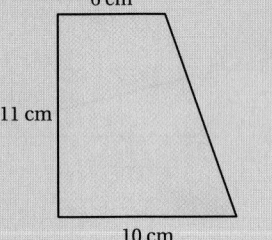

6 cm

11 cm

10 cm

AREA OF A TRAPEZOID

The **area of a trapezoid** is half the product of the height and the sum of the lengths of the parallel sides (bases):

$$A = \frac{1}{2} \cdot h \cdot (a + b), \quad \text{or} \quad A = \frac{a + b}{2} \cdot h.$$

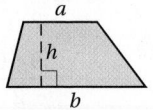

EXAMPLE 9 Find the area of this trapezoid.

$$A = \frac{1}{2} \cdot h \cdot (a + b)$$

$$= \frac{1}{2} \cdot 7 \, \text{cm} \cdot (12 + 18) \, \text{cm}$$

$$= \frac{7 \cdot 30}{2} \cdot \text{cm}^2 = \frac{7 \cdot 15 \cdot 2}{1 \cdot 2} \, \text{cm}^2$$

$$= \frac{2}{2} \cdot \frac{7 \cdot 15}{1} \, \text{cm}^2$$

$$= 105 \, \text{cm}^2$$

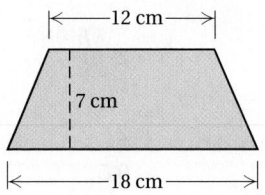

12 cm

7 cm

18 cm

Do Exercises 11 and 12.

(C) Solving Applied Problems

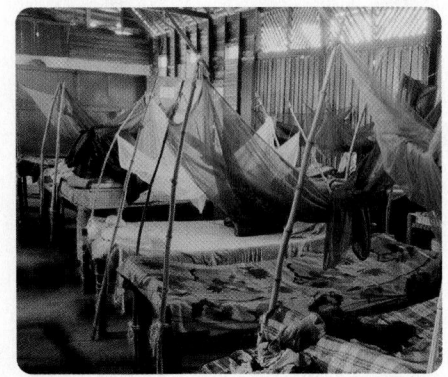

EXAMPLE 10 *Mosquito Netting.* Malaria is the leading cause of death among children in Africa. Bed nets prevent malaria transmission by creating a protective barrier against mosquitoes at night. In November 2006, the United Nations Foundation, the United Methodist Church, and the National Basketball Association launched the Nothing But Nets campaign to distribute mosquito netting in Africa. Two years later, 2,194,124 insecticide-treated bed nets had been sent to seven African countries. A medium-sized net measures approximately 9.843 ft by 8.2025 ft. A large-sized net measures approximately 13.124 ft by 8.2025 ft. Find the area of each net. How much larger is the area of the large net than that of the medium net?

Source: www.nothingbutnets.net

We find the area of each net using the area formula $A = l \cdot w$ and substituting values for l and w:

$A = l \times w$ $A = l \times w$

$A \approx 9.843 \, \text{ft} \times 8.2025 \, \text{ft}$ $A \approx 13.124 \, \text{ft} \times 8.2025 \, \text{ft}$

$A \approx 80.74 \, \text{ft}^2;$ $A \approx 107.65 \, \text{ft}^2.$

The area of the medium bed net is about $80.74 \, \text{ft}^2$; the area of the large bed net is about $107.65 \, \text{ft}^2$. The large net is approximately $107.65 - 80.74$, or $26.91 \, \text{ft}^2$, larger than the medium net.

Answers

11. $100 \, \text{m}^2$ **12.** $88 \, \text{cm}^2$

EXAMPLE 11 *Lucas Oil Stadium.* The retractable roof of Lucas Oil Stadium, the home of the Indianapolis Colts football team, divides lengthwise. Each half measures 600 ft by 160 ft. The roof opens and closes in approximately 9–11 min. The opening measures 293 ft across. What is the total area of the rectangular roof? What is the area of the opening?

Source: HKS Sports and Entertainment

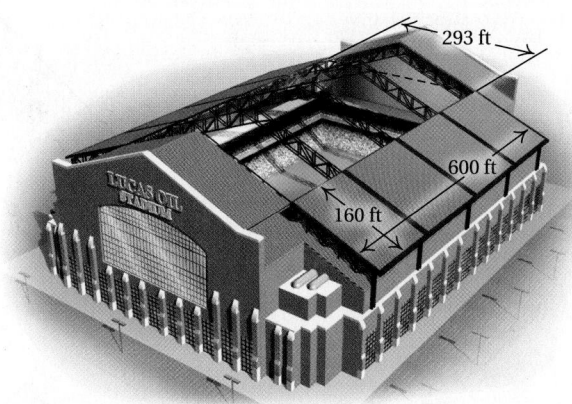

Each half of the retractable roof is a rectangle that measures 600 ft by 160 ft. The area of a rectangle is length times width, so we have

$$A = l \cdot w$$
$$= 600 \text{ ft} \times 160 \text{ ft}$$
$$= 96{,}000 \text{ ft}^2.$$

The total area of the two halves of the retractable roof is

$$\text{Total area} = 2 \times 96{,}000 \text{ ft}^2$$
$$= 192{,}000 \text{ ft}^2.$$

When the retractable roof is open, the dimensions of the opening are 600 ft by 293 ft. The area of this rectangle is

$$A = l \cdot w$$
$$= 600 \text{ ft} \times 293 \text{ ft}$$
$$= 175{,}800 \text{ ft}^2.$$

When the roof is open, the opening is 175,800 ft^2.

Do Exercise 13.

13. Find the area of this kite.

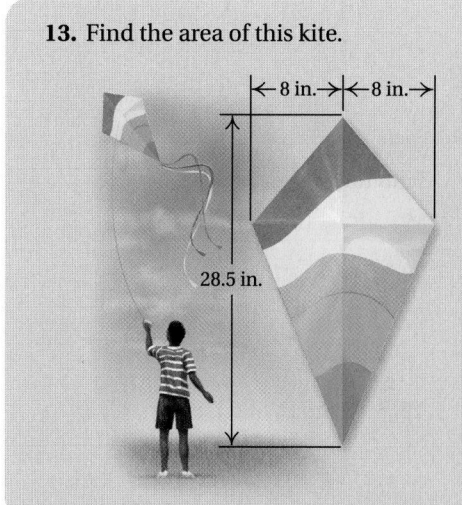

Answer

13. 228 in^2

a Find the area.

1.

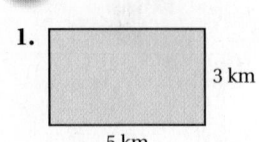

3 km

5 km

2.

1.5 ft

1.5 ft

3.

2 in.

0.7 in.

4.

2.2 m

3.8 m

5.

$2\frac{1}{2}$ yd

$2\frac{1}{2}$ yd

6.

$3\frac{1}{2}$ mi

$3\frac{1}{2}$ mi

7.

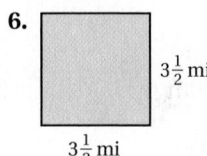

90 ft

90 ft

8.

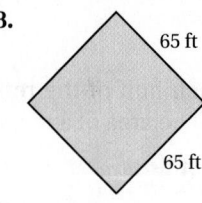

65 ft

65 ft

Find the area of each rectangle.

9. 5 ft by 10 ft

10. 14 yd by 8 yd

11. 34.67 cm by 4.9 cm

12. 2.45 km by 100 km

13. $4\frac{2}{3}$ in. by $8\frac{5}{6}$ in.

14. $10\frac{1}{3}$ mi by $20\frac{2}{3}$ mi

Find the area of the square.

15. 22 ft on a side

16. 18 yd on a side

17. 56.9 km on a side

18. 45.5 m on a side

19. $5\frac{3}{8}$ yd on a side

20. $7\frac{2}{3}$ ft on a side

Copyright © 2012 Pearson Education, Inc.

Find the area.

21.

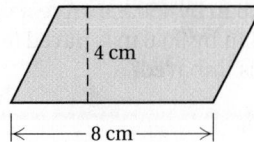

4 cm

8 cm

22.

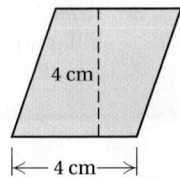

4 cm

4 cm

23.

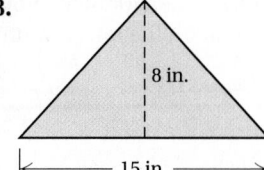

8 in.

15 in.

24.

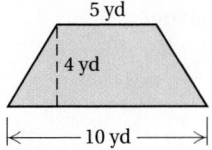

5 yd

4 yd

10 yd

25.

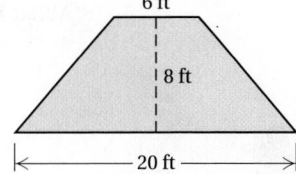

6 ft

8 ft

20 ft

26.

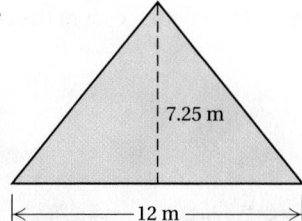

7.25 m

12 m

27.

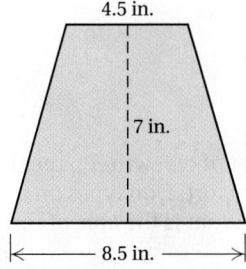

4.5 in.

7 in.

8.5 in.

28.

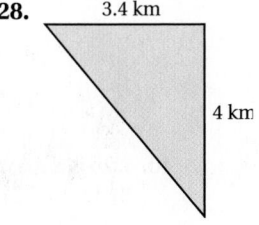

3.4 km

4 km

29.

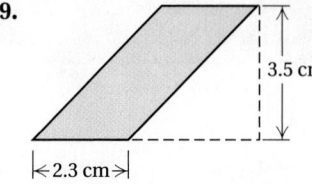

3.5 cm

2.3 cm

30.

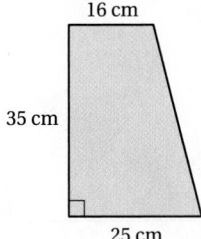

16 cm

35 cm

25 cm

31.

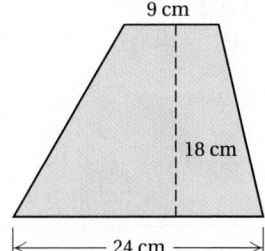

9 cm

18 cm

24 cm

32.

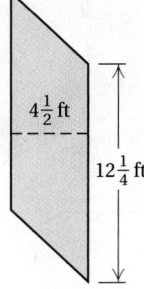

$4\frac{1}{2}$ ft

$12\frac{1}{4}$ ft

33.

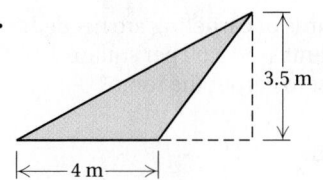

3.5 m

4 m

34.

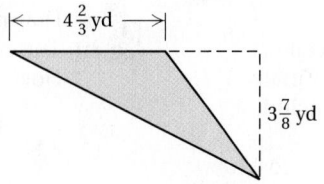

$4\frac{2}{3}$ yd

$3\frac{7}{8}$ yd

 Solve.

35. *Area of a Lawn.* A lot is 40 m by 36 m. A house 27 m by 9 m is built on the lot. How much area is left over for a lawn?

36. *Area of a Field.* A field is 240.8 m by 450.2 m. A rectangular area that measures 160.4 m by 90.6 m is paved for a parking lot. How much area is unpaved?

37. *Mowing Expense.* A square basketball court $19\frac{1}{2}$ ft on a side is placed on an 80-ft by $110\frac{2}{3}$-ft lawn.

  a) Find the area of the lawn.
  b) It costs \$0.012 per square foot to have the lawn mowed. What is the total cost of the mowing?

38. *Mowing Expense.* A square flower bed 10.5 ft on a side is dug on a 90-ft by $67\frac{1}{4}$-ft lawn.

  a) Find the area of the lawn.
  b) It costs \$0.03 per square foot to have the lawn mowed. What is the total cost of the mowing?

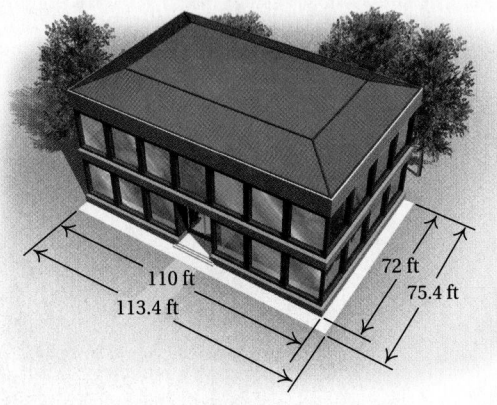

80 ft $19\frac{1}{2}$ ft $19\frac{1}{2}$ ft

39. *Area of a Sidewalk.* Franklin Construction Company builds a sidewalk around two sides of a new library, as shown in the figure. What is the area of the sidewalk?

40. *Margin Area.* A standard sheet of typewriter paper is $8\frac{1}{2}$ in. by 11 in. For a quarterly report, Don types on a 7-in. by 9-in. area of the paper. What is the area of the margins?

110 ft   72 ft
113.4 ft   75.4 ft

41. *Painting Costs.* A room is 15 ft by 20 ft. The ceiling is 8 ft above the floor. There are two windows in the room, each 3 ft by 4 ft. The door is $2\frac{1}{2}$ ft by $6\frac{1}{2}$ ft.

  a) What is the total area of the walls and the ceiling?
  b) A gallon of paint will cover 360.625 ft^2. How many gallons of paint are needed for the room, including the ceiling?
  c) Paint costs \$24.95 a gallon. How much will it cost to paint the room?

42. *Carpeting Costs.* A restaurant owner wants to carpet a 15-yd by 20-yd room.

  a) How many square yards of carpeting are needed?
  b) The carpeting she wants is \$18.50 per square yard. How much will it cost to carpet the room?

Copyright © 2012 Pearson Education, Inc.

Find the area of the shaded region in each figure.

43.

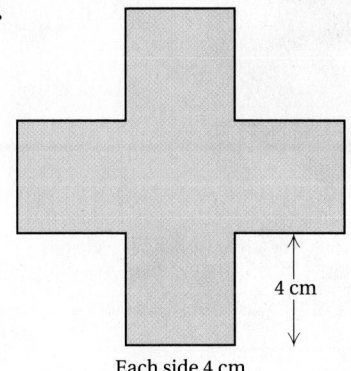

4 cm

Each side 4 cm

44.

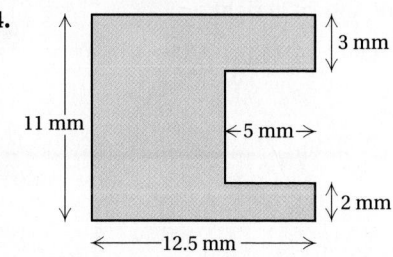

3 mm

11 mm

←5 mm→

2 mm

12.5 mm

45.

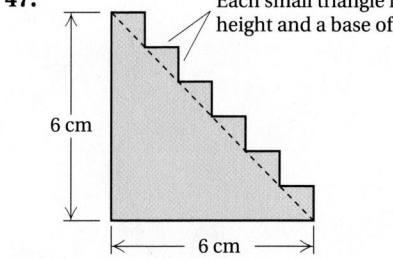

15 cm

30 cm

30 cm

46.

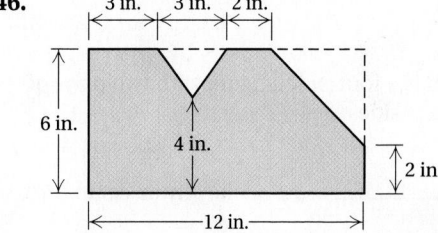

3 in.   3 in.   2 in.

6 in.

4 in.

2 in

12 in.

47.

Each small triangle has a
height and a base of 1 cm

6 cm

6 cm

48.

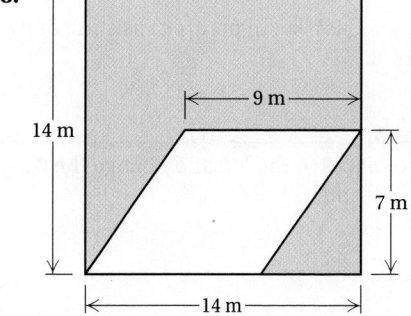

14 m

9 m

7 m

14 m

49. *Triangular Sail.*   Jane's Custom Sails is making a
custom sail for a laser sailboat. From a rectangular piece
of dacron sailcloth that measures 18 ft by 12 ft, she cuts
out a right triangular area plus a rectangular extension
on each side for the hems, with the dimensions shown at
right. How much fabric (area) is left over?

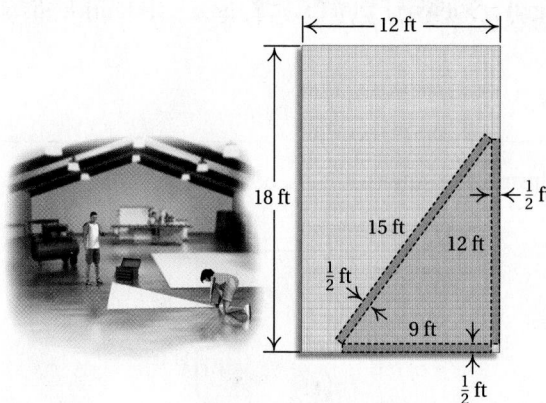

12 ft

18 ft

15 ft

12 ft

$\frac{1}{2}$ ft

$\frac{1}{2}$ ft

9 ft

$\frac{1}{2}$ ft

50. *Building Area.* Find the total area of the sides and the ends of the building shown at right.

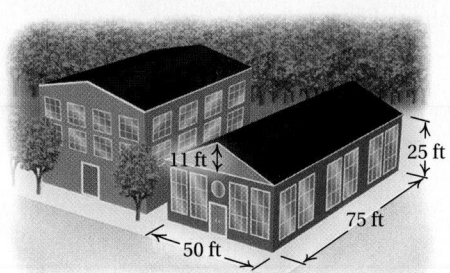

Skill Maintenance

In each of Exercises 51–58, fill in the blank with the correct term from the given list. Some of the choices may not be used.

51. A number is divisible by 8 if the number named by the last _____ digits of the given number is divisible by 8. [1.8a]

52. A parallelogram is a four-sided figure with two pairs of _____ sides. [6.3b]

53. Two lines are _____ if they intersect to form a right angle. [6.1d]

54. A natural number, other than 1, that is not _____ is composite. [1.7c]

55. A(n) _____ is a set of points consisting of two rays with a common endpoint. [6.1b]

56. To convert from _____ to _____ , move the decimal point two places to the left and change the ¢ sign at the end to the $ sign in front. [3.3b]

57. The _____ of a polygon is the sum of the lengths of its sides. [6.2a]

58. The number 1 is known as the _____ identity, and the number 0 is known as the _____ identity. [1.3a], [1.2a]

prime

composite

two

three

dollars

cents

perimeter

parallel

perpendicular

additive

multiplicative

parallel

perpendicular

vertex

angle

area

Synthesis

59. Find the area, in square inches, of the shaded region.

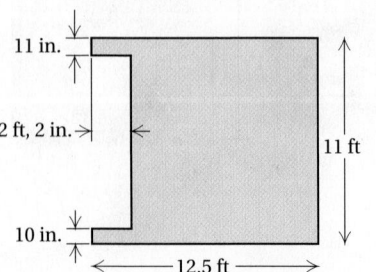

60. Find the area, in square feet, of the shaded region.

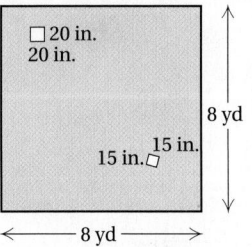

Copyright © 2012 Pearson Education, Inc.

6.4   Circles

a   Radius and Diameter

Shown below is a circle with center O. Segment $\overline{AC}$ is a *diameter*. A **diameter** is a segment that passes through the center of the circle and has endpoints on the circle. Segment $\overline{OB}$ is called a *radius*. A **radius** is a segment with one endpoint on the center and the other endpoint on the circle.

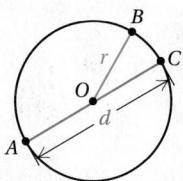

DIAMETER AND RADIUS

Suppose that d is the length of the diameter of a circle and r is the length of the radius. Then

$$d = 2 \cdot r \quad \text{and} \quad r = \frac{d}{2}.$$

EXAMPLE 1   Find the length of a radius of this circle.

$$r = \frac{d}{2}$$

$$= \frac{12 \text{ m}}{2}$$

$$= 6 \text{ m}$$

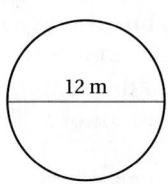

The radius is 6 m.

EXAMPLE 2   Find the length of a diameter of this circle.

$$d = 2 \cdot r$$

$$= 2 \cdot \frac{1}{4} \text{ ft}$$

$$= \frac{1}{2} \text{ ft}$$

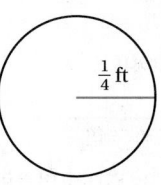

The diameter is $\frac{1}{2}$ ft.

Do Margin Exercises 1 and 2.

OBJECTIVES

a Find the length of a radius of a circle given the length of a diameter, and find the length of a diameter given the length of a radius.

b Find the circumference of a circle given the length of a diameter or a radius.

c Find the area of a circle given the length of a diameter or a radius.

d Solve applied problems involving circles.

SKILL TO REVIEW
Objective 2.1c: Multiply a fraction by a whole number.

Multiply.

1. $9 \times \frac{3}{8}$ **2.** $\frac{1}{10} \cdot 7$

1. Find the length of a radius.

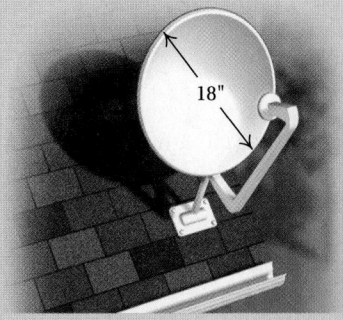

2. Find the length of a diameter.

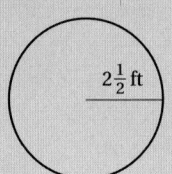

Answers
See p. 418.

b Circumference

The **circumference** of a circle is the distance around it. Calculating circumference is similar to finding the perimeter of a polygon.

To find a formula for the circumference of any circle given its diameter, we first need to consider the ratio C/d. Take a dinner plate and measure the circumference C with a tape measure. Also measure the diameter d. The results for a specific plate are shown in the figure below.

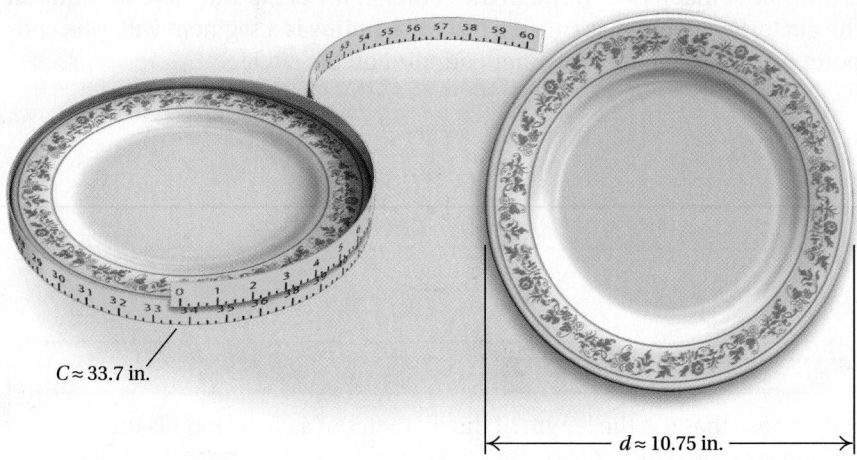

$C \approx 33.7$ in.

$d \approx 10.75$ in.

Then we have

$$\frac{C}{d} = \frac{33.7 \text{ in.}}{10.75 \text{ in.}} \approx 3.1.$$

Suppose we do this with plates and circles of several sizes. We get different values for C and d, but always a number close to 3.1 for C/d. For any circle, if we divide the circumference C by the diameter d, we get the same number. We call this number π (pi). The *exact* value of the ratio C/d is π; 3.14 and 22/7 are approximations of π. If $C/d = \pi$, then $C = \pi \cdot d$.

> ### CIRCUMFERENCE AND DIAMETER
>
> The circumference C of a circle of diameter d is given by
>
> $$C = \pi \cdot d.$$
>
> The number π is about 3.14, or about $\dfrac{22}{7}$.

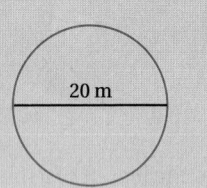

3. Find the circumference of this circle. Use 3.14 for π.

20 m

EXAMPLE 3 Find the circumference of this circle. Use 3.14 for π.

$C = \pi \cdot d$
$\quad \approx 3.14 \times 6 \text{ cm}$
$\quad = 18.84 \text{ cm}$

6 cm

The circumference is about 18.84 cm.

Do Exercise 3.

Answers

Skill to Review:

1. $\dfrac{27}{8}$ **2.** $\dfrac{7}{10}$

Margin Exercises:

1. 9" **2.** 5 ft **3.** 62.8 m

Since $d = 2 \cdot r$, where r is the length of a radius, it follows that

$$C = \pi \cdot d = \pi \cdot (2 \cdot r), \text{ or } 2 \cdot \pi \cdot r.$$

CIRCUMFERENCE AND RADIUS

The circumference C of a circle of radius r is given by

$$C = 2 \cdot \pi \cdot r.$$

EXAMPLE 4 Find the circumference of this circle. Use $\frac{22}{7}$ for π.

$C = 2 \cdot \pi \cdot r$

$\approx 2 \cdot \dfrac{22}{7} \cdot 70$ in.

$= 2 \cdot 22 \cdot \dfrac{70}{7}$ in.

$= 44 \cdot 10$ in.

$= 440$ in.

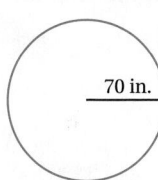

70 in.

The circumference is about 440 in.

EXAMPLE 5 Find the perimeter of this figure. Use 3.14 for π.

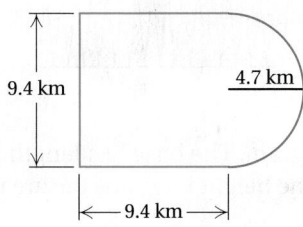

9.4 km

4.7 km

9.4 km

We let $P =$ the perimeter. We see that we have half a circle attached to a square. Thus we add half the circumference of the circle to the lengths of the three sides of the square.

$P = \begin{matrix} \text{Length of} \\ \text{three sides} \\ \text{of the square} \end{matrix} + \begin{matrix} \text{Half of the} \\ \text{circumference} \\ \text{of the circle} \end{matrix}$

$= 3 \times 9.4 \text{ km} + \dfrac{1}{2} \times 2 \times \pi \times 4.7 \text{ km}$

$\approx 28.2 \text{ km} + 3.14 \times 4.7 \text{ km}$

$= 28.2 \text{ km} + 14.758 \text{ km}$

$= 42.958 \text{ km}$

The perimeter is about 42.958 km.

Do Exercises 4 and 5.

Calculator Corner

The $\boxed{\pi}$ Key Many calculators have a $\boxed{\pi}$ key that can be used to enter the value of π in a computation. It might be necessary to press a $\boxed{\text{2nd}}$ or $\boxed{\text{SHIFT}}$ key before pressing the $\boxed{\pi}$ key on some calculators. Since 3.14 is a rounded value for π, results obtained using the $\boxed{\pi}$ key might be slightly different from those obtained when 3.14 is used for the value of π in a computation.

To find the circumference of the circle in Example 3, we press $\boxed{\text{2nd}}$ $\boxed{\pi}$ $\boxed{\times}$ $\boxed{6}$ $\boxed{=}$ or $\boxed{\text{SHIFT}}$ $\boxed{\pi}$ $\boxed{\times}$ $\boxed{6}$ $\boxed{=}$. The result is approximately 18.85. Note that this is slightly different from the result found using 3.14 for the value of π.

Exercises:

1. Use a calculator with a $\boxed{\pi}$ key to perform the computations in Examples 4 and 5.
2. Use a calculator with a $\boxed{\pi}$ key to perform the computations in Margin Exercises 3–5.

4. Find the circumference of this circle. Use $\frac{22}{7}$ for π.

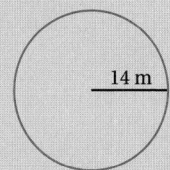

14 m

5. Find the perimeter of this figure. Use 3.14 for π.

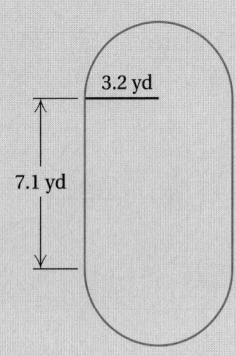

3.2 yd

7.1 yd

Answers

4. 88 m **5.** 34.296 yd

STUDY TIPS

BEGINNING TO STUDY FOR THE FINAL EXAM

It is never too soon to begin to study for the final examination. Take a few minutes each week to review the highlighted information, such as formulas, properties, and procedures. Make special use of the Mid-Chapter Reviews, Summary and Reviews, and Chapter Tests.

 **Area**

Below is a circle of radius r.

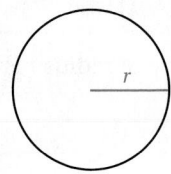

Think of cutting half the circular region into small pieces and arranging them as shown below.

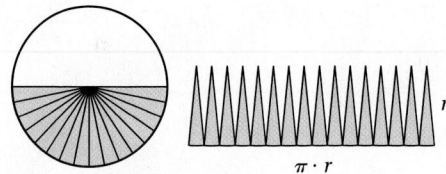

Then imagine cutting the other half of the circular region and arranging the pieces in with the others as shown below.

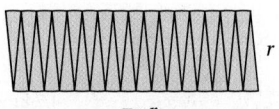

This is almost a parallelogram. The base has length $\frac{1}{2} \cdot 2 \cdot \pi \cdot r$, or $\pi \cdot r$ (half the circumference), and the height is r. Thus the area is

$$(\pi \cdot r) \cdot r.$$

This is the area of a circle.

AREA OF A CIRCLE

The **area of a circle** with radius of length r is given by

$$A = \pi \cdot r \cdot r, \quad \text{or} \quad A = \pi \cdot r^2.$$

---

6. Find the area of this circle. Use $\frac{22}{7}$ for π.

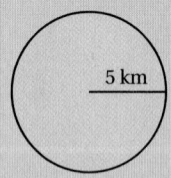

EXAMPLE 6 Find the area of this circle. Use $\frac{22}{7}$ for π.

$$A = \pi \cdot r \cdot r$$

$$\approx \frac{22}{7} \cdot 14\,\text{cm} \cdot 14\,\text{cm}$$

$$= \frac{22}{7} \cdot 196\,\text{cm}^2$$

$$= 616\,\text{cm}^2$$

The area is about $616\,\text{cm}^2$.

Do Exercise 6.

Answer

6. $78\frac{4}{7}$ km^2

EXAMPLE 7 Find the area of this circle. Use 3.14 for π. Round to the nearest hundredth.

The diameter is 4.2 m; the radius is 4.2 m ÷ 2, or 2.1 m.

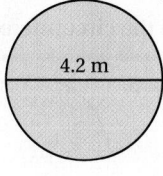

$$A = \pi \cdot r \cdot r$$
$$\approx 3.14 \times 2.1\,\text{m} \times 2.1\,\text{m}$$
$$= 3.14 \times 4.41\,\text{m}^2$$
$$= 13.8474\,\text{m}^2$$
$$\approx 13.85\,\text{m}^2$$

The area is about 13.85 m².

------------------------------ *Caution!* ------------------------------

Remember that circumference is always measured in linear units like ft, m, cm, yd, and so on. But area is measured in square units like ft², m², cm², yd², and so on.

Do Exercise 7.

7. Find the area of this circle. Use 3.14 for π. Round to the nearest hundredth.

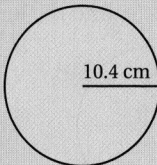

10.4 cm

(d) Solving Applied Problems

EXAMPLE 8 *Area of Pizza Pans.* How much larger is a pizza made in a 16-in.-square pizza pan than a pizza made in a 16-in.-diameter circular pan?

First, we make a drawing of each.

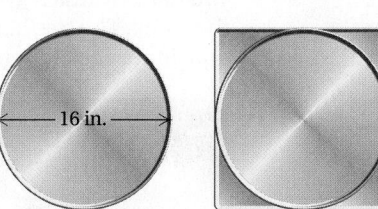

Then we compute areas.
The area of the square is

$$A = s \cdot s$$
$$= 16\,\text{in.} \times 16\,\text{in.} = 256\,\text{in}^2.$$

The diameter of the circle is 16 in., so the radius is 16 in./2, or 8 in. The area of the circle is

$$A = \pi \cdot r \cdot r$$
$$\approx 3.14 \times 8\,\text{in.} \times 8\,\text{in.} = 200.96\,\text{in}^2.$$

The square pizza is larger by about

$$256\,\text{in}^2 - 200.96\,\text{in}^2, \quad \text{or} \quad 55.04\,\text{in}^2.$$

Do Exercise 8.

8. Which is larger and by how much: a 10-ft-square flower bed or a 12-ft-diameter flower bed?

Answers

7. 339.62 cm²   **8.** 12-ft-diameter flower bed, by about 13.04 ft²

a, **b**, **c**   For each circle, find the length of a diameter, the circumference, and the area. Use $\frac{22}{7}$ for π.

1.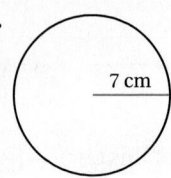
7 cm

2.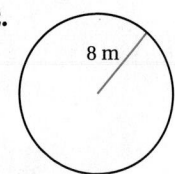
8 m

3.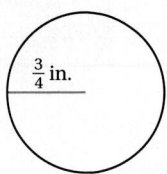
$\frac{3}{4}$ in.

4.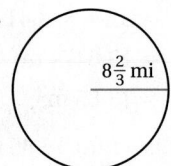
$8\frac{2}{3}$ mi

For each circle, find the length of a radius, the circumference, and the area. Use 3.14 for π.

5.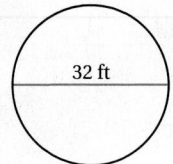
32 ft

6.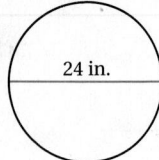
24 in.

7.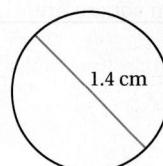
1.4 cm

8.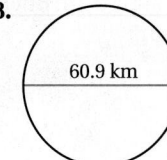
60.9 km

d   Solve. Use 3.14 for π.

9. *Treated Mosquito Net.*   The Adventure II treated mosquito net is perfect for the rural or tropic traveler. This net is circular with a radius of 6.37 ft. What is its diameter? its circumference? its area? Compare its area to that of the rectangular nets described in Example 10 of Section 6.3. How much larger is this net?

Source: www.travelhealthhelp.com/nets1.html

10. *Gypsy-Moth Tape.*   To protect a tree in your backyard, you need to attach gypsy moth caterpillar tape around the trunk. The tree has a 1.1-ft diameter. What length of tape is needed?

11. *Area of Pizza Pans.*   How much larger is a pizza made in a 12-in.-square pizza pan than a pizza made in a 12-in.-diameter circular pan?

12. *Penny.*   A penny has a 1-cm radius. What is its diameter? its circumference? its area?

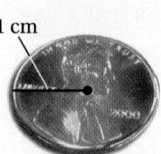
1 cm

Copyright © 2012 Pearson Education, Inc.

13. *Earth.*   The diameter of the earth at the equator is 7926.41 mi. What is the circumference of the earth at the equator?

14. *Dimensions of a Quarter.*   The circumference of a quarter is 7.85 cm. What is the diameter? the radius? the area?

15. *Circumference of a Baseball Bat.*   In Major League Baseball, the diameter of the barrel of a bat cannot be more than $2\frac{3}{4}$ in., and the diameter of the bat handle can be no thinner than $\frac{16}{19}$ in. Find the maximum circumference of the barrel of a bat and the minimum circumference of the bat handle. Use $\frac{22}{7}$ for π.
Source: Major League Baseball

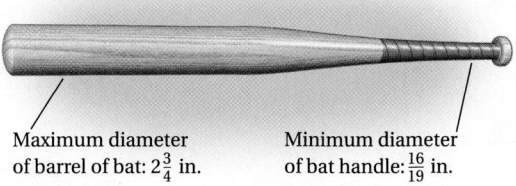

Maximum diameter
of barrel of bat: $2\frac{3}{4}$ in.

Minimum diameter
of bat handle: $\frac{16}{19}$ in.

16. *Trampoline.*   The standard backyard trampoline has a diameter of 14 ft. What is its area?
Source: International Trampoline Industry Association, Inc.

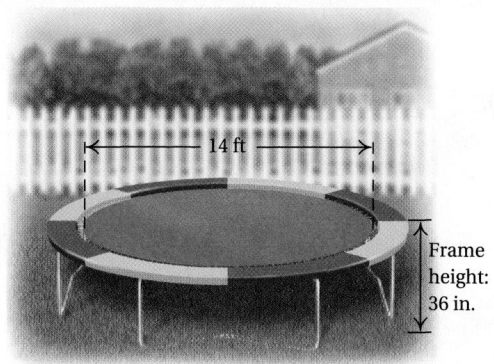

14 ft

Frame
height:
36 in.

17. *Swimming-Pool Walk.*   You want to install a 1-yd-wide walk around a circular swimming pool. The diameter of the pool is 20 yd. What is the area of the walk?

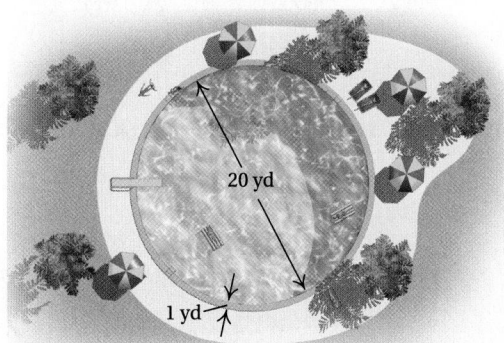

20 yd

1 yd

18. *Roller-Rink Floor.*   A roller-rink floor is shown below. Each end is a semicircle. What is its area? If hardwood flooring costs $32.50 per square meter, how much will the flooring cost?

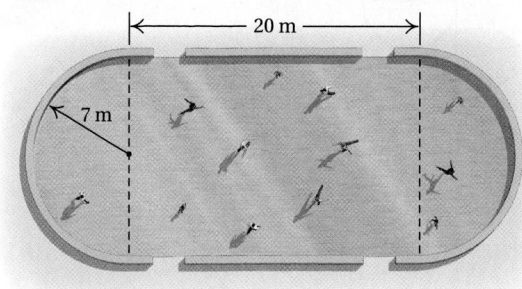

20 m

7 m

Find the perimeter of each figure. Use 3.14 for π.

19.

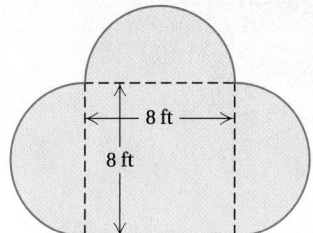

8 ft

8 ft

20.

4 cm   4 cm

4 cm

21.

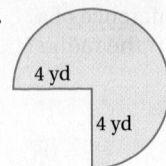

22.

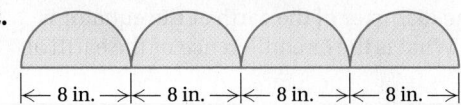

23.

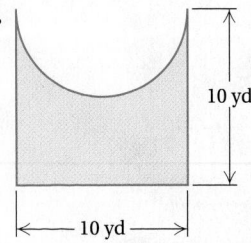

24.

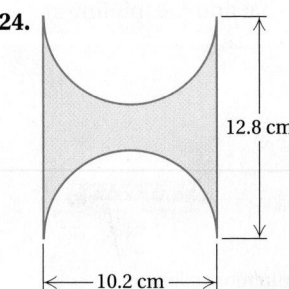

Find the area of the shaded region in each figure. Use 3.14 for π.

25.

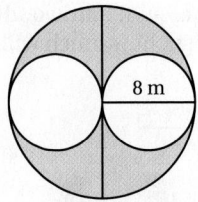

26.

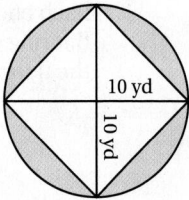

27.

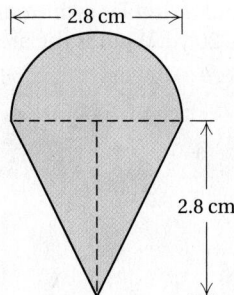

28.

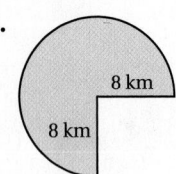

29.

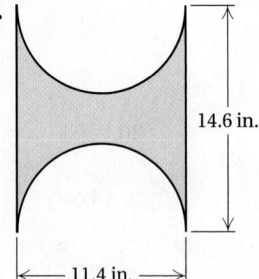

30.

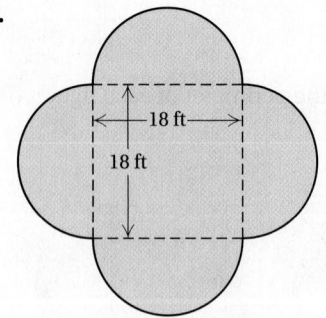

Copyright © 2012 Pearson Education, Inc.

Skill Maintenance

Evaluate. [1.6b]

31. 2^4 **32.** 17^2

Convert to percent notation. [4.3a]

33. $\dfrac{3}{8}$ **34.** $\dfrac{2}{3}$

35. The weight of a human brain is 2.5% of total body weight. A person weighs 200 lb. What does the brain weigh? [4.6a]

36. Jack's commission is increased according to how much he sells. He receives a commission of 6% for the first $3000 and 10% on the amount over $3000. What is the total commission on sales of $8500? [4.7b]

Synthesis

Comparing Perimeters and Fencing Costs. An **acre** is a unit of area that is defined to be 43,560 ft². A farmer needs to fence an acre of land. She is using 32-in. fencing that costs $149.99 for a 330-ft roll. Complete the following table for Exercises 37–41 and then use the data to answer Exercise 42. Use 3.14 for π.

	FIGURE	AREA	PERIMETER OR CIRCUMFERENCE	COST OF FENCING
37.	75 ft / 580.8 ft			
38.	100 ft / 435.6 ft			
39.	117.83 ft			
40.	208.71 ft / 208.71 ft			
41.	180 ft / 242 ft			

42. Which dimensions of the acre yield the fence with **(a)** the shortest perimeter? **(b)** the least area? **(c)** the lowest cost and the largest area?

Mid-Chapter Review

Concept Reinforcement

Determine whether each statement is true or false.

_____ **1.** The area of a parallelogram with base 8 cm and height 5 cm is the same as the area of a rectangle with length 8 cm and width 5 cm. [6.3a]

_____ **2.** The area of a square that is 4 in. on a side is less than the area of a circle whose radius is 4 in. [6.3a], [6.4c]

_____ **3.** The perimeter of a rectangle that is 6 ft by 3 ft is greater than the circumference of a circle whose radius is 3 ft. [6.2a], [6.4b]

_____ **4.** The exact value of the ratio C/d is π. [6.4b]

Guided Solutions

Fill in each blank with the number that creates a correct solution.

5. Find the area. [6.3b]

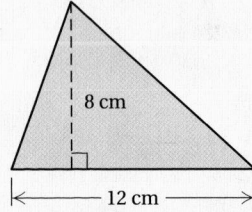

$A = \frac{1}{2} \cdot b \cdot h$

$A = \frac{1}{2} \cdot \square \text{ cm} \cdot \square \text{ cm}$

$A = \frac{\square \cdot \square}{2} \text{ cm}^{\square}$

$A = \frac{\square}{2} \text{ cm}^{\square}, \text{ or } \square \text{ cm}^{\square}$

6. Find the circumference and the area. Use 3.14 for π. [6.4b, c]

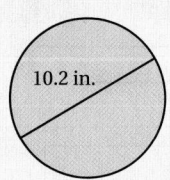
10.2 in.

$C = \pi \cdot d$
$C \approx \square \cdot \square \text{ in.}$
$C = \square \text{ in.}$

$A = \pi \cdot r \cdot r$
$A \approx \square \cdot \square \text{ in.} \cdot \square \text{ in.}$
$A = \square \text{ in}^{\square}$

Mixed Review

7. Find the sum of the angle measures of a 19-sided polygon. [6.1f]

8. Find the missing angle measure. [6.1f]

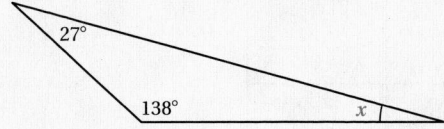

9. Classify the polygon by name. [6.1e]

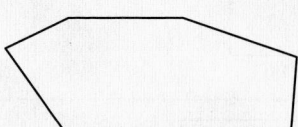

Classify each triangle as equilateral, isosceles, or scalene. Then classify it as right, obtuse, or acute. [6.1e]

10.
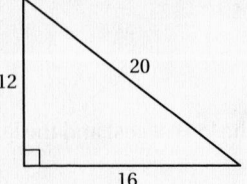

11.
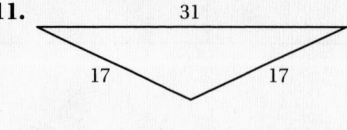

12.
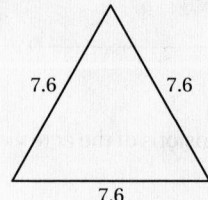

Copyright © 2012 Pearson Education, Inc.

13. Find the perimeter. [6.2a]

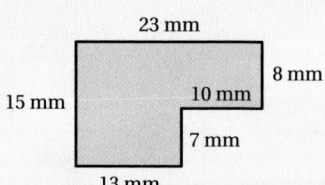

14. Find the perimeter and the area.
[6.2a], [6.3a]

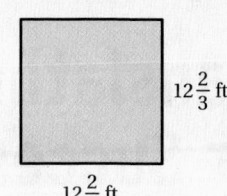

15. Find the area. [6.3b]

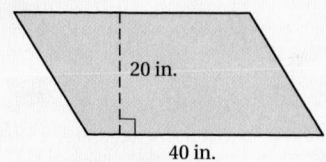

Find the area. [6.3b]

16.

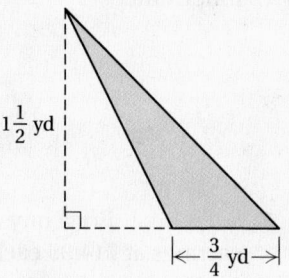

17.

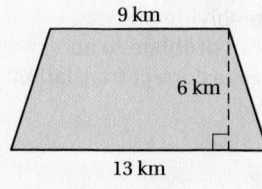

Find the circumference and the area. Use 3.14 for π. [6.4b, c]

18.

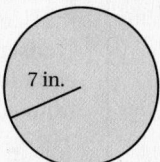

19.

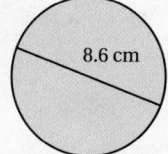

20. *Matching.* Match each item in the first column with the appropriate item in the second column by drawing connecting lines. Some expressions in the second column might be used more than once. Some expressions might not be used.
[6.2a], [6.3a, b], [6.4b, c]

Area of a circle with radius 4 ft

Area of a square with side 4 ft

Circumference of a circle with radius 4 ft

Area of a rectangle with length 8 ft and width 4 ft

Area of a triangle with base 4 ft and height 8 ft

Perimeter of a square with side 4 ft

Perimeter of a rectangle with length 8 ft and width 4 ft

24 ft

16 ft

$16 \cdot \pi$ ft^2

$8 \cdot \pi$ ft^2

32 ft^2

$4 \cdot \pi$ ft

$8 \cdot \pi$ ft

64 ft

16 ft^2

Understanding Through Discussion and Writing

21. Explain why a 16-in.-diameter pizza that costs $16.25 is a better buy than a 10-in.-diameter pizza that costs $7.85. [6.4d]

22. The length and the width of one rectangle are each three times the length and the width of another rectangle. Is the area of the first rectangle three times the area of the other rectangle? Why or why not? [6.3a]

23. The length of a side of a square is $\frac{1}{2}$ the length of a side of another square. Is the perimeter of the first square $\frac{1}{2}$ the perimeter of the other square? Why or why not? [6.2a]

24. Create for a fellow student a development of the formula
$$P = 2 \cdot (l + w) = 2 \cdot l + 2 \cdot w$$
for the perimeter of a rectangle. [6.2a]

25. Explain how the area of a triangle can be found by considering the area of a parallelogram. [6.3b]

26. The radius of one circle is twice the length of another circle's radius. Is the area of the first circle twice the area of the other circle? Why or why not? [6.4c]

Translating for Success

1. *Servings of Pork.* An 8-lb pork roast contains 37 servings of meat. How many pounds of pork would be needed for 55 servings?

2. *Height of a Ladder.* A 14.5-ft ladder leans against a house. The bottom of the ladder is 9.4 ft from the house. How high is the top of the ladder?

3. *Cruise Cost.* A group of 6 college students pays $4608 for a spring break cruise. What is each person's share?

4. *Sales Tax Rate.* The sales tax is $14.95 on the purchase of a new ladder that costs $299. What is the sales tax rate?

5. *Volume of a Sphere.* Find the volume of a sphere whose radius is 7.2 cm.

The goal of these matching questions is to practice step (2), *Translate*, of the five-step problem-solving process. Translate each word problem to an equation and select a correct translation from equations A–O.

A. $x = \dfrac{1}{3}\pi \cdot 6^2 \cdot (7.2)$

B. $6 \cdot x = \$4608$

C. $x = \dfrac{4}{3} \cdot \pi \cdot 6^2 \cdot (7.2)$

D. $x = \pi \cdot \left(5\dfrac{1}{2} \div 2\right)^2 \cdot 7$

E. $x = 6\% \times 5 \times \$14.95$

F. $x = \dfrac{1}{3}\pi\left(5\dfrac{1}{2}\right)^2$

G. $(9.4)^2 + x^2 = (14.5)^2$

H. $\$14.95 = x \cdot \$299$

I. $x = 2(14.5 + 9.4)$

J. $(9.4 + 14.5)^2 = x$

K. $\dfrac{8}{37} = \dfrac{x}{55}$

L. $x = 4(14.5 + 9.4)$

M. $x = 6 \cdot \$4608$

N. $8 \cdot 37 = 55 \cdot x$

O. $x = \dfrac{4}{3}\pi(7.2)^3$

Answers on page A-11

6. *Inheritance.* Six children each inherit $4608 from their mother's estate. What is the total inheritance?

7. *Sales Tax.* Erica buys 5 pairs of earrings at $14.95 each. The sales tax rate is 6%. How much sales tax will be charged?

8. *Volume of a Cone.* Find the volume of a circular cone with a 6-cm base radius and a height of 7.2 cm.

9. *Volume of a Storage Tank.* The diameter of a cylindrical grain-storage tank is $5\frac{1}{2}$ yd. Its height is 7 yd. Find its volume.

10. *Perimeter of a Photo.* A rectangular photo is 14.5 cm by 9.4 cm. What is the perimeter of the photo?

Summary and Review

Key Terms and Formulas

geometric figure, p. 390
segment, p. 390
ray, p. 390
line, p. 390
coplanar, p. 391
parallel lines, p. 391
intersecting lines, p. 391
angle, p. 391
vertex, p. 391
protractor, p. 392
right angle, p. 393
straight angle, p. 393
acute angle, p. 393
obtuse angle, p. 393
perpendicular lines, p. 394
polygon, pp. 394, 401
triangle, pp. 394, 408

equilateral triangle, p. 394
isosceles triangle, p. 394
scalene triangle, p. 394
right triangle, p. 394
obtuse triangle, p. 394
acute triangle, p. 394
perimeter, p. 401
rectangle, p. 401
square, p. 402
area, p. 406
parallelogram, p. 407
trapezoid, p. 409
circle, p. 417
diameter, p. 417
radius, p. 417
circumference, p. 418
pi (π), p. 418

volume, p. 428
rectangular solid, p. 428
surface area, p. 429
circular cylinder, p. 430
sphere, p. 431
circular cone, p. 432
complementary angles, p. 439
supplementary angles, p. 440
congruent, p. 441
vertical angles, p. 442
transversal, p. 443
corresponding angles, p. 443
interior angles, p. 444
alternate interior angles, p. 444
congruent triangles, p. 449
diagonal, p. 454
similar triangles, p. 462

Perimeter of a Rectangle:	$P = 2 \cdot (l + w)$, or $P = 2 \cdot l + 2 \cdot w$
Perimeter of a Square:	$P = 4 \cdot s$
Area of a Rectangle:	$A = l \cdot w$
Area of a Square:	$A = s \cdot s$, or $A = s^2$
Area of a Parallelogram:	$A = b \cdot h$
Area of a Triangle:	$A = \frac{1}{2} \cdot b \cdot h$
Area of a Trapezoid:	$A = \frac{1}{2} \cdot h \cdot (a + b)$
Radius and Diameter of a Circle:	$d = 2 \cdot r$, or $r = \dfrac{d}{2}$

Circumference of a Circle:	$C = \pi \cdot d$, or $C = 2 \cdot \pi \cdot r$
Area of a Circle:	$A = \pi \cdot r \cdot r$, or $A = \pi \cdot r^2$
Volume of a Rectangular Solid:	$V = l \cdot w \cdot h$
Surface Area of a Rectangular Solid:	$SA = 2lw + 2lh + 2wh$, or $2(lw + lh + wh)$
Volume of a Circular Cylinder:	$V = \pi \cdot r^2 \cdot h$
Volume of a Sphere:	$V = \frac{4}{3} \cdot \pi \cdot r^3$
Volume of a Cone:	$V = \frac{1}{3} \cdot \pi \cdot r^2 \cdot h$
Sum of Angle Measures of a Triangle:	$m\angle A + m\angle B + m\angle C = 180°$
Sum of Angle Measures of a Polygon:	$(n - 2) \cdot 180°$

Concept Reinforcement

Determine whether each statement is true or false.

_____ **1.** The acute angles of a right triangle are complementary. [6.1e], [6.6a]

_____ **2.** Two angles are supplementary if the sum of their measures is between 90° and 180°. [6.6a]

_____ **3.** The number π is greater than 3.14 and $\dfrac{22}{7}$. [6.4b]

_____ **4.** The volume of a sphere with diameter 6 ft is less than the volume of a rectangular solid that measures 6 ft by 6 ft by 6 ft. [6.5a, c]

_____ **5.** The measure of any obtuse angle is larger than the measure of any acute angle. [6.1c]

Important Concepts

Objective 6.1b   Name an angle in five different ways, and given an angle, measure it with a protractor.

Example   Name this angle in five different ways and measure it with a protractor.

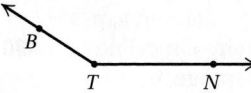

We can name this angle as

     angle *BTN*,   angle *NTB*,   ∠*BTN*,   ∠*NTB*,   or   ∠*T*.

The measure of the angle is 148°.

Practice Exercise

1. Name this angle in five different ways and measure it with a protractor.

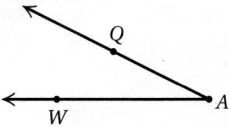

Objective 6.1c   Classify an angle as right, straight, acute, or obtuse.

Example   Classify each angle as right, straight, acute, or obtuse.

a)

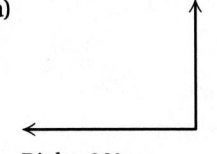

Right: 90°

b)

Obtuse: Greater than 90° and less than 180°

c)

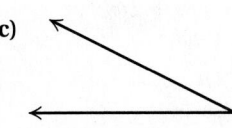

Acute: Greater than 0° and less than 90°

d)

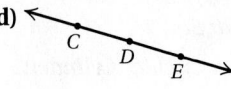

Straight: 180°

Practice Exercise

2. Classify each angle as right, straight, acute, or obtuse.

a)

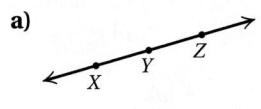

b)

c)

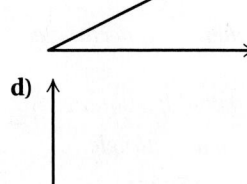

d)

Objective 6.1e   Classify a triangle as equilateral, isosceles, or scalene and as right, obtuse, or acute.

Example   Classify each triangle as equilateral, isosceles, or scalene. Then classify it as right, obtuse, or acute.

a)

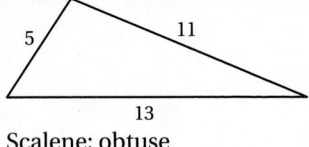

Scalene; obtuse

b)

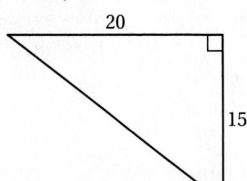

Scalene; right

c)

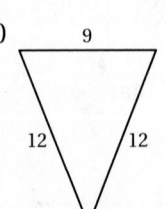

Isosceles; acute

d)

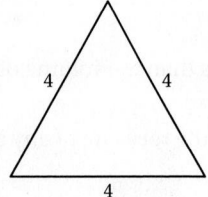

Equilateral; acute

Practice Exercise

3. Classify each triangle as equilateral, isosceles, or scalene. Then classify it as right, obtuse or acute.

a)

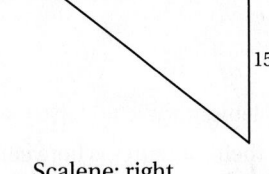

b)

c)

d)

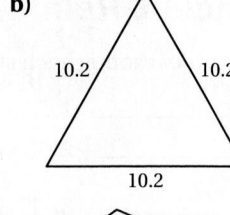

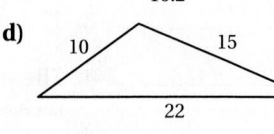

Objective 6.1f   Given two of the angle measures of a triangle, find the third.

Example   Find the missing angle measure.

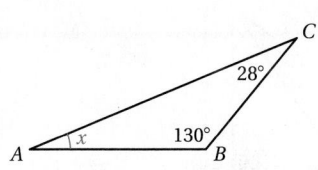

$$m\angle A + m\angle B + m\angle C = 180°$$
$$x + 130° + 28° = 180°$$
$$x + 158° = 180°$$
$$x = 180° - 158°$$
$$x = 22°$$

The measure of $\angle A$ is 22°.

Practice Exercise

4. Find the missing angle measure.

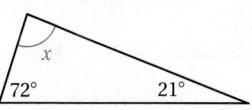

Objective 6.1f   Given a polygon of n sides, find the sum of its angle measures using the formula $(n - 2) \cdot 180°$.

Example   Find the sum of the angle measures of a 12-sided (dodecagon) polygon.

$$(n - 2) \cdot 180° = (12 - 2) \cdot 180° = 10 \cdot 180°$$
$$= 1800°$$

Practice Exercise

5. Find the sum of the angle measures of a 9-sided (nonagon) polygon.

Objectives 6.2a and 6.3a   Find the perimeter of a polygon. Find the area of a rectangle and a square.

Example   Find the perimeter and the area of this rectangle.

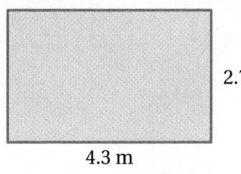

2.7 m

4.3 m

$$P = 2 \cdot (l + w)$$
$$= 2 \cdot (4.3\,\text{m} + 2.7\,\text{m})$$
$$= 2 \cdot (7\,\text{m})$$
$$= 14\,\text{m}$$
$$A = l \cdot w$$
$$= 4.3\,\text{m} \cdot 2.7\,\text{m}$$
$$= 11.61\,\text{m}^2$$

Practice Exercise

6. Find the perimeter and the area of this rectangle.

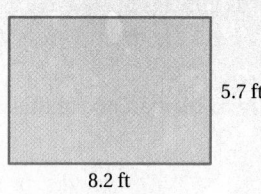

5.7 ft

8.2 ft

Objective 6.3b   Find the area of a parallelogram, a triangle, and a trapezoid.

Example   Find the area of this parallelogram.

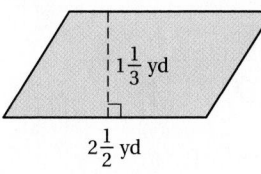

$1\frac{1}{3}$ yd

$2\frac{1}{2}$ yd

$$A = b \cdot h$$
$$= 2\frac{1}{2}\,\text{yd} \cdot 1\frac{1}{3}\,\text{yd}$$
$$= \frac{5}{2} \cdot \frac{4}{3} \cdot \text{yd} \cdot \text{yd}$$
$$= \frac{20}{6}\,\text{yd}^2$$
$$= \frac{10}{3}\,\text{yd}^2, \text{ or } 3\frac{1}{3}\,\text{yd}^2$$

Practice Exercises

7. Find the area of this parallelogram.

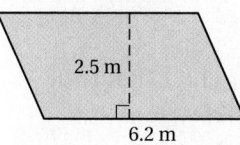

2.5 m

6.2 m

Objective 6.3b *(continued)*

Find the area of this triangle.

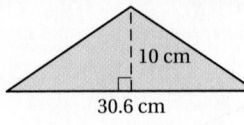

$$A = \frac{1}{2} \cdot b \cdot h$$

$$= \frac{1}{2} \cdot 30.6 \text{ cm} \cdot 10 \text{ cm}$$

$$= \frac{1}{2} \cdot 30.6 \cdot 10 \cdot \text{cm}^2$$

$$= 153 \text{ cm}^2$$

Find the area of this trapezoid.

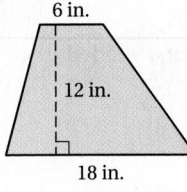

$$A = \frac{1}{2} \cdot h \cdot (a + b)$$

$$= \frac{1}{2} \times 12 \text{ in.} \times (6 \text{ in.} + 18 \text{ in.})$$

$$= \frac{1}{2} \times 12 \text{ in.} \times (24 \text{ in.})$$

$$= \frac{12 \times 24}{2} \text{ in}^2$$

$$= 144 \text{ in}^2$$

8. Find the area of this triangle.

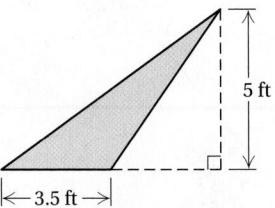

9. Find the area of this trapezoid.

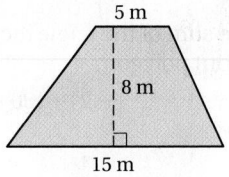

Objective 6.4b   Find the circumference of a circle given the length of a diameter or a radius.

Example   Find the circumference of this circle. Use 3.14 for π.

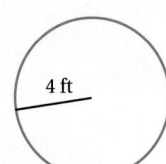

$$C = \pi \cdot d, \quad \text{or} \quad 2 \cdot \pi \cdot r$$

$$\approx 2 \times 3.14 \times 4 \text{ ft}$$

$$= 25.12 \text{ ft}$$

Practice Exercise

10. Find the circumference of this circle. Use 3.14 for π.

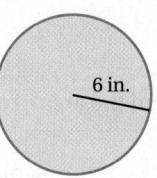

Objective 6.4c   Find the area of a circle given the length of a diameter or a radius.

Example   Find the area of this circle. Use $\frac{22}{7}$ for π.

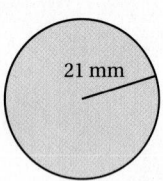

$$A = \pi \cdot r \cdot r, \quad \text{or} \quad \pi \cdot r^2$$

$$\approx \frac{22}{7} \cdot 21 \text{ mm} \cdot 21 \text{ mm}$$

$$= \frac{22 \cdot 21 \cdot 21}{7} \text{ mm}^2$$

$$= 1386 \text{ mm}^2$$

Practice Exercise

11. Find the area of this circle. Use $\frac{22}{7}$ for π.

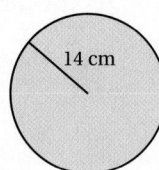

Review Exercises

Use a protractor to measure each angle.   [6.1b]

1.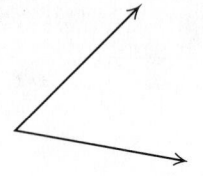

2.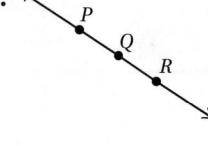

3.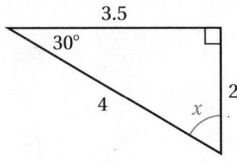

4.

5.–8. Classify each of the angles in Exercises 1–4 as right, straight, acute, or obtuse.   [6.1c]

Use the following triangle for Exercises 9–11.

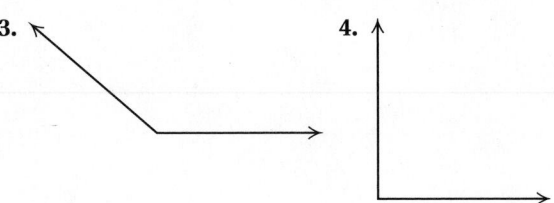

9. Find the missing angle measure.   [6.1f]

10. Classify the triangle as equilateral, isosceles, or scalene.   [6.1e]

11. Classify the triangle as right, obtuse, or acute.   [6.1e]

12. Find the sum of the angle measures of a hexagon.   [6.1f]

Find the perimeter.   [6.2a]

13.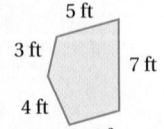

14.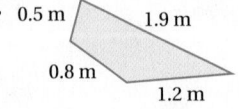

15. *Tennis Court.*   The dimensions of a standard-sized tennis court are 78 ft by 36 ft. Find the perimeter and the area of the tennis court.   [6.2b], [6.3c]

Find the perimeter and the area.   [6.2a], [6.3a]

16.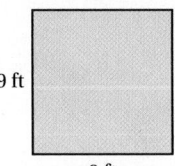

17.

7 cm

1.8 cm

Find the area.   [6.3b]

18.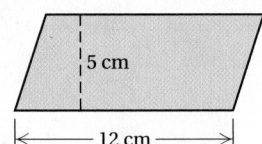

19.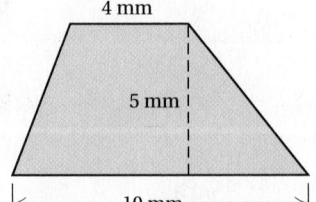

Copyright © 2012 Pearson Education, Inc.

20.

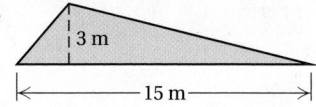

21.

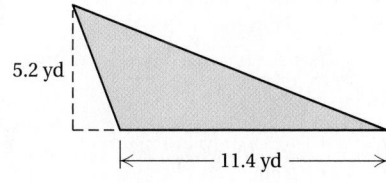

22.

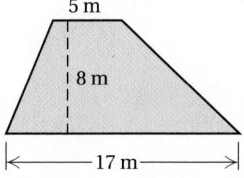

23.

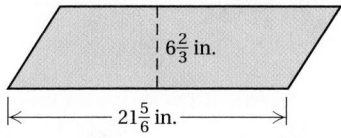

24. *Seeded Area.* A grassy area is to be seeded around three sides of a building and has equal width on the three sides, as shown below. What is the area of the seeded area? [6.3c]

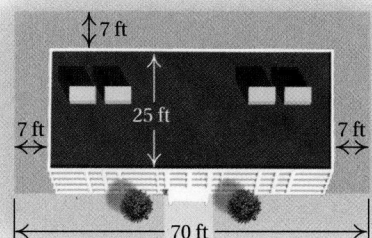

Find the length of a radius of each circle. [6.4a]

25.

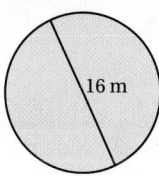

26.

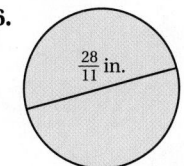

Find the length of a diameter of each circle. [6.4a]

27.

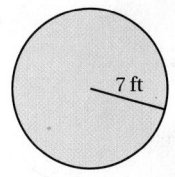

28.

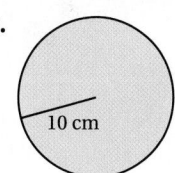

29. Find the circumference of the circle in Exercise 25. Use 3.14 for π. [6.4b]

30. Find the circumference of the circle in Exercise 26. Use $\frac{22}{7}$ for π. [6.4b]

31. Find the area of the circle in Exercise 25. Use 3.14 for π. [6.4c]

32. Find the area of the circle in Exercise 26. Use $\frac{22}{7}$ for π.
[6.4c]

33. Find the area of the shaded region. Use 3.14 for π.
[6.4d]

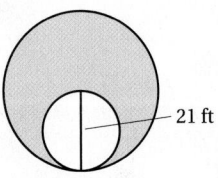

21 ft

34. A "Norman" window is designed with dimensions as shown. Find its area and its perimeter. Use 3.14 for π.
[6.4d]

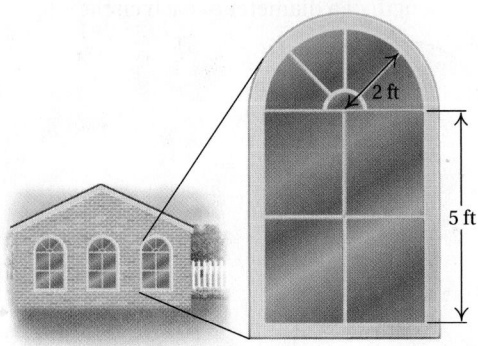

2 ft

5 ft

Find the volume and the surface area. [6.5a]

35.

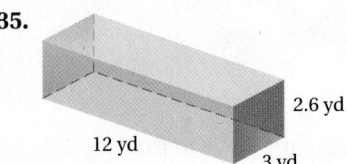

2.6 yd

12 yd

3 yd

36.

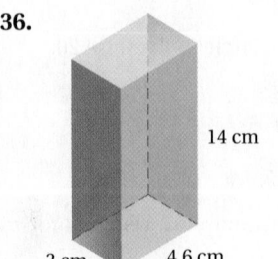

14 cm

3 cm   4.6 cm

Find the volume. Use 3.14 for π.

37.   [6.5b]

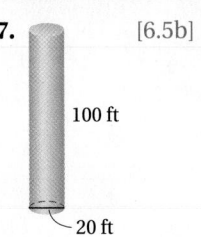

100 ft

20 ft

38.   [6.5c]

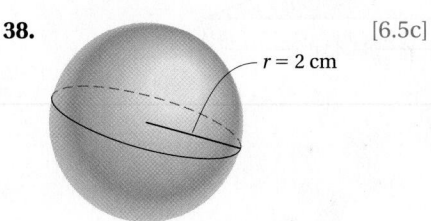

$r = 2$ cm

39.   [6.5d]

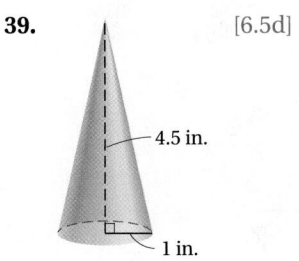

4.5 in.

1 in.

40.   [6.5b]

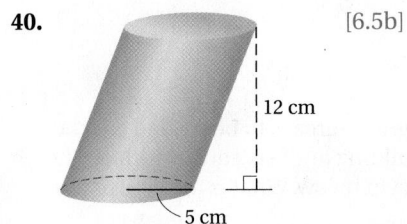

12 cm

5 cm

41. Find the measure of a complement of $\angle BAC$. [6.6a]

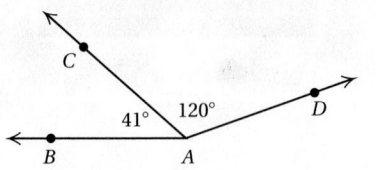

C

41°   120°   D

B   A

Copyright © 2012 Pearson Education, Inc.

Find the measure of a complement of an angle with the given measure. [6.6a]

42. 82°   **43.** 5°

Find the measure of a supplement of an angle with the given measure. [6.6a]

44. 33°   **45.** 133°

46. In this figure, $m\angle 1 = 38°$ and $m\angle 5 = 105°$. Find $m\angle 2$, $m\angle 3$, $m\angle 4$, and $m\angle 6$. [6.6c]

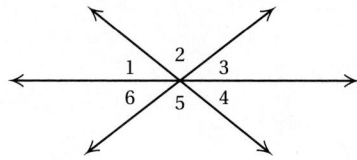

47. In this figure, identify **(a)** all pairs of corresponding angles, **(b)** all interior angles, and **(c)** all pairs of alternate interior angles. [6.6d]

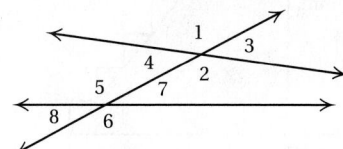

48. If $m \parallel n$ and $m\angle 4 = 135°$, what are the measures of the other angles? [6.6d]

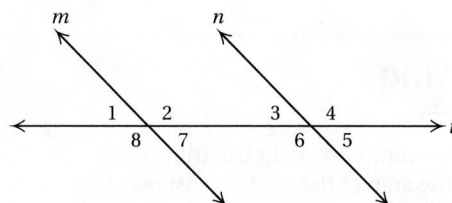

Name the corresponding parts of these congruent triangles. [6.7a]

49. $\triangle DHJ \cong \triangle RZK$

50.

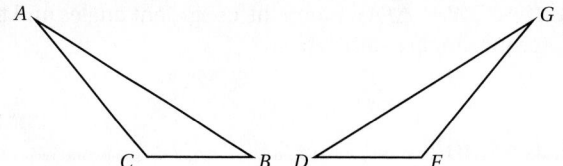

Which property (if any) should be used to show that the pair of triangles is congruent? [6.7a]

51.

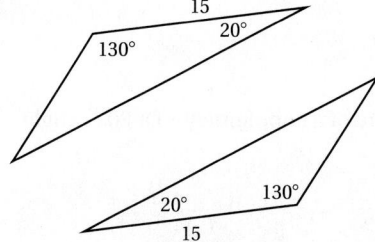

52.

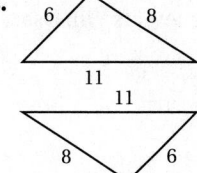

53.

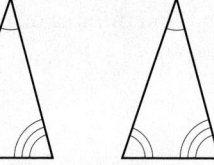

54. J is the midpoint of $\overline{IK}$ and $\overline{HI} \parallel \overline{KL}$. Explain why $\triangle JIH \cong \triangle JKL$. [6.7a]

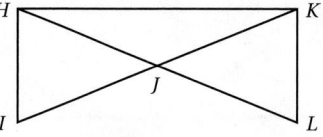

55. Find the measures of the angles and the lengths of the sides of this parallelogram. [6.7b]

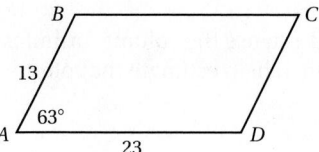

56. If $\triangle CQW \sim \triangle FAS$, name the congruent angles and the proportional sides. [6.8a]

57. If $\triangle NMO \sim \triangle STR$, find *MO*. [6.8b]

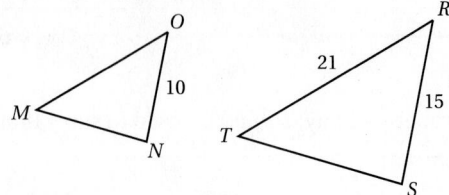

58. Find the measure of a supplement of a $20\frac{3}{4}°$ angle. [6.6a]

A. $339\frac{1}{4}°$ **B.** $159\frac{1}{4}°$

C. $69\frac{1}{4}°$ **D.** $70\frac{1}{4}°$

59. Find the area of a circle whose diameter is $\frac{7}{9}$ in. Use $\frac{22}{7}$ for π. [6.4c]

A. $\frac{11}{9}$ in^2 **B.** $\frac{77}{162}$ in^2

C. $\frac{22}{9}$ in^2 **D.** $\frac{154}{81}$ in^2

Synthesis

60. A square is cut in half so that the perimeter of the resulting rectangle is 30 ft. Find the area of the original square. [6.2a], [6.3a]

61. Find the area, in square meters, of the shaded region. [6.3c]

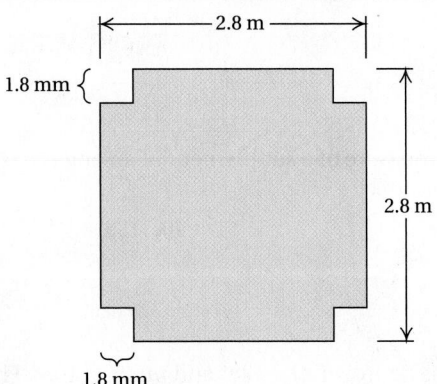

62. Find the area, in square centimeters, of the shaded region. [6.3c]

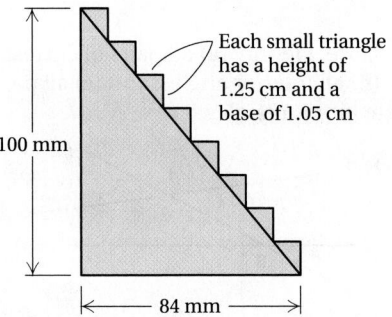

Each small triangle has a height of 1.25 cm and a base of 1.05 cm

Understanding Through Discussion and Writing

1. Explain a procedure that could be used to determine the measure of an angle's supplement from the measure of the angle's complement. [6.6a]

2. How could you use the volume formulas given in this section to help estimate the volume of an egg? [5.5a, b, c, e]

3. Describe the difference among linear, area, and volume units of measure. [6.2a], [6.3a], [6.5a]

4. Explain how you might use triangles to find the sum of the angle measures of this figure. [6.1f]

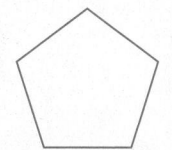

5. The design of a home includes a cylindrical tower that will be capped with either a 10-ft-high dome (half of a sphere) or a 10-ft-high cone. Which type of cap will be more energy-efficient and why? [6.5c, d]

6. Which occupies more volume: two spheres, each with radius r, or one sphere with radius $2r$? Explain why. [6.5c]

Copyright © 2012 Pearson Education, Inc.

CHAPTER
6

Test

For Extra Help

CHAPTER
Test Prep
VIDEOS

Step-by-step test solutions are found on the Chapter Test Prep Videos available via the Video Resources on DVD, in *MyMathLab*, and on You Tube (search "BittingerDevMath" and click on "Channels").

Use a protractor to measure each angle.

1.

2.

3.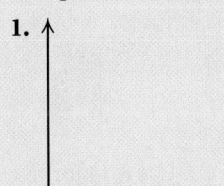

4.

5.–8. Classify each of the angles in Exercises 1–4 as right, straight, acute, or obtuse.

Use the following triangle for Exercises 9–11.

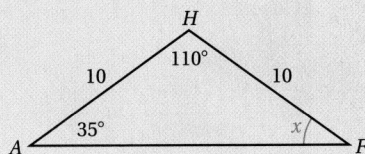

9. Find the missing angle measure.

10. Classify the triangle as equilateral, isosceles, or scalene.

11. Classify the triangle as right, obtuse, or acute.

12. Find the sum of the angle measures of a pentagon.

Find the perimeter and the area.

13.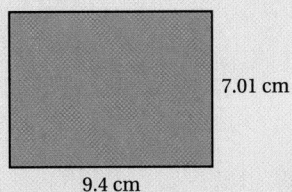

7.01 cm

9.4 cm

14.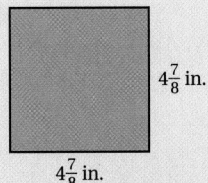

$4\frac{7}{8}$ in.

$4\frac{7}{8}$ in.

Find the area.

15.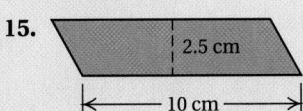

2.5 cm

10 cm

16.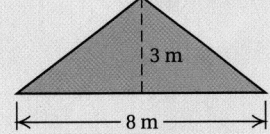

3 m

8 m

17.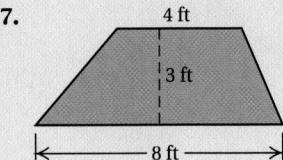

4 ft

3 ft

8 ft

18. Find the length of a diameter of this circle.

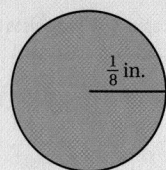

$\frac{1}{8}$ in.

19. Find the length of a radius of this circle.

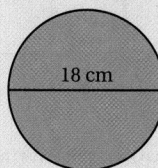

18 cm

20. Find the circumference of the circle in Exercise 18. Use $\frac{22}{7}$ for π.

21. Find the area of the circle in Exercise 19. Use 3.14 for π.

22. Find the perimeter and the area of the shaded region. Use 3.14 for π.

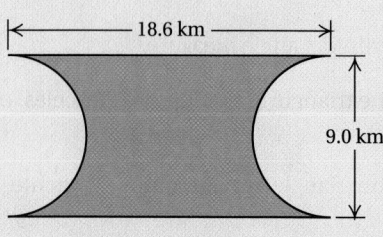

18.6 km

9.0 km

23. Find the volume and the surface area.

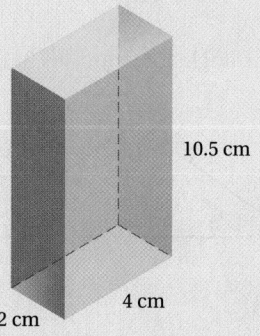

10.5 cm

4 cm

2 cm

24. A twelve-box rectangular carton of 12-oz juice boxes measures $10\frac{1}{2}$ in. by 8 in. by 5 in. What is the volume of the carton?

Find the volume. Use 3.14 for π.

25.

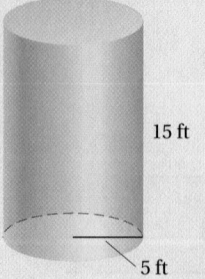

15 ft

5 ft

26.

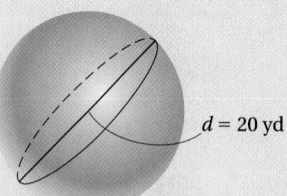

$d = 20$ yd

27.

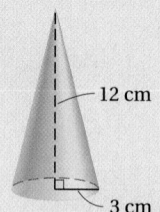

12 cm

3 cm

Copyright © 2012 Pearson Education, Inc.

28. Find the measure of a complement and a supplement of ∠CAD.

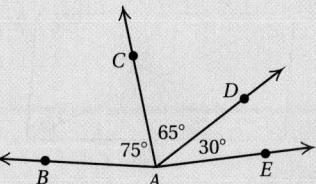

29. In the figure, $m\angle 1 = 62°$ and $m\angle 5 = 110°$. Find $m\angle 2$, $m\angle 3$, $m\angle 4$, and $m\angle 6$.

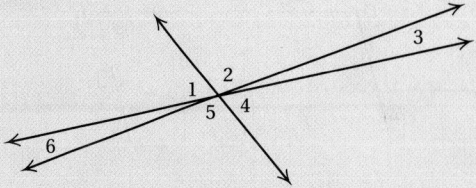

30. If $m \parallel n$ and $m\angle 4 = 120°$, what are the measures of the other angles?

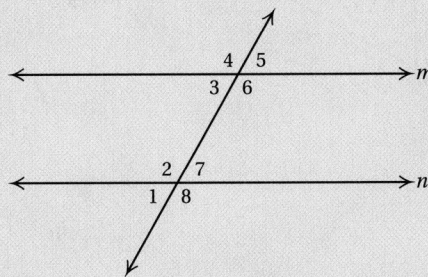

31. Name the corresponding parts of these congruent triangles: $\triangle CWS \cong \triangle ATZ$.

Which property (if any) would you use to show that $\triangle RST \cong \triangle DEF$ with the given information?

32. $\overline{RS} \cong \overline{DE}$, $\overline{RT} \cong \overline{DF}$, and $\angle R \cong \angle D$

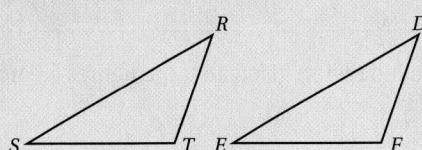

33. $\angle R \cong \angle D$, $\angle S \cong \angle E$, and $\angle T \cong \angle F$

34. $\overline{RS} \cong \overline{DE}$, $\angle R \cong \angle D$, and $\angle S \cong \angle E$

35. $\angle R \cong \angle D$, $\overline{RT} \cong \overline{DF}$, and $\overline{ST} \cong \overline{EF}$

36. The perimeter of □*DEFG* is 62. Find the measures of the angles and the lengths of the sides.

37. In □*JKLM*, *JN* = 3.2 and *KN* = 3. Find the lengths of the diagonals, $\overline{LJ}$ and $\overline{KM}$.

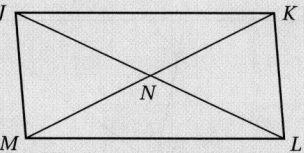

38. If △*ERS* ∼ △*TGF*, name the congruent angles and the proportional sides.

39. If △*GTR* ∼ △*ZEK*, find *EK* and *ZK*.

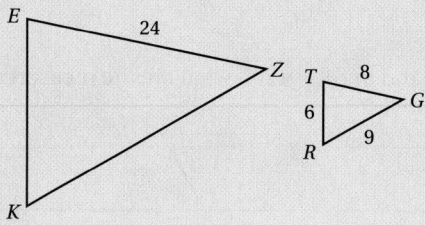

40. Find the volume of a sphere whose diameter is 42 cm. Use $\frac{22}{7}$ for π.

A. 310, 464 cm^3 **B.** 9702 cm^3
C. 1848 cm^3 **D.** 38,808 cm^3

Synthesis

Find the area of the shaded region. (Note that the figures are not drawn in perfect proportion.) Give the answer in square feet.

41.

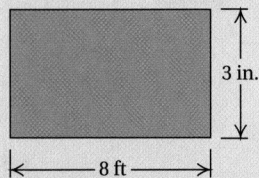

42.

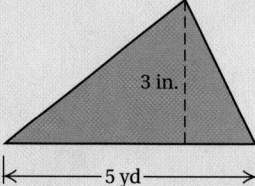

Find the volume of the solid. (Note that the solids are not drawn in perfect proportion.) Give the answer in cubic feet. Use 3.14 for π and round to the nearest thousandth in Exercises 44 and 45.

43.

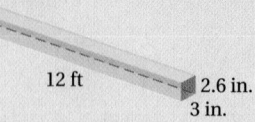

44.

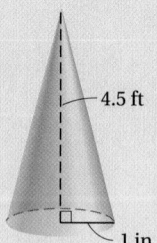

45.

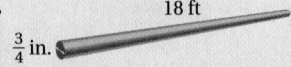

Copyright © 2012 Pearson Education, Inc.

Introduction to Real Numbers and Algebraic Expressions

Real-World Application

The tallest mountain in the world, when measured from base to peak, is Mauna Kea (White Mountain) in Hawaii. From its base 19,684 ft below sea level in the Hawaiian Trough, it rises 33,480 ft. What is the elevation of the peak above sea level?

Source: The Guinness Book of Records

This problem appears as Exercise 71 in Exercise Set 7.3.

7.1

Introduction to Algebra

OBJECTIVES

a Evaluate algebraic expressions by substitution.

b Translate phrases to algebraic expressions.

The study of algebra involves the use of equations to solve problems. Equations are constructed from algebraic expressions. The purpose of this section is to introduce you to the types of expressions encountered in algebra.

a Evaluating Algebraic Expressions

In arithmetic, you have worked with expressions such as

$$49 + 75, \quad 8 \times 6.07, \quad 29 - 14, \quad \text{and} \quad \frac{5}{6}.$$

In algebra, we can use letters to represent numbers and work with *algebraic expressions* such as

$$x + 75, \quad 8 \times y, \quad 29 - t, \quad \text{and} \quad \frac{a}{b}.$$

Sometimes a letter can represent various numbers. In that case, we call the letter a **variable**. Let a = your age. Then a is a variable since a changes from year to year. Sometimes a letter can stand for just one number. In that case, we call the letter a **constant**. Let b = your date of birth. Then b is a constant.

Where do algebraic expressions occur? Most often we encounter them when we are solving applied problems. For example, consider the bar graph shown at left, one that we might find in a book or a magazine. Suppose we want to know how much higher Mt. McKinley is than Mt. Evans. Using arithmetic, we might simply subtract. But let's see how we can determine this using algebra. We translate the problem into a statement of equality, an equation. It could be done as follows:

Height of Mt. Evans	plus	How much more	is	Height of Mt. McKinley
14,264	+	x	=	20,320.

Note that we have an algebraic expression, $14{,}264 + x$, on the left of the equals sign. To find the number x, we can subtract 14,264 on both sides of the equation:

$$14{,}264 + x = 20{,}320$$
$$14{,}264 + x - 14{,}264 = 20{,}320 - 14{,}264$$
$$x = 6056.$$

This value of x gives the answer, 6056 ft.

We call $14{,}264 + x$ an *algebraic expression* and $14{,}264 + x = 20{,}320$ an *algebraic equation*. Note that there is no equals sign, =, in an algebraic expression.

In arithmetic, you probably would do this subtraction without ever considering an equation. *In algebra, more complex problems are difficult to solve without first writing an equation.*

Do Exercise 1.

Mountain Peaks in the United States

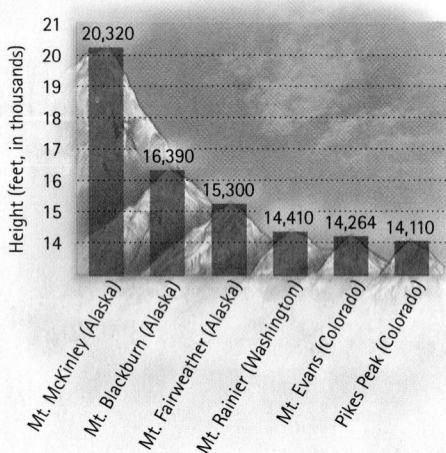

SOURCE: U.S. Department of the Interior, Geological Survey

1. Translate this problem to an equation. Then solve the equation.

Mountain Peaks. There are 92 mountain peaks in the United States that are higher than 14,000 ft. The bar graph above shows data for six of these. How much higher is Mt. Fairweather than Mt. Rainier?

Answer

1. $14{,}410 + x = 15{,}300$; 890 ft

An **algebraic expression** consists of variables, constants, numerals, operation signs, and/or grouping symbols. When we replace a variable with a number, we say that we are **substituting** for the variable. When we replace all of the variables in an expression with numbers and carry out the operations in the expression, we are **evaluating the expression**.

EXAMPLE 1 Evaluate $x + y$ when $x = 37$ and $y = 29$.

We substitute 37 for x and 29 for y and carry out the addition:

$$x + y = 37 + 29 = 66.$$

The number 66 is called the **value** of the expression when $x = 37$ and $y = 29$.

Algebraic expressions involving multiplication can be written in several ways. For example, "8 times a" can be written as

$$8 \times a, \quad 8 \cdot a, \quad 8(a), \quad \text{or simply} \quad 8a.$$

Two letters written together without an operation symbol, such as ab, also indicate a multiplication.

2. Evaluate $a + b$ when $a = 38$ and $b = 26$.

3. Evaluate $x - y$ when $x = 57$ and $y = 29$.

4. Evaluate $4t$ when $t = 15$.

EXAMPLE 2 Evaluate $3y$ when $y = 14$.

$$3y = 3(14) = 42$$

Do Exercises 2–4.

EXAMPLE 3 *Area of a Rectangle.* The area A of a rectangle of length l and width w is given by the formula $A = lw$. Find the area when l is 24.5 in. and w is 16 in.

We substitute 24.5 in. for l and 16 in. for w and carry out the multiplication:

$$\begin{aligned} A = lw &= (24.5\text{ in.})(16\text{ in.}) \\ &= (24.5)(16)(\text{in.})(\text{in.}) \\ &= 392\text{ in}^2, \text{ or } 392 \text{ square inches.} \end{aligned}$$

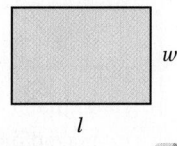

Do Exercise 5.

5. Find the area of a rectangle when l is 24 ft and w is 8 ft.

Algebraic expressions involving division can also be written in several ways. For example, "8 divided by t" can be written as

$$8 \div t, \quad \frac{8}{t}, \quad 8/t, \quad \text{or} \quad 8 \cdot \frac{1}{t},$$

where the fraction bar is a division symbol.

EXAMPLE 4 Evaluate $\dfrac{a}{b}$ when $a = 63$ and $b = 9$.

We substitute 63 for a and 9 for b and carry out the division:

$$\frac{a}{b} = \frac{63}{9} = 7.$$

EXAMPLE 5 Evaluate $\dfrac{12m}{n}$ when $m = 8$ and $n = 16$.

$$\frac{12m}{n} = \frac{12 \cdot 8}{16} = \frac{96}{16} = 6$$

Answers
2. 64 **3.** 28 **4.** 60 **5.** 192 ft^2

6. Evaluate a/b when $a = 200$ and $b = 8$.

7. Evaluate $10p/q$ when $p = 40$ and $q = 25$.

8. Motorcycle Travel. Find the time it takes to travel 660 mi if the speed is 55 mph.

To the student: At the front of the text, you will find a Student Organizer card. This pullout card will help you keep track of important dates and useful contact information. You can also use it to plan time for class, study, work, and relaxation. By managing your time wisely, you will provide yourself the best possible opportunity to be successful in this course.

Do Exercises 6 and 7.

EXAMPLE 6 *Motorcycle Travel.* Ed wants to travel 660 mi on his motorcycle on a particular day. The time t, in hours, that it takes to travel 660 mi is given by

$$t = \frac{660}{r},$$

where r is the speed of Ed's motorcycle. Find the time of travel if the speed r is 60 mph.

We substitute 60 for r and carry out the division:

$$t = \frac{660}{r} = \frac{660}{60} = 11 \text{ hr.}$$

Do Exercise 8.

(b) Translating to Algebraic Expressions

In algebra, we translate problems to equations. The different parts of an equation are translations of word phrases to algebraic expressions. It is easier to translate if we know that certain words often translate to certain operation symbols.

KEY WORDS, PHRASES, AND CONCEPTS

ADDITION (+)	SUBTRACTION (−)	MULTIPLICATION (·)	DIVISION (÷)
add	subtract	multiply	divide
added to	subtracted from	multiplied by	divided by
sum	difference	product	quotient
total	minus	times	
plus	less than	of	
more than	decreased by		
increased by	take away		

EXAMPLE 7 Translate to an algebraic expression:

Twice (or two times) some number.

Think of some number, say, 8. We can write 2 times 8 as 2×8, or $2 \cdot 8$. We multiplied by 2. Do the same thing using a variable. We can use any variable we wish, such as $x, y, m,$ or n. Let's use y to stand for some number. If we multiply by 2, we get an expression

$$y \times 2, \quad 2 \times y, \quad 2 \cdot y, \quad \text{or} \quad 2y.$$

In algebra, $2y$ is the expression generally used.

EXAMPLE 8 Translate to an algebraic expression:

Thirty-eight percent of some number.

Let $n =$ the number. The word "of" translates to a multiplication symbol, so we could write any of the following expressions as a translation:

$$38\% \cdot n, \quad 0.38 \times n, \quad \text{or} \quad 0.38n.$$

Answers

6. 25   **7.** 16   **8.** 12 hr

EXAMPLE 9 Translate to an algebraic expression:

Seven less than some number.

We let x represent the number. If the number were 10, then 7 less than 10 is $10 - 7$, or 3. If we knew the number to be 34, then 7 less than the number would be $34 - 7$. Thus if the number is x, then the translation is

$$x - 7.$$

Caution!

Note that $7 - x$ is *not* a correct translation of the expression in Example 9. The expression $7 - x$ is a translation of "seven minus some number" or "some number less than seven."

EXAMPLE 10 Translate to an algebraic expression:

Eighteen more than a number.

We let t = the number. Now if the number were 6, then the translation would be $6 + 18$, or $18 + 6$. If we knew the number to be 17, then the translation would be $17 + 18$, or $18 + 17$. If the number is t, then the translation is

$$t + 18, \quad \text{or} \quad 18 + t.$$

EXAMPLE 11 Translate to an algebraic expression:

A number divided by 5.

We let m = the number. Now if the number were 7, then the translation would be $7 \div 5$, or $7/5$, or $\frac{7}{5}$. If the number were 21, then the translation would be $21 \div 5$, or $21/5$, or $\frac{21}{5}$. If the number is m, then the translation is

$$m \div 5, \quad m/5, \quad \text{or} \quad \frac{m}{5}.$$

EXAMPLE 12 Translate each phrase to an algebraic expression.

PHRASE	ALGEBRAIC EXPRESSION
Five more than some number	$n + 5$, or $5 + n$
Half of a number	$\frac{1}{2}t$, $\frac{t}{2}$, or $t/2$
Five more than three times some number	$3p + 5$, or $5 + 3p$
The difference of two numbers	$x - y$
Six less than the product of two numbers	$mn - 6$
Seventy-six percent of some number	$76\%z$, or $0.76z$
Four less than twice some number	$2x - 4$

Do Exercises 9–17.

Translate each phrase to an algebraic expression.

9. Eight less than some number

10. Eight more than some number

11. Four less than some number

12. Half of some number

13. Six more than eight times some number

14. The difference of two numbers

15. Fifty-nine percent of some number

16. Two hundred less than the product of two numbers

17. The sum of two numbers

Answers

9. $x - 8$ 10. $y + 8$, or $8 + y$
11. $m - 4$ 12. $\frac{1}{2} \cdot p$, or $\frac{p}{2}$
13. $8x + 6$, or $6 + 8x$ 14. $a - b$
15. $59\%x$, or $0.59x$ 16. $xy - 200$
17. $p + q$

a Substitute to find values of the expressions in each of the following applied problems.

1. *Commuting Time.* It takes Erin 24 min less time to commute to work than it does George. Suppose that the variable x stands for the time it takes George to get to work. Then $x - 24$ stands for the time it takes Erin to get to work. How long does it take Erin to get to work if it takes George 56 min? 93 min? 105 min?

2. *Enrollment Costs.* At Emmett Community College, it costs $600 to enroll in the 8 A.M. section of Elementary Algebra. Suppose that the variable n stands for the number of students who enroll. Then $600n$ stands for the total amount of money collected for this course. How much is collected if 34 students enroll? 78 students? 250 students?

3. *Area of a Triangle.* The area A of a triangle with base b and height h is given by $A = \frac{1}{2}bh$. Find the area when $b = 45$ m (meters) and $h = 86$ m.

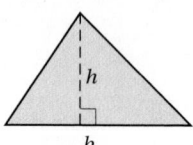

4. *Area of a Parallelogram.* The area A of a parallelogram with base b and height h is given by $A = bh$. Find the area of the parallelogram when the height is 15.4 cm (centimeters) and the base is 6.5 cm.

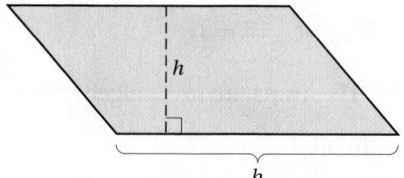

5. *Distance Traveled.* A driver who drives at a constant speed of r miles per hour for t hours will travel a distance of d miles given by $d = rt$ miles. How far will a driver travel at a speed of 65 mph for 4 hr?

6. *Simple Interest.* The simple interest I on a principal of P dollars at interest rate r for time t, in years, is given by $I = Prt$. Find the simple interest on a principal of $4800 at 9% for 2 years. (*Hint*: 9% = 0.09.)

7. *Hockey Goal.* The front of a regulation hockey goal is a rectangle that is 6 ft wide and 4 ft high. Find its area.

Source: National Hockey League

8. *Zoology.* A great white shark has triangular teeth. Each tooth measures about 5 cm across the base and has a height of 6 cm. Find the surface area of one side of one tooth. (See Exercise 3.)

Copyright © 2012 Pearson Education, Inc.

Evaluate.

9. $8x$, when $x = 7$

10. $6y$, when $y = 7$

11. $\dfrac{c}{d}$, when $c = 24$ and $d = 3$

12. $\dfrac{p}{q}$, when $p = 16$ and $q = 2$

13. $\dfrac{3p}{q}$, when $p = 2$ and $q = 6$

14. $\dfrac{5y}{z}$, when $y = 15$ and $z = 25$

15. $\dfrac{x + y}{5}$, when $x = 10$ and $y = 20$

16. $\dfrac{p + q}{2}$, when $p = 2$ and $q = 16$

17. $\dfrac{x - y}{8}$, when $x = 20$ and $y = 4$

18. $\dfrac{m - n}{5}$, when $m = 16$ and $n = 6$

b   Translate each phrase to an algebraic expression. Use any letter for the variable(s) unless directed otherwise.

19. Seven more than some number

20. Nine more than some number

21. Twelve less than some number

22. Fourteen less than some number

23. Some number increased by four

24. Some number increased by thirteen

25. b more than a

26. c more than d

27. x divided by y

28. c divided by h

29. x plus w

30. s added to t

31. m subtracted from n

32. p subtracted from q

33. The sum of two numbers

34. The sum of nine and some number

35. Twice some number

36. Three times some number

37. Three multiplied by some number

38. The product of eight and some number

39. Six more than four times some number

40. Two more than six times some number

41. Eight less than the product of two numbers

42. The product of two numbers minus seven

43. Five less than twice some number

44. Six less than seven times some number

45. Three times some number plus eleven

46. Some number times 8 plus 5

47. The sum of four times a number plus three times another number

48. Five times a number minus eight times another number

49. The product of 89% and your salary

50. 67% of the women attending

51. Your salary after a 5% salary increase if your salary before the increase was s

52. The price of a blouse after a 30% reduction if the price before the reduction was P

53. Danielle drove at a speed of 65 mph for t hours. How far did Danielle travel? (See Exercise 5.)

54. Dino drove his pickup truck at 55 mph for t hours. How far did he travel? (See Exercise 5.)

55. Lisa had $50 before spending x dollars on pizza. How much money remains?

56. Juan has d dollars before spending $29.95 on a DVD of the movie *Chicago*. How much did Juan have after the purchase?

57. Robert's part-time job pays $8.50 per hour. How much does he earn for working n hours?

58. Meredith pays her babysitter $10 per hour. What does it cost her to hire the sitter for m hours?

Skill Maintenance

Find the prime factorization.   [1.7d]

59. 54　　　　**60.** 32　　　　**61.** 108　　　　**62.** 192　　　　**63.** 1023

Find the LCM.   [1.9a]

64. 6, 18　　　　**65.** 6, 24, 32　　　　**66.** 10, 20, 30　　　　**67.** 16, 24, 32　　　　**68.** 18, 36, 44

Synthesis

Evaluate.

69. $\dfrac{a - 2b + c}{4b - a}$, when $a = 20, b = 10,$ and $c = 5$

70. $\dfrac{x}{y} - \dfrac{5}{x} + \dfrac{2}{y}$, when $x = 30$ and $y = 6$

71. $\dfrac{12 - c}{c + 12b}$, when $b = 1$ and $c = 12$

72. $\dfrac{2w - 3z}{7y}$, when $w = 5, y = 6,$ and $z = 1$

Copyright © 2012 Pearson Education, Inc.

7.2 The Real Numbers

A **set** is a collection of objects. (See Appendix E for more on sets.) For our purposes, we will most often be considering sets of numbers. One way to name a set uses what is called **roster notation**. For example, roster notation for the set containing the numbers 0, 2, and 5 is $\{0, 2, 5\}$.

Sets that are part of other sets are called **subsets**. In this section, we become acquainted with the set of *real numbers* and its various subsets.

Two important subsets of the real numbers are listed below using roster notation.

NATURAL NUMBERS

The set of **natural numbers** $= \{1, 2, 3, \ldots\}$. These are the numbers used for counting.

WHOLE NUMBERS

The set of **whole numbers** $= \{0, 1, 2, 3, \ldots\}$. This is the set of natural numbers and 0.

We can represent these sets on the number line. The natural numbers are to the right of zero. The whole numbers are the natural numbers and zero.

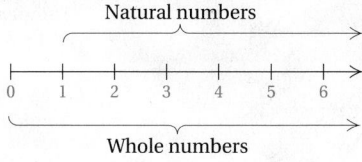

We create a new set, called the *integers*, by starting with the whole numbers, 0, 1, 2, 3, and so on. For each natural number 1, 2, 3, and so on, we obtain a new number to the left of zero on the number line:

For the number 1, there will be an *opposite* number -1 (negative 1).

For the number 2, there will be an *opposite* number -2 (negative 2).

For the number 3, there will be an *opposite* number -3 (negative 3), and so on.

The **integers** consist of the whole numbers and these new numbers.

INTEGERS

The set of **integers** $= \{\ldots, -5, -4, -3, -2, -1, 0, 1, 2, 3, 4, 5, \ldots\}$.

OBJECTIVES

a State the integer that corresponds to a real-world situation.

b Graph rational numbers on the number line.

c Convert from fraction notation for a rational number to decimal notation.

d Determine which of two real numbers is greater and indicate which, using < or >. Given an inequality like $a > b$, write another inequality with the same meaning. Determine whether an inequality like $-3 \leq 5$ is true or false.

e Find the absolute value of a real number.

We picture the integers on the number line as follows.

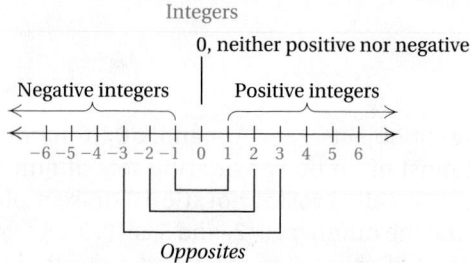

We call the integers to the left of zero **negative integers**. The natural numbers are also called **positive integers**. Zero is neither positive nor negative. We call −1 and 1 **opposites** of each other. Similarly, −2 and 2 are opposites, −3 and 3 are opposites, −100 and 100 are opposites, and 0 is its own opposite. Pairs of opposite numbers like −3 and 3 are the same distance from zero. The integers extend infinitely on the number line to the left and right of zero.

(a) Integers and the Real World

Integers correspond to many real-world problems and situations. The following examples will help you get ready to translate problem situations that involve integers to mathematical language.

EXAMPLE 1 Tell which integer corresponds to this situation: The temperature is 4 degrees below zero.

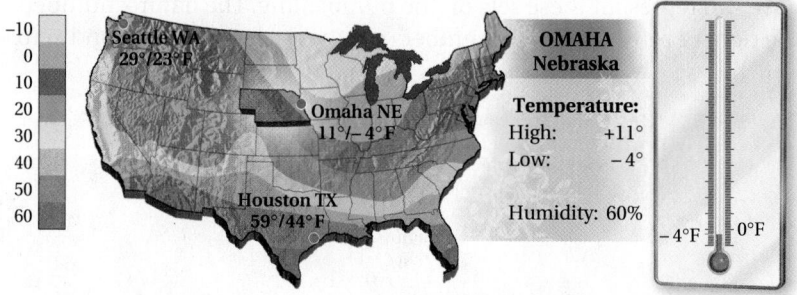

The integer −4 corresponds to the situation. The temperature is −4°.

EXAMPLE 2 *"Jeopardy."* Tell which integer corresponds to this situation: A contestant missed a $600 question on the television game show "Jeopardy."

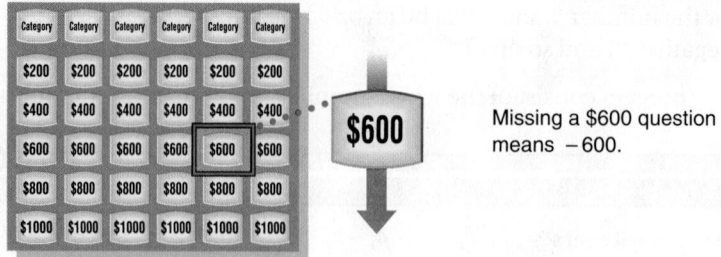

Missing a $600 question causes a $600 loss on the score—that is, the contestant earns −600 dollars.

EXAMPLE 3 *Elevation.* Tell which integer corresponds to this situation: The shores of California's largest lake, the Salton Sea, are 227 ft below sea level.

Source: Salton Sea Authority

The integer -227 corresponds to the situation. The elevation is -227 ft.

EXAMPLE 4 *Stock Price Change.* Tell which integers correspond to this situation: Hal owns a stock whose price decreased $16 per share over a recent period. He owns another stock whose price increased $2 per share over the same period.

The integer -16 corresponds to the decrease in the value of the first stock. The integer 2 represents the increase in the value of the second stock.

Do Exercises 1–5.

Tell which integers correspond to each situation.

1. **Temperature High and Low.** The highest recorded temperature in Nevada is 125°F on June 29, 1994, in Laughlin. The lowest recorded temperature in Nevada is 50°F below zero on January 8, 1937, in San Jacinto.
Source: National Climatic Data Center, Asheville, NC, and Storm Phillips, STORMFAX, INC.

2. **Stock Decrease.** The price of a stock decreased $3 per share over a recent period.

3. At 10 sec before liftoff, ignition occurs. At 148 sec after liftoff, the first stage is detached from the rocket.

4. The halfback gained 8 yd on first down. The quarterback was sacked for a 5-yd loss on second down.

5. A submarine dove 120 ft, rose 50 ft, and then dove 80 ft.

b) The Rational Numbers

We created the set of integers by obtaining a negative number for each natural number and also including 0. To create a larger number system, called the set of **rational numbers**, we consider quotients of integers with nonzero divisors. The following are some examples of rational numbers:

$$\frac{2}{3}, \quad -\frac{2}{3}, \quad \frac{7}{1}, \quad 4, \quad -3, \quad 0, \quad \frac{23}{-8}, \quad 2.4, \quad -0.17, \quad 10\frac{1}{2}.$$

The number $-\frac{2}{3}$ (read "negative two-thirds") can also be named $\frac{-2}{3}$ or $\frac{2}{-3}$; that is,

$$-\frac{a}{b} = \frac{-a}{b} = \frac{a}{-b}.$$

The number 2.4 can be named $\frac{24}{10}$ or $\frac{12}{5}$, and -0.17 can be named $-\frac{17}{100}$. We can describe the set of rational numbers as follows.

RATIONAL NUMBERS

The set of **rational numbers** = the set of numbers $\frac{a}{b}$,

where a and b are integers and b is not equal to 0 ($b \neq 0$).

Answers

1. 125; -50 2. The integer -3 corresponds to the decrease in the stock's value.
3. -10; 148 4. 8; -5 5. -120; 50; -80

Note that this new set of numbers, the rational numbers, contains the whole numbers, the integers, the arithmetic numbers (also called the non-negative rational numbers), and the negative rational numbers.

We picture the rational numbers on the number line as follows.

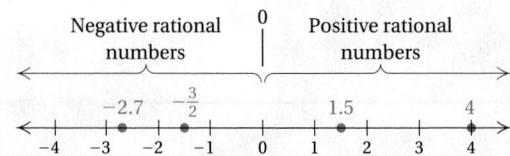

To **graph** a number means to find and mark its point on the number line. Some rational numbers are graphed in the preceding figure.

EXAMPLE 5   Graph: $\frac{5}{2}$.

The number $\frac{5}{2}$ can also be named $2\frac{1}{2}$, or 2.5. Its graph is halfway between 2 and 3.

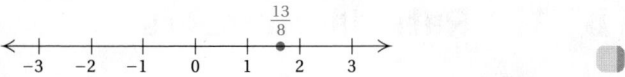

EXAMPLE 6   Graph: -3.2.

The graph of -3.2 is $\frac{2}{10}$ of the way from -3 to -4.

EXAMPLE 7   Graph: $\frac{13}{8}$.

The number $\frac{13}{8}$ can also be named $1\frac{5}{8}$, or 1.625. The graph is $\frac{5}{8}$ of the way from 1 to 2.

Do Exercises 6–8.

(c) Notation for Rational Numbers

Each rational number can be named using fraction notation or decimal notation.

EXAMPLE 8   Convert to decimal notation: $-\frac{5}{8}$.

We first find decimal notation for $\frac{5}{8}$. Since $\frac{5}{8}$ means $5 \div 8$, we divide.

$$
\begin{array}{r}
0.625 \\
8\overline{)5.000} \\
\underline{48} \\
20 \\
\underline{16} \\
40 \\
\underline{40} \\
0
\end{array}
$$

Thus, $\frac{5}{8} = 0.625$, so $-\frac{5}{8} = -0.625$.

Graph on the number line.

6. $-\frac{7}{2}$

7. 1.4

8. $-\frac{11}{4}$

Answers

6.
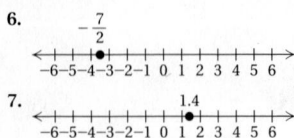

7.

8.

Decimal notation for $-\frac{5}{8}$ is -0.625. We consider -0.625 to be a **terminating decimal**. Decimal notation for some numbers repeats.

EXAMPLE 9 Convert to decimal notation: $\frac{7}{11}$.

$$
\begin{array}{r}
0.6\ 3\ 6\ 3\ \ldots \\
11\,\overline{)7.0\ 0\ 0\ 0} \\
\underline{6\ 6} \\
4\ 0 \\
\underline{3\ 3} \\
7\ 0 \\
\underline{6\ 6} \\
4\ 0 \\
\underline{3\ 3} \\
7
\end{array}
$$

Dividing

We can abbreviate **repeating decimal** notation by writing a bar over the repeating part—in this case, we write $0.\overline{63}$. Thus, $\frac{7}{11} = 0.\overline{63}$.

> Each rational number can be expressed in either terminating or repeating decimal notation.

The following are other examples showing how rational numbers can be named using fraction notation or decimal notation:

$$0 = \frac{0}{8}, \qquad \frac{27}{100} = 0.27, \qquad -8\frac{3}{4} = -8.75, \qquad -\frac{13}{6} = -2.1\overline{6}.$$

Do Exercises 9–11.

(d) The Real Numbers and Order

Every rational number has a point on the number line. However, there are some points on the line for which there is no rational number. These points correspond to what are called **irrational numbers**.

What kinds of numbers are irrational? One example is the number π, which is used in finding the area and the circumference of a circle: $A = \pi r^2$ and $C = 2\pi r$.

Another example of an irrational number is the square root of 2, named $\sqrt{2}$. It is the length of the diagonal of a square with sides of length 1. It is also the number that when multiplied by itself gives 2—that is, $\sqrt{2} \cdot \sqrt{2} = 2$. There is no rational number that can be multiplied by itself to get 2. But the following are rational *approximations*:

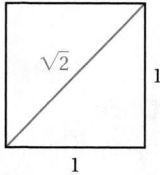

1.4 is an approximation of $\sqrt{2}$ because $(1.4)^2 = 1.96$;

1.41 is a better approximation because $(1.41)^2 = 1.9881$;

1.4142 is an even better approximation because $(1.4142)^2 = 1.99996164$.

We can find rational approximations for square roots using a calculator.

Find decimal notation.

9. $-\dfrac{3}{8}$

10. $-\dfrac{6}{11}$

11. $\dfrac{4}{3}$

Calculator Corner

Approximating Square Roots and π Square roots are found by pressing **2ND** **√**. ($\sqrt{}$ is the second operation associated with the **x²** key.)

To find an approximation for $\sqrt{48}$, we press **2ND** **√** **4** **8** **ENTER**. The approximation 6.92820323 is displayed.

To find $8 \cdot \sqrt{13}$, we press **8** **2ND** **√** **1** **3** **ENTER**. The approximation 28.8444102 is displayed. The number π is used widely enough to have its own key. (π is the second operation associated with the **^** key.)

To approximate π, we press **2ND** **π** **ENTER**. The approximation 3.141592654 is displayed.

Exercises: Approximate.

1. $\sqrt{76}$
2. $\sqrt{317}$
3. $15 \cdot \sqrt{20}$
4. $29 + \sqrt{42}$
5. π
6. $29 \cdot \pi$
7. $\pi \cdot 13^2$
8. $5 \cdot \pi + 8 \cdot \sqrt{237}$

Answers

9. -0.375 **10.** $-0.5\overline{4}$ **11.** $1.\overline{3}$

> Decimal notation for rational numbers *either* terminates *or* repeats.
>
> Decimal notation for irrational numbers *neither* terminates *nor* repeats.

Some other examples of irrational numbers are $\sqrt{3}, -\sqrt{8}, \sqrt{11}$, and $0.121221222122221\ldots$. Whenever we take the square root of a number that is not a perfect square, we will get an irrational number.

The rational numbers and the irrational numbers together correspond to all the points on the number line and make up what is called the **real-number system**.

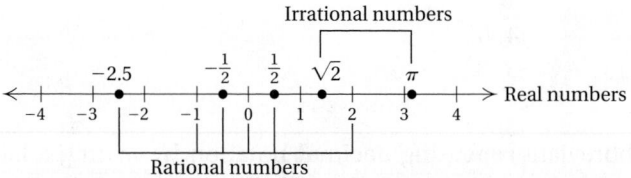

REAL NUMBERS

> The set of **real numbers** = The set of all numbers corresponding to points on the number line.

The real numbers consist of the rational numbers and the irrational numbers. The following figure shows the relationships among various kinds of numbers.

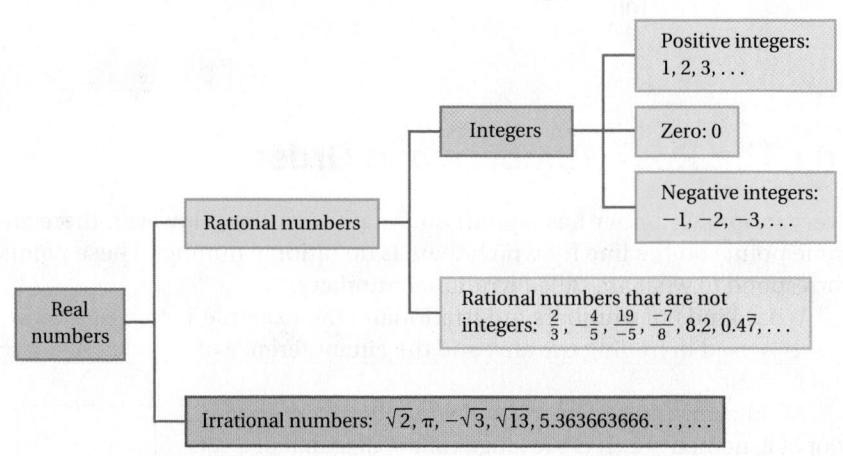

Order

Real numbers are named in order on the number line, increasing as we move from left to right. For any two numbers on the line, the one on the left is less than the one on the right.

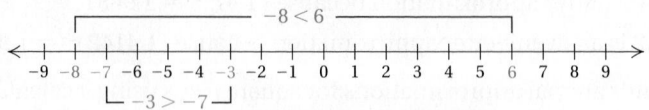

We use the symbol **<** to mean "**is less than**." The sentence $-8 < 6$ means "-8 is less than 6." The symbol **>** means "**is greater than**." The sentence $-3 > -7$ means "-3 is greater than -7." The sentences $-8 < 6$ and $-3 > -7$ are **inequalities**.

Calculator Corner

Negative Numbers on a Calculator; Converting to Decimal Notation We use the opposite key ⊖ to enter negative numbers on a graphing calculator. Note that this is different from the ⊖ key, which is used for the operation of subtraction. To convert $-\frac{5}{8}$ to decimal notation, as in Example 8, we press ⊖ ⑤ ÷ ⑧ ENTER. The result is -0.625.

```
-5/8
           -.625
```

Exercises: Convert each of the following negative numbers to decimal notation.

1. $-\dfrac{3}{4}$ 2. $-\dfrac{9}{20}$

3. $-\dfrac{1}{8}$ 4. $-\dfrac{9}{5}$

5. $-\dfrac{27}{40}$ 6. $-\dfrac{11}{16}$

7. $-\dfrac{7}{2}$ 8. $-\dfrac{19}{25}$

EXAMPLES Use either $<$ or $>$ for ☐ to write a true sentence.

10. $2 ☐ 9$ Since 2 is to the left of 9, 2 is less than 9, so $2 < 9$.

11. $-7 ☐ 3$ Since -7 is to the left of 3, we have $-7 < 3$.

12. $6 ☐ -12$ Since 6 is to the right of -12, then $6 > -12$.

13. $-18 ☐ -5$ Since -18 is to the left of -5, we have $-18 < -5$.

14. $-2.7 ☐ -\frac{3}{2}$ The answer is $-2.7 < -\frac{3}{2}$.

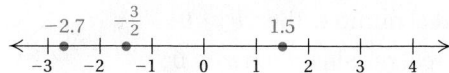

15. $1.5 ☐ -2.7$ The answer is $1.5 > -2.7$.

16. $1.38 ☐ 1.83$ The answer is $1.38 < 1.83$.

17. $-3.45 ☐ 1.32$ The answer is $-3.45 < 1.32$.

18. $-4 ☐ 0$ The answer is $-4 < 0$.

19. $5.8 ☐ 0$ The answer is $5.8 > 0$.

20. $\frac{5}{8} ☐ \frac{7}{11}$ We convert to decimal notation: $\frac{5}{8} = 0.625$ and $\frac{7}{11} = 0.6363\ldots$. Thus, $\frac{5}{8} < \frac{7}{11}$.

21. $-\frac{1}{2} ☐ -\frac{1}{3}$ The answer is $-\frac{1}{2} < -\frac{1}{3}$.

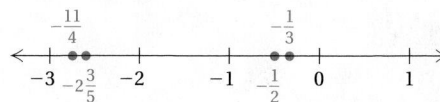

22. $-2\frac{3}{5} ☐ -\frac{11}{4}$ The answer is $-2\frac{3}{5} > -\frac{11}{4}$.

Do Exercises 12–19.

Note that both $-8 < 6$ and $6 > -8$ are true. Every true inequality yields another true inequality when we interchange the numbers or variables and reverse the direction of the inequality sign.

> **ORDER; $>$, $<$**
>
> $a < b$ also has the meaning $b > a$.

EXAMPLES Write another inequality with the same meaning.

23. $-3 > -8$ The inequality $-8 < -3$ has the same meaning.

24. $a < -5$ The inequality $-5 > a$ has the same meaning.

A helpful mental device is to think of an inequality sign as an "arrow" with the arrowhead pointing to the smaller number.

Do Exercises 20 and 21.

Use either $<$ or $>$ for ☐ to write a true sentence.

12. $-3 ☐ 7$

13. $-8 ☐ -5$

14. $7 ☐ -10$

15. $3.1 ☐ -9.5$

16. $-4.78 ☐ -5.01$

17. $-\frac{2}{3} ☐ -\frac{5}{9}$

18. $-\frac{11}{8} ☐ \frac{23}{15}$

19. $0 ☐ -9.9$

Write another inequality with the same meaning.

20. $-5 < 7$

21. $x > 4$

Answers

12. $<$ **13.** $<$ **14.** $>$ **15.** $>$ **16.** $>$
17. $<$ **18.** $<$ **19.** $>$ **20.** $7 > -5$
21. $4 < x$

Note that all positive real numbers are greater than zero and all negative real numbers are less than zero.

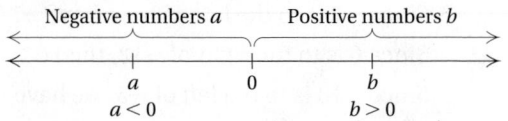

If b is a positive real number, then $b > 0$.
If a is a negative real number, then $a < 0$.

Expressions like $a \leq b$ and $b \geq a$ are also inequalities. We read $a \leq b$ as "a **is less than or equal to** b." We read $a \geq b$ as "a **is greater than or equal to** b."

EXAMPLES   Write true or false for each statement.

25. $-3 \leq 5.4$ True since $-3 < 5.4$ is true
26. $-3 \leq -3$ True since $-3 = -3$ is true
27. $-5 \geq 1\frac{2}{3}$ False since neither $-5 > 1\frac{2}{3}$ nor $-5 = 1\frac{2}{3}$ is true

Do Exercises 22–24.

e Absolute Value

From the number line, we see that numbers like 4 and -4 are the same distance from zero. Distance is always a nonnegative number. We call the distance of a number from zero on the number line the **absolute value** of the number.

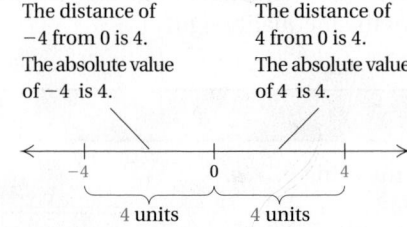

> **ABSOLUTE VALUE**
>
> The **absolute value** of a number is its distance from zero on the number line. We use the symbol $|x|$ to represent the absolute value of a number x.

Write true or false.
22. $-4 \leq -6$

23. $7.8 \geq 7.8$

24. $-2 \leq \frac{3}{8}$

Calculator Corner

Absolute Value   The absolute-value operation is the first item in the Catalog on the T1-84 Plus graphing calculator. To find $|-7|$, as in Example 28 on the following page, we first press **2ND** **CATALOG** **ENTER** to copy "abs(" to the home screen. (CATALOG is the second operation associated with the **0** numeric key.) Then we press **(-)** **7** **)** **ENTER**. The result is 7. To find $|-\frac{1}{2}|$ and express the result as a fraction, we press **2ND** **CATALOG** **ENTER** **(-)** **1** **÷** **2** **)** **MATH** **1** **ENTER**. The result is $\frac{1}{2}$.

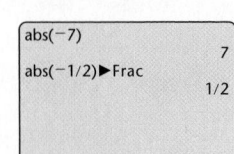

```
abs(-7)
                    7
abs(-1/2)►Frac
                  1/2
```

Exercises: Find the absolute value.

1. $|-5|$ **2.** $|17|$
3. $|0|$ **4.** $|6.48|$
5. $|-12.7|$ **6.** $|-0.9|$
7. $\left|-\dfrac{5}{7}\right|$ **8.** $\left|\dfrac{4}{3}\right|$

Answers
22. False   **23.** True   **24.** True

> **FINDING ABSOLUTE VALUE**
>
> **a)** If a number is negative, its absolute value is its opposite.
>
> **b)** If a number is positive or zero, its absolute value is the same as the number.

EXAMPLES Find the absolute value.

28. $|-7|$ The distance of -7 from 0 is 7, so $|-7| = 7$.

29. $|12|$ The distance of 12 from 0 is 12, so $|12| = 12$.

30. $|0|$ The distance of 0 from 0 is 0, so $|0| = 0$.

31. $\left|\frac{3}{2}\right| = \frac{3}{2}$

32. $|-2.73| = 2.73$

Do Exercises 25–28.

Find the absolute value.

25. $|8|$ **26.** $|-9|$

27. $\left|-\frac{2}{3}\right|$ **28.** $|5.6|$

STUDY TIPS

USING THIS TEXTBOOK

You will find many Study Tips throughout the book. An index of all Study Tips can be found on the Bittinger Student Organizer at the front of the book. One of the most important ways to improve your math study skills is to learn the proper use of the textbook. Here we highlight a few points that we consider most helpful.

- **Be sure to note the special symbols** (a), (b), (c), **and so on, that correspond to the objectives you are to be able to master.** The first time you see them is in the margin at the beginning of each section; the second time is in the subheadings of each section; and the third time is in the exercise set for the section. You will also find them referred to in the skill maintenance exercises in each exercise set, in the mid-chapter review, and in the review exercises at the end of the chapter, as well as in the answers to the chapter tests. These objective symbols allow you to refer to the appropriate place in the text whenever you need to review a topic.

- **Read and study each step of each example.** The examples include important side comments that explain each step. These carefully chosen examples and notes prepare you for success in the exercise set.

- **Stop and do the margin exercises as you study a section.** Doing the margin exercises is one of the most effective ways to enhance your ability to learn mathematics from this text. Don't deprive yourself of its benefits!

- **Note the icons listed at the top of each exercise set.** These refer to the many distinctive multimedia study aids that accompany the book.

- **Odd-numbered exercises.** Usually an instructor assigns some odd-numbered exercises. When you complete these, you can check your answers at the back of the book. If you miss any, check your work in the *Student's Solutions Manual* or ask your instructor for guidance.

- **Even-numbered exercises.** Whether or not your instructor assigns the even-numbered exercises, always do some on your own. Remember, there are no answers given for the class tests, so you need to practice doing exercises without answers. Check your answers later with a friend or your instructor.

Answers

25. 8   **26.** 9   **27.** $\frac{2}{3}$ **28.** 5.6

a State the integers that correspond to the situation.

1. *Death Valley.* With an elevation of 282 ft below sea level, Badwater Basin in California's Death Valley has the lowest elevation in the United States.
   Source: Desert USA

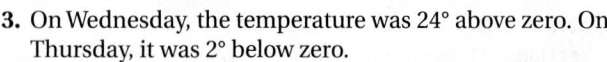

2. *Pollution Fine.* The Massey Energy Company, the nation's fourth largest coal producer, was fined $20 million for water pollution in 2008.
   Source: Environmental Protection Agency

3. On Wednesday, the temperature was 24° above zero. On Thursday, it was 2° below zero.

4. A student deposited her tax refund of $750 in a savings account. Two weeks later, she withdrew $125 to pay technology fees.

5. *Temperature Extremes.* The highest temperature ever created in a lab is 3,600,000,000°F. The lowest temperature ever created is approximately 460°F below zero.
   Sources: Live Science; Guinness Book of World Records

6. *Extreme Climate.* Verkhoyansk, a river port in northeast Siberia, has the most extreme climate on the planet. Its average monthly winter temperature is 58.5°F below zero, and its average monthly summer temperature is 56.5°F.
   Source: Guinness Book of World Records

7. In bowling, the Alley Cats are 34 pins behind the Strikers going into the last frame. Describe the situation of each team.

8. During a video game, Maggie intercepted a missile worth 20 points, lost a starship worth 150 points, and captured a landing base worth 300 points.

b Graph the number on the number line.

9. $\frac{10}{3}$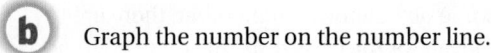

10. $-\frac{17}{4}$

11. -5.2

12. 4.78

13. $-4\frac{2}{5}$

14. $2\frac{6}{11}$

Copyright © 2012 Pearson Education, Inc.

c Convert to decimal notation.

15. $-\dfrac{7}{8}$

16. $-\dfrac{3}{16}$

17. $\dfrac{5}{6}$

18. $\dfrac{5}{3}$

19. $-\dfrac{7}{6}$

20. $-\dfrac{5}{12}$

21. $\dfrac{2}{3}$

22. $-\dfrac{11}{9}$

23. $\dfrac{1}{10}$

24. $\dfrac{1}{4}$

25. $-\dfrac{1}{2}$

26. $\dfrac{9}{8}$

27. $\dfrac{4}{25}$

28. $-\dfrac{7}{20}$

d Use either < or > for ☐ to write a true sentence.

29. 8 ☐ 0

30. 3 ☐ 0

31. −8 ☐ 3

32. 6 ☐ −6

33. −8 ☐ 8

34. 0 ☐ −9

35. −8 ☐ −5

36. −4 ☐ −3

37. −5 ☐ −11

38. −3 ☐ −4

39. −6 ☐ −5

40. −10 ☐ −14

41. 2.14 ☐ 1.24

42. −3.3 ☐ −2.2

43. −14.5 ☐ 0.011

44. 17.2 ☐ −1.67

45. −12.88 ☐ −6.45

46. −14.34 ☐ −17.88

47. $-\dfrac{1}{2}$ ☐ $-\dfrac{2}{3}$

48. $-\dfrac{5}{4}$ ☐ $-\dfrac{3}{4}$

49. $-\dfrac{2}{3}$ ☐ $\dfrac{1}{3}$

50. $\dfrac{3}{4}$ ☐ $-\dfrac{5}{4}$

51. $\dfrac{5}{12}$ ☐ $\dfrac{11}{25}$

52. $-\dfrac{13}{16}$ ☐ $-\dfrac{5}{9}$

Write an inequality with the same meaning.

53. $-6 > x$ **54.** $x < 8$ **55.** $-10 \le y$ **56.** $12 \ge t$

Write true or false.

57. $-5 \le -6$ **58.** $-7 \ge -10$ **59.** $4 \ge 4$ **60.** $7 \le 7$

61. $-3 \ge -11$ **62.** $-1 \le -5$ **63.** $0 \ge 8$ **64.** $-5 \le 7$

(e) Find the absolute value.

65. $|-3|$ **66.** $|-6|$ **67.** $|10|$ **68.** $|11|$ **69.** $|0|$

70. $|-2.7|$ **71.** $|-30.4|$ **72.** $|325|$ **73.** $\left|-\dfrac{2}{3}\right|$ **74.** $\left|-\dfrac{10}{7}\right|$

75. $\left|\dfrac{0}{4}\right|$ **76.** $|14.8|$ **77.** $|-2.65|$ **78.** $\left|-3\dfrac{5}{8}\right|$ **79.** $\left|-7\dfrac{4}{5}\right|$

Skill Maintenance

Convert to decimal notation.   [4.2b]

80. $23\dfrac{4}{5}\%$ **81.** 63% **82.** 22.76% **83.** 110%

Convert to percent notation.   [4.3a]

84. $\dfrac{5}{4}$ **85.** $\dfrac{13}{25}$ **86.** $\dfrac{19}{32}$ **87.** $\dfrac{5}{6}$

Synthesis

List in order from the least to the greatest.

88. $-\dfrac{2}{3}, \dfrac{1}{2}, -\dfrac{3}{4}, -\dfrac{5}{6}, \dfrac{3}{8}, \dfrac{1}{6}$

89. $\dfrac{2}{3}, -\dfrac{1}{7}, \dfrac{1}{3}, -\dfrac{2}{7}, -\dfrac{2}{3}, \dfrac{2}{5}, -\dfrac{1}{3}, -\dfrac{2}{5}, \dfrac{9}{8}$

90. $-5.16, -4.24, -8.76, 5.23, 1.85, -2.13$

91. $-8\dfrac{7}{8}, 7^1, -5, |-6|, 4, |3|, -8\dfrac{5}{8}, -100, 0, 1^7, \dfrac{14}{4}, -\dfrac{67}{8}$

Given that $0.\overline{3} = \frac{1}{3}$ and $0.\overline{6} = \frac{2}{3}$, express each of the following as a quotient or a ratio of two integers.

92. $0.\overline{1}$ **93.** $0.\overline{9}$ **94.** $5.\overline{5}$

Copyright © 2012 Pearson Education, Inc.

7.3

Addition of Real Numbers

In this section, we consider addition of real numbers. First, to gain an understanding, we add using the number line. Then we consider rules for addition.

OBJECTIVES

a Add real numbers without using the number line.

b Find the opposite, or additive inverse, of a real number.

c Solve applied problems involving addition of real numbers.

> **ADDITION ON THE NUMBER LINE**
>
> To do the addition $a + b$ on the number line, start at 0, move to a, and then move according to b.
>
> **a)** If b is positive, move from a to the right.
> **b)** If b is negative, move from a to the left.
> **c)** If b is 0, stay at a.

EXAMPLE 1 Add: $3 + (-5)$.

We start at 0 and move to 3. Then we move 5 units left since -5 is negative.

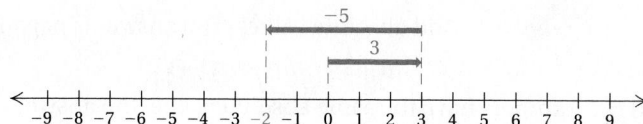

$3 + (-5) = -2$

EXAMPLE 2 Add: $-4 + (-3)$.

We start at 0 and move to -4. Then we move 3 units left since -3 is negative.

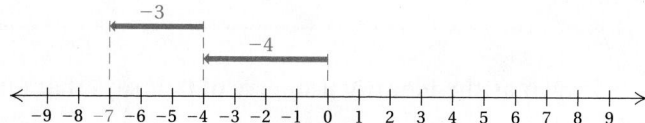

$-4 + (-3) = -7$

EXAMPLE 3 Add: $-4 + 9$.

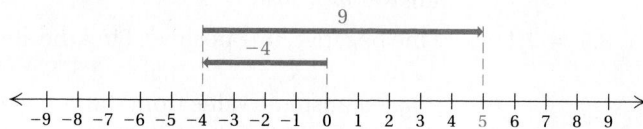

$-4 + 9 = 5$

STUDY TIPS

SMALL STEPS LEAD TO GREAT SUCCESS

What is your long-term goal for getting an education? How does math help you to attain that goal? As you begin this course, approach each short-term task, such as going to class, asking questions, using your time wisely, and doing your homework, as part of the framework of your long-term goal.

Add using the number line.

1. $0 + (-3)$

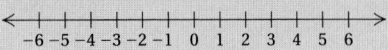

2. $1 + (-4)$

3. $-3 + (-2)$

4. $-3 + 7$

5. $-2.4 + 2.4$

6. $-\dfrac{5}{2} + \dfrac{1}{2}$

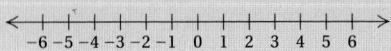

EXAMPLE 4 Add: $-5.2 + 0$.

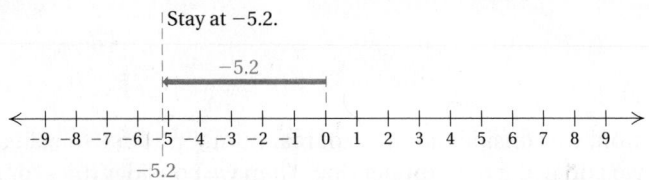

Stay at -5.2.

$-5.2 + 0 = -5.2$

Do Exercises 1–6.

(a) Adding Without the Number Line

You may have noticed some patterns in the preceding examples. These lead us to rules for adding without using the number line that are more efficient for adding larger numbers.

> **RULES FOR ADDITION OF REAL NUMBERS**
>
> 1. *Positive numbers*: Add the same as arithmetic numbers. The answer is positive.
> 2. *Negative numbers*: Add absolute values. The answer is negative.
> 3. *A positive number and a negative number*:
>   - If the numbers have the same absolute value, the answer is 0.
>   - If the numbers have different absolute values, subtract the smaller absolute value from the larger. Then:
>   a) If the positive number has the greater absolute value, the answer is positive.
>   b) If the negative number has the greater absolute value, the answer is negative.
> 4. *One number is zero*: The sum is the other number.

Rule 4 is known as the **identity property of 0.** It says that for any real number a, $a + 0 = a$.

EXAMPLES Add without using the number line.

5. $-12 + (-7) = -19$ Two negatives. Add the absolute values: $|-12| + |-7| = 12 + 7 = 19$. Make the answer *negative*: -19.

6. $-1.4 + 8.5 = 7.1$ One negative, one positive. Find the absolute values: $|-1.4| = 1.4$; $|8.5| = 8.5$. Subtract the smaller absolute value from the larger: $8.5 - 1.4 = 7.1$. The *positive* number, 8.5, has the larger absolute value, so the answer is *positive*: 7.1.

7. $-36 + 21 = -15$ One negative, one positive. Find the absolute values: $|-36| = 36$; $|21| = 21$. Subtract the smaller absolute value from the larger: $36 - 21 = 15$. The *negative* number, -36, has the larger absolute value, so the answer is *negative*: -15.

Answers

1. -3 2. -3 3. -5
4. 4 5. 0 6. -2

8. $1.5 + (-1.5) = 0$ The numbers have the same absolute value. The sum is 0.

9. $-\dfrac{7}{8} + 0 = -\dfrac{7}{8}$ One number is zero. The sum is $-\dfrac{7}{8}$.

10. $-9.2 + 3.1 = -6.1$

11. $-\dfrac{3}{2} + \dfrac{9}{2} = \dfrac{6}{2} = 3$

12. $-\dfrac{2}{3} + \dfrac{5}{8} = -\dfrac{16}{24} + \dfrac{15}{24} = -\dfrac{1}{24}$

> Do Exercises 7–20.

Suppose we want to add several numbers, some positive and some negative, as follows. How can we proceed?

$$15 + (-2) + 7 + 14 + (-5) + (-12)$$

We can change grouping and order as we please when adding. For instance, we can group the positive numbers together and the negative numbers together and add them separately. Then we add the two results.

EXAMPLE 13 Add: $15 + (-2) + 7 + 14 + (-5) + (-12)$.

a) $15 + 7 + 14 = 36$ Adding the positive numbers

b) $-2 + (-5) + (-12) = -19$ Adding the negative numbers

$36 + (-19) = 17$ Adding the results in (a) and (b)

We can also add the numbers in any other order we wish, say, from left to right as follows:

$$
\begin{aligned}
15 + (-2) + 7 + 14 + (-5) + (-12) &= 13 + 7 + 14 + (-5) + (-12) \\
&= 20 + 14 + (-5) + (-12) \\
&= 34 + (-5) + (-12) \\
&= 29 + (-12) \\
&= 17
\end{aligned}
$$

> Do Exercises 21–24.

(b) Opposites, or Additive Inverses

Suppose we add two numbers that are **opposites**, such as 6 and -6. The result is 0. When opposites are added, the result is always 0. Opposites are also called **additive inverses**. Every real number has an opposite, or additive inverse.

> **OPPOSITES, OR ADDITIVE INVERSES**
>
> Two numbers whose sum is 0 are called **opposites**, or **additive inverses**, of each other.

Add without using the number line.

7. $-5 + (-6)$ **8.** $-9 + (-3)$

9. $-4 + 6$ **10.** $-7 + 3$

11. $5 + (-7)$ **12.** $-20 + 20$

13. $-11 + (-11)$ **14.** $10 + (-7)$

15. $-0.17 + 0.7$ **16.** $-6.4 + 8.7$

17. $-4.5 + (-3.2)$

18. $-8.6 + 2.4$

19. $\dfrac{5}{9} + \left(-\dfrac{7}{9}\right)$

20. $-\dfrac{1}{5} + \left(-\dfrac{3}{4}\right)$

Add.

21. $(-15) + (-37) + 25 + 42 + (-59) + (-14)$

22. $42 + (-81) + (-28) + 24 + 18 + (-31)$

23. $-2.5 + (-10) + 6 + (-7.5)$

24. $-35 + 17 + 14 + (-27) + 31 + (-12)$

Answers

7. -11 **8.** -12 **9.** 2   **10.** -4
11. -2 **12.** 0   **13.** -22 **14.** 3
15. 0.53   **16.** 2.3   **17.** -7.7 **18.** -6.2
19. $-\dfrac{2}{9}$ **20.** $-\dfrac{19}{20}$ **21.** -58 **22.** -56
23. -14 **24.** -12

Find the opposite, or additive inverse, of each number.

25. −4   **26.** 8.7

27. −7.74   **28.** $-\dfrac{8}{9}$

29. 0   **30.** 12

EXAMPLES Find the opposite, or additive inverse, of each number.

14. 34   The opposite of 34 is -34 because $34 + (-34) = 0$.

15. −8   The opposite of -8 is 8 because $-8 + 8 = 0$.

16. 0   The opposite of 0 is 0 because $0 + 0 = 0$.

17. $-\dfrac{7}{8}$ The opposite of $-\dfrac{7}{8}$ is $\dfrac{7}{8}$ because $-\dfrac{7}{8} + \dfrac{7}{8} = 0$.

Do Exercises 25–30.

To name the opposite, we use the symbol −, as follows.

SYMBOLIZING OPPOSITES

The opposite, or additive inverse, of a number a can be named $-a$ (read "the opposite of a," or "the additive inverse of a").

Note that if we take a number, say, 8, and find its opposite, -8, and then find the opposite of the result, we will have the original number, 8, again.

THE OPPOSITE OF AN OPPOSITE

The **opposite of the opposite** of a number is the number itself. (The additive inverse of the additive inverse of a number is the number itself.) That is, for any number a,

$$-(-a) = a.$$

EXAMPLE 18 Evaluate $-x$ and $-(-x)$ when $x = 16$.

If $x = 16$, then $-x = -16$.   The opposite of 16 is -16.

If $x = 16$, then $-(-x) = -(-16) = 16$.   The opposite of the opposite of 16 is 16.

EXAMPLE 19 Evaluate $-x$ and $-(-x)$ when $x = -3$.

If $x = -3$, then $-x = -(-3) = 3$.

If $x = -3$, then $-(-x) = -(-(-3)) = -(3) = -3$.

Note that in Example 19 we used a second set of parentheses to show that we are substituting the negative number -3 for x. Symbolism like $--x$ is not considered meaningful.

Evaluate $-x$ and $-(-x)$ when:

31. $x = 14$.   **32.** $x = 1$.

33. $x = -19$.   **34.** $x = -1.6$.

35. $x = \dfrac{2}{3}$.   **36.** $x = -\dfrac{9}{8}$.

Do Exercises 31–36.

A symbol such as -8 is usually read "negative 8." It could be read "the additive inverse of 8," because the additive inverse of 8 is negative 8. It could also be read "the opposite of 8," because the opposite of 8 is -8. Thus a symbol like -8 can be read in more than one way. It is never correct to read -8 as "minus 8."

Caution!

A symbol like $-x$, which has a variable, should be read "the opposite of x" or "the additive inverse of x" and *not* "negative x," because we do not know whether x represents a positive number, a negative number, or 0. You can check this in Examples 18 and 19.

Answers

25. 4   **26.** −8.7   **27.** 7.74   **28.** $\dfrac{8}{9}$

29. 0   **30.** −12   **31.** −14; 14

32. −1; 1   **33.** 19; −19   **34.** 1.6; −1.6

35. $-\dfrac{2}{3}; \dfrac{2}{3}$ **36.** $\dfrac{9}{8}; -\dfrac{9}{8}$

We can use the symbolism $-a$ to restate the definition of opposite, or additive inverse.

> **OPPOSITES, OR ADDITIVE INVERSES**
>
> For any real number a, the **opposite**, or **additive inverse**, of a, denoted $-a$, is such that
> $$a + (-a) = (-a) + a = 0.$$

Signs of Numbers

A negative number is sometimes said to have a "negative sign." A positive number is said to have a "positive sign." When we replace a number with its opposite, we can say that we have "changed its sign."

EXAMPLES Find the opposite. (Change the sign.)

20. -3 $\quad -(-3) = 3$

21. $-\dfrac{2}{13}$ $\quad -\left(-\dfrac{2}{13}\right) = \dfrac{2}{13}$

22. 0 $\quad -(0) = 0$

23. 14 $\quad -(14) = -14$

Do Exercises 37–40.

Find the opposite. (Change the sign.)

37. -4

38. -13.4

39. 0

40. $\dfrac{1}{4}$

(c) Applications and Problem Solving

Addition of real numbers occurs in many real-world situations.

EXAMPLE 24 *Lake Level.* In the course of one four-month period, the water level of Lake Clearwater went down 2 ft, up 1 ft, down 5 ft, and up 3 ft. By how much had the lake level changed at the end of the four months?

We let $T =$ the total change in the level of the lake. Then the problem translates to a sum:

Total change	is	1st change	plus	2nd change	plus	3rd change	plus	4th change
T	$=$	-2	$+$	1	$+$	(-5)	$+$	$3.$

Adding from left to right, we have

$$T = -2 + 1 + (-5) + 3 = -1 + (-5) + 3$$
$$= -6 + 3$$
$$= -3.$$

The lake level had dropped 3 ft at the end of the four-month period.

Do Exercise 41.

41. Change in Class Size. During the first two weeks of the semester in Jim's algebra class, 4 students withdrew, 8 students enrolled late, and 6 students were dropped as "no shows." By how many students had the class size changed at the end of the first two weeks?

Answers

37. 4 **38.** 13.4 **39.** 0
40. $-\dfrac{1}{4}$ **41.** -2 students

a   Add. Do not use the number line except as a check.

1. $2 + (-9)$

2. $-5 + 2$

3. $-11 + 5$

4. $4 + (-3)$

5. $-6 + 6$

6. $8 + (-8)$

7. $-3 + (-5)$

8. $-4 + (-6)$

9. $-7 + 0$

10. $-13 + 0$

11. $0 + (-27)$

12. $0 + (-35)$

13. $17 + (-17)$

14. $-15 + 15$

15. $-17 + (-25)$

16. $-24 + (-17)$

17. $18 + (-18)$

18. $-13 + 13$

19. $-28 + 28$

20. $11 + (-11)$

21. $8 + (-5)$

22. $-7 + 8$

23. $-4 + (-5)$

24. $10 + (-12)$

25. $13 + (-6)$

26. $-3 + 14$

27. $-25 + 25$

28. $50 + (-50)$

29. $53 + (-18)$

30. $75 + (-45)$

31. $-8.5 + 4.7$

32. $-4.6 + 1.9$

33. $-2.8 + (-5.3)$

34. $-7.9 + (-6.5)$

35. $-\dfrac{3}{5} + \dfrac{2}{5}$

36. $-\dfrac{4}{3} + \dfrac{2}{3}$

37. $-\dfrac{2}{9} + \left(-\dfrac{5}{9}\right)$

38. $-\dfrac{4}{7} + \left(-\dfrac{6}{7}\right)$

39. $-\dfrac{5}{8} + \dfrac{1}{4}$

40. $-\dfrac{5}{6} + \dfrac{2}{3}$

41. $-\dfrac{5}{8} + \left(-\dfrac{1}{6}\right)$

42. $-\dfrac{5}{6} + \left(-\dfrac{2}{9}\right)$

43. $-\dfrac{3}{8} + \dfrac{5}{12}$

44. $-\dfrac{7}{16} + \dfrac{7}{8}$

45. $-\dfrac{1}{6} + \dfrac{7}{10}$

46. $-\dfrac{11}{18} + \left(-\dfrac{3}{4}\right)$

47. $\dfrac{7}{15} + \left(-\dfrac{1}{9}\right)$

48. $-\dfrac{4}{21} + \dfrac{3}{14}$

Copyright © 2012 Pearson Education, Inc.

49. $76 + (-15) + (-18) + (-6)$

50. $29 + (-45) + 18 + 32 + (-96)$

51. $-44 + \left(-\dfrac{3}{8}\right) + 95 + \left(-\dfrac{5}{8}\right)$

52. $24 + 3.1 + (-44) + (-8.2) + 63$

53. $98 + (-54) + 113 + (-998) + 44 + (-612)$

54. $-458 + (-124) + 1025 + (-917) + 218$

 Find the opposite, or additive inverse.

55. 24

56. -64

57. -26.9

58. 48.2

Evaluate $-x$ when:

59. $x = 8.$

60. $x = -27.$

61. $x = -\dfrac{13}{8}.$

62. $x = \dfrac{1}{236}.$

Evaluate $-(-x)$ when:

63. $x = -43.$

64. $x = 39.$

65. $x = \dfrac{4}{3}.$

66. $x = -7.1.$

Find the opposite. (Change the sign.)

67. -24

68. -12.3

69. $-\dfrac{3}{8}$

70. 10

 Solve.

71. *Tallest Mountain.* The tallest mountain in the world, when measured from base to peak, is Mauna Kea (White Mountain) in Hawaii. From its base 19,684 ft below sea level in the Hawaiian Trough, it rises 33,480 ft. What is the elevation of the peak above sea level?
Source: *The Guinness Book of Records*

72. *Telephone Bills.* Erika's cell-phone bill for July was $82. She sent a check for $50 and then made $37 worth of calls in August. How much did she then owe on her cell-phone bill?

73. *Temperature Changes.* One day the temperature in Lawrence, Kansas, is 32°F at 6:00 A.M. It rises 15° by noon, but falls 50° by midnight when a cold front moves in. What is the final temperature?

74. *Stock Changes.* On a recent day, the price of a stock opened at a value of $61.38. During the day, it rose $4.75, dropped $7.38, and rose $5.13. Find the value of the stock at the end of the day.

75. *Profits and Losses.* The profit of a business is expressed as a positive number and referred to as operating "in the black." A loss is expressed as a negative number and is referred to as operating "in the red." The profits and losses of Xponent Corporation over various years are shown in the bar graph below. Find the sum of the profits and losses.

Xponent Corporation

76. *Football Yardage.* In a college football game, the quarterback attempted passes with the following results. Find the total gain or loss.

TRY	GAIN OR LOSS
1st	13-yd gain
2nd	12-yd loss
3rd	21-yd gain

77. *Credit-Card Bills.* On August 1, Lyle's credit-card bill shows that he owes $470. During the month of August, Lyle sends a check for $45 to the credit-card company, charges another $160 in merchandise, and then pays off another $500 of his bill. What is the new amount that Lyle owes at the end of August?

78. *Account Balance.* Leah has $460 in a checking account. She writes a check for $530, makes a deposit of $75, and then writes a check for $90. What is the balance in her account?

Skill Maintenance

Convert to decimal notation. [4.2b]

79. 71.3%

80. $92\frac{7}{8}\%$

Convert to percent notation. [4.3a]

81. $\frac{1}{8}$

82. $\frac{13}{32}$

83. Divide and simplify: $\frac{2}{3} \div \frac{5}{12}$. [2.2c]

84. Subtract and simplify: $\frac{2}{3} - \frac{5}{12}$. [2.3b]

Synthesis

85. For what numbers x is $-x$ negative?

86. For what numbers x is $-x$ positive?

87. If a is positive and b is negative, then $-a + b$ is:
   A. Positive.
   B. Negative.
   C. 0.
   D. Cannot be determined without more information

88. If $a = b$ and a and b are negative, then $-a + (-b)$ is:
   A. Positive.
   B. Negative.
   C. 0.
   D. Cannot be determined without more information

Copyright © 2012 Pearson Education, Inc.

7.4 Subtraction of Real Numbers

a Subtraction

We now consider subtraction of real numbers.

SUBTRACTION

The difference $a - b$ is the number c for which $a = b + c$.

Consider, for example, $45 - 17$. *Think*: What number can we add to 17 to get 45? Since $45 = 17 + 28$, we know that $45 - 17 = 28$. Let's consider an example whose answer is a negative number.

EXAMPLE 1 Subtract: $3 - 7$.

Think: What number can we add to 7 to get 3? The number must be negative. Since $7 + (-4) = 3$, we know the number is -4: $3 - 7 = -4$. That is, $3 - 7 = -4$ because $7 + (-4) = 3$.

> Do Exercises 1–3.

The definition above does not provide the most efficient way to do subtraction. We can develop a faster way to subtract. As a rationale for the faster way, let's compare $3 + 7$ and $3 - 7$ on the number line.

To find $3 + 7$ on the number line, we start at 0, move to 3, and then move 7 units farther to the right since 7 is positive.

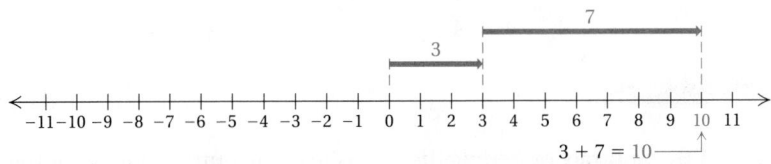

To find $3 - 7$, we do the "opposite" of adding 7: We move 7 units to the *left* to do the subtracting. This is the same as *adding* the opposite of 7, -7, to 3.

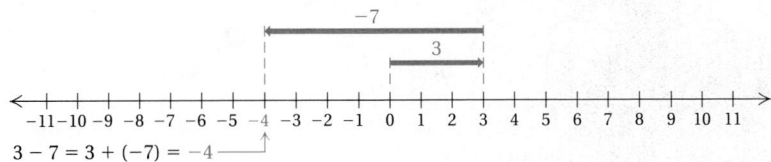

> Do Exercises 4–6.

Look for a pattern in the examples shown at right.

SUBTRACTING	ADDING AN OPPOSITE
$5 - 8 = -3$	$5 + (-8) = -3$
$-6 - 4 = -10$	$-6 + (-4) = -10$
$-7 - (-2) = -5$	$-7 + 2 = -5$

OBJECTIVES

a Subtract real numbers and simplify combinations of additions and subtractions.

b Solve applied problems involving subtraction of real numbers.

Subtract.

1. $-6 - 4$

   Think: What number can be added to 4 to get -6:

   $$\square + 4 = -6?$$

2. $-7 - (-10)$

   Think: What number can be added to -10 to get -7:

   $$\square + (-10) = -7?$$

3. $-7 - (-2)$

   Think: What number can be added to -2 to get -7:

   $$\square + (-2) = -7?$$

Subtract. Use the number line, doing the "opposite" of addition.

4. $5 - 9$

5. $-3 - 2$

6. $-4 - (-3)$

Answers

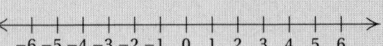

1. -10 2. 3 3. -5 4. -4
5. -5 6. -1

Complete the addition and compare with the subtraction.

7. $4 - 6 = -2;$
$4 + (-6) = $ _____

8. $-3 - 8 = -11;$
$-3 + (-8) = $ _____

9. $-5 - (-9) = 4;$
$-5 + 9 = $ _____

10. $-5 - (-3) = -2;$
$-5 + 3 = $ _____

Do Exercises 7-10.

Perhaps you have noticed that we can subtract by adding the opposite of the number being subtracted. This can always be done.

SUBTRACTING BY ADDING THE OPPOSITE

For any real numbers a and b,

$$a - b = a + (-b).$$

(To subtract, add the opposite, or additive inverse, of the number being subtracted.)

This is the method generally used for quick subtraction of real numbers.

EXAMPLES Subtract.

2. $2 - 6 = 2 + (-6) = -4$ | The opposite of 6 is -6. We change the subtraction to addition and add the opposite. *Check:* $-4 + 6 = 2.$

3. $4 - (-9) = 4 + 9 = 13$ | The opposite of -9 is 9. We change the subtraction to addition and add the opposite. *Check:* $13 + (-9) = 4.$

4. $-4.2 - (-3.6) = -4.2 + 3.6 = -0.6$ | Adding the opposite. *Check:* $-0.6 + (-3.6) = -4.2.$

5. $-\dfrac{1}{2} - \left(-\dfrac{3}{4}\right) = -\dfrac{1}{2} + \dfrac{3}{4}$ | Adding the opposite. *Check:* $\dfrac{1}{4} + \left(-\dfrac{3}{4}\right) = -\dfrac{1}{2}.$

$$= -\dfrac{2}{4} + \dfrac{3}{4} = \dfrac{1}{4}$$

Subtract.

11. $2 - 8$ **12.** $-6 - 10$

13. $12.4 - 5.3$ **14.** $-8 - (-11)$

15. $-8 - (-8)$ **16.** $\dfrac{2}{3} - \left(-\dfrac{5}{6}\right)$

Do Exercises 11-16.

EXAMPLES Subtract by adding the opposite of the number being subtracted.

6. $3 - 5$ *Think:* "Three minus five is three plus the opposite of five"
$3 - 5 = 3 + (-5) = -2$

7. $\dfrac{1}{8} - \dfrac{7}{8}$ *Think:* "One-eighth minus seven-eighths is one-eighth plus the opposite of seven-eighths"

$$\dfrac{1}{8} - \dfrac{7}{8} = \dfrac{1}{8} + \left(-\dfrac{7}{8}\right) = -\dfrac{6}{8}, \text{ or } -\dfrac{3}{4}$$

8. $-4.6 - (-9.8)$ *Think:* "Negative four point six minus negative nine point eight is negative four point six plus the opposite of negative nine point eight"

$$-4.6 - (-9.8) = -4.6 + 9.8 = 5.2$$

9. $-\dfrac{3}{4} - \dfrac{7}{5}$ *Think:* "Negative three-fourths minus seven-fifths is negative three-fourths plus the opposite of seven-fifths"

$$-\dfrac{3}{4} - \dfrac{7}{5} = -\dfrac{3}{4} + \left(-\dfrac{7}{5}\right) = -\dfrac{15}{20} + \left(-\dfrac{28}{20}\right) = -\dfrac{43}{20}$$

Subtract by adding the opposite of the number being subtracted.

17. $3 - 11$

18. $12 - 5$

19. $-12 - (-9)$

20. $-12.4 - 10.9$

21. $-\dfrac{4}{5} - \left(-\dfrac{4}{5}\right)$

Do Exercises 17-21.

Answers

7. -2 **8.** -11 **9.** 4 **10.** -2 **11.** -6
12. -16 **13.** 7.1 **14.** 3 **15.** 0 **16.** $\dfrac{3}{2}$
17. -8 **18.** 7 **19.** -3 **20.** -23.3
21. 0

When several additions and subtractions occur together, we can make them all additions.

EXAMPLES Simplify.

10. $8 - (-4) - 2 - (-4) + 2 = 8 + 4 + (-2) + 4 + 2$ Adding the opposite

$$= 16$$

11. $8.2 - (-6.1) + 2.3 - (-4) = 8.2 + 6.1 + 2.3 + 4 = 20.6$

12. $\dfrac{3}{4} - \left(-\dfrac{1}{12}\right) - \dfrac{5}{6} - \dfrac{2}{3} = \dfrac{9}{12} + \dfrac{1}{12} + \left(-\dfrac{10}{12}\right) + \left(-\dfrac{8}{12}\right)$

$$= \dfrac{9 + 1 + (-10) + (-8)}{12}$$

$$= \dfrac{-8}{12} = -\dfrac{8}{12} = -\dfrac{2}{3}$$

> Do Exercises 22–24.

Simplify.

22. $-6 - (-2) - (-4) - 12 + 3$

23. $\dfrac{2}{3} - \dfrac{4}{5} - \left(-\dfrac{11}{15}\right) + \dfrac{7}{10} - \dfrac{5}{2}$

24. $-9.6 + 7.4 - (-3.9) - (-11)$

(b) Applications and Problem Solving

Let's now see how we can use subtraction of real numbers to solve applied problems.

EXAMPLE 13 *Surface Temperatures on Mars.* Surface temperatures on Mars vary from $-128°$C during polar night to $27°$C at the equator during mid-day at the closest point in orbit to the sun. Find the difference between the highest value and the lowest value in this temperature range.

Source: Mars Institute

We let $D =$ the difference in the temperatures. Then the problem translates to the following subtraction:

Difference in temperature	is	Highest temperature	minus	Lowest temperature
↓	↓	↓	↓	↓
D	$=$	27	$-$	(-128)
D	$= 27 + 128 = 155.$			

The difference in the temperatures is $155°$C.

> Do Exercise 25.

25. Temperature Extremes.
The highest temperature ever recorded in the United States is 134°F in Greenland Ranch, California, on July 10, 1913. The lowest temperature ever recorded is $-80°$F in Prospect Creek, Alaska, on January 23, 1971. How much higher was the temperature in Greenland Ranch than the temperature in Prospect Creek?

Source: National Oceanographic and Atmospheric Administration

Answers

22. -9 **23.** $-\dfrac{6}{5}$ **24.** 12.7   **25.** 214°F

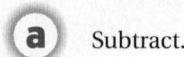
a   Subtract.

1. $2 - 9$

2. $3 - 8$

3. $-8 - (-2)$

4. $-6 - (-8)$

5. $-11 - (-11)$

6. $-6 - (-6)$

7. $12 - 16$

8. $14 - 19$

9. $20 - 27$

10. $30 - 4$

11. $-9 - (-3)$

12. $-7 - (-9)$

13. $-40 - (-40)$

14. $-9 - (-9)$

15. $7 - (-7)$

16. $4 - (-4)$

17. $8 - (-3)$

18. $-7 - 4$

19. $-6 - 8$

20. $6 - (-10)$

21. $-4 - (-9)$

22. $-14 - 2$

23. $-6 - (-5)$

24. $-4 - (-3)$

25. $8 - (-10)$

26. $5 - (-6)$

27. $-5 - (-2)$

28. $-3 - (-1)$

29. $-7 - 14$

30. $-9 - 16$

31. $0 - (-5)$

32. $0 - (-1)$

33. $-8 - 0$

34. $-9 - 0$

35. $7 - (-5)$

36. $7 - (-4)$

37. $2 - 25$

38. $18 - 63$

39. $-42 - 26$

40. $-18 - 63$

Copyright © 2012 Pearson Education, Inc.

41. $-71 - 2$

42. $-49 - 3$

43. $24 - (-92)$

44. $48 - (-73)$

45. $-50 - (-50)$

46. $-70 - (-70)$

47. $-\dfrac{3}{8} - \dfrac{5}{8}$

48. $\dfrac{3}{9} - \dfrac{9}{9}$

49. $\dfrac{3}{4} - \dfrac{2}{3}$

50. $\dfrac{5}{8} - \dfrac{3}{4}$

51. $-\dfrac{3}{4} - \dfrac{2}{3}$

52. $-\dfrac{5}{8} - \dfrac{3}{4}$

53. $-\dfrac{5}{8} - \left(-\dfrac{3}{4}\right)$

54. $-\dfrac{3}{4} - \left(-\dfrac{2}{3}\right)$

55. $6.1 - (-13.8)$

56. $1.5 - (-3.5)$

57. $-2.7 - 5.9$

58. $-3.2 - 5.8$

59. $0.99 - 1$

60. $0.87 - 1$

61. $-79 - 114$

62. $-197 - 216$

63. $0 - (-500)$

64. $500 - (-1000)$

65. $-2.8 - 0$

66. $6.04 - 1.1$

67. $7 - 10.53$

68. $8 - (-9.3)$

69. $\dfrac{1}{6} - \dfrac{2}{3}$

70. $-\dfrac{3}{8} - \left(-\dfrac{1}{2}\right)$

71. $-\dfrac{4}{7} - \left(-\dfrac{10}{7}\right)$

72. $\dfrac{12}{5} - \dfrac{12}{5}$

73. $-\dfrac{7}{10} - \dfrac{10}{15}$

74. $-\dfrac{4}{18} - \left(-\dfrac{2}{9}\right)$

75. $\dfrac{1}{5} - \dfrac{1}{3}$

76. $-\dfrac{1}{7} - \left(-\dfrac{1}{6}\right)$

77. $\dfrac{5}{12} - \dfrac{7}{16}$

78. $-\dfrac{1}{35} - \left(-\dfrac{9}{40}\right)$

79. $-\dfrac{2}{15} - \dfrac{7}{12}$

80. $\dfrac{2}{21} - \dfrac{9}{14}$

Simplify.

81. $18 - (-15) - 3 - (-5) + 2$

82. $22 - (-18) + 7 + (-42) - 27$

83. $-31 + (-28) - (-14) - 17$

84. $-43 - (-19) - (-21) + 25$

85. $-34 - 28 + (-33) - 44$

86. $39 + (-88) - 29 - (-83)$

87. $-93 - (-84) - 41 - (-56)$

88. $84 + (-99) + 44 - (-18) - 43$

89. $-5.4 - (-30.9) + 30.8 + 40.2 - (-12)$

90. $14.9 - (-50.7) + 20 - (-32.8)$

91. $-\dfrac{7}{12} + \dfrac{3}{4} - \left(-\dfrac{5}{8}\right) - \dfrac{13}{24}$

92. $-\dfrac{11}{16} + \dfrac{5}{32} - \left(-\dfrac{1}{4}\right) + \dfrac{7}{8}$

 Solve.

93. *Ocean Depth.* The deepest point in the Pacific Ocean is the Marianas Trench, with a depth of 10,924 m. The deepest point in the Atlantic Ocean is the Puerto Rico Trench, with a depth of 8605 m. What is the difference in the elevation of the two trenches?

Source: *The World Almanac and Book of Facts*

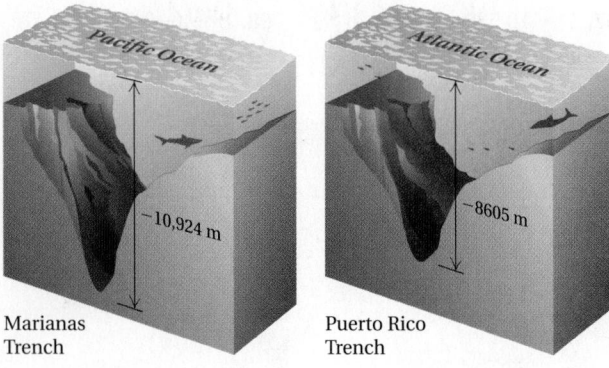

Marianas Trench —10,924 m

Puerto Rico Trench —8605 m

94. *Elevations in Africa.* The elevation of the highest point in Africa, Mt. Kilimanjaro, Tanzania, is 19,340 ft. The lowest elevation, at Lake Assal, Djibouti, is −512 ft. What is the difference in the elevations of the two locations?

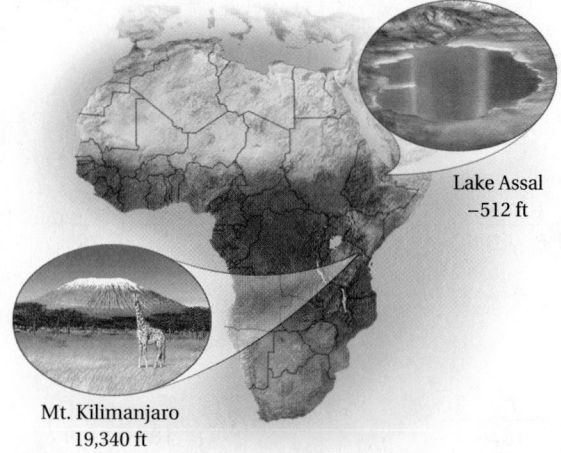

Lake Assal −512 ft

Mt. Kilimanjaro 19,340 ft

95. Claire has a charge of $476.89 on her credit card, but she then returns a sweater that cost $128.95. How much does she now owe on her credit card?

96. Chris has $720 in a checking account. He writes a check for $970 to pay for a sound system. What is the balance in his checking account?

Copyright © 2012 Pearson Education, Inc.

97. *Difference in Elevation.* At its highest point, the elevation of Denver, Colorado, is 5672 ft above sea level. At its lowest point, the elevation of New Orleans, Louisiana, is 4 ft below sea level. Find the difference in the elevations.
Source: *Information Please Almanac*

98. *Difference in Elevation.* The lowest elevation in North America, Death Valley, California, is 282 ft below sea level. The highest elevation in North America, Mount McKinley, Alaska, is 20,320 ft. Find the difference in elevation between the highest point and the lowest point.
Source: National Geographic Society

99. *Low Points on Continents.* The lowest point in Africa is Lake Assal, which is 512 ft below sea level. The lowest point in South America is the Valdes Peninsula, which is 131 ft below sea level. How much lower is Lake Assal than the Valdes Peninsula?
Source: National Geographic Society

100. *Temperature Records.* The greatest recorded temperature change in one 24-hr period occurred between January 23 and January 24, 1916, in Browning, Montana, where the temperature fell from to 44°F to −56°F. By how much did the temperature drop?
Source: *The Guinness Book of Records*

101. *Surface Temperature on Mercury.* Surface temperatures on Mercury vary from 840°F on the equator when the planet is closest to the sun to −290°F at night. Find the difference between these two temperatures.

102. *Run Differential.* In baseball, the difference between the number of runs that a team scores and the number of runs that it allows its opponents to score is called the *run differential.* That is,

$$\text{Run differential} = \frac{\text{Number of}}{\text{runs scored}} - \frac{\text{Number of}}{\text{runs allowed}}.$$

Teams strive for a positive run differential.
Source: Major League Baseball

a) In a recent season, the Chicago White Sox scored 810 runs and allowed 729 runs to be scored on them. Find the run differential.

b) In a recent season, the Pittsburgh Pirates scored 735 runs and allowed 884 runs to be scored on them. Find the run differential.

Skill Maintenance

Simplify. [1.6c]

103. $256 \div 64 \div 2^3 + 100$

104. $5 \cdot 6 + (7 \cdot 2)^2$

105. $2^5 \div 4 + 20 \div 2^2$

106. $65 - 5^2 \div 5 - 5 \cdot 2$

107. Add and simplify: $\dfrac{1}{8} + \dfrac{7}{12} + \dfrac{5}{24}$. [2.3a]

108. Simplify: $\dfrac{164}{256}$. [2.1e]

Synthesis

Determine whether each statement is true or false for all integers a and b. If false, give an example to show why. Examples may vary.

109. $a - 0 = 0 - a$

110. $0 - a = a$

111. If $a \neq b$, then $a - b \neq 0$.

112. If $a = -b$, then $a + b = 0$.

113. If $a + b = 0$, then a and b are opposites.

114. If $a - b = 0$, then $a = -b$.

Mid-Chapter Review

Concept Reinforcement

Determine whether each statement is true or false.

_____ **1.** All rational numbers can be named using fraction notation.   [7.2c]

_____ **2.** If $a > b$, then a lies to the left of b on the number line.   [7.2d]

_____ **3.** The absolute value of a number is always nonnegative.   [7.2e]

_____ **4.** We can translate "7 less than y" as $7 - y$.   [7.1b]

Guided Solutions

Fill in each blank with the number that creates a correct statement or solution.

5. Evaluate $-x$ and $-(-x)$ when $x = -4$.   [7.3b]

$-x = -(\square) = \square$;

$-(-x) = -(-(\square)) = -(\square) = \square$

Subtract.   [7.4a]

6. $5 - 13 = 5 + (\square) = \square$

7. $-6 - 7 = -6 + (\square) = \square$

Mixed Review

Evaluate.   [7.1a]

8. $\dfrac{3m}{n}$, when $m = 8$ and $n = 6$

9. $\dfrac{a + b}{2}$, when $a = 5$ and $b = 17$

Translate each phrase to an algebraic expression. Use any letter for the variable.   [7.1b]

10. Three times some number

11. Five less than some number

12. State the integers that correspond to this situation: Jerilyn deposited \$450 in her checking account. Later that week, she wrote a check for \$79.   [7.2a]

13. Graph -3.5 on the number line.   [7.2b]

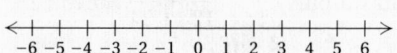

Convert to decimal notation.   [7.2c]

14. $-\dfrac{4}{5}$

15. $\dfrac{7}{3}$

Use either $<$ or $>$ for $\square$ to write a true sentence.   [7.2d]

16. $-5 \;\square\; -3$

17. $-9.9 \;\square\; -10.1$

Copyright © 2012 Pearson Education, Inc.

Write true or false.   [7.2d]

18. $-8 \geq -5$

19. $-4 \leq -4$

Write an inequality with the same meaning.   [7.2d]

20. $y < 5$

21. $-3 \geq t$

Find the absolute value.   [7.2e]

22. $|15.6|$

23. $|-18|$

24. $|0|$

25. $\left|-\dfrac{12}{5}\right|$

Find the opposite, or additive inverse, of the number.   [7.3b]

26. -5.6

27. $\dfrac{7}{4}$

28. 0

29. -49

30. Evaluate $-x$ when x is -19.   [7.3b]

31. Evaluate $-(-x)$ when x is 2.3.   [7.3b]

Compute and simplify.   [7.3a], [7.4a]

32. $7 + (-9)$

33. $-\dfrac{3}{8} + \dfrac{1}{4}$

34. $3.6 + (-3.6)$

35. $-8 + (-9)$

36. $\dfrac{2}{3} + \left(-\dfrac{9}{8}\right)$

37. $-4.2 + (-3.9)$

38. $-14 + 5$

39. $19 + (-21)$

40. $-4.1 - 6.3$

41. $5 - (-11)$

42. $-\dfrac{1}{4} - \left(-\dfrac{3}{5}\right)$

43. $12 - 24$

44. $-8 - (-4)$

45. $-\dfrac{1}{2} - \dfrac{5}{6}$

46. $12.3 - 14.1$

47. $6 - (-7)$

48. $16 - (-9) - 20 - (-4)$

49. $-4 + (-10) - (-3) - 12$

50. $17 - (-25) + 15 - (-18)$

51. $-9 + (-3) + 16 - (-10)$

Solve.   [7.3c], [7.4b]

52. *Temperature Change.*   In chemistry lab, Ben works with a substance whose initial temperature is 25°C. During an experiment, the temperature falls to −8°C. Find the difference between the two temperatures.

53. *Stock Price Change.*   The price of a stock opened at $56.12. During the day, it dropped $1.18, then rose $1.22, and then dropped $1.36. Find the value of the stock at the end of the day.

Understanding Through Discussion and Writing

54. Give three examples of rational numbers that are not integers. Explain.   [7.2b]

55. Give three examples of irrational numbers. Explain the difference between an irrational number and a rational number.   [7.2b, d]

56. Explain in your own words why the sum of two negative numbers is always negative.   [7.3a]

57. If a negative number is subtracted from a positive number, will the result always be positive? Why or why not?   [7.4a]

7.5

Multiplication of Real Numbers

OBJECTIVES

a Multiply real numbers.

b Solve applied problems involving multiplication of real numbers.

a Multiplication

Multiplication of real numbers is very much like multiplication of arithmetic numbers. The only difference is that we must determine whether the answer is positive or negative.

Multiplication of a Positive Number and a Negative Number

To see how to multiply a positive number and a negative number, consider the pattern of the following.

This number decreases by 1 each time.

$$
\begin{aligned}
4 \cdot 5 &= 20 \\
3 \cdot 5 &= 15 \\
2 \cdot 5 &= 10 \\
1 \cdot 5 &= 5 \\
0 \cdot 5 &= 0 \\
-1 \cdot 5 &= -5 \\
-2 \cdot 5 &= -10 \\
-3 \cdot 5 &= -15
\end{aligned}
$$

This number decreases by 5 each time.

Do Exercise 1.

According to this pattern, it looks as though the product of a negative number and a positive number is negative. That is the case, and we have the first part of the rule for multiplying real numbers.

> **THE PRODUCT OF A POSITIVE NUMBER AND A NEGATIVE NUMBER**
>
> To multiply a positive number and a negative number, multiply their absolute values. The answer is negative.

1. Complete, as in the example.

$$
\begin{aligned}
4 \cdot 10 &= 40 \\
3 \cdot 10 &= 30 \\
2 \cdot 10 &= \\
1 \cdot 10 &= \\
0 \cdot 10 &= \\
-1 \cdot 10 &= \\
-2 \cdot 10 &= \\
-3 \cdot 10 &=
\end{aligned}
$$

Multiply.

2. $-3 \cdot 6$

3. $20 \cdot (-5)$

4. $4 \cdot (-20)$

5. $-\dfrac{2}{3} \cdot \dfrac{5}{6}$

6. $-4.23(7.1)$

7. $\dfrac{7}{8}\left(-\dfrac{4}{5}\right)$

EXAMPLES Multiply.

1. $8(-5) = -40$

2. $-\dfrac{1}{3} \cdot \dfrac{5}{7} = -\dfrac{5}{21}$

3. $(-7.2)5 = -36$

Do Exercises 2–7.

Answers

1. 20; 10; 0; −10; −20; −30   **2.** −18

3. −100   **4.** −80   **5.** $-\dfrac{5}{9}$

6. −30.033   **7.** $-\dfrac{7}{10}$

Multiplication of Two Negative Numbers

How do we multiply two negative numbers? Again, we look for a pattern.

This number decreases by 1 each time.

$4 \cdot (-5) = -20$
$3 \cdot (-5) = -15$
$2 \cdot (-5) = -10$
$1 \cdot (-5) = -5$
$0 \cdot (-5) = 0$
$-1 \cdot (-5) = 5$
$-2 \cdot (-5) = 10$
$-3 \cdot (-5) = 15$

This number increases by 5 each time.

Do Exercise 8.

According to the pattern, it appears that the product of two negative numbers is positive. That is actually so, and we have the second part of the rule for multiplying real numbers.

THE PRODUCT OF TWO NEGATIVE NUMBERS

To multiply two negative numbers, multiply their absolute values. The answer is positive.

Do Exercises 9–14.

The following is another way to consider the rules we have for multiplication.

To multiply two nonzero real numbers:

a) Multiply the absolute values.
b) If the signs are the same, the answer is positive.
c) If the signs are different, the answer is negative.

Multiplication by Zero

The only case that we have not considered is multiplying by zero. As with nonnegative numbers, the product of any real number and 0 is 0.

THE MULTIPLICATION PROPERTY OF ZERO

For any real number a,

$$a \cdot 0 = 0 \cdot a = 0.$$

(The product of 0 and any real number is 0.)

EXAMPLES Multiply.

4. $(-3)(-4) = 12$

5. $-1.6(2) = -3.2$

6. $-19 \cdot 0 = 0$

7. $\left(-\dfrac{5}{6}\right)\left(-\dfrac{1}{9}\right) = \dfrac{5}{54}$

8. $0 \cdot (-452) = 0$

9. $23 \cdot 0 \cdot \left(-8\frac{2}{3}\right) = 0$

Do Exercises 15–20.

---

8. Complete, as in the example.

$3 \cdot (-10) = -30$
$2 \cdot (-10) = -20$
$1 \cdot (-10) =$
$0 \cdot (-10) =$
$-1 \cdot (-10) =$
$-2 \cdot (-10) =$
$-3 \cdot (-10) =$

Multiply.

9. $-9 \cdot (-3)$

10. $-16 \cdot (-2)$

11. $-7 \cdot (-5)$

12. $-\dfrac{4}{7}\left(-\dfrac{5}{9}\right)$

13. $-\dfrac{3}{2}\left(-\dfrac{4}{9}\right)$

14. $-3.25(-4.14)$

Multiply.

15. $5(-6)$

16. $(-5)(-6)$

17. $(-3.2) \cdot 10$

18. $\left(-\dfrac{4}{5}\right)\left(\dfrac{10}{3}\right)$

19. $0 \cdot (-34.2)$

20. $-\dfrac{5}{7} \cdot 0 \cdot \left(-4\frac{2}{3}\right)$

Answers

8. $-10; 0; 10; 20; 30$ **9.** 27   **10.** 32
11. 35   **12.** $\dfrac{20}{63}$ **13.** $\dfrac{2}{3}$ **14.** 13.455
15. -30 **16.** 30   **17.** -32 **18.** $-\dfrac{8}{3}$
19. 0   **20.** 0

Multiplying More Than Two Numbers

When multiplying more than two real numbers, we can choose order and grouping as we please.

EXAMPLES Multiply.

10. $-8 \cdot 2(-3) = -16(-3)$ Multiplying the first two numbers

$ = 48$

11. $-8 \cdot 2(-3) = 24 \cdot 2$ Multiplying the negatives. Every pair of negative numbers gives a positive product.

$ = 48$

12. $-3(-2)(-5)(4) = 6(-5)(4)$ Multiplying the first two numbers

$ = (-30)4$

$ = -120$

13. $\left(-\dfrac{1}{2}\right)(8)\left(-\dfrac{2}{3}\right)(-6) = (-4)4$ Multiplying the first two numbers and the last two numbers

$\phantom{\left(-\dfrac{1}{2}\right)(8)\left(-\dfrac{2}{3}\right)(-6)} = -16$

14. $-5 \cdot (-2) \cdot (-3) \cdot (-6) = 10 \cdot 18 = 180$

15. $(-3)(-5)(-2)(-3)(-6) = (-30)(18) = -540$

Considering that the product of a pair of negative numbers is positive, we see the following pattern.

> The product of an even number of negative numbers is positive.
>
> The product of an odd number of negative numbers is negative.

Do Exercises 21–26.

EXAMPLE 16 Evaluate $2x^2$ when $x = 3$ and when $x = -3$.

$2x^2 = 2(3)^2 = 2(9) = 18;$

$2x^2 = 2(-3)^2 = 2(9) = 18$

Let's compare the expressions $(-x)^2$ and $-x^2$.

EXAMPLE 17 Evaluate $(-x)^2$ and $-x^2$ when $x = 5$.

$(-x)^2 = (-5)^2 = (-5)(-5) = 25;$ Substitute 5 for x. Then evaluate the power.

$-x^2 = -(5)^2 = -(25) = -25$ Substitute 5 for x. Evaluate the power. Then find the opposite.

In Example 17, we see that the expressions $(-x)^2$ and $-x^2$ are *not* equivalent. That is, they do not have the same value for every allowable replacement of the variable by a real number. To find $(-x)^2$, we take the opposite and then square. To find $-x^2$, we find the square and then take the opposite.

Multiply.

21. $5 \cdot (-3) \cdot 2$

22. $-3 \times (-4.1) \times (-2.5)$

23. $-\dfrac{1}{2} \cdot \left(-\dfrac{4}{3}\right) \cdot \left(-\dfrac{5}{2}\right)$

24. $-2 \cdot (-5) \cdot (-4) \cdot (-3)$

25. $(-4)(-5)(-2)(-3)(-1)$

26. $(-1)(-1)(-2)(-3)(-1)(-1)$

Answers

21. -30 **22.** -30.75 **23.** $-\dfrac{5}{3}$

24. 120 **25.** -120 **26.** 6

EXAMPLE 18 Evaluate $(-a)^2$ and $-a^2$ when $a = -4$.

To make sense of the substitutions and computations, we introduce extra grouping symbols into the expressions.

$$(-a)^2 = [-(-4)]^2 = [4]^2 = 16;$$
$$-a^2 = -(-4)^2 = -(16) = -16$$

Do Exercises 27–29.

27. Evaluate $3x^2$ when $x = 4$ and when $x = -4$.

28. Evaluate $(-x)^2$ and $-x^2$ when $x = 2$.

29. Evaluate $(-x)^2$ and $-x^2$ when $x = -3$.

b Applications and Problem Solving

We now consider multiplication of real numbers in real-world applications.

EXAMPLE 19 *Chemical Reaction.* During a chemical reaction, the temperature in a beaker decreased by 2°C every minute until 10:23 A.M. If the temperature was 17°C at 10:00 A.M., when the reaction began, what was the temperature at 10:23 A.M.?

This is a multistep problem. We first find the total number of degrees that the temperature dropped, using −2° for each minute. Since it dropped 2° for each of the 23 minutes, we know that the total drop d is given by

$$d = 23 \cdot (-2) = -46.$$

To determine the temperature after this time period, we find the sum of 17 and −46, or

$$T = 17 + (-46) = -29.$$

Thus the temperature at 10:23 A.M. was −29°C.

Do Exercise 30.

30. Chemical Reaction. During a chemical reaction, the temperature in a beaker increased by 3°C every minute until 1:34 P.M. If the temperature was −17°C at 1:10 P.M., when the reaction began, what was the temperature at 1:34 P.M.?

STUDY TIPS

MAKING POSITIVE CHOICES

Making the right choices can give you the power to succeed in learning mathematics.

You can choose to improve your attitude and raise the academic goals that you have set for yourself. Projecting a positive attitude toward your study of mathematics and expecting a positive outcome can make it easier for you to learn and to perform well in this course.

Here are some positive choices you can make:

• Choose to make a strong commitment to learning.

• Choose to allocate the proper amount of time to learn.

• Choose to place the primary responsibility for learning on yourself.

Well-known American psychologist William James once said, "The one thing that will guarantee the successful conclusion of a doubtful undertaking is faith in the beginning that you can do it."

Answers

27. 48; 48   **28.** 4; −4
29. 9; −9   **30.** 55°C

a Multiply.

1. $-4 \cdot 2$

2. $-3 \cdot 5$

3. $-8 \cdot 6$

4. $-5 \cdot 2$

5. $8 \cdot (-3)$

6. $9 \cdot (-5)$

7. $-9 \cdot 8$

8. $-10 \cdot 3$

9. $-8 \cdot (-2)$

10. $-2 \cdot (-5)$

11. $-7 \cdot (-6)$

12. $-9 \cdot (-2)$

13. $15 \cdot (-8)$

14. $-12 \cdot (-10)$

15. $-14 \cdot 17$

16. $-13 \cdot (-15)$

17. $-25 \cdot (-48)$

18. $39 \cdot (-43)$

19. $-3.5 \cdot (-28)$

20. $97 \cdot (-2.1)$

21. $9 \cdot (-8)$

22. $7 \cdot (-9)$

23. $4 \cdot (-3.1)$

24. $3 \cdot (-2.2)$

25. $-5 \cdot (-6)$

26. $-6 \cdot (-4)$

27. $-7 \cdot (-3.1)$

28. $-4 \cdot (-3.2)$

29. $\frac{2}{3} \cdot \left(-\frac{3}{5}\right)$

30. $\frac{5}{7} \cdot \left(-\frac{2}{3}\right)$

31. $-\frac{3}{8} \cdot \left(-\frac{2}{9}\right)$

32. $-\frac{5}{8} \cdot \left(-\frac{2}{5}\right)$

33. -6.3×2.7

34. -4.1×9.5

35. $-\frac{5}{9} \cdot \frac{3}{4}$

36. $-\frac{8}{3} \cdot \frac{9}{4}$

37. $7 \cdot (-4) \cdot (-3) \cdot 5$

38. $9 \cdot (-2) \cdot (-6) \cdot 7$

39. $-\frac{2}{3} \cdot \frac{1}{2} \cdot \left(-\frac{6}{7}\right)$

40. $-\frac{1}{8} \cdot \left(-\frac{1}{4}\right) \cdot \left(-\frac{3}{5}\right)$

41. $-3 \cdot (-4) \cdot (-5)$

42. $-2 \cdot (-5) \cdot (-7)$

43. $-2 \cdot (-5) \cdot (-3) \cdot (-5)$

44. $-3 \cdot (-5) \cdot (-2) \cdot (-1)$

45. $\frac{1}{5}\left(-\frac{2}{9}\right)$

46. $-\frac{3}{5}\left(-\frac{2}{7}\right)$

47. $-7 \cdot (-21) \cdot 13$

48. $-14 \cdot (34) \cdot 12$

Copyright © 2012 Pearson Education, Inc.

49. $-4 \cdot (-1.8) \cdot 7$

50. $-8 \cdot (-1.3) \cdot (-5)$

51. $-\dfrac{1}{9}\left(-\dfrac{2}{3}\right)\left(\dfrac{5}{7}\right)$

52. $-\dfrac{7}{2}\left(-\dfrac{5}{7}\right)\left(-\dfrac{2}{5}\right)$

53. $4 \cdot (-4) \cdot (-5) \cdot (-12)$

54. $-2 \cdot (-3) \cdot (-4) \cdot (-5)$

55. $0.07 \cdot (-7) \cdot 6 \cdot (-6)$

56. $80 \cdot (-0.8) \cdot (-90) \cdot (-0.09)$

57. $\left(-\dfrac{5}{6}\right)\left(\dfrac{1}{8}\right)\left(-\dfrac{3}{7}\right)\left(-\dfrac{1}{7}\right)$

58. $\left(\dfrac{4}{5}\right)\left(-\dfrac{2}{3}\right)\left(-\dfrac{15}{7}\right)\left(\dfrac{1}{2}\right)$

59. $(-14) \cdot (-27) \cdot 0$

60. $7 \cdot (-6) \cdot 5 \cdot (-4) \cdot 3 \cdot (-2) \cdot 1 \cdot 0$

61. $(-8)(-9)(-10)$

62. $(-7)(-8)(-9)(-10)$

63. $(-6)(-7)(-8)(-9)(-10)$

64. $(-5)(-6)(-7)(-8)(-9)(-10)$

65. $(-1)^{12}$

66. $(-1)^9$

67. Evaluate $(-x)^2$ and $-x^2$ when $x = 4$ and when $x = -4$.

68. Evaluate $(-x)^2$ and $-x^2$ when $x = 10$ and when $x = -10$.

69. Evaluate $(-3x)^2$ and $-3x^2$ when $x = 7$.

70. Evaluate $(-2x)^2$ and $-2x^2$ when $x = 3$.

71. Evaluate $5x^2$ when $x = 2$ and when $x = -2$.

72. Evaluate $2x^2$ when $x = 5$ and when $x = -5$.

73. Evaluate $-2x^3$ when $x = 1$ and when $x = -1$.

74. Evaluate $-3x^3$ when $x = 2$ and when $x = -2$.

 Solve.

75. *Weight Loss.* Dave lost 2 lb each week for a period of 10 weeks. Express his total weight change as an integer.

76. *Stock Loss.* Emma lost $3 each day for a period of 5 days in the value of a stock she owned. Express her total loss as an integer.

77. *Chemical Reaction.* The temperature of a chemical compound was 0°C at 11:00 A.M. During a reaction, it dropped 3°C per minute until 11:18 A.M. What was the temperature at 11:18 A.M.?

78. *Chemical Reaction.* The temperature of a chemical compound was −5°C at 3:20 P.M. During a reaction, it increased 2°C per minute until 3:52 P.M. What was the temperature at 3:52 P.M.?

79. *Stock Price.*   The price of a stock began the day at $23.75 per share and dropped $1.38 per hour for 8 hr. What was the price of the stock after 8 hr?

80. *Population Decrease.*   The population of Bloomtown was 12,500. It decreased 380 each year for 4 yr. What was the population of the town after 4 yr?

81. *Diver's Position.*   After diving 95 m below the sea level, a diver rises at a rate of 7 m/min for 9 min. Where is the diver in relation to the surface at the end of the 9-min period?

82. *Checking Account Balance.*   Karen had $68 in her checking account. After she had written checks to make seven purchases at $13 each, what was the balance in her checking account?

83. *Drop in Temperature.*   The temperature in Osgood was 62°F at 2:00 P.M. It dropped 6°F per hour for the next 4 hr. What was the temperature at the end of the 4-hr period?

84. *Juice Consumption.*   Eliza bought a 64-oz container of cranberry juice and drank 8 oz per day for a week. How much juice was left in the container at the end of the week?

Skill Maintenance

85. Find the LCM of 36 and 60.   [1.9a]

86. Find the prime factorization of 4608.   [1.7d]

Simplify.   [2.1e]

87. $\dfrac{26}{39}$

88. $\dfrac{48}{54}$

89. $\dfrac{264}{484}$

90. $\dfrac{1025}{6625}$

91. $\dfrac{275}{800}$

92. $\dfrac{111}{201}$

93. $\dfrac{11}{264}$

94. $\dfrac{78}{13}$

Synthesis

95. If a is positive and b is negative, then $-ab$ is:
   A. Positive.
   B. Negative.
   C. 0.
   D. Cannot be determined without more information

96. If a is positive and b is negative, then $(-a)(-b)$ is:
   A. Positive.
   B. Negative.
   C. 0.
   D. Cannot be determined without more information

97. Below is a number line showing 0 and two positive numbers x and y. Use a compass or ruler to locate the following as best you can:

   $2x, \quad 3x, \quad 2y, \quad -x, \quad -y, \quad x + y, \quad x - y, \quad x - 2y.$

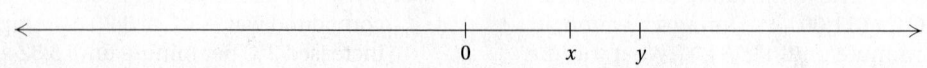

98. Of all possible quotients of the numbers $10, -\frac{1}{2}, -5,$ and $\frac{1}{5}$, which two produce the largest quotient? Which two produce the smallest quotient?

Copyright © 2012 Pearson Education, Inc.

7.6

Division of Real Numbers

We now consider division of real numbers. The definition of division results in rules for division that are the same as those for multiplication.

a Division of Integers

DIVISION

The quotient $a \div b$, or $\frac{a}{b}$, where $b \neq 0$, is that unique real number c for which $a = b \cdot c$.

Let's use the definition to divide integers.

EXAMPLES Divide, if possible. Check your answer.

1. $14 \div (-7) = -2$ *Think*: What number multiplied by -7 gives 14? That number is -2. *Check*: $(-2)(-7) = 14$.

2. $\frac{-32}{-4} = 8$ *Think*: What number multiplied by -4 gives -32? That number is 8. *Check*: $8(-4) = -32$.

3. $\frac{-10}{7} = -\frac{10}{7}$ *Think*: What number multiplied by 7 gives -10? That number is $-\frac{10}{7}$. *Check*: $-\frac{10}{7} \cdot 7 = -10$.

4. $\frac{-17}{0}$ is **not defined**.   *Think*: What number multiplied by 0 gives -17? There is no such number because the product of 0 and *any* number is 0.

The rules for division are the same as those for multiplication.

To multiply or divide two real numbers (where the divisor is nonzero):

a) Multiply or divide the absolute values.

b) If the signs are the same, the answer is positive.

c) If the signs are different, the answer is negative.

> Do Margin Exercises 1–6.

Excluding Division by 0

Example 4 shows why we cannot divide -17 by 0. We can use the same argument to show why we cannot divide any nonzero number b by 0. Consider $b \div 0$. We look for a number that when multiplied by 0 gives b. There is no such number because the product of 0 and any number is 0. Thus we cannot divide a nonzero number b by 0.

On the other hand, if we divide 0 by 0, we look for a number c such that $0 \cdot c = 0$. But $0 \cdot c = 0$ for any number c. Thus it appears that $0 \div 0$ could be any number we choose. Getting any answer we want when we divide 0 by 0 would be very confusing. Thus we agree that division by 0 is not defined.

OBJECTIVES

a Divide integers.

b Find the reciprocal of a real number.

c Divide real numbers.

d Solve applied problems involving division of real numbers.

SKILL TO REVIEW
Objective 2.2c: Divide and simplify using fraction notation.

Divide and simplify.

1. $\frac{6}{5} \div \frac{9}{2}$ **2.** $30 \div \frac{5}{6}$

Divide.

1. $6 \div (-3)$

Think: What number multiplied by -3 gives 6?

2. $\frac{-15}{-3}$

Think: What number multiplied by -3 gives -15?

3. $-24 \div 8$

Think: What number multiplied by 8 gives -24?

4. $\frac{-48}{-6}$ **5.** $\frac{30}{-5}$

6. $\frac{30}{-7}$

Answers

Skill to Review:

1. $\frac{4}{15}$ 2. 36

Margin Exercises:

1. -2 2. 5   3. -3 4. 8

5. -6 6. $-\frac{30}{7}$

EXCLUDING DIVISION BY 0

Division by 0 is not defined.

$$a \div 0, \text{ or } \frac{a}{0}, \text{ is not defined for all real numbers } a.$$

Dividing 0 by Other Numbers

Note that

$$0 \div 8 = 0 \text{ because } 0 = 0 \cdot 8; \qquad \frac{0}{-5} = 0 \text{ because } 0 = 0 \cdot (-5).$$

DIVIDENDS OF 0

Zero divided by any nonzero real number is 0:

$$\frac{0}{a} = 0; \qquad a \neq 0.$$

EXAMPLES Divide.

5. $0 \div (-6) = 0$ **6.** $\dfrac{0}{12} = 0$ **7.** $\dfrac{-3}{0}$ is not defined.

Do Exercises 7 and 8.

> Divide, if possible.
>
> **7.** $\dfrac{-5}{0}$ **8.** $\dfrac{0}{-3}$

b Reciprocals

When two numbers like $\frac{1}{2}$ and 2 are multiplied, the result is 1. Such numbers are called **reciprocals** of each other. Every nonzero real number has a reciprocal, also called a **multiplicative inverse**.

RECIPROCALS

Two numbers whose product is 1 are called **reciprocals**, or **multiplicative inverses**, of each other.

EXAMPLES Find the reciprocal.

8. $\dfrac{7}{8}$ The reciprocal of $\dfrac{7}{8}$ is $\dfrac{8}{7}$ because $\dfrac{7}{8} \cdot \dfrac{8}{7} = 1$.

9. -5 The reciprocal of -5 is $-\dfrac{1}{5}$ because $-5\left(-\dfrac{1}{5}\right) = 1$.

10. 3.9 The reciprocal of 3.9 is $\dfrac{1}{3.9}$ because $3.9\left(\dfrac{1}{3.9}\right) = 1$.

11. $-\dfrac{1}{2}$ The reciprocal of $-\dfrac{1}{2}$ is -2 because $\left(-\dfrac{1}{2}\right)(-2) = 1$.

12. $-\dfrac{2}{3}$ The reciprocal of $-\dfrac{2}{3}$ is $-\dfrac{3}{2}$ because $\left(-\dfrac{2}{3}\right)\left(-\dfrac{3}{2}\right) = 1$.

13. $\dfrac{3y}{8x}$ The reciprocal of $\dfrac{3y}{8x}$ is $\dfrac{8x}{3y}$ because $\left(\dfrac{3y}{8x}\right)\left(\dfrac{8x}{3y}\right) = 1$.

Answers
7. Not defined   **8.** 0

RECIPROCAL PROPERTIES

For $a \neq 0$, the reciprocal of a can be named $\frac{1}{a}$ and the reciprocal of $\frac{1}{a}$ is a.

The reciprocal of a nonzero number $\frac{a}{b}$ can be named $\frac{b}{a}$.

The number 0 has no reciprocal.

Do Exercises 9-14.

The reciprocal of a positive number is also a positive number, because the product of the two numbers must be the positive number 1. The reciprocal of a negative number is also a negative number, because the product of the two numbers must be the positive number 1.

THE SIGN OF A RECIPROCAL

The reciprocal of a number has the same sign as the number itself.

--------- *Caution!* ---------

It is important *not* to confuse *opposite* with *reciprocal*. Keep in mind that the opposite, or additive inverse, of a number is what we add to the number to get 0. The reciprocal, or multiplicative inverse, is what we multiply the number by to get 1.

Compare the following.

NUMBER	OPPOSITE (Change the sign.)	RECIPROCAL (Invert but do not change the sign.)
$-\frac{3}{8}$	$\frac{3}{8}$	$-\frac{8}{3}$
19	-19	$\frac{1}{19}$
$\frac{18}{7}$	$-\frac{18}{7}$	$\frac{7}{18}$
-7.9	7.9	$-\frac{1}{7.9}$, or $-\frac{10}{79}$
0	0	Not defined

$\left(-\frac{3}{8}\right)\left(-\frac{8}{3}\right) = 1$

$-\frac{3}{8} + \frac{3}{8} = 0$

Do Exercise 15.

Find the reciprocal.

9. $\frac{2}{3}$

10. $-\frac{5}{4}$

11. -3

12. $-\frac{1}{5}$

13. 1.3

14. $\frac{a}{6b}$

15. Complete the following table.

NUMBER	OPPOSITE	RECIPROCAL
$\frac{2}{3}$		
$-\frac{5}{4}$		
0		
1		
-8		
-4.7		

Answers

9. $\frac{3}{2}$ 10. $-\frac{4}{5}$ 11. $-\frac{1}{3}$ 12. -5 13. $\frac{1}{1.3}$, or $\frac{10}{13}$ 14. $\frac{6b}{a}$ 15. $-\frac{2}{3}$ and $\frac{3}{2}$; $\frac{5}{4}$ and $-\frac{4}{5}$; 0 and not defined; -1 and 1; 8 and $-\frac{1}{8}$; 4.7 and $-\frac{1}{4.7}$, or $-\frac{10}{47}$

7.6   Division of Real Numbers   **531**

c Division of Real Numbers

We know that we can subtract by adding an opposite. Similarly, we can divide by multiplying by a reciprocal.

RECIPROCALS AND DIVISION

For any real numbers a and b, $b \neq 0$,

$$a \div b = \frac{a}{b} = a \cdot \frac{1}{b}.$$

(To divide, multiply by the reciprocal of the divisor.)

EXAMPLES Rewrite each division as a multiplication.

14. $-4 \div 3$ $\qquad$ $-4 \div 3$ is the same as $-4 \cdot \dfrac{1}{3}$

15. $\dfrac{6}{-7}$ $\qquad$ $\dfrac{6}{-7} = 6\left(-\dfrac{1}{7}\right)$

16. $\dfrac{3}{5} \div \left(-\dfrac{9}{7}\right)$ $\qquad$ $\dfrac{3}{5} \div \left(-\dfrac{9}{7}\right) = \dfrac{3}{5}\left(-\dfrac{7}{9}\right)$

17. $\dfrac{x+2}{5}$ $\qquad$ $\dfrac{x+2}{5} = (x+2)\dfrac{1}{5}$ $\qquad$ Parentheses are necessary here.

18. $\dfrac{-17}{1/b}$ $\qquad$ $\dfrac{-17}{1/b} = -17 \cdot b$

Do Exercises 16–20.

When actually doing division calculations, we sometimes multiply by a reciprocal and we sometimes divide directly. With fraction notation, it is usually better to multiply by a reciprocal. With decimal notation, it is usually better to divide directly.

EXAMPLES Divide by multiplying by the reciprocal of the divisor.

19. $\dfrac{2}{3} \div \left(-\dfrac{5}{4}\right) = \dfrac{2}{3} \cdot \left(-\dfrac{4}{5}\right) = -\dfrac{8}{15}$

20. $-\dfrac{5}{6} \div \left(-\dfrac{3}{4}\right) = -\dfrac{5}{6} \cdot \left(-\dfrac{4}{3}\right) = \dfrac{20}{18} = \dfrac{10 \cdot 2}{9 \cdot 2} = \dfrac{10}{9} \cdot \dfrac{2}{2} = \dfrac{10}{9}$

---------------------------- *Caution!* ----------------------------

Be careful *not* to change the sign when taking a reciprocal!

----

21. $-\dfrac{3}{4} \div \dfrac{3}{10} = -\dfrac{3}{4} \cdot \left(\dfrac{10}{3}\right) = -\dfrac{30}{12} = -\dfrac{5 \cdot 6}{2 \cdot 6} = -\dfrac{5}{2} \cdot \dfrac{6}{6} = -\dfrac{5}{2}$

Do Exercises 21 and 22.

Rewrite each division as a multiplication.

16. $\dfrac{4}{7} \div \left(-\dfrac{3}{5}\right)$

17. $\dfrac{5}{-8}$

18. $\dfrac{a-b}{7}$

19. $\dfrac{-23}{1/a}$

20. $-5 \div 7$

Divide by multiplying by the reciprocal of the divisor.

21. $\dfrac{4}{7} \div \left(-\dfrac{3}{5}\right)$

22. $-\dfrac{12}{7} \div \left(-\dfrac{3}{4}\right)$

Answers

16. $\dfrac{4}{7} \cdot \left(-\dfrac{5}{3}\right)$ $\quad$ **17.** $5 \cdot \left(-\dfrac{1}{8}\right)$

18. $(a-b) \cdot \dfrac{1}{7}$ $\quad$ **19.** $-23 \cdot a$

20. $-5 \cdot \left(\dfrac{1}{7}\right)$ $\quad$ **21.** $-\dfrac{20}{21}$ $\quad$ **22.** $\dfrac{16}{7}$

With decimal notation, it is easier to carry out long division than to multiply by the reciprocal.

EXAMPLES Divide.

22. $-27.9 \div (-3) = \dfrac{-27.9}{-3} = 9.3$ Do the long division $3\overline{)27.9}$.

The answer is positive.

23. $-6.3 \div 2.1 = -3$ Do the long division $2.1\overline{)6.3}$.

The answer is negative.

Do Exercises 23 and 24.

Consider the following:

1. $\dfrac{2}{3} = \dfrac{2}{3} \cdot 1 = \dfrac{2}{3} \cdot \dfrac{-1}{-1} = \dfrac{2(-1)}{3(-1)} = \dfrac{-2}{-3}$.   Thus, $\dfrac{2}{3} = \dfrac{-2}{-3}$.

(A negative number divided by a negative number is positive.)

2. $-\dfrac{2}{3} = -1 \cdot \dfrac{2}{3} = \dfrac{-1}{1} \cdot \dfrac{2}{3} = \dfrac{-1 \cdot 2}{1 \cdot 3} = \dfrac{-2}{3}$.   Thus, $-\dfrac{2}{3} = \dfrac{-2}{3}$.

(A negative number divided by a positive number is negative.)

3. $\dfrac{-2}{3} = \dfrac{-2}{3} \cdot 1 = \dfrac{-2}{3} \cdot \dfrac{-1}{-1} = \dfrac{-2(-1)}{3(-1)} = \dfrac{2}{-3}$.   Thus, $-\dfrac{2}{3} = \dfrac{2}{-3}$.

(A positive number divided by a negative number is negative.)

We can use the following properties to make sign changes in fraction notation.

SIGN CHANGES IN FRACTION NOTATION

For any numbers a and b, $b \neq 0$:

1. $\dfrac{-a}{-b} = \dfrac{a}{b}$

(The opposite of a number a divided by the opposite of another number b is the same as the quotient of the two numbers a and b.)

2. $\dfrac{-a}{b} = \dfrac{a}{-b} = -\dfrac{a}{b}$

(The opposite of a number a divided by another number b is the same as the number a divided by the opposite of the number b, and both are the same as the opposite of a *divided by b*.)

Do Exercises 25–27.

Divide.

23. $21.7 \div (-3.1)$

24. $-20.4 \div (-4)$

Find two equal expressions for each number with negative signs in different places.

25. $\dfrac{-5}{6}$

26. $-\dfrac{8}{7}$

27. $\dfrac{10}{-3}$

Answers

23. -7 **24.** 5.1 **25.** $\dfrac{5}{-6}; -\dfrac{5}{6}$ **26.** $\dfrac{8}{-7}; \dfrac{-8}{7}$

27. $\dfrac{-10}{3}; -\dfrac{10}{3}$

(d) Applications and Problem Solving

EXAMPLE 24 *Chemical Reaction.* During a chemical reaction, the temperature in a beaker decreased every minute by the same number of degrees. The temperature was 56°F at 10:10 A.M. By 10:42 A.M., the temperature had dropped to −12°F. By how many degrees did it change each minute?

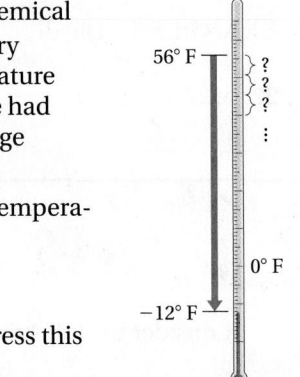

We first determine by how many degrees d the temperature changed altogether. We subtract −12 from 56:

$$d = 56 - (-12) = 56 + 12 = 68.$$

The temperature changed a total of 68°. We can express this as −68° since the temperature dropped.

The amount of time t that passed was 42 − 10, or 32 min. Thus the number of degrees T that the temperature dropped each minute is given by

$$T = \frac{d}{t} = \frac{-68}{32} = -2.125.$$

The change was −2.125°F per minute.

> **28. Chemical Reaction.** During a chemical reaction, the temperature in a beaker decreased every minute by the same number of degrees. The temperature was 71°F at 2:12 P.M. By 2:37 P.M., the temperature had changed to −14°F. By how many degrees did it change each minute?

Do Exercise 28.

Calculator Corner

Operations on the Real Numbers We can perform operations on the real numbers on a graphing calculator. Recall that negative numbers are entered using the opposite key, (−), rather than the subtraction operation key, −. Consider the sum −5 + (−3.8). We use parentheses when we write this sum in order to separate the addition symbol and the "opposite of" symbol and thus make the expression more easily read. When we enter this calculation on a graphing calculator, however, the parentheses are not necessary. We can press (−) 5 + (−) 3 . 8 **ENTER**. The result is −8.8. Note that it is not incorrect to enter the parentheses. The result will be the same if this is done.

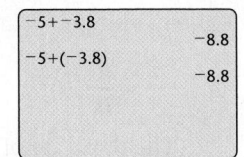

To find the difference 10 − (−17), we press 1 0 − (−) 1 7 **ENTER**. The result is 27. We can also multiply and divide real numbers. To find −5 · (−7), we press (−) 5 × (−) 7 **ENTER**, and to find 45 ÷ (−9), we press 4 5 ÷ (−) 9 **ENTER**. Note that it is not necessary to use parentheses in any of these calculations.

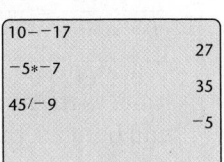

Exercises: Use a calculator to perform each operation.

1. −8 + 4	**2.** 1.2 + (−1.5)	**3.** −7 + (−5)	**4.** −7.6 + (−1.9)
5. −8 − 4	**6.** 1.2 − (−1.5)	**7.** −7 − (−5)	**8.** −7.6 − (−1.9)
9. −8 · 4	**10.** 1.2 · (−1.5)	**11.** −7 · (−5)	**12.** −7.6 · (−1.9)
13. −8 ÷ 4	**14.** 1.2 ÷ (−1.5)	**15.** −7 ÷ (−5)	**16.** −7.6 ÷ (−1.9)

Answer

28. −3.4°F per minute

a Divide, if possible. Check each answer.

1. $48 \div (-6)$

2. $\dfrac{42}{-7}$

3. $\dfrac{28}{-2}$

4. $24 \div (-12)$

5. $\dfrac{-24}{8}$

6. $-18 \div (-2)$

7. $\dfrac{-36}{-12}$

8. $-72 \div (-9)$

9. $\dfrac{-72}{9}$

10. $\dfrac{-50}{25}$

11. $-100 \div (-50)$

12. $\dfrac{-200}{8}$

13. $-108 \div 9$

14. $\dfrac{-63}{-7}$

15. $\dfrac{200}{-25}$

16. $-300 \div (-16)$

17. $\dfrac{75}{0}$

18. $\dfrac{0}{-5}$

19. $\dfrac{0}{-2.6}$

20. $\dfrac{-23}{0}$

b Find the reciprocal.

21. $\dfrac{15}{7}$

22. $\dfrac{3}{8}$

23. $-\dfrac{47}{13}$

24. $-\dfrac{31}{12}$

25. 13

26. -10

27. -32

28. 15

29. $\dfrac{1}{-7.1}$

30. $\dfrac{1}{-4.9}$

31. $\dfrac{1}{9}$

32. $\dfrac{1}{16}$

33. $\dfrac{1}{4y}$

34. $\dfrac{-1}{8a}$

35. $\dfrac{2a}{3b}$

36. $\dfrac{-4y}{3x}$

© Rewrite each division as a multiplication.

37. $4 \div 17$

38. $5 \div (-8)$

39. $\dfrac{8}{-13}$

40. $-\dfrac{13}{47}$

41. $\dfrac{13.9}{-1.5}$

42. $-\dfrac{47.3}{21.4}$

43. $\dfrac{2}{3} \div \left(-\dfrac{4}{5}\right)$

44. $\dfrac{3}{4} \div \left(-\dfrac{7}{10}\right)$

45. $\dfrac{\frac{x}{1}}{y}$

46. $\dfrac{13}{\frac{1}{x}}$

47. $\dfrac{3x + 4}{5}$

48. $\dfrac{4y - 8}{-7}$

Divide.

49. $\dfrac{3}{4} \div \left(-\dfrac{2}{3}\right)$

50. $\dfrac{7}{8} \div \left(-\dfrac{1}{2}\right)$

51. $-\dfrac{5}{4} \div \left(-\dfrac{3}{4}\right)$

52. $-\dfrac{5}{9} \div \left(-\dfrac{5}{6}\right)$

53. $-\dfrac{2}{7} \div \left(-\dfrac{4}{9}\right)$

54. $-\dfrac{3}{5} \div \left(-\dfrac{5}{8}\right)$

55. $-\dfrac{3}{8} \div \left(-\dfrac{8}{3}\right)$

56. $-\dfrac{5}{8} \div \left(-\dfrac{6}{5}\right)$

57. $-\dfrac{5}{6} \div \dfrac{2}{3}$

58. $-\dfrac{7}{16} \div \dfrac{3}{8}$

59. $-\dfrac{9}{4} \div \dfrac{5}{12}$

60. $-\dfrac{3}{5} \div \dfrac{7}{10}$

61. $\dfrac{-11}{-13}$

62. $\dfrac{-21}{-25}$ ___

63. $-6.6 \div 3.3$

64. $-44.1 \div (-6.3)$

Copyright © 2012 Pearson Education, Inc.

65. $\dfrac{48.6}{-3}$ **66.** $\dfrac{-1.9}{20}$ **67.** $\dfrac{-12.5}{5}$ **68.** $\dfrac{-17.8}{3.2}$

69. $11.25 \div (-9)$ **70.** $-9.6 \div (-6.4)$ **71.** $\dfrac{-9}{17 - 17}$ **72.** $\dfrac{-8}{-5 + 5}$

 Percent of Increase or Decrease in Employment. A percent of increase is generally positive and a percent of decrease is generally negative. The table below lists estimates of the number of job opportunities for various occupations in 2006 and 2016. In Exercises 73–76, find the missing numbers.

	OCCUPATION	NUMBER OF JOBS IN 2006 (in thousands)	NUMBER OF JOBS IN 2016 (in thousands)	CHANGE	PERCENT OF INCREASE OR DECREASE
	Electrician	705	757	52	7.4%
	File clerk	234	137	−97	−41.5%
73.	Athletic trainer	17	21	4	
74.	Child-care worker	1388	1636	248	
75.	Cashier	3527	3411	−116	
76.	Fisherman	38	32	−6	

SOURCE: U.S. Bureau of Labor Statistics *Occupational Outlook Handbook*

Skill Maintenance

Simplify.   [1.6c]

77. $2^3 - 5 \cdot 3 + 8 \cdot 10 \div 2$

78. $16 \cdot 2^3 - 5 \cdot 3 + 80 \div 10 \cdot 2$

79. $1000 \div 100 \div 10$

80. $216 \cdot 6^3 \div 6^2$

81. Simplify: $\dfrac{264}{468}$.   [2.1e]

82. Convert to decimal notation: 47.7%.   [4.2b]

83. Convert to percent notation: $\dfrac{7}{8}$.   [4.3a]

84. Simplify: $\dfrac{40}{60}$.   [2.1e]

85. Divide and simplify: $\dfrac{12}{25} \div \dfrac{32}{75}$.   [2.2c]

86. Multiply and simplify: $\dfrac{12}{25} \cdot \dfrac{32}{75}$.   [2.2a]

Synthesis

87. Find the reciprocal of -10.5. What happens if you take the reciprocal of the result?

88. Determine those real numbers a for which the opposite of a is the same as the reciprocal of a.

Determine whether each expression represents a positive number or a negative number when a and b are negative.

89. $\dfrac{-a}{b}$ **90.** $\dfrac{-a}{-b}$ **91.** $-\left(\dfrac{a}{-b}\right)$ **92.** $-\left(\dfrac{-a}{b}\right)$ **93.** $-\left(\dfrac{-a}{-b}\right)$

7.7

Properties of Real Numbers

OBJECTIVES

a Find equivalent fraction expressions and simplify fraction expressions.

b Use the commutative and associative laws to find equivalent expressions.

c Use the distributive laws to multiply expressions like 8 and $x - y$.

d Use the distributive laws to factor expressions like $4x - 12 + 24y$.

e Collect like terms.

a Equivalent Expressions

In solving equations and doing other kinds of work in algebra, we manipulate expressions in various ways. For example, instead of $x + x$, we might write $2x$, knowing that the two expressions represent the same number for any allowable replacement of x. In that sense, the expressions $x + x$ and $2x$ are **equivalent**, as are $\dfrac{3}{x}$ and $\dfrac{3x}{x^2}$, even though 0 is not an allowable replacement because division by 0 is not defined.

> ### EQUIVALENT EXPRESSIONS
>
> Two expressions that have the same value for all allowable replacements are called **equivalent**.

The expressions $x + 3x$ and $5x$ are *not* equivalent, as we see in Margin Exercise 2.

Do Exercises 1 and 2.

In this section, we will consider several laws of real numbers that will allow us to find equivalent expressions. The first two laws are the *identity properties of 0 and 1*.

> ### THE IDENTITY PROPERTY OF 0
>
> For any real number a,
>
> $$a + 0 = 0 + a = a.$$
>
> (The number 0 is the *additive identity*.)

> ### THE IDENTITY PROPERTY OF 1
>
> For any real number a,
>
> $$a \cdot 1 = 1 \cdot a = a.$$
>
> (The number 1 is the *multiplicative identity*.)

We often refer to the use of the identity property of 1 as "multiplying by 1." We can use this method to find equivalent fraction expressions. Recall from arithmetic that to multiply with fraction notation, we multiply the numerators and multiply the denominators. (See also Section 2.2.)

EXAMPLE 1 Write a fraction expression equivalent to $\frac{2}{3}$ with a denominator of $3x$:

$$\frac{2}{3} = \frac{\square}{3x}.$$

Complete the table by evaluating each expression for the given values.

1.

Value	$x + x$	$2x$
$x = 3$		
$x = -6$		
$x = 4.8$		

2.

Value	$x + 3x$	$5x$
$x = 2$		
$x = -6$		
$x = 4.8$		

Answers

1. 6, 6; −12, −12; 9.6, 9.6   **2.** 8, 10; −24, −30; 19.2, 24

Note that $3x = 3 \cdot x$. We want fraction notation for $\frac{2}{3}$ that has a denominator of $3x$, but the denominator 3 is missing a factor of x. Thus we multiply by 1, using x/x as an equivalent expression for 1:

$$\frac{2}{3} = \frac{2}{3} \cdot 1 = \frac{2}{3} \cdot \frac{x}{x} = \frac{2x}{3x}.$$

The expressions $2/3$ and $2x/(3x)$ are equivalent. They have the same value for any allowable replacement. Note that $2x/3x$ is not defined for a replacement of 0, but for all nonzero real numbers, the expressions $2/3$ and $2x/(3x)$ have the same value.

Do Exercises 3 and 4.

In algebra, we consider an expression like $2/3$ to be "simplified" from $2x/(3x)$. To find such simplified expressions, we use the identity property of 1 to remove a factor of 1. (See also Section 2.1.)

EXAMPLE 2 Simplify: $-\dfrac{20x}{12x}$.

$$-\frac{20x}{12x} = -\frac{5 \cdot 4x}{3 \cdot 4x} \qquad \text{We look for the largest factor common to both the numerator and the denominator and factor each.}$$

$$= -\frac{5}{3} \cdot \frac{4x}{4x} \qquad \text{Factoring the fraction expression}$$

$$= -\frac{5}{3} \cdot 1 \qquad \frac{4x}{4x} = 1$$

$$= -\frac{5}{3} \qquad \text{Removing a factor of 1 using the identity property of 1}$$

EXAMPLE 3 Simplify: $\dfrac{14ab}{56a}$.

$$\frac{14ab}{56a} = \frac{14a \cdot b}{14a \cdot 4} = \frac{14a}{14a} \cdot \frac{b}{4} = 1 \cdot \frac{b}{4} = \frac{b}{4}$$

Do Exercises 5–8.

(b) The Commutative and Associative Laws

The Commutative Laws

Let's examine the expressions $x + y$ and $y + x$, as well as xy and yx.

EXAMPLE 4 Evaluate $x + y$ and $y + x$ when $x = 4$ and $y = 3$.

We substitute 4 for x and 3 for y in both expressions:

$$x + y = 4 + 3 = 7; \qquad y + x = 3 + 4 = 7.$$

EXAMPLE 5 Evaluate xy and yx when $x = 3$ and $y = -12$.

We substitute 3 for x and -12 for y in both expressions:

$$xy = 3 \cdot (-12) = -36; \qquad yx = (-12) \cdot 3 = -36.$$

Do Exercises 9 and 10.

3. Write a fraction expression equivalent to $\frac{3}{4}$ with a denominator of 8:

$$\frac{3}{4} = \frac{\square}{8}.$$

4. Write a fraction expression equivalent to $\frac{3}{4}$ with a denominator of $4t$:

$$\frac{3}{4} = \frac{\square}{4t}.$$

Simplify.

5. $\dfrac{3y}{4y}$

6. $-\dfrac{16m}{12m}$

7. $\dfrac{5xy}{40y}$

8. $\dfrac{18p}{24pq}$

9. Evaluate $x + y$ and $y + x$ when $x = -2$ and $y = 3$.

10. Evaluate xy and yx when $x = -2$ and $y = 5$.

Answers

3. $\dfrac{6}{8}$ 4. $\dfrac{3t}{4t}$ 5. $\dfrac{3}{4}$ 6. $-\dfrac{4}{3}$

7. $\dfrac{x}{8}$ 8. $\dfrac{3}{4q}$ 9. 1; 1   10. -10; -10

The expressions $x + y$ and $y + x$ have the same values no matter what the variables stand for. Thus they are equivalent. Therefore, when we add two numbers, the order in which we add does not matter. Similarly, the expressions xy and yx are equivalent. They also have the same values, no matter what the variables stand for. Therefore, when we multiply two numbers, the order in which we multiply does not matter.

The following are examples of general patterns or laws.

THE COMMUTATIVE LAWS

Addition. For any numbers a and b,

$$a + b = b + a.$$

(We can change the order when adding without affecting the answer.)

Multiplication. For any numbers a and b,

$$ab = ba.$$

(We can change the order when multiplying without affecting the answer.)

Using a commutative law, we know that $x + 2$ and $2 + x$ are equivalent. Similarly, $3x$ and $x(3)$ are equivalent. Thus, in an algebraic expression, we can replace one with the other and the result will be equivalent to the original expression.

EXAMPLE 6 Use the commutative laws to write an equivalent expression: **(a)** $y + 5$; **(b)** mn; **(c)** $7 + xy$.

a) An expression equivalent to $y + 5$ is $5 + y$ by the commutative law of addition.

b) An expression equivalent to mn is nm by the commutative law of multiplication.

c) An expression equivalent to $7 + xy$ is $xy + 7$ by the commutative law of addition. Another expression equivalent to $7 + xy$ is $7 + yx$ by the commutative law of multiplication. Another equivalent expression is $yx + 7$.

Use a commutative law to write an equivalent expression.

11. $x + 9$

12. pq

13. $xy + t$

Do Exercises 11–13.

The Associative Laws

Now let's examine the expressions $a + (b + c)$ and $(a + b) + c$. Note that these expressions involve the use of parentheses as *grouping* symbols, and they also involve three numbers. Calculations within parentheses are to be done first.

EXAMPLE 7 Calculate and compare: $3 + (8 + 5)$ and $(3 + 8) + 5$.

$$3 + (8 + 5) = 3 + 13 \qquad \text{Calculating within parentheses first;}$$
$$\text{adding the 8 and the 5}$$

$$= 16;$$

$$(3 + 8) + 5 = 11 + 5 \qquad \text{Calculating within parentheses first;}$$
$$\text{adding the 3 and the 8}$$

$$= 16$$

Answers

11. $9 + x$ **12.** qp
13. $t + xy$, or $yx + t$, or $t + yx$

The two expressions in Example 7 name the same number. Moving the parentheses to group the additions differently does not affect the value of the expression.

EXAMPLE 8 Calculate and compare: $3 \cdot (4 \cdot 2)$ and $(3 \cdot 4) \cdot 2$.

$$3 \cdot (4 \cdot 2) = 3 \cdot 8 = 24; \qquad (3 \cdot 4) \cdot 2 = 12 \cdot 2 = 24$$

Do Exercises 14 and 15.

You may have noted that when only addition is involved, numbers can be grouped any way we please without affecting the answer. When only multiplication is involved, numbers can also be grouped any way we please without affecting the answer.

THE ASSOCIATIVE LAWS

Addition. For any numbers a, b, and c,

$$a + (b + c) = (a + b) + c.$$

(Numbers can be grouped in any manner for addition.)

Multiplication. For any numbers a, b, and c,

$$a \cdot (b \cdot c) = (a \cdot b) \cdot c.$$

(Numbers can be grouped in any manner for multiplication.)

EXAMPLE 9 Use an associative law to write an equivalent expression: **(a)** $(y + z) + 3$; **(b)** $8(xy)$.

a) An expression equivalent to $(y + z) + 3$ is $y + (z + 3)$ by the associative law of addition.

b) An expression equivalent to $8(xy)$ is $(8x)y$ by the associative law of multiplication.

Do Exercises 16 and 17.

The associative laws say that numbers can be grouped any way we please when only additions or only multiplications are involved. Thus we often omit the parentheses. For example,

$$x + (y + 2) \quad \text{means} \quad x + y + 2, \qquad \text{and} \qquad (lw)h \quad \text{means} \quad lwh.$$

Using the Commutative and Associative Laws Together

EXAMPLE 10 Use the commutative and associative laws to write at least three expressions equivalent to $(x + 5) + y$.

a) $(x + 5) + y = x + (5 + y)$ Using the associative law first and then using
$\qquad\qquad\quad = x + (y + 5)$ the commutative law

b) $(x + 5) + y = y + (x + 5)$ Using the commutative law twice
$\qquad\qquad\quad = y + (5 + x)$

c) $(x + 5) + y = (5 + x) + y$ Using the commutative law first and then the
$\qquad\qquad\quad = 5 + (x + y)$ associative law

14. Calculate and compare:
$$8 + (9 + 2) \text{ and } (8 + 9) + 2.$$

15. Calculate and compare:
$$10 \cdot (5 \cdot 3) \text{ and } (10 \cdot 5) \cdot 3.$$

Use an associative law to write an equivalent expression.

16. $r + (s + 7)$

17. $9(ab)$

Answers

14. 19; 19   **15.** 150; 150   **16.** $(r + s) + 7$
17. $(9a)b$

7.7 Properties of Real Numbers   **541**

EXAMPLE 11   Use the commutative and associative laws to write at least three expressions equivalent to $(3x)y$.

a) $(3x)y = 3(xy)$ Using the associative law first and then using the
    $\quad\quad\quad = 3(yx)$ commutative law

b) $(3x)y = y(3x)$ Using the commutative law twice
    $\quad\quad\quad = y(x \cdot 3)$

c) $(3x)y = (x \cdot 3)y$ Using the commutative law, and then the associative law,
    $\quad\quad\quad = x(3y)$ and then the commutative law again
    $\quad\quad\quad = x(y \cdot 3)$

Do Exercises 18 and 19.

Use the commutative and associative laws to write at least three equivalent expressions.

18. $4(tu)$

19. $r + (2 + s)$

(c) The Distributive Laws

The *distributive laws* are the basis of many procedures in both arithmetic and algebra. They are probably the most important laws that we use to manipulate algebraic expressions. The distributive law of multiplication over addition involves two operations: addition and multiplication.

Let's begin by considering a multiplication problem from arithmetic:

$$
\begin{array}{r}
4\ 5 \\
7 \\
\hline
3\ 5 \\
2\ 8\ 0 \\
3\ 1\ 5 \\
\end{array}
$$

← This is $7 \cdot 5$.
← This is $7 \cdot 40$.
← This is the sum $7 \cdot 5 + 7 \cdot 40$.

To carry out the multiplication, we actually added two products. That is,

$$7 \cdot 45 = 7(5 + 40) = 7 \cdot 5 + 7 \cdot 40.$$

Let's examine this further. If we wish to multiply a sum of several numbers by a factor, we can either add and then multiply, or multiply and then add.

EXAMPLE 12   Compute in two ways: $5 \cdot (4 + 8)$.

a) $5 \cdot (4 + 8)$ Adding within parentheses first, and then multiplying

$\quad = 5 \cdot \quad 12$

$\quad = 60$

b) $5 \cdot (4 + 8) = (5 \cdot 4) + (5 \cdot 8)$ Distributing the multiplication to terms
within parentheses first and then adding

$\quad\quad\quad = \quad 20 \quad + \quad 40$

$\quad\quad\quad = \quad 60$

Do Exercises 20–22.

Compute.

20. a) $7 \cdot (3 + 6)$

  b) $(7 \cdot 3) + (7 \cdot 6)$

21. a) $2 \cdot (10 + 30)$

  b) $(2 \cdot 10) + (2 \cdot 30)$

22. a) $(2 + 5) \cdot 4$

  b) $(2 \cdot 4) + (5 \cdot 4)$

> **THE DISTRIBUTIVE LAW OF MULTIPLICATION OVER ADDITION**
>
> For any numbers a, b, and c,
>
> $$a(b + c) = ab + ac.$$

Answers

18. $(4t)u, (tu)4, t(4u)$; answers may vary
19. $(2 + r) + s, (r + s) + 2, s + (r + 2)$;
answers may vary   **20. (a)** $7 \cdot 9 = 63$;
(b) $21 + 42 = 63$ **21. (a)** $2 \cdot 40 = 80$;
(b) $20 + 60 = 80$ **22. (a)** $7 \cdot 4 = 28$;
(b) $8 + 20 = 28$

In the statement of the distributive law, we know that in an expression such as $ab + ac$, the multiplications are to be done first according to the rules for order of operations. (See Section 1.6.) So, instead of writing $(4 \cdot 5) + (4 \cdot 7)$, we can write $4 \cdot 5 + 4 \cdot 7$. However, in $a(b + c)$, we cannot omit the parentheses. If we did, we would have $ab + c$, which means $(ab) + c$. For example, $3(4 + 2) = 3(6) = 18$, but $3 \cdot 4 + 2 = 12 + 2 = 14$.

There is another distributive law that relates multiplication and subtraction. This law says that to multiply by a difference, we can either subtract and then multiply, or multiply and then subtract.

THE DISTRIBUTIVE LAW OF MULTIPLICATION OVER SUBTRACTION

For any numbers a, b, and c,

$$a(b - c) = ab - ac.$$

We often refer to "*the* distributive law" when we mean *either* or *both* of these laws.

Do Exercises 23–25.

What do we mean by the *terms* of an expression? **Terms** are separated by addition signs. If there are subtraction signs, we can find an equivalent expression that uses addition signs.

EXAMPLE 13 What are the terms of $3x - 4y + 2z$?

We have

$$3x - 4y + 2z = 3x + (-4y) + 2z. \quad \text{Separating parts with } + \text{ signs}$$

The terms are $3x$, $-4y$, and $2z$.

Do Exercises 26 and 27.

The distributive laws are a basis for a procedure in algebra called **multiplying**. In an expression like $8(a + 2b - 7)$, we multiply each term inside the parentheses by 8:

$$8(a + 2b - 7) = 8 \cdot a + 8 \cdot 2b - 8 \cdot 7 = 8a + 16b - 56.$$

EXAMPLES Multiply.

14. $9(x - 5) = 9 \cdot x - 9 \cdot 5$ Using the distributive law of multiplication over subtraction

$$= 9x - 45$$

15. $\frac{2}{3}(w + 1) = \frac{2}{3} \cdot w + \frac{2}{3} \cdot 1$ Using the distributive law of multiplication over addition

$$= \frac{2}{3}w + \frac{2}{3}$$

16. $\frac{4}{3}(s - t + w) = \frac{4}{3}s - \frac{4}{3}t + \frac{4}{3}w$ Using both distributive laws

Do Exercises 28–30.

Calculate.

23. a) $4(5 - 3)$

   b) $4 \cdot 5 - 4 \cdot 3$

24. a) $-2 \cdot (5 - 3)$

   b) $-2 \cdot 5 - (-2) \cdot 3$

25. a) $5 \cdot (2 - 7)$

   b) $5 \cdot 2 - 5 \cdot 7$

What are the terms of each expression?

26. $5x - 8y + 3$

27. $-4y - 2x + 3z$

Multiply.

28. $3(x - 5)$

29. $5(x + 1)$

30. $\frac{3}{5}(p + q - t)$

Answers

23. (a) $4 \cdot 2 = 8$; (b) $20 - 12 = 8$
24. (a) $-2 \cdot 2 = -4$; (b) $-10 + 6 = -4$
25. (a) $5(-5) = -25$; (b) $10 - 35 = -25$
26. $5x, -8y, 3$ 27. $-4y, -2x, 3z$
28. $3x - 15$ 29. $5x + 5$
30. $\frac{3}{5}p + \frac{3}{5}q - \frac{3}{5}t$

EXAMPLE 17 Multiply: $-4(x - 2y + 3z)$.

$$-4(x - 2y + 3z) = -4 \cdot x - (-4)(2y) + (-4)(3z) \quad \text{Using both distributive laws}$$

$$= -4x - (-8y) + (-12z) \quad \text{Multiplying}$$

$$= -4x + 8y - 12z$$

We can also do this problem by first finding an equivalent expression with all plus signs and then multiplying:

$$-4(x - 2y + 3z) = -4[x + (-2y) + 3z]$$

$$= -4 \cdot x + (-4)(-2y) + (-4)(3z)$$

$$= -4x + 8y - 12z.$$

Do Exercises 31–33.

EXAMPLES Name the property or law illustrated by each equation.

Equation	*Property*
18. $5x = x(5)$	Commutative law of multiplication
19. $a + (8.5 + b) = (a + 8.5) + b$	Associative law of addition
20. $0 + 11 = 11$	Identity property of 0
21. $(-5s)t = -5(st)$	Associative law of multiplication
22. $\dfrac{3}{4} \cdot 1 = \dfrac{3}{4}$	Identity property of 1
23. $12.5(w - 3) = 12.5w - 12.5(3)$	Distributive law of multiplication over subtraction
24. $y + \dfrac{1}{2} = \dfrac{1}{2} + y$	Commutative law of addition

Do Exercises 34–40.

(d) Factoring

Factoring is the reverse of multiplying. To factor, we can use the distributive laws in reverse:

$$ab + ac = a(b + c) \quad \text{and} \quad ab - ac = a(b - c).$$

> **FACTORING**
>
> To **factor** an expression is to find an equivalent expression that is a product.

To factor $9x - 45$, for example, we find an equivalent expression that is a product: $9(x - 5)$. This reverses the multiplication that we did in Example 14. When all the terms of an expression have a factor in common, we can "factor it out" using the distributive laws. Note the following.

$9x$ has the factors $9, -9, 3, -3, 1, -1, x, -x, 3x, -3x, 9x, -9x;$

-45 has the factors $1, -1, 3, -3, 5, -5, 9, -9, 15, -15, 45, -45$

Multiply.

31. $-2(x - 3)$

32. $5(x - 2y + 4z)$

33. $-5(x - 2y + 4z)$

Name the property or law illustrated by each equation.

34. $(-8a)b = -8(ab)$

35. $p \cdot 1 = p$

36. $m + 34 = 34 + m$

37. $2(t + 5) = 2t + 2(5)$

38. $0 + k = k$

39. $-8x = x(-8)$

40. $x + (4.3 + b) = (x + 4.3) + b$

Answers

31. $-2x + 6$ **32.** $5x - 10y + 20z$
33. $-5x + 10y - 20z$ **34.** Associative law of multiplication   **35.** Identity property of 1
36. Commutative law of addition
37. Distributive law of multiplication over addition   **38.** Identity property of 0
39. Commutative law of multiplication
40. Associative law of addition

We generally remove the largest common factor. In this case, that factor is 9. Thus,

$$9x - 45 = 9 \cdot x - 9 \cdot 5$$
$$= 9(x - 5).$$

Remember that an expression has been factored when we have found an equivalent expression that is a product. Above, we note that $9x - 45$ and $9(x - 5)$ are equivalent expressions. The expression $9x - 45$ is the difference of $9x$ and 45; the expression $9(x - 5)$ is the product of 9 and $(x - 5)$.

EXAMPLES Factor.

25. $5x - 10 = 5 \cdot x - 5 \cdot 2$ Try to do this step mentally.

       $= 5(x - 2)$ You can check by multiplying.

26. $ax - ay + az = a(x - y + z)$

27. $9x + 27y - 9 = 9 \cdot x + 9 \cdot 3y - 9 \cdot 1 = 9(x + 3y - 1)$

Note in Example 27 that you might, at first, just factor out a 3, as follows:

$$9x + 27y - 9 = 3 \cdot 3x + 3 \cdot 9y - 3 \cdot 3$$
$$= 3(3x + 9y - 3).$$

At this point, the mathematics is correct, but the answer is not because there is another factor of 3 that can be factored out, as follows:

$$3 \cdot 3x + 3 \cdot 9y - 3 \cdot 3 = 3(3x + 9y - 3)$$
$$= 3(3 \cdot x + 3 \cdot 3y - 3 \cdot 1)$$
$$= 3 \cdot 3(x + 3y - 1)$$
$$= 9(x + 3y - 1).$$

We now have a correct answer, but it took more work than we did in Example 27. Thus it is better to look for the *greatest common factor* at the outset.

EXAMPLES Factor. Try to write just the answer, if you can.

28. $5x - 5y = 5(x - y)$

29. $-3x + 6y - 9z = -3(x - 2y + 3z)$

We usually factor out a negative factor when the first term is negative. The way we factor can depend on the situation in which we are working. We might also factor the expression in Example 29 as follows:

$$-3x + 6y - 9z = 3(-x + 2y - 3z).$$

30. $18z - 12x - 24 = 6(3z - 2x - 4)$

31. $\frac{1}{2}x + \frac{3}{2}y - \frac{1}{2} = \frac{1}{2}(x + 3y - 1)$

Remember that you can always check factoring by multiplying. Keep in mind that an expression is factored when it is written as a product.

Do Exercises 41–46.

Factor.

41. $6x - 12$

42. $3x - 6y + 9$

43. $bx + by - bz$

44. $16a - 36b + 42$

45. $\dfrac{3}{8}x - \dfrac{5}{8}y + \dfrac{7}{8}$

46. $-12x + 32y - 16z$

Answers

41. $6(x - 2)$ **42.** $3(x - 2y + 3)$
43. $b(x + y - z)$ **44.** $2(8a - 18b + 21)$
45. $\dfrac{1}{8}(3x - 5y + 7)$ **46.** $-4(3x - 8y + 4z)$,
or $4(-3x + 8y - 4z)$

(e) Collecting Like Terms

Terms such as $5x$ and $-4x$, whose variable factors are exactly the same, are called **like terms**. Similarly, numbers, such as -7 and 13, are like terms. Also, $3y^2$ and $9y^2$ are like terms because the variables are raised to the same power. Terms such as $4y$ and $5y^2$ are not like terms, and $7x$ and $2y$ are not like terms.

The process of **collecting like terms** is also based on the distributive laws. We can apply a distributive law when a factor is on the right because of the commutative law of multiplication.

Later in this text, terminology like "collecting like terms" and "combining like terms" will also be referred to as "simplifying."

EXAMPLES Collect like terms. Try to write just the answer, if you can.

32. $4x + 2x = (4 + 2)x = 6x$ Factoring out the x using a distributive law

33. $2x + 3y - 5x - 2y = 2x - 5x + 3y - 2y$
$$= (2 - 5)x + (3 - 2)y = -3x + 1y = -3x + y$$

34. $3x - x = 3x - 1x = (3 - 1)x = 2x$

35. $x - 0.24x = 1 \cdot x - 0.24x = (1 - 0.24)x = 0.76x$

36. $x - 6x = 1 \cdot x - 6 \cdot x = (1 - 6)x = -5x$

37. $4x - 7y + 9x - 5 + 3y - 8 = 13x - 4y - 13$

38. $\frac{2}{3}a - b + \frac{4}{5}a + \frac{1}{4}b - 10 = \frac{2}{3}a - 1 \cdot b + \frac{4}{5}a + \frac{1}{4}b - 10$
$$= \left(\frac{2}{3} + \frac{4}{5}\right)a + \left(-1 + \frac{1}{4}\right)b - 10$$
$$= \left(\frac{10}{15} + \frac{12}{15}\right)a + \left(-\frac{4}{4} + \frac{1}{4}\right)b - 10$$
$$= \frac{22}{15}a - \frac{3}{4}b - 10$$

Do Exercises 47–53.

Collect like terms.

47. $6x - 3x$ **48.** $7x - x$

49. $x - 9x$ **50.** $x - 0.41x$

51. $5x + 4y - 2x - y$

52. $3x - 7x - 11 + 8y + 4 - 13y$

53. $-\dfrac{2}{3} - \dfrac{3}{5}x + y + \dfrac{7}{10}x - \dfrac{2}{9}y$

STUDY TIPS

LEARNING RESOURCES

Please see the preface for more information on these resources and others. To order any of our products, call (800) 824-7799 in the United States or (201) 767-5021 outside the United States, or visit your campus bookstore.

- The *Student's Solutions Manual* contains fully worked-out solutions to the odd-numbered exercises in the exercise sets, as well as solutions to all exercises in the Mid-Chapter Reviews, end-of-chapter Review Exercises, and Chapter Tests.

Answers

47. $3x$ **48.** $6x$ **49.** $-8x$ **50.** $0.59x$
51. $3x + 3y$ **52.** $-4x - 5y - 7$
53. $\dfrac{1}{10}x + \dfrac{7}{9}y - \dfrac{2}{3}$

a Find an equivalent expression with the given denominator.

1. $\dfrac{3}{5} = \dfrac{\square}{5y}$

2. $\dfrac{5}{8} = \dfrac{\square}{8t}$

3. $\dfrac{2}{3} = \dfrac{\square}{15x}$

4. $\dfrac{6}{7} = \dfrac{\square}{14y}$

5. $\dfrac{2}{x} = \dfrac{\square}{x^2}$

6. $\dfrac{4}{9x} = \dfrac{\square}{9xy}$

Simplify.

7. $-\dfrac{24a}{16a}$

8. $-\dfrac{42t}{18t}$

9. $-\dfrac{42ab}{36ab}$

10. $-\dfrac{64pq}{48pq}$

11. $\dfrac{20st}{15t}$

12. $\dfrac{21w}{7wz}$

b Write an equivalent expression. Use a commutative law.

13. $y + 8$

14. $x + 3$

15. mn

16. yz

17. $9 + xy$

18. $11 + ab$

19. $ab + c$

20. $rs + t$

Write an equivalent expression. Use an associative law.

21. $a + (b + 2)$

22. $3(vw)$

23. $(8x)y$

24. $(y + z) + 7$

25. $(a + b) + 3$

26. $(5 + x) + y$

27. $3(ab)$

28. $(6x)y$

Use the commutative and associative laws to write three equivalent expressions.

29. $(a + b) + 2$

30. $(3 + x) + y$

31. $5 + (v + w)$

32. $6 + (x + y)$

33. $(xy)3$

34. $(ab)5$

35. $7(ab)$

36. $5(xy)$

c Multiply.

37. $2(b + 5)$

38. $4(x + 3)$

39. $7(1 + t)$

40. $4(1 + y)$

41. $6(5x + 2)$

42. $9(6m + 7)$

43. $7(x + 4 + 6y)$

44. $4(5x + 8 + 3p)$

45. $7(x - 3)$ **46.** $15(y - 6)$ **47.** $-3(x - 7)$

48. $1.2(x - 2.1)$ **49.** $\dfrac{2}{3}(b - 6)$ **50.** $\dfrac{5}{8}(y + 16)$

51. $7.3(x - 2)$ **52.** $5.6(x - 8)$ **53.** $-\dfrac{3}{5}(x - y + 10)$

54. $-\dfrac{2}{3}(a + b - 12)$ **55.** $-9(-5x - 6y + 8)$ **56.** $-7(-2x - 5y + 9)$

57. $-4(x - 3y - 2z)$ **58.** $8(2x - 5y - 8z)$

59. $3.1(-1.2x + 3.2y - 1.1)$ **60.** $-2.1(-4.2x - 4.3y - 2.2)$

List the terms of each expression.

61. $4x + 3z$ **62.** $8x - 1.4y$ **63.** $7x + 8y - 9z$ **64.** $8a + 10b - 18c$

d   Factor. Check by multiplying.

65. $2x + 4$ **66.** $5y + 20$ **67.** $30 + 5y$ **68.** $7x + 28$

69. $14x + 21y$ **70.** $18a + 24b$ **71.** $14t - 7$ **72.** $25m - 5$

73. $8x - 24$ **74.** $10x - 50$ **75.** $18a - 24b$ **76.** $32x - 20y$

Copyright © 2012 Pearson Education, Inc.

77. $-4y + 32$ **78.** $-6m + 24$ **79.** $5x + 10 + 15y$ **80.** $9a + 27b + 81$

81. $16m - 32n + 8$ **82.** $6x + 10y - 2$ **83.** $12a + 4b - 24$ **84.** $8m - 4n + 12$

85. $8x + 10y - 22$ **86.** $9a + 6b - 15$ **87.** $ax - a$ **88.** $by - 9b$

89. $ax - ay - az$ **90.** $cx + cy - cz$ **91.** $-18x + 12y + 6$ **92.** $-14x + 21y + 7$

93. $\frac{2}{3}x - \frac{5}{3}y + \frac{1}{3}$ **94.** $\frac{3}{5}a + \frac{4}{5}b - \frac{1}{5}$ **95.** $36x - 6y + 18z$ **96.** $8a - 4b + 20c$

  Collect like terms.

97. $9a + 10a$ **98.** $12x + 2x$ **99.** $10a - a$

100. $-16x + x$ **101.** $2x + 9z + 6x$ **102.** $3a - 5b + 7a$

103. $7x + 6y^2 + 9y^2$ **104.** $12m^2 + 6q + 9m^2$ **105.** $41a + 90 - 60a - 2$

106. $42x - 6 - 4x + 2$ **107.** $23 + 5t + 7y - t - y - 27$ **108.** $45 - 90d - 87 - 9d + 3 + 7d$

109. $\frac{1}{2}b + \frac{1}{2}b$ **110.** $\frac{2}{3}x + \frac{1}{3}x$ **111.** $2y + \frac{1}{4}y + y$

112. $\frac{1}{2}a + a + 5a$ **113.** $11x - 3x$ **114.** $9t - 17t$

115. $6n - n$

116. $100t - t$

117. $y - 17y$

118. $3m - 9m + 4$

119. $-8 + 11a - 5b + 6a - 7b + 7$

120. $8x - 5x + 6 + 3y - 2y - 4$

121. $9x + 2y - 5x$

122. $8y - 3z + 4y$

123. $11x + 2y - 4x - y$

124. $13a + 9b - 2a - 4b$

125. $2.7x + 2.3y - 1.9x - 1.8y$

126. $6.7a + 4.3b - 4.1a - 2.9b$

127. $\dfrac{13}{2}a + \dfrac{9}{5}b - \dfrac{2}{3}a - \dfrac{3}{10}b - 42$

128. $\dfrac{11}{4}x + \dfrac{2}{3}y - \dfrac{4}{5}x - \dfrac{1}{6}y + 12$

Skill Maintenance

Find the LCM.   [1.9a]

129. 16, 18

130. 18, 24

131. 16, 18, 24

132. 12, 15, 20

133. 16, 32

134. 24, 72

135. 15, 45, 90

136. 18, 54, 108

137. Add and simplify: $\dfrac{11}{12} + \dfrac{15}{16}$.   [2.3a]

138. Subtract and simplify: $\dfrac{7}{8} - \dfrac{2}{3}$.   [2.3b]

139. Subtract and simplify: $\dfrac{1}{8} - \dfrac{1}{3}$.   [2.3b]

140. Convert to percent notation: $\dfrac{3}{10}$.   [4.3a]

Synthesis

Determine whether the expressions are equivalent. Explain why if they are. Give an example if they are not. Examples may vary.

141. $3t + 5$ and $3 \cdot 5 + t$

142. $4x$ and $x + 4$

143. $5m + 6$ and $6 + 5m$

144. $(x + y) + z$ and $z + (x + y)$

145. Factor: $q + qr + qrs + qrst$.

146. Collect like terms:

$$21x + 44xy + 15y - 16x - 8y - 38xy + 2y + xy.$$

Copyright © 2012 Pearson Education, Inc.

7.8

Simplifying Expressions; Order of Operations

We now expand our ability to manipulate expressions by first considering opposites of sums and differences. Then we simplify expressions involving parentheses.

a Opposites of Sums

What happens when we multiply a real number by -1? Consider the following products:

$$-1(7) = -7, \quad -1(-5) = 5, \quad -1(0) = 0.$$

From these examples, it appears that when we multiply a number by -1, we get the opposite, or additive inverse, of that number.

> ### THE PROPERTY OF -1
>
> For any real number a,
>
> $$-1 \cdot a = -a.$$
>
> (Negative one times a is the opposite, or additive inverse, of a.)

The property of -1 enables us to find expressions equivalent to opposites of sums.

EXAMPLES Find an equivalent expression without parentheses.

1.
$$
\begin{aligned}
-(3 + x) &= -1(3 + x) && \text{Using the property of } -1 \\
&= -1 \cdot 3 + (-1)x && \text{Using a distributive law, multiplying} \\
& && \text{each term by } -1 \\
&= -3 + (-x) && \text{Using the property of } -1 \\
&= -3 - x
\end{aligned}
$$

2.
$$
\begin{aligned}
-(3x + 2y + 4) &= -1(3x + 2y + 4) && \text{Using the property of } -1 \\
&= -1(3x) + (-1)(2y) + (-1)4 && \text{Using a distributive} \\
& && \text{law} \\
&= -3x - 2y - 4 && \text{Using the property of } -1
\end{aligned}
$$

Do Exercises 1 and 2.

Suppose we want to remove parentheses in an expression like

$$-(x - 2y + 5).$$

We can first rewrite any subtractions inside the parentheses as additions. Then we take the opposite of each term:

$$
\begin{aligned}
-(x - 2y + 5) &= -[x + (-2y) + 5] \\
&= -x + 2y + (-5) = -x + 2y - 5.
\end{aligned}
$$

The most efficient method for removing parentheses is to replace each term in the parentheses with its opposite ("change the sign of every term"). Doing so for $-(x - 2y + 5)$, we obtain $-x + 2y - 5$ as an equivalent expression.

OBJECTIVES

a Find an equivalent expression for an opposite without parentheses, where an expression has several terms.

b Simplify expressions by removing parentheses and collecting like terms.

c Simplify expressions with parentheses inside parentheses.

d Simplify expressions using the rules for order of operations.

Find an equivalent expression without parentheses.

1. $-(x + 2)$

2. $-(5x + 2y + 8)$

Answers

1. $-x - 2$ **2.** $-5x - 2y - 8$

Find an equivalent expression without parentheses. Try to do this in one step.

3. $-(6 - t)$

4. $-(x - y)$

5. $-(-4a + 3t - 10)$

6. $-(18 - m - 2n + 4z)$

EXAMPLES Find an equivalent expression without parentheses.

3. $-(5 - y) = -5 + y$ Changing the sign of each term

4. $-(2a - 7b - 6) = -2a + 7b + 6$

5. $-(-3x + 4y + z - 7w - 23) = 3x - 4y - z + 7w + 23$

Do Exercises 3–6.

b Removing Parentheses and Simplifying

When a sum is added to another expression, as in $5x + (2x + 3)$, we can simply remove, or drop, the parentheses and collect like terms because of the associative law of addition:

$$5x + (2x + 3) = 5x + 2x + 3 = 7x + 3.$$

On the other hand, when a sum is subtracted from another expression, as in $3x - (4x + 2)$, we cannot simply drop the parentheses. However, we can subtract by adding an opposite. We then remove parentheses by changing the sign of each term inside the parentheses and collecting like terms.

EXAMPLE 6 Remove parentheses and simplify.

$$\begin{aligned}
3x - (4x + 2) &= 3x + [-(4x + 2)] &&\text{Adding the opposite of } (4x + 2) \\
&= 3x + (-4x - 2) &&\text{Changing the sign of each term inside the parentheses} \\
&= 3x - 4x - 2 \\
&= -x - 2 &&\text{Collecting like terms}
\end{aligned}$$

------------------------------------ *Caution!* ------------------------------------

Note that $3x - (4x + 2) \neq 3x - 4x + 2$. You cannot simply drop the parentheses.

Do Exercises 7 and 8.

Remove parentheses and simplify.

7. $5x - (3x + 9)$

8. $5y - 2 - (2y - 4)$

In practice, the first three steps of Example 6 are usually combined by changing the sign of each term in parentheses and then collecting like terms.

EXAMPLES Remove parentheses and simplify.

7. $5y - (3y + 4) = 5y - 3y - 4$ Removing parentheses by changing the sign of every term inside the parentheses

$\qquad\qquad\qquad = 2y - 4$ Collecting like terms

8. $3x - 2 - (5x - 8) = 3x - 2 - 5x + 8$

$\qquad\qquad\qquad\qquad = -2x + 6$

9. $(3a + 4b - 5) - (2a - 7b + 4c - 8)$

$\qquad = 3a + 4b - 5 - 2a + 7b - 4c + 8$

$\qquad = a + 11b - 4c + 3$

Do Exercises 9–11.

Remove parentheses and simplify.

9. $6x - (4x + 7)$

10. $8y - 3 - (5y - 6)$

11. $(2a + 3b - c) - (4a - 5b + 2c)$

Answers

3. $-6 + t$ 4. $-x + y$ 5. $4a - 3t + 10$
6. $-18 + m + 2n - 4z$ 7. $2x - 9$
8. $3y + 2$ 9. $2x - 7$ 10. $3y + 3$
11. $-2a + 8b - 3c$

Next, consider subtracting an expression consisting of several terms multiplied by a number other than 1 or −1.

EXAMPLE 10 Remove parentheses and simplify.

$$x - 3(x + y) = x + [-3(x + y)] \qquad \text{Adding the opposite of } 3(x + y)$$
$$= x + [-3x - 3y] \qquad \text{Multiplying } x + y \text{ by } -3$$
$$= x - 3x - 3y$$
$$= -2x - 3y \qquad \text{Collecting like terms}$$

EXAMPLES Remove parentheses and simplify

11. $3y - 2(4y - 5) = 3y - 8y + 10$ Multiplying each term in the parentheses by -2

$$= -5y + 10$$

12. $(2a + 3b - 7) - 4(-5a - 6b + 12)$
$$= 2a + 3b - 7 + 20a + 24b - 48 = 22a + 27b - 55$$

13. $2y - \frac{1}{3}(9y - 12) = 2y - 3y + 4 = -y + 4$

14. $6(5x - 3y) - 2(8x + y) = 30x - 18y - 16x - 2y = 14x - 20y$

> Do Exercises 12–16.

Remove parentheses and simplify.

12. $y - 9(x + y)$

13. $5a - 3(7a - 6)$

14. $4a - b - 6(5a - 7b + 8c)$

15. $5x - \frac{1}{4}(8x + 28)$

16. $4.6(5x - 3y) - 5.2(8x + y)$

(c) Parentheses Within Parentheses

In addition to parentheses, some expressions contain other grouping symbols such as brackets [ ] and braces { }.

> When more than one kind of grouping symbol occurs, do the computations in the innermost ones first. Then work from the inside out.

EXAMPLES Simplify.

15. $[3 - (7 + 3)] = [3 - 10] = -7$

16. $\{8 - [9 - (12 + 5)]\} = \{8 - [9 - 17]\}$ Computing $12 + 5$
$$= \{8 - [-8]\} \qquad \text{Computing } 9 - 17$$
$$= 8 + 8 = 16$$

17. $\left[(-4) \div \left(-\frac{1}{4}\right)\right] \div \frac{1}{4} = [(-4) \cdot (-4)] \div \frac{1}{4}$ Working within the brackets; computing $(-4) \div \left(-\frac{1}{4}\right)$
$$= 16 \div \frac{1}{4}$$
$$= 16 \cdot 4 = 64$$

18. $4(2 + 3) - \{7 - [4 - (8 + 5)]\}$
$$= 4 \cdot 5 - \{7 - [4 - 13]\} \qquad \text{Working with the innermost parentheses first}$$
$$= 20 - \{7 - [-9]\} \qquad \text{Computing } 4 \cdot 5 \text{ and } 4 - 13$$
$$= 20 - 16 \qquad \text{Computing } 7 - [-9]$$
$$= 4$$

> Do Exercises 17–20.

Simplify.

17. $12 - (8 + 2)$

18. $9 - [10 - (13 + 6)]$

19. $[24 \div (-2)] \div (-2)$

20. $5(3 + 4) - \{8 - [5 - (9 + 6)]\}$

Answers

12. $-9x - 8y$ 13. $-16a + 18$
14. $-26a + 41b - 48c$ 15. $3x - 7$
16. $-18.6x - 19y$ 17. 2   18. 18
19. 6   20. 17

EXAMPLE 19 Simplify.

$$[5(x + 2) - 3x] - [3(y + 2) - 7(y - 3)]$$
$$= [5x + 10 - 3x] - [3y + 6 - 7y + 21] \quad \text{Working with the innermost parentheses first}$$

$$= [2x + 10] - [-4y + 27] \quad \text{Collecting like terms within brackets}$$
$$= 2x + 10 + 4y - 27 \quad \text{Removing brackets}$$
$$= 2x + 4y - 17 \quad \text{Collecting like terms}$$

Do Exercise 21.

21. Simplify:
$$[3(x + 2) + 2x] -$$
$$[4(y + 2) - 3(y - 2)].$$

(d) Order of Operations

When several operations are to be done in a calculation or a problem, we apply the same rules that we did in Section 1.6. We repeat them here for review. (If you did not study that section earlier, you may wish to do so now.)

RULES FOR ORDER OF OPERATIONS

1. Do all calculations within grouping symbols before operations outside.
2. Evaluate all exponential expressions.
3. Do all multiplications and divisions in order from left to right.
4. Do all additions and subtractions in order from left to right.

These rules are consistent with the way in which most computers and scientific calculators perform calculations.

EXAMPLE 20 Simplify: $-34 \cdot 56 - 17$.

There are no parentheses or powers, so we start with the third step.

$$-34 \cdot 56 - 17 = -1904 - 17 \quad \text{Doing all multiplications and divisions in order from left to right}$$

$$= -1921 \quad \text{Doing all additions and subtractions in order from left to right}$$

EXAMPLE 21 Simplify: $25 \div (-5) + 50 \div (-2)$.

There are no calculations inside parentheses and no powers. The parentheses with (-5) and (-2) are used only to represent the negative numbers. We begin by doing all multiplications and divisions.

$$\underbrace{25 \div (-5)} + \underbrace{50 \div (-2)}$$

$$= -5 + (-25) \quad \text{Doing all multiplications and divisions in order from left to right}$$

$$= -30 \quad \text{Doing all additions and subtractions in order from left to right}$$

Do Exercises 22–24.

Simplify.
22. $23 - 42 \cdot 30$

23. $32 \div 8 \cdot 2$

24. $-24 \div 3 - 48 \div (-4)$

Answers

21. $5x - y - 8$ **22.** -1237 **23.** 8 **24.** 4

EXAMPLE 22 Simplify: $-2^4 + 51 \cdot 4 - (37 + 23 \cdot 2)$.

$$-2^4 + 51 \cdot 4 - (37 + 23 \cdot 2)$$
$$= -2^4 + 51 \cdot 4 - (37 + 46) \qquad \text{Working within the parentheses}$$
$$= -2^4 + 51 \cdot 4 - 83$$
$$= -16 + 51 \cdot 4 - 83 \qquad \text{Evaluating exponential expressions.}$$
$$\text{Note that } -2^4 \neq (-2)^4.$$
$$= -16 + 204 - 83 \qquad \text{Doing the multiplication}$$
$$= 188 - 83 \qquad \text{Doing all additions and subtractions}$$
$$\text{in order from left to right}$$
$$= 105$$

A fraction bar can play the role of a grouping symbol.

EXAMPLE 23 Simplify: $\dfrac{-64 \div (-16) \div (-2)}{2^3 - 3^2}$.

An equivalent expression with brackets as grouping symbols is

$$[-64 \div (-16) \div (-2)] \div [2^3 - 3^2].$$

This shows, in effect, that we do the calculations in the numerator and then in the denominator, and divide the results:

$$\frac{-64 \div (-16) \div (-2)}{2^3 - 3^2} = \frac{4 \div (-2)}{8 - 9} = \frac{-2}{-1} = 2.$$

Do Exercises 25 and 26.

Simplify.

25. $-4^3 + 52 \cdot 5 + 5^3 - (4^2 - 48 \div 4)$

26. $\dfrac{5 - 10 - 5 \cdot 23}{2^3 + 3^2 - 7}$

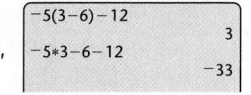

Calculator Corner

Order of Operations and Grouping Symbols Parentheses are necessary in some calculations in order to ensure that operations are performed in the desired order. To simplify $-5(3 - 6) - 12$, we press (−) 5 (3 − 6) − 1 2 ENTER. The result is 3. Without parentheses, the computation is $-5 \cdot 3 - 6 - 12$, and the result is -33.

When a negative number is raised to an even power, parentheses must also be used. To find $(-3)^4$, we press ((−) 3) ^ 4 ENTER. The result is 81. Without parentheses, the computation is $-3^4 = -1 \cdot 3^4 = -1 \cdot 81 = -81$.

To simplify an expression like $\dfrac{49 - 104}{7 + 4}$, we must enter it as $(49 - 104) \div (7 + 4)$. We press (4 9 − 1 0 4) ÷ (7 + 4) ENTER. The result is -5.

```
-5(3-6)-12
              3
-5*3-6-12
            -33
```

```
(-3)^4
             81
-3^4
            -81
```

```
(49-104)/(7+4)
             -5
```

Exercises: Calculate.

1. $-8 + 4(7 - 9) + 5$

2. $-3[2 + (-5)]$

3. $7[4 - (-3)] + 5[3^2 - (-4)]$

4. $(-7)^6$

5. $(-17)^5$

6. $(-104)^3$

7. -7^6

8. -17^5

9. -104^3

10. $\dfrac{38 - 178}{5 + 30}$

11. $\dfrac{311 - 17^2}{2 - 13}$

12. $785 - \dfrac{285 - 5^4}{17 + 3 \cdot 51}$

Translating for Success

1. **Calories in Cereal.** There are 140 calories in a $1\frac{1}{2}$-cup serving of Brand A cereal. How many calories are there in 6 cups of the cereal?

2. **Calories in Cereal.** There are 140 calories in 6 cups of Brand B cereal. How many calories are there in a $1\frac{1}{2}$-cup serving of the cereal?

3. **Gallons of Gasoline.** Jared's SUV traveled 310 mi on 15.5 gal of gasoline. At this rate, how many gallons would be needed to travel 465 mi?

4. **Gallons of Gasoline.** Elizabeth's new fuel-efficient car traveled 465 mi on 15.5 gal of gasoline. At this rate, how many gallons will be needed to travel 310 mi?

5. **Perimeter.** Find the perimeter of a rectangular field that measures 83.7 m by 62.4 m.

The goal of these matching questions is to practice step (2), *Translate*, of the five-step problem-solving process. Translate each word problem to an equation and select a correct translation from equations A–O.

A. $\dfrac{310}{15.5} = \dfrac{465}{x}$

B. $180 = 1\frac{1}{2} \cdot x$

C. $x = 71\frac{1}{8} - 76\frac{1}{2}$

D. $71\frac{1}{8} \cdot x = 74$

E. $74 \cdot 71\frac{1}{8} = x$

F. $x = 83.7 + 62.4$

G. $71\frac{1}{8} + x = 76\frac{1}{2}$

H. $x = 1\frac{2}{3} \cdot 180$

I. $\dfrac{140}{6} = \dfrac{x}{1\frac{1}{2}}$

J. $x = 2(83.7 + 62.4)$

K. $\dfrac{465}{15.5} = \dfrac{310}{x}$

L. $x = 83.7 \cdot 62.4$

M. $x = 180 \div 1\frac{2}{3}$

N. $\dfrac{140}{1\frac{1}{2}} = \dfrac{x}{6}$

O. $x = 1\frac{2}{3} \div 180$

Answers on page A-14

---

6. **Electric Bill.** Last month Todd's electric bills for his two rentals were $83.70 and $62.40. What was the total electric bill for the two properties?

7. **Package Tape.** A postal service center uses rolls of package tape that each contain 180 ft of tape. If it takes an average of $1\frac{2}{3}$ ft per package, how many packages can be taped with one roll?

8. **Online Price.** Jane spent $180 for an area rug in a department store. Later she saw the same rug for sale online and realized she had paid $1\frac{1}{2}$ times the online price. What was the online price?

9. **Heights of Sons.** Henry's three sons played basketball on three different college teams, Jeff, Jason, and Jared's heights are 74 in., $71\frac{1}{8}$ in., and $76\frac{1}{2}$ in., respectively. How much taller is Jared than Jason?

10. **Total Investment.** An investor bought 74 shares of stock at $71\frac{1}{8}$ per share. What was the total investment?

a Find an equivalent expression without parentheses.

1. $-(2x + 7)$

2. $-(8x + 4)$

3. $-(8 - x)$

4. $-(a - b)$

5. $-(4a - 3b + 7c)$

6. $-(x - 4y - 3z)$

7. $-(6x - 8y + 5)$

8. $-(4x + 9y + 7)$

9. $-(3x - 5y - 6)$

10. $-(6a - 4b - 7)$

11. $-(-8x - 6y - 43)$

12. $-(-2a + 9b - 5c)$

b Remove parentheses and simplify.

13. $9x - (4x + 3)$

14. $4y - (2y + 5)$

15. $2a - (5a - 9)$

16. $12m - (4m - 6)$

17. $2x + 7x - (4x + 6)$

18. $3a + 2a - (4a + 7)$

19. $2x - 4y - 3(7x - 2y)$

20. $3a - 9b - 1(4a - 8b)$

21. $15x - y - 5(3x - 2y + 5z)$

22. $4a - b - 4(5a - 7b + 8c)$

23. $(3x + 2y) - 2(5x - 4y)$

24. $(-6a - b) - 5(2b + a)$

25. $(12a - 3b + 5c) - 5(-5a + 4b - 6c)$

26. $(-8x + 5y - 12) - 6(2x - 4y - 10)$

c Simplify.

27. $9 - 2(5 - 4)$

28. $6 - 5(8 - 4)$

29. $8[7 - 6(4 - 2)]$

30. $10[7 - 4(7 - 5)]$

31. $[4(9 - 6) + 11] - [14 - (6 + 4)]$

32. $[7(8 - 4) + 16] - [15 - (7 + 8)]$

33. $[10(x + 3) - 4] + [2(x - 1) + 6]$

34. $[9(x + 5) - 7] + [4(x - 12) + 9]$

35. $[7(x + 5) - 19] - [4(x - 6) + 10]$

36. $[6(x + 4) - 12] - [5(x - 8) + 14]$

37. $3\{[7(x - 2) + 4] - [2(2x - 5) + 6]\}$

38. $4\{[8(x - 3) + 9] - [4(3x - 2) + 6]\}$

39. $4\{[5(x - 3) + 2] - 3[2(x + 5) - 9]\}$

40. $3\{[6(x - 4) + 5] - 2[5(x + 8) - 3]\}$

d Simplify.

41. $8 - 2 \cdot 3 - 9$

42. $8 - (2 \cdot 3 - 9)$

43. $(8 - 2 \cdot 3) - 9$

44. $(8 - 2)(3 - 9)$

45. $[(-24) \div (-3)] \div \left(-\frac{1}{2}\right)$

46. $[32 \div (-2)] \div \left(-\frac{1}{4}\right)$

47. $16 \cdot (-24) + 50$

48. $10 \cdot 20 - 15 \cdot 24$

49. $2^4 + 2^3 - 10$

50. $40 - 3^2 - 2^3$

51. $5^3 + 26 \cdot 71 - (16 + 25 \cdot 3)$

52. $4^3 + 10 \cdot 20 + 8^2 - 23$

Copyright © 2012 Pearson Education, Inc.

53. $4 \cdot 5 - 2 \cdot 6 + 4$

54. $4 \cdot (6 + 8)/(4 + 3)$

55. $4^3/8$

56. $5^3 - 7^2$

57. $8(-7) + 6(-5)$

58. $10(-5) + 1(-1)$

59. $19 - 5(-3) + 3$

60. $14 - 2(-6) + 7$

61. $9 \div (-3) + 16 \div 8$

62. $-32 - 8 \div 4 - (-2)$

63. $-4^2 + 6$

64. $-5^2 + 7$

65. $-8^2 - 3$

66. $-9^2 - 11$

67. $12 - 20^3$

68. $20 + 4^3 \div (-8)$

69. $2 \cdot 10^3 - 5000$

70. $-7(3^4) + 18$

71. $6[9 - (3 - 4)]$

72. $8[(6 - 13) - 11]$

73. $-1000 \div (-100) \div 10$

74. $256 \div (-32) \div (-4)$

75. $8 - (7 - 9)$

76. $(8 - 7) - 9$

77. $\dfrac{10 - 6^2}{9^2 + 3^2}$

78. $\dfrac{5^2 - 4^3 - 3}{9^2 - 2^2 - 1^5}$

79. $\dfrac{3(6 - 7) - 5 \cdot 4}{6 \cdot 7 - 8(4 - 1)}$

80. $\dfrac{20(8 - 3) - 4(10 - 3)}{10(2 - 6) - 2(5 + 2)}$

81. $\dfrac{|2^3 - 3^2| + |12 \cdot 5|}{-32 \div (-16) \div (-4)}$

82. $\dfrac{|3 - 5|^2 - |7 - 13|}{|12 - 9| + |11 - 14|}$

Skill Maintenance

In each of Exercises 83–90, fill in the blank with the correct term from the given list. Some of the choices may not be used and some may be used more than once.

83. The set of _____ is $\{\ldots, -5, -4, -3, -2, -1, 0, 1, 2, 3, \ldots\}$. [7.2a]

84. Two numbers whose sum is 0 are called _____ of each other. [7.3b]

85. The _____ of addition says that $a + b = b + a$ for any real numbers a and b. [7.7b]

86. The _____ states that for any real number a, $a \cdot 1 = 1 \cdot a = a$. [7.7a]

87. The _____ of addition says that $a + (b + c) = (a + b) + c$ for any real numbers a, b, and c. [7.7b]

88. The _____ of multiplication says that $a(bc) = (ab)c$ for any real numbers a, b, and c. [7.7b]

89. Two numbers whose product is 1 are called _____ of each other. [7.6b]

90. The equation $y + 0 = y$ illustrates the _____. [7.7a]

natural numbers
whole numbers
integers
real numbers
multiplicative inverses
additive inverses
commutative law
associative law
distributive law
identity property of 0
identity property of 1
property of −1

Synthesis

Find an equivalent expression by enclosing the last three terms in parentheses preceded by a minus sign.

91. $6y + 2x - 3a + c$

92. $x - y - a - b$

93. $6m + 3n - 5m + 4b$

Simplify.

94. $z - \{2z - [3z - (4z - 5z) - 6z] - 7z\} - 8z$

95. $\{x - [f - (f - x)] + [x - f]\} - 3x$

96. $x - \{x - 1 - [x - 2 - (x - 3 - \{x - 4 - [x - 5 - (x - 6)]\})]\}$

97. 🖩 Use your calculator to do the following.
   a) Evaluate $x^2 + 3$ when $x = 7$, when $x = -7$, and when $x = -5.013$.
   b) Evaluate $1 - x^2$ when $x = 5$, when $x = -5$, and when $x = -10.455$.

98. Express $3^3 + 3^3 + 3^3$ as a power of 3.

Find the average.

99. $-15, 20, 50, -82, -7, -2$

100. $-1, 1, 2, -2, 3, -8, -10$

Copyright © 2012 Pearson Education, Inc.

Key Terms and Properties

variable, p. 486
constant, p. 486
algebraic expression, p. 487
substitute, p. 487
evaluate, p. 487
natural numbers, p. 493
whole numbers, p. 493
integers, p. 493

opposites, p. 494
rational numbers, p. 495
terminating decimal, p. 497
repeating decimal, p. 497
irrational numbers, p. 497
real numbers, p. 498
absolute value, p. 500
additive inverse, p. 507

reciprocals, p. 530
multiplicative inverse, p. 530
equivalent expressions, p. 538
factor, p. 544
like terms, p. 546
collect like terms, p. 546

Properties of the Real-Number System

The Commutative Laws: $a + b = b + a, \quad ab = ba$

The Associative Laws: $a + (b + c) = (a + b) + c, \quad a(bc) = (ab)c$

The Identity Properties: $a + 0 = 0 + a = a, \quad a \cdot 1 = 1 \cdot a = a$

The Inverse Properties: For any real number a, there is an opposite $-a$ such that $a + (-a) = (-a) + a = 0$.

For any nonzero real number a, there is a reciprocal $\frac{1}{a}$ such that $a \cdot \frac{1}{a} = \frac{1}{a} \cdot a = 1$.

The Distributive Laws: $a(b + c) = ab + ac, \quad a(b - c) = ab - ac$

The Property of -1: $-1 \cdot a = -a$

Concept Reinforcement

Determine whether each statement is true or false.

_____ **1.** Every whole number is also an integer. [7.2d]

_____ **2.** The product of an even number of negative numbers is positive. [7.5a]

_____ **3.** The product of a number and its multiplicative inverse is -1. [7.6b]

_____ **4.** $a < b$ also has the meaning $b \geq a$. [7.2d]

Important Concepts

Objective 7.1a Evaluate algebraic expressions by substitution.

Example Evaluate $y - z$ when $y = 5$ and $z = -7$. $y - z = 5 - (-7) = 5 + 7 = 12$	**Practice Exercise** **1.** Evaluate $2a + b$ when $a = -1$ and $b = 16$.

Objective 7.2d Determine which of two real numbers is greater and indicate which, using $<$ or $>$.

Example Use $<$ or $>$ for $\square$ to write a true sentence: $-5 \;\square\; -12$. Since -5 is to the right of -12 on the number line, we have $-5 > -12$.	**Practice Exercise** **2.** Use $<$ or $>$ for $\square$ to write a true sentence: $-6 \;\square\; -3$.

Objective 7.2e Find the absolute value of a real number.

Example Find the absolute value: **(a)** $|21|$; **(b)** $|-3.2|$; **(c)** $|0|$.

a) The number is positive, so the absolute value is the same as the number.
$$|21| = 21$$

b) The number is negative, so we make it positive.
$$|-3.2| = 3.2$$

c) The number is 0, so the absolute value is the same as the number.
$$|0| = 0$$

Practice Exercise

3. Find: $\left|-\dfrac{5}{4}\right|$.

Objective 7.3a Add real numbers without using the number line.

Example Add without using the number line:
(a) $-13 + 4$; **(b)** $-2 + (-3)$.

a) We have a negative number and a positive number. The absolute values are 13 and 4. The difference is 9. The negative number has the larger absolute value, so the answer is negative.
$$-13 + 4 = -9$$

b) We have two negative numbers. The sum of the absolute values is $2 + 3$, or 5. The answer is negative.
$$-2 + (-3) = -5$$

Practice Exercise

4. Add without using the number line: $-5.6 + (-2.9)$.

Objective 7.4a Subtract real numbers.

Example Subtract: $-4 - (-6)$.
$$-4 - (-6) = -4 + 6 = 2$$

Practice Exercise

5. Subtract: $7 - 9$.

Objective 7.5a Multiply real numbers.

Example Multiply: **(a)** $-1.9(4)$; **(b)** $-7(-6)$.

a) The signs are different, so the answer is negative.
$$-1.9(4) = -7.6$$

b) The signs are the same, so the answer is positive.
$$-7(-6) = 42$$

Practice Exercise

6. Multiply: $-8(-7)$.

Objective 7.6a Divide integers.

Example Divide: **(a)** $15 \div (-3)$; **(b)** $-72 \div (-9)$.

a) The signs are different, so the answer is negative.
$$15 \div (-3) = -5$$

b) The signs are the same, so the answer is positive.
$$-72 \div (-9) = 8$$

Practice Exercise

7. Divide: $-48 \div 6$.

Objective 7.6c Divide real numbers.

Example   Divide: **(a)** $-\dfrac{1}{4} \div \dfrac{3}{5}$; **(b)** $-22.4 \div (-4)$.

a) We multiply by the reciprocal of the divisor:

$$-\frac{1}{4} \div \frac{3}{5} = -\frac{1}{4} \cdot \frac{5}{3} = -\frac{5}{12}.$$

b) We carry out the long division:

$$-22.4 \div (-4) = 5.6.$$

Practice Exercise

8. Divide: $-\dfrac{3}{4} \div \left(-\dfrac{5}{3}\right)$.

Objective 7.7a Simplify fraction expressions.

Example   Simplify: $-\dfrac{18x}{15x}$.

$$-\frac{18x}{15x} = -\frac{6 \cdot 3x}{5 \cdot 3x}$$ Factoring the numerator and the denominator

$$= -\frac{6}{5} \cdot \frac{3x}{3x}$$ Factoring the fraction expression

$$= -\frac{6}{5} \cdot 1 \qquad \frac{3x}{3x} = 1$$

$$= -\frac{6}{5}$$ Removing a factor of 1

Practice Exercise

9. Simplify: $\dfrac{45y}{27y}$.

Objective 7.7c Use the distributive laws to multiply expressions like 8 and $x - y$.

Example   Multiply: $3(4x - y + 2z)$.

$$3(4x - y + 2z)$$
$$= 3 \cdot 4x - 3 \cdot y + 3 \cdot 2z$$
$$= 12x - 3y + 6z$$

Practice Exercise

10. Multiply: $5(x + 3y - 4z)$.

Objective 7.7d Use the distributive laws to factor expressions like $4x - 12 + 24y$.

Example   Factor: $12a - 8b + 4c$.

$$12a - 8b + 4c$$
$$= 4 \cdot 3a - 4 \cdot 2b + 4 \cdot c$$
$$= 4(3a - 2b + c)$$

Practice Exercise

11. Factor: $27x + 9y - 36z$.

Objective 7.7e Collect like terms.

Example   Collect like terms: $3x - 5y + 8x + y$.

$$3x - 5y + 8x + y$$
$$= 3x + 8x - 5y + y$$
$$= 3x + 8x - 5y + 1 \cdot y$$
$$= (3 + 8)x + (-5 + 1)y$$
$$= 11x - 4y$$

Practice Exercise

12. Collect like terms: $6a - 4b - a + 2b$.

Objective 7.8b   Simplify expressions by removing parentheses and collecting like terms.

Example   Remove parentheses and simplify:

$$5x - 2(3x - y).$$
$$5x - 2(3x - y) = 5x - 6x + 2y = -x + 2y$$

Practice Exercise

13. Remove parentheses and simplify:

$$8a - b - (4a + 3b).$$

Objective 7.8d   Simplify expressions using the rules for order of operations.

Example   Simplify: $12 - (7 - 3 \cdot 6)$.

$$\begin{aligned} 12 - (7 - 3 \cdot 6) &= 12 - (7 - 18) \\ &= 12 - (-11) \\ &= 12 + 11 \\ &= 23 \end{aligned}$$

Practice Exercise

14. Simplify: $75 \div (-15) + 24 \div 8$.

Review Exercises

The review exercises that follow are for practice. Answers are at the back of the book. If you miss an exercise, restudy the objective indicated in red after the exercise or the direction line that precedes it.

1. Evaluate $\dfrac{x - y}{3}$ when $x = 17$ and $y = 5$.   [7.1a]

2. Translate to an algebraic expression: [7.1b]
   Nineteen percent of some number.

3. Tell which integers correspond to this situation: [7.2a]
   David has a debt of $45 and Joe has $72 in his savings account.

Find the absolute value.   [7.2e]

4. $|-38|$ 5. $|126|$

Graph the number on the number line.   [7.2b]

6. -2.5 7. $\dfrac{8}{9}$

Use either $<$ or $>$ for $\square$ to write a true sentence.   [7.2d]

8. $-3 \ \square \ 10$ 9. $-1 \ \square \ -6$

10. $0.126 \ \square \ -12.6$ 11. $-\dfrac{2}{3} \ \square \ -\dfrac{1}{10}$

12. Write another inequality with the same meaning as $-3 < x$.   [7.2d]

Write true or false.   [7.2d]

13. $-9 \le 11$ 14. $-11 \ge -3$

Find the opposite.   [7.3b]

15. 3.8 16. $-\dfrac{3}{4}$

Find the reciprocal.   [7.6b]

17. $\dfrac{3}{8}$ 18. -7

19. Evaluate $-x$ when $x = -34$.   [7.3b]

20. Evaluate $-(-x)$ when $x = 5$.   [7.3b]

Compute and simplify.

21. $4 + (-7)$ [7.3a]

22. $6 + (-9) + (-8) + 7$ [7.3a]

Copyright © 2012 Pearson Education, Inc.

23. $-3.8 + 5.1 + (-12) + (-4.3) + 10$ [7.3a]

24. $-3 - (-7) + 7 - 10$ [7.4a]

25. $-\dfrac{9}{10} - \dfrac{1}{2}$ [7.4a]

26. $-3.8 - 4.1$ [7.4a]

27. $-9 \cdot (-6)$ [7.5a]

28. $-2.7(3.4)$ [7.5a]

29. $\dfrac{2}{3} \cdot \left(-\dfrac{3}{7}\right)$ [7.5a]

30. $3 \cdot (-7) \cdot (-2) \cdot (-5)$ [7.5a]

31. $35 \div (-5)$ [7.6a]

32. $-5.1 \div 1.7$ [7.6c]

33. $-\dfrac{3}{11} \div \left(-\dfrac{4}{11}\right)$ [7.6c]

Simplify. [7.8d]

34. $(-3.4 - 12.2) - 8(-7)$

35. $\dfrac{-12(-3) - 2^3 - (-9)(-10)}{3 \cdot 10 + 1}$

36. $-16 \div 4 - 30 \div (-5)$

37. $\dfrac{-4[7 - (10 - 13)]}{|-2(8) - 4|}$

Solve.

38. On the first, second, and third downs, a football team had these gains and losses: 5-yd gain, 12-yd loss, and 15-yd gain, respectively. Find the total gain (or loss). [7.3c]

39. Kaleb's total assets are $170. He borrows $300. What are his total assets now? [7.4b]

40. *Stock Price.* The value of EFX Corp. stock began the day at $17.68 per share and dropped $1.63 per hour for 8 hr. What was the price of the stock after 8 hr? [7.5b]

41. *Checking Account Balance.* Yuri had $68 in his checking account. After writing a check to buy seven equally priced purchases of DVDs, the balance in his account was −$64.65. What was the price of each DVD? [7.6d]

Multiply. [7.7c]

42. $5(3x - 7)$

43. $-2(4x - 5)$

44. $10(0.4x + 1.5)$

45. $-8(3 - 6x)$

Factor. [7.7d]

46. $2x - 14$

47. $-6x + 6$

48. $5x + 10$

49. $-3x + 12y - 12$

Collect like terms. [7.7e]

50. $11a + 2b - 4a - 5b$

51. $7x - 3y - 9x + 8y$

52. $6x + 3y - x - 4y$

53. $-3a + 9b + 2a - b$

Remove parentheses and simplify.

54. $2a - (5a - 9)$ [7.8b]

55. $3(b + 7) - 5b$ [7.8b]

56. $3[11 - 3(4 - 1)]$ [7.8c]

57. $2[6(y - 4) + 7]$ [7.8c]

58. $[8(x + 4) - 10] - [3(x - 2) + 4]$ [7.8c]

59. $5\{[6(x - 1) + 7] - [3(3x - 4) + 8]\}$ [7.8c]

60. Factor out the greatest common factor:
$18x - 6y + 30.$ [7.7d]

    A. $2(9x - 2y + 15)$ **B.** $3(6x - 2y + 10)$
    C. $6(3x + 5)$ **D.** $6(3x - y + 5)$

61. Which expression is *not* equivalent to $mn + 5$?
[7.7b]

    A. $nm + 5$ **B.** $5n + m$
    C. $5 + mn$ **D.** $5 + nm$

Synthesis

Simplify. [7.2e], [7.4a], [7.6a], [7.8d]

62. $-\left| \dfrac{7}{8} - \left(-\dfrac{1}{2} \right) - \dfrac{3}{4} \right|$

63. $(|2.7 - 3| + 3^2 - |-3|) \div (-3)$

64. $2000 - 1990 + 1980 - 1970 + \cdots + 20 - 10$

65. Find a formula for the perimeter of the figure below.
[7.7e]

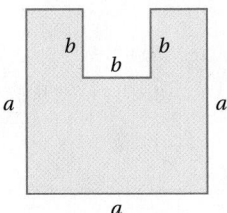

Understanding Through Discussion and Writing

1. Without actually performing the addition, explain why the sum of all integers from -50 to 50 is 0. [7.3b]

2. What rule have we developed that would tell you the sign of $(-7)^8$ and of $(-7)^{11}$ without doing the computations? Explain. [7.5a]

3. Explain how multiplication can be used to justify why a negative number divided by a negative number is positive. [7.6c]

4. Explain how multiplication can be used to justify why a negative number divided by a positive number is negative. [7.6c]

5. The distributive law was introduced before the discussion on collecting like terms. Why do you think this was done? [7.7c, e]

6. ▦ Jake keys in $18/2 \cdot 3$ on his calculator and expects the result to be 3. What mistake is he making? [7.8d]

Copyright © 2012 Pearson Education, Inc.

Test

For Extra Help

Step-by-step test solutions are found on the Chapter Test Prep Videos available via the Video Resources on DVD, in *MyMathLab* , and on YouTube (search "BittingerDevMath" and click on "Channels").

1. Evaluate $\dfrac{3x}{y}$ when $x = 10$ and $y = 5$.

2. Translate to an algebraic expression: Nine less than some number.

Use either $<$ or $>$ for $\square$ to write a true sentence.

3. $-3 \ \square \ -8$

4. $-\dfrac{1}{2} \ \square \ -\dfrac{1}{8}$

5. $-0.78 \ \square \ -0.87$

6. Write an inequality with the same meaning as $x < -2$.

7. Write true or false: $-13 \leq -3$.

Simplify.

8. $|-7|$

9. $\left|\dfrac{9}{4}\right|$

10. $|-2.7|$

Find the opposite.

11. $\dfrac{2}{3}$

12. -1.4

Find the reciprocal.

13. -2

14. $\dfrac{4}{7}$

15. Evaluate $-x$ when $x = -8$.

Compute and simplify.

16. $3.1 - (-4.7)$

17. $-8 + 4 + (-7) + 3$

18. $-\dfrac{1}{5} + \dfrac{3}{8}$

19. $2 - (-8)$

20. $3.2 - 5.7$

21. $\dfrac{1}{8} - \left(-\dfrac{3}{4}\right)$

22. $4 \cdot (-12)$

23. $-\dfrac{1}{2} \cdot \left(-\dfrac{3}{8}\right)$

24. $-45 \div 5$

25. $-\dfrac{3}{5} \div \left(-\dfrac{4}{5}\right)$

26. $4.864 \div (-0.5)$

27. $-2(16) - |2(-8) - 5^3|$

28. $-20 \div (-5) + 36 \div (-4)$

29. Maureen kept track of the changes in the stock market over a period of 5 weeks. By how many points had the market risen or fallen over this time?

WEEK 1	WEEK 2	WEEK 3	WEEK 4	WEEK 5
Down 13 pts	Down 16 pts	Up 36 pts	Down 11 pts	Up 19 pts

30. *Antarctica Highs and Lows.* The continent of Antarctica, which lies in the southern hemisphere, experiences winter in July. The average high temperature is −67°F and the average low temperature is −81°F. How much higher is the average high than the average low?

Source: National Climatic Data Center

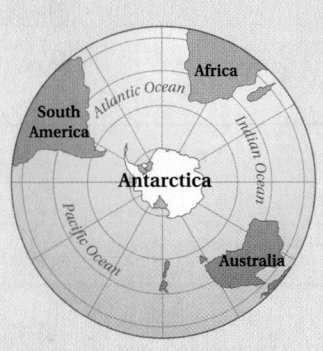

31. *Population Decrease.* The population of Mapleton was 18,600. It dropped 420 each year for 6 yr. What was the population of the city after 6 yr?

32. *Chemical Experiment.* During a chemical reaction, the temperature in a beaker decreased every minute by the same number of degrees. The temperature was 16°C at 11:08 A.M. By 11:52 A.M., the temperature had dropped to −17°C. By how many degrees did it change each minute?

Multiply.

33. $3(6 - x)$

34. $-5(y - 1)$

Factor.

35. $12 - 22x$

36. $7x + 21 + 14y$

Simplify.

37. $6 + 7 - 4 - (-3)$

38. $5x - (3x - 7)$

39. $4(2a - 3b) + a - 7$

40. $4\{3[5(y - 3) + 9] + 2(y + 8)\}$

41. $256 \div (-16) \div 4$

42. $2^3 - 10[4 - (-2 + 18)3]$

43. Which of the following is *not* a true statement?

    A. $-5 \leq -5$ **B.** $-5 < -5$

    C. $-5 \geq -5$ **D.** $-5 = -5$

Synthesis

Simplify.

44. $|-27 - 3(4)| - |-36| + |-12|$

45. $a - \{3a - [4a - (2a - 4a)]\}$

46. Find a formula for the perimeter of the figure shown here.

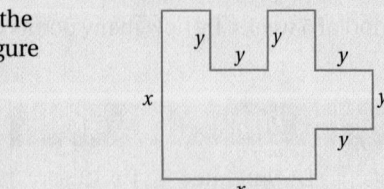

Copyright © 2012 Pearson Education, Inc.

Solving Equations and Inequalities

Real-World Application

The manatee, Florida's state marine mammal, is an endangered species. An aerial wintertime manatee census counted 2817 of these animals in 2007. This was 296 fewer than the number counted in 2006. What was Florida's manatee population in 2006?

Source: Florida Fish and Wildlife Conservation Commission

This problem appears as Exercise 1 in Exercise Set 8.6.

8.1

Solving Equations: The Addition Principle

OBJECTIVES

a Determine whether a given number is a solution of a given equation.

b Solve equations using the addition principle.

SKILL TO REVIEW

Objective 7.1a: Evaluate algebraic expressions by substitution.

1. Evaluate $x - 7$ when $x = 5$.
2. Evaluate $2x + 3$ when $x = -1$.

Determine whether each equation is true, false, or neither.

1. $5 - 8 = -4$

2. $12 + 6 = 18$

3. $x + 6 = 7 - x$

---

a Equations and Solutions

In order to solve problems, we must learn to solve equations.

> **EQUATION**
>
> An **equation** is a number sentence that says that the expressions on either side of the equals sign, =, represent the same number.

Here are some examples of equations:

$$3 + 2 = 5, \quad 14 - 10 = 1 + 3, \quad x + 6 = 13, \quad 3x - 2 = 7 - x.$$

Equations have expressions on each side of the equals sign. The sentence "$14 - 10 = 1 + 3$" asserts that the expressions $14 - 10$ and $1 + 3$ name the same number.

Some equations are true. Some are false. Some are neither true nor false.

EXAMPLES Determine whether each equation is true, false, or neither.

1. $3 + 2 = 5$ The equation is *true*.
2. $7 - 2 = 4$ The equation is *false*.
3. $x + 6 = 13$ The equation is *neither* true nor false, because we do not know what number x represents.

Do Margin Exercises 1–3.

> **SOLUTION OF AN EQUATION**
>
> Any replacement for the variable that makes an equation true is called a **solution** of the equation. To solve an equation means to find *all* of its solutions.

One way to determine whether a number is a solution of an equation is to evaluate the expression on each side of the equals sign by substitution. If the values are the same, then the number is a solution.

EXAMPLE 4 Determine whether 7 is a solution of $x + 6 = 13$.

We have

$$\begin{array}{ll} x + 6 = 13 & \text{Writing the equation} \\ 7 + 6 \ ? \ 13 & \text{Substituting 7 for } x \\ \quad 13 \ | & \text{TRUE} \end{array}$$

Since the left-hand and the right-hand sides are the same, 7 is a solution. No other number makes the equation true, so the only solution is the number 7.

Answers

Skill to Review:
1. -2 2. 1

Margin Exercises:
1. False   2. True   3. Neither

EXAMPLE 5 Determine whether 19 is a solution of $7x = 141$.

$$7x = 141 \quad \text{Writing the equation}$$
$$7(19) \; ? \; 141 \quad \text{Substituting 19 for } x$$
$$133 \;|\; \quad \text{FALSE}$$

Since the left-hand and the right-hand sides are not the same, 19 is not a solution of the equation.

Do Exercises 4–7.

b Using the Addition Principle

Consider the equation

$$x = 7.$$

We can easily see that the solution of this equation is 7. If we replace x with 7, we get

$$7 = 7, \quad \text{which is true.}$$

Now consider the equation of Example 4: $x + 6 = 13$. In Example 4, we discovered that the solution of this equation is also 7, but the fact that 7 is the solution is not as obvious. We now begin to consider principles that allow us to start with an equation like $x + 6 = 13$ and end up with an *equivalent equation*, like $x = 7$, in which the variable is alone on one side and for which the solution is easier to find.

EQUIVALENT EQUATIONS

Equations with the same solutions are called **equivalent equations**.

One of the principles that we use in solving equations involves addition. An equation $a = b$ says that a and b stand for the same number. Suppose this is true, and we add a number c to the number a. We get the same answer if we add c to b, because a and b are the same number.

THE ADDITION PRINCIPLE FOR EQUATIONS

For any real numbers a, b, and c,

$$a = b \quad \text{is equivalent to} \quad a + c = b + c.$$

Let's solve the equation $x + 6 = 13$ using the addition principle. We want to get x alone on one side. To do so, we use the addition principle, choosing to add -6 because $6 + (-6) = 0$:

$$x + 6 = 13$$
$$x + 6 + (-6) = 13 + (-6) \quad \text{Using the addition principle: adding } -6 \text{ on both sides}$$
$$x + 0 = 7 \quad \text{Simplifying}$$
$$x = 7. \quad \text{Identity property of 0: } x + 0 = x$$

The solution of $x + 6 = 13$ is 7.

Do Exercise 8.

Determine whether the given number is a solution of the given equation.

4. 8; $x + 4 = 12$

5. 0; $x + 4 = 12$

6. -3; $7 + x = -4$

7. $-\dfrac{3}{5}$; $-5x = 3$

8. Solve using the addition principle:

$$x + 2 = 11.$$

Answers

4. Yes **5.** No **6.** No **7.** Yes **8.** 9

When we use the addition principle, we sometimes say that we "add the same number on both sides of the equation." This is also true for subtraction, since we can express every subtraction as an addition. That is, since

$$a - c = b - c \quad \text{is equivalent to} \quad a + (-c) = b + (-c),$$

the addition principle tells us that we can "subtract the same number on both sides of the equation."

EXAMPLE 6 Solve: $x + 5 = -7$.

We have

$$\begin{aligned} x + 5 &= -7 \\ x + 5 - 5 &= -7 - 5 \qquad &\text{Using the addition principle: adding } -5 \text{ on} \\ & &\text{both sides or subtracting 5 on both sides} \\ x + 0 &= -12 &\text{Simplifying} \\ x &= -12. &\text{Identity property of 0} \end{aligned}$$

To check the answer, we substitute -12 in the original equation.

Check:
$$\begin{array}{c|c} x + 5 = -7 \\ \hline -12 + 5 \;?\; -7 \\ -7 \;\big|\; \qquad \text{TRUE} \end{array}$$

The solution of the original equation is -12.

In Example 6, to get x alone, we used the addition principle and subtracted 5 on both sides. This eliminated the 5 on the left. We started with $x + 5 = -7$, and, using the addition principle, we found a simpler equation $x = -12$ for which it was easy to "see" the solution. The equations $x + 5 = -7$ and $x = -12$ are *equivalent*.

Do Exercise 9.

Now we use the addition principle to solve an equation that involves a subtraction.

EXAMPLE 7 Solve: $a - 4 = 10$.

We have

$$\begin{aligned} a - 4 &= 10 \\ a - 4 + 4 &= 10 + 4 \qquad &\text{Using the addition principle: adding 4 on} \\ & &\text{both sides} \\ a + 0 &= 14 &\text{Simplifying} \\ a &= 14. &\text{Identity property of 0} \end{aligned}$$

Check:
$$\begin{array}{c|c} a - 4 = 10 \\ \hline 14 - 4 \;?\; 10 \\ 10 \;\big|\; \qquad \text{TRUE} \end{array}$$

The solution is 14.

Do Exercise 10.

9. Solve using the addition principle, subtracting 5 on both sides:
$$x + 5 = -8.$$

10. Solve: $t - 3 = 19$.

Answers

9. -13 **10.** 22

EXAMPLE 8 Solve: $-6.5 = y - 8.4$.

We have

$$-6.5 = y - 8.4$$

$$-6.5 + 8.4 = y - 8.4 + 8.4 \qquad \text{Using the addition principle: adding } 8.4 \text{ on both sides to eliminate } -8.4 \text{ on the right}$$

$$1.9 = y.$$

Check: $\dfrac{-6.5 = y - 8.4}{-6.5 \ ? \ 1.9 - 8.4}$
$\qquad \qquad \ \ | \ -6.5 \qquad \text{TRUE}$

The solution is 1.9.

Note that equations are reversible. That is, if $a = b$ is true, then $b = a$ is true. Thus when we solve $-6.5 = y - 8.4$, we can reverse it and solve $y - 8.4 = -6.5$ if we wish.

Do Exercises 11 and 12.

Solve.

11. $8.7 = n - 4.5$

12. $y + 17.4 = 10.9$

EXAMPLE 9 Solve: $-\dfrac{2}{3} + x = \dfrac{5}{2}$.

We have

$$-\frac{2}{3} + x = \frac{5}{2}$$

$$\frac{2}{3} - \frac{2}{3} + x = \frac{2}{3} + \frac{5}{2} \qquad \text{Adding } \tfrac{2}{3} \text{ on both sides}$$

$$x = \frac{2}{3} + \frac{5}{2}$$

$$x = \frac{2}{3} \cdot \frac{2}{2} + \frac{5}{2} \cdot \frac{3}{3} \qquad \text{Multiplying by 1 to obtain equivalent fraction expressions with the least common denominator 6}$$

$$x = \frac{4}{6} + \frac{15}{6}$$

$$x = \frac{19}{6}.$$

Check: $-\dfrac{2}{3} + x = \dfrac{5}{2}$

$$\frac{-\dfrac{2}{3} + \dfrac{19}{6} \ ? \ \dfrac{5}{2}}{\ \ -\dfrac{4}{6} + \dfrac{19}{6}}$$

$$\frac{15}{6}$$

$$\frac{5}{2} \qquad \text{TRUE}$$

The solution is $\dfrac{19}{6}$.

Do Exercises 13 and 14.

Solve.

13. $x + \dfrac{1}{2} = -\dfrac{3}{2}$

14. $t - \dfrac{13}{4} = \dfrac{5}{8}$

Answers

11. 13.2   **12.** −6.5   **13.** −2   **14.** $\dfrac{31}{8}$

a Determine whether the given number is a solution of the given equation.

1. 15; $x + 17 = 32$

2. 35; $t + 17 = 53$

3. 21; $x - 7 = 12$

4. 36; $a - 19 = 17$

5. -7; $6x = 54$

6. -9; $8y = -72$

7. 30; $\dfrac{x}{6} = 5$

8. 49; $\dfrac{y}{8} = 6$

9. 20; $5x + 7 = 107$

10. 9; $9x + 5 = 86$

11. -10; $7(y - 1) = 63$

12. -5; $6(y - 2) = 18$

b Solve using the addition principle. Don't forget to check!

13. $x + 2 = 6$

Check: $x + 2 = 6$
$\overset{?}{}$

14. $y + 4 = 11$

Check: $y + 4 = 11$
$\overset{?}{}$

15. $x + 15 = -5$

Check: $x + 15 = -5$
$\overset{?}{}$

16. $t + 10 = 44$

Check: $t + 10 = 44$
$\overset{?}{}$

17. $x + 6 = -8$

Check: $x + 6 = -8$
$\overset{?}{}$

18. $z + 9 = -14$

19. $x + 16 = -2$

20. $m + 18 = -13$

21. $x - 9 = 6$

22. $x - 11 = 12$

23. $x - 7 = -21$

24. $x - 3 = -14$

25. $5 + t = 7$

26. $8 + y = 12$

27. $-7 + y = 13$

28. $-8 + y = 17$

29. $-3 + t = -9$

30. $-8 + t = -24$

31. $x + \dfrac{1}{2} = 7$

32. $24 = -\dfrac{7}{10} + r$

Copyright © 2012 Pearson Education, Inc.

33. $12 = a - 7.9$

34. $2.8 + y = 11$

35. $r + \dfrac{1}{3} = \dfrac{8}{3}$

36. $t + \dfrac{3}{8} = \dfrac{5}{8}$

37. $m + \dfrac{5}{6} = -\dfrac{11}{12}$

38. $x + \dfrac{2}{3} = -\dfrac{5}{6}$

39. $x - \dfrac{5}{6} = \dfrac{7}{8}$

40. $y - \dfrac{3}{4} = \dfrac{5}{6}$

41. $-\dfrac{1}{5} + z = -\dfrac{1}{4}$

42. $-\dfrac{1}{8} + y = -\dfrac{3}{4}$

43. $7.4 = x + 2.3$

44. $8.4 = 5.7 + y$

45. $7.6 = x - 4.8$

46. $8.6 = x - 7.4$

47. $-9.7 = -4.7 + y$

48. $-7.8 = 2.8 + x$

49. $5\dfrac{1}{6} + x = 7$

50. $5\dfrac{1}{4} = 4\dfrac{2}{3} + x$

51. $q + \dfrac{1}{3} = -\dfrac{1}{7}$

52. $52\dfrac{3}{8} = -84 + x$

Skill Maintenance

53. Add: $-3 + (-8)$. [7.3a]

54. Subtract: $-3 - (-8)$. [7.4a]

55. Multiply: $-\dfrac{2}{3} \cdot \dfrac{5}{8}$. [7.5a]

56. Divide: $-\dfrac{3}{7} \div \left(-\dfrac{9}{7}\right)$. [7.6c]

57. Divide: $\dfrac{2}{3} \div \left(-\dfrac{4}{9}\right)$. [7.6c]

58. Add: $-8.6 + 3.4$. [7.3a]

59. Subtract: $-\dfrac{2}{3} - \left(-\dfrac{5}{8}\right)$. [7.4a]

60. Multiply: $(-25.4)(-6.8)$. [7.5a]

Translate to an algebraic expression. [7.1b]

61. Jane had $83 before paying x dollars for a pair of tennis shoes. How much does she have left?

62. Justin drove his S-10 pickup truck 65 mph for t hours. How far did he drive?

Synthesis

Solve.

63. $-356.788 = -699.034 + t$

64. $-\dfrac{4}{5} + \dfrac{7}{10} = x - \dfrac{3}{4}$

65. $x + \dfrac{4}{5} = -\dfrac{2}{3} - \dfrac{4}{15}$

66. $8 - 25 = 8 + x - 21$

67. $16 + x - 22 = -16$

68. $x + x = x$

69. $x + 3 = 3 + x$

70. $x + 4 = 5 + x$

71. $-\dfrac{3}{2} + x = -\dfrac{5}{17} - \dfrac{3}{2}$

72. $|x| = 5$

73. $|x| + 6 = 19$

8.2 Solving Equations: The Multiplication Principle

OBJECTIVE

a Solve equations using the multiplication principle.

SKILL TO REVIEW
Objective 7.6b: Find the reciprocal of a real number.

Find the reciprocal.

1. 5

2. $-\dfrac{5}{4}$

a Using the Multiplication Principle

Suppose that $a = b$ is true, and we multiply a by some number c. We get the same number if we multiply b by c, because a and b are the same number.

> **THE MULTIPLICATION PRINCIPLE FOR EQUATIONS**
>
> For any real numbers a, b, and c, $c \neq 0$,
>
> $$a = b \quad \text{is equivalent to} \quad a \cdot c = b \cdot c.$$

When using the multiplication principle, we sometimes say that we "multiply on both sides of the equation by the same number."

EXAMPLE 1 Solve: $5x = 70$.

To get x alone, we multiply by the *multiplicative inverse*, or *reciprocal*, of 5. Then we get the *multiplicative identity* 1 times x, or $1 \cdot x$, which simplifies to x. This allows us to eliminate 5 on the left.

$$5x = 70 \qquad \text{The reciprocal of 5 is } \tfrac{1}{5}.$$

$$\frac{1}{5} \cdot 5x = \frac{1}{5} \cdot 70 \qquad \text{Multiplying by } \tfrac{1}{5} \text{ to get } 1 \cdot x \text{ and eliminate 5 on the left}$$

$$1 \cdot x = 14 \qquad \text{Simplifying}$$

$$x = 14 \qquad \text{Identity property of 1: } 1 \cdot x = x$$

Check:
$$\begin{array}{c|c} 5x = 70 \\ \hline 5 \cdot 14 \;?\; 70 \\ 70 \;\big|\; \quad \text{TRUE} \end{array}$$

The solution is 14.

The multiplication principle also tells us that we can "divide on both sides of the equation by the same nonzero number." This is because dividing is the same as multiplying by a reciprocal. That is,

$$\frac{a}{c} = \frac{b}{c} \quad \text{is equivalent to} \quad a \cdot \frac{1}{c} = b \cdot \frac{1}{c}, \quad \text{when } c \neq 0.$$

In an expression like $5x$ in Example 1, the number 5 is called the **coefficient**. Example 1 could be done as follows, dividing on both sides by 5, the coefficient of x.

EXAMPLE 2 Solve: $5x = 70$.

$$5x = 70$$

$$\frac{5x}{5} = \frac{70}{5} \qquad \text{Dividing by 5 on both sides}$$

$$1 \cdot x = 14 \qquad \text{Simplifying}$$

$$x = 14 \qquad \text{Identity property of 1. The solution is 14.}$$

Answers

Skill to Review:

1. $\dfrac{1}{5}$ 2. $-\dfrac{4}{5}$

Do Exercises 1 and 2.

1. Solve. Multiply on both sides.
$$6x = 90$$

2. Solve. Divide on both sides.
$$4x = -7$$

EXAMPLE 3 Solve: $-4x = 92$.

We have

$$-4x = 92$$

$$\frac{-4x}{-4} = \frac{92}{-4}$$ Using the multiplication principle. Dividing by -4 on both sides is the same as multiplying by $-\frac{1}{4}$.

$$1 \cdot x = -23$$ Simplifying

$$x = -23.$$ Identity property of 1

Check:
$$\frac{-4x = 92}{-4(-23) \;?\; 92}$$
$$92 \;\mid\; \quad \text{TRUE}$$

The solution is -23.

Do Exercise 3.

3. Solve: $-6x = 108$.

EXAMPLE 4 Solve: $-x = 9$.

We have

$$-x = 9$$

$$-1 \cdot x = 9$$ Using the property of -1: $-x = -1 \cdot x$

$$\frac{-1 \cdot x}{-1} = \frac{9}{-1}$$ Dividing by -1 on both sides: $-1/(-1) = 1$

$$1 \cdot x = -9$$

$$x = -9.$$

Check:
$$\frac{-x = 9}{-(-9) \;?\; 9}$$
$$9 \;\mid\; \quad \text{TRUE}$$

The solution is -9.

Do Exercise 4.

4. Solve. Divide on both sides.
$$-x = -10$$

We can also solve the equation $-x = 9$ by multiplying as follows.

EXAMPLE 5 Solve: $-x = 9$.

We have

$$-x = 9$$

$$-1 \cdot (-x) = -1 \cdot 9$$ Multiplying by -1 on both sides

$$-1 \cdot (-1) \cdot x = -9$$ $-x = (-1) \cdot x$

$$1 \cdot x = -9$$ $-1 \cdot (-1) = 1$

$$x = -9.$$

The solution is -9.

Do Exercise 5.

5. Solve. Multiply on both sides.
$$-x = -10$$

Answers

1. 15   2. $-\dfrac{7}{4}$ 3. -18 4. 10   5. 10

In practice, it is generally more convenient to divide on both sides of the equation if the coefficient of the variable is in decimal notation or is an integer. If the coefficient is in fraction notation, it is usually more convenient to multiply by a reciprocal.

EXAMPLE 6   Solve: $\frac{3}{8} = -\frac{5}{4}x$.

$$\frac{3}{8} = -\frac{5}{4}x$$

The reciprocal of $-\frac{5}{4}$ is $-\frac{4}{5}$. There is no sign change.

$$-\frac{4}{5} \cdot \frac{3}{8} = -\frac{4}{5} \cdot \left(-\frac{5}{4}x\right)$$ Multiplying by $-\frac{4}{5}$ to get $1 \cdot x$ and eliminate $-\frac{5}{4}$ on the right

$$-\frac{12}{40} = 1 \cdot x$$

$$-\frac{3}{10} = 1 \cdot x$$ Simplifying

$$-\frac{3}{10} = x$$ Identity property of 1

Check: $$\frac{3}{8} = -\frac{5}{4}x$$

$$\frac{3}{8} \; ? \; -\frac{5}{4}\left(-\frac{3}{10}\right)$$

$$\frac{3}{8} \qquad \text{TRUE}$$

The solution is $-\frac{3}{10}$.

As noted in Section 8.1, if $a = b$ is true, then $b = a$ is true. Thus we can reverse the equation $\frac{3}{8} = -\frac{5}{4}x$ and solve $-\frac{5}{4}x = \frac{3}{8}$ if we wish.

Do Exercise 6.

6. Solve: $\frac{2}{3} = -\frac{5}{6}y$.

EXAMPLE 7   Solve: $1.16y = 9744$.

$$1.16y = 9744$$

$$\frac{1.16y}{1.16} = \frac{9744}{1.16}$$ Dividing by 1.16 on both sides

$$y = \frac{9744}{1.16}$$

$$y = 8400$$ Simplifying

Check: $$1.16y = 9744$$

$$1.16(8400) \; ? \; 9744$$

$$9744 \qquad \text{TRUE}$$

The solution is 8400.

Do Exercises 7 and 8.

Solve.

7. $1.12x = 8736$

8. $6.3 = -2.1y$

Answers

6. $-\frac{4}{5}$ 7. 7800   8. −3

Now we use the multiplication principle to solve an equation that involves division.

EXAMPLE 8   Solve: $\dfrac{-y}{9} = 14$.

$$\frac{-y}{9} = 14$$

$$9 \cdot \frac{-y}{9} = 9 \cdot 14 \qquad \text{Multiplying by 9 on both sides}$$

$$-y = 126$$

$$-1 \cdot (-y) = -1 \cdot 126 \qquad \text{Multiplying by } -1 \text{ on both sides}$$

$$y = -126$$

Check:

$$\frac{-y}{9} = 14$$

$$\frac{-(-126)}{9} \overset{?}{\,\bigm|\,} 14$$

$$\frac{126}{9}$$

$$14 \bigm| \quad \text{TRUE}$$

The solution is -126.

There are other ways to solve the equation in Example 8. One is by multiplying by -9 on both sides as follows:

$$-9 \cdot \frac{-y}{9} = -9 \cdot 14$$

$$\frac{(-9)(-y)}{9} = -126$$

$$\frac{9y}{9} = -126$$

$$y = -126.$$

> Do Exercise 9.

9. Solve: $-14 = \dfrac{-y}{2}$.

STUDY TIPS

TIME MANAGEMENT

Having enough time to study is a critical factor in any course. Have realistic expectations about the amount of time you need to study for this course.

- **A rule of thumb for study time.**   Budget two to three hours for homework and study per week for each hour of class time.

- **Balancing work and study.**   Working 40 hours per week and taking 12 credit hours is equivalent to having two full-time jobs. It is challenging to handle such a load. If you work 40 hours per week, you will probably have more success in school if you take 3 to 6 credit hours. If you are carrying a full class-load, you can probably work 5 to 10 hours per week. Be honest with yourself about how much time you have available to work, attend class, and study.

Answer

9. 28

a) Solve using the multiplication principle. Don't forget to check!

1. $6x = 36$

Check: $6x = 36$
$\overline{}$
?

2. $3x = 51$

Check: $3x = 51$
$\overline{}$
?

3. $5y = 45$

Check: $5y = 45$
$\overline{}$
?

4. $8y = 72$

Check: $8y = 72$
$\overline{}$
?

5. $84 = 7x$

6. $63 = 9x$

7. $-x = 40$

8. $-x = 53$

9. $-1 = -z$

10. $-47 = -t$

11. $7x = -49$

12. $8x = -56$

13. $-12x = 72$

14. $-15x = 105$

15. $-21w = -126$

16. $-13w = -104$

17. $\dfrac{t}{7} = -9$

18. $\dfrac{y}{5} = -6$

19. $\dfrac{n}{-6} = 8$

20. $\dfrac{y}{-8} = 11$

21. $\dfrac{3}{4}x = 27$

22. $\dfrac{4}{5}x = 16$

23. $-\dfrac{2}{3}x = 6$

24. $-\dfrac{3}{8}x = 12$

25. $\dfrac{-t}{3} = 7$

26. $\dfrac{-x}{6} = 9$

27. $-\dfrac{m}{3} = \dfrac{1}{5}$

28. $\dfrac{1}{8} = -\dfrac{y}{5}$

Copyright © 2012 Pearson Education, Inc.

29. $-\dfrac{3}{5}r = \dfrac{9}{10}$

30. $-\dfrac{2}{5}y = \dfrac{4}{15}$

31. $-\dfrac{3}{2}r = -\dfrac{27}{4}$

32. $-\dfrac{3}{8}x = -\dfrac{15}{16}$

33. $6.3x = 44.1$

34. $2.7y = 54$

35. $-3.1y = 21.7$

36. $-3.3y = 6.6$

37. $38.7m = 309.6$

38. $29.4m = 235.2$

39. $-\dfrac{2}{3}y = -10.6$

40. $-\dfrac{9}{7}y = 12.06$

41. $\dfrac{-x}{5} = 10$

42. $\dfrac{-x}{8} = -16$

43. $-\dfrac{t}{2} = 7$

44. $\dfrac{m}{-3} = 10$

Skill Maintenance

Collect like terms.   [7.7e]

45. $3x + 4x$

46. $6x + 5 - 7x$

47. $-4x + 11 - 6x + 18x$

48. $8y - 16y - 24y$

Remove parentheses and simplify.   [7.8b]

49. $3x - (4 + 2x)$

50. $2 - 5(x + 5)$

51. $8y - 6(3y + 7)$

52. $-2a - 4(5a - 1)$

Translate to an algebraic expression.   [7.1b]

53. Patty drives her van for 8 hr at a speed of r miles per hour. How far does she drive?

54. A triangle has a height of 10 meters and a base of b meters. What is the area of the triangle?

Synthesis

Solve.

55. $-0.2344m = 2028.732$

56. $0 \cdot x = 0$

57. $0 \cdot x = 9$

58. $4|x| = 48$

59. $2|x| = -12$

Solve for x.

60. $ax = 5a$

61. $3x = \dfrac{b}{a}$

62. $cx = a^2 + 1$

63. $\dfrac{a}{b}x = 4$

64. A student makes a calculation and gets an answer of 22.5. On the last step, she multiplies by 0.3 when she should have divided by 0.3. What is the correct answer?

8.3

Using the Principles Together

OBJECTIVES

a Solve equations using both the addition principle and the multiplication principle.

b Solve equations in which like terms may need to be collected.

c Solve equations by first removing parentheses and collecting like terms; solve equations with an infinite number of solutions and equations with no solutions.

a Applying Both Principles

Consider the equation $3x + 4 = 13$. It is more complicated than those we discussed in the preceding two sections. In order to solve such an equation, we first isolate the x-term, $3x$, using the addition principle. Then we apply the multiplication principle to get x by itself.

EXAMPLE 1 Solve: $3x + 4 = 13$.

$$3x + 4 = 13$$
$$3x + 4 - 4 = 13 - 4 \qquad \text{Using the addition principle:} \\ \text{subtracting 4 on both sides}$$

First isolate the x-term. $\rightarrow 3x = 9$ Simplifying

$$\frac{3x}{3} = \frac{9}{3} \qquad \text{Using the multiplication principle:} \\ \text{dividing by 3 on both sides}$$

Then isolate x. $\rightarrow x = 3$ Simplifying

Check: $$\begin{array}{r} 3x + 4 = 13 \\ \hline 3 \cdot 3 + 4 \; ? \; 13 \\ 9 + 4 \\ 13 \; | \qquad \text{TRUE} \end{array}$$

We use the rules for order of operations to carry out the check. We find the product $3 \cdot 3$. Then we add 4.

The solution is 3.

1. Solve: $9x + 6 = 51$.

> Do Exercise 1.

EXAMPLE 2 Solve: $-5x - 6 = 16$.

$$-5x - 6 = 16$$
$$-5x - 6 + 6 = 16 + 6 \qquad \text{Adding 6 on both sides}$$
$$-5x = 22$$
$$\frac{-5x}{-5} = \frac{22}{-5} \qquad \text{Dividing by } -5 \text{ on both sides}$$
$$x = -\frac{22}{5}, \text{ or } -4\frac{2}{5} \qquad \text{Simplifying}$$

Check: $$\begin{array}{r} -5x - 6 = 16 \\ \hline -5\left(-\dfrac{22}{5}\right) - 6 \; ? \; 16 \\ 22 - 6 \\ 16 \; | \qquad \text{TRUE} \end{array}$$

Solve.

2. $8x - 4 = 28$

3. $-\dfrac{1}{2}x + 3 = 1$

The solution is $-\frac{22}{5}$.

> Do Exercises 2 and 3.

Answers

1. 5   2. 4   3. 4

EXAMPLE 3 Solve: $45 - t = 13$.

$$45 - t = 13$$
$$-45 + 45 - t = -45 + 13 \qquad \text{Adding } -45 \text{ on both sides}$$
$$-t = -32$$
$$-1(-t) = -1(-32) \qquad \text{Multiplying by } -1 \text{ on both sides}$$
$$t = 32$$

The number 32 checks and is the solution.

Do Exercise 4.

4. Solve: $-18 - m = -57$.

EXAMPLE 4 Solve: $16.3 - 7.2y = -8.18$.

$$16.3 - 7.2y = -8.18$$
$$-16.3 + 16.3 - 7.2y = -16.3 + (-8.18) \qquad \text{Adding } -16.3 \text{ on both sides}$$
$$-7.2y = -24.48$$
$$\frac{-7.2y}{-7.2} = \frac{-24.48}{-7.2} \qquad \text{Dividing by } -7.2 \text{ on both sides}$$
$$y = 3.4$$

Check:

$$\begin{array}{c|c} 16.3 - 7.2y = -8.18 \\ \hline 16.3 - 7.2(3.4) \; ? \; -8.18 \\ 16.3 - 24.48 \; | \\ -8.18 \; | \qquad \text{TRUE} \end{array}$$

The solution is 3.4.

Do Exercises 5 and 6.

Solve.

5. $-4 - 8x = 8$

6. $41.68 = 4.7 - 8.6y$

b Collecting Like Terms

If there are like terms on one side of the equation, we collect them before using the addition principle or the multiplication principle.

EXAMPLE 5 Solve: $3x + 4x = -14$.

$$3x + 4x = -14$$
$$7x = -14 \qquad \text{Collecting like terms}$$
$$\frac{7x}{7} = \frac{-14}{7} \qquad \text{Dividing by 7 on both sides}$$
$$x = -2$$

The number -2 checks, so the solution is -2.

Do Exercises 7 and 8.

Solve.

7. $4x + 3x = -21$

8. $x - 0.09x = 728$

If there are like terms on opposite sides of the equation, we get them on the same side by using the addition principle. Then we collect them. In other words, we get all the terms with a variable on one side of the equation and all the terms without a variable on the other side.

Answers

4. 39 **5.** $-\dfrac{3}{2}$ **6.** -4.3
7. -3 **8.** 800

EXAMPLE 6 Solve: $2x - 2 = -3x + 3$.

$$2x - 2 = -3x + 3$$

$$2x - 2 + 2 = -3x + 3 + 2 \qquad \text{Adding 2}$$

$$2x = -3x + 5 \qquad \text{Collecting like terms}$$

$$2x + 3x = -3x + 3x + 5 \qquad \text{Adding } 3x$$

$$5x = 5 \qquad \text{Simplifying}$$

$$\frac{5x}{5} = \frac{5}{5} \qquad \text{Dividing by 5}$$

$$x = 1 \qquad \text{Simplifying}$$

Check:

$$\begin{array}{c|c} 2x - 2 = -3x + 3 \\ \hline 2 \cdot 1 - 2 \; ? \; -3 \cdot 1 + 3 \\ 2 - 2 \;\big|\; -3 + 3 \\ 0 \;\big|\; 0 \quad \text{TRUE} \end{array}$$

Substituting in the original equation

The solution is 1.

Do Exercises 9 and 10.

In Example 6, we used the addition principle to get all the terms with an x on one side of the equation and all the terms without an x on the other side. Then we collected like terms and proceeded as before. If there are like terms on one side at the outset, they should be collected first.

EXAMPLE 7 Solve: $6x + 5 - 7x = 10 - 4x + 3$.

$$6x + 5 - 7x = 10 - 4x + 3$$

$$-x + 5 = 13 - 4x \qquad \text{Collecting like terms}$$

$$4x - x + 5 = 13 - 4x + 4x \qquad \begin{array}{l}\text{Adding } 4x \text{ to get all terms with a} \\ \text{variable on one side}\end{array}$$

$$3x + 5 = 13 \qquad \begin{array}{l}\text{Simplifying; that is, collecting} \\ \text{like terms}\end{array}$$

$$3x + 5 - 5 = 13 - 5 \qquad \text{Subtracting 5}$$

$$3x = 8 \qquad \text{Simplifying}$$

$$\frac{3x}{3} = \frac{8}{3} \qquad \text{Dividing by 3}$$

$$x = \frac{8}{3} \qquad \text{Simplifying}$$

The number $\frac{8}{3}$ checks, so it is the solution.

Do Exercises 11 and 12.

Clearing Fractions and Decimals

In general, equations are easier to solve if they do not contain fractions or decimals. Consider, for example, the equations

$$\frac{1}{2}x + 5 = \frac{3}{4} \quad \text{and} \quad 2.3x + 7 = 5.4.$$

Solve.

9. $7y + 5 = 2y + 10$

10. $5 - 2y = 3y - 5$

Solve.

11. $7x - 17 + 2x = 2 - 8x + 15$

12. $3x - 15 = 5x + 2 - 4x$

Answers

9. 1   **10.** 2   **11.** 2   **12.** $\frac{17}{2}$

If we multiply by 4 on both sides of the first equation and by 10 on both sides of the second equation, we have

$$4\left(\frac{1}{2}x + 5\right) = 4 \cdot \frac{3}{4} \quad \text{and} \quad 10(2.3x + 7) = 10 \cdot 5.4$$

$$4 \cdot \frac{1}{2}x + 4 \cdot 5 = 4 \cdot \frac{3}{4} \quad \text{and} \quad 10 \cdot 2.3x + 10 \cdot 7 = 10 \cdot 5.4$$

$$2x + 20 = 3 \quad \text{and} \quad 23x + 70 = 54.$$

The first equation has been "cleared of fractions" and the second equation has been "cleared of decimals." Both resulting equations are equivalent to the original equations and are easier to solve. *It is your choice* whether to clear fractions or decimals, but doing so often eases computations.

The easiest way to clear an equation of fractions is to multiply *every term on both sides* by the **least common multiple of all the denominators**.

EXAMPLE 8 Solve: $\frac{2}{3}x - \frac{1}{6} + \frac{1}{2}x = \frac{7}{6} + 2x.$

The denominators are 3, 6, and 2. The number 6 is the least common multiple of all the denominators. We multiply by 6 on both sides of the equation.

$$6\left(\frac{2}{3}x - \frac{1}{6} + \frac{1}{2}x\right) = 6\left(\frac{7}{6} + 2x\right) \qquad \text{Multiplying by 6 on both sides}$$

$$6 \cdot \frac{2}{3}x - 6 \cdot \frac{1}{6} + 6 \cdot \frac{1}{2}x = 6 \cdot \frac{7}{6} + 6 \cdot 2x \qquad \text{Using the distributive law (Caution! Be sure to multiply all the terms by 6.)}$$

$$4x - 1 + 3x = 7 + 12x \qquad \text{Simplifying. Note that the fractions are cleared.}$$

$$7x - 1 = 7 + 12x \qquad \text{Collecting like terms}$$

$$7x - 1 - 12x = 7 + 12x - 12x \qquad \text{Subtracting } 12x$$

$$-5x - 1 = 7 \qquad \text{Collecting like terms}$$

$$-5x - 1 + 1 = 7 + 1 \qquad \text{Adding 1}$$

$$-5x = 8 \qquad \text{Collecting like terms}$$

$$\frac{-5x}{-5} = \frac{8}{-5} \qquad \text{Dividing by } -5$$

$$x = -\frac{8}{5}$$

Check:

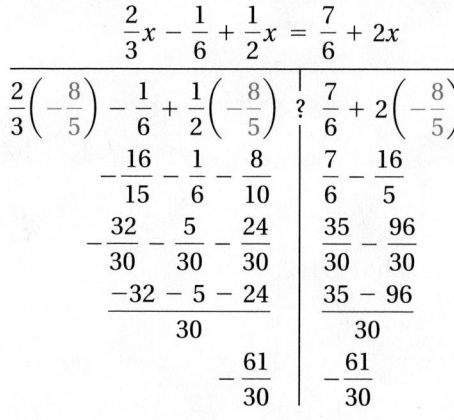

$$\frac{2}{3}x - \frac{1}{6} + \frac{1}{2}x = \frac{7}{6} + 2x$$

TRUE

Calculator Corner

Checking Possible Solutions There are several ways to check the possible solutions of an equation on a calculator. One of the most straightforward methods is to substitute and carry out the calculations on each side of the equation just as we do when we check by hand. To check the possible solution, 1, in Example 6, for instance, we first substitute 1 for x in the expression on the left side of the equation. We press 2 ✕ 1 − 2 **ENTER**. We get 0. Next, we substitute 1 for x in the expression on the right side of the equation. We then press (−) 3 ✕ 1 + 3 **ENTER**. Again we get 0. Since the two sides of the equation have the same value when x is 1, we know that 1 is the solution of the equation.

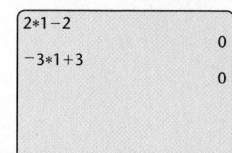

Exercise:

1. Use substitution to check the solutions found in Examples 1–5.

---------- *Caution!* ----------

Check the possible solution in the *original* equation rather than in the equation that has been cleared of fractions.

----

13. Solve: $\dfrac{7}{8}x - \dfrac{1}{4} + \dfrac{1}{2}x = \dfrac{3}{4} + x.$

The solution is $-\dfrac{8}{5}$.

Do Exercise 13.

To illustrate clearing decimals, we repeat Example 4, but this time we clear the equation of decimals first. Compare both methods.

To clear an equation of decimals, we count the greatest number of decimal places in any one number. If the greatest number of decimal places is 1, we multiply every term on both sides by 10; if it is 2, we multiply by 100; and so on.

EXAMPLE 9 Solve: $16.3 - 7.2y = -8.18.$

The greatest number of decimal places in any one number is *two*. Multiplying by 100, which has *two* 0's, will clear all decimals.

$$100(16.3 - 7.2y) = 100(-8.18) \quad \text{Multiplying by 100 on both sides}$$

$$100(16.3) - 100(7.2y) = 100(-8.18) \quad \text{Using the distributive law}$$

$$1630 - 720y = -818 \quad \text{Simplifying}$$

$$1630 - 720y - 1630 = -818 - 1630 \quad \text{Subtracting 1630}$$

$$-720y = -2448 \quad \text{Collecting like terms}$$

$$\dfrac{-720y}{-720} = \dfrac{-2448}{-720} \quad \text{Dividing by } -720$$

$$y = \dfrac{17}{5}, \text{ or } 3.4$$

The number $\dfrac{17}{5}$, or 3.4, checks, as shown in Example 4, so it is the solution.

14. Solve: $41.68 = 4.7 - 8.6y.$

Do Exercise 14.

(c) Equations Containing Parentheses

To solve certain kinds of equations that contain parentheses, we first use the distributive laws to remove the parentheses. Then we proceed as before.

EXAMPLE 10 Solve: $8x = 2(12 - 2x).$

$$8x = 2(12 - 2x)$$

$$8x = 24 - 4x \quad \text{Using the distributive laws to multiply and remove parentheses}$$

$$8x + 4x = 24 - 4x + 4x \quad \text{Adding } 4x \text{ to get all the } x\text{-terms on one side}$$

$$12x = 24 \quad \text{Collecting like terms}$$

$$\dfrac{12x}{12} = \dfrac{24}{12} \quad \text{Dividing by 12}$$

$$x = 2$$

The number 2 checks, so the solution is 2.

Solve.

15. $2(2y + 3) = 14$

16. $5(3x - 2) = 35$

Do Exercises 15 and 16.

Answers

13. $\dfrac{8}{3}$ **14.** $-\dfrac{43}{10}$, or -4.3

15. 2   **16.** 3

Here is a procedure for solving the types of equation discussed in this section.

AN EQUATION-SOLVING PROCEDURE

1. Multiply on both sides to clear the equation of fractions or decimals. (This is optional, but it can ease computations.)
2. If parentheses occur, multiply to remove them using the *distributive laws*.
3. Collect like terms on each side, if necessary.
4. Get all terms with variables on one side and all numbers (constant terms) on the other side, using the *addition principle*.
5. Collect like terms again, if necessary.
6. Multiply or divide to solve for the variable, using the *multiplication principle*.
7. Check all possible solutions in the original equation.

EXAMPLE 11 Solve: $2 - 5(x + 5) = 3(x - 2) - 1$.

$$2 - 5(x + 5) = 3(x - 2) - 1$$

$2 - 5x - 25 = 3x - 6 - 1$ Using the distributive laws to multiply and remove parentheses

$-5x - 23 = 3x - 7$ Collecting like terms

$-5x - 23 + 5x = 3x - 7 + 5x$ Adding $5x$

$-23 = 8x - 7$ Collecting like terms

$-23 + 7 = 8x - 7 + 7$ Adding 7

$-16 = 8x$ Collecting like terms

$\dfrac{-16}{8} = \dfrac{8x}{8}$ Dividing by 8

$-2 = x$

Check: $\dfrac{2 - 5(x + 5) = 3(x - 2) - 1}{}$

$\begin{array}{c|c} 2 - 5(-2 + 5) \overset{?}{} & 3(-2 - 2) - 1 \\ 2 - 5(3) & 3(-4) - 1 \\ 2 - 15 & -12 - 1 \\ -13 & -13 \quad \text{TRUE} \end{array}$

The solution is -2.

> Do Exercises 17 and 18.

Equations with Infinitely Many Solutions

The types of equations we have considered thus far in Sections 8.1–8.3 have all had exactly one solution. We now look at two other possibilities.

Consider

$$3 + x = x + 3.$$

Let's explore the equation and possible solutions in Margin Exercises 19–22.

> Do Exercises 19–22.

Solve.

17. $3(7 + 2x) = 30 + 7(x - 1)$

18. $4(3 + 5x) - 4 = 3 + 2(x - 2)$

Determine whether the given number is a solution of the given equation.

19. 10; $3 + x = x + 3$

20. -7; $3 + x = x + 3$

21. $\dfrac{1}{2}$; $3 + x = x + 3$

22. 0; $3 + x = x + 3$

Answers

17. -2 **18.** $-\dfrac{1}{2}$ **19.** Yes   **20.** Yes
21. Yes   **22.** Yes

We know by the commutative law of addition that the equation $3 + x = x + 3$ holds for any replacement of x with a real number. (See Section 7.7.) We have confirmed some of these solutions in Margin Exercises 19–22. Suppose we try to solve this equation using the addition principle:

$$3 + x = x + 3$$
$$-x + 3 + x = -x + x + 3 \qquad \text{Adding } -x$$
$$3 = 3. \qquad\qquad \text{True}$$

We end with a true equation. The original equation holds for all real-number replacements. Every real number is a solution. Thus the number of solutions is **infinite**.

EXAMPLE 12 Solve: $7x - 17 = 4 + 7(x - 3)$.

$$7x - 17 = 4 + 7(x - 3)$$
$$7x - 17 = 4 + 7x - 21 \qquad \text{Using the distributive law to multiply and remove parentheses}$$
$$7x - 17 = 7x - 17 \qquad\qquad \text{Collecting like terms}$$
$$-7x + 7x - 17 = -7x + 7x - 17 \qquad \text{Adding } -7x$$
$$-17 = -17 \qquad\qquad \text{True for all real numbers}$$

Every real number is a solution. There are infinitely many solutions.

Equations with No Solution

Now consider

$$3 + x = x + 8.$$

Let's explore the equation and possible solutions in Margin Exercises 23–26.

> Do Exercises 23–26.

None of the replacements in Margin Exercises 23–26 is a solution of the given equation. In fact, there are no solutions. Let's try to solve this equation using the addition principle:

$$3 + x = x + 8$$
$$-x + 3 + x = -x + x + 8 \qquad \text{Adding } -x$$
$$3 = 8. \qquad\qquad \text{False}$$

We end with a false equation. The original equation is false for all real-number replacements. Thus it has **no** solution.

EXAMPLE 13 Solve: $3x + 4(x + 2) = 11 + 7x$.

$$3x + 4(x + 2) = 11 + 7x$$
$$3x + 4x + 8 = 11 + 7x \qquad \text{Using the distributive law to multiply and remove parentheses}$$
$$7x + 8 = 11 + 7x \qquad\qquad \text{Collecting like terms}$$
$$7x + 8 - 7x = 11 + 7x - 7x \qquad \text{Subtracting } 7x$$
$$8 = 11 \qquad\qquad \text{False}$$

There are no solutions.

> Do Exercises 27 and 28.

Determine whether the given number is a solution of the given equation.

23. 10; $3 + x = x + 8$

24. -7; $3 + x = x + 8$

25. $\dfrac{1}{2}$; $3 + x = x + 8$

26. 0; $3 + x = x + 8$

Solve.

27. $30 + 5(x + 3) = -3 + 5x + 48$

28. $2x + 7(x - 4) = 13 + 9x$

When solving an equation, if the result is:

- an equation of the form $x = a$, where a is a real number, then there is one solution, the number a;
- a true equation like $3 = 3$ or $-1 = -1$, then every real number is a solution;
- a false equation like $3 = 8$ or $-4 = 5$, then there is no solution.

Answers

23. No   **24.** No   **25.** No   **26.** No
27. All real numbers   **28.** No solution

a Solve. Don't forget to check!

1. $5x + 6 = 31$

Check: $\underline{5x + 6 = 31}$
?

2. $7x + 6 = 13$

Check: $\underline{7x + 6 = 13}$
?

3. $8x + 4 = 68$

Check: $\underline{8x + 4 = 68}$
?

4. $4y + 10 = 46$

Check: $\underline{4y + 10 = 46}$
?

5. $4x - 6 = 34$

6. $5y - 2 = 53$

7. $3x - 9 = 33$

8. $4x - 19 = 5$

9. $7x + 2 = -54$

10. $5x + 4 = -41$

11. $-45 = 3 + 6y$

12. $-91 = 9t + 8$

13. $-4x + 7 = 35$

14. $-5x - 7 = 108$

15. $\dfrac{5}{4}x - 18 = -3$

16. $\dfrac{3}{2}x - 24 = -36$

b Solve.

17. $5x + 7x = 72$

Check: $\underline{5x + 7x = 72}$
?

18. $8x + 3x = 55$

Check: $\underline{8x + 3x = 55}$
?

19. $8x + 7x = 60$

Check: $\underline{8x + 7x = 60}$
?

20. $8x + 5x = 104$

Check: $\underline{8x + 5x = 104}$
?

21. $4x + 3x = 42$

22. $7x + 18x = 125$

23. $-6y - 3y = 27$

24. $-5y - 7y = 144$

25. $-7y - 8y = -15$

26. $-10y - 3y = -39$

27. $x + \dfrac{1}{3}x = 8$

28. $x + \dfrac{1}{4}x = 10$

29. $10.2y - 7.3y = -58$ **30.** $6.8y - 2.4y = -88$ **31.** $8y - 35 = 3y$ **32.** $4x - 6 = 6x$

33. $8x - 1 = 23 - 4x$ **34.** $5y - 2 = 28 - y$ **35.** $2x - 1 = 4 + x$ **36.** $4 - 3x = 6 - 7x$

37. $6x + 3 = 2x + 11$ **38.** $14 - 6a = -2a + 3$ **39.** $5 - 2x = 3x - 7x + 25$

40. $-7z + 2z - 3z - 7 = 17$ **41.** $4 + 3x - 6 = 3x + 2 - x$ **42.** $5 + 4x - 7 = 4x - 2 - x$

43. $4y - 4 + y + 24 = 6y + 20 - 4y$ **44.** $5y - 7 + y = 7y + 21 - 5y$

Solve. Clear fractions or decimals first.

45. $\dfrac{7}{2}x + \dfrac{1}{2}x = 3x + \dfrac{3}{2} + \dfrac{5}{2}x$ **46.** $\dfrac{7}{8}x - \dfrac{1}{4} + \dfrac{3}{4}x = \dfrac{1}{16} + x$

47. $\dfrac{2}{3} + \dfrac{1}{4}t = \dfrac{1}{3}$ **48.** $-\dfrac{3}{2} + x = -\dfrac{5}{6} - \dfrac{4}{3}$

49. $\dfrac{2}{3} + 3y = 5y - \dfrac{2}{15}$ **50.** $\dfrac{1}{2} + 4m = 3m - \dfrac{5}{2}$

51. $\dfrac{5}{3} + \dfrac{2}{3}x = \dfrac{25}{12} + \dfrac{5}{4}x + \dfrac{3}{4}$ **52.** $1 - \dfrac{2}{3}y = \dfrac{9}{5} - \dfrac{y}{5} + \dfrac{3}{5}$

53. $2.1x + 45.2 = 3.2 - 8.4x$ **54.** $0.96y - 0.79 = 0.21y + 0.46$

55. $1.03 - 0.62x = 0.71 - 0.22x$ **56.** $1.7t + 8 - 1.62t = 0.4t - 0.32 + 8$

Copyright © 2012 Pearson Education, Inc.

57. $\frac{2}{7}x - \frac{1}{2}x = \frac{3}{4}x + 1$

58. $\frac{5}{16}y + \frac{3}{8}y = 2 + \frac{1}{4}y$

c Solve.

59. $3(2y - 3) = 27$

60. $8(3x + 2) = 30$

61. $40 = 5(3x + 2)$

62. $9 = 3(5x - 2)$

63. $-23 + y = y + 25$

64. $17 - t = -t + 68$

65. $-23 + x = x - 23$

66. $y - \frac{2}{3} = -\frac{2}{3} + y$

67. $2(3 + 4m) - 9 = 45$

68. $5x + 5(4x - 1) = 20$

69. $5r - (2r + 8) = 16$

70. $6b - (3b + 8) = 16$

71. $6 - 2(3x - 1) = 2$

72. $10 - 3(2x - 1) = 1$

73. $5x + 5 - 7x = 15 - 12x + 10x - 10$

74. $3 - 7x + 10x - 14 = 9 - 6x + 9x - 20$

75. $22x - 5 - 15x + 3 = 10x - 4 - 3x + 11$

76. $11x - 6 - 4x + 1 = 9x - 8 - 2x + 12$

77. $5(d + 4) = 7(d - 2)$

78. $3(t - 2) = 9(t + 2)$

79. $8(2t + 1) = 4(7t + 7)$

80. $7(5x - 2) = 6(6x - 1)$

81. $3(r - 6) + 2 = 4(r + 2) - 21$

82. $5(t + 3) + 9 = 3(t - 2) + 6$

83. $19 - (2x + 3) = 2(x + 3) + x$

84. $13 - (2c + 2) = 2(c + 2) + 3c$

85. $2[4 - 2(3 - x)] - 1 = 4[2(4x - 3) + 7] - 25$

86. $5[3(7 - t) - 4(8 + 2t)] - 20 = -6[2(6 + 3t) - 4]$

87. $11 - 4(x + 1) - 3 = 11 + 2(4 - 2x) - 16$

88. $6(2x - 1) - 12 = 7 + 12(x - 1)$

89. $22x - 1 - 12x = 5(2x - 1) + 4$

90. $2 + 14x - 9 = 7(2x + 1) - 14$

91. $0.7(3x + 6) = 1.1 - (x + 2)$

92. $0.9(2x + 8) = 20 - (x + 5)$

Skill Maintenance

93. Divide: $-22.1 \div 3.4$.   [7.6c]

94. Multiply: $-22.1(3.4)$.   [7.5a]

95. Factor: $7x - 21 - 14y$.   [7.7d]

96. Factor: $8y - 88x + 8$.   [7.7d]

Simplify.

97. $-3 + 2(-5)^2(-3) - 7$ [7.8d]

98. $3x + 2[4 - 5(2x - 1)]$ [7.8c]

99. $23(2x - 4) - 15(10 - 3x)$ [7.8b]

100. $256 \div 64 \div 4^2$ [7.8d]

Synthesis

Solve.

101. $\dfrac{2}{3}\left(\dfrac{7}{8} - 4x\right) - \dfrac{5}{8} = \dfrac{3}{8}$

102. $\dfrac{1}{4}(8y + 4) - 17 = -\dfrac{1}{2}(4y - 8)$

103. $\dfrac{4 - 3x}{7} = \dfrac{2 + 5x}{49} - \dfrac{x}{14}$

104. The width of a rectangle is 5 ft, its length is $(3x + 2)$ ft, and its area is 75 ft^2. Find x.

Copyright © 2012 Pearson Education, Inc.

8.4 Formulas

(a) Evaluating Formulas

A **formula** is a "recipe" for doing a certain type of calculation. Formulas are often given as equations. When we replace the variables in an equation with numbers and calculate the result, we are **evaluating** the formula. Evaluating was introduced in Section 7.1.

Let's consider a formula that has to do with weather. Suppose you see a flash of lightning during a storm. Then a few seconds later, you hear the thunder that accompanies that lightning.

Your distance from the place where the lightning struck is given by the formula $M = \frac{1}{5}t$, where t is the number of seconds from the lightning flash to the sound of the thunder and M is in miles.

EXAMPLE 1 *Distance from Lightning.* Consider the formula $M = \frac{1}{5}t$. Suppose it takes 10 sec for the sound of thunder to reach you after you have seen a flash of lightning. How far away did the lightning strike?

We substitute 10 for t and calculate M:

$$M = \frac{1}{5}t = \frac{1}{5}(10) = 2.$$

The lightning struck 2 mi away.

EXAMPLE 2 *Socks from Cotton.* Consider the formula $S = 4321x$, where S is the number of socks of average size that can be produced from x bales of cotton. You see a shipment of 300 bales of cotton taken off a ship. How many socks can be made from the cotton?

Source: *Country Woman Magazine*

We substitute 300 for x and calculate S:

$$S = 4321x = 4321(300) = 1{,}296{,}300.$$

Thus, 1,296,300 socks can be made from 300 bales of cotton.

Do Exercises 1 and 2.

OBJECTIVES

(a) Evaluate a formula.

(b) Solve a formula for a specified letter.

---

1. **Storm Distance.** Refer to Example 1. Suppose that it takes the sound of thunder 14 sec to reach you. How far away is the storm?

2. **Socks from Cotton.** Refer to Example 2. Determine the number of socks that can be made from 65 bales of cotton.

Answers

1. 2.8 mi **2.** 280,865 socks

EXAMPLE 3 *Distance, Rate, and Time.*   The distance d that a car will travel at a rate, or speed, r in time t is given by

$$d = rt.$$

A car travels at 75 miles per hour (mph) for 4.5 hr. How far will it travel?

We substitute 75 for r and 4.5 for t and calculate d:

$$d = rt = (75)(4.5) = 337.5 \text{ mi.}$$

The car will travel 337.5 mi.

Do Exercise 3.

3. Distance, Rate, and Time.
A car travels at 55 mph for 6.2 hr. How far will it travel?

(b) Solving Formulas

Refer to Example 2. Suppose a clothing company wants to produce S socks and needs to know how many bales of cotton to order. If this calculation is to be repeated many times, it might be helpful to first solve the formula for x:

$$S = 4321x$$

$$\frac{S}{4321} = x. \qquad \text{Dividing by 4321}$$

Then we can substitute a number for S and calculate x. For example, if the number of socks S to be produced is 432,100, then

$$x = \frac{S}{4321} = \frac{432,100}{4321} = 100.$$

The company would need to order 100 bales of cotton.

EXAMPLE 4   Solve for z: $H = \frac{1}{4}z$.

$$H = \frac{1}{4}z \qquad \text{We want this letter alone.}$$
$$4 \cdot H = 4 \cdot \frac{1}{4}z \qquad \text{Multiplying by 4 on both sides}$$
$$4H = z$$

For $H = 2$ in Example 4, $z = 4H = 4(2)$, or 8.

EXAMPLE 5   *Distance, Rate, and Time.*   Solve for t: $d = rt$.

$$d = rt \qquad \text{We want this letter alone.}$$
$$\frac{d}{r} = \frac{rt}{r} \qquad \text{Dividing by } r$$
$$\frac{d}{r} = \frac{r}{r} \cdot t$$
$$\frac{d}{r} = t \qquad \text{Simplifying}$$

Do Exercises 4–6.

4. Solve for q: $B = \frac{1}{3}q$.

5. Solve for m: $n = mz$.

6. Electricity.   Solve for I: $E = IR$. (This formula relates voltage E, current I, and resistance R.)

Answers

3. 341 mi   **4.** $q = 3B$
5. $m = \dfrac{n}{z}$ **6.** $I = \dfrac{E}{R}$

EXAMPLE 6 Solve for x: $y = x + 3$.

$y = x + 3$ We want this letter alone.

$y - 3 = x + 3 - 3$ Subtracting 3

$y - 3 = x$ Simplifying

EXAMPLE 7 Solve for x: $y = x - a$.

$y = x - a$ We want this letter alone.

$y + a = x - a + a$ Adding a

$y + a = x$ Simplifying

Do Exercises 7–9.

Solve for x.

7. $y = x + 5$

8. $y = x - 7$

9. $y = x - b$

EXAMPLE 8 Solve for y: $6y = 3x$.

$6y = 3x$ We want this letter alone.

$\dfrac{6y}{6} = \dfrac{3x}{6}$ Dividing by 6

$y = \dfrac{x}{2}$, or $\dfrac{1}{2}x$ Simplifying

EXAMPLE 9 Solve for y: $by = ax$.

$by = ax$ We want this letter alone.

$\dfrac{by}{b} = \dfrac{ax}{b}$ Dividing by b

$y = \dfrac{ax}{b}$ Simplifying

Do Exercises 10 and 11.

10. Solve for y: $9y = 5x$.

11. Solve for p: $ap = bt$.

EXAMPLE 10 Solve for x: $ax + b = c$.

$ax + b = c$ We want this letter alone.

$ax + b - b = c - b$ Subtracting b

$ax = c - b$ Simplifying

$\dfrac{ax}{a} = \dfrac{c - b}{a}$ Dividing by a

$x = \dfrac{c - b}{a}$ Simplifying

12. Solve for x: $y = mx + b$.

13. Solve for Q: $tQ - p = a$.

Do Exercises 12 and 13.

Answers

7. $x = y - 5$ **8.** $x = y + 7$

9. $x = y + b$ **10.** $y = \dfrac{5x}{9}$, or $\dfrac{5}{9}x$

11. $p = \dfrac{bt}{a}$ **12.** $x = \dfrac{y - b}{m}$

13. $Q = \dfrac{a + p}{t}$

To solve a formula for a given letter, identify the letter and:

1. Multiply on both sides to clear fractions or decimals, if that is needed.
2. Collect like terms on each side, if necessary.
3. Get all terms with the letter to be solved for on one side of the equation and all other terms on the other side.
4. Collect like terms again, if necessary.
5. Solve for the letter in question.

EXAMPLE 11 *Circumference.* Solve for r: $C = 2\pi r$. This is a formula for the circumference C of a circle of radius r.

$$C = 2\pi r \qquad \text{We want this letter alone.}$$

$$\frac{C}{2\pi} = \frac{2\pi r}{2\pi} \qquad \text{Dividing by } 2\pi$$

$$\frac{C}{2\pi} = r$$

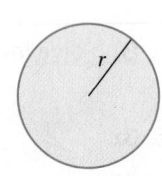

EXAMPLE 12 *Averages.* Solve for a: $A = \dfrac{a + b + c}{3}$. This is a formula for the average A of three numbers a, b, and c.

$$A = \frac{a + b + c}{3} \qquad \text{We want the letter } a \text{ alone.}$$

$$3 \cdot A = 3 \cdot \frac{a + b + c}{3} \qquad \text{Multiplying by 3 on both sides}$$

$$3A = a + b + c \qquad \text{Simplifying}$$

$$3A - b - c = a \qquad \text{Subtracting } b \text{ and } c$$

Do Exercises 14 and 15.

14. Circumference. Solve for D:
$$C = \pi D.$$
This is a formula for the circumference C of a circle of diameter D.

15. Averages. Solve for c:
$$A = \frac{a + b + c + d}{4}.$$

STUDY TIPS

HIGHLIGHTING

- **Try to keep one section ahead of your syllabus.** Reading and highlighting a section before your instructor lectures on it allows you to listen carefully and concentrate on what is being said in class. Then you can take notes only on special points and on questions related to the lecture.

- **Highlight important points.** You are probably used to highlighting key points as you study. If that works for you, continue to do so. But you will notice many design features throughout this book that already highlight important points. Thus you may not need to highlight as much as you generally do.

- **Highlight points that you do not understand.** Use a special marker to indicate trouble spots that can lead to questions to be asked during class or in a tutoring session.

Answers

14. $D = \dfrac{C}{\pi}$ 15. $c = 4A - a - b - d$

 Solve.

1. *Furnace Output.* The formula

$$B = 30a$$

is used in New England to estimate the minimum furnace output B, in Btu's, for a modern house with a square feet of flooring.

Source: U.S. Department of Energy

a) Determine the minimum furnace output for a 1900-ft^2 modern house.

b) Solve for a. That is, solve $B = 30a$ for a.

3. *Distance from Lightning.* The formula

$$M = \tfrac{1}{5}t$$

can be used to determine how far M, in miles, you are from lightning when its thunder takes t seconds to reach your ears.

a) It takes 8 sec for the sound of thunder to reach you after you have seen the lightning. How far away did the lightning strike?

b) Solve for t.

5. *College Enrollment.* At many colleges, the number of "full-time-equivalent" students f is given by

$$f = \frac{n}{15},$$

where n is the total number of credits for which students have enrolled in a given semester.

a) Determine the number of full-time-equivalent students on a campus in which students registered for a total of 21,345 credits.

b) Solve for n.

2. *Furnace Output.* The formula

$$B = 50a$$

is used in New England to estimate the minimum furnace output B, in Btu's, for an old, poorly insulated house with a square feet of flooring.

Source: U.S. Department of Energy

a) Determine the minimum furnace output for a 3200-ft^2 old, poorly insulated house.

b) Solve for a. That is, solve $B = 50a$ for a.

4. *Electrical Power.* The power rating P, in watts, of an electrical appliance is determined by

$$P = I \cdot V,$$

where I is the current, in amperes, and V is measured in volts.

a) A microwave oven requires 12 amps of current and the voltage in the house is 115 volts. What is the wattage of the microwave?

b) Solve for I; for V.

6. *Surface Area of a Cube.* The surface area A of a cube with side s is given by

$$A = 6s^2.$$

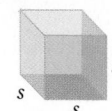

a) Find the surface area of a cube with sides of 3 in.

b) Solve for s^2.

7. *Calorie Density.* The calorie density D, in calories per ounce, of a food that contains c calories and weighs w ounces is given by

$$D = \frac{c}{w}.$$

Eight ounces of fat-free milk contains 84 calories. Find the calorie density of fat-free milk.

Source: *Nutrition Action Healthletter*, March 2000, p. 9. Center for Science in the Public Interest, Suite 300; 1875 Connecticut Ave NW, Washington, D.C. 20008.

8. *Wavelength of a Musical Note.* The wavelength w, in meters per cycle, of a musical note is given by

$$w = \frac{r}{f},$$

where r is the speed of the sound, in meters per second, and f is the frequency, in cycles per second. The speed of sound in air is 344 m/sec. What is the wavelength of a note whose frequency in air is 24 cycles per second?

9. *Size of a League Schedule.* When all n teams in a league play every other team twice, a total of N games are played, where

$$N = n^2 - n.$$

A soccer league has 7 teams and all teams play each other twice. How many games are played?

10. *Size of a League Schedule.* When all n teams in a league play every other team twice, a total of N games are played, where

$$N = n^2 - n.$$

A basketball league has 11 teams and all teams play each other twice. How many games are played?

b   Solve for the indicated letter.

11. $y = 5x$, for x

12. $d = 55t$, for t

13. $a = bc$, for c

14. $y = mx$, for x

15. $n = m + 11$, for m

16. $z = t + 21$, for t

17. $y = x - \dfrac{3}{5}$, for x

18. $y = x - \dfrac{2}{3}$, for x

19. $y = 13 + x$, for x

20. $t = 6 + s$, for s

21. $y = x + b$, for x

22. $y = x + A$, for x

23. $y = 5 - x$, for x

24. $y = 10 - x$, for x

25. $y = a - x$, for x

Copyright © 2012 Pearson Education, Inc.

26. $y = q - x$, for x

27. $8y = 5x$, for y

28. $10y = -5x$, for y

29. $By = Ax$, for x

30. $By = Ax$, for y

31. $W = mt + b$, for t

32. $W = mt - b$, for t

33. $y = bx + c$, for x

34. $y = bx - c$, for x

35. *Area of a Parallelogram:*
$A = bh$, for h
(Area A, base b, height h)

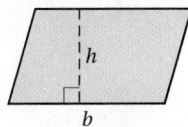

36. *Distance, Rate, Time:*
$d = rt$, for r
(Distance d, speed r, time t)

Speed, r Time, t

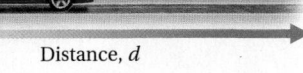

Distance, d

37. *Perimeter of a Rectangle:*
$P = 2l + 2w$, for w
(Perimeter P, length l, width w)

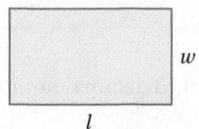

38. *Area of a Circle:*
$A = \pi r^2$, for r^2
(Area A, radius r)

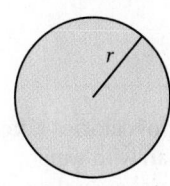

39. *Average of Two Numbers:*
$A = \dfrac{a + b}{2}$, for a

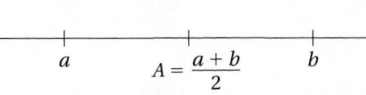

a $A = \dfrac{a+b}{2}$ b

40. *Area of a Triangle:*
$A = \dfrac{1}{2}bh$, for b

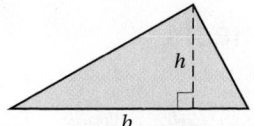

41. $A = \dfrac{a + b + c}{3}$, for b

42. $A = \dfrac{a + b + c}{3}$, for c

43. $A = at + b$, for t

44. $S = rx + s$, for x

45. $Ax + By = c$, for x

46. $Q = \dfrac{p - q}{2}$, for p

47. *Force:*

$$F = ma, \text{ for } a$$

(Force F, mass m, acceleration a)

48. *Simple Interest:*

$$I = Prt, \text{ for } P$$

(Interest I, principal P, interest rate r, time t)

49. *Relativity:*

$$E = mc^2, \text{ for } c^2$$

(Energy E, mass m, speed of light c)

50. $Ax + By = c$, for y

51. $v = \dfrac{3k}{t}$, for t

52. $P = \dfrac{ab}{c}$, for c

Skill Maintenance

53. Convert to decimal notation: $\dfrac{23}{25}$.   [3.1b]

54. Add: $-23 + (-67)$.   [7.3a]

55. Add: $0.082 + (-9.407)$.   [7.3a]

56. Subtract: $-23 - (-67)$.   [7.4a]

57. Subtract: $-45.8 - (-32.6)$.   [7.4a]

58. Remove parentheses and simplify: [7.8b]
$$4a - 8b - 5(5a - 4b).$$

Convert to decimal notation.   [4.2b]

59. 3.1%

60. 67.1%

61. Add: $-\dfrac{2}{3} + \dfrac{5}{6}$.   [7.3a]

62. Subtract: $-\dfrac{2}{3} - \dfrac{5}{6}$.   [7.4a]

Synthesis

63. *Female Caloric Needs.*   The number of calories K needed each day by a moderately active woman who weighs w pounds, is h inches tall, and is a years old can be estimated by the formula

$$K = 917 + 6(w + h - a).$$

Source: Parker, M., *She Does Math.* Mathematical Association of America, p. 96

a) Elaine is moderately active, weighs 120 lb, is 67 in. tall, and is 23 yr old. What are her caloric needs?

b) Solve the formula for a; for h; for w.

64. *Male Caloric Needs.*   The number of calories K needed each day by a moderately active man who weighs w kilograms, is h centimeters tall, and is a years old can be estimated by the formula

$$K = 19.18w + 7h - 9.52a + 92.4.$$

Source: Parker, M., *She Does Math.* Mathematical Association of America, p. 96

a) Marv is moderately active, weighs 97 kg, is 185 cm tall, and is 55 yr old. What are his caloric needs?

b) Solve the formula for a; for h; for w.

Solve.

65. $H = \dfrac{2}{a - b}$, for b; for a

66. $P = 4m + 7mn$, for m

67. In $A = lw$, if l and w both double, what is the effect on A?

68. In $P = 2a + 2b$, if P doubles, do a and b necessarily both double?

69. In $A = \frac{1}{2}bh$, if b increases by 4 units and h does not change, what happens to A?

70. Solve for F: $D = \dfrac{1}{E + F}$.

Copyright © 2012 Pearson Education, Inc.

Mid-Chapter Review

Concept Reinforcement

Determine whether each statement is true or false.

_____ 1. $3 - x = 4x$ and $5x = -3$ are equivalent equations. [8.1b]

_____ 2. For any real numbers a, b, and c, $a = b$ is equivalent to $a + c = b + c$. [8.1b]

_____ 3. We can use the multiplication principle to divide on both sides of an equation by the same nonzero number. [8.2a]

_____ 4. Every equation has at least one solution. [8.3c]

Guided Solutions

Fill in each blank with the number, variable, or expression that creates a correct statement or solution.

Solve. [8.1b], [8.2a]

5.
$$x + 5 = -3$$
$$x + 5 - 5 = -3 - \square$$
$$x + \square = -8$$
$$x = \square$$

6.
$$-6x = 42$$
$$\frac{-6x}{-6} = \frac{42}{\square}$$
$$\square \cdot x = -7$$
$$x = \square$$

7. Solve for y: $5y + z = t$. [8.4b]
$$5y + z = t$$
$$5y + z - z = t - \square$$
$$5y = \square$$
$$\frac{5y}{5} = \frac{t - z}{\square}$$
$$y = \frac{\square}{5}$$

Mixed Review

Solve. [8.1b], [8.2a], [8.3a, b, c]

8. $x + 5 = 11$

9. $x + 9 = -3$

10. $8 = t + 1$

11. $-7 = y + 3$

12. $x - 6 = 14$

13. $y - 7 = -2$

14. $-\dfrac{3}{2} + z = -\dfrac{3}{4}$

15. $-3.3 = -1.9 + t$

16. $7x = 42$

17. $17 = -t$

18. $6x = -54$

19. $-5y = -85$

20. $\dfrac{x}{7} = 3$

21. $\dfrac{2}{3}x = 12$

22. $-\dfrac{t}{5} = 3$

23. $\dfrac{3}{4}x = -\dfrac{9}{8}$

24. $3x + 2 = 5$

25. $5x + 4 = -11$

26. $6x - 7 = 2$

27. $-4x - 9 = -5$

28. $6x + 5x = 33$

29. $-3y - 4y = 49$

30. $3x - 4 = 12 - x$

31. $5 - 6x = 9 - 8x$

32. $4y - \dfrac{3}{2} = \dfrac{3}{4} + 2y$

33. $\dfrac{4}{5} + \dfrac{1}{6}t = \dfrac{1}{10}$

34. $0.21n - 1.05 = 2.1 - 0.14n$

35. $5(3y - 1) = -35$

36. $7 - 2(5x + 3) = 1$

37. $-8 + t = t - 8$

38. $z + 12 = -12 + z$

39. $4(3x + 2) = 5(2x - 1)$

40. $8x - 6 - 2x = 3(2x - 4) + 6$

Solve for the indicated letter. [8.4b]

41. $A = 4b$, for b

42. $y = x - 1.5$, for x

43. $n = s - m$, for m

44. $4t = 9w$, for t

45. $B = at - c$, for t

46. $M = \dfrac{x + y + z}{2}$, for y

Understanding Through Discussion and Writing

47. Explain the difference between equivalent expressions and equivalent equations. [7.7a], [8.1b]

48. Are the equations $x = 5$ and $x^2 = 25$ equivalent? Why or why not? [8.1b]

49. When solving an equation using the addition principle, how do you determine which number to add or subtract on both sides of the equation? [8.1b]

50. Explain the following mistake made by a fellow student. [8.1b]

$$x + \dfrac{1}{3} = -\dfrac{5}{3}$$

$$x = -\dfrac{4}{3}$$

51. When solving an equation using the multiplication principle, how do you determine by what number to multiply or divide on both sides of the equation? [8.2a]

52. Devise an application in which it would be useful to solve the equation $d = rt$ for r. [8.4b]

Copyright © 2012 Pearson Education, Inc.

8.5 Applications of Percent

a Translating and Solving

Many applied problems involve percent. Here we begin to see how equation solving can enhance our problem-solving skills. For background on the manipulative skills of percent notation, see Sections 4.2–4.5.

In solving percent problems, we first *translate* the problem to an equation. Then we *solve* the equation using the techniques discussed in Sections 8.1–8.3. The key words in the translation are as follows.

> **KEY WORDS IN PERCENT TRANSLATIONS**
>
> "**Of**" translates to "·" or "×".
>
> "**Is**" translates to "=".
>
> "**What number**" or "**what percent**" translates to any letter.
>
> "**%**" translates to "$\times \frac{1}{100}$" or "$\times 0.01$".

EXAMPLE 1 Translate:

$$\begin{array}{ccccc} 28\% & \text{of} & 5 & \text{is} & \text{what number?} \\ \downarrow & \downarrow & \downarrow & \downarrow & \downarrow \\ 28\% & \cdot & 5 & = & a \end{array}$$ This is a percent equation.

EXAMPLE 2 Translate:

$$\begin{array}{cccccc} 45\% & \text{of} & \text{what number} & \text{is} & 28? \\ \downarrow & \downarrow & \downarrow & \downarrow & \downarrow \\ 45\% & \times & b & = & 28 \end{array}$$

EXAMPLE 3 Translate:

$$\begin{array}{ccccc} \underline{\text{What percent}} & \text{of} & 90 & \text{is} & 7? \\ \downarrow & \downarrow & \downarrow & \downarrow \\ n & \cdot & 90 & = & 7 \end{array}$$

> Do Exercises 1–6.

Percent problems are actually of three different types. Although the method we present does *not* require that you be able to identify which type we are studying, it is helpful to know them. Let's begin by using a specific example to find a standard form for a percent problem.

We know that

15 is 25% of 60,   or $15 = 25\% \times 60$.

We can think of this as:

> Amount = Percent number × Base.

Translate to an equation. Do not solve.

1. 13% of 80 is what number?

2. What number is 60% of 70?

3. 43 is 20% of what number?

4. 110% of what number is 30?

5. 16 is what percent of 80?

6. What percent of 94 is 10.5?

Answers

1. $13\% \cdot 80 = a$ **2.** $a = 60\% \cdot 70$
3. $43 = 20\% \cdot b$ **4.** $110\% \cdot b = 30$
5. $16 = n \cdot 80$ **6.** $n \cdot 94 = 10.5$

STUDY TIPS

SOLVING APPLIED PROBLEMS

Don't be discouraged if, at first, you find the exercises in this section to be more challenging than those in earlier sections or if you have had difficulty doing applied problems in the past. Your skill will improve with each problem you solve. After you have done your homework for this section, you might want to do extra problems from the text. As you gain experience solving applied problems, you will find yourself becoming comfortable with them.

Each of the three types of percent problem depends on which of the three pieces of information is missing in the statement

$$\text{Amount} = \text{Percent number} \times \text{Base}.$$

1. Finding the *amount* (the result of taking the percent)

   Example: What number   is   25%   of   60?

   Translation: y $=$ 25%   ·   60

2. Finding the *base* (the number you are taking the percent of)

   Example: 15   is   25%   of   what number?

   Translation: 15 $=$ 25%   · y

3. Finding the *percent number* (the percent itself)

   Example: 15   is   what percent   of   60?

   Translation: 15 $=$ y ·   60

Finding the Amount

EXAMPLE 4   What number is 11% of 49?

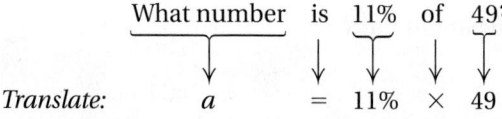

What number   is   11%   of   49?

Translate: a $=$ 11% $\times$ 49

Solve: The letter is by itself. To solve the equation, we need only convert 11% to decimal notation and multiply:

$$a = 11\% \times 49 = 0.11 \times 49 = 5.39.$$

Thus, 5.39 is 11% of 49. The answer is 5.39.

7. What number is 2.4% of 80?

Do Exercise 7.

Finding the Base

EXAMPLE 5   3 is 16% of what number?

3   is   16%   of   what number?

Translate: 3 $=$ 16% $\times$ b

$3 = 0.16 \times b$ Converting 16% to decimal notation

Solve: In this case, the letter is not by itself. To solve the equation, we divide by 0.16 on both sides:

$$3 = 0.16 \times b$$

$$\frac{3}{0.16} = \frac{0.16 \times b}{0.16} \qquad \text{Dividing by 0.16}$$

$$18.75 = b. \qquad \text{Simplifying}$$

The answer is 18.75.

8. 25.3 is 22% of what number?

Answers

7. 1.92   **8.** 115

Do Exercise 8.

Finding the Percent Number

In solving these problems, you *must* remember to convert to percent notation after you have solved the equation.

EXAMPLE 6 $32 is what percent of $50?

$$\underbrace{\$32} \quad \text{is} \quad \underbrace{\text{what percent}} \quad \text{of} \quad \underbrace{\$50?}$$

Translate: $32 = p \times 50$

Solve: To solve the equation, we divide by 50 on both sides and convert the answer to percent notation:

$$32 = p \times 50$$

$$\frac{32}{50} = \frac{p \times 50}{50} \qquad \text{Dividing by 50}$$

$$0.64 = p$$

$$64\% = p. \qquad \text{Converting to percent notation}$$

Thus, $32 is 64% of $50. The answer is 64%.

Do Exercise 9.

9. What percent of $50 is $18?

EXAMPLE 7 *Foreign Visitors to China.* About 22 million foreign travelers visited China in 2006. Of this number, 9% were from the United States. How many Americans visited China in 2006?

Source: *TIME Magazine*, March 8, 2007

To solve this problem, we first reword and then translate. We let a = the number of Americans, in millions, who visited China in 2006.

Rewording: $\underbrace{\text{What number}}$ is 9% of 22?

Translating: $a = 9\% \times 22$

Solve: The letter is by itself. To solve the equation, we need only convert 9% to decimal notation and multiply:

$$a = 9\% \times 22 = 0.09 \times 22 = 1.98.$$

Thus, 1.98 million is 9% of 22 million, so 1.98 million Americans visited China in 2006.

Do Exercise 10.

10. Chinese Visitors to the United States. About 51 million foreign travelers visited the United States in 2006. Of this number, 1% were from China. How many Chinese travelers visited the United States in 2006?
Source: *TIME Magazine*, March 8, 2007

EXAMPLE 8 *Public School Enrollment.* In the fall of 2008, 14.9 million students enrolled in grades 9–12 in U.S. public schools. This was 30% of the total enrollment in public schools. What was the total enrollment?

Source: National Center for Educational Statistics

To solve this problem, we first reword and then translate. We let T = the total enrollment, in millions, in U.S. public schools in 2008.

Rewording: 14.9 is 30% of $\underbrace{\text{what number?}}$

Translating: $14.9 = 30\% \times T$

Answers
9. 36%   **10.** 0.51 million travelers

11. Areas of Texas and Alaska.
The area of the second largest state, Texas, is 268,581 mi². This is about 40.5% of the area of the largest state, Alaska. What is the area of Alaska?

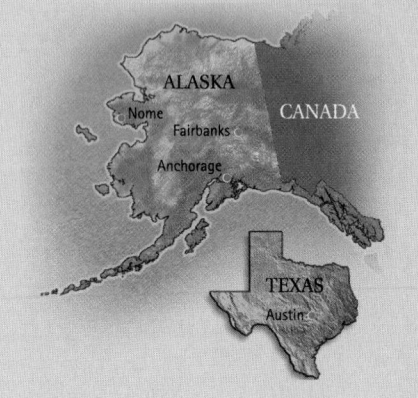

ALASKA
Nome
Fairbanks
CANADA
Anchorage

TEXAS
Austin

Solve: To solve the equation, we convert 30% to decimal notation and divide by 0.3 on both sides:

$$14.9 = 30\% \times T$$

$$14.9 = 0.3 \times T \qquad \text{Converting to decimal notation}$$

$$\frac{14.9}{0.3} = \frac{0.3 \times T}{0.3} \qquad \text{Dividing by 0.3}$$

$$49.7 \approx T. \qquad \text{Simplifying and rounding to the nearest tenth}$$

About 49.7 million students enrolled in U.S. public schools in 2008.

Do Exercise 11.

EXAMPLE 9 *Employment Outlook.* There were 280 thousand dental assistants in 2006. This number is expected to grow to 362 thousand in 2016. What is the percent of increase?

Source: *Occupational Outlook Handbook*

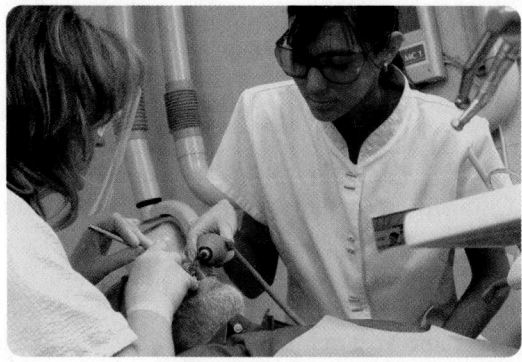

To solve the problem, we must first determine the amount of the increase, in thousands:

Jobs in 2016	minus	Jobs in 2006	=	Increase
362	−	280	=	82.

Using the job increase of 82 thousand, we reword and then translate. We let p = the percent of increase. We want to know, "what percent of the number of jobs in 2006 is 82 thousand?"

Rewording:	82	is	what percent	of	280?
Translating:	82	=	p	×	280

Solve: To solve the equation, we divide by 280 on both sides and convert the answer to percent notation:

$$82 = p \times 280$$

$$\frac{82}{280} = \frac{p \times 280}{280} \qquad \text{Dividing by 280}$$

$$0.293 \approx p \qquad \text{Simplifying}$$

$$29.3\% \approx p. \qquad \text{Converting to percent notation}$$

The percent of increase is about 29.3%.

Do Exercise 12.

12. Employment Outlook. There were 234 thousand file clerks in 2006. This number is expected to decrease to 137 thousand in 2016. What is the percent of decrease?

Source: *Occupational Outlook Handbook*

Answers

11. About 663,163 mi²
12. About 41.5%

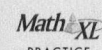 
a Solve.

1. What percent of 180 is 36?

2. What percent of 76 is 19?

3. 45 is 30% of what number?

4. 20.4 is 24% of what number?

5. What number is 65% of 840?

6. What number is 50% of 50?

7. 30 is what percent of 125?

8. 57 is what percent of 300?

9. 12% of what number is 0.3?

10. 7 is 175% of what number?

11. 2 is what percent of 40?

12. 16 is what percent of 40?

13. What percent of 68 is 17?

14. What percent of 150 is 39?

15. What number is 35% of 240?

16. What number is 1% of one million?

17. What percent of 125 is 30?

18. What percent of 60 is 75?

19. What percent of 300 is 48?

20. What percent of 70 is 70?

21. 14 is 30% of what number?

22. 54 is 24% of what number?

23. What number is 2% of 40?

24. What number is 40% of 2?

25. 0.8 is 16% of what number?

26. 40 is 2% of what number?

27. 54 is 135% of what number?

28. 8 is 2% of what number?

Amount Spent on Pets.   In 2007, $41.2 billion was spent on pets in the United States. The circle graph below shows the breakdown of this spending.

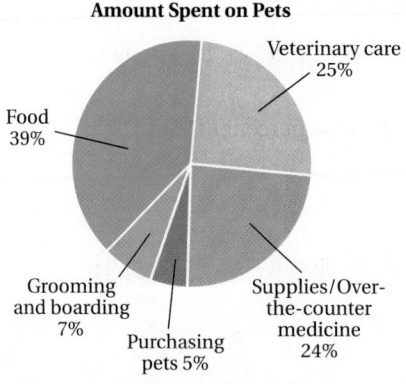

Amount Spent on Pets

Veterinary care 25%

Food 39%

Grooming and boarding 7%

Purchasing pets 5%

Supplies/Over-the-counter medicine 24%

SOURCE: American Pet Products Association

Complete the following table of amounts spent on pets. Round to the nearest tenth.

	CATEGORY	AMOUNT (in billions)		CATEGORY	AMOUNT (in billions)
29.	Food		30.	Veterinary care	
31.	Purchasing pets		32.	Grooming and boarding	

33. *Smart TV Market.*   Smart TVs, which are designed to be easily connected to the Internet or to a home computer network, are a small but growing part of the TV market. Total TV sales in 2010 are projected to be 209 million units, with smart TVs comprising 25.1 million units. What percent of total sales are projected to be smart TV sales?
Source: IDC

34. *Automobile Sales.*   Sales of cars averaged $26 million per dealership in 2007. Of this amount, new car sales accounted for receipts of $24 million. What percent of total sales are new cars?
Source: U.S. Census Bureau

35. *Graduation Gifts.*   American consumers spent $4.5 billion on graduation gifts in 2008. Cash accounted for 58.8% of this amount. How much cash was given as graduation gifts?
Source: National Retail Federation

36. *Graduation Gifts.*   Refer to Exercise 35. Gift cards accounted for 35.7% of the amount spent on graduation gifts in 2008. What is the total value of these gift cards?
Source: National Retail Federation

Copyright © 2012 Pearson Education, Inc.

37. *Student Loans.* To finance her community college education, Sarah takes out a Stafford loan for $6500. After a year, Sarah decides to pay off the interest, which is 6% of $6500. How much will she pay?

38. *Student Loans.* Paul takes out a PLUS loan for $5400. After a year, Paul decides to pay off the interest, which is 8.5% of $5400. How much will he pay?

39. *Tipping.* Leon left a $4 tip for a meal that cost $25.

a) What percent of the cost of the meal was the tip?
b) What was the total cost of the meal including the tip?

40. *Tipping.* Selena left a $12.76 tip for a meal that cost $58.

a) What percent of the cost of the meal was the tip?
b) What was the total cost of the meal including the tip?

41. *Tipping.* Leon left a 15% tip for a meal that cost $25.

a) How much was the tip?
b) What was the total cost of the meal including the tip?

42. *Tipping.* Sam, Selena, Rachel, and Clement left a 15% tip for a meal that cost $58.

a) How much was the tip?
b) What was the total cost of the meal including the tip?

43. *Tipping.* Leon left a 15% tip of $4.50 for a meal.

a) What was the cost of the meal before the tip?
b) What was the total cost of the meal including the tip?

44. *Tipping.* Selena left a 15% tip of $8.40 for a meal.

a) What was the cost of the meal before the tip?
b) What was the total cost of the meal including the tip?

45. *City Park Space.* Portland, Oregon, has 12,959 acres of park space. This is 15.1% of the acreage of the entire city. What is the total acreage of Portland?

Source: Indy Parks and Recreation master plan

46. *Junk Mail.* About 46.2 billion pieces of unopened junk mail ends up in landfills each year. This is about 44% of all the junk mail that is sent annually. How many pieces of junk mail are sent annually?

Source: Globaljunkmailcrisis.org

47. *Size of New Homes.* The median size of a new single-family home grew from 1879 ft^2 in 1997 to 2304 ft^2 in 2008. What is the percent of increase?

Source: U.S. Census Bureau

48. *Health Technology Spending.* With growth in traditional technology markets slowing, many companies are developing products for the health-care market. Worldwide, $68.4 billion was spent on health-care technology in 2005. This amount was expected to increase to $83.6 billion in 2009. What is the percent of increase?

Source: Gartner

49. *Renewable Fuel.* In 2006, about 4 billion gal of renewable fuels, such as ethanol and other biofuels, were used in the United States. The energy law passed in 2007 requires that 36 billion gal of such fuels be used by 2022. What is the percent of increase?
Source: U.S. Senate Committee on Energy and Natural Resources

50. *Accidents at Railroad Crossings.* In 1997, 3865 accidents occurred at railroad crossings in the United States. This number dropped to 2918 in 2006. What is the percent of decrease?
Source: Federal Railroad Administration

51. *Employment Outlook.* In 2006, there were 50 thousand pharmacy aides in the United States. This number is expected to drop to 45 thousand by 2016. What is the percent of decrease?
Source: Occupational Outlook Handbook

52. *Employment Outlook.* In 2006, there were 767,000 personal and home-care aides in the United States. This number is expected to grow to 1,156,000 by 2016. What is the percent of increase?
Source: Occupational Outlook Handbook

53. *Debit IDs.* A growing number of colleges are teaming up with banks to issue student ID cards that double as debit cards. There were 52 such partnerships in 2002. This number grew to 127 in 2007. What is the percent of increase?
Source: CR80News

54. *Decline in Tuberculosis Cases.* The number of cases of tuberculosis in the United States has plunged from 69,895 in 1956 to 13,299 in 2007. What is the percent of decrease?
Source: U.S. Centers for Disease Control and Prevention

Skill Maintenance

Compute.

55. $9.076 \div 0.05$ [3.4a]

56. 9.076×0.05 [3.3a]

57. $1.089 + 10.89 + 0.1089$ [3.2a]

58. $1000.23 - 156.0893$ [3.2b]

Remove parentheses and simplify. [7.8b]

59. $-5a + 3c - 2(c - 3a)$

60. $4(x - 2y) - (y - 3x)$

Add. [7.3a]

61. $-6.5 + 2.6$

62. $-\dfrac{3}{8} + (-5) + \dfrac{1}{4} + (-1)$

Fill in each blank with a word that makes the statement true. [7.8d]

63. To simplify the calculation $18 - 24 \div 3 - 48 \div (-4)$, do all the _____ calculations first, and then the _____ calculations.

64. To simplify the calculation $18 - 24^3 \div 48 \div (-4)^2$, do all the _____ calculations first, and then the _____ calculations, and finally the _____ calculation.

Synthesis

65. It has been determined that at the age of 15, a boy has reached 96.1% of his final adult height. Jaraan is 6 ft 4 in. at the age of 15. What will his final adult height be?

66. It has been determined that at the age of 10, a girl has reached 84.4% of her final adult height. Dana is 4 ft 8 in. at the age of 10. What will her final adult height be?

Copyright © 2012 Pearson Education, Inc.

8.6

Applications and Problem Solving

(a) Five Steps for Solving Problems

OBJECTIVE

(a) Solve applied problems by translating to equations.

We have discussed many new equation-solving tools in this chapter and used them for applications and problem solving. Here we consider a five-step strategy that can be very helpful in solving problems.

> **FIVE STEPS FOR PROBLEM SOLVING IN ALGEBRA**
>
> 1. *Familiarize* yourself with the problem situation.
> 2. *Translate* the problem to an equation.
> 3. *Solve* the equation.
> 4. *Check* the answer in the original problem.
> 5. *State* the answer to the problem clearly.

SKILL TO REVIEW

Objective 7.1b: Translate phrases to algebraic expressions.

Translate each phrase to an algebraic expression.

1. One-third of a number
2. Two more than a number

Of the five steps, the most important is probably the first one: becoming familiar with the problem situation. The box below lists some hints for familiarization.

> **TO FAMILIARIZE YOURSELF WITH A PROBLEM**
>
> - If a problem is given in words, read it carefully. Reread the problem, perhaps aloud. Try to verbalize the problem as if you were explaining it to someone else.
>
> - Choose a variable (or variables) to represent the unknown and clearly state what the variable represents. Be descriptive! For example, let L = the length, d = the distance, and so on.
>
> - Make a drawing and label it with known information, using specific units if given. Also, indicate unknown information.
>
> - Find further information. Look up formulas or definitions with which you are not familiar. (Geometric formulas appear on the inside back cover of this text.) Consult a reference librarian or the Internet.
>
> - Create a table that lists all the information you have available. Look for patterns that may help in the translation to an equation.
>
> - Think of a possible answer and check the guess. Note the manner in which the guess is checked.

EXAMPLE 1 *Knitted Scarf.* Lily knitted a scarf in three shades of blue, starting with a light-blue section, then a medium-blue section, and finally a dark-blue section. The medium-blue section is one-half the length of the light-blue section. The dark-blue section is one-fourth the length of the light-blue section. The scarf is 7 ft long. Find the length of each section of the scarf.

Answers

Skill to Review:

1. $\frac{1}{3}n$, or $\frac{n}{3}$ 2. $x + 2$, or $2 + x$

1. **Familiarize.**   Because the lengths of the medium-blue section and the dark-blue section are expressed in terms of the length of the light-blue section, we let

$$x = \text{the length of the light-blue section.}$$

Then $\frac{1}{2}x = $ the length of the medium-blue section

and $\frac{1}{4}x = $ the length of the dark-blue section.

We make a drawing and label it.

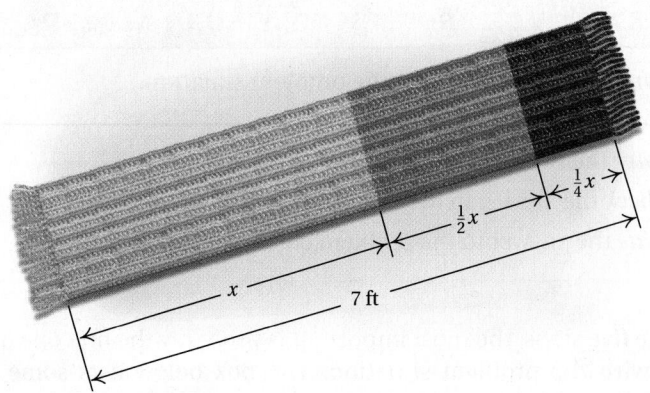

2. **Translate.**   From the statement of the problem and the drawing, we know that the lengths add up to 7 ft. This gives us our translation:

Length of light-blue section	plus	Length of medium-blue section	plus	Length of dark-blue section	is	Total length
↓	↓	↓	↓	↓	↓	↓
x	$+$	$\frac{1}{2}x$	$+$	$\frac{1}{4}x$	$=$	$7.$

3. **Solve.**   First, we clear fractions and then carry out the solution as follows:

$$x + \frac{1}{2}x + \frac{1}{4}x = 7 \qquad \text{The LCM of the denominators is 4.}$$

$$4\left(x + \frac{1}{2}x + \frac{1}{4}x\right) = 4 \cdot 7 \qquad \text{Multiplying by the LCM, 4}$$

$$4 \cdot x + 4 \cdot \frac{1}{2}x + 4 \cdot \frac{1}{4}x = 4 \cdot 7 \qquad \text{Using the distributive law}$$

$$4x + 2x + x = 28 \qquad \text{Simplifying}$$

$$7x = 28 \qquad \text{Collecting like terms}$$

$$\frac{7x}{7} = \frac{28}{7} \qquad \text{Dividing by 7}$$

$$x = 4.$$

4. **Check.**   Do we have an answer to the *original problem*? If the length of the light-blue section is 4 ft, then the length of the medium-blue section is $\frac{1}{2} \cdot 4$ ft, or 2 ft, and the length of the dark-blue section is $\frac{1}{4} \cdot 4$ ft, or 1 ft. The sum of these lengths is 7 ft, so the answer checks.

5. State. The length of the light-blue section is 4 ft, the length of the medium-blue section is 2 ft, and the length of the dark-blue section is 1 ft. (Note that we must include the unit, feet, in the answer.)

> Do Exercise 1.

EXAMPLE 2 *Hiking.* At age 79, Earl Shaffer became the oldest person to through-hike all 2100 miles of the Appalachian Trail—from Springer Mountain, Georgia, to Mount Katahdin, Maine. Shaffer through-hiked the trail three times, in 1948 (Georgia to Maine), in 1965 (Maine to Georgia), and in 1998 (Georgia to Maine) near the 50th anniversary of his first hike. At one point in 1998, Shaffer stood atop Big Walker Mountain, Virginia, which is three times as far from the northern end as from the southern end. How far was Shaffer from each end of the trail?

Source: Appalachian Trail Conference; Earl Shaffer Foundation

1. Familiarize. Let's consider a drawing.

To become familiar with the problem, let's guess a possible distance that Shaffer stood from Springer Mountain—say, 600 mi. Three times 600 mi is 1800 mi. Since 600 mi + 1800 mi = 2400 mi and 2400 mi is greater than 2100 mi, we see that our guess is too large. Rather than guess again, let's use the equation-solving skills that we have learned in this chapter. We let

d = the distance, in miles, to the southern end,   and

$3d$ = the distance, in miles, to the northern end.

(We could also let x = the distance to the northern end and $\frac{1}{3}x$ = the distance to the southern end.)

2. Translate. From the drawing, we see that the lengths of the two parts of the trail must add up to 2100 mi. This leads to our translation:

Distance to southern end plus Distance to northern end is 2100 mi

$$d + 3d = 2100.$$

1. Gourmet Sandwiches. A sandwich shop specializes in sandwiches prepared in buns of length 18 in. Jenny, Emma, and Sarah buy one of these sandwiches and take it back to their apartment. Since they have different appetites, Jenny cuts the sandwich in such a way that Emma gets one-half of what Jenny gets and Sarah gets three-fourths of what Jenny gets. Find the length of each person's sandwich.

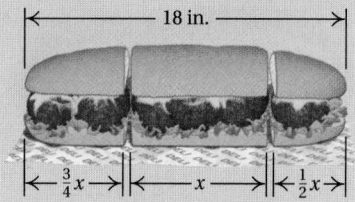

Answer

1. Jenny: 8 in.; Emma: 4 in.; Sarah: 6 in.

2. Running. Yiannis Kouros of Australia holds the record for the greatest distance run in 24 hr by running 188 mi. After 8 hr, he was approximately twice as far from the finish line as he was from the start. How far had he run?

Source: Australian Ultra Runners Association

3. **Solve.** We solve the equation:

$$d + 3d = 2100$$
$$4d = 2100 \quad \text{Collecting like terms}$$
$$\frac{4d}{4} = \frac{2100}{4} \quad \text{Dividing by 4}$$
$$d = 525.$$

4. **Check.** As expected, d is less than 600 mi. If $d = 525$ mi, then $3d = 1575$ mi. Since 525 mi + 1575 mi = 2100 mi, we have a check.

5. **State.** Atop Big Walker Mountain, Shaffer stood 525 mi from Springer Mountain and 1575 mi from Mount Katahdin.

Do Exercise 2.

Recall that the set of integers = $\{\ldots, -5, -4, -3, -2, -1, 0, 1, 2, 3, 4, 5, \ldots\}$. Before we solve the next problem, we need to learn some additional terminology regarding integers.

The following are examples of **consecutive integers:** 16, 17, 18, 19, 20; and −31, −30, −29, −28. Note that consecutive integers can be represented in the form $x, x + 1, x + 2$, and so on.

The following are examples of **consecutive even integers:** 16, 18, 20, 22, 24; and −52, −50, −48, −46. Note that consecutive even integers can be represented in the form $x, x + 2, x + 4$, and so on.

The following are examples of **consecutive odd integers:** 21, 23, 25, 27, 29; and −71, −69, −67, −65. Note that consecutive odd integers can be represented in the form $x, x + 2, x + 4$, and so on.

EXAMPLE 3 *Interstate Mile Markers.* U.S. interstate highways post numbered markers every mile to indicate location in case of an accident or breakdown. In many states, the numbers on the markers increase from west to east. The sum of two consecutive mile markers on I-70 in Kansas is 559. Find the numbers on the markers.

Source: Federal Highway Administration, Ed Rotalewski

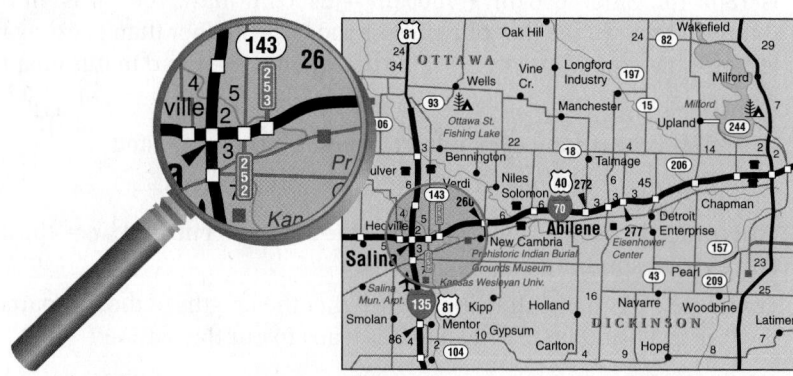

1. **Familiarize.** The numbers on the mile markers are consecutive positive integers. Thus if we let $x =$ the smaller number, then $x + 1 =$ the larger number.

To become familiar with the problem, we can make a table, as shown at left. First, we guess a value for x; then we find $x + 1$. Finally, we add the two numbers and check the sum.

x	$x + 1$	Sum of x and $x + 1$
114	115	229
252	253	505
302	303	605

Answer

2. $62\frac{2}{3}$ mi

From the table, we see that the first marker will be between 252 and 302. We could continue guessing and solve the problem this way, but let's work on developing our algebra skills.

2. Translate. We reword the problem and translate as follows.

Rewording: First integer plus Second integer is 559

Translating: x $+$ $(x + 1)$ $=$ 559

3. Solve. We solve the equation:

$$x + (x + 1) = 559$$
$$2x + 1 = 559 \qquad \text{Collecting like terms}$$
$$2x + 1 - 1 = 559 - 1 \qquad \text{Subtracting 1}$$
$$2x = 558$$
$$\frac{2x}{2} = \frac{558}{2} \qquad \text{Dividing by 2}$$
$$x = 279.$$

If x is 279, then $x + 1$ is 280.

4. Check. Our possible answers are 279 and 280. These are consecutive positive integers and $279 + 280 = 559$, so the answers check.

5. State. The mile markers are 279 and 280.

Do Exercise 3.

3. Interstate Mile Markers. The sum of two consecutive mile markers on I-90 in upstate New York is 627. (On I-90 in New York, the marker numbers increase from east to west.) Find the numbers on the markers.

Source: New York State Department of Transportation

EXAMPLE 4 *Copy Machine Rental.* It costs the Drake law firm $225 per month plus 1.2¢ per copy to rent a copy machine. The firm needs to lease a machine for use during a special case that they anticipate will take 3 months. If they allot a budget of $1100, how many copies can they make?

Copy Machine Rental
$225 per month
plus 1.2¢ per copy

1. Familiarize. Suppose that the law firm makes 20,000 copies. Then the cost is given by monthly charges plus copy charges, or

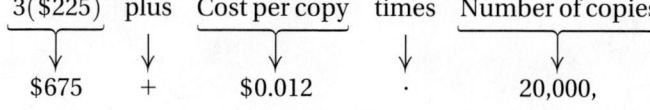

3($225) plus Cost per copy times Number of copies

$675 $+$ $0.012 · 20,000,

Answer

3. 313 and 314

which is $915. We see that the firm can make more than 20,000 copies. This process familiarizes us with the way in which a calculation is made. Note that we convert 1.2¢ to $0.012 so that all information is in the same unit, dollars. Otherwise, we will not get the correct answer.

We let c = the number of copies that can be made for the budget of $1100.

2. **Translate.** We reword the problem and translate as follows:

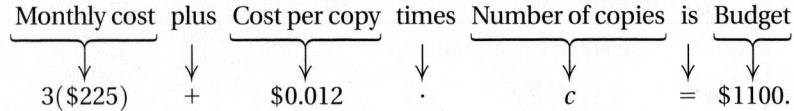

Monthly cost	plus	Cost per copy	times	Number of copies	is	Budget
3($225)	+	$0.012	·	c	=	$1100.

3. **Solve.** We solve the equation:

$$3(225) + 0.012c = 1100$$
$$675 + 0.012c = 1100$$
$$0.012c = 425 \qquad \text{Subtracting 675}$$
$$\frac{0.012c}{0.012} = \frac{425}{0.012} \qquad \text{Dividing by 0.012}$$
$$c \approx 35{,}417. \qquad \text{Rounding to the nearest one}$$

4. **Check.** We check in the original problem. The cost for 35,417 pages is 35,417($0.012) = $425.004. The rental for 3 months is 3($225) = $675. The total cost is then $425.004 + $675 ≈ $1100, which is the $1100 that was allotted.

5. **State.** The law firm can make 35,417 copies on the copy rental allotment of $1100.

Do Exercise 4.

---

4. Copy Machine Rental. The Drake law firm in Example 4 decides to increase its budget to $1400 for the 3-month period. How many copies can they make for $1400?

EXAMPLE 5 *Perimeter of NBA Court.* The perimeter of an NBA basketball court is 288 ft. The length is 44 ft longer than the width. Find the dimensions of the court.

Source: National Basketball Association

1. **Familiarize.** We first make a drawing.

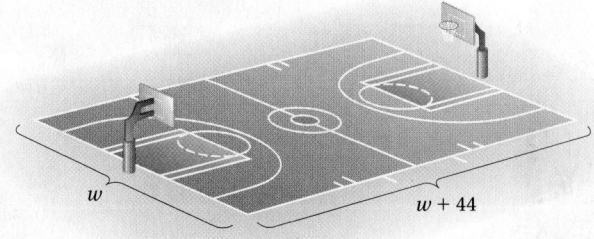

We let w = the width of the rectangle. Then $w + 44$ = the length. The perimeter P of a rectangle is the distance around the rectangle and is given by the formula $2l + 2w = P$, where

$$l = \text{the length} \quad \text{and} \quad w = \text{the width.}$$

Answer

4. 60,417 copies

---

2. **Translate.** To translate the problem, we substitute $w + 44$ for l and 288 for P:

$$2l + 2w = P$$

$$2(w + 44) + 2w = 288.$$

--- *Caution!* ---

Parentheses are necessary here.

3. **Solve.** We solve the equation:

$$2(w + 44) + 2w = 288$$

$$2 \cdot w + 2 \cdot 44 + 2w = 288 \qquad \text{Using the distributive law}$$

$$4w + 88 = 288 \qquad \text{Collecting like terms}$$

$$4w + 88 - 88 = 288 - 88 \qquad \text{Subtracting 88}$$

$$4w = 200$$

$$\frac{4w}{4} = \frac{200}{4} \qquad \text{Dividing by 4}$$

$$w = 50.$$

Thus possible dimensions are

$$w = 50 \text{ ft} \quad \text{and} \quad l = w + 44 = 50 + 44, \text{ or } 94 \text{ ft}.$$

4. **Check.** If the width is 50 ft and the length is 94 ft, then the perimeter is $2(50 \text{ ft}) + 2(94 \text{ ft})$, or 288 ft. This checks.

5. **State.** The width is 50 ft and the length is 94 ft.

Do Exercise 5.

5. Perimeter of High School Basketball Court. The perimeter of a standard high school basketball court is 268 ft. The length is 34 ft longer than the width. Find the dimensions of the court.

Source: Indiana High School Athletic Association

Caution!

Always be sure to answer the original problem completely. For instance, in Example 2, we need to find *two* numbers: the distances from *each* end of the trail to the hiker. Similarly, in Example 3, we need to find two mile markers, and in Example 5, we need to find two dimensions, not just the width.

EXAMPLE 6 *Roof Gable.* In a triangular gable end of a roof, the angle of the peak is twice as large as the angle of the back side of the house. The measure of the angle on the front side is 20° greater than the angle on the back side. How large are the angles?

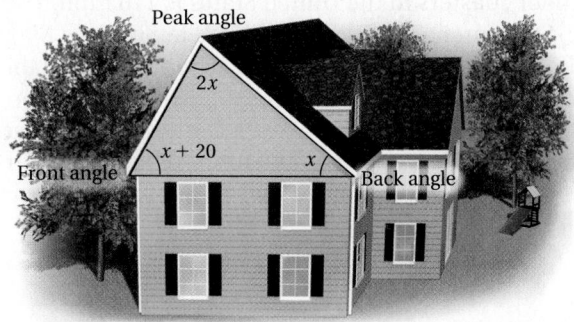

Peak angle

$2x$

$x + 20$

Front angle

x

Back angle

1. **Familiarize.** We first make a drawing as shown above. We let

measure of back angle $= x$.

Then measure of peak angle $= 2x$

and measure of front angle $= x + 20$.

Answer

5. Length: 84 ft; width: 50 ft

2. Translate. To translate, we need to know that the sum of the measures of the angles of a triangle is 180°. You might recall this fact from geometry or you can look it up in a geometry book or in the list of formulas inside the back cover of this book. We translate as follows:

Measure of back angle	plus	Measure of peak angle	plus	Measure of front angle	is	180°
↓	↓	↓	↓	↓	↓	↓
x	$+$	$2x$	$+$	$(x + 20)$	$=$	$180°.$

3. Solve. We solve the equation:

$$x + 2x + (x + 20) = 180$$
$$4x + 20 = 180$$
$$4x + 20 - 20 = 180 - 20$$
$$4x = 160$$
$$\frac{4x}{4} = \frac{160}{4}$$
$$x = 40.$$

Possible measures for the angles are as follows:

Back angle: $x = 40°$;

Peak angle: $2x = 2(40) = 80°$;

Front angle: $x + 20 = 40 + 20 = 60°.$

4. Check. Consider our answers: 40°, 80°, and 60°. The peak is twice the back and the front is 20° greater than the back. The sum is 180°. The angles check.

5. State. The measures of the angles are 40°, 80°, and 60°.

--------------------------------------- *Caution!* ---------------------------------------

Units are important in answers. Remember to include them, where appropriate.

----

6. The second angle of a triangle is three times as large as the first. The third angle measures 30° more than the first angle. Find the measures of the angles.

Do Exercise 6.

EXAMPLE 7 *Fastest Roller Coasters.* The average top speed of the three fastest steel roller coasters in the United States is 116 mph. The third-fastest roller coaster, Superman: The Escape (located at Six Flags Magic Mountain, Valencia, California), reaches a top speed of 28 mph less than the fastest roller coaster, Kingda Ka (located at Six Flags Great Adventure, Jackson, New Jersey). The second-fastest roller coaster, Top Thrill Dragster (located at Cedar Point, Sandusky, Ohio), has a top speed of 120 mph. What is the top speed of the fastest steel roller coaster?

Source: Coaster Grotto

Answer

6. First: 30°; second: 90°; third: 60°

1. **Familiarize.** The **average** of a set of numbers is the sum of the numbers divided by the number of addends.

We are given that the second-fastest speed is 120 mph. Suppose the three top speeds are 131, 120, and 103. The average is then

$$\frac{131 + 120 + 103}{3} = \frac{354}{3} = 118,$$

which is too high. Instead of continuing to guess, let's use the equation-solving skills we have learned in this chapter. We let x represent the top speed of the fastest roller coaster. Then $x - 28$ is the top speed of the third-fastest roller coaster.

2. **Translate.** We reword the problem and translate as follows:

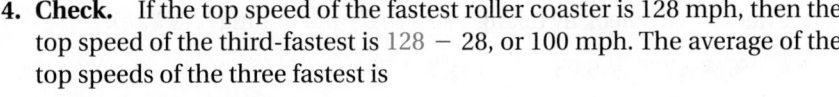

$$\frac{\text{Speed of fastest coaster} + \text{Speed of second-fastest coaster} + \text{Speed of third-fastest coaster}}{\text{Number of roller coasters}} = \frac{\text{Average speed of three fastest roller coasters}}{}$$

$$\frac{x + 120 + (x - 28)}{3} = 116.$$

3. **Solve.** We solve as follows:

$$\frac{x + 120 + (x - 28)}{3} = 116$$

$$3 \cdot \frac{x + 120 + (x - 28)}{3} = 3 \cdot 116 \qquad \text{Multiplying by 3 on both sides to clear the fraction}$$

$$x + 120 + (x - 28) = 348$$

$$2x + 92 = 348 \qquad \text{Collecting like terms}$$

$$2x = 256 \qquad \text{Subtracting 92}$$

$$x = 128. \qquad \text{Dividing by 2}$$

4. **Check.** If the top speed of the fastest roller coaster is 128 mph, then the top speed of the third-fastest is $128 - 28$, or 100 mph. The average of the top speeds of the three fastest is

$$\frac{128 + 120 + 100}{3} = \frac{348}{3} = 116 \text{ mph.}$$

The answer checks.

5. **State.** The top speed of the fastest steel roller coaster in the United States is 128 mph.

Do Exercise 7.

7. **Average Test Score.** Sam's average score on his first three math tests is 77. He scored 62 on the first test. On the third test, he scored 9 more than he scored on his second test. What did he score on the second and third tests?

Answer

7. Second: 80; third: 89

EXAMPLE 8 *Simple Interest.*   An investment is made at 3% simple interest for 1 year. It grows to $746.75. How much was originally invested (the principal)?

1. **Familiarize.**   Suppose that $100 was invested. Recalling the formula for simple interest, $I = Prt$, we know that the interest for 1 year on $100 at 3% simple interest is given by $I = \$100 \cdot 0.03 \cdot 1 = \$3$. Then, at the end of the year, the amount in the account is found by adding the principal and the interest:

$$
\begin{array}{ccccc}
\text{Principal} & + & \text{Interest} & = & \text{Amount} \\
\downarrow & & \downarrow & & \downarrow \\
\$100 & + & \$3 & = & \$103.
\end{array}
$$

In this problem, we are working backward. We are trying to find the principal, which is the original investment. We let x = the principal. Then the interest earned is 3%x.

2. **Translate.**   We reword the problem and then translate:

$$
\begin{array}{ccccc}
\text{Principal} & + & \text{Interest} & = & \text{Amount} \\
\downarrow & & \downarrow & & \downarrow \\
x & + & 3\%x & = & 746.75.
\end{array}
$$

Interest is 3% of the principal.

3. **Solve**.   We solve the equation:

$$
\begin{aligned}
x + 3\%x &= 746.75 \\
x + 0.03x &= 746.75 \qquad \text{Converting to decimal notation} \\
1x + 0.03x &= 746.75 \qquad \text{Identity property of 1} \\
(1 + 0.03)x &= 746.75 \\
1.03x &= 746.75 \qquad \text{Collecting like terms} \\
\frac{1.03x}{1.03} &= \frac{746.75}{1.03} \qquad \text{Dividing by 1.03} \\
x &= 725.
\end{aligned}
$$

4. **Check.**   We check by taking 3% of $725 and adding it to $725:

$3\% \times \$725 = 0.03 \times 725 = \$21.75.$

Then $725 + $21.75 = $746.75, so $725 checks.

5. **State.**   The original investment was $725.

Do Exercise 8.

8. Simple Interest.   An investment is made at 7% simple interest for 1 year. It grows to $8988. How much was originally invested (the principal)?

EXAMPLE 9 *Selling a Home.*   The Landers are planning to sell their home. If they want to be left with $117,500 after paying 6% of the selling price to a realtor as a commission, for how much must they sell the house?

1. **Familiarize.**   Suppose the Landers sell the house for $120,000. A 6% commission can be determined by finding 6% of $120,000:

6% of $120,000 = 0.06($120,000) = $7200.

Subtracting this commission from $120,000 would leave the Landers with

$120,000 − $7200 = $112,800.

This shows that in order for the Landers to clear $117,500, the house must sell for more than $120,000. Our guess shows us how to translate to an equation. We let x = the selling price, in dollars. With a 6% commission, the realtor would receive 0.06x.

Answer

8. $8400

2. Translate.   We reword the problem and translate as follows:

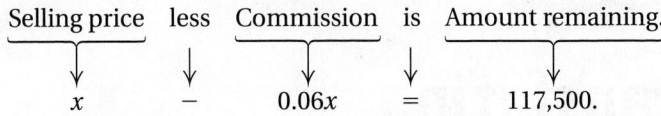

$$x - 0.06x = 117{,}500.$$

3. Solve.   We solve the equation:

$$x - 0.06x = 117{,}500$$
$$1x - 0.06x = 117{,}500$$
$$(1 - 0.06)x = 117{,}500$$
$$0.94x = 117{,}500$$

Collecting like terms. Had we noted that after the commission has been paid, 94% remains, we could have begun with this equation.

$$\frac{0.94x}{0.94} = \frac{117{,}500}{0.94}$$

Dividing by 0.94

$$x = 125{,}000.$$

4. Check.   To check, we first find 6% of $125,000:

$$6\% \text{ of } \$125{,}000 = 0.06(\$125{,}000) = \$7500.$$ This is the commission.

Next, we subtract the commission to find the remaining amount:

$$\$125{,}000 - \$7500 = \$117{,}500.$$

Since, after the commission, the Landers are left with $117,500, our answer checks. Note that the $125,000 selling price is greater than $120,000, as predicted in the *Familiarize* step.

5. State.   To be left with $117,500, the Landers must sell the house for $125,000.

> Do Exercise 9.

> **9. Price Before Sale.**   The price of a suit was decreased to a sale price of $526.40. This was a 20% reduction. What was the former price?

------------------------------ *Caution!* ------------------------------

The problem in Example 9 is easy to solve with algebra. Without algebra, it is not. A common error in such a problem is to take 6% of the price after commission and then subtract or add. Note that 6% of the selling price $(6\% \cdot \$125{,}000 = \$7500)$ is not equal to 6% of the amount that the Landers want to be left with $(6\% \cdot \$117{,}500 = \$7050)$.

STUDY TIPS

PROBLEM-SOLVING TIPS

The more problems you solve, the more your skills will improve.

1. Look for patterns when solving problems. Each time you study an example in a text, you may observe a pattern for problems that you will encounter later in the exercise sets or in other practical situations.

2. When translating in mathematics, consider the dimensions of the variables and the constants in the equation. The variables that represent length should all be in the same unit, those that represent money should all be in dollars or all in cents, and so on.

3. Make sure that units appear in the answer whenever appropriate and that you have completely answered the original problem.

Answer

9. $658

Translating for Success

1. *Angle Measures.* The measure of the second angle of a triangle is 51° more than that of the first angle. The measure of the third angle is 3° less than twice the first angle. Find the measures of the angles.

2. *Sales Tax.* Tina paid $3976 for a used car. This amount included 5% for sales tax. How much did the car cost before tax?

3. *Perimeter.* The perimeter of a rectangle is 2347 ft. The length is 28 ft greater than the width. Find the length and the width.

4. *Fraternity or Sorority Membership.* At Arches Tech University, 3976 students belong to a fraternity or a sorority. This is 35% of the total enrollment. What is the total enrollment at Arches Tech?

5. *Fraternity or Sorority Membership.* At Moab Tech University, thirty-five percent of the students belong to a fraternity or a sorority. The total enrollment of the university is 11,360 students. How many students belong to either a fraternity or a sorority?

The goal of these matching questions is to practice step (2), *Translate,* of the five-step problem-solving process. Translate each word problem to an equation and select a correct translation from equations A–O.

A. $x + (x - 3) + \frac{4}{5}x = 384$

B. $x + (x + 51) + (2x - 3) = 180$

C. $x + (x + 96) = 180$

D. $2 \cdot 96 + 2x = 3976$

E. $x + (x + 1) + (x + 2) = 384$

F. $3976 = x \cdot 11{,}360$

G. $2x + 2(x + 28) = 2347$

H. $3976 = x + 5\%x$

I. $x + (x + 28) = 2347$

J. $x = 35\% \cdot 11{,}360$

K. $x + 96 = 3976$

L. $x + (x + 3) + \frac{4}{5}x = 384$

M. $x + (x + 2) + (x + 4) = 384$

N. $35\% \cdot x = 3976$

O. $2x + (x + 28) = 2347$

Answers on page A-15

6. *Island Population.* There are 180 thousand people living on a small Caribbean island. The women outnumber the men by 96 thousand. How many men live on the island?

7. *Wire Cutting.* A 384-m wire is cut into three pieces. The second piece is 3 m longer than the first. The third is four-fifths as long as the first. How long is each piece?

8. *Locker Numbers.* The numbers on three adjoining lockers are consecutive integers whose sum is 384. Find the integers.

9. *Fraternity or Sorority Membership.* The total enrollment at Canyonlands Tech University is 11,360 students. Of these, 3976 students belong to a fraternity or a sorority. What percent of the students belong to a fraternity or a sorority?

10. *Width of a Rectangle.* The length of a rectangle is 96 ft. The perimeter of the rectangle is 3976 ft. Find the width.

8.6 Exercise Set

For Extra Help

MyMathLab

Math XL
PRACTICE

WATCH

DOWNLOAD

READ

REVIEW

a Solve. *Although you might find the answer quickly in some other way, practice using the five-step problem-solving strategy.*

1. *Manatee Population.* The manatee, Florida's state marine mammal, is an endangered species. An aerial wintertime manatee census counted 2817 of these animals in 2007. This was 296 fewer than the number counted in 2006. What was Florida's manatee population in 2006?

Source: Florida Fish and Wildlife Conservation Commission

2. *Mass Transit Boom.* Americans took 2.8 billion rides on public transit from April through June in 2008. This was the highest ridership for that period in 50 yr and represented an increase of 0.7 billion rides over the same period in 1998. How many rides were taken from April through June in 1998?

Source: American Public Transportation Association

3. *Pipe Cutting.* A 240-in. pipe is cut into two pieces. One piece is three times the length of the other. Find the lengths of the pieces.

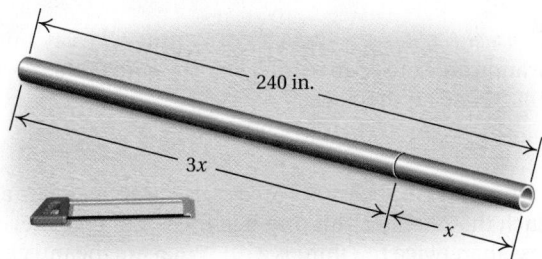

240 in.

3x

x

4. *Board Cutting.* A 72-in. board is cut into two pieces. One piece is 2 in. longer than the other. Find the lengths of the pieces.

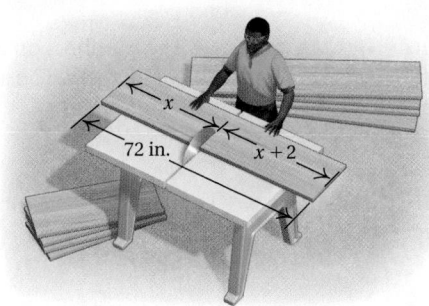

x

72 in.

x + 2

5. *Cost of Movie Tickets.* The average cost of movie tickets for a family of four was $28.32 in 2008. This was $11.76 more than the cost in 1993. What was the average cost of movie tickets for a family of four in 1993? (These prices include senior discounts and children's prices.)

Source: Motion Picture Association of America

6. *Area of Lake Ontario.* The area of Lake Superior is about four times the area of Lake Ontario. The area of Lake Superior is 30,172 mi^2. What is the area of Lake Ontario?

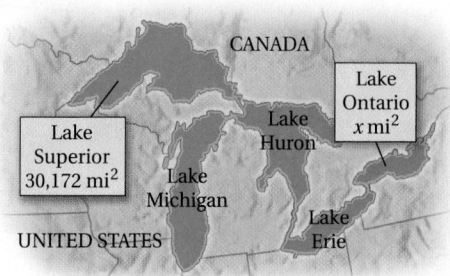

CANADA

Lake Ontario x mi^2

Lake Huron

Lake Superior 30,172 mi^2

Lake Michigan

Lake Erie

UNITED STATES

7. *Iditarod Race.* The Iditarod sled dog race in Alaska extends for 1049 mi from Anchorage to Nome. If a musher is twice as far from Anchorage as from Nome, how many miles of the race has the musher completed?

Source: Iditarod Trail Commission

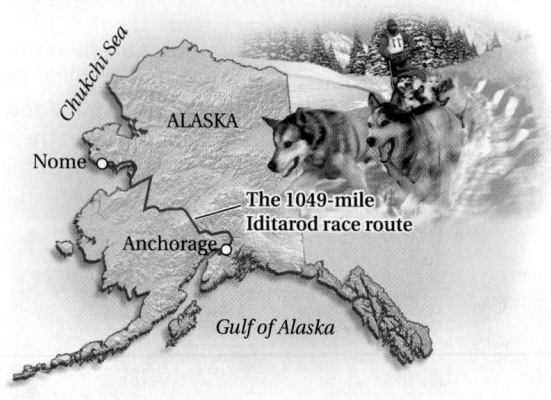

8. *Statue of Liberty.* The height of the Eiffel Tower is 974 ft, which is about 669 ft higher than the Statue of Liberty. What is the height of the Statue of Liberty?

9. *Consecutive Apartment Numbers.* The apartments in Vincent's apartment house are numbered consecutively on each floor. The sum of his number and his next-door neighbor's number is 2409. What are the two numbers?

10. *Consecutive Post Office Box Numbers.* The sum of the numbers on two consecutive post office boxes is 547. What are the numbers?

11. *Consecutive Ticket Numbers.* The numbers on Sam's three raffle tickets are consecutive integers. The sum of the numbers is 126. What are the numbers?

12. *Consecutive Ages.* The ages of Whitney, Wesley, and Wanda are consecutive integers. The sum of their ages is 108. What are their ages?

13. *Consecutive Odd Integers.* The sum of three consecutive odd integers is 189. What are the integers?

14. *Consecutive Integers.* Three consecutive integers are such that the first plus one-half the second plus seven less than twice the third is 2101. What are the integers?

15. *Standard Billboard Sign.* A standard rectangular highway billboard sign has a perimeter of 124 ft. The length is 6 ft more than three times the width. Find the dimensions of the sign.

16. *Two-by-Four.* The perimeter of a cross section or end of a "two-by-four" piece of lumber is 10 in. The length is 2 in. more than the width. Find the actual dimensions of the cross section of a two-by-four.

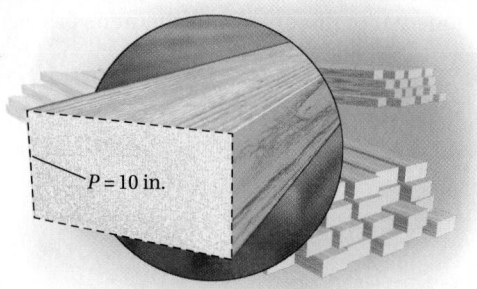

Copyright © 2012 Pearson Education, Inc.

17. *Price of Walking Shoes.* Amy paid $63.75 for a pair of walking shoes during a 15%-off sale. What was the regular price?

18. *Price of a CD Player.* Doug paid $72 for a shockproof portable CD player during a 20%-off sale. What was the regular price?

19. *Price of a Jacket.* Evelyn paid $89.25, including 5% tax, for a jacket. How much did the jacket itself cost?

20. *Price of a Printer.* Jake paid $100.70, including 6% tax, for a color printer. How much did the printer itself cost?

21. *Parking Costs.* A hospital parking lot charges $1.50 for the first hour or part thereof, and $1.00 for each additional hour or part thereof. A weekly pass costs $27.00 and allows unlimited parking for 7 days. Suppose that each visit Ed makes to the hospital lasts $1\frac{1}{2}$ hr. What is the minimum number of times that Ed would have to visit per week to make it worthwhile for him to buy the pass?

22. *Van Rental.* Value Rent-A-Car rents vans at a daily rate of $84.45 plus 55¢ per mile. Molly rents a van to deliver electrical parts to her customers. She is allotted a daily budget of $250. How many miles can she drive for $250? (*Hint:* 60¢ = $0.60.)

23. *Triangular Field.* The second angle of a triangular field is three times as large as the first angle. The third angle is 40° greater than the first angle. How large are the angles?

24. *Triangular Parking Lot.* The second angle of a triangular parking lot is four times as large as the first angle. The third angle is 45° less than the sum of the other two angles. How large are the angles?

25. *Triangular Backyard.* A home has a triangular backyard. The second angle of the triangle is 5° more than the first angle. The third angle is 10° more than three times the first angle. Find the angles of the triangular yard.

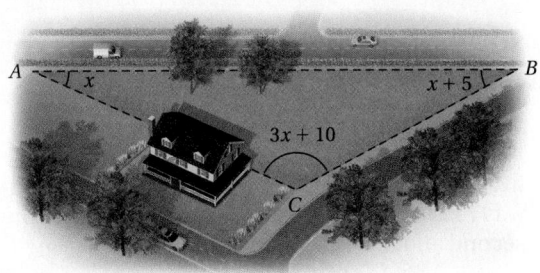

26. *Boarding Stable.* A rancher needs to form a triangular horse pen using ropes next to a stable. The second angle is three times the first angle. The third angle is 15° less than the first angle. Find the angles of the triangular pen.

27. *Stock Prices.* Sarah's investment in a technology stock grew 28% to $448. How much did she invest?

28. *Savings Interest.* Sharon invested money in a savings account at a rate of 6% simple interest. After 1 year, she has $6996 in the account. How much did Sharon originally invest?

29. *Credit Cards.* The balance on Will's credit card grew 2%, to $870, in one month. What was his balance at the beginning of the month?

30. *Loan Interest.* Alvin borrowed money from a cousin at a rate of 10% simple interest. After 1 year, $7194 paid off the loan. How much did Alvin borrow?

31. *Taxi Fares.* In Beniford, taxis charge $3 plus 75¢ per mile for an airport pickup. How far from the airport can Courtney travel for $12?

32. *Taxi Fares.* In Cranston, taxis charge $4 plus 90¢ per mile for an airport pickup. How far from the airport can Ralph travel for $17.50?

33. *Tipping.* Leon left a 15% tip for a meal. The total cost of the meal, including the tip, was $41.40. What was the cost of the meal before the tip was added?

34. *Tipping.* Selena left an 18% tip for a meal. The total cost of the meal, including the tip, was $40.71. What was the cost of the meal before the tip was added?

35. *Average Price.* Tom paid an average of $34 per tie for a recent purchase of three ties. The price of one tie was twice as much as another, and the remaining tie cost $27. What were the prices of the other two ties?

36. *Average Test Score.* Jaci averaged 84 on her first three history exams. The first score was 67. The second score was 7 less than the third score. What did she score on the second and third exams?

Copyright © 2012 Pearson Education, Inc.

37. If you double a number and then add 16, you get $\frac{2}{3}$ of the original number. What is the original number?

38. If you double a number and then add 85, you get $\frac{3}{4}$ of the original number. What is the original number?

Skill Maintenance

Calculate.

39. $-\frac{4}{5} - \frac{3}{8}$ [7.4a]

40. $-\frac{4}{5} + \frac{3}{8}$ [7.3a]

41. $-\frac{4}{5} \cdot \frac{3}{8}$ [7.5a]

42. $-\frac{4}{5} \div \frac{3}{8}$ [7.6c]

43. $\frac{1}{10} \div \left(-\frac{1}{100}\right)$ [7.6c]

44. $-25.6 \div (-16)$ [7.6c]

45. $-25.6(-16)$ [7.5a]

46. $-25.6 - (-16)$ [7.4a]

47. $-25.6 + (-16)$ [7.3a]

48. $(-0.02) \div (-0.2)$ [7.6c]

Synthesis

49. Apples are collected in a basket for six people. One-third, one-fourth, one-eighth, and one-fifth are given to four people, respectively. The fifth person gets ten apples, leaving one apple for the sixth person. Find the original number of apples in the basket.

50. *Test Questions.*   A student scored 78 on a test that had 4 seven-point fill-ins and 24 three-point multiple-choice questions. The student answered one fill-in incorrectly. How many multiple-choice questions did the student answer correctly?

51. The area of this triangle is 2.9047 in². Find x.

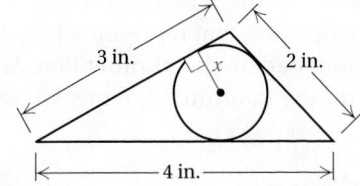

52. Susanne goes to the bank to get $20 in quarters, dimes, and nickels to use to make change at her yard sale. She gets twice as many quarters as dimes and 10 more nickels than dimes. How many of each type of coin does she get?

53. In Connerville, a sales tax of 9% was added to the price of gasoline as registered on the pump. Suppose a driver asked for $10 worth of gas. The attendant filled the tank until the pump read $9.10 and charged the driver $10. Something was wrong. Use algebra to correct the error.

8.7

Solving Inequalities

OBJECTIVES

a Determine whether a given number is a solution of an inequality.

b Graph an inequality on the number line.

c Solve inequalities using the addition principle.

d Solve inequalities using the multiplication principle.

e Solve inequalities using the addition principle and the multiplication principle together.

SKILL TO REVIEW

Objective 7.2d: Determine whether an inequality like $-3 \leq 5$ is true or false.

Write true or false.

1. $-6 \leq -8$ 2. $1 \geq 1$

Determine whether each number is a solution of the inequality.

1. $x > 3$

    a) 2   b) 0

    c) -5 d) 15.4

    e) 3   f) $-\dfrac{2}{5}$

2. $x \leq 6$

    a) 6   b) 0

    c) -4.3 d) 25

    e) -6 f) $\dfrac{5}{8}$

We now extend our equation-solving principles to the solving of inequalities.

a Solutions of Inequalities

In Section 7.2, we defined the symbols $>$ (is greater than), $<$ (is less than), $\geq$ (is greater than or equal to), and $\leq$ (is less than or equal to).

An **inequality** is a number sentence with $>$, $<$, $\geq$, or $\leq$ as its verb—for example,

$$-4 > t, \qquad x < 3, \qquad 2x + 5 \geq 0, \quad \text{and} \quad -3y + 7 \leq -8.$$

Some replacements for a variable in an inequality make it true and some make it false. (There are some exceptions to this statement, but we will not consider them here.)

> **SOLUTION**
>
> A replacement that makes an inequality true is called a **solution**. The set of all solutions is called the **solution set**. When we have found the set of all solutions of an inequality, we say that we have **solved** the inequality.

EXAMPLES Determine whether each number is a solution of $x < 2$.

1. -2.7 Since $-2.7 < 2$ is true, -2.7 is a solution.

2. 2   Since $2 < 2$ is false, 2 is not a solution.

EXAMPLES Determine whether each number is a solution of $y \geq 6$.

3. 6   Since $6 \geq 6$ is true, 6 is a solution.

4. $-\dfrac{4}{3}$ Since $-\dfrac{4}{3} \geq 6$ is false, $-\dfrac{4}{3}$ is not a solution.

Do Margin Exercises 1 and 2.

b Graphs of Inequalities

Some solutions of $x < 2$ are $-3, 0, 1, 0.45, -8.9, -\pi, \frac{5}{8}$, and so on. In fact, there are infinitely many real numbers that are solutions. Because we cannot list them all individually, it is helpful to make a drawing that represents all the solutions.

A **graph** of an inequality is a drawing that represents its solutions. An inequality in one variable can be graphed on the number line. An inequality in two variables can be graphed on the coordinate plane. We will study such graphs in Chapter 9.

Answers

Skill to Review:
1. False   2. True

Margin Exercises:
1. (a) No; (b) no; (c) no; (d) yes; (e) no; (f) no
2. (a) Yes; (b) yes; (c) yes; (d) no; (e) yes; (f) yes

EXAMPLE 5 Graph: $x < 2$.

The solutions of $x < 2$ are all those numbers less than 2. They are shown on the number line by shading all points to the left of 2. The open circle at 2 indicates that 2 is *not* part of the graph.

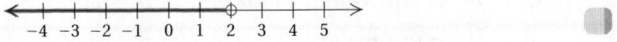

EXAMPLE 6 Graph: $x \geq -3$.

The solutions of $x \geq -3$ are shown on the number line by shading the point for -3 and all points to the right of -3. The closed circle at -3 indicates that -3 *is* part of the graph.

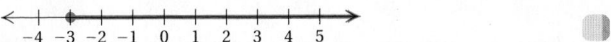

EXAMPLE 7 Graph: $-3 \leq x < 2$.

The inequality $-3 \leq x < 2$ is read "-3 is less than or equal to x *and* x is less than 2," or "x is greater than or equal to -3 *and* x is less than 2." In order to be a solution of this inequality, a number must be a solution of both $-3 \leq x$ and $x < 2$. The number 1 is a solution, as are -1.7, 0, 1.5, and $\frac{3}{8}$. We can see from the graphs below that the solution set consists of the numbers that overlap in the two solution sets in Examples 5 and 6.

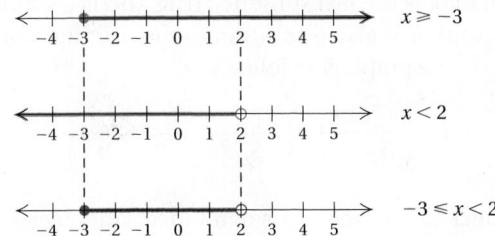

The open circle at 2 means that 2 is *not* part of the graph. The closed circle at -3 means that -3 *is* part of the graph. The other solutions are shaded.

Do Exercises 3–5.

c) Solving Inequalities Using the Addition Principle

Consider the true inequality $3 < 7$. If we add 2 on both sides, we get another true inequality:

$$3 + 2 < 7 + 2, \quad \text{or} \quad 5 < 9.$$

Similarly, if we add -4 on both sides of $x + 4 < 10$, we get an *equivalent* inequality:

$$x + 4 + (-4) < 10 + (-4),$$

or $\qquad\qquad x < 6.$

To say that $x + 4 < 10$ and $x < 6$ are **equivalent** is to say that they have the same solution set. For example, the number 3 is a solution of $x + 4 < 10$. It is also a solution of $x < 6$. The number -2 is a solution of $x < 6$. It is also a solution of $x + 4 < 10$. Any solution of one inequality is a solution of the other—they are equivalent.

Graph.

3. $x \leq 4$

```
←—+——+——+——+——+——+——+——+——+——+——+—→
 -5  -4  -3  -2  -1   0   1   2   3   4   5
```

4. $x > -2$

```
←—+——+——+——+——+——+——+——+——+——+——+—→
 -5  -4  -3  -2  -1   0   1   2   3   4   5
```

5. $-2 < x \leq 4$

```
←—+——+——+——+——+——+——+——+——+——+——+—→
 -5  -4  -3  -2  -1   0   1   2   3   4   5
```

Answers

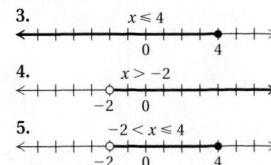

> ## THE ADDITION PRINCIPLE FOR INEQUALITIES
>
> For any real numbers a, b, and c:
>
> $a < b$ is equivalent to $a + c < b + c$;
>
> $a > b$ is equivalent to $a + c > b + c$;
>
> $a \leq b$ is equivalent to $a + c \leq b + c$;
>
> $a \geq b$ is equivalent to $a + c \geq b + c$.
>
> In other words, when we add or subtract the same number on both sides of an inequality, the direction of the inequality symbol is not changed.

STUDY TIPS

USING THE SUPPLEMENTS

The new mathematical skills and concepts presented in lectures will be of increased value to you if you begin the homework assignment as soon as possible after the lecture. Then if you still have difficulty with any of the exercises, you have time to access supplementary resources such as the *Student's Solutions Manual.* Please see the Preface for more information on this and other supplements.

As with equation solving, when solving inequalities, our goal is to isolate the variable on one side. Then it is easier to determine the solution set.

EXAMPLE 8 Solve: $x + 2 > 8$. Then graph.

We use the addition principle, subtracting 2 on both sides:

$$x + 2 - 2 > 8 - 2$$
$$x > 6.$$

From the inequality $x > 6$, we can determine the solutions directly. Any number greater than 6 makes the last sentence true and is a solution of that sentence. Any such number is also a solution of the original sentence. Thus the inequality is solved. The graph is as follows:

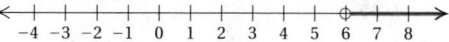

We cannot check all the solutions of an inequality by substitution, as we usually can for an equation, because there are too many of them. A partial check can be done by substituting a number greater than 6—say, 7—into the original inequality:

$$\frac{x + 2 > 8}{7 + 2 \; ? \; 8}$$
$$9 \; | \quad \text{TRUE}$$

Since $9 > 8$ is true, 7 is a solution. This is a partial check that any number greater than 6 is a solution.

EXAMPLE 9 Solve: $3x + 1 \leq 2x - 3$. Then graph.

We have

$$3x + 1 \leq 2x - 3$$
$$3x + 1 - 1 \leq 2x - 3 - 1 \qquad \text{Subtracting 1}$$
$$3x \leq 2x - 4 \qquad \text{Simplifying}$$
$$3x - 2x \leq 2x - 4 - 2x \qquad \text{Subtracting } 2x$$
$$x \leq -4. \qquad \text{Simplifying}$$

Any number less than or equal to -4 is a solution. The graph is as follows:

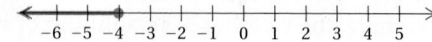

In Example 9, any number less than or equal to -4 is a solution. The following are some solutions:

$$-4, \quad -5, \quad -6, \quad -\frac{13}{3}, \quad -204.5, \quad \text{and} \quad -18\pi.$$

Besides drawing a graph, we can also describe all the solutions of an inequality using **set notation**. We could just begin to list them in a set using roster notation (see p. 493), as follows:

$$\left\{ -4, -5, -6, -\frac{13}{3}, -204.5, -18\pi, \dots \right\}.$$

We can never list them all this way, however. Seeing this set without knowing the inequality makes it difficult for us to know what real numbers we are considering. There is, however, another kind of notation that we can use. It is

$$\{x \mid x \leq -4\},$$

which is read

"The set of all x such that x is less than or equal to -4."

This shorter notation for sets is called **set-builder notation**.
From now on, we will use this notation when solving inequalities.

> Do Exercises 6–8.

EXAMPLE 10 Solve: $x + \frac{1}{3} > \frac{5}{4}$.

We have

$$\begin{aligned}
x + \tfrac{1}{3} &> \tfrac{5}{4} \\
x + \tfrac{1}{3} - \tfrac{1}{3} &> \tfrac{5}{4} - \tfrac{1}{3} &&\text{Subtracting } \tfrac{1}{3} \\
x &> \tfrac{5}{4} \cdot \tfrac{3}{3} - \tfrac{1}{3} \cdot \tfrac{4}{4} &&\text{Multiplying by 1 to obtain} \\
&&&\text{a common denominator} \\
x &> \tfrac{15}{12} - \tfrac{4}{12} \\
x &> \tfrac{11}{12}.
\end{aligned}$$

Any number greater than $\frac{11}{12}$ is a solution. The solution set is

$$\left\{ x \mid x > \tfrac{11}{12} \right\},$$

which is read

"The set of all x such that x is greater than $\frac{11}{12}$."

When solving inequalities, you may obtain an answer like $\frac{11}{12} < x$. Recall from Chapter 7 that this has the same meaning as $x > \frac{11}{12}$. Thus the solution set in Example 10 can be described as $\left\{ x \mid \frac{11}{12} < x \right\}$ or as $\left\{ x \mid x > \frac{11}{12} \right\}$. The latter is used most often.

> Do Exercises 9 and 10.

(d) Solving Inequalities Using the Multiplication Principle

There is a multiplication principle for inequalities that is similar to that for equations, but it must be modified. When we are multiplying on both sides by a negative number, the direction of the inequality symbol must be changed.

Solve. Then graph.

6. $x + 3 > 5$

$$\xleftarrow[\;-5\;-4\;-3\;-2\;-1\;\;\;0\;\;\;1\;\;\;2\;\;\;3\;\;\;4\;\;\;5\;]{}\rightarrow$$

7. $x - 1 \leq 2$

$$\xleftarrow[\;-5\;-4\;-3\;-2\;-1\;\;\;0\;\;\;1\;\;\;2\;\;\;3\;\;\;4\;\;\;5\;]{}\rightarrow$$

8. $5x + 1 < 4x - 2$

$$\xleftarrow[\;-5\;-4\;-3\;-2\;-1\;\;\;0\;\;\;1\;\;\;2\;\;\;3\;\;\;4\;\;\;5\;]{}\rightarrow$$

Solve.

9. $x + \dfrac{2}{3} \geq \dfrac{4}{5}$

10. $5y + 2 \leq -1 + 4y$

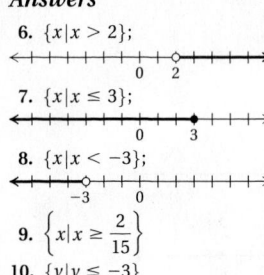

Answers

6. $\{x \mid x > 2\};$

7. $\{x \mid x \leq 3\};$

8. $\{x \mid x < -3\};$

9. $\left\{ x \mid x \geq \dfrac{2}{15} \right\}$

10. $\{y \mid y \leq -3\}$

Consider the true inequality $3 < 7$. If we multiply on both sides by a *positive* number, like 2, we get another true inequality:

$$3 \cdot 2 < 7 \cdot 2, \quad \text{or} \quad 6 < 14. \qquad \text{True}$$

If we multiply on both sides by a *negative* number, like -2, and we do not change the direction of the inequality symbol, we get a *false* inequality:

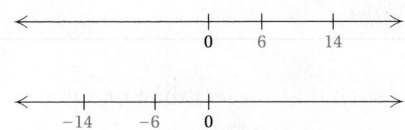

$$3 \cdot (-2) < 7 \cdot (-2), \quad \text{or} \quad -6 < -14. \qquad \text{False}$$

The fact that $6 < 14$ is true but $-6 < -14$ is false stems from the fact that the negative numbers, in a sense, mirror the positive numbers. That is, whereas 14 is to the *right* of 6 on the number line, the number -14 is to the *left* of -6. Thus, if we reverse (change the direction of) the inequality symbol, we get a *true* inequality: $-6 > -14$.

0   6   14

−14   −6   0

THE MULTIPLICATION PRINCIPLE FOR INEQUALITIES

For any real numbers a and b, and any *positive* number c:

$a < b$ is equivalent to $ac < bc$;

$a > b$ is equivalent to $ac > bc$.

For any real numbers a and b, and any *negative* number c:

$a < b$ is equivalent to $ac > bc$;

$a > b$ is equivalent to $ac < bc$.

Similar statements hold for $\leq$ and $\geq$.

In other words, when we multiply or divide by a positive number on both sides of an inequality, the direction of the inequality symbol stays the same. When we multiply or divide by a negative number on both sides of an inequality, the direction of the inequality symbol is reversed.

EXAMPLE 11   Solve: $4x < 28$. Then graph.

We have

$$4x < 28$$

$$\frac{4x}{4} < \frac{28}{4} \qquad \text{Dividing by 4}$$

The symbol stays the same.

$$x < 7. \qquad \text{Simplifying}$$

The solution set is $\{x \mid x < 7\}$. The graph is as follows:

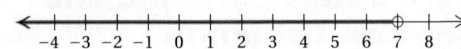

−4 −3 −2 −1 0 1 2 3 4 5 6 7 8

Do Exercises 11 and 12.

Solve. Then graph.

11. $8x < 64$

−12 −8 −4 0 4 8 12

12. $5y \geq 160$

−80 −60 −40 −20 0 20 40 60 80

Answers

11. $\{x \mid x < 8\}$;

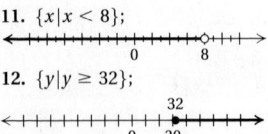

0   8

12. $\{y \mid y \geq 32\}$;

32

0   30

EXAMPLE 12 Solve: $-2y < 18$. Then graph.

$$-2y < 18$$

$$\frac{-2y}{-2} > \frac{18}{-2} \quad \text{Dividing by } -2$$

The symbol must be reversed!

$$y > -9. \quad \text{Simplifying}$$

The solution set is $\{y \mid y > -9\}$. The graph is as follows:

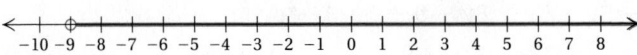

Do Exercises 13 and 14.

Do Exercises 13 and 14.

Solve.

13. $-4x \leq 24$

14. $-5y > 13$

(e) Using the Principles Together

All of the equation-solving techniques used in Sections 8.1–8.3 can be used with inequalities, provided we remember to reverse the inequality symbol when multiplying or dividing on both sides by a negative number.

EXAMPLE 13 Solve: $6 - 5x > 7$.

$$6 - 5x > 7$$

$$-6 + 6 - 5x > -6 + 7 \quad \text{Adding } -6. \text{ The symbol stays the same.}$$

$$-5x > 1 \quad \text{Simplifying}$$

$$\frac{-5x}{-5} < \frac{1}{-5} \quad \text{Dividing by } -5$$

The symbol must be reversed because we are dividing by a *negative* number, -5.

$$x < -\frac{1}{5}. \quad \text{Simplifying}$$

The solution set is $\left\{x \mid x < -\frac{1}{5}\right\}$.

Do Exercise 15.

Do Exercise 15.

15. Solve: $7 - 4x < 8$.

EXAMPLE 14 Solve: $17 - 5y > 8y - 9$.

$$-17 + 17 - 5y > -17 + 8y - 9 \quad \text{Adding } -17. \text{ The symbol stays the same.}$$

$$-5y > 8y - 26 \quad \text{Simplifying}$$

$$-8y - 5y > -8y + 8y - 26 \quad \text{Adding } -8y$$

$$-13y > -26 \quad \text{Simplifying}$$

$$\frac{-13y}{-13} < \frac{-26}{-13} \quad \text{Dividing by } -13$$

The symbol must be reversed because we are dividing by a *negative* number, -13.

$$y < 2$$

The solution set is $\{y \mid y < 2\}$.

Do Exercise 16.

Do Exercise 16.

16. Solve. Begin by subtracting 24 on both sides.

$$24 - 7y \leq 11y - 14$$

Answers

13. $\{x \mid x \geq -6\}$ **14.** $\left\{y \mid y < -\frac{13}{5}\right\}$

15. $\left\{x \mid x > -\frac{1}{4}\right\}$ **16.** $\left\{y \mid y \geq \frac{19}{9}\right\}$

Typically, we solve an equation or an inequality by isolating the variable on the left side. When we are solving an inequality, however, there are situations in which isolating the variable on the right side will eliminate the need to reverse the inequality symbol. Let's solve the inequality in Example 14 again, but this time we will isolate the variable on the right side.

EXAMPLE 15   Solve: $17 - 5y > 8y - 9$.

Note that if we add $5y$ on both sides, the coefficient of the y-term will be positive after like terms have been collected.

$$17 - 5y + 5y > 8y - 9 + 5y \qquad \text{Adding } 5y$$
$$17 > 13y - 9 \qquad \text{Simplifying}$$
$$17 + 9 > 13y - 9 + 9 \qquad \text{Adding } 9$$
$$26 > 13y \qquad \text{Simplifying}$$
$$\frac{26}{13} > \frac{13y}{13} \qquad \text{Dividing by 13. We leave the inequality symbol the same because we are dividing by a positive number.}$$
$$2 > y$$

The solution set is $\{y|2 > y\}$, or $\{y|y < 2\}$.

> **17.** Solve. Begin by adding $7y$ on both sides.
> $$24 - 7y \le 11y - 14$$

Do Exercise 17.

EXAMPLE 16   Solve: $3(x - 2) - 1 < 2 - 5(x + 6)$.

First, we use the distributive law to remove parentheses. Next, we collect like terms and then use the addition and multiplication principles for inequalities to get an equivalent inequality with x alone on one side.

$$3(x - 2) - 1 < 2 - 5(x + 6)$$
$$3x - 6 - 1 < 2 - 5x - 30 \qquad \text{Using the distributive law to multiply and remove parentheses}$$
$$3x - 7 < -5x - 28 \qquad \text{Collecting like terms}$$
$$3x + 5x < -28 + 7 \qquad \text{Adding } 5x \text{ and 7 to get all } x\text{-terms on one side and all other terms on the other side}$$
$$8x < -21 \qquad \text{Simplifying}$$
$$x < \frac{-21}{8}, \text{ or } -\frac{21}{8}. \qquad \text{Dividing by 8}$$

The solution set is $\left\{x|x < -\frac{21}{8}\right\}$.

> **18.** Solve:
> $$3(7 + 2x) \le 30 + 7(x - 1).$$

Do Exercise 18.

Answers

17. $\left\{y|y \ge \frac{19}{9}\right\}$ **18.** $\{x|x \ge -2\}$

EXAMPLE 17 Solve: $16.3 - 7.2p \le -8.18$.

The greatest number of decimal places in any one number is *two*. Multiplying by 100, which has two 0's, will clear decimals. Then we proceed as before.

$$16.3 - 7.2p \le -8.18$$

$$100(16.3 - 7.2p) \le 100(-8.18) \qquad \text{Multiplying by 100}$$

$$100(16.3) - 100(7.2p) \le 100(-8.18) \qquad \text{Using the distributive law}$$

$$1630 - 720p \le -818 \qquad \text{Simplifying}$$

$$1630 - 720p - 1630 \le -818 - 1630 \qquad \text{Subtracting 1630}$$

$$-720p \le -2448 \qquad \text{Simplifying}$$

$$\frac{-720p}{-720} \ge \frac{-2448}{-720} \qquad \text{Dividing by } -720$$

The symbol must be reversed.

$$p \ge 3.4$$

The solution set is $\{p \mid p \ge 3.4\}$.

Do Exercise 19.

19. Solve:
$$2.1x + 43.2 \ge 1.2 - 8.4x.$$

EXAMPLE 18 Solve: $\dfrac{2}{3}x - \dfrac{1}{6} + \dfrac{1}{2}x > \dfrac{7}{6} + 2x$.

The number 6 is the least common multiple of all the denominators. Thus we first multiply by 6 on both sides to clear the fractions.

$$\frac{2}{3}x - \frac{1}{6} + \frac{1}{2}x > \frac{7}{6} + 2x$$

$$6\left(\frac{2}{3}x - \frac{1}{6} + \frac{1}{2}x\right) > 6\left(\frac{7}{6} + 2x\right) \qquad \text{Multiplying by 6 on both sides}$$

$$6 \cdot \frac{2}{3}x - 6 \cdot \frac{1}{6} + 6 \cdot \frac{1}{2}x > 6 \cdot \frac{7}{6} + 6 \cdot 2x \qquad \text{Using the distributive law}$$

$$4x - 1 + 3x > 7 + 12x \qquad \text{Simplifying}$$

$$7x - 1 > 7 + 12x \qquad \text{Collecting like terms}$$

$$7x - 1 - 7x > 7 + 12x - 7x \qquad \text{Subtracting } 7x. \text{ The coefficient of the } x\text{-term will be positive.}$$

$$-1 > 7 + 5x \qquad \text{Simplifying}$$

$$-1 - 7 > 7 + 5x - 7 \qquad \text{Subtracting 7}$$

$$-8 > 5x \qquad \text{Simplifying}$$

$$\frac{-8}{5} > \frac{5x}{5} \qquad \text{Dividing by 5}$$

$$-\frac{8}{5} > x$$

The solution set is $\left\{x \mid -\frac{8}{5} > x\right\}$, or $\left\{x \mid x < -\frac{8}{5}\right\}$.

Do Exercise 20.

20. Solve:
$$\frac{3}{4} + x < \frac{7}{8}x - \frac{1}{4} + \frac{1}{2}x.$$

Answers

19. $\{x \mid x \ge -4\}$ **20.** $\left\{x \mid x > \frac{8}{3}\right\}$

a Determine whether each number is a solution of the given inequality.

1. $x > -4$
   a) 4
   b) 0
   c) −4
   d) 6
   e) 5.6

2. $x \leq 5$
   a) 0
   b) 5
   c) −1
   d) −5
   e) $7\frac{1}{4}$

3. $x \geq 6.8$
   a) −6
   b) 0
   c) 6
   d) 8
   e) $-3\frac{1}{2}$

4. $x < 8$
   a) 8
   b) −10
   c) 0
   d) 11
   e) −4.7

b Graph on the number line.

5. $x > 4$

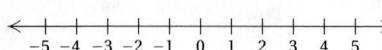

6. $x < 0$

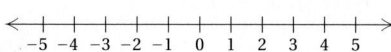

7. $t < -3$

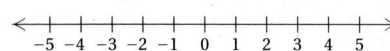

8. $y > 5$

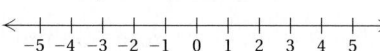

9. $m \geq -1$

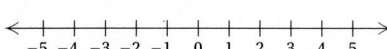

10. $x \leq -2$

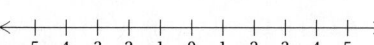

11. $-3 < x \leq 4$

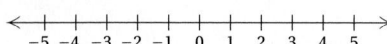

12. $-5 \leq x < 2$

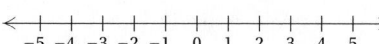

13. $0 < x < 3$

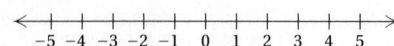

14. $-5 \leq x \leq 0$

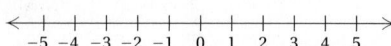

c Solve using the addition principle. Then graph.

15. $x + 7 > 2$

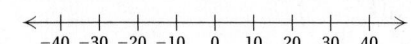

16. $x + 5 > 2$

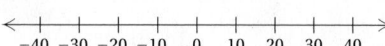

17. $x + 8 \leq -10$

18. $x + 8 \leq -11$

Copyright © 2012 Pearson Education, Inc.

Solve using the addition principle.

19. $y - 7 > -12$ **20.** $y - 9 > -15$ **21.** $2x + 3 > x + 5$ **22.** $2x + 4 > x + 7$

23. $3x + 9 \leq 2x + 6$ **24.** $3x + 18 \leq 2x + 16$ **25.** $5x - 6 < 4x - 2$ **26.** $9x - 8 < 8x - 9$

27. $-9 + t > 5$ **28.** $-8 + p > 10$ **29.** $y + \dfrac{1}{4} \leq \dfrac{1}{2}$ **30.** $x - \dfrac{1}{3} \leq \dfrac{5}{6}$

31. $x - \dfrac{1}{3} > \dfrac{1}{4}$ **32.** $x + \dfrac{1}{8} > \dfrac{1}{2}$

(d)   Solve using the multiplication principle. Then graph.

33. $5x < 35$

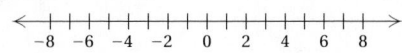

34. $8x \geq 32$

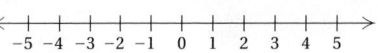

35. $-12x > -36$

36. $-16x > -64$

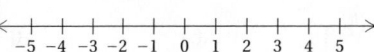

Solve using the multiplication principle.

37. $5y \geq -2$ **38.** $3x < -4$ **39.** $-2x \leq 12$ **40.** $-3x \leq 15$

41. $-4y \geq -16$ **42.** $-7x < -21$ **43.** $-3x < -17$ **44.** $-5y > -23$

45. $-2y > \dfrac{1}{7}$ **46.** $-4x \leq \dfrac{1}{9}$ **47.** $-\dfrac{6}{5} \leq -4x$ **48.** $-\dfrac{7}{9} > 63x$

Solve using the addition principle and the multiplication principle.

49. $4 + 3x < 28$

50. $3 + 4y < 35$

51. $3x - 5 \leq 13$

52. $5y - 9 \leq 21$

53. $13x - 7 < -46$

54. $8y - 6 < -54$

55. $30 > 3 - 9x$

56. $48 > 13 - 7y$

57. $4x + 2 - 3x \leq 9$

58. $15x + 5 - 14x \leq 9$

59. $-3 < 8x + 7 - 7x$

60. $-8 < 9x + 8 - 8x - 3$

61. $6 - 4y > 4 - 3y$

62. $9 - 8y > 5 - 7y + 2$

63. $5 - 9y \leq 2 - 8y$

64. $6 - 18x \leq 4 - 12x - 5x$

65. $19 - 7y - 3y < 39$

66. $18 - 6y - 4y < 63 + 5y$

67. $0.9x + 19.3 > 5.3 - 2.6x$

68. $0.96y - 0.79 \leq 0.21y + 0.46$

69. $\dfrac{x}{3} - 2 \leq 1$

70. $\dfrac{2}{3} + \dfrac{x}{5} < \dfrac{4}{15}$

71. $\dfrac{y}{5} + 1 \leq \dfrac{2}{5}$

72. $\dfrac{3x}{4} - \dfrac{7}{8} \geq -15$

73. $3(2y - 3) < 27$

74. $4(2y - 3) > 28$

75. $2(3 + 4m) - 9 \geq 45$

76. $3(5 + 3m) - 8 \leq 88$

77. $8(2t + 1) > 4(7t + 7)$

78. $7(5y - 2) > 6(6y - 1)$

Copyright © 2012 Pearson Education, Inc.

79. $3(r - 6) + 2 < 4(r + 2) - 21$

80. $5(x + 3) + 9 \le 3(x - 2) + 6$

81. $0.8(3x + 6) \ge 1.1 - (x + 2)$

82. $0.4(2x + 8) \ge 20 - (x + 5)$

83. $\dfrac{5}{3} + \dfrac{2}{3}x < \dfrac{25}{12} + \dfrac{5}{4}x + \dfrac{3}{4}$

84. $1 - \dfrac{2}{3}y \ge \dfrac{9}{5} - \dfrac{y}{5} + \dfrac{3}{5}$

Skill Maintenance

Add or subtract.   [7.3a], [7.4a]

85. $-56 + (-18)$

86. $-2.3 + 7.1$

87. $-\dfrac{3}{4} + \dfrac{1}{8}$

88. $8.12 - 9.23$

89. $-56 - (-18)$

90. $-\dfrac{3}{4} - \dfrac{1}{8}$

91. $-2.3 - 7.1$

92. $-8.12 + 9.23$

Simplify.

93. $5 - 3^2 + (8 - 2)^2 \cdot 4$ [7.8d]

94. $10 \div 2 \cdot 5 - 3^2 + (-5)^2$ [7.8d]

95. $5(2x - 4) - 3(4x + 1)$ [7.8b]

96. $9(3 + 5x) - 4(7 + 2x)$ [7.8b]

Synthesis

97. Determine whether each number is a solution of the inequality $|x| < 3$.
- **a)** 0
- **b)** -2
- **c)** -3
- **d)** 4
- **e)** 3
- **f)** 1.7
- **g)** -2.8

98. Graph $|x| < 3$ on the number line.

$$\xleftarrow{\hspace{0.5em}} \overset{\textstyle-5\ -4\ -3\ -2\ -1\ \ 0\ \ 1\ \ 2\ \ 3\ \ 4\ \ 5}{|\ \ |\ \ |\ \ |\ \ |\ \ |\ \ |\ \ |\ \ |\ \ |\ \ |} \xrightarrow{\hspace{0.5em}}$$

Solve.

99. $x + 3 < 3 + x$

100. $x + 4 > 3 + x$

8.8

Applications and Problem Solving with Inequalities

OBJECTIVES

a Translate number sentences to inequalities.

b Solve applied problems using inequalities.

The five steps for problem solving can be used for problems involving inequalities.

a Translating to Inequalities

Before solving problems that involve inequalities, we list some important phrases to look for. Sample translations are listed as well.

IMPORTANT WORDS	SAMPLE SENTENCE	TRANSLATION
is at least	Bill is at least 21 years old.	$b \geq 21$
is at most	At most 5 students dropped the course.	$n \leq 5$
cannot exceed	To qualify, earnings cannot exceed $12,000.	$r \leq 12{,}000$
must exceed	The speed must exceed 15 mph.	$s > 15$
is less than	Tucker's weight is less than 50 lb.	$w < 50$
is more than	Boston is more than 200 mi away.	$d > 200$
is between	The film was between 90 and 100 min long.	$90 < t < 100$
no more than	Bing weighs no more than 90 lb.	$w \leq 90$
no less than	Valerie scored no less than 8.3.	$s \geq 8.3$

The following phrases deserve special attention.

Translate.

1. Maggie worked no fewer than 15 hr last week.

2. The price of that PT Cruiser is at most $21,900.

3. The time of the test was between 45 and 55 min.

4. Tania's weight is less than 110 lb.

5. That number is more than −2.

6. The costs of production of that CD-ROM cannot exceed $12,500.

7. At most 1250 people attended the concert.

8. Yesterday, at least 23 people got tickets for speeding.

> ### TRANSLATING "AT LEAST" AND "AT MOST"
>
> A quantity x is at least some amount q: $x \geq q$.
> (If x is at least q, it cannot be less than q.)
>
> A quantity x is at most some amount q: $x \leq q$.
> (If x is at most q, it cannot be more than q.)

Do Exercises 1–8.

b Solving Problems

EXAMPLE 1 *Catering Costs.* To cater a party, Curtis' Barbeque charges a $150 setup fee plus $15.50 per person. The cost of Berry Manufacturing's annual picnic cannot exceed $2100. How many people can attend the picnic?

Source: Curtis' All American Barbeque, Putney, Vermont

1. **Familiarize.** Suppose that 110 people were to attend the picnic. The cost would then be $150 + $15.50(110), or $1855. This shows that more than 110 people could attend the picnic without exceeding $2100. Instead of making another guess, we let n = the number of people in attendance.

Answers

1. $h \geq 15$ 2. $p \leq 21{,}900$
3. $45 < t < 55$ 4. $w < 110$
5. $n > -2$ 6. $c \leq 12{,}500$
7. $p \leq 1250$ 8. $s \geq 23$

2. **Translate.** Our guess shows us how to translate. The cost of the picnic will be the $150 setup fee plus $15.50 times the number of people attending. We translate to an inequality:

Rewording: The setup fee plus the cost of the meals cannot exceed $2100.

Translating: 150 $+$ $15.50n$ $\leq$ $2100.$

3. **Solve.** We solve the inequality for n:

$$150 + 15.50n \leq 2100$$
$$150 + 15.50n - 150 \leq 2100 - 150 \quad \text{Subtracting 150}$$
$$15.50n \leq 1950 \quad \text{Simplifying}$$
$$\frac{15.50n}{15.50} \leq \frac{1950}{15.50} \quad \text{Dividing by 15.50}$$
$$n \leq 125.8. \quad \text{Rounding to the nearest tenth}$$

4. **Check.** Although the solution set of the inequality is all numbers less than or equal to about 125.8, since n = the number of people in attendance, we round *down* to 125 people. If 125 people attend, the cost will be $150 + $15.50(125)$, or $2087.50. If 126 attend, the cost will exceed $2100.

5. **State.** At most, 125 people can attend the picnic.

Do Exercise 9.

Translate to an inequality and solve.

9. **Butter Temperatures.** Butter stays solid at Fahrenheit temperatures below 88°. The formula
$$F = \tfrac{9}{5}C + 32$$
can be used to convert Celsius temperatures C to Fahrenheit temperatures F. Determine (in terms of an inequality) those Celsius temperatures for which butter stays solid.

---------------------------------- *Caution!* ----------------------------------

Solutions of problems should always be checked using the original wording of the problem. In some cases, answers might need to be whole numbers or integers or rounded off in a particular direction.

EXAMPLE 2 *Nutrition.* The U.S. Department of Agriculture recommends that for a typical 2000-calorie daily diet, no more than 20 g of saturated fat be consumed. In the first three days of a four-day vacation, Anthony consumed 26 g, 17 g, and 22 g of saturated fat. Determine (in terms of an inequality) how many grams of saturated fat Anthony can consume on the fourth day if he is to average no more than 20 g of saturated fat per day.

Exercise
Grains   Vegetables   Fruit   Oils   Milk   Meat and beans

SOURCES: U.S. Department of Health and Human Services; U.S. Department of Agriculture

Answer

9. $\frac{9}{5}C + 32 < 88$; $\left\{C | C < 31\frac{1}{9}°\right\}$

1. **Familiarize.** Suppose Anthony consumed 19 g of saturated fat on the fourth day. His daily average for the vacation would then be

$$\frac{26\,\text{g} + 17\,\text{g} + 22\,\text{g} + 19\,\text{g}}{4} = \frac{84\,\text{g}}{4} = 21\,\text{g}.$$

This shows that Anthony cannot consume 19 g of saturated fat on the fourth day, if he is to average no more than 20 g of fat per day. We let x = the number of grams of fat that Anthony consumes on the fourth day.

2. **Translate.** We reword the problem and translate to an inequality as follows:

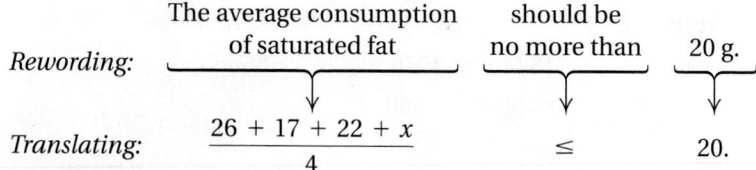

Rewording: The average consumption of saturated fat   should be no more than   20 g.

Translating: $\dfrac{26 + 17 + 22 + x}{4}$ $\leq$ 20.

3. **Solve.** Because of the fraction expression, it is convenient to use the multiplication principle first to solve the inequality:

$$\frac{26 + 17 + 22 + x}{4} \leq 20$$

$$4\left(\frac{26 + 17 + 22 + x}{4}\right) \leq 4 \cdot 20 \qquad \text{Multiplying by 4}$$

$$26 + 17 + 22 + x \leq 80$$

$$65 + x \leq 80 \qquad \text{Simplifying}$$

$$x \leq 15. \qquad \text{Subtracting 65}$$

4. **Check.** As a partial check, we show that Anthony can consume 15 g of saturated fat on the fourth day and not exceed a 20-g average for the four days:

$$\frac{26 + 17 + 22 + 15}{4} = \frac{80}{4} = 20.$$

5. **State.** Anthony's average intake of saturated fat for the vacation will not exceed 20 g per day if he consumes no more than 15 g of saturated fat on the fourth day.

Do Exercise 10.

Translate to an inequality and solve.

10. Test Scores. A pre-med student is taking a chemistry course in which four tests are given. To get an A, she must average at least 90 on the four tests. The student got scores of 91, 86, and 89 on the first three tests. Determine (in terms of an inequality) what scores on the last test will allow her to get an A.

STUDY TIPS

CHECKLIST

- Are you approaching your study of mathematics with a positive attitude?
- Are you making use of the textbook supplements, such as the *Student's Solutions Manual*?
- Have you determined the location of the learning resource centers on your campus, such as a math lab, a tutor center, and your instructor's office?
- Are you stopping to work the margin exercises when directed to do so?
- Are you keeping one section ahead in your syllabus?

Answer

10. $\dfrac{91 + 86 + 89 + s}{4} \geq 90; \{s \mid s \geq 94\}$

a   Translate to an inequality.

1. A number is at least 7.

2. A number is greater than or equal to 5.

3. The baby weighs more than 2 kilograms (kg).

4. Between 75 and 100 people attended the concert.

5. The speed of the train was between 90 and 110 mph.

6. The attendance was no more than 180.

7. Leah works no more than 20 hr per week.

8. The amount of acid must exceed 40 liters (L).

9. The cost of gasoline is no less than $1.50 per gallon.

10. The temperature is at most $-2°$.

11. A number is greater than 8.

12. A number is less than 5.

13. A number is less than or equal to -4.

14. A number is greater than or equal to 18.

15. The number of people is at least 1300.

16. The cost is at most $4857.95.

17. The amount of water is not to exceed 500 liters.

18. The cost of lettuce is no less than 94 cents per pound.

19. Two more than three times a number is less than 13.

20. Five less than one-half a number is greater than 17.

b   Solve.

21. *Test Scores.* James is taking a literature course in which four tests are given. To get a B, he must average at least 80 on the four tests. He got scores of 82, 76, and 78 on the first three tests. Determine (in terms of an inequality) what scores on the last test will allow him to get at least a B.

22. *Test Scores.* Rebecca's quiz grades are 73, 75, 89, and 91. Determine (in terms of an inequality) what scores on the last quiz will allow her to get an average quiz grade of at least 85.

23. *Gold Temperatures.* Gold stays solid at Fahrenheit temperatures below 1945.4°. Determine (in terms of an inequality) those Celsius temperatures for which gold stays solid. Use the formula given in Margin Exercise 9.

24. *Body Temperatures.* The human body is considered to be fevered when its temperature is higher than 98.6°F. Using the formula given in Margin Exercise 9, determine (in terms of an inequality) those Celsius temperatures for which the body is fevered.

25. *World Records in the 1500-m Run.* The formula

$$R = -0.075t + 3.85$$

can be used to predict the world record in the 1500-m run t years after 1930. Determine (in terms of an inequality) those years for which the world record will be less than 3.5 min.

26. *World Records in the 200-m Dash.* The formula

$$R = -0.028t + 20.8$$

can be used to predict the world record in the 200-m dash t years after 1920. Determine (in terms of an inequality) those years for which the world record will be less than 19.0 sec.

27. *Envelope Size.* For a direct-mail campaign, Laramore Advertising determines that any envelope with a fixed width of $3\frac{1}{2}$ in. and an area of at least $17\frac{1}{2}$ in^2 can be used. Determine (in terms of an inequality) those lengths that will satisfy the company constraints.

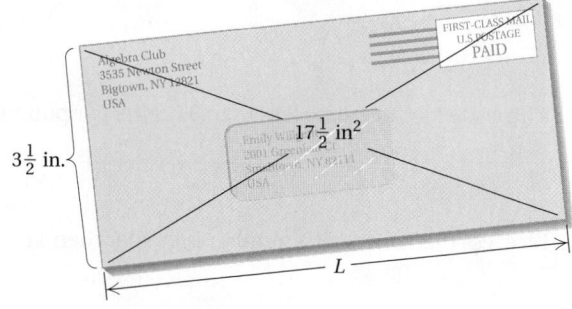

28. *Package Sizes.* Logan Delivery Service accepts packages of up to 165 in. in length and girth combined. (Girth is the distance around the package.) A package has a fixed girth of 53 in. Determine (in terms of an inequality) those lengths for which a package is acceptable.

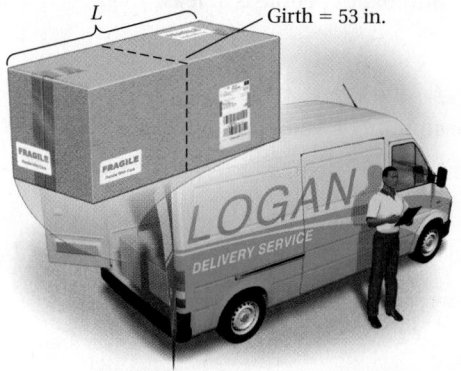

29. *Blueprints.* To make copies of blueprints, Vantage Reprographics charges a $5 setup fee plus $4 per copy. Myra can spend no more than $65 for copying her blueprints. What numbers of copies will allow her to stay within budget?

30. *Banquet Costs.* The Shepard College women's volleyball team can spend at most $450 for its awards banquet at a local restaurant. If the restaurant charges a $40 setup fee plus $16 per person, at most how many can attend?

Copyright © 2012 Pearson Education, Inc.

31. *Phone Costs.*   Simon claims that it costs him at least $3.00 every time he calls an overseas customer. If his typical call costs 75¢ plus 45¢ for each minute, how long do his calls typically last? (*Hint*: 75¢ = $0.75.)

32. *Parking Costs.*   Laura is certain that every time she parks in the municipal garage it costs her at least $6.75. If the garage charges $1.50 plus 75¢ for each half hour, for how long is Laura's car generally parked?

33. *College Tuition.*   Angelica's financial aid stipulates that her tuition cannot exceed $1000. If her local community college charges a $35 registration fee plus $375 per course, what is the greatest number of courses for which Angelica can register?

34. *Furnace Repairs.*   RJ's Plumbing and Heating charges $45 plus $30 per hour for emergency service. Gary remembers being billed over $150 for an emergency call. How long was RJ's there?

35. *Nutrition.*   Following the guidelines of the Food and Drug Administration, Dale tries to eat at least 5 servings of fruits or vegetables each day. For the first six days of one week, he had 4, 6, 7, 4, 6, and 4 servings. How many servings of fruits or vegetables should Dale eat on Saturday, in order to average at least 5 servings per day for the week?

36. *College Course Load.*   To remain on financial aid, Millie needs to complete an average of at least 7 credits per quarter each year. In the first three quarters of 2009, Millie completed 5, 7, and 8 credits. How many credits of course work must Millie complete in the fourth quarter if she is to remain on financial aid?

37. *Perimeter of a Rectangle.*   The width of a rectangle is fixed at 8 ft. What lengths will make the perimeter at least 200 ft? at most 200 ft?

38. *Perimeter of a Triangle.*   One side of a triangle is 2 cm shorter than the base. The other side is 3 cm longer than the base. What lengths of the base will allow the perimeter to be greater than 19 cm?

39. *Area of a Rectangle.*   The width of a rectangle is fixed at 4 cm. For what lengths will the area be less than 86 cm^2?

40. *Area of a Rectangle.*   The width of a rectangle is fixed at 16 yd. For what lengths will the area be at least 264 yd^2?

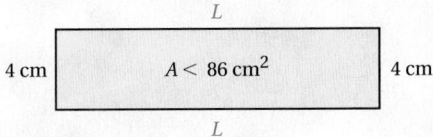

41. *Insurance-Covered Repairs.* Most insurance companies will replace a vehicle if an estimated repair exceeds 80% of the "blue-book" value of the vehicle. Michelle's insurance company paid $8500 for repairs to her Subaru after an accident. What can be concluded about the blue-book value of the car?

42. *Insurance-Covered Repairs.* Following an accident, Jeff's Ford pickup was replaced by his insurance company because the damage was so extensive. Before the damage, the blue-book value of the truck was $21,000. How much would it have cost to repair the truck? (See Exercise 41.)

43. *Reduced-Fat Foods.* In order for a food to be labeled "reduced fat," it must have at least 25% less fat than the regular item. One brand of reduced-fat peanut butter contains 12 g of fat per serving. What can you conclude about the fat content in a serving of the brand's regular peanut butter?

44. *Reduced-Fat Foods.* One brand of reduced-fat chocolate chip cookies contains 5 g of fat per serving. What can you conclude about the fat content of the brand's regular chocolate chip cookies? (See Exercise 43.)

45. *Pond Depth.* On July 1, Garrett's Pond was 25 ft deep. Since that date, the water level has dropped $\frac{2}{3}$ ft per week. For what dates will the water level not exceed 21 ft?

46. *Weight Gain.* A 3-lb puppy is gaining weight at a rate of $\frac{3}{4}$ lb per week. When will the puppy's weight exceed $22\frac{1}{2}$ lb?

47. *Area of a Triangular Flag.* As part of an outdoor education course, Wendy needs to make a bright-colored triangular flag with an area of at least 3 ft^2. What heights can the triangle be if the base is $1\frac{1}{2}$ ft?

48. *Area of a Triangular Sign.* Zoning laws in Harrington prohibit displaying signs with areas exceeding 12 ft^2. If Flo's Marina is ordering a triangular sign with an 8-ft base, how tall can the sign be?

49. *Electrician Visits.* Dot's Electric made 17 customer calls last week and 22 calls this week. How many calls must be made next week in order to maintain a weekly average of at least 20 calls for the three-week period?

50. *Volunteer Work.* George and Joan do volunteer work at a hospital. Joan worked 3 more hr than George, and together they worked more than 27 hr. What possible numbers of hours did each work?

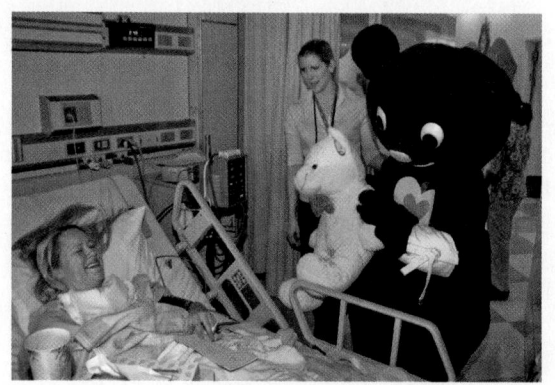

Copyright © 2012 Pearson Education, Inc.

Skill Maintenance

In each of Exercises 51–58, fill in the blank with the correct term from the given list. Some of the choices may not be used.

51. The product of a(n) _____ number of negative numbers is always positive.   [7.5a]

52. The product of a(n) _____ number of negative numbers is always negative.   [7.5a]

53. The _____ inverse of a negative number is always positive.   [7.3b]

54. The _____ inverse of a negative number is always negative.   [7.6b]

55. Equations with the same solutions are called _____ equations.   [8.1b]

56. The _____ for equations asserts that when we add the same number to the expressions on each side of the equation, we get equivalent equations.   [8.1b]

57. The _____ for inequalities asserts that when we multiply or divide by a negative number on both sides of an inequality, the direction of the inequality symbol _____.   [8.7d]

58. Any replacement for the variable that makes an equation true is called a(n) _____ of the equation.   [8.1a]

addition principle

multiplication principle

solution

value

is reversed

stays the same

even

odd

multiplicative

additive

equivalent

Synthesis

59. *Ski Wax.*   Green ski wax works best between 5° and 15° Fahrenheit. Determine those Celsius temperatures for which green ski wax works best. Use the formula given in Margin Exercise 9.

60. *Parking Fees.*   Mack's Parking Garage charges $4.00 for the first hour and $2.50 for each additional hour. For how long has a car been parked when the charge exceeds $16.50?

61. *Low-Fat Foods.*   In order for a food to be labeled "low fat," it must have fewer than 3 g of fat per serving. One brand of reduced-fat tortilla chips contains 60% less fat than regular nacho cheese tortilla chips, but still cannot be labeled low fat. What can you conclude about the fat content of a serving of nacho cheese tortilla chips?

62. *Parking Fees.*   When asked how much the parking charge is for a certain car, Mack replies "between 14 and 24 dollars." For how long has the car been parked? (See Exercise 60.)

Summary and Review

Key Terms and Properties

equation, p. 570
solution of an equation, p. 570
equivalent equations, p. 571
clearing fractions, p. 585

clearing decimals, p. 585
formula, p. 593
evaluating a formula, p. 593
inequality, p. 628

solution set, p. 628
graph of an inequality, p. 628
equivalent inequalities, p. 629
set-builder notation, p. 631

The Addition Principle for Equations:	For any real numbers a, b, and c, $a = b$ is equivalent to $a + c = b + c$.
The Multiplication Principle for Equations:	For any real numbers a, b, and c, $c \neq 0$: $a = b$ is equivalent to $a \cdot c = b \cdot c$.
The Addition Principle for Inequalities:	For any real numbers a, b, and c: $a < b$ is equivalent to $a + c < b + c$; $a > b$ is equivalent to $a + c > b + c$. Similar statements hold for $\leq$ and $\geq$.
The Multiplication Principle for Inequalities:	For any real numbers a and b, and any *positive* number c: $a < b$ is equivalent to $ac < bc$; $a > b$ is equivalent to $ac > bc$. For any real numbers a and b, and any *negative* number c: $a < b$ is equivalent to $ac > bc$; $a > b$ is equivalent to $ac < bc$. Similar statements hold for $\leq$ and $\geq$.

Concept Reinforcement

Determine whether each statement is true or false.

_____ **1.** Some equations have no solution.   [8.3c]

_____ **2.** For any number n, $n \geq n$.   [8.7a]

_____ **3.** $2x - 7 < 11$ and $x < 2$ are equivalent inequalities.   [8.7e]

_____ **4.** If $x > y$, then $-x < -y$.   [8.7d]

Important Concepts

Objective 8.3a   Solve equations using both the addition principle and the multiplication principle.

Objective 8.3b   Solve equations in which like terms may need to be collected.

Objective 8.3c   Solve equations by first removing parentheses and collecting like terms.

Example   Solve: $6y - 2(2y - 3) = 12$.

$$6y - 2(2y - 3) = 12$$

$6y - 4y + 6 = 12$	Removing parentheses
$2y + 6 = 12$	Collecting like terms
$2y + 6 - 6 = 12 - 6$	Subtracting 6
$2y = 6$	
$\dfrac{2y}{2} = \dfrac{6}{2}$	Dividing by 2
$y = 3$	

Practice Exercise

1. Solve: $4(x - 3) = 6(x + 2)$.

Objective 8.3c Solve equations with no solutions and equations with an infinite number of solutions.

Example Solve: $8 + 2x - 4 = 6 + 2(x - 1)$.

$$8 + 2x - 4 = 6 + 2(x - 1)$$
$$8 + 2x - 4 = 6 + 2x - 2$$
$$2x + 4 = 2x + 4$$
$$2x + 4 - 2x = 2x + 4 - 2x$$
$$4 = 4$$

Every real number is a solution of the equation $4 = 4$, so all real numbers are solutions of the original equation. The equation has infinitely many solutions.

Example Solve: $2 + 5(x - 1) = -6 + 5x + 7$.

$$2 + 5(x - 1) = -6 + 5x + 7$$
$$2 + 5x - 5 = -6 + 5x + 7$$
$$5x - 3 = 5x + 1$$
$$5x - 3 - 5x = 5x + 1 - 5x$$
$$-3 = 1$$

This is a false equation, so the original equation has no solution.

Practice Exercises

2. Solve: $4 + 3y - 7 = 3 + 3(y - 2)$.

3. Solve: $4(x - 3) + 7 = -5 + 4x + 10$.

Objective 8.4b Solve a formula for a specified letter.

Example Solve for n: $M = \dfrac{m + n}{5}$.

$$M = \frac{m + n}{5}$$
$$5 \cdot M = 5\left(\frac{m + n}{5}\right)$$
$$5M = m + n$$
$$5M - m = m + n - m$$
$$5M - m = n$$

Practice Exercise

4. Solve for b: $A = \dfrac{1}{2}bh$.

Objective 8.7b Graph an inequality on the number line.

Example Graph each inequality: **(a)** $x < 2$; **(b)** $x \geq -3$.

a) The solutions of $x < 2$ are all numbers less than 2. We shade all points to the left of 2, and we use an open circle at 2 to indicate that 2 *is not* part of the graph.

$x < 2$

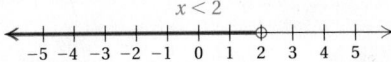

b) The solutions of $x \geq -3$ are all numbers greater than -3 and the number -3 as well. We shade all points to the right of -3, and we use a closed circle at -3 to indicate that -3 *is* part of the graph.

$x \geq -3$

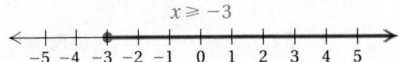

Practice Exercises

5. Graph: $x > 1$.

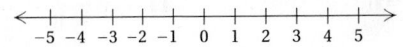

6. Graph: $x \leq -1$.

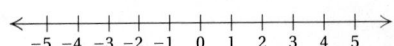

Objective 8.7e Solve inequalities using the addition principle and the multiplication principle together.

Example Solve: $8y - 7 \leq 5y + 2$.

$$8y - 7 \leq 5y + 2$$
$$8y - 7 - 8y \leq 5y + 2 - 8y$$
$$-7 \leq -3y + 2$$
$$-7 - 2 \leq -3y + 2 - 2$$
$$-9 \leq -3y$$
$$\frac{-9}{-3} \geq \frac{-3y}{-3} \quad \text{Reversing the symbol}$$
$$3 \geq y$$

The solution set is $\{y \mid 3 \geq y\}$, or $\{y \mid y \leq 3\}$.

Practice Exercise

7. Solve: $6y + 5 > 3y - 7$.

Review Exercises

Solve. [8.1b]

1. $x + 5 = -17$

2. $n - 7 = -6$

3. $x - 11 = 14$

4. $y - 0.9 = 9.09$

Solve. [8.2a]

5. $-\dfrac{2}{3}x = -\dfrac{1}{6}$

6. $-8x = -56$

7. $-\dfrac{x}{4} = 48$

8. $15x = -35$

9. $\dfrac{4}{5}y = -\dfrac{3}{16}$

Solve. [8.3a]

10. $5 - x = 13$

11. $\dfrac{1}{4}x - \dfrac{5}{8} = \dfrac{3}{8}$

Solve. [8.3b, c]

12. $5t + 9 = 3t - 1$

13. $7x - 6 = 25x$

14. $14y = 23y - 17 - 10$

15. $0.22y - 0.6 = 0.12y + 3 - 0.8y$

16. $\dfrac{1}{4}x - \dfrac{1}{8}x = 3 - \dfrac{1}{16}x$

17. $14y + 17 + 7y = 9 + 21y + 8$

18. $4(x + 3) = 36$

19. $3(5x - 7) = -66$

20. $8(x - 2) - 5(x + 4) = 20 + x$

21. $-5x + 3(x + 8) = 16$

22. $6(x - 2) - 16 = 3(2x - 5) + 11$

Determine whether the given number is a solution of the inequality $x \leq 4$. [8.7a]

23. -3

24. 7

25. 4

Copyright © 2012 Pearson Education, Inc.

Solve. Write set notation for the answers. [8.7c, d, e]

26. $y + \dfrac{2}{3} \geq \dfrac{1}{6}$

27. $9x \geq 63$

28. $2 + 6y > 14$

29. $7 - 3y \geq 27 + 2y$

30. $3x + 5 < 2x - 6$

31. $-4y < 28$

32. $4 - 8x < 13 + 3x$

33. $-4x \leq \dfrac{1}{3}$

Graph on the number line. [8.7b, e]

34. $4x - 6 < x + 3$

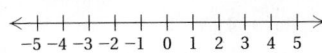

35. $-2 < x \leq 5$

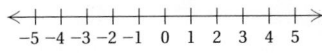

36. $y > 0$

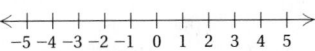

Solve. [8.4b]

37. $C = \pi d$, for d

38. $V = \dfrac{1}{3} Bh$, for B

39. $A = \dfrac{a + b}{2}$, for a

40. $y = mx + b$, for x

Solve. [8.6a]

41. *Dimensions of Wyoming.* The state of Wyoming is roughly in the shape of a rectangle whose perimeter is 1280 mi. The length is 90 mi more than the width. Find the dimensions.

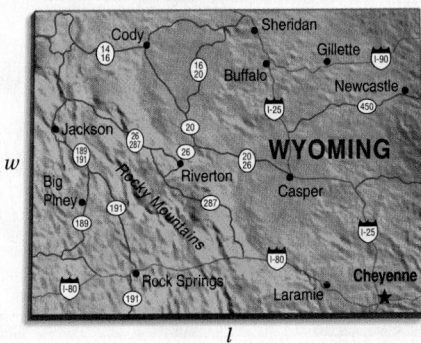

42. *Interstate Mile Markers.* The sum of two consecutive mile markers on I-5 in California is 691. Find the numbers on the markers.

43. An entertainment center sold for $2449 in June. This was $332 more than the cost in February. What was the cost in February?

44. Ty is paid a commission of $4 for each magazine subscription he sells. One week, he received $108 in commissions. How many subscriptions did he sell?

45. The measure of the second angle of a triangle is 50° more than that of the first angle. The measure of the third angle is 10° less than twice the first angle. Find the measures of the angles.

Solve. [8.5a]

46. What number is 20% of 75?

47. Fifteen is what percent of 80?

48. 18 is 3% of what number?

49. *Job Opportunities.* There were 1.388 million child-care workers in 2006. The number of job opportunities in that field is expected to grow to 1.636 million by 2016. What is the percent of increase?

Source: *Occupational Outlook Handbook*

Solve. [8.6a]

50. After a 30% reduction, a bread maker is on sale for $154. What was the marked price (the price before the reduction)?

51. A hotel manager's salary is $61,410, which is a 15% increase over the previous year's salary. What was the previous salary?

52. A tax-exempt organization received a bill of $145.90 for janitorial supplies. The bill incorrectly included sales tax of 5%. How much does the organization actually owe?

Solve. [8.8b]

53. *Test Scores.* Jacinda's test grades are 71, 75, 82, and 86. What is the lowest grade that she can get on the next test and still have an average test score of at least 80?

54. The length of a rectangle is 43 cm. What widths will make the perimeter greater than 120 cm?

55. The solution of the equation $4(3x - 5) + 6 = 8 + x$ is which of the following? [8.3c]

A. Less than -1 **B.** Between -1 and 1
C. Between 1 and 5   **D.** Greater than 5

56. Solve for y: $3x + 4y = P$. [8.4b]

A. $y = \dfrac{P - 3x}{4}$ **B.** $y = \dfrac{P + 3x}{4}$

C. $y = P - \dfrac{3x}{4}$ **D.** $y = \dfrac{P}{4} - 3x$

Synthesis

Solve.

57. $2|x| + 4 = 50$ [7.2e], [8.3a]

58. $|3x| = 60$ [7.2e], [8.2a]

59. $y = 2a - ab + 3$, for a [8.4b]

Understanding Through Discussion and Writing

1. Would it be better to receive a 5% raise and then an 8% raise or the other way around? Why? [8.5a]

2. Erin returns a tent that she bought during a storewide 25%-off sale that has ended. She is offered store credit for 125% of what she paid (not to be used on sale items). Is this fair to Erin? Why or why not? [8.5a]

3. Are the inequalities $x > -5$ and $-x < 5$ equivalent? Why or why not? [8.7d]

4. Explain in your own words why it is necessary to reverse the inequality symbol when multiplying on both sides of an inequality by a negative number. [8.7d]

5. If f represents Fran's age and t represents Todd's age, write a sentence that would translate to $t + 3 < f$. [8.8a]

6. Explain how the meanings of "Five more than a number" and "Five is more than a number" differ. [8.8a]

Copyright © 2012 Pearson Education, Inc.

Test   For Extra Help

CHAPTER
Test Prep
VIDEOS

Step-by-step test solutions are found on the Chapter Test Prep Videos available via the Video Resources on DVD, in *MyMathLab* , and on You Tube (search "BittingerDevMath" and click on "Channels").

Solve.

1. $x + 7 = 15$

2. $t - 9 = 17$

3. $3x = -18$

4. $-\frac{4}{7}x = -28$

5. $3t + 7 = 2t - 5$

6. $\frac{1}{2}x - \frac{3}{5} = \frac{2}{5}$

7. $8 - y = 16$

8. $-\frac{2}{5} + x = -\frac{3}{4}$

9. $3(x + 2) = 27$

10. $-3x - 6(x - 4) = 9$

11. $0.4p + 0.2 = 4.2p - 7.8 - 0.6p$

12. $4(3x - 1) + 11 = 2(6x + 5) - 8$

13. $-2 + 7x + 6 = 5x + 4 + 2x$

Solve. Write set notation for the answers.

14. $x + 6 \le 2$

15. $14x + 9 > 13x - 4$

16. $12x \le 60$

17. $-2y \ge 26$

18. $-4y \le -32$

19. $-5x \ge \frac{1}{4}$

20. $4 - 6x > 40$

21. $5 - 9x \ge 19 + 5x$

Graph on the number line.

22. $y \le 9$

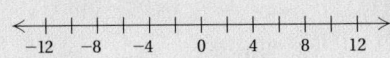

23. $6x - 3 < x + 2$

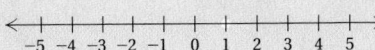

24. $-2 \le x \le 2$

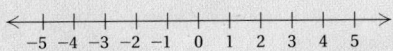

Solve.

25. What number is 24% of 75?

26. 15.84 is what percent of 96?

27. 800 is 2% of what number?

28. *Job Opportunities.* The number of job opportunities for physician's assistants is expected to increase from 66,000 in 2006 to 83,000 in 2016. What is the percent of increase?

Source: *Occupational Outlook Handbook*

29. *Perimeter of a Photograph.* The perimeter of a rectangular photograph is 36 cm. The length is 4 cm greater than the width. Find the width and the length.

30. *Charitable Contributions.* About $102.3 billion was given to religious organizations in 2007. This represents 33% of all charitable donations that year. How much was donated to all charities?

Sources: Giving USA Foundation; Center on Philanthropy at Indiana University

31. *Raffle Tickets.* The numbers on three raffle tickets are consecutive integers whose sum is 7530. Find the integers.

32. *Savings Account.* Money is invested in a savings account at 5% simple interest. After 1 year, there is $924 in the account. How much was originally invested?

33. *Board Cutting.* An 8-m board is cut into two pieces. One piece is 2 m longer than the other. How long are the pieces?

34. *Lengths of a Rectangle.* The width of a rectangle is 96 yd. Find all possible lengths such that the perimeter of the rectangle will be at least 540 yd.

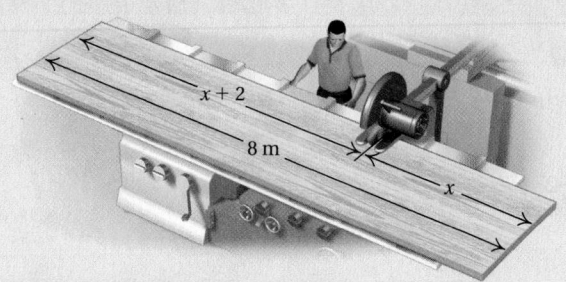

35. *Budgeting.* Jason has budgeted an average of $95 per month for entertainment. For the first five months of the year, he has spent $98, $89, $110, $85, and $83. How much can Jason spend in the sixth month without exceeding his average budget?

36. *Copy Machine Rental.* A catalog publisher needs to lease a copy machine for use during a special project that they anticipate will take 3 months. It costs $225 per month plus 1.2¢ per copy to rent the machine. The company must stay within a budget of $2400 for copies. Determine (in terms of an inequality) the number of copies they can make and still remain within budget.

37. Solve $A = 2\pi rh$ for r.

38. Solve $y = 8x + b$ for x.

39. *Senior Population.* The number of Americans age 65 and older is projected to grow from 40.4 million to 70.3 million between 2011 and 2030. Find the percent of increase.

Source: U.S. Census Bureau

A. 42.5%   **B.** 47%
C. 57.5%   **D.** 74%

Synthesis

40. Solve $c = \dfrac{1}{a - d}$ for d.

41. Solve: $3|w| - 8 = 37$.

42. A movie theater had a certain number of tickets to give away. Five people got the tickets. The first got one-third of the tickets, the second got one-fourth of the tickets, and the third got one-fifth of the tickets. The fourth person got eight tickets, and there were five tickets left for the fifth person. Find the total number of tickets given away.

Copyright © 2012 Pearson Education, Inc.

Graphs of Linear Equations

Real-World Application

The maximum grade allowed between two stations in a rapid-transit rail system is 3.5%. Between station A and station B, which are 280 ft apart, the tracks rise $8\frac{1}{2}$ ft. What is the grade of the tracks between these two stations? Round the answer to the nearest tenth of a percent. Does this grade meet the rapid-transit rail standards?

Source: Brian Burell, *Merriam Webster's Guide to Everyday Math*, Merriam-Webster, Inc., Springfield MA

This problem appears as Exercise 53 in Section 9.3.

Graphs and Applications of Linear Equations

OBJECTIVES

a Plot points associated with ordered pairs of numbers; determine the quadrant in which a point lies.

b Find the coordinates of a point on a graph.

c Determine whether an ordered pair is a solution of an equation with two variables.

d Graph linear equations of the type $y = mx + b$ and $Ax + By = C$, identifying the y-intercept.

e Solve applied problems involving graphs of linear equations.

SKILL TO REVIEW
Objective 8.1a: Determine whether a given number is a solution of a given equation.

Determine whether -3 is a solution of each equation.

1. $8(w - 3) = 0$
2. $15 = -2y + 9$

You probably have seen bar graphs like the following in newspapers and magazines. Note that a straight line can be drawn along the tops of the bars. Such a line is a *graph of a linear equation*. In this chapter, we study how to graph linear equations and consider properties such as slope and intercepts. Many applications of these topics will also be considered.

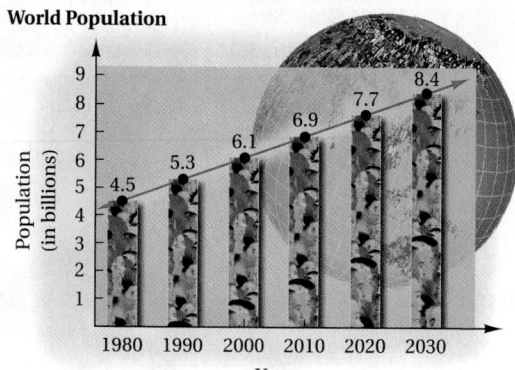

World Population

SOURCE: U.S. Census Bureau; International Data Base

a Plotting Ordered Pairs

In Chapter 8, we graphed numbers and inequalities in one variable on a line. To enable us to graph an equation that contains two variables, we now learn to graph number pairs on a plane.

On the number line, each point is the graph of a number. On a plane, each point is the graph of a number pair. To form the plane, we use two perpendicular number lines called **axes**. They cross at a point called the **origin**. The arrows show the positive directions.

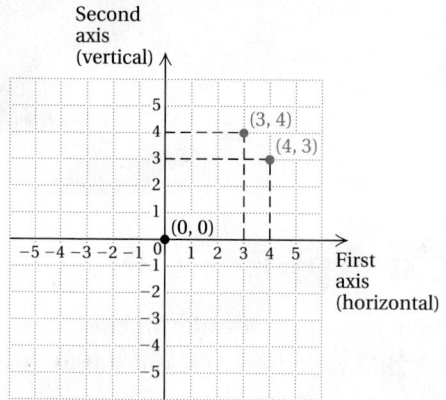

Consider the **ordered pair** $(3, 4)$. The numbers in an ordered pair are called **coordinates**. In $(3, 4)$, the **first coordinate** (the **abscissa**) is 3 and the **second coordinate** (the **ordinate**) is 4. To plot $(3, 4)$, we start at the origin and move horizontally to the 3. Then we move up vertically 4 units and make a "dot."

The point $(4, 3)$ is also plotted above. Note that $(3, 4)$ and $(4, 3)$ represent different points. The order of the numbers in the pair is important. We use the term *ordered* pairs because it makes a difference which number comes first. The coordinates of the origin are $(0, 0)$.

Answers
Skill to Review:
1. -3 is not a solution.   2. -3 is a solution.

EXAMPLE 1 Plot the point $(-5, 2)$.

The first number, -5, is negative. Starting at the origin, we move -5 units in the horizontal direction (5 units to the left). The second number, 2, is positive. We move 2 units in the vertical direction (up).

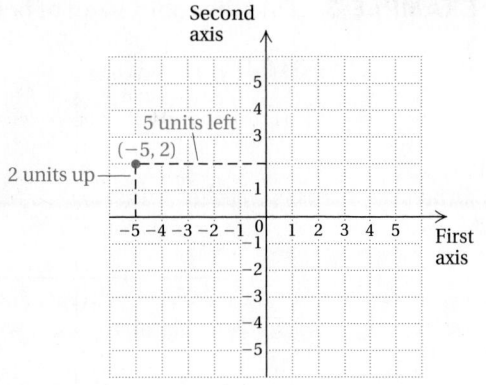

Plot these points on the graph below.

1. $(4, 5)$ **2.** $(5, 4)$

3. $(-2, 5)$ **4.** $(-3, -4)$

5. $(5, -3)$ **6.** $(-2, -1)$

7. $(0, -3)$ **8.** $(2, 0)$

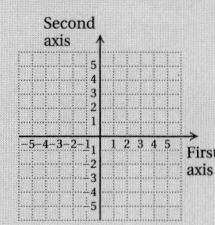

------------------------------ *Caution!* ------------------------------

The *first* coordinate of an ordered pair is always graphed in a *horizontal* direction and the *second* coordinate is always graphed in a *vertical* direction.

Do Exercises 1–8.

The figure below shows some points and their coordinates. In region I (the *first quadrant*), both coordinates of any point are positive. In region II (the *second quadrant*), the first coordinate is negative and the second positive. In region III (the *third quadrant*), both coordinates are negative. In region IV (the *fourth quadrant*), the first coordinate is positive and the second is negative.

EXAMPLE 2 In which quadrant, if any, are the points $(-4, 5)$, $(5, -5)$, $(2, 4)$, $(-2, -5)$, and $(-5, 0)$ located?

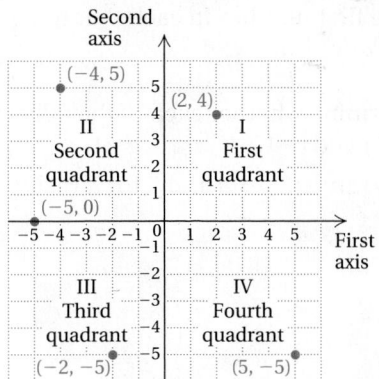

9. What can you say about the coordinates of a point in the third quadrant?

10. What can you say about the coordinates of a point in the fourth quadrant?

In which quadrant, if any, is each point located?

11. $(5, 3)$ **12.** $(-6, -4)$

13. $(10, -14)$ **14.** $(-13, 9)$

15. $(0, -3)$ **16.** $\left(-\frac{1}{2}, \frac{1}{4}\right)$

The point $(-4, 5)$ is in the second quadrant. The point $(5, -5)$ is in the fourth quadrant. The point $(2, 4)$ is in the first quadrant. The point $(-2, -5)$ is in the third quadrant. The point $(-5, 0)$ is on an axis and is *not in any quadrant*.

Do Exercises 9–16.

b Finding Coordinates

To find the coordinates of a point, we see how far to the right or left of the origin it is located and how far up or down from the origin.

Answers

1–8.

Second axis

(−2, 5) (4, 5)

(5, 4)

(2, 0)

(−2, −1) First axis

(0, −3)

(5, −3)

(−3, −4)

9. Both are negative numbers.   **10.** First, positive; second, negative   **11.** I   **12.** III
13. IV   **14.** II   **15.** On an axis, not in any quadrant   **16.** II

find coordinate

EXAMPLE 3 Find the coordinates of points *A, B, C, D, E, F,* and *G.*

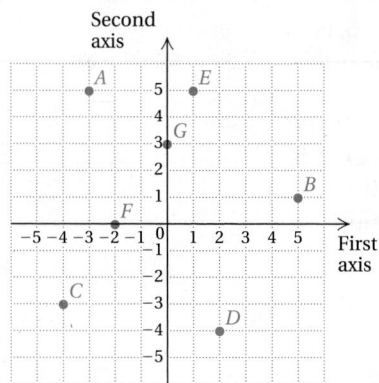

Point *A* is 3 units to the left (horizontal direction) and 5 units up (vertical direction). Its coordinates are $(-3, 5)$. Point *D* is 2 units to the right and 4 units down. Its coordinates are $(2, -4)$. The coordinates of the other points are as follows:

B: $(5, 1)$; C: $(-4, -3)$;

E: $(1, 5)$; F: $(-2, 0)$; G: $(0, 3)$.

Do Exercise 17.

17. Find the coordinates of points *A, B, C, D, E, F,* and *G* on the graph below.

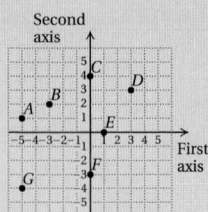

(c) Solutions of Equations

Now we begin to learn how graphs can be used to represent solutions of equations. When an equation contains two variables, the solutions of the equation are *ordered pairs* in which each number in the pair corresponds to a letter in the equation. Unless stated otherwise, to determine whether a pair is a solution, we use the first number in each pair to replace the variable that occurs first *alphabetically.*

EXAMPLE 4 Determine whether each of the following pairs is a solution of $4q - 3p = 22$: $(2, 7)$ and $(-1, 6)$.

For $(2, 7)$, we substitute 2 for *p* and 7 for *q* (using alphabetical order of variables):

$$
\begin{array}{c|c}
4q - 3p = 22 & \\
\hline
4 \cdot 7 - 3 \cdot 2 \ ? \ 22 & \\
28 - 6 & \\
22 & \text{TRUE}
\end{array}
$$

handwritten:
$4 \cdot 7 - 3 \cdot 2 \overset{?}{=} 22 \qquad 28$
$28 - 6 \overset{?}{=} 22 \qquad -6$
Yes, true. $\qquad 22$

Thus, $(2, 7)$ is a solution of the equation.

For $(-1, 6)$, we substitute -1 for *p* and 6 for *q*:

$$
\begin{array}{c|c}
4q - 3p = 22 & \\
\hline
4 \cdot 6 - 3 \cdot (-1) \ ? \ 22 & \\
24 + 3 & \\
27 & \text{FALSE}
\end{array}
$$

handwritten:
$4 \cdot 6 - 3 \cdot -1 \overset{?}{=} 22$
$24 - -3 \overset{?}{=} 22$
No, $24 + 3 \neq 22$
false.

Thus, $(-1, 6)$ is *not* a solution of the equation.

Do Exercises 18 and 19.

18. Determine whether $(2, -4)$ is a solution of $4q - 3p = 22$.

19. Determine whether $(2, -4)$ is a solution of $7a + 5b = -6$.

Answers

17. *A:* $(-5, 1)$; *B:* $(-3, 2)$; *C:* $(0, 4)$; *D:* $(3, 3)$; *E:* $(1, 0)$; *F:* $(0, -3)$; *G:* $(-5, -4)$
18. No   **19.** Yes

EXAMPLE 5 Show that the pairs $(3, 7)$, $(0, 1)$, and $(-3, -5)$ are solutions of $y = 2x + 1$. Then graph the three points and use the graph to determine another pair that is a solution.

To show that a pair is a solution, we substitute, replacing x with the first coordinate and y with the second coordinate of each pair:

$$\begin{array}{c|c} y = 2x + 1 \\ \hline 7 \ ? \ 2 \cdot 3 + 1 \\ \quad\ \, 6 + 1 \\ \quad\ \, 7 \qquad \text{TRUE} \end{array} \qquad \begin{array}{c|c} y = 2x + 1 \\ \hline 1 \ ? \ 2 \cdot 0 + 1 \\ \quad\ \, 0 + 1 \\ \quad\ \, 1 \qquad \text{TRUE} \end{array}$$

$$\begin{array}{c|c} y = 2x + 1 \\ \hline -5 \ ? \ 2(-3) + 1 \\ \quad\ \, -6 + 1 \\ \quad\ \, -5 \qquad \text{TRUE} \end{array}$$

In each of the three cases, the substitution results in a true equation. Thus the pairs are all solutions.

We plot the points as shown at right. The order of the points follows the alphabetical order of the variables. That is, x comes before y, so x-values are first coordinates and y-values are second coordinates. Similarly, we also label the horizontal axis as the x-axis and the vertical axis as the y-axis.

Note that the three points appear to "line up." That is, they appear to be on a straight line. Will other points that line up with these points also represent solutions of $y = 2x + 1$? To find out, we use a straightedge and sketch a line passing through $(3, 7)$, $(0, 1)$, and $(-3, -5)$.

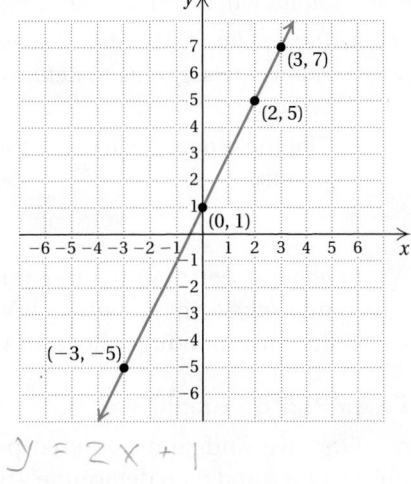

The line appears to pass through $(2, 5)$ as well. Let's see if this pair is a solution of $y = 2x + 1$:

$$\begin{array}{c|c} y = 2x + 1 \\ \hline 5 \ ? \ 2 \cdot 2 + 1 \\ \quad\ \, 4 + 1 \\ \quad\ \, 5 \qquad \text{TRUE} \end{array}$$

Thus, $(2, 5)$ is a solution.

Do Exercise 20.

Example 5 leads us to suspect that any point on the line that passes through $(3, 7)$, $(0, 1)$, and $(-3, -5)$ represents a solution of $y = 2x + 1$. In fact, every solution of $y = 2x + 1$ is represented by a point on that line and every point on that line represents a solution. The line is the *graph* of the equation.

STUDY TIPS

LEARNING RESOURCES ON CAMPUS

Your college or university probably has resources to support your learning.

1. There may be a learning lab or a tutoring center for drop-in tutoring.

2. There may be group tutoring sessions for this specific course.

3. The math department may have a bulletin board or a network for locating private tutors.

4. Visit your instructor during office hours if you need additional help. Also, many instructors welcome e-mails from students with questions.

20. Use the graph in Example 5 to find at least two more points that are solutions of $y = 2x + 1$.

Answer

20. $(-2, -3)$, $(1, 3)$; answers may vary

[Handwritten at top: $y = mx + b$ $Ax + By = C$ where $m, b, A, B + C$ are constants are Linear (as long as both aren't zero)]

Calculator Corner

Finding Solutions of Equations   A table of values representing ordered pairs that are solutions of an equation can be displayed on a graphing calculator. To do this for the equation in Example 6, $y = 2x$, we first press ⟨Y=⟩ to access the equation-editor screen. Then we clear any equations that are present. Next, we enter the equation by positioning the cursor beside "$Y_1 =$" and press ② ⟨X,T,Θ,n⟩. Now we press ⟨2ND⟩ ⟨TBLSET⟩ to display the table set-up screen. We then set both INDPNT and DEPEND to AUTO by positioning the cursor over AUTO and pressing ⟨ENTER⟩.

We will display a table of values that starts with $x = -2$ (TBLSTART) and adds 1 (ΔTBL) to the preceding x-value. We press ⟨(-)⟩ ② ⟨▽⟩ ① or ⟨(-)⟩ ② ⟨ENTER⟩ ① to do this. To display the table, we press ⟨2ND⟩ ⟨TABLE⟩.

X	Y₁
-2	-4
-1	-2
0	0
1	2
2	4
3	6
4	8
X = -2	

You can use the ⟨△⟩ and ⟨▽⟩ keys to scroll up and down through the table to see other solutions of the equation.

Exercise:

1. Create a table of ordered pairs that are solutions of the equations in Examples 7 and 8.

[Handwritten notes in left margin:]

$ex, 6.$

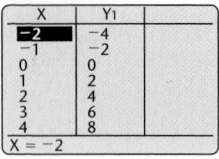

[Handwritten table:]

x	y	x,y
0	0	
2	4	
4	8	
3	6	
-3	-6	

[Handwritten: $y = 0$ $y = 4$ $y = 8$]

GRAPH OF AN EQUATION

The **graph** of an equation is a drawing that represents all of its solutions.

d Graphs of Linear Equations

Equations like $y = 2x + 1$ and $4q - 3p = 22$ are said to be **linear** because the graph of each equation is a straight line. In general, any equation equivalent to one of the form $y = mx + b$ or $Ax + By = C$, where $m, b, A, B,$ and C are constants (not variables) and A and B are not both 0, is linear.

> To graph a linear equation:
>
> 1. Select a value for one variable and calculate the corresponding value of the other variable. Form an ordered pair using alphabetical order as indicated by the variables.
>
> 2. Repeat step (1) to obtain at least two other ordered pairs. Two points are essential to determine a straight line. A third point serves as a check.
>
> 3. Plot the ordered pairs and draw a straight line passing through the points.

In general, calculating three (or more) ordered pairs is not difficult for equations of the form $y = mx + b$. We simply substitute values for x and calculate the corresponding values for y.

EXAMPLE 6   Graph: $y = 2x$.

First, we find some ordered pairs that are solutions. We choose *any* number for x and then determine y by substitution. Since $y = 2x$, we find y by doubling x. Suppose that we choose 3 for x. Then

$$y = 2x = 2 \cdot 3 = 6.$$

We get a solution: the ordered pair $(3, 6)$.
Suppose that we choose 0 for x. Then

$$y = 2x = 2 \cdot 0 = 0.$$

We get another solution: the ordered pair $(0, 0)$.
For a third point, we make a negative choice for x. If x is -3, we have

$$y = 2x = 2 \cdot (-3) = -6.$$

This gives us the ordered pair $(-3, -6)$.
We now have enough points to plot the line, but if we wish, we can compute more. If a number takes us off the graph paper, we either do not use it or we use larger paper or rescale the axes. Continuing in this manner, we create a table like the one shown on the following page.

Now we plot these points. Then we draw the line, or graph, with a straightedge and label it $y = 2x$.

x	y y = 2x	(x, y)
3	6	(3, 6)
1	2	(1, 2)
0	0	(0, 0)
-2	-4	(-2, -4)
-3	-6	(-3, -6)

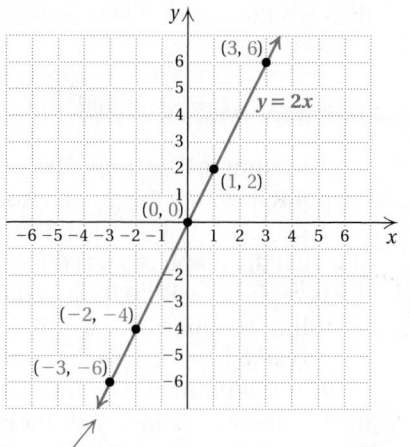

(1) Choose x.
(2) Compute y.
(3) Form the pair (x, y).
(4) Plot the points.

Caution!

Keep in mind that you can choose *any* number for x and then compute y. Our choice of certain numbers in the examples does not dictate those that you must choose.

> Do Exercises 21 and 22.

EXAMPLE 7 Graph: $y = -3x + 1$.

We select a value for x, compute y, and form an ordered pair. Then we repeat the process for other choices of x.

If $x = 2$, then $y = -3 \cdot 2 + 1 = -5$, and $(2, -5)$ is a solution.
If $x = 0$, then $y = -3 \cdot 0 + 1 = 1$, and $(0, 1)$ is a solution.
If $x = -1$, then $y = -3 \cdot (-1) + 1 = 4$, and $(-1, 4)$ is a solution.

Results are listed in the table below. The points corresponding to each pair are then plotted.

x	y y = -3x + 1	(x, y)
2	-5	(2, -5)
0	1	(0, 1)
-1	4	(-1, 4)

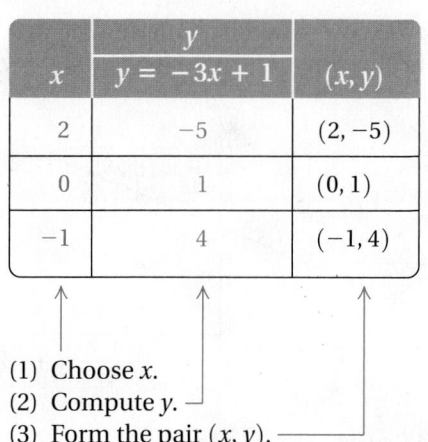

(1) Choose x.
(2) Compute y.
(3) Form the pair (x, y).
(4) Plot the points.

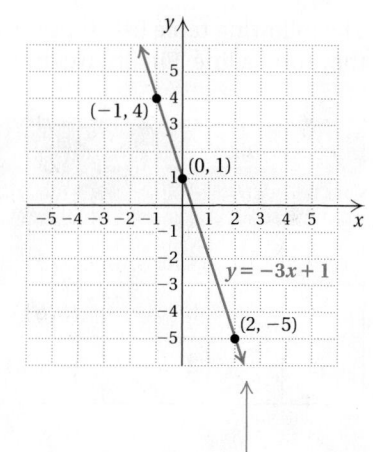

Complete each table and graph.

21. $y = -2x$

x	y	(x, y)
-3	6	-3, 6
-1	2	-1, 2
0	0	0, 0
1	-2	1, -2
3	-6	3, -6

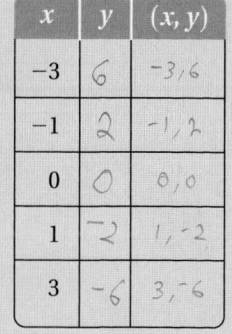
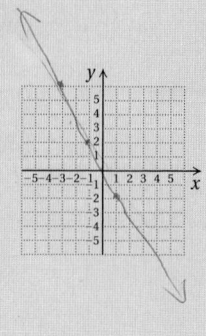

22. $y = \frac{1}{2}x$

x	y	(x, y)
4	2	
2	1	
0	0	
-2	-1	
-4	-2	
-1	-.5	

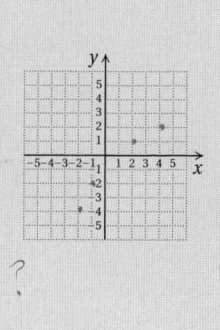

Answers

21.

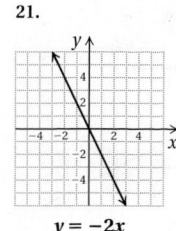

$y = -2x$

22.

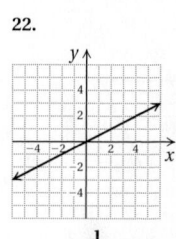

$y = \frac{1}{2}x$

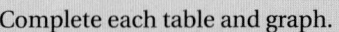
$b = y$ intercept

Complete each table and graph.

23. $y = 2x + 3$

x,y
0 | 3
2 | 7
-2 | -1
-3 | -3
-1 | 3

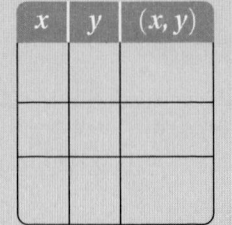

x	y	(x, y)

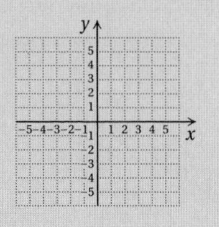

24. $y = -\dfrac{1}{2}x - 3$

x | y
0 | -3
4 | -5
-4 | -1
6 | 0

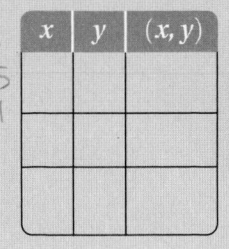

x	y	(x, y)

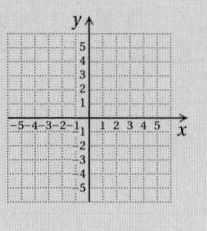

$y = \dfrac{2}{5}x + 4$

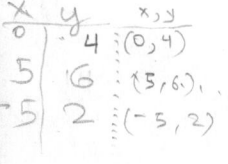

x | y | x,y
0 | 4 | (0, 4)
5 | 6 | (5, 6),
-5 | 2 | (-5, 2)

simplify fraction than add b

Note that all three points line up. If they did not, we would know that we had made a mistake. When only two points are plotted, a mistake is harder to detect. We use a ruler or other straightedge to draw a line through the points. Every point on the line represents a solution of $y = -3x + 1$.

> **Do Exercises 23 and 24.**

In Example 6, we saw that $(0, 0)$ is a solution of $y = 2x$. It is also the point at which the graph crosses the y-axis. Similarly, in Example 7, we saw that $(0, 1)$ is a solution of $y = -3x + 1$. It is also the point at which the graph crosses the y-axis. A generalization can be made: If x is replaced with 0 in the equation $y = mx + b$, then the corresponding y-value is $m \cdot 0 + b$, or b. Thus any equation of the form $y = mx + b$ has a graph that passes through the point $(0, b)$. Since $(0, b)$ is the point at which the graph crosses the y-axis, it is called the **y-intercept**. Sometimes, for convenience, we simply refer to b as the y-intercept.

---

y-INTERCEPT

The graph of the equation
$y = mx + b$ passes through the
y-intercept $(0, b)$.

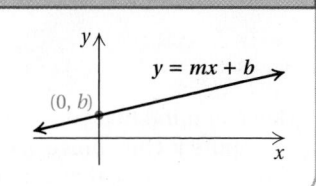

EXAMPLE 8   Graph $y = \frac{2}{5}x + 4$ and identify the y-intercept.

We select a value for x, compute y, and form an ordered pair. Then we repeat the process for other choices of x. In this case, using multiples of 5 avoids fractions. We try to avoid graphing ordered pairs with fractions because they are difficult to graph accurately.

$$\text{If } x = 0, \quad \text{then } y = \frac{2}{5} \cdot 0 + 4 = 4, \qquad \text{and } (0, 4) \text{ is a solution.}$$

$$\text{If } x = 5, \quad \text{then } y = \frac{2}{5} \cdot 5 + 4 = 6, \qquad \text{and } (5, 6) \text{ is a solution.}$$

$$\text{If } x = -5, \quad \text{then } y = \frac{2}{5} \cdot (-5) + 4 = 2, \quad \text{and } (-5, 2) \text{ is a solution.}$$

The following table lists these solutions. Next, we plot the points and see that they form a line. Finally, we draw and label the line.

x	y $y = \frac{2}{5}x + 4$	(x, y)
0	4	(0, 4)
5	6	(5, 6)
-5	2	(-5, 2)

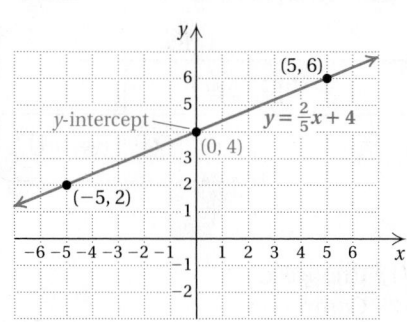

Answers

23.

24.

$y = 2x + 3$ $y = -\dfrac{1}{2}x - 3$

We see that $(0, 4)$ is a solution of $y = \frac{2}{5}x + 4$. It is the y-intercept. Because the equation is in the form $y = mx + b$, we can read the y-intercept directly from the equation as follows:

$$y = \frac{2}{5}x + 4 \qquad (0, 4) \text{ is the } y\text{-intercept.}$$

Do Exercises 25 and 26.

Calculating ordered pairs is generally easiest when y is isolated on one side of the equation, as in $y = mx + b$. To graph an equation in which y is not isolated, we can use the addition and multiplication principles to solve for y. (See Sections 8.3 and 8.4.)

EXAMPLE 9 Graph $3y + 5x = 0$ and identify the y-intercept.

To find an equivalent equation in the form $y = mx + b$, we solve for y:

$$3y + 5x = 0$$
$$3y + 5x - 5x = 0 - 5x \qquad \text{Subtracting } 5x$$
$$3y = -5x \qquad \text{Collecting like terms}$$
$$\frac{3y}{3} = \frac{-5x}{3} \qquad \text{Dividing by 3}$$
$$y = -\frac{5}{3}x.$$

Because all the equations above are equivalent, we can use $y = -\frac{5}{3}x$ to draw the graph of $3y + 5x = 0$. To graph $y = -\frac{5}{3}x$, we select x-values and compute y-values. In this case, if we select multiples of 3, we can avoid fractions.

$$\text{If } x = 0, \quad \text{then } y = -\frac{5}{3} \cdot 0 = 0.$$

$$\text{If } x = 3, \quad \text{then } y = -\frac{5}{3} \cdot 3 = -5.$$

$$\text{If } x = -3, \quad \text{then } y = -\frac{5}{3} \cdot (-3) = 5.$$

We list these solutions in a table. Next, we plot the points and see that they form a line. Finally, we draw and label the line. The y-intercept is $(0, 0)$.

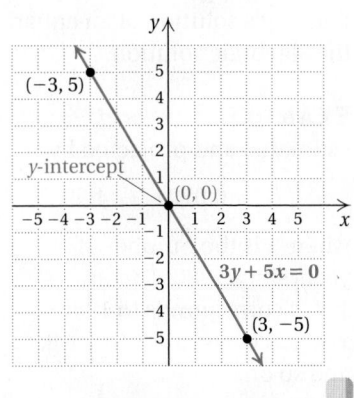

x	y	
0	0	← y-intercept
3	−5	
−3	5	

Do Exercises 27 and 28.

Graph each equation and identify the y-intercept.

25. $y = \frac{3}{5}x + 2$

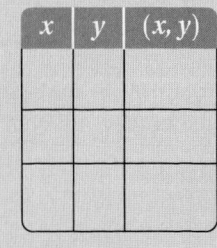 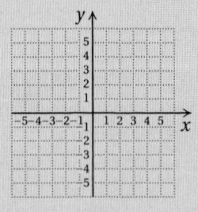

26. $y = -\frac{3}{5}x - 1$

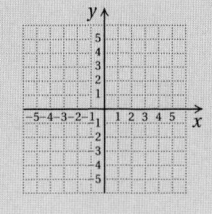

Graph each equation and identify the y-intercept.

27. $5y + 4x = 0$

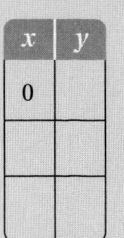 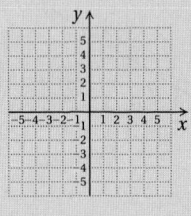

28. $4y = 3x$

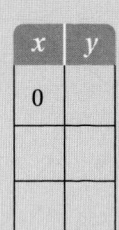 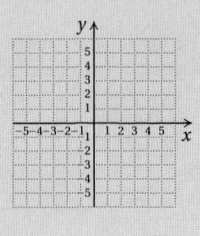

Answers

Answers to Margin Exercises 25–28 are on p. 664.

EXAMPLE 10 Graph $4y + 3x = -8$ and identify the y-intercept.

To find an equivalent equation in the form $y = mx + b$, we solve for y:

$$4y + 3x = -8$$

$$4y + 3x - 3x = -8 - 3x \qquad \text{Subtracting } 3x$$

$$4y = -3x - 8 \qquad \text{Simplifying}$$

$$\frac{1}{4} \cdot 4y = \frac{1}{4} \cdot (-3x - 8) \qquad \text{Multiplying by } \tfrac{1}{4} \text{ or dividing by 4}$$

$$y = \frac{1}{4} \cdot (-3x) - \frac{1}{4} \cdot 8 \qquad \text{Using the distributive law}$$

$$y = -\frac{3}{4}x - 2. \qquad \text{Simplifying}$$

Thus, $4y + 3x = -8$ is equivalent to $y = -\frac{3}{4}x - 2$. The y-intercept is $(0, -2)$. We find two other pairs using multiples of 4 for x to avoid fractions. We then complete and label the graph as shown.

x	y
0	−2	← y-intercept
4	−5
−4	1

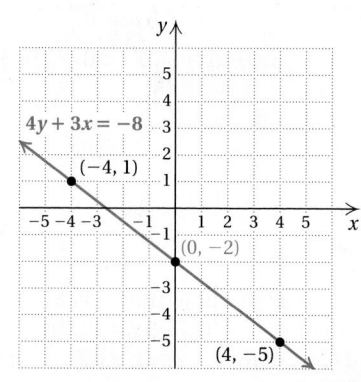

Graph each equation and identify the y-intercept.

29. $5y - 3x = -10$

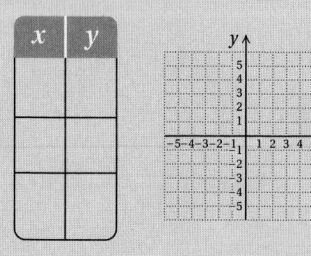

30. $5y + 3x = 20$

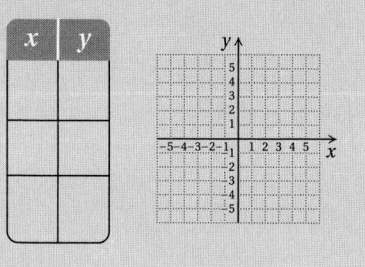

Do Exercises 29 and 30.

(e) Applications of Linear Equations

Mathematical concepts become more understandable through visualization. Throughout this text, you will occasionally see the heading ※ Algebraic–Graphical Connection, as in Example 11, which follows. In this feature, the algebraic approach is enhanced and expanded with a graphical connection. Relating a solution of an equation to a graph can often give added meaning to the algebraic solution.

EXAMPLE 11 *World Population.* The world population, in billions, is estimated and projected by

$$y = 0.072x + 4.593,$$

where x is the number of years since 1980. That is, $x = 0$ corresponds to 1980, $x = 12$ corresponds to 1992, and so on.

Source: U.S. Census Bureau

Answers

25.

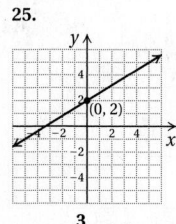

$y = \frac{3}{5}x + 2$

26.

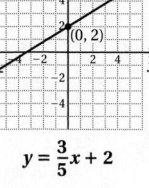

$y = -\frac{3}{5}x - 1$

27.

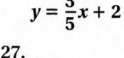

$5y + 4x = 0$

28.

$4y = 3x$

29.

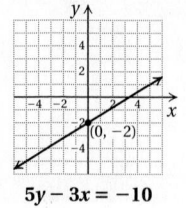

$5y - 3x = -10$

30.

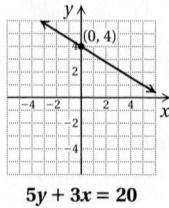

$5y + 3x = 20$

a) Determine the world population in 1980, in 2005, and in 2030.

b) Graph the equation and then use the graph to estimate the world population in 2015.

c) In what year would we estimate the world population to be 7.761 billion?

a) The years 1980, 2005, and 2030 correspond to $x = 0$, $x = 25$, and $x = 50$, respectively. We substitute 0, 25, and 50 for x and then calculate y:

$y = 0.072(0) + 4.593 = 0 + 4.593 = 4.593;$

$y = 0.072(25) + 4.593 = 1.8 + 4.593 = 6.393;$

$y = 0.072(50) + 4.593 = 3.6 + 4.593 = 8.193.$

The world population in 1980, in 2005, and in 2030 is estimated to be 4.593 billion, 6.393 billion, and 8.193 billion, respectively.

STUDY TIPS

FORMING A STUDY GROUP

Consider forming a study group with some of your fellow students. Exchange e-mail addresses, telephone numbers, and schedules so that you can coordinate study time for homework and tests.

※ Algebraic-Graphical Connection

b) We have three ordered pairs from part (a). We plot these points and see that they line up. Thus our calculations are probably correct. Since we are considering only the year 2015 and the number of years since 1980 ($x \geq 0$) and since the population, in billions, for those years will be positive ($y > 0$), we need only the first quadrant for the graph. We use the three points we have plotted to draw a straight line. (See Figure 1.)

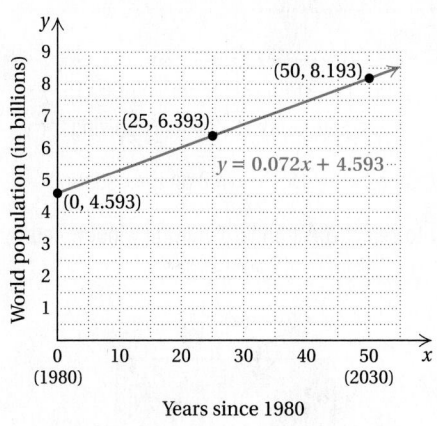

FIGURE 1

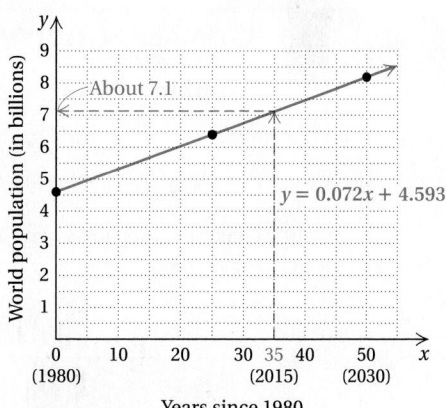

FIGURE 2

     To use the graph to estimate world population in 2015, we first note in Figure 2 that this year corresponds to $x = 35$. We need to determine which y-value is paired with $x = 35$. We locate the point on the graph by moving up vertically from $x = 35$, and then find the value on the y-axis that corresponds to that point. It appears that the world population in 2015 will be about 7.1 billion.

     To find a more accurate value, we can simply substitute into the equation:

$y = 0.072(35) + 4.593 = 7.113.$

The world population in 2015 is projected to be 7.113 billion.

※

31. Milk Consumption. Milk consumption per capita (per person) in the United States is given by

$$M = -0.271t + 27.952,$$

where M is the consumption, in gallons, t years from 1980.

Source: U.S. Department of Agriculture

a) Find the per capita consumption of milk in 1980, in 1995, and in 2015.

b) Graph the equation and use the graph to estimate milk consumption in 2010.

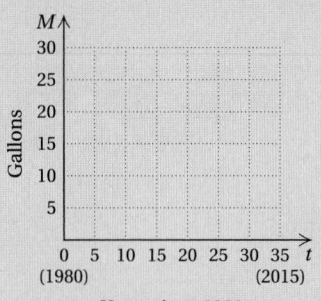

Years since 1980

c) In which year would the per capita consumption of milk be 19.28 gal?

c) We substitute 7.761 for y and solve for x:

$$y = 0.072x + 4.593$$
$$7.761 = 0.072x + 4.593$$
$$3.168 = 0.072x$$
$$44 = x.$$

In 44 yr after 1980, or in 2024, the world population will be approximately 7.761 billion.

Do Exercise 31.

Many equations in two variables have graphs that are not straight lines. Three such nonlinear graphs are shown below. We will cover some such graphs in the optional Calculator Corners throughout the text and in Chapter 15.

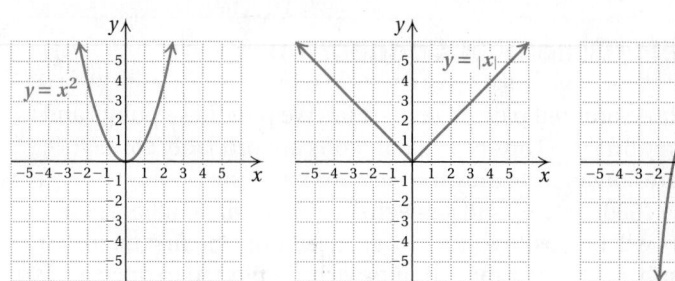

Calculator Corner

Graphing Equations Equations must be solved for y before they can be graphed on the TI-84 Plus. Consider the equation $3x + 2y = 6$. Solving for y, we get $y = \dfrac{6 - 3x}{2}$. We enter this equation as $y_1 = (6 - 3x)/2$ on the equation-editor screen. Then we press ⌈ZOOM⌉ ⌈6⌉ to select the standard viewing window and display the graph.

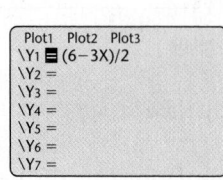

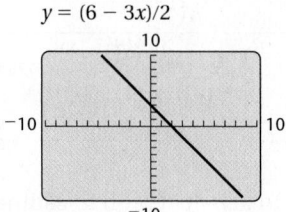

Exercises: Graph each equation in the standard viewing window $[-10, 10, -10, 10]$, with Xscl = 1 and Yscl = 1.

1. $y = 2x + 1$

2. $y = -3x + 1$

3. $y = -5x + 3$

4. $y = 4x - 5$

5. $4x - 5y = -10$

6. $5y + 5 = -3x$

7. $y = 2.085x + 5.08$

8. $y = -3.45x - 1.68$

Answer

31. (a) 27.952 gal; 23.887 gal; 18.467 gal;
(b) about 19.8 gal;

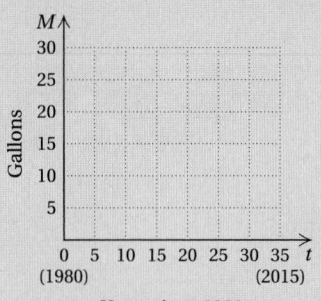

Years since 1980

(c) in 32 years, or in 2012

a

1. Plot these points.

$(2, 5)$ $(-1, 3)$ $(3, -2)$ $(-2, -4)$

$(0, 4)$ $(0, -5)$ $(5, 0)$ $(-5, 0)$

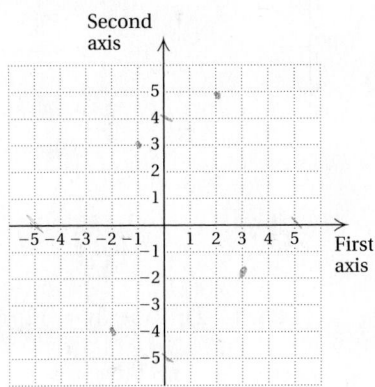

2. Plot these points.

$(4, 4)$ $(-2, 4)$ $(5, -3)$ $(-5, -5)$

$(0, 2)$ $(0, -4)$ $(3, 0)$ $(-4, 0)$

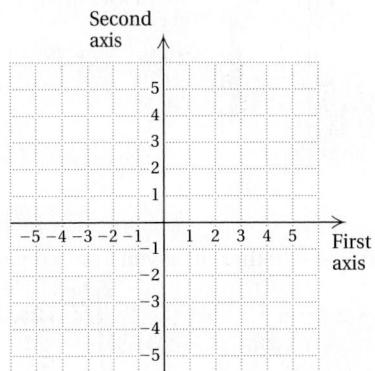

In which quadrant, if any, is each point located?

3. $(-5, 3)$

4. $(1, -12)$

5. $(100, -1)$

6. $(-2.5, 35.6)$

7. $(-6, -29)$

8. $(3.6, 105.9)$

9. $(3.8, 0)$

10. $(0, -492)$

11. $\left(-\dfrac{1}{3}, \dfrac{15}{7}\right)$

12. $\left(-\dfrac{2}{3}, -\dfrac{9}{8}\right)$

13. $\left(12\dfrac{7}{8}, -1\dfrac{1}{2}\right)$

14. $\left(23\dfrac{5}{8}, 81.74\right)$

In which quadrant(s) can the point described be located?

15. The first coordinate is negative and the second coordinate is positive.

16. The first and second coordinates are positive.

17. The first coordinate is positive.

18. The second coordinate is negative.

19. The first and second coordinates are equal.

20. The first coordinate is the additive inverse of the second coordinate.

b Find the coordinates of points *A, B, C, D,* and *E.*

21.

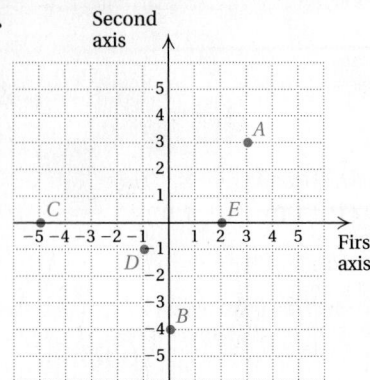

22.

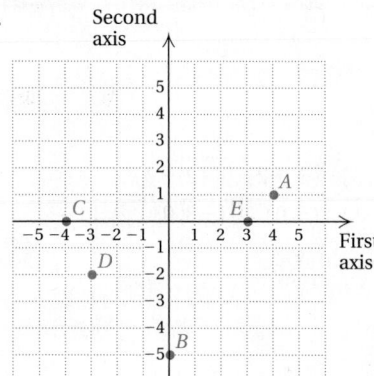

c Determine whether the given ordered pair is a solution of the equation.

23. $(2, 9)$; $y = 3x - 1$

24. $(1, 7)$; $y = 2x + 5$

25. $(4, 2)$; $2x + 3y = 12$

26. $(0, 5)$; $5x - 3y = 15$

27. $(3, -1)$; $3a - 4b = 13$

28. $(-5, 1)$; $2p - 3q = -13$

In Exercises 29–34, an equation and two ordered pairs are given. Show that each pair is a solution of the equation. Then use the graph of the equation to determine another solution. Answers may vary.

29. $y = x - 5$; $(4, -1)$ and $(1, -4)$

30. $y = x + 3$; $(-1, 2)$ and $(3, 6)$

31. $y = \frac{1}{2}x + 3$; $(4, 5)$ and $(-2, 2)$

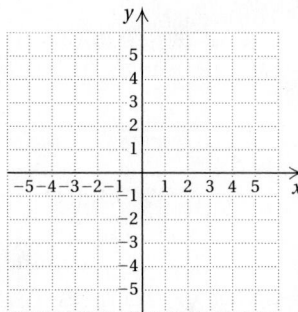

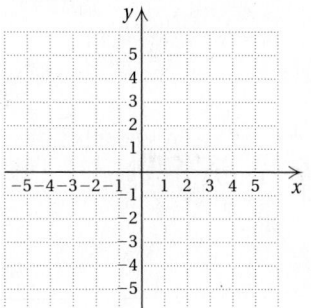

32. $3x + y = 7$; $(2, 1)$ and $(4, -5)$

33. $4x - 2y = 10$; $(0, -5)$ and $(4, 3)$

34. $6x - 3y = 3$; $(1, 1)$ and $(-1, -3)$

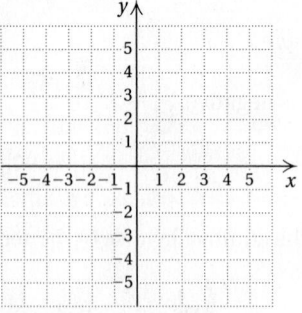

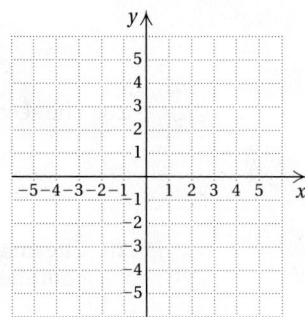

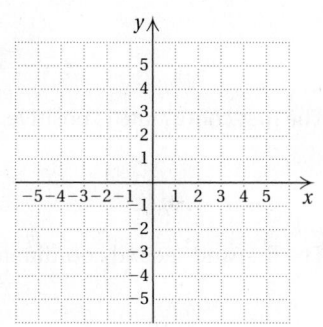

Copyright © 2012 Pearson Education, Inc.

Graph each equation and identify the *y*-intercept.

35. $y = x + 1$

x	y
−2	
−1	
0	
1	
2	
3	

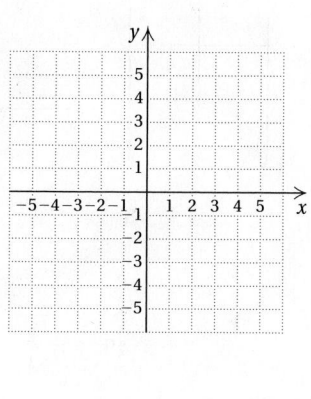

36. $y = x - 1$

x	y
−2	
−1	
0	
1	
2	
3	

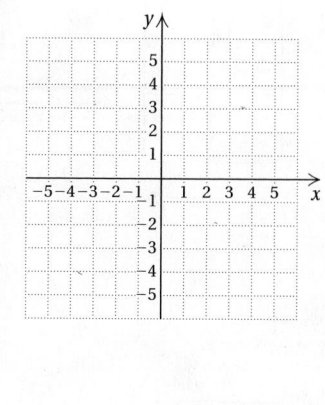

37. $y = x$

x	y
−2	
−1	
0	
1	
2	
3	

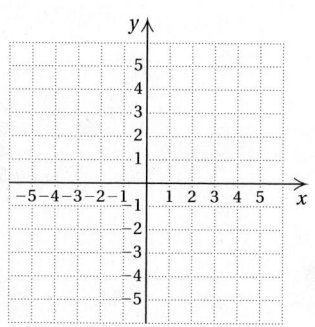

38. $y = -x$

x	y
−2	
−1	
0	
1	
2	
3	

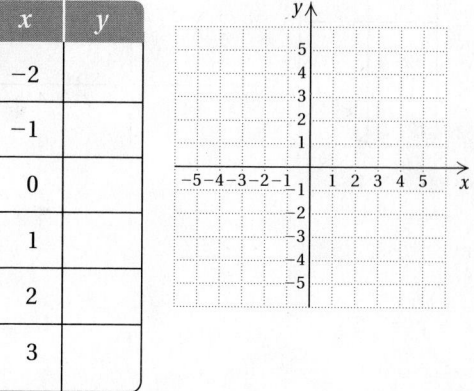

39. $y = \dfrac{1}{2}x$

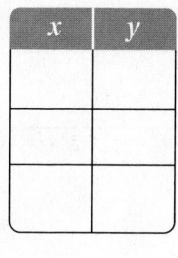

x	y
−2	
0	
4	

40. $y = \dfrac{1}{3}x$

x	y
−6	
0	
3	

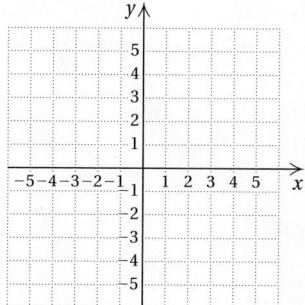

41. $y = x - 3$

x	y

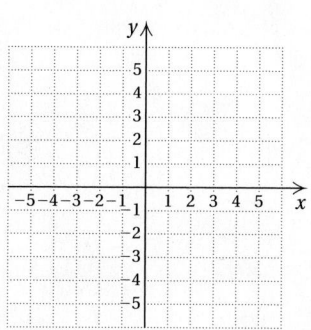

42. $y = x + 3$

x	y

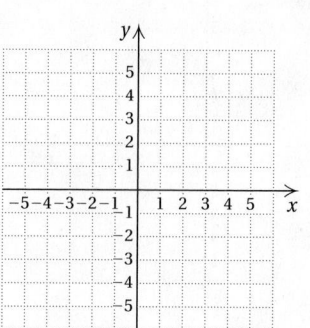

43. $y = 3x - 2$

x	y

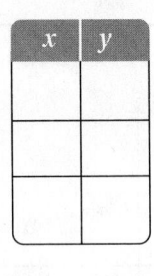

44. $y = 2x + 2$

x	y

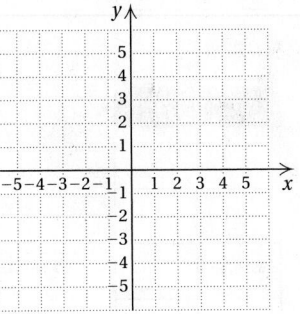

45. $y = \frac{1}{2}x + 1$

x	y

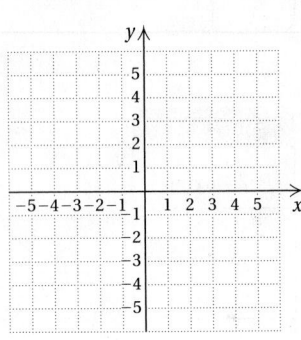

46. $y = \frac{1}{3}x - 4$

x	y

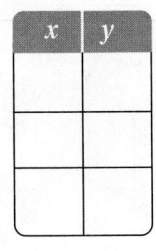

47. $x + y = -5$

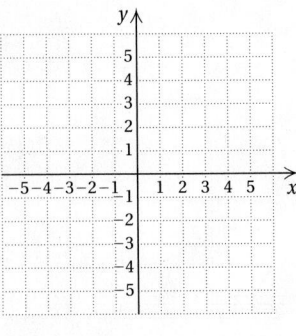

48. $x + y = 4$

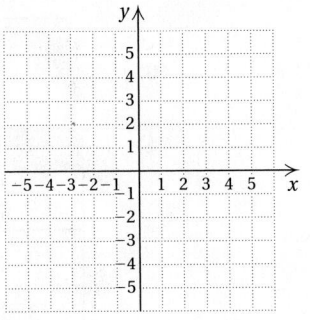

49. $y = \frac{5}{3}x - 2$

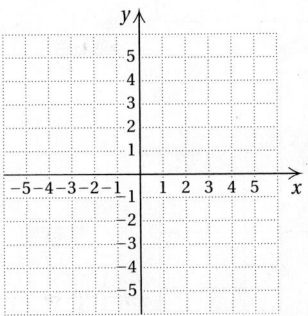

50. $y = \frac{5}{2}x + 3$

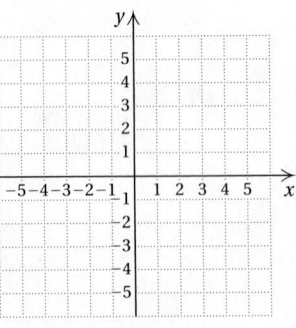

51. $x + 2y = 8$

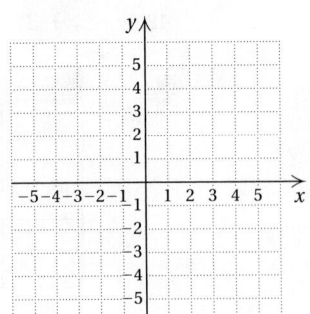

52. $x + 2y = -6$

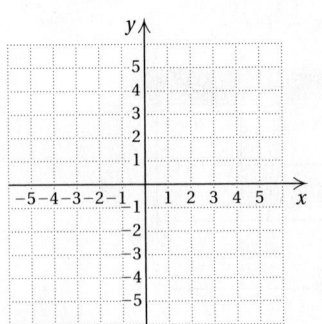

Copyright © 2012 Pearson Education, Inc.

53. $y = \dfrac{3}{2}x + 1$

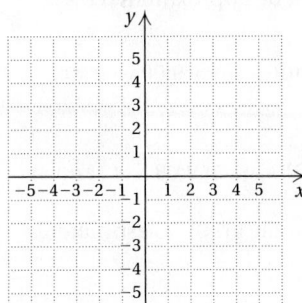

54. $y = -\dfrac{1}{2}x - 3$

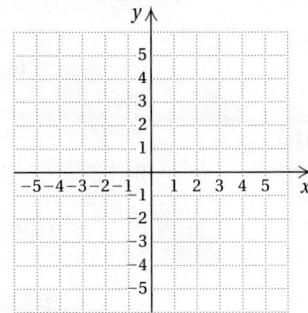

55. $8x - 2y = -10$

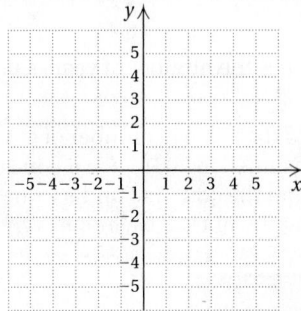

56. $6x - 3y = 9$

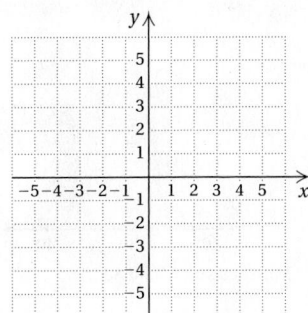

57. $8y + 2x = -4$

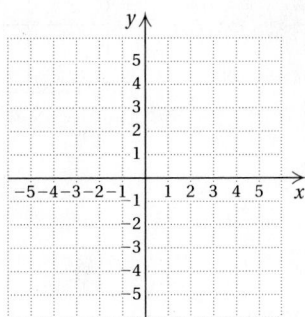

58. $6y + 2x = 8$

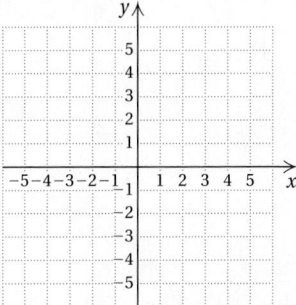

  Solve.

59. *Realtor Income.* The median annual income R, in dollars, for realtors has declined in recent years and can be approximated by

$$R = -1698t + 52{,}620,$$

where t is the number of years since 2002.

Source: National Association of Realtors

a) Find the median income in 2002, in 2007, and in 2010.

b) Graph the equation and then use the graph to estimate the median income in 2005.

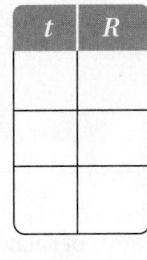

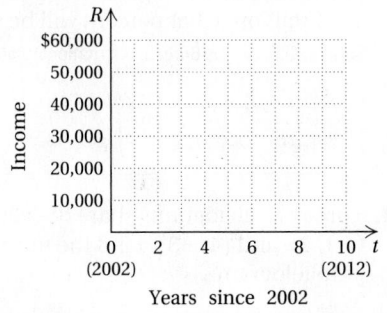

Years since 2002

c) At this rate of decline, in what year will the median income be $37,338?

60. *International Visitors.* The number of international visitors V, in millions, to the United States each year can be estimated and projected by

$$V = 2.18t + 46.46,$$

where t is the number of years since 2004.

Sources: TIA's Travel Forecast Model; U.S. Bureau of Labor Statistics, Office of Travel and Tourism Industries

a) Find the number of international visitors in 2004, in 2007, and in 2012.

b) Graph the equation and use the graph to estimate the number of visitors in 2009.

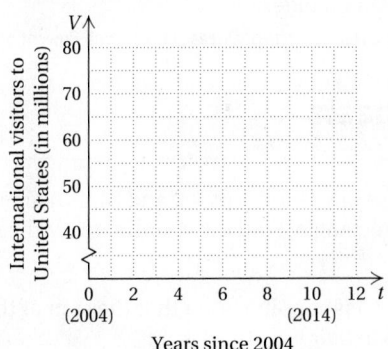

Years since 2004

c) In what year will the number of visitors be about 68.3 million?

61. *Bottled Water Consumption.* The average number of gallons W of bottled water consumed each year by the U.S. consumer can be approximated by

$$W = 1.8d + 16.44,$$

where d is the number of years since 2000.

Source: USDA/Economic Research Service

a) Find the average number of gallons of bottled water consumed in 2001 ($d = 1$), in 2010, and in 2015.

b) Graph the equation and use the graph to estimate what the bottled water consumption was in 2008.

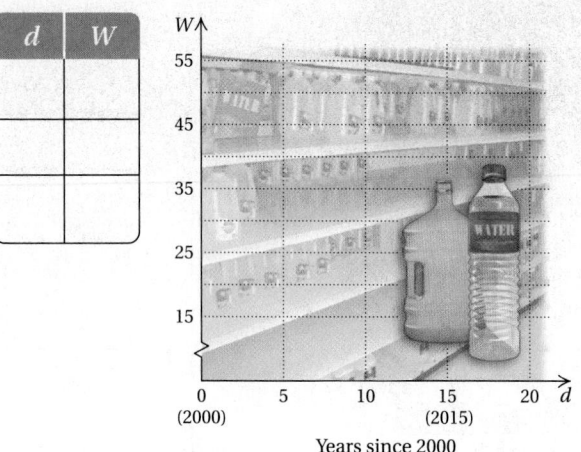

Years since 2000

c) In what year will bottled water consumption be about 36 gal?

62. *Record Temperature Drop.* On 22 January 1943, the temperature T, in degrees Fahrenheit, in Spearfish, South Dakota, could be approximated by

$$T = -2.15m + 54,$$

where m is the number of minutes since 9:00 that morning.

Source: *Information Please Almanac*

a) Find the temperature at 9:01 A.M., at 9:08 A.M., and at 9:20 A.M.

b) Graph the equation and use the graph to estimate the temperature at 9:15 A.M.

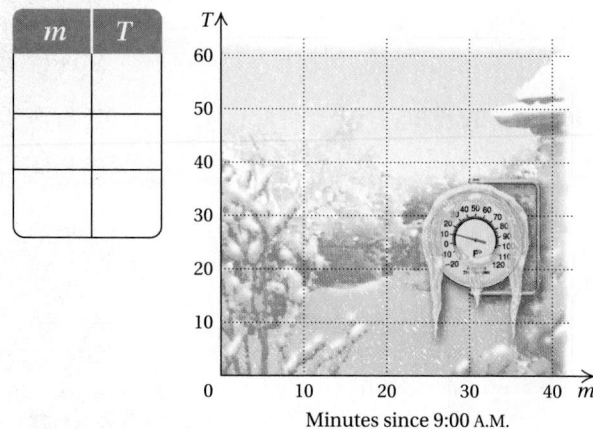

Minutes since 9:00 A.M.

c) The temperature stopped dropping when it reached $-4°F$. At what time did this occur?

Skill Maintenance

Find the absolute value. [7.2e]

63. $|-12|$

64. $|4.89|$

65. $|0|$

66. $\left|-\frac{4}{5}\right|$

67. $|-3.4|$

68. $|\sqrt{2}|$

69. $\left|\frac{2}{3}\right|$

70. $\left|-\frac{7}{8}\right|$

Solve. [8.5a]

71. *Older Patients.* In recent years, 24% of U.S. hospital patients are age 75 and older. For a hospital with 200 beds, approximately how many patients will be age 75 and older?

Source: U.S. Centers for Disease Control and Prevention

72. *Under 15 Years Old in India.* It is projected that by 2010, 363.5 million people in India will be under 15 years old. If the projected population in India in 2010 is 1184 million, what percent will be under 15 years old?

Source: U.S. Census Bureau, International Data Base

Synthesis

73. The points $(-1, 1)$, $(4, 1)$, and $(4, -5)$ are three vertices of a rectangle. Find the coordinates of the fourth vertex.

74. Three parallelograms share the vertices $(-2, -3)$, $(-1, 2)$, and $(4, -3)$. Find the fourth vertex of each parallelogram.

75. Graph eight points such that the sum of the coordinates in each pair is 6.

76. Graph eight points such that the first coordinate minus the second coordinate is 1.

77. Find the perimeter of a rectangle whose vertices have coordinates $(5, 3)$, $(5, -2)$, $(-3, -2)$, and $(-3, 3)$.

78. Find the area of a triangle whose vertices have coordinates $(0, 9)$, $(0, -4)$, and $(5, -4)$.

Copyright © 2012 Pearson Education, Inc.

9.2

More with Graphing and Intercepts

(a) Graphing Using Intercepts

In Section 9.1, we graphed linear equations of the form $Ax + By = C$ by first solving for y to find an equivalent equation in the form $y = mx + b$. We did so because it is then easier to calculate the y-value that corresponds to a given x-value. Another convenient way to graph $Ax + By = C$ is to use **intercepts**. Look at the graph of $-2x + y = 4$ shown below.

The y-intercept is $(0, 4)$. It occurs where the line crosses the y-axis and thus will always have 0 as the first coordinate. The x-intercept is $(-2, 0)$. It occurs where the line crosses the x-axis and thus will always have 0 as the second coordinate.

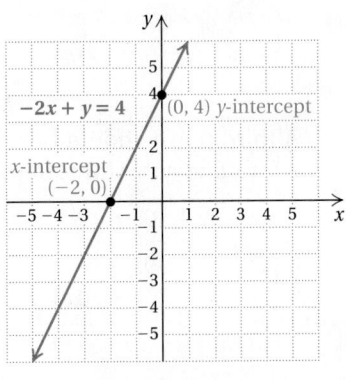

Do Margin Exercise 1.

We find intercepts as follows.

> ### INTERCEPTS
>
> The **y-intercept** is $(0, b)$. To find b, let $x = 0$ and solve the equation for y.
>
> The **x-intercept** is $(a, 0)$. To find a, let $y = 0$ and solve the equation for x.
>
>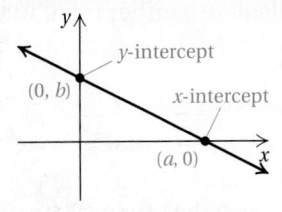

Now let's draw a graph using intercepts.

EXAMPLE 1 Consider $4x + 3y = 12$. Find the intercepts. Then graph the equation using the intercepts.

To find the y-intercept, we let $x = 0$. Then we solve for y:

$$4 \cdot 0 + 3y = 12$$
$$3y = 12$$
$$y = 4.$$

Thus, $(0, 4)$ is the y-intercept. Note that finding this intercept amounts to covering up the x-term and solving the rest of the equation for y.

To find the x-intercept, we let $y = 0$. Then we solve for x:

$$4x + 3 \cdot 0 = 12$$
$$4x = 12$$
$$x = 3.$$

OBJECTIVES

a Find the intercepts of a linear equation, and graph using intercepts.

b Graph equations equivalent to those of the type $x = a$ and $y = b$.

SKILL TO REVIEW

Objective 8.3a: Solve equations using both the addition principle and the multiplication principle.

Solve.

1. $5x - 7 = -10$

2. $-20 = \dfrac{7}{4}x + 8$

1. Look at the graph shown below.

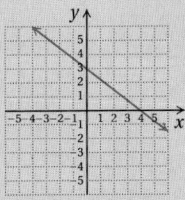

a) Find the coordinates of the y-intercept.

b) Find the coordinates of the x-intercept.

Answers

Skill to Review:

1. $-\dfrac{3}{5}$ **2.** -16

Margin Exercises:

1. (a) $(0, 3)$; (b) $(4, 0)$

For each equation, find the intercepts. Then graph the equation using the intercepts.

2. $2x + 3y = 6$

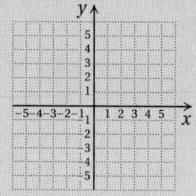

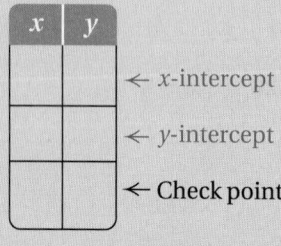

3. $3y - 4x = 12$

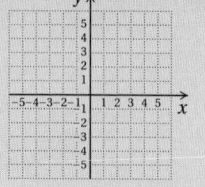

Thus, $(3, 0)$ is the *x*-intercept. Note that finding this intercept amounts to covering up the *y*-term and solving the rest of the equation for *x*.

We plot these points and draw the line, or graph.

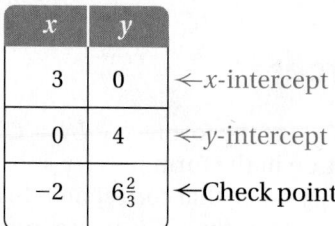

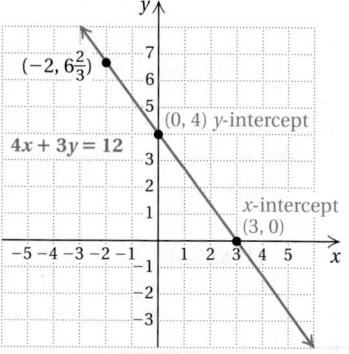

A third point should be used as a check. We substitute any convenient value for *x* and solve for *y*. In this case, we choose $x = -2$. Then

$$4(-2) + 3y = 12 \qquad \text{Substituting } -2 \text{ for } x$$
$$-8 + 3y = 12$$
$$3y = 20 \qquad \text{Adding 8 on both sides}$$
$$y = \tfrac{20}{3}, \text{ or } 6\tfrac{2}{3}. \qquad \text{Solving for } y$$

It appears that the point $\left(-2, 6\tfrac{2}{3}\right)$ is on the graph, though graphing fraction values can be inexact. The graph is probably correct.

> Do Exercises 2 and 3.

Graphs of equations of the type $y = mx$ pass through the origin. Thus the *x*-intercept and the *y*-intercept are the same, $(0, 0)$. In such cases, we must calculate another point in order to complete the graph. Another point would also need to be calculated if a check is desired.

EXAMPLE 2 Graph: $y = 3x$.

We know that $(0, 0)$ is both the *x*-intercept and the *y*-intercept. We calculate values at two other points and complete the graph, knowing that it passes through the origin $(0, 0)$.

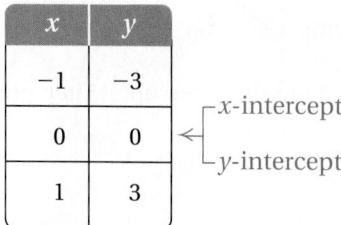

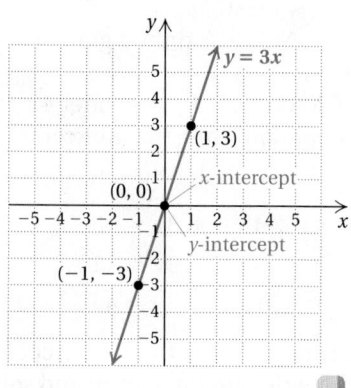

> Do Exercises 4 and 5 on the following page.

Answers

2.
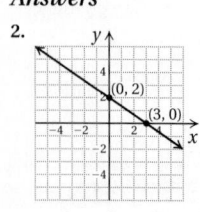
$2x + 3y = 6$

3.
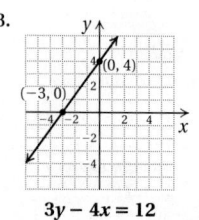
$3y - 4x = 12$

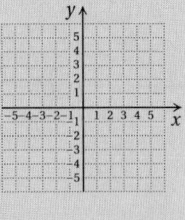

x	y
-1	
0	
1	

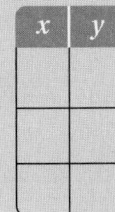

5. $y = -\dfrac{2}{3}x$

x	y

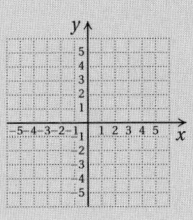

Calculator Corner

Viewing the Intercepts Knowing the intercepts of a linear equation helps us to determine a good viewing window for the graph of the equation. For example, when we graph the equation $y = -x + 15$ in the standard window, we see only a small portion of the graph in the upper righthand corner of the screen, as shown on the left below.

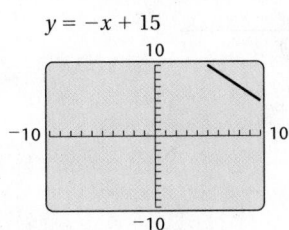

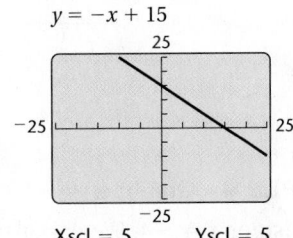

Using algebra, as we did in Example 1, we find that the intercepts of the graph of this equation are $(0, 15)$ and $(15, 0)$. This tells us that, if we are to see more of the graph than is shown on the left above, both Xmax and Ymax should be greater than 15. We can try different window settings until we find one that suits us. One good choice is $[-25, 25, -25, 25]$, with Xscl $= 5$ and Yscl $= 5$, shown on the right above.

Exercises: Find the intercepts of each equation algebraically. Then graph the equation on a graphing calculator, choosing window settings that allow the intercepts to be seen clearly. (Settings may vary.)

1. $y = -7.5x - 15$ **2.** $y - 2.15x = 43$

3. $6x - 5y = 150$ **4.** $y = 0.2x - 4$

5. $y = 1.5x - 15$ **6.** $5x - 4y = 2$

b Equations Whose Graphs Are Horizontal or Vertical Lines

EXAMPLE 3 Graph: $y = 3$.

The equation $y = 3$ tells us that y must be 3, but it doesn't give us any information about x. We can also think of this equation as $0 \cdot x + y = 3$. No matter what number we choose for x, we find that y is 3. We make up a table with all 3's in the y-column.

x	y
	3
	3
	3

Choose any number for x. →

y must be 3.

x	y
-2	3
0	3	← y-intercept
4	3

Answers

4.

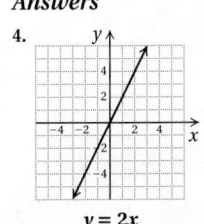

$y = 2x$

5.

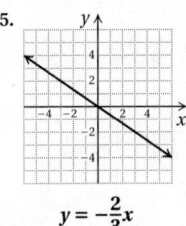

$y = -\dfrac{2}{3}x$

Graph.

6. $x = 5$

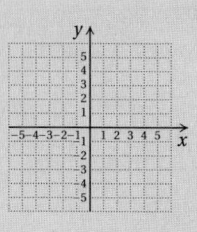

7. $y = -2$

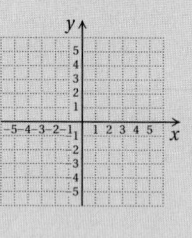

8. $x = -3$

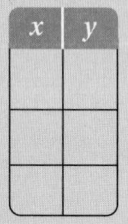 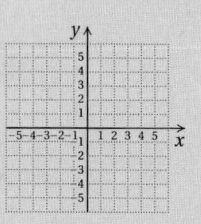

9. $x = 0$

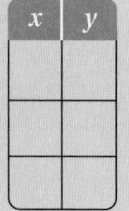 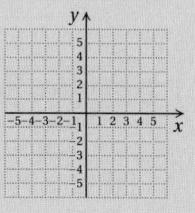

Answers

6.
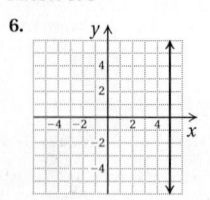

$x = 5$

7.
(image with graph)

$y = -2$

8.
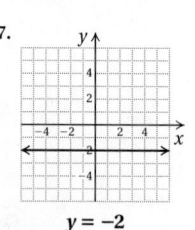

$x = -3$

9.
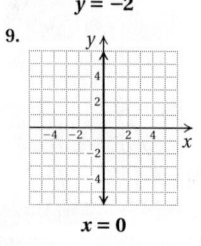

$x = 0$

When we plot the ordered pairs $(-2, 3)$, $(0, 3)$, and $(4, 3)$ and connect the points, we obtain a horizontal line. Any ordered pair $(x, 3)$ is a solution. So the line is parallel to the x-axis with y-intercept $(0, 3)$.

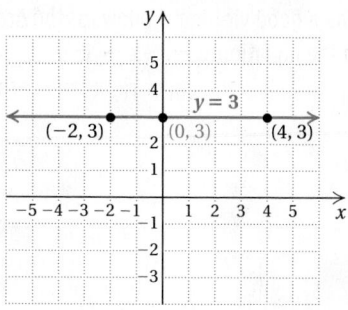

EXAMPLE 4 Graph: $x = -4$.

Consider $x = -4$. We can also think of this equation as $x + 0 \cdot y = -4$. We make up a table with all -4's in the x-column.

x	y
-4	
-4	
-4	
-4	

x must be -4.

x-intercept →

x	y
-4	-5
-4	1
-4	3
-4	0

← Choose any number for y.

When we plot the ordered pairs $(-4, -5)$, $(-4, 1)$, $(-4, 3)$, and $(-4, 0)$ and connect the points, we obtain a vertical line. Any ordered pair $(-4, y)$ is a solution. So the line is parallel to the y-axis with x-intercept $(-4, 0)$.

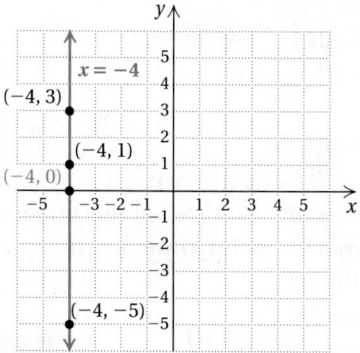

HORIZONTAL AND VERTICAL LINES

The graph of $y = b$ is a **horizontal line**. The y-intercept is $(0, b)$.

The graph of $x = a$ is a **vertical line**. The x-intercept is $(a, 0)$.

Do Exercises 6–9.

The following is a general procedure for graphing linear equations.

STUDY TIPS

ASKING QUESTIONS

Don't be afraid to ask questions in class. Most instructors welcome and encourage this. Other students often have the same questions you do.

GRAPHING LINEAR EQUATIONS

1. If the equation is of the type $x = a$ or $y = b$, the graph will be a line parallel to an axis; $x = a$ is vertical and $y = b$ is horizontal.

   Examples.

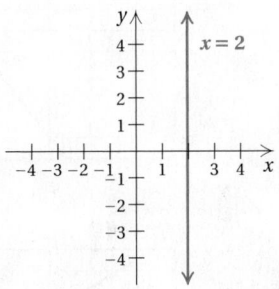 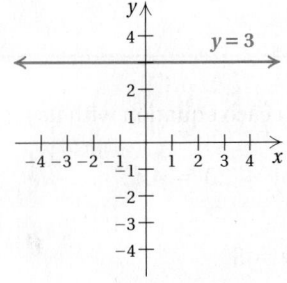

2. If the equation is of the type $y = mx$, both intercepts are the origin, $(0, 0)$. Plot $(0, 0)$ and two other points.

   Example.

3. If the equation is of the type $y = mx + b$, plot the y-intercept $(0, b)$ and two other points.

   Example.

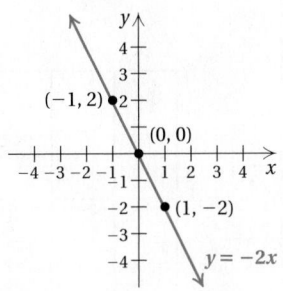 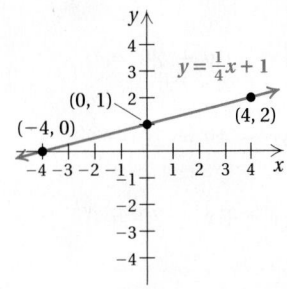

4. If the equation is of the type $Ax + By = C$, but not of the type $x = a$ or $y = b$, then either solve for y and proceed as with the equation $y = mx + b$, or graph using intercepts. If the intercepts are too close together, choose another point or points farther from the origin.

   Examples.

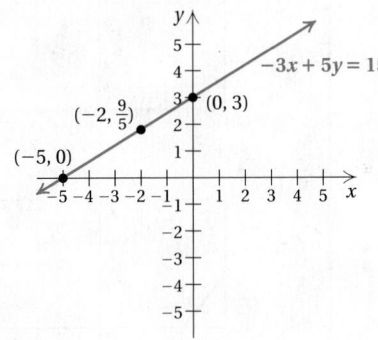 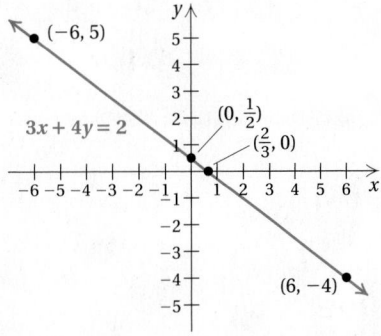

Visualizing
for Success

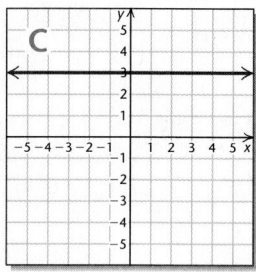

Match each equation with its graph.

1. $5y + 20 = 4x$

2. $y = 3$

3. $3x + 5y = 15$

4. $5y + 4x = 20$

5. $5y = 10 - 2x$

6. $4x + 5y + 20 = 0$

7. $5x - 4y = 20$

8. $4y + 5x + 20 = 0$

9. $5y - 4x = 20$

10. $x = -3$

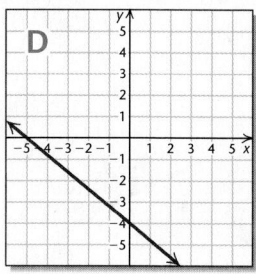

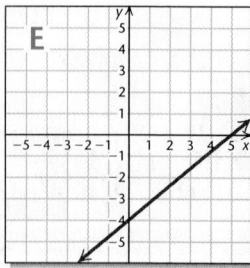

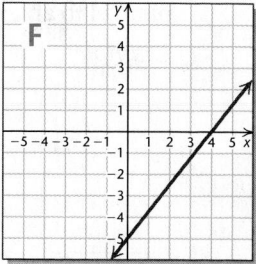

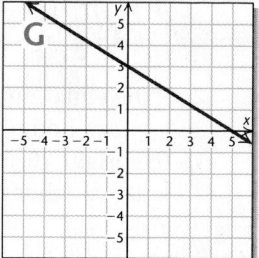

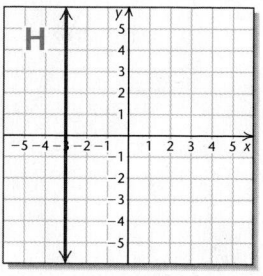

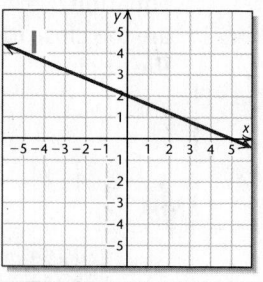

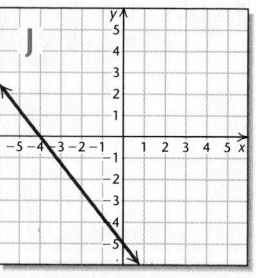

Answers on page A-18

For Exercises 1–4, find **(a)** the coordinates of the *y*-intercept and **(b)** the coordinates of the *x*-intercept.

1.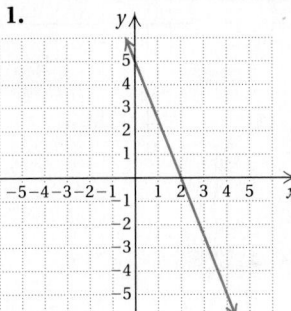

2.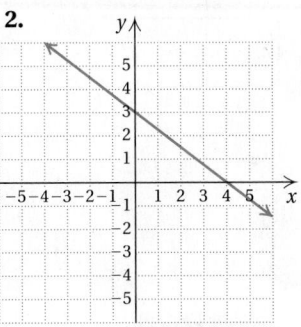

3.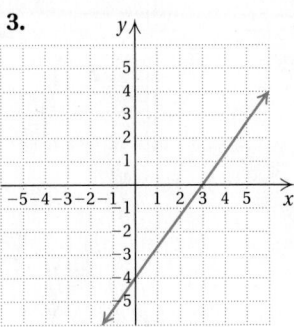

4.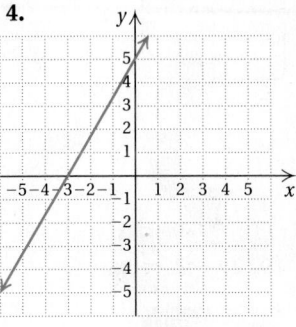

For Exercises 5–12, find **(a)** the coordinates of the *y*-intercept and **(b)** the coordinates of the *x*-intercept. Do not graph.

5. $3x + 5y = 15$

6. $5x + 2y = 20$

7. $7x - 2y = 28$

8. $3x - 4y = 24$

9. $-4x + 3y = 10$

10. $-2x + 3y = 7$

11. $6x - 3 = 9y$

12. $4y - 2 = 6x$

For each equation, find the intercepts. Then use the intercepts to graph the equation.

13. $x + 3y = 6$

x	*y*	
0		← *y*-intercept
	0	← *x*-intercept

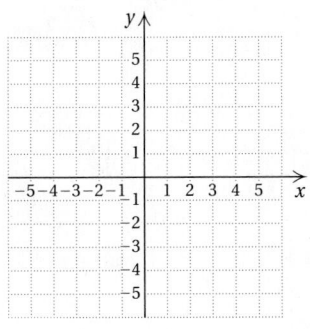

14. $x + 2y = 2$

x	*y*	
0		← *y*-intercept
	0	← *x*-intercept

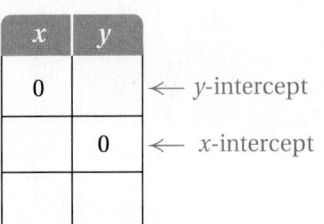

15. $-x + 2y = 4$

x	*y*	
0		← *y*-intercept
	0	← *x*-intercept

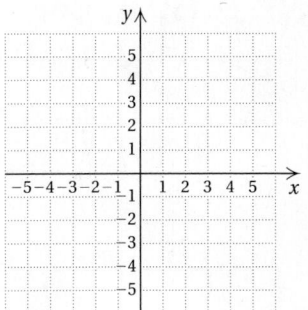

16. $-x + y = 5$

x	*y*	
0		← *y*-intercept
	0	← *x*-intercept

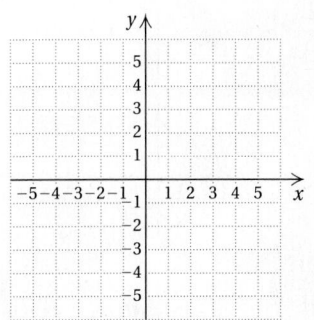

17. $3x + y = 6$

x	y
0		← *y*-intercept
	0	← *x*-intercept

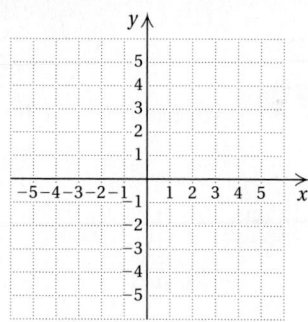

18. $2x + y = 6$

x	y
0		← *y*-intercept
	0	← *x*-intercept

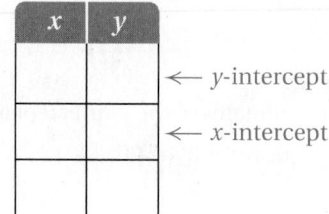

19. $2y - 2 = 6x$

x	y
		← *y*-intercept
		← *x*-intercept

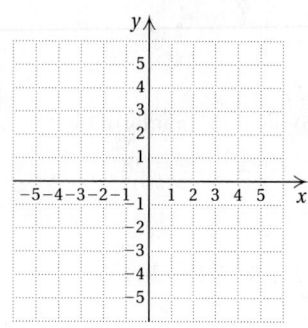

20. $3y - 6 = 9x$

x	y
		← *y*-intercept
		← *x*-intercept

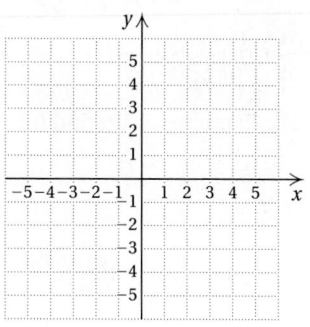

21. $3x - 9 = 3y$

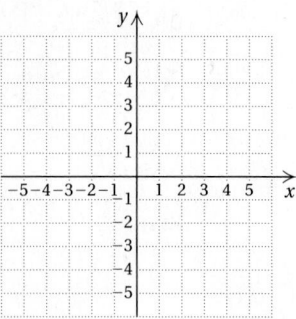

22. $5x - 10 = 5y$

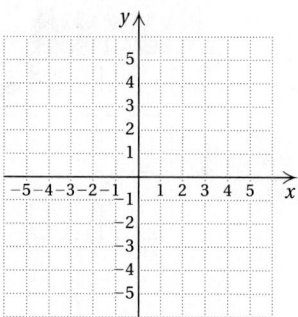

23. $2x - 3y = 6$

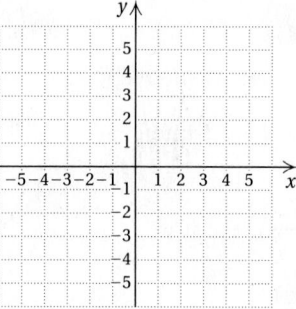

24. $2x - 5y = 10$

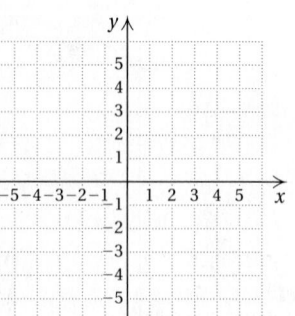

25. $4x + 5y = 20$

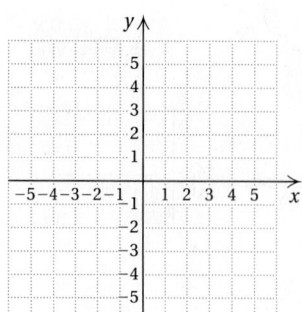

26. $2x + 6y = 12$

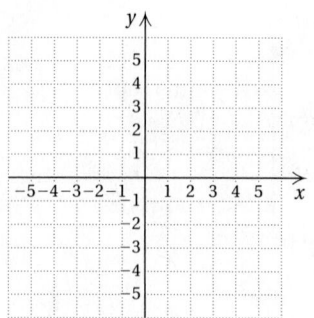

Copyright © 2012 Pearson Education, Inc.

27. $2x + 3y = 8$

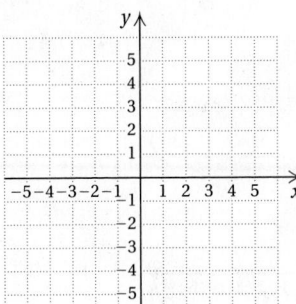

28. $x - 1 = y$

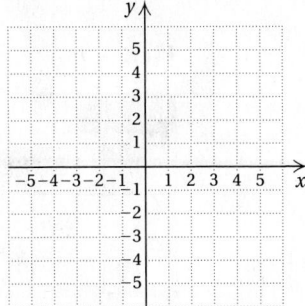

29. $3x + 4y = 5$

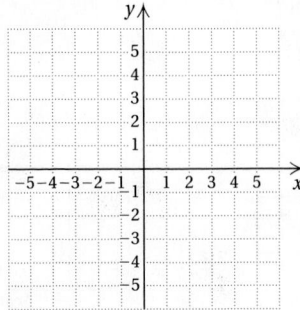

30. $2x - 1 = y$

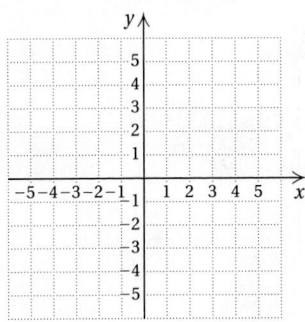

31. $3x - 2 = y$

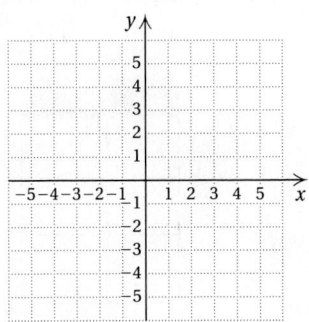

32. $4x - 3y = 12$

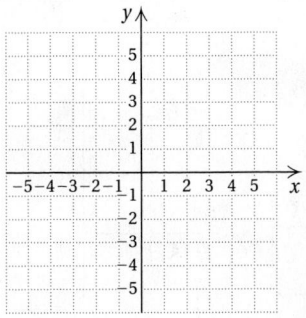

33. $6x - 2y = 12$

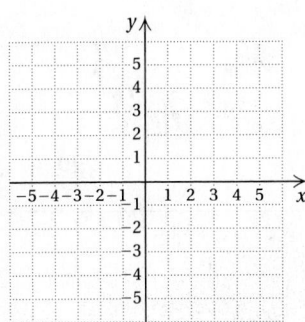

34. $7x + 2y = 6$

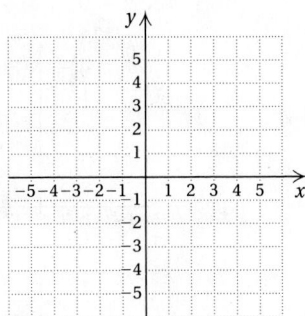

35. $y = -3 - 3x$

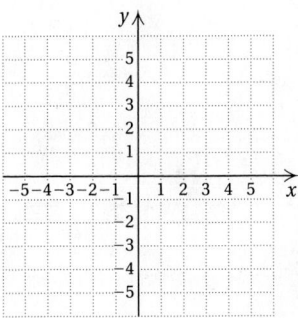

36. $-3x = 6y - 2$

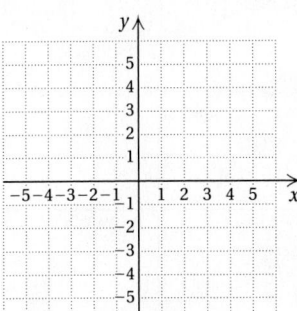

37. $y - 3x = 0$

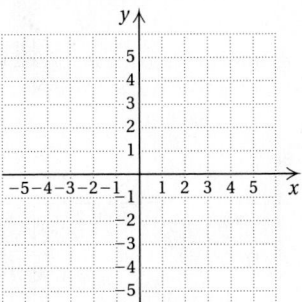

38. $x + 2y = 0$

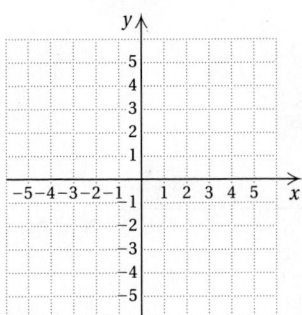

b Graph.

39. $x = -2$

x	y
-2	
-2	
-2	

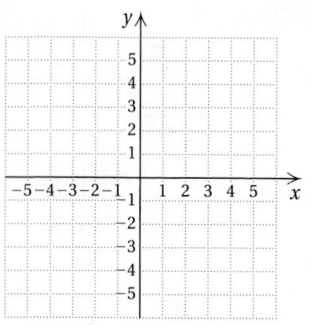

40. $x = 1$

x	y
1	
1	
1	

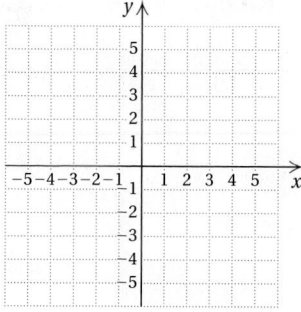

41. $y = 2$

x	y
	2
	2
	2

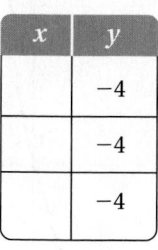

42. $y = -4$

x	y
	-4
	-4
	-4

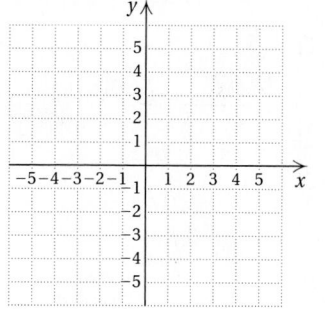

43. $x = 2$

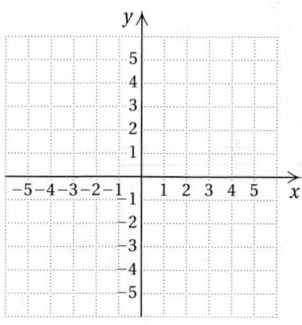

44. $x = 3$

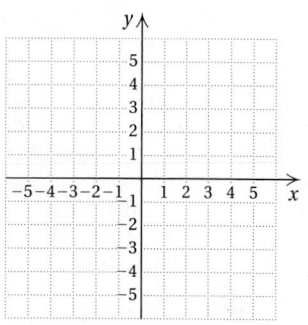

45. $y = 0$

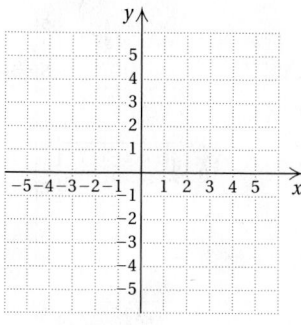

46. $y = -1$

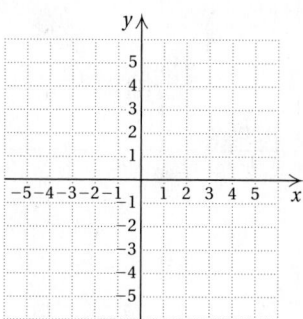

47. $x = \dfrac{3}{2}$

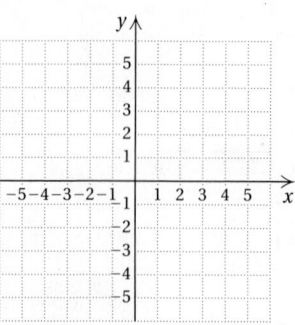

48. $x = -\dfrac{5}{2}$

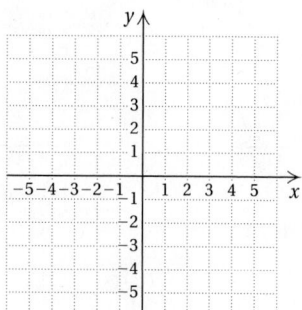

49. $3y = -5$

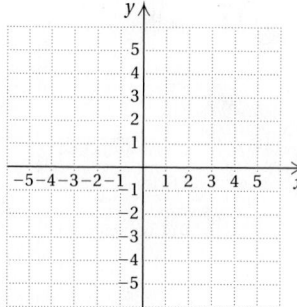

50. $12y = 45$

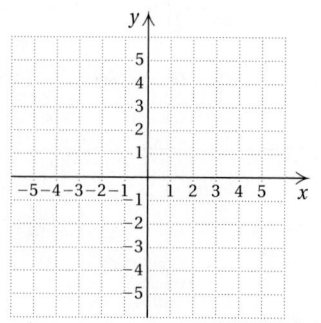

Copyright © 2012 Pearson Education, Inc.

51. $4x + 3 = 0$

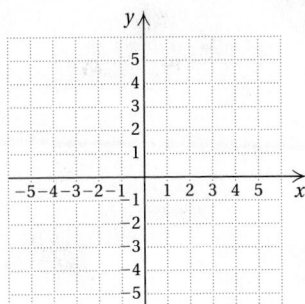

52. $-3x + 12 = 0$

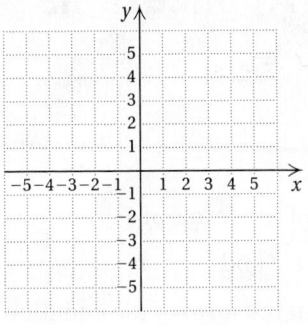

53. $48 - 3y = 0$

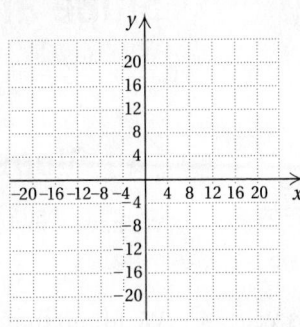

54. $63 + 7y = 0$

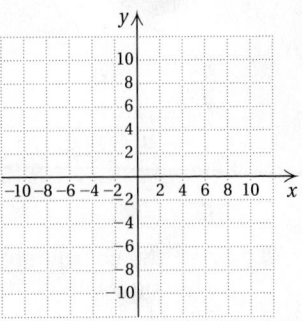

Write an equation for the graph shown.

55.

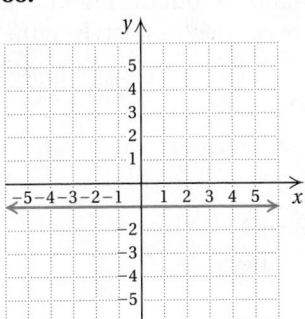

56.

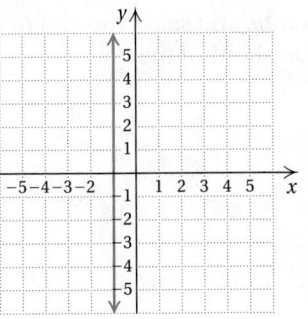

57.

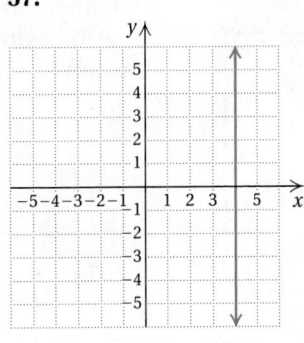

58.

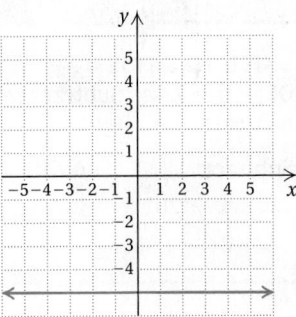

Skill Maintenance

Solve.   [8.7e]

59. $-1.6x < 64$

60. $-12x - 71 \geq 13$

61. $x + (x - 1) < (x + 2) - (x + 1)$

62. $6 - 18x \leq 4 - 12x - 5x$

63. $\dfrac{2x}{7} - 4 \leq -2$

64. $\dfrac{1}{4} + \dfrac{x}{3} > \dfrac{7}{12}$

Solve.   [8.5a]

65. *Foreign-Born Residents.*   The population of Detroit is 1,027,974, and it is estimated that 8.7% are foreign-born. How many of the residents of Detroit are foreign-born?
Source: U.S. Census Bureau

66. *Food Expenditure.*   The average American family spends 7% of its income on food. The Wilsons spent $3024 on food in a year. Estimate their annual income.
Source: "Going Hungry in America," by Peter Jaret. *AARP Bulletin,* Spring 2008

Synthesis

67. Write an equation of a line parallel to the *x*-axis and passing through $(-3, -4)$.

68. Find the value of *m* such that the graph of $y = mx + 6$ has an *x*-intercept of $(2, 0)$.

69. Find the value of *k* such that the graph of $3x + k = 5y$ has an *x*-intercept of $(-4, 0)$.

70. Find the value of *k* such that the graph of $4x = k - 3y$ has a *y*-intercept of $(0, -8)$.

9.3

Slope and Applications

OBJECTIVES

a Given the coordinates of two points on a line, find the slope of the line, if it exists.

b Find the slope of a line from an equation.

c Find the slope, or rate of change, in an applied problem involving slope.

SKILL TO REVIEW
Objective 7.4a: Subtract real numbers.

Subtract.

1. $-4 - 20$

2. $-21 - (-5)$

a Slope

We have considered two forms of a linear equation,

$$Ax + By = C \quad \text{and} \quad y = mx + b.$$

We found that from the form of the equation $y = mx + b$, we know that the y-intercept of the line is $(0, b)$.

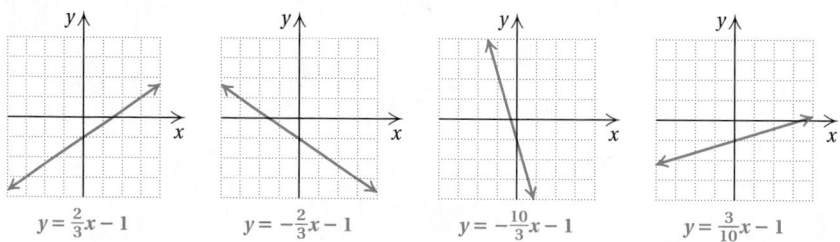

$$y = mx + b.$$

? ← The y-intercept is $(0, b)$.

What about the constant m? Does it give us information about the line? Look at the following graphs and see if you can make any connection between the constant m and the "slant" of the line.

$$y = \frac{2}{3}x - 1 \qquad y = -\frac{2}{3}x - 1 \qquad y = -\frac{10}{3}x - 1 \qquad y = \frac{3}{10}x - 1$$

The graphs of some linear equations slant upward from left to right. Others slant downward. Some are vertical and some are horizontal. Some slant more steeply than others. We now look for a way to describe such possibilities with numbers.

Consider a line with two points marked P and Q. As we move from P to Q, the y-coordinate changes from 1 to 3 and the x-coordinate changes from 2 to 6. The change in y is $3 - 1$, or 2. The change in x is $6 - 2$, or 4.

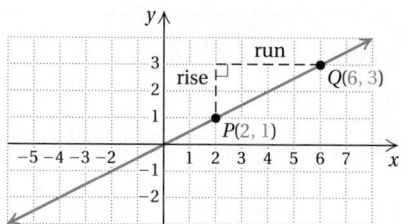

STUDY TIPS

TUNE OUT DISTRACTIONS

Do you often study in noisy places? If there is constant noise in your home, dorm, or other study area, consider finding a quiet place in the library—preferably a spot that is away from the main traffic areas so that distractions are kept to a minimum.

We call the change in y the **rise** and the change in x the **run**. The ratio rise/run is the same for any two points on a line. We call this ratio the **slope** of the line. Slope describes the slant of a line. The slope of the line in the graph above is given by

$$\frac{\text{rise}}{\text{run}} = \frac{\text{the change in } y}{\text{the change in } x}, \text{ or } \frac{2}{4}, \text{ or } \frac{1}{2}.$$

SLOPE

The **slope** of a line containing points (x_1, y_1) and (x_2, y_2) is given by

$$m = \frac{\text{rise}}{\text{run}} = \frac{\text{the change in } y}{\text{the change in } x} = \frac{y_2 - y_1}{x_2 - x_1}.$$

Answers

Skill to Review:
1. -24 2. -16

In the preceding definition, (x_1, y_1) and (x_2, y_2)—read "x sub-one, y sub-one and x sub-two, y sub-two"—represent two different points on a line. It does not matter which point is considered (x_1, y_1) and which is considered (x_2, y_2) so long as coordinates are subtracted in the same order in both the numerator and the denominator:

$$\frac{y_2 - y_1}{x_2 - x_1} = \frac{y_1 - y_2}{x_1 - x_2}.$$

EXAMPLE 1 Graph the line containing the points $(-4, 3)$ and $(2, -6)$ and find the slope.

The graph is shown below. We consider (x_1, y_1) to be $(-4, 3)$ and (x_2, y_2) to be $(2, -6)$. From $(-4, 3)$ and $(2, -6)$, we see that the change in y, or the rise, is $-6 - 3$, or -9. The change in x, or the run, is $2 - (-4)$, or 6.

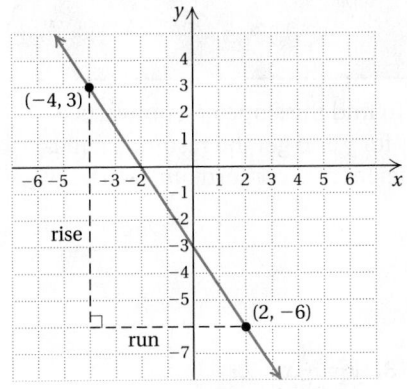

$$\text{Slope} = \frac{\text{rise}}{\text{run}} = \frac{\text{change in } y}{\text{change in } x}$$

$$= \frac{y_2 - y_1}{x_2 - x_1}$$

$$= \frac{-6 - 3}{2 - (-4)}$$

$$= \frac{-9}{6} = -\frac{9}{6}, \text{ or } -\frac{3}{2}.$$

When we use the formula

$$m = \frac{y_2 - y_1}{x_2 - x_1},$$

we must remember to subtract the y-coordinates in the same order that we subtract the x-coordinates. Let's redo Example 1, where we consider (x_1, y_1) to be $(2, -6)$ and (x_2, y_2) to be $(-4, 3)$:

$$\text{Slope} = \frac{\text{change in } y}{\text{change in } x} = \frac{3 - (-6)}{-4 - 2} = \frac{9}{-6} = -\frac{9}{6} = -\frac{3}{2}.$$

Do Exercises 1 and 2.

The slope of a line tells how it slants. A line with positive slope slants up from left to right. The larger the slope, the steeper the slant. A line with negative slope slants downward from left to right.

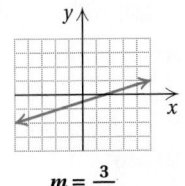

$m = \frac{3}{10}$

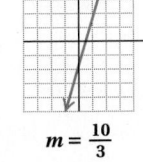

$m = \frac{10}{3}$

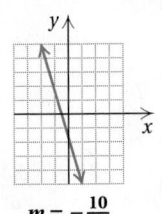

$m = -\frac{10}{3}$

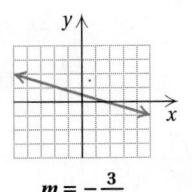

$m = -\frac{3}{10}$

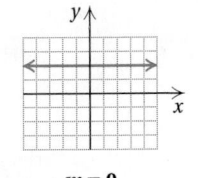

$m = 0$

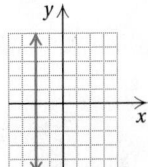

m is not defined.

Later in this section, in Examples 7 and 8, we will discuss the slope of a horizontal line and of a vertical line.

Graph the line containing the points and find the slope in two different ways.

1. $(-2, 3)$ and $(3, 5)$

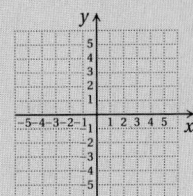

2. $(0, -3)$ and $(-3, 2)$

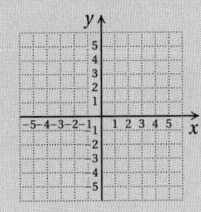

Answers

Answers to Margin Exercises 1 and 2 are on p. 686.

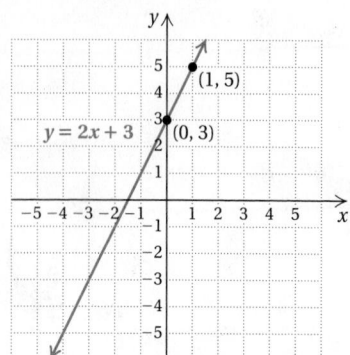

$y = 2x + 3$

b Finding the Slope from an Equation

It is possible to find the slope of a line from its equation. Let's consider the equation $y = 2x + 3$, which is in the form $y = mx + b$. The graph of this equation is shown at left. We can find two points by choosing convenient values for x—say, 0 and 1—and substituting to find the corresponding y-values. We find the two points on the line to be $(0, 3)$ and $(1, 5)$. The slope of the line is found using the definition of slope:

$$m = \frac{\text{change in } y}{\text{change in } x} = \frac{5 - 3}{1 - 0} = \frac{2}{1} = 2.$$

The slope is 2. Note that this is also the coefficient of the x-term in the equation $y = 2x + 3$.

> ### DETERMINING SLOPE FROM THE EQUATION $y = mx + b$
>
> The slope of the line $y = mx + b$ is m. To find the slope of a nonvertical line, solve the linear equation in x and y for y and get the resulting equation in the form $y = mx + b$. The coefficient of the x-term, m, is the slope of the line.

Find the slope of each line.

3. $y = 4x + 11$

4. $y = -17x + 8$

5. $y = -x + \dfrac{1}{2}$

6. $y = \dfrac{2}{3}x - 1$

EXAMPLES Find the slope of each line.

2. $y = -3x + \dfrac{2}{9}$
  $\longrightarrow m = -3 = $ Slope

3. $y = \dfrac{4}{5}x$
  $\longrightarrow m = \dfrac{4}{5} = $ Slope

4. $y = x + 6$
  $\longrightarrow m = 1 = $ Slope

5. $y = -0.6x - 3.5$
  $\longrightarrow m = -0.6 = $ Slope

Do Exercises 3–6.

To find slope from an equation, we may need to first find an equivalent form of the equation.

EXAMPLE 6 Find the slope of the line $2x + 3y = 7$.

We solve for y to get the equation in the form $y = mx + b$:

$$2x + 3y = 7$$
$$3y = -2x + 7$$
$$y = \frac{1}{3}(-2x + 7)$$
$$y = -\frac{2}{3}x + \frac{7}{3}. \qquad \text{This is } y = mx + b.$$

The slope is $-\frac{2}{3}$.

Find the slope of each line.

7. $4x + 4y = 7$

8. $5x - 4y = 8$

Do Exercises 7 and 8.

Answers

1. $\dfrac{2}{5}$ 2. $-\dfrac{5}{3}$

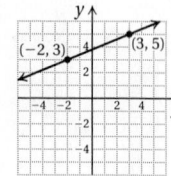

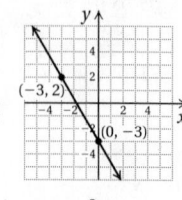

3. 4   4. -17 5. -1 6. $\dfrac{2}{3}$
7. -1 8. $\dfrac{5}{4}$

What about the slope of a horizontal line or a vertical line?

EXAMPLE 7 Find the slope of the line $y = 5$.

We can think of $y = 5$ as $y = 0x + 5$. Then from this equation, we see that $m = 0$. Consider the points $(-3, 5)$ and $(4, 5)$, which are on the line. The change in $y = 5 - 5$, or 0. The change in $x = -3 - 4$, or -7. We have

$$m = \frac{5 - 5}{-3 - 4}$$

$$= \frac{0}{-7}$$

$$= 0.$$

Any two points on a horizontal line have the same y-coordinate. The change in y is 0. Thus the slope of a horizontal line is 0.

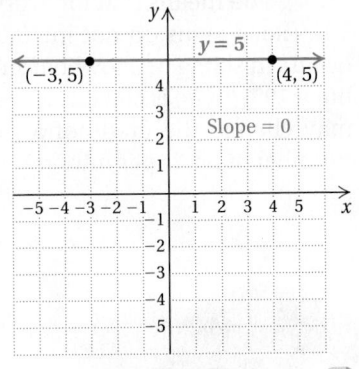

Calculator Corner

Visualizing Slope

Exercises: Graph each of the following sets of equations using the window settings $[-6, 6, -4, 4]$, with Xscl $= 1$ and Yscl $= 1$.

1. $y = x$, $y = 2x$,
$y = 5x$, $y = 10x$
What do you think the graph of $y = 123x$ will look like?

2. $y = x$, $y = \frac{3}{4}x$,
$y = 0.38x$, $y = \frac{5}{32}x$
What do you think the graph of $y = 0.000043x$ will look like?

3. $y = -x$, $y = -2x$,
$y = -5x$, $y = -10x$
What do you think the graph of $y = -123x$ will look like?

4. $y = -x$, $y = -\frac{3}{4}x$,
$y = -0.38x$, $y = -\frac{5}{32}x$
What do you think the graph of $y = -0.000043x$ will look like?

EXAMPLE 8 Find the slope of the line $x = -4$.

Consider the points $(-4, 3)$ and $(-4, -2)$, which are on the line. The change in $y = 3 - (-2)$, or 5. The change in $x = -4 - (-4)$, or 0. We have

$$m = \frac{3 - (-2)}{-4 - (-4)}$$

$$= \frac{5}{0}. \quad \text{Not defined}$$

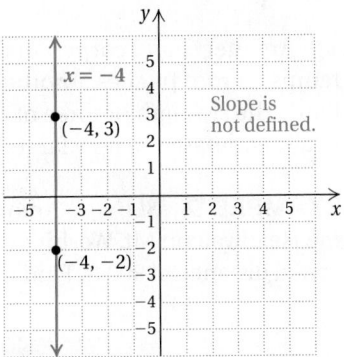

Since division by 0 is not defined, the slope of this line is not defined. The answer in this example is "The slope of this line is not defined."

SLOPE 0; SLOPE NOT DEFINED

The slope of a horizontal line is 0.

The slope of a vertical line is not defined.

Do Exercises 9 and 10.

Find the slope, if it exists, of each line.

9. $x = 7$

10. $y = -5$

Answers

9. Not defined   **10.** 0

c) Applications of Slope; Rates of Change

Slope has many real-world applications. For example, numbers like 2%, 3%, and 6% are often used to represent the *grade* of a road, a measure of how steep a road on a hill or mountain is. For example, a 3% grade $\left(3\% = \frac{3}{100}\right)$ means that for every horizontal distance of 100 ft, the road rises 3 ft, and a −3% grade means that for every horizontal distance of 100 ft, the road drops 3 ft. (Road signs do not include negative signs.) The concept of grade also occurs in skiing or snowboarding, where a 7% grade is considered very tame, but a 70% grade is considered extremely steep. And in cardiology, a physician may change the grade of a treadmill to measure its effect on heart rate (number of beats per minute).

Architects and carpenters use slope when designing and building stairs, ramps, or roof pitches. Another application occurs in hydrology. When a river flows, the strength or force of the river depends on how far the river falls vertically compared to how far it flows horizontally.

EXAMPLE 9 *Skiing.* Among the steepest skiable terrain in North America, the Headwall on Mt. Washington, in New Hampshire, drops 720 ft over a horizontal distance of 900 ft. Find the grade of the Headwall.

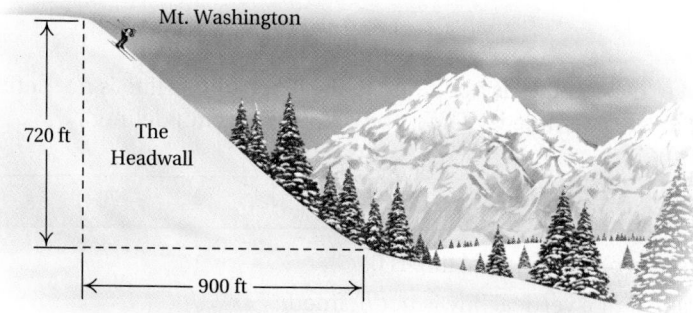

The grade of the Headwall is its slope, expressed as a percent:

$$m = \frac{720 \leftarrow \text{Vertical change}}{900 \leftarrow \text{Horizontal change}}$$

$$= \frac{8}{10} = 80\%.$$

Do Exercise 11.

11. Construction. Public buildings regularly include steps with 7-in. risers and 11-in. treads. Find the grade of such a stairway.

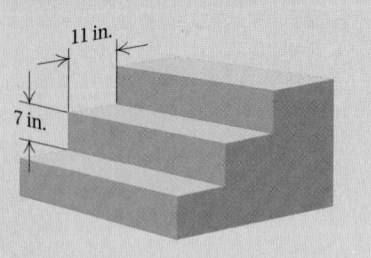

Answer

11. $63\frac{7}{11}\%$, or $63.\overline{63}\%$

Slope can also be considered as a **rate of change**.

EXAMPLE 10 *Masonry.* Jacob, an experienced mason, prepared a graph displaying data from a recent day's work. Use the graph to determine the slope, or the rate of change of the number of bricks he can lay with respect to time.

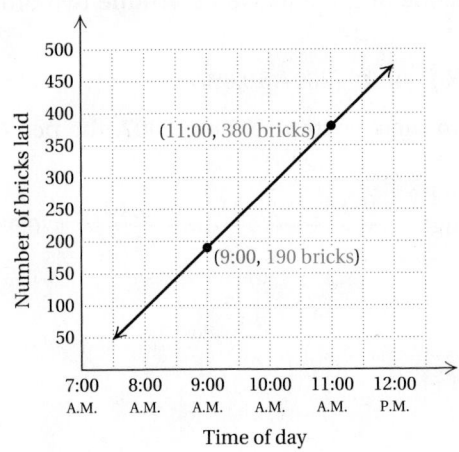

The vertical axis of the graph shows the number of bricks he has laid and the horizontal axis shows the time, in units of one hour. We can describe the rate of change of the number of bricks laid with respect to time as

$$\frac{\text{Bricks}}{\text{Hour}}, \quad \text{or} \quad \text{number of bricks laid per hour.}$$

This value is the slope of the line. We see two ordered pairs on the graph—in this case,

(9:00, 190 bricks)   and   (11:00, 380 bricks).

This tells us that in the 2 hr between 9:00 and 11:00, 380 − 190, or 190, bricks were laid. Thus,

$$\text{Rate of change} = \frac{380 \text{ bricks} - 190 \text{ bricks}}{11:00 - 9:00}$$

$$= \frac{190 \text{ bricks}}{2 \text{ hours}} = 95 \text{ bricks per hour.}$$

Do Exercise 12.

12. Hair Cutting. Kiddie Kutters has a graph displaying data for a recent day's work. Use the graph to determine the slope, or rate of change of the number of haircuts with respect to time.

EXAMPLE 11 *Decreased Smoking.* Each year in the United States, the percent of the adult population who smoke declines. Use the graph at right to determine the slope, or rate of change of the percent of the adult population who smoke with respect to time.

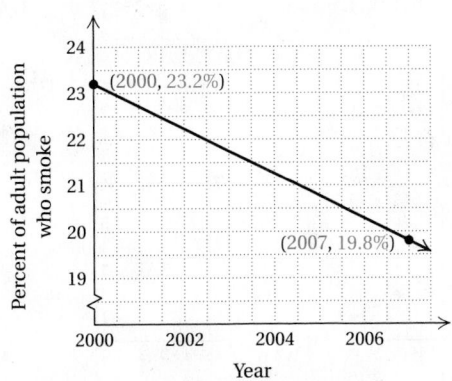

SOURCES: U.S. Centers for Disease Control and Prevention, National Center for Health Statistics; WebMD Health News

Answer

12. 3 haircuts per hour

13. Farms with Milk Cows. Use the graph below to determine the rate of change of the number of farms in the United States with milk cows.

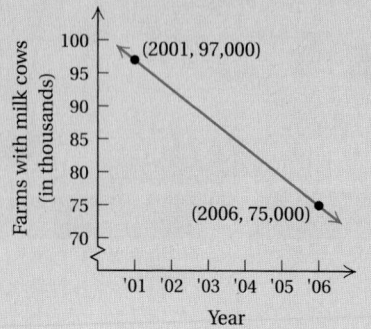

The vertical axis of the graph shows the percent of the adult population who smoke and the horizontal axis shows the years. We can describe the rate of change of the percent who smoke with respect to time as

$$\frac{\text{Change in percent who smoke}}{\text{Years}}, \quad \text{or} \quad \text{change in percent who smoke per year.}$$

This value is the slope of the line. We determine two ordered pairs on the graph—in this case,

(2000, 23.2%)   and   (2007, 19.8%).

This tells us that in the 7 yr from 2000 to 2007, the percent dropped from 23.2% to 19.8%. Thus,

$$\text{Rate of change} = \frac{19.8\% - 23.2\%}{2007 - 2000} = \frac{-3.4\%}{7} \approx -0.5\% \text{ per year.}$$

Do Exercise 13.

Answer

13. −4400 farms with milk cows per year

9.3 Exercise Set

For Extra Help
MyMathLab   Math XL PRACTICE   WATCH   DOWNLOAD   READ   REVIEW

a   Find the slope, if it exists, of each line.

1.
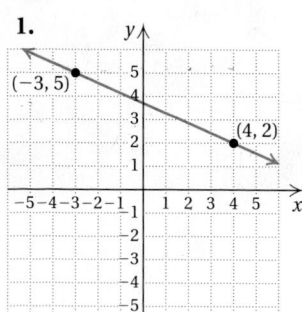

2.
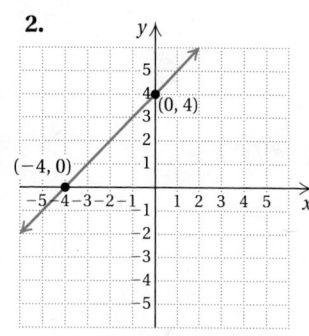

3.
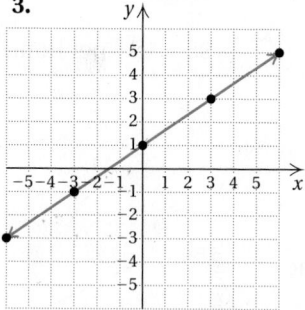

4.
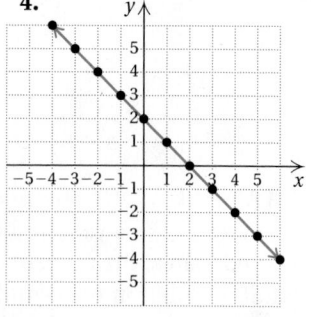

5.
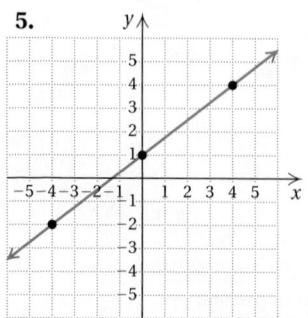

6.
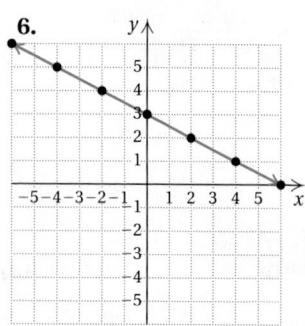

7.
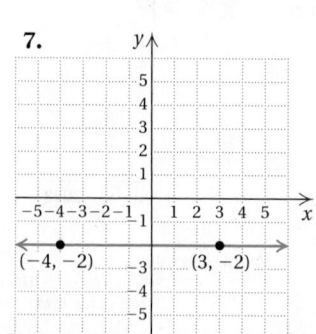

8.
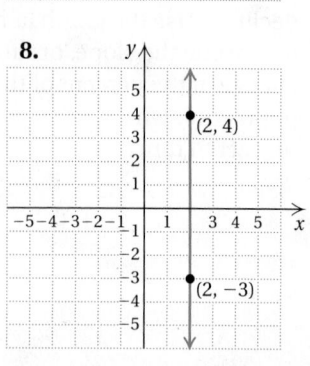

Copyright © 2012 Pearson Education, Inc.

Graph the line containing the given pair of points and find the slope.

9. $(-2, 4), (3, 0)$

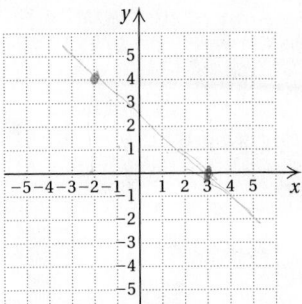

10. $(2, -4), (-3, 2)$

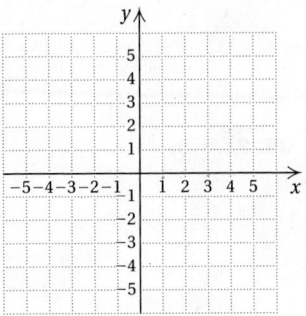

11. $(-4, 0), (-5, -3)$

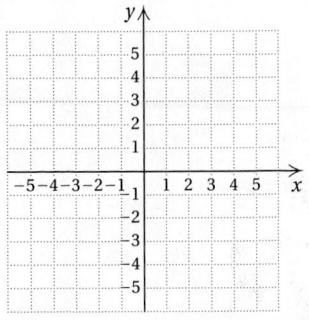

12. $(-3, 0), (-5, -2)$

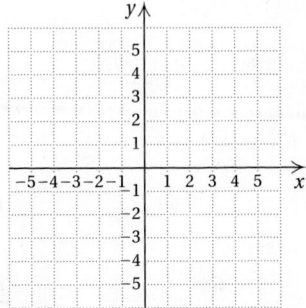

13. $(-4, 1), (2, -3)$

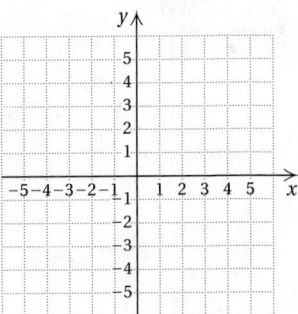

14. $(-3, 5), (4, -3)$

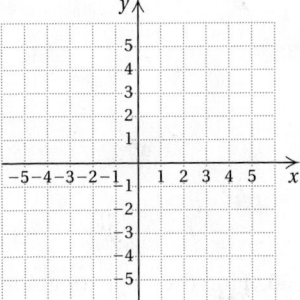

15. $(5, 3), (-3, -4)$

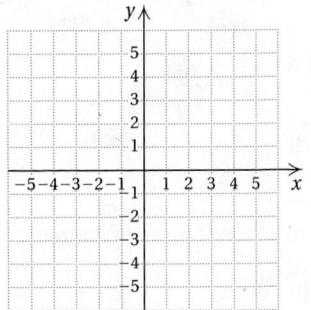

16. $(-4, -3), (2, 5)$

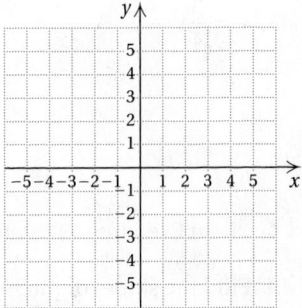

Find the slope, if it exists, of the line containing the given pair of points.

17. $\left(2, -\frac{1}{2}\right), \left(5, \frac{3}{2}\right)$

18. $\left(\frac{2}{3}, -1\right), \left(\frac{5}{3}, 2\right)$

19. $(4, -2), (4, 3)$

20. $(4, -3), (-2, -3)$

21. $(-11, 7), (15, -3)$

22. $(-13, 22), (8, -17)$

23. $\left(-\frac{1}{2}, \frac{3}{11}\right), \left(\frac{5}{4}, \frac{3}{11}\right)$

24. $(0.2, 4), (0.2, -0.04)$

b Find the slope, if it exists, of each line.

25. $y = -10x$

26. $y = \frac{10}{3}x$

27. $y = 3.78x - 4$

28. $y = -\frac{3}{5}x + 28$

29. $3x - y = 4$

30. $-2x + y = 8$

31. $x + 5y = 10$

32. $x - 4y = 8$

33. $3x + 2y = 6$

34. $2x - 4y = 8$

35. $x = \dfrac{2}{15}$

36. $y = -\dfrac{1}{3}$

37. $y = 2 - x$

38. $y = \dfrac{3}{4} + x$

39. $9x = 3y + 5$

40. $4y = 9x - 7$

41. $5x - 4y + 12 = 0$

42. $16 + 2x - 8y = 0$

43. $y = 4$

44. $x = -3$

45. $x = \dfrac{3}{4}y - 2$

46. $3x - \dfrac{1}{5}y = -4$

47. $\dfrac{2}{3}y = -\dfrac{7}{4}x$

48. $-x = \dfrac{2}{11}y$

C   In Exercises 49–52, find the slope (or rate of change).

49. Find the slope (or pitch) of the roof.

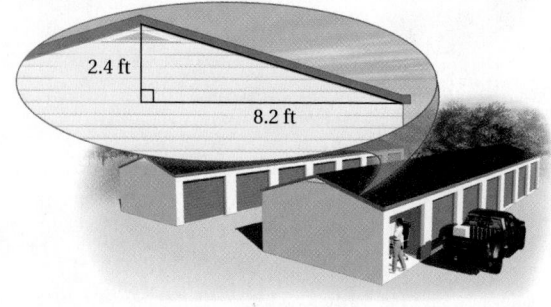

50. Find the slope (or grade) of the road.

51. Find the slope of the river.

52. Find the slope of the treadmill.

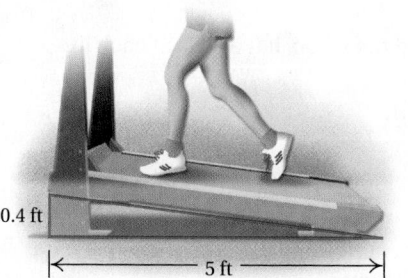

Copyright © 2012 Pearson Education, Inc.

53. *Grade of Transit System.* The maximum grade allowed between two stations in a rapid-transit rail system is 3.5%. Between station A and station B, which are 280 ft apart, the tracks rise $8\frac{1}{2}$ ft. What is the grade of the tracks between these two stations? Round the answer to the nearest tenth of a percent. Does this grade meet the rapid-transit rail standards?

Source: Brian Burell, *Merriam Webster's Guide to Everyday Math*, Merriam-Webster, Inc., Springfield MA

54. *Slope of Long's Peak.* From a base elevation of 9600 ft, Long's Peak in Colorado rises to a summit elevation of 14,255 ft over a horizontal distance of 15,840 ft. Find the grade of Long's Peak.

In Exercises 55–58, use the graph to calculate a rate of change in which the units of the horizontal axis are used in the denominator.

55. *Farmland.* The amount of farmland in the United States, in millions of acres, is represented in the following graph. Find the rate of change, rounded to the nearest ten thousand, of the number of acres with respect to time.

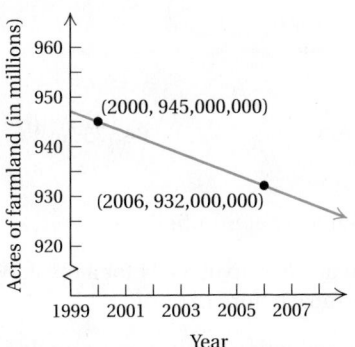

SOURCE: U.S. Department of Agriculture

56. *Movie Cost.* The cost of movie tickets for a family of four is represented in the following graph. Find the rate of change, rounded to the nearest cent, of the cost of four tickets with respect to time.

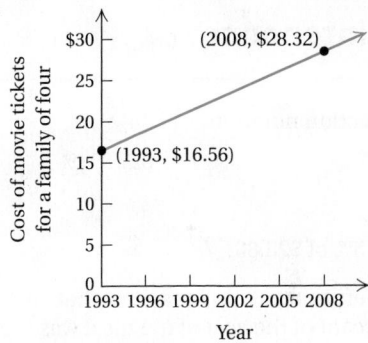

SOURCE: Motion Picture Association of America

57. *Population Growth of Nevada.* The population of Nevada is illustrated in the following graph. Find the rate of change, to the nearest hundred, of the population with respect to time.

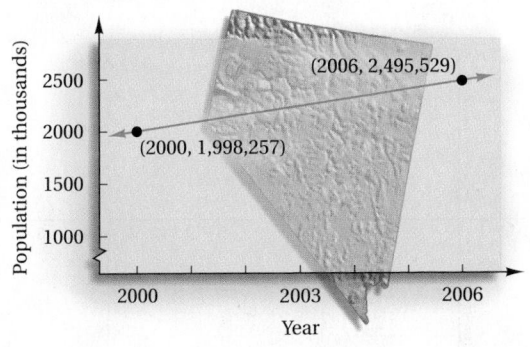

58. *Population Growth of Georgia.* The population of Georgia is illustrated in the following graph. Find the rate of change, to the nearest hundred, of the population with respect to time.

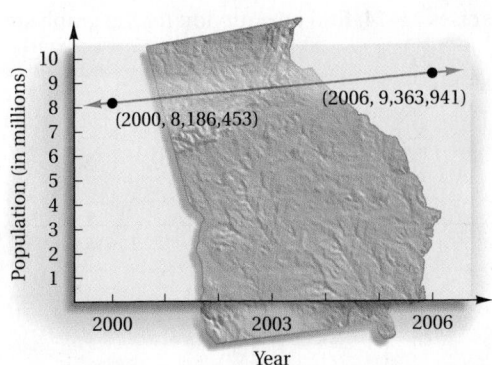

59. *Production of Blueberries.* U.S. production of blueberries is continually increasing. In 2004, 137,000 tons of blueberries were produced. By 2006, this amount had increased to 175,000 tons. Find the rate of change of the production of blueberries with respect to time.

Source: U.S. Department of Agriculture

60. *Manufacturing Jobs.* Employment in manufacturing in the United States has declined for decades. In 1960, approximately 28.5% of all jobs were in manufacturing. By 2007, this number had fallen to 10.1% of all jobs. Find the rate of change, rounded to the nearest tenth of a percent, of the percentage of jobs in manufacturing with respect to time.

Source: U.S. Department of Labor

Skill Maintenance

Convert to fraction notation. [4.3b]

61. 16%

62. $33\frac{1}{3}\%$

63. 37.5%

64. 75%

Solve. [8.5a]

65. What is 15% of $23.80?

66. $7.29 is 15% of what number?

67. Jennifer left an $8.50 tip for a meal that cost $42.50. What percent of the cost of the meal was the tip?

68. Kristen left an 18% tip of $3.24 for a meal. What was the cost of the meal before the tip?

69. Juan left a 15% tip for a meal. The total cost of the meal, including the tip, was $51.92. What was the cost of the meal before the tip was added?

70. After a 25% reduction, a sweater is on sale for $41.25. What was the original price?

Synthesis

In Exercises 71–74, find an equation for the graph shown.

71.

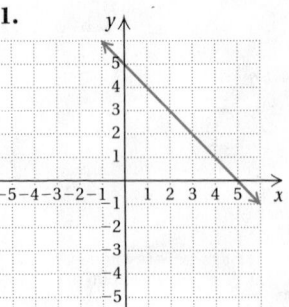

72.

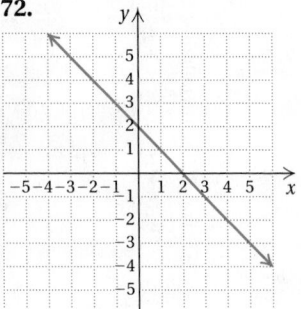

73.

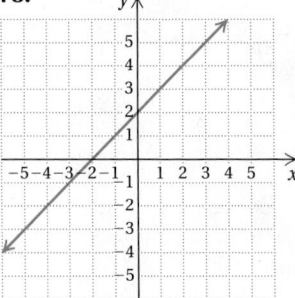

74.

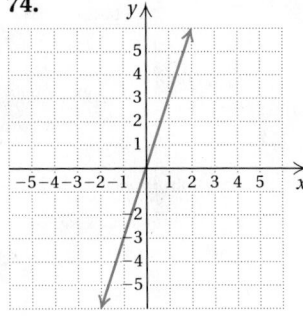

Copyright © 2012 Pearson Education, Inc.

9.5 Graphing Using the Slope and the y-Intercept

(a) Graphs Using the Slope and the y-Intercept

We can graph a line if we know the coordinates of two points on that line. We can also graph a line if we know the slope and the y-intercept.

EXAMPLE 1 Draw a line that has slope $\frac{1}{4}$ and y-intercept $(0, 2)$.

We plot $(0, 2)$ and from there move *up* 1 unit (since the numerator of $\frac{1}{4}$ is *positive* and corresponds to the change in y) and *to the right* 4 units (since the denominator is *positive* and corresponds to the change in x). This locates the point $(4, 3)$. We plot $(4, 3)$ and draw a line passing through $(0, 2)$ and $(4, 3)$ as shown on the right below.

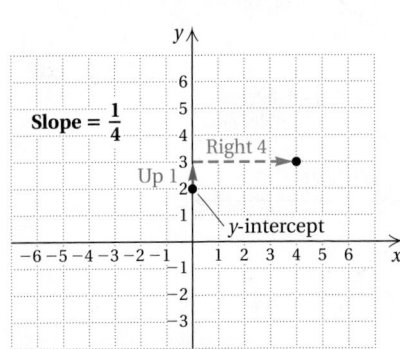
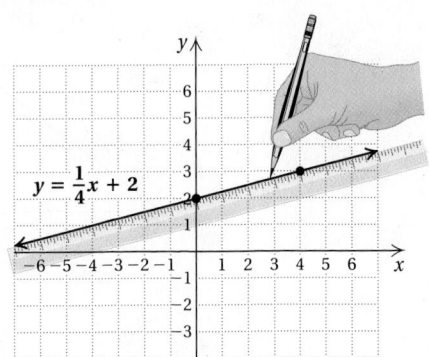

We are actually graphing the equation $y = \frac{1}{4}x + 2$.

EXAMPLE 2 Draw a line that has slope $-\frac{2}{3}$ and y-intercept $(0, 4)$.

We can think of $-\frac{2}{3}$ as $\frac{-2}{3}$. We plot $(0, 4)$ and from there move *down* 2 units (since the numerator is *negative*) and *to the right* 3 units (since the denominator is *positive*). We plot the point $(3, 2)$ and draw a line passing through $(0, 4)$ and $(3, 2)$.

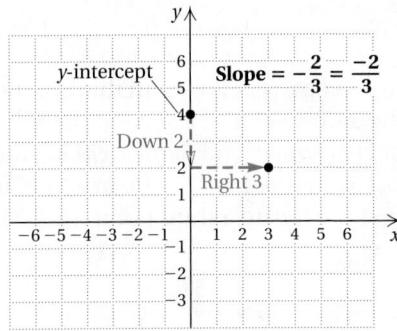
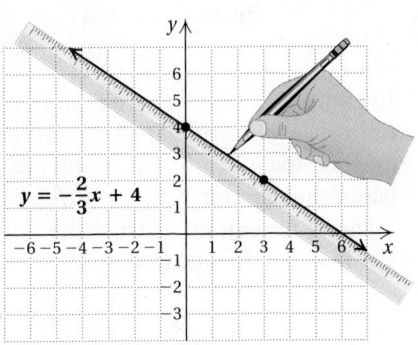

We are actually graphing the equation $y = -\frac{2}{3}x + 4$.

Do Exercises 1–3.

1. Draw a line that has slope $\frac{2}{5}$ and y-intercept $(0, -3)$. What equation is graphed?

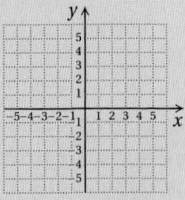

2. Draw a line that has slope $-\frac{2}{5}$ and y-intercept $(0, -3)$. What equation is graphed?

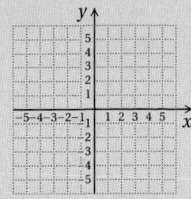

3. Draw a line that has slope 6 and y-intercept $(0, -3)$. Think of 6 as $\frac{6}{1}$. What equation is graphed?

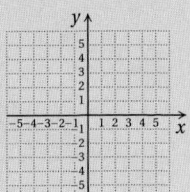

Answers

Answers to Margin Exercises 1–3 are on p. 704.

We now use our knowledge of the slope–intercept equation to graph linear equations.

EXAMPLE 3 Graph $y = \frac{3}{4}x + 5$ using the slope and the y-intercept.

From the equation $y = \frac{3}{4}x + 5$, we see that the slope of the graph is $\frac{3}{4}$ and the y-intercept is $(0, 5)$. We plot $(0, 5)$ and then consider the slope, $\frac{3}{4}$. Starting at $(0, 5)$, we plot a second point by moving *up* 3 units (since the numerator is *positive*) and *to the right* 4 units (since the denominator is *positive*). We reach a new point, $(4, 8)$.

We can also rewrite the slope as $\frac{-3}{-4}$. We again start at the y-intercept, $(0, 5)$, but move *down* 3 units (since the numerator is *negative* and corresponds to the change in y) and *to the left* 4 units (since the denominator is *negative* and corresponds to the change in x). We reach another point, $(-4, 2)$. Once two or three points have been plotted, the line representing all solutions of $y = \frac{3}{4}x + 5$ can be drawn.

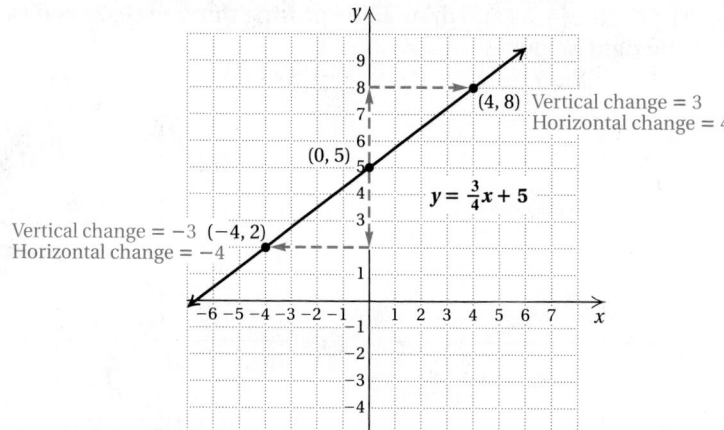

4. Graph $y = \frac{3}{5}x - 4$ using the slope and the y-intercept.

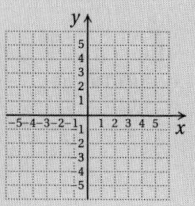

Do Exercise 4.

EXAMPLE 4 Graph $2x + 3y = 3$ using the slope and the y-intercept.

To graph $2x + 3y = 3$, we first rewrite the equation in slope–intercept form:

$$2x + 3y = 3$$

$$3y = -2x + 3 \qquad \text{Adding } -2x$$

$$\frac{1}{3} \cdot 3y = \frac{1}{3}(-2x + 3) \qquad \text{Multiplying by } \frac{1}{3}$$

$$y = -\frac{2}{3}x + 1. \qquad \text{Simplifying}$$

To graph $y = -\frac{2}{3}x + 1$, we first plot the y-intercept, $(0, 1)$. We can think of the slope as $\frac{-2}{3}$. Starting at $(0, 1)$ and using the slope, we find a second point by moving *down* 2 units (since the numerator is *negative*) and *to the right* 3 units (since the denominator is *positive*). We plot the new point, $(3, -1)$. In a similar manner, we can move from the point $(3, -1)$ to locate a third point, $(6, -3)$. The line can then be drawn.

Answers

1.
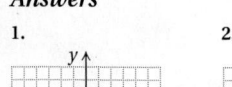

2.

$y = \frac{2}{5}x - 3$ $y = -\frac{2}{5}x - 3$

3.
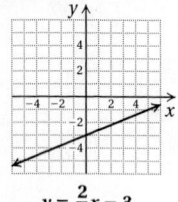

4.
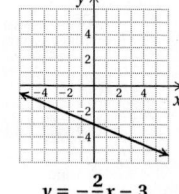

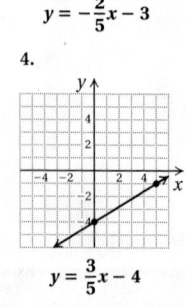

$y = 6x - 3$ $y = \frac{3}{5}x - 4$

Since $-\frac{2}{3} = \frac{2}{-3}$, an alternative approach is to again plot $(0, 1)$, but this time we move *up* 2 units (since the numerator is *positive*) and *to the left* 3 units (since the denominator is *negative*). This leads to another point on the graph, $(-3, 3)$.

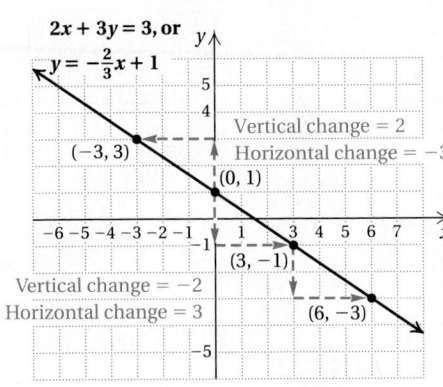

Do Exercise 5.

5. Graph: $3x + 4y = 12$.

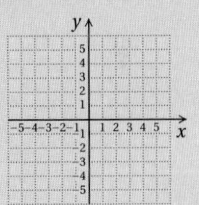

Answer

5.

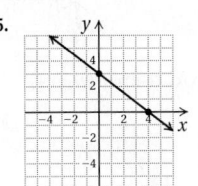

$3x + 4y = 12$

9.5 **Exercise Set**

For Extra Help

MyMathLab | Math XL PRACTICE | WATCH | DOWNLOAD | READ | REVIEW

a Draw a line that has the given slope and y-intercept.

1. Slope $\frac{2}{5}$; y-intercept $(0, 1)$

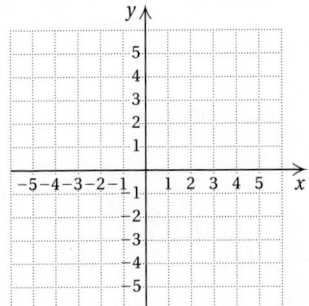

2. Slope $\frac{3}{5}$; y-intercept $(0, -1)$

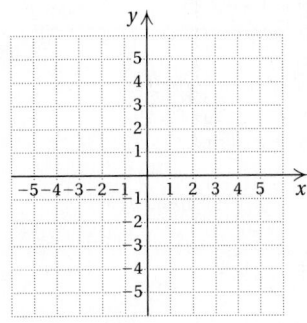

3. Slope $\frac{5}{3}$; y-intercept $(0, -2)$

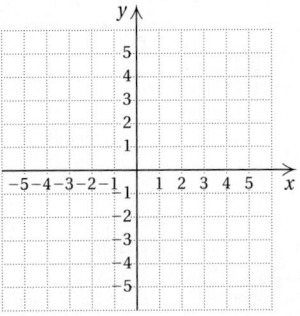

4. Slope $\frac{5}{2}$; y-intercept $(0, 1)$

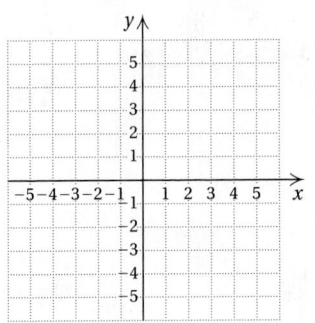

5. Slope $-\frac{3}{4}$; y-intercept $(0, 5)$

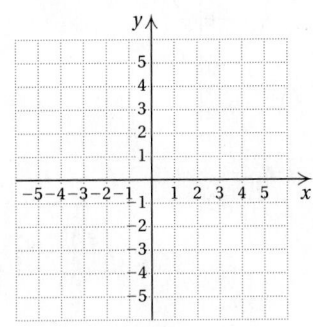

6. Slope $-\frac{4}{5}$; y-intercept $(0, 6)$

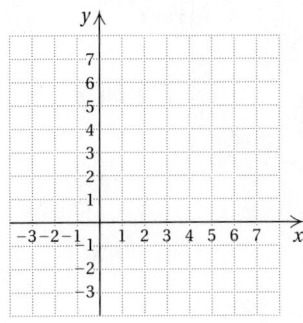

7. Slope $-\frac{1}{2}$; y-intercept $(0, 3)$

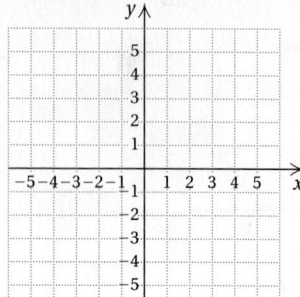

8. Slope $\frac{1}{3}$; y-intercept $(0, -4)$

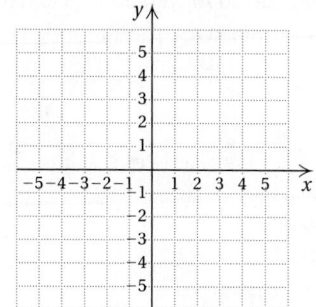

9. Slope 2; y-intercept $(0, -4)$

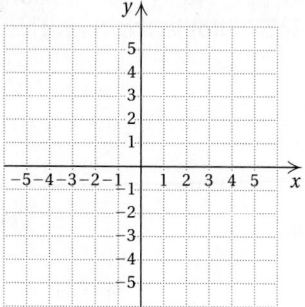

10. Slope -2; y-intercept $(0, -3)$

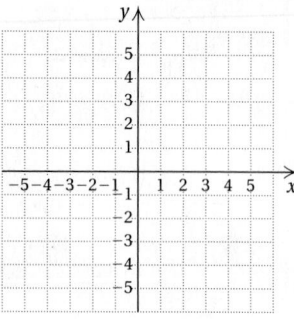

11. Slope -3; y-intercept $(0, 2)$

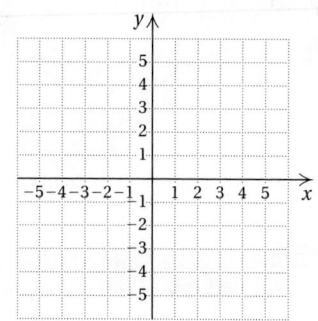

12. Slope 3; y-intercept $(0, 4)$

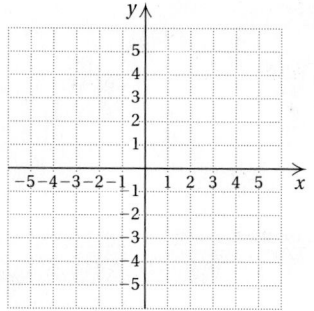

Graph using the slope and the y-intercept.

13. $y = \frac{3}{5}x + 2$

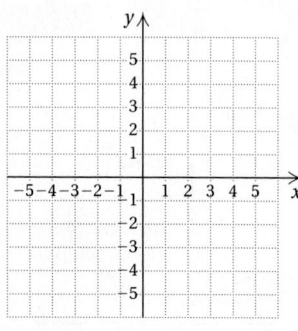

14. $y = -\frac{3}{5}x - 1$

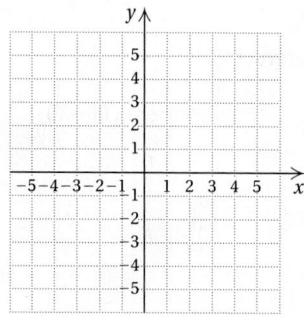

15. $y = -\frac{3}{5}x + 1$

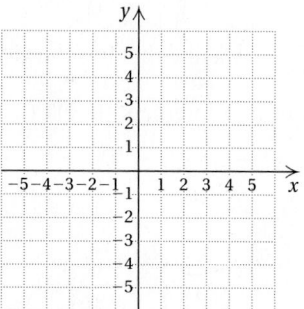

16. $y = \frac{3}{5}x - 2$

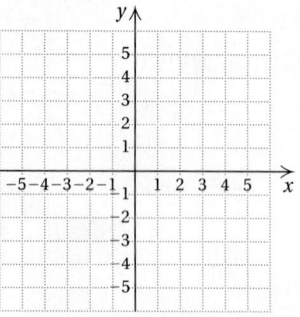

17. $y = \frac{5}{3}x + 3$

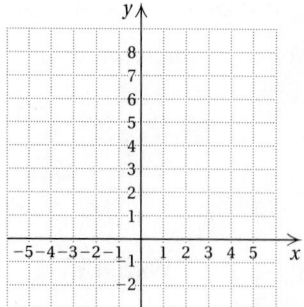

18. $y = \frac{5}{3}x - 2$

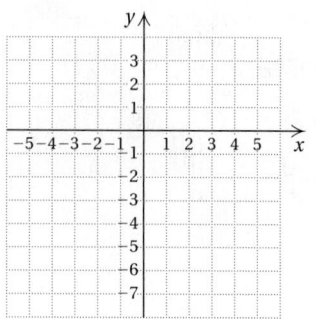

Copyright © 2012 Pearson Education, Inc.

19. $y = -\frac{3}{2}x - 2$

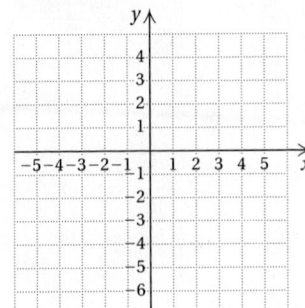

20. $y = -\frac{4}{3}x + 3$

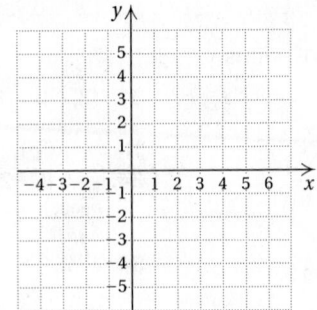

21. $2x + y = 1$

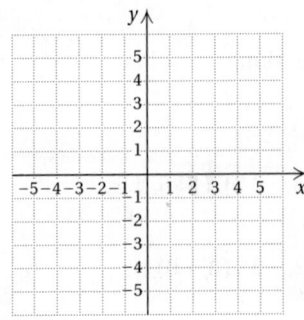

22. $3x + y = 2$

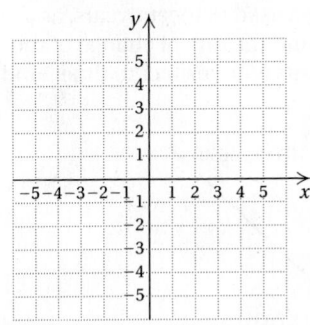

23. $3x - y = 4$

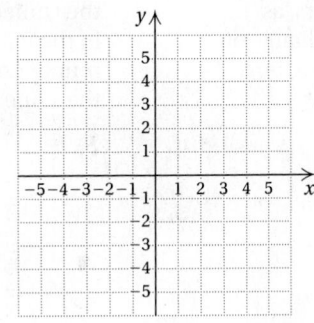

24. $2x - y = 5$

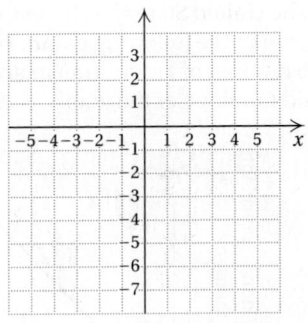

25. $2x + 3y = 9$

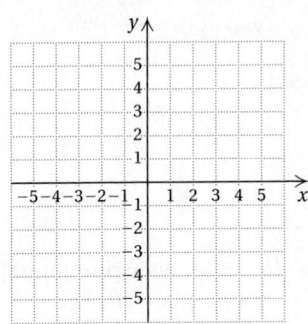

26. $4x + 5y = 15$

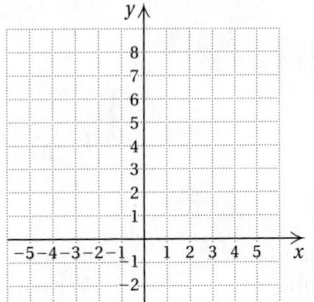

27. $x - 4y = 12$

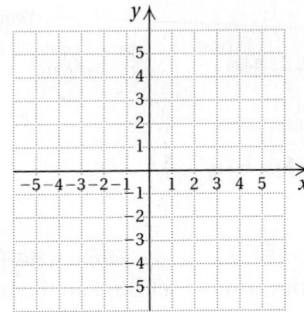

28. $x + 5y = 20$

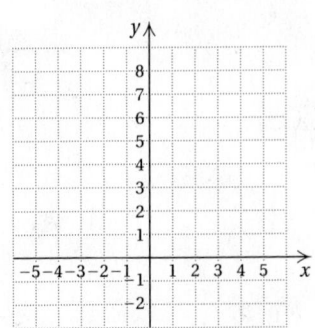

29. $x + 2y = 6$

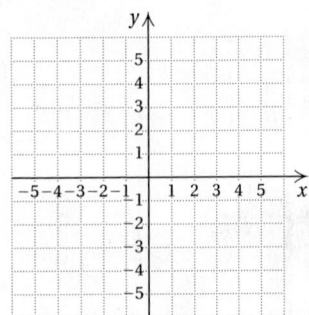

30. $x - 3y = 9$

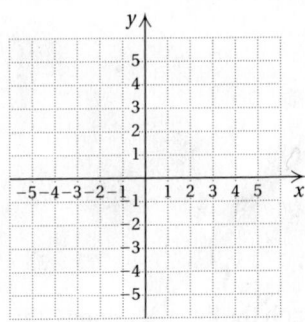

Skill Maintenance

Find the slope of the line containing the given pair of points.   [9.3a]

31. $(-2, -6), (8, 7)$

32. $(2, -6), (8, -7)$

33. $(4.5, -2.3), (14.5, 4.6)$

34. $(-0.8, -2.3), (-4.8, 0.1)$

35. $(-2, -6), (8, -6)$

36. $(-2, -6), (-2, 7)$

37. $(11, -1), (11, -4)$

38. $(-3, 5), (8, 5)$

39. *Kidney Transplants.*   The number of kidney transplants in the United States has increased in recent years, as shown in the following graph. Find the rate of change of the number of kidney transplants with respect to time. Find the slope of the graph.   [9.3c]

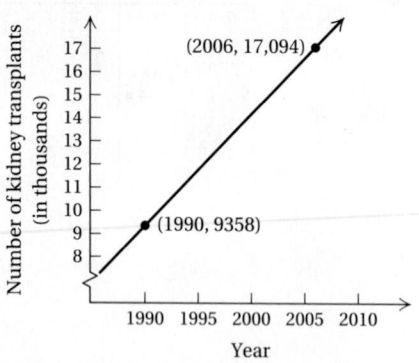

SOURCE: U.S. Department of Health and Human Services, Division of Transplantation

40. *Liver Transplants.*   The number of liver transplants in the United States has increased in recent years, as shown in the following graph. Find the rate of change of the number of liver transplants with respect to time. Find the slope of the graph.   [9.3c]

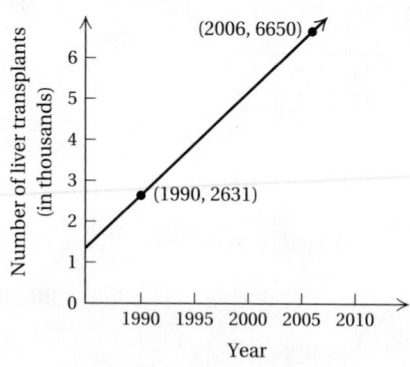

SOURCE: U.S. Department of Health and Human Services, Division of Transplantation

Synthesis

41. *Refrigerator Size.*   Kitchen designers recommend that a refrigerator be selected on the basis of the number of people in the household. For 1–2 people, a 16 ft^3 model is suggested. For each additional person, an additional 1.5 ft^3 is recommended. If x is the number of residents in excess of 2, find the slope–intercept equation for the recommended size of a refrigerator.

42. *Wireless Service.*   In a recent nationwide promotion, Verizon charged a monthly phone-plan fee of $39.99 plus 45¢ for each minute to non-Verizon customers above the 450 min included in the plan. If x is the number of minutes of calls above the 450-min limit, find the slope–intercept equation for the monthly bill.
Source: Verizon

43. Graph the line with slope 2 that passes through the point $(-3, 1)$.

Copyright © 2012 Pearson Education, Inc.

Summary and Review

Key Terms, Properties, and Formulas

axes, p. 656
origin, p. 656
coordinates, p. 656
first coordinate, p. 656
abscissa, p. 656
second coordinate, p. 656
ordinate, p. 656
ordered pairs, p. 656
first quadrant, p. 657

second quadrant, p. 657
third quadrant, p. 657
fourth quadrant, p. 657
graph, p. 659
x-intercept, p. 673
y-intercept, p. 673
horizontal line, p. 676
vertical line, p. 676
rise, p. 684

run, p. 684
slope, p. 684
rate of change, p. 689
slope–intercept equation, p. 695
parallel lines, p. 709
perpendicular lines, p. 710
half-plane, p. 715
linear inequality, p. 715

$Slope = m = \dfrac{y_2 - y_1}{x_2 - x_1}$

Slope–Intercept Equation: $y = mx + b$

Parallel Lines: Slopes equal, y-intercepts different

Perpendicular Lines: Product of slopes $= -1$

Concept Reinforcement

Determine whether each statement is true or false.

_____ **1.** The x- and y-intercepts of $y = mx$ are both $(0, 0)$. [9.2a]

_____ **2.** Parallel lines have the same y-intercept. [9.6a]

_____ **3.** Lines $y = mx + s$ and $y = -\dfrac{1}{m}x + t$, $m \neq 0$, are perpendicular. [9.6b]

_____ **4.** The ordered pair $(0, 0)$ is a solution of $y > x$. [9.7a]

_____ **5.** The second coordinate of all points in quadrant III is negative. [9.1a]

_____ **6.** The x-intercept of $Ax + By = C$, $C \neq 0$, is $\left(\dfrac{A}{C}, 0\right)$. [9.2a]

_____ **7.** The slope of the line that passes through $(0, t)$ and $(-t, 0)$ is $\dfrac{1}{t}$. [9.3a]

Important Concepts

Objective 9.1b Find the coordinates of a point on a graph.

Example Find the coordinates of points Q, R, and S.

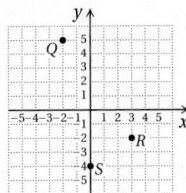

Point Q is 2 units to the left and 5 units up. Its coordinates are $(-2, 5)$.

Point R is 3 units to the right and 2 units down. Its coordinates are $(3, -2)$.

Point S is 0 units to the left or right and 4 units down. Its coordinates are $(0, -4)$.

Practice Exercise

1. Find the coordinates of points F, G, and H.

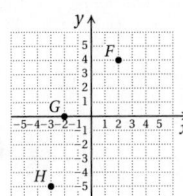

Objective 9.1d Graph linear equations of the type $y = mx + b$ and $Ax + By = C$, identifying the y-intercept.

Example Graph $2y + 2 = -3x$ and identify the y-intercept.

To find an equivalent equation in the form $y = mx + b$, we solve for y: $y = -\frac{3}{2}x - 1$. The y-intercept is $(0, -1)$.

We then find two other pairs using multiples of 2 for x to avoid fractions.

x	y
0	-1	$\leftarrow$ y-intercept
-2	2
2	-4

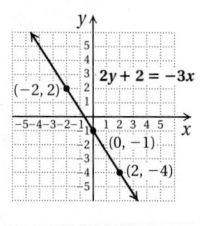

Practice Exercise

2. Graph $x + 2y = 8$ and identify the y-intercept.

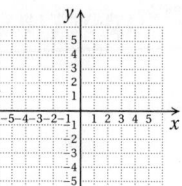

Objective 9.2a Find the intercepts of a linear equation, and graph using intercepts.

Example For $2x - y = -6$, find the intercepts. Then use the intercepts to graph the equation.

To find the y-intercept, we let $x = 0$ and solve for y:

$2 \cdot 0 - y = -6$ and $y = 6$.

The y-intercept is $(0, 6)$.

To find the x-intercept, we let $y = 0$ and solve for x:

$2x - 0 = -6$ and $x = -3$.

The x-intercept is $(-3, 0)$.

We find a third point as a check.

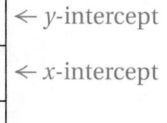

x	y
0	6	$\leftarrow$ y-intercept
-3	0	$\leftarrow$ x-intercept
-1	4

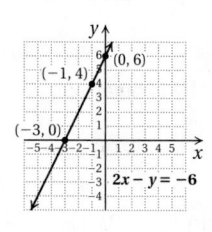

Practice Exercise

3. For $y - 2x = -4$, find the intercepts. Then use the intercepts to graph the equation.

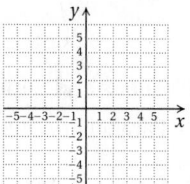

Objective 9.2b Graph equations equivalent to those of the type $x = a$ and $y = b$.

Example Graph: $y = 1$ and $x = -\frac{3}{2}$.

For $y = 1$, no matter what number we choose for x, $y = 1$. The graph is a horizontal line. For $x = -\frac{3}{2}$, no matter what number we choose for y, $x = -\frac{3}{2}$. The graph is a vertical line.

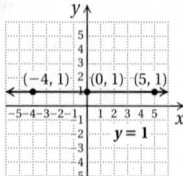

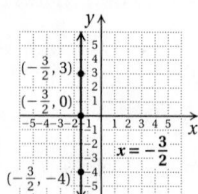

Practice Exercises

Graph.

4. $y = -\frac{5}{2}$

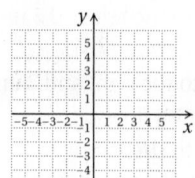

5. $x = 2$

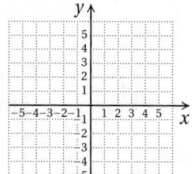

Objective 9.3a Given the coordinates of two points on a line, find the slope of the line, if it exists.

Example Find the slope, if it exists, of the line containing the given points.

$(-9, 3)$ and $(5, -6)$: $\quad m = \dfrac{-6 - 3}{5 - (-9)} = \dfrac{-9}{14} = -\dfrac{9}{14}$;

$\left(7, \dfrac{1}{2}\right)$ and $\left(-13, \dfrac{1}{2}\right)$: $\quad m = \dfrac{\frac{1}{2} - \frac{1}{2}}{-13 - 7} = \dfrac{0}{-20} = 0$;

$(0.6, 1.5)$ and $(0.6, -1.5)$: $\quad m = \dfrac{-1.5 - 1.5}{0.6 - 0.6} = \dfrac{-3}{0}$,

m is not defined.

Practice Exercises

Find the slope, if it exists, of the line containing the given points.

6. $(-8, 20), (-8, 14)$

7. $(2, -1), (16, 20)$

8. $(0.5, 2.8), (1.5, 2.8)$

Objective 9.3b Find the slope of a line from an equation.

Example Find the slope, if it exists, of each line.

a) $5x - 20y = -10$

We first solve for y: $y = \frac{1}{4}x + \frac{1}{2}$. The slope is $\frac{1}{4}$.

b) $y = -\frac{4}{5}$

Think: $y = 0 \cdot x - \frac{4}{5}$. This line is horizontal. The slope is 0.

c) $x = 6$

This line is vertical. The slope is not defined.

Practice Exercises

Find the slope, if it exists, of the line.

9. $x = 0.25$

10. $7y + 14x = -28$

11. $y = -5$

Review Exercises

Find the coordinates of each point.   [9.1b]

1. *A*   **2.** *B*   **3.** *C*

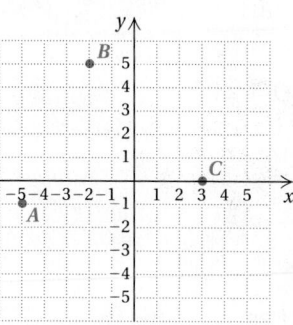

Plot each point.   [9.1a]

4. $(2, 5)$ **5.** $(0, -3)$ **6.** $(-4, -2)$

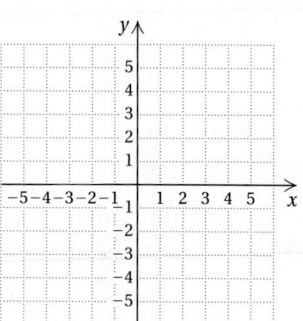

Copyright © 2012 Pearson Education, Inc.

In which quadrant is each point located? [9.1a]

7. $(3, -8)$ **8.** $(-20, -14)$ **9.** $(4.9, 1.3)$

Determine whether each ordered pair is a solution of $2y - x = 10$. [9.1c]

10. $(2, -6)$ **11.** $(0, 5)$

12. Show that the ordered pairs $(0, -3)$ and $(2, 1)$ are solutions of the equation $2x - y = 3$. Then use the graph of the equation to determine another solution. Answers may vary. [9.1c]

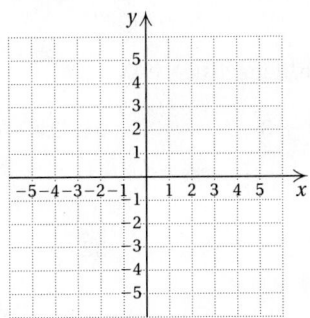

Graph each equation, identifying the *y*-intercept. [9.1d]

13. $y = 2x - 5$ **14.** $y = -\dfrac{3}{4}x$

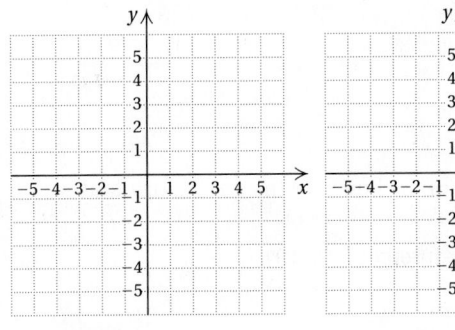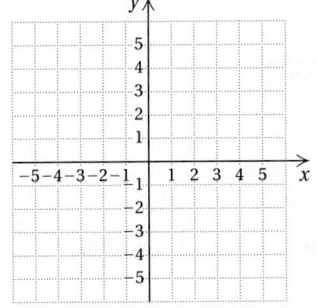

15. $y = -x + 4$ **16.** $y = 3 - 4x$

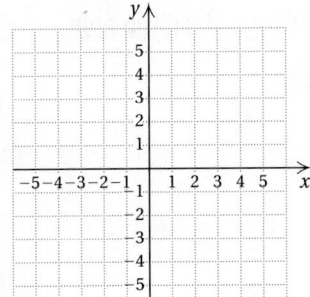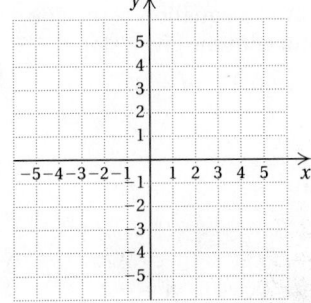

Graph each equation. [9.2b]

17. $y = 3$ **18.** $5x - 4 = 0$

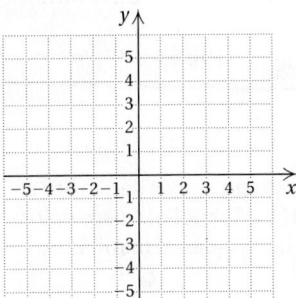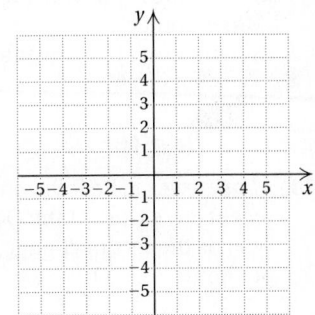

Find the intercepts of each equation. Then graph the equation. [9.2a]

19. $x - 2y = 6$ **20.** $5x - 2y = 10$

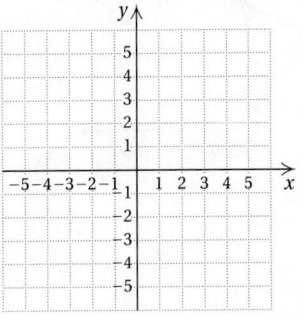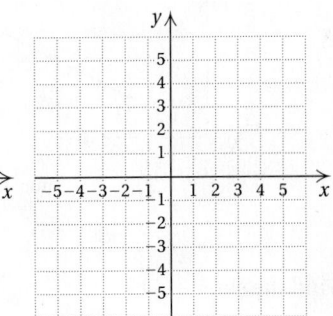

Solve. [9.1e]

21. *Kitchen Design.* Kitchen designers recommend that a refrigerator be selected on the basis of the number of people n in the household. The appropriate size S, in cubic feet, is given by

$$S = \frac{3}{2}n + 13.$$

  a) Determine the recommended size of a refrigerator if the number of people is 1, 2, 5, and 10.

  b) Graph the equation and use the graph to estimate the recommended size of a refrigerator for 4 people sharing an apartment.

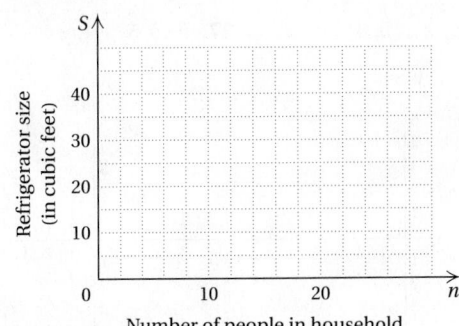

  c) A refrigerator is 22 ft³. For how many residents is it the recommended size?

22. *Snow Removal.*   By 3:00 P.M., Erin had plowed 7 drive-ways and by 5:30 P.M., she had completed 13.

   a) Find Erin's plowing rate, in number of driveways per hour.   [9.3c]

   b) Find Erin's plowing rate, in minutes per driveway. [9.3c]

23. *Manicures.*   The following graph shows data from a recent day's work at the O'Hara School of Cosmetology. What is the rate of change, in number of manicures per hour?   [9.3c]

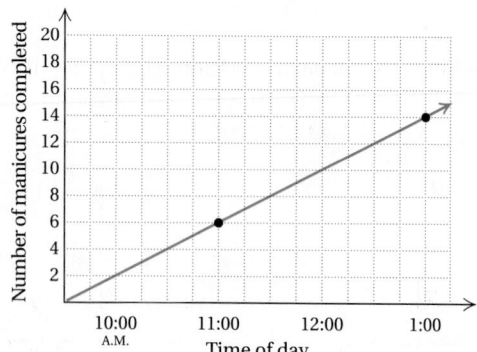

Find the slope.   [9.3a]

24.

25.

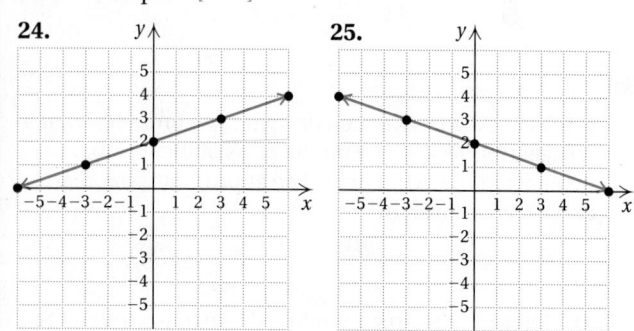

Graph the line containing the given pair of points and find the slope.   [9.3a]

26. $(-5, -2), (5, 4)$

27. $(-5, 5), (4, -4)$

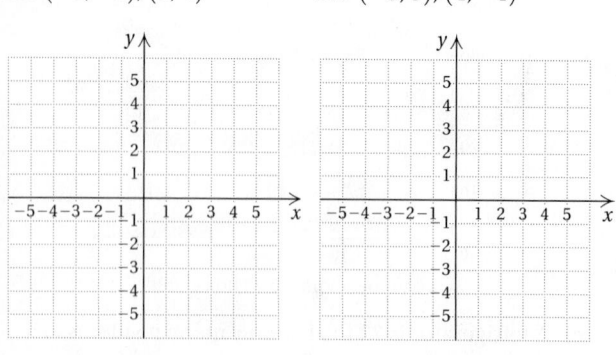

28. *Road Grade.*   At one point, Beartooth Highway in Yellowstone National Park rises 315 ft over a horizontal distance of 4500 ft. Find the slope, or grade, of the road.   [9.3c]

Find the slope, if it exists.   [9.3b]

29. $y = -\dfrac{5}{8}x - 3$

30. $2x - 4y = 8$

31. $x = -2$

32. $y = 9$

Find the slope and the y-intercept.   [9.4a]

33. $y = -9x + 46$

34. $x + y = 9$

35. $3x - 5y = 4$

Find an equation of the line with the given slope and y-intercept.   [9.4a]

36. Slope: -2.8; y-intercept: $(0, 19)$

37. Slope: $\frac{5}{8}$; y-intercept: $\left(0, -\frac{7}{8}\right)$

Find an equation of the line containing the given point and with the given slope.   [9.4b]

38. $(1, 2)$, $m = 3$

39. $(-2, -5)$, $m = \frac{2}{3}$

40. $(0, -4)$, $m = -2$

Copyright © 2012 Pearson Education, Inc.

Find an equation of the line containing the given pair of points.   [9.4c]

41. $(5, 7)$ and $(-1, 1)$

42. $(2, 0)$ and $(-4, -3)$

Solve.   [9.4c]

43. *Prescriptions.*   The line graph below illustrates the number of prescriptions per year that are filled in the United States for years since 1997.

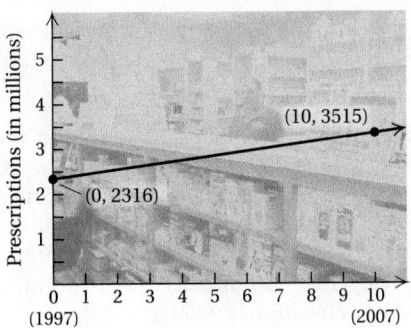

Years since 1997

SOURCE: IMS Health and NACDS Economics Department

a) Find an equation of the line. Let x = the number of years since 1997.
b) What is the rate of change of the number of prescriptions filled annually with respect to time?
c) Use the equation to find the number of prescriptions filled in 2006.

44. Draw a line that has slope -1 and y-intercept $(0, 4)$.   [9.5a]

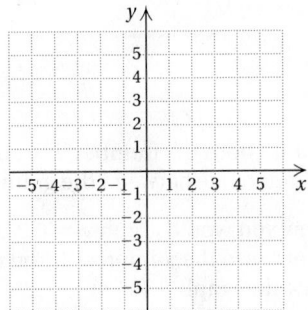

45. Draw a line that has slope $\frac{5}{3}$ and y-intercept $(0, -3)$.   [9.5a]

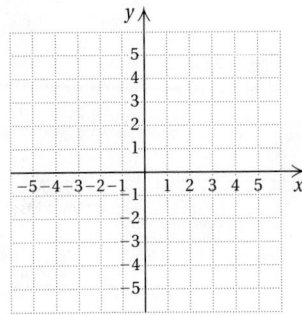

46. Graph $y = -\frac{3}{5}x + 2$ using the slope and the y-intercept.   [9.5a]

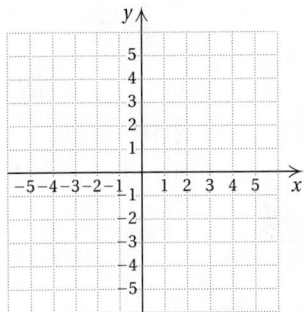

47. Graph $2y - 3x = 6$ using the slope and the y-intercept.   [9.5a]

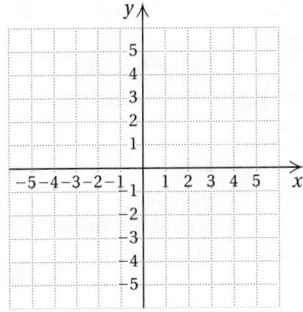

Determine whether the graphs of the equations are parallel, perpendicular, or neither.   [9.6a, b]

48. $4x + y = 6$,
$4x + y = 8$

49. $2x + y = 10$,
$y = \frac{1}{2}x - 4$

50. $x + 4y = 8$,
$x = -4y - 10$

51. $3x - y = 6$,
$3x + y = 8$

Determine whether the given point is a solution of the inequality $x - 2y > 1$.   [9.7a]

52. $(0, 0)$

53. $(1, 3)$

54. $(4, -1)$

Graph on a plane. [9.7b]

55. $x < y$

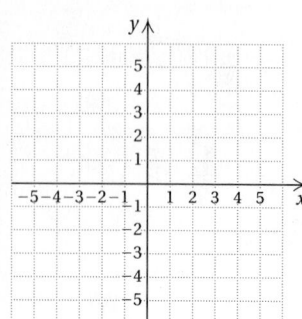

56. $x + 2y \geq 4$

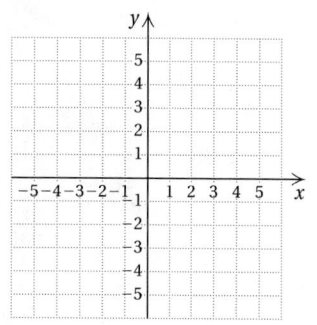

57. $x > -2$

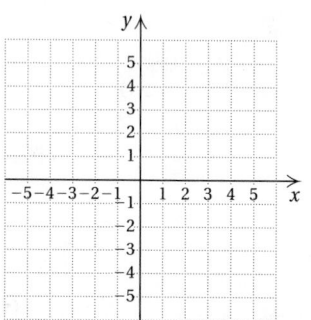

58. Select the statement that describes the graphs of the lines $-x + \frac{1}{2}y = -2$ and $2y + x - 8 = 0$. [9.6a, b]

  A. The lines are parallel.
  B. The lines are the same.
  C. The lines intersect and are not perpendicular.
  D. The lines are perpendicular.

59. Find the equation of the line with slope $-\frac{8}{3}$ and containing the point $(-3, 8)$. [9.4b]

  A. $y = -\frac{8}{3}x + \frac{55}{3}$ **B.** $y = -\frac{3}{8}$

  C. $y = -\frac{8}{3}x$ **D.** $8y + 3x = -3$

Synthesis

60. Find the area and the perimeter of a rectangle for which $(-2, 2)$, $(7, 2)$, and $(7, -3)$ are three of the vertices. [9.1a]

61. *Gondola Aerial Lift.* In Telluride, Colorado, there is a free gondola ride that provides a spectacular view of the town and the surrounding mountains. The gondolas that begin in the town at an elevation of 8725 ft travel 5750 ft to Station St. Sophia, whose altitude is 10,550 ft. They then continue 3913 ft to Mountain Village, whose elevation is 9500 ft. [9.3c]

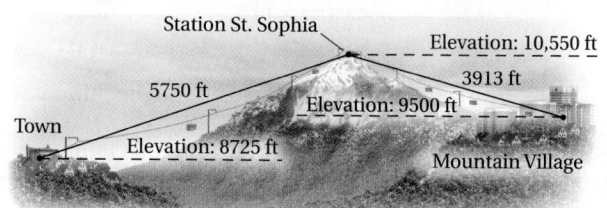

A visitor departs from the town at 11:55 A.M. and with no stop at Station St. Sophia reaches Mountain Village at 12:07 P.M.

  a) Find the gondola's average rate of ascent and descent, in feet per minute.
  b) Find the gondola's average rate of ascent and descent, in minutes per foot.

Understanding Through Discussion and Writing

1. Consider two equations of the type $Ax + By = C$. Explain how you would go about showing that their graphs are perpendicular. [9.6b]

2. Is the graph of any inequality in the form $y > mx + b$ shaded *above* the line $y = mx + b$? Why or why not? [9.7b]

3. Explain why the first coordinate of the y-intercept is always 0. [9.1d]

4. Graph $x < 1$ on both the number line and a plane, and explain the difference between the graphs. [9.7b]

5. Describe how you would graph $y = 0.37x + 2458$ using the slope and the y-intercept. You need not actually draw the graph. [9.5a]

6. Consider two equations of the type $Ax + By = C$. Explain how you would go about showing that their graphs are parallel. [9.6a]

Copyright © 2012 Pearson Education, Inc.

Test **For Extra Help**

CHAPTER Test Prep VIDEOS

Step-by-step test solutions are found on the Chapter Test Prep Videos available via the Video Resources on DVD, in *MyMathLab*, and on YouTube (search "BittingerDevMath" and click on "Channels").

In which quadrant is each point located?

1. $\left(-\frac{1}{2}, 7\right)$

2. $(-5, -6)$

Find the coordinates of each point.

3. A **4.** B

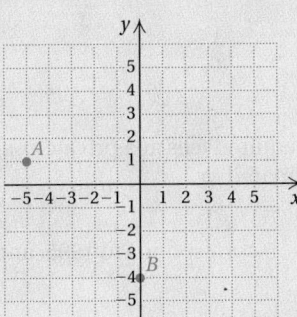

5. Show that the ordered pairs $(-4, -3)$ and $(-1, 3)$ are solutions of the equation $y - 2x = 5$. Then use the graph of the straight line containing the two points to determine another solution. Answers may vary.

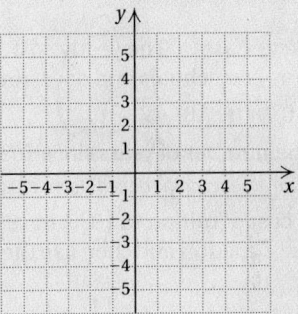

Graph each equation. Identify the y-intercept.

6. $y = 2x - 1$

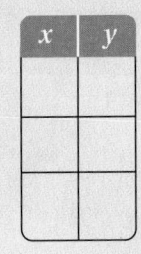
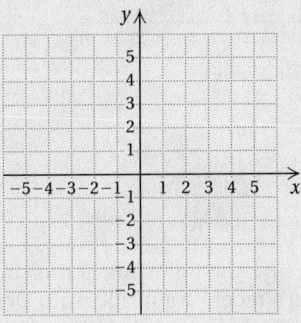

7. $y = -\frac{3}{2}x$

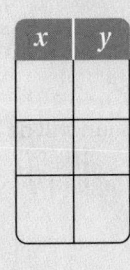
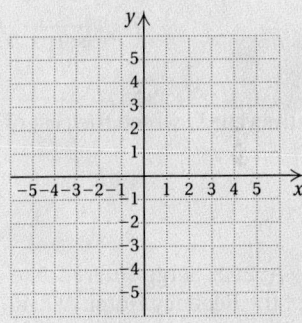

Graph each equation.

8. $2x + 8 = 0$

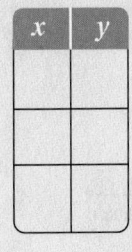
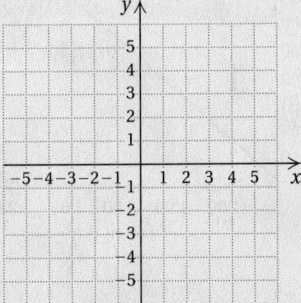

9. $y = 5$

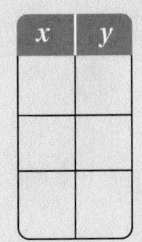
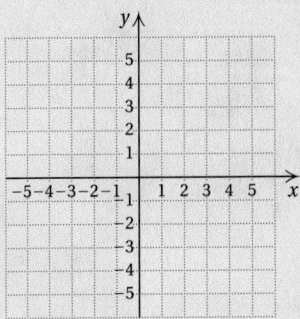

Find the intercepts of each equation. Then graph the equation.

10. $2x - 4y = -8$

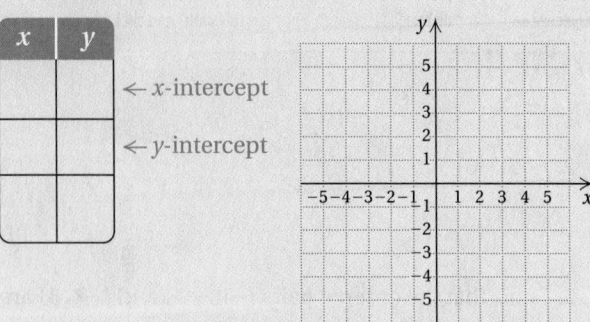

11. $2x - y = 3$

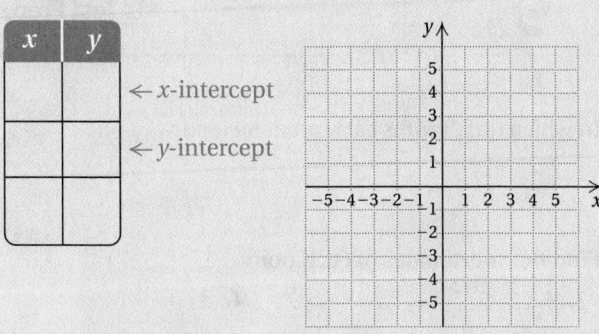

12. *Private-College Costs.* The yearly cost T, in thousands of dollars, of tuition and required fees at a private college (includes two- and four-year schools and does not include room and board) can be approximated by

$$T = 0.7n + 7.8,$$

where n is the number of years since 1990. That is, $n = 0$ corresponds to 1990, $n = 5$ corresponds to 1995, and so on.

Source: *Statistical Abstract of the United States*, 2009

a) Find the cost of tuition in 1990, in 1996, in 2005, and in 2010.

b) Graph the equation and then use the graph to estimate the cost of tuition in 2015.

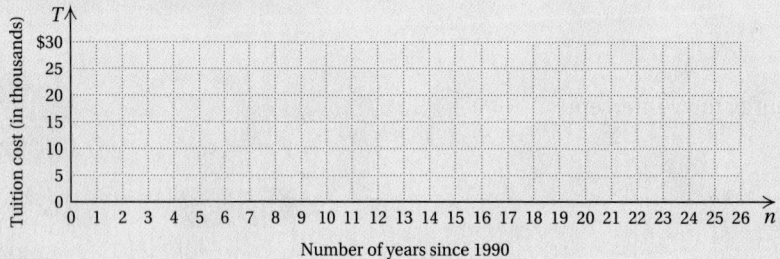

c) Predict the year in which the cost of tuition will be $28,800.

13. *Elevators.* At 2:38, Serge entered an elevator on the 34th floor of the Regency Hotel. At 2:40, he stepped off at the 5th floor.

a) Find the elevator's average rate of travel, in number of floors per minute.

b) Find the elevator's average rate of travel, in seconds per floor.

14. *Train Travel.* The following graph shows data concerning a recent train ride from Denver to Kansas City. At what rate did the train travel?

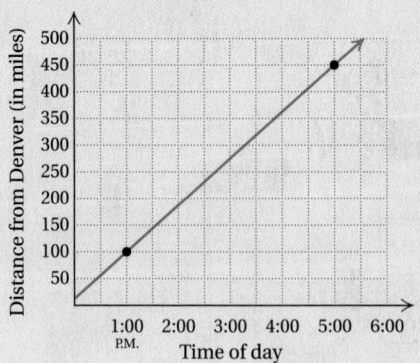

Copyright © 2012 Pearson Education, Inc.

15. Find the slope.

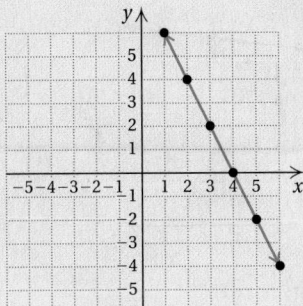

16. Graph the line containing $(-3, 1)$ and $(5, 4)$ and find the slope.

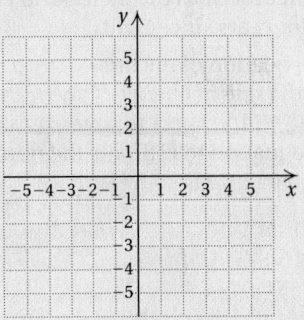

17. Find the slope, if it exists.
   a) $2x - 5y = 10$
   b) $x = -2$

18. *Navigation.* Capital Rapids drops 54 ft vertically over a horizontal distance of 1080 ft. What is the slope of the rapids?

19. Draw a graph of the line with slope $-\frac{3}{2}$ and y-intercept $(0, 1)$.

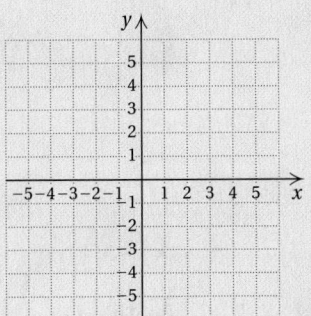

20. Graph $y = 2x - 3$ using the slope and the y-intercept.

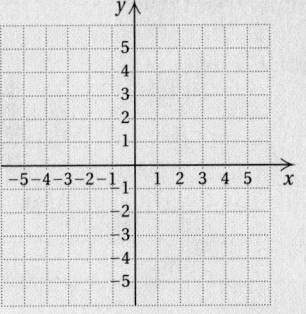

Find the slope and the y-intercept.

21. $y = 2x - \frac{1}{4}$

22. $-4x + 3y = -6$

Find an equation of the line with the given slope and y-intercept.

23. Slope: 1.8; y-intercept: $(0, -7)$

24. Slope: $-\frac{3}{8}$; y-intercept: $\left(0, -\frac{1}{8}\right)$

Find an equation of the line containing the given point and with the given slope.

25. $(3, 5), m = 1$

26. $(-2, 0), m = -3$

Find an equation of the line containing the given pair of points.

27. $(1, 1)$ and $(2, -2)$

28. $(4, -1)$ and $(-4, -3)$

29. *Egg Production.* The number of eggs produced in the United States has increased in recent years. The line graph at right describes the increase in egg production, in billions, for years since 2000.

   a) Find an equation of the line.
   b) What is the rate of change of the number of eggs produced with respect to time?
   c) Use the equation to estimate the number of eggs produced in 2012.

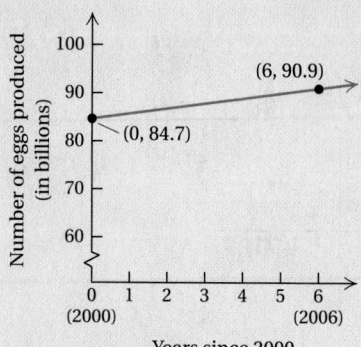

SOURCE: U.S. Department of Agriculture

Determine whether the graphs of the equations are parallel, perpendicular, or neither.

30. $2x + y = 8$,
    $2x + y = 4$

31. $2x + 5y = 2$,
    $y = 2x + 4$

32. $x + 2y = 8$,
    $-2x + y = 8$

Determine whether the given point is a solution of the inequality $3y - 2x < -2$.

33. $(0, 0)$

34. $(-4, -10)$

Graph on a plane.

35. $y > x - 1$

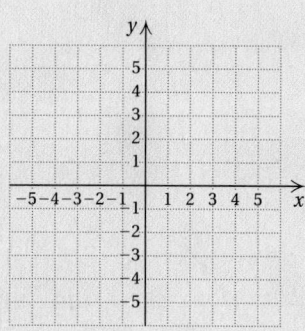

36. $2x - y \le 4$

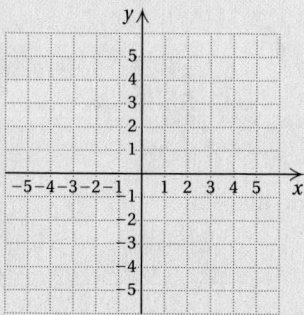

37. Select the statement that best describes the graphs of the lines $15x + 21y = 7$ and $35y + 14 = -25x$.

   A. The lines are parallel.
   B. The lines are the same.
   C. The lines intersect and are not perpendicular.
   D. The lines are perpendicular.

Synthesis

38. A diagonal of a square connects the points $(-3, -1)$ and $(2, 4)$. Find the area and the perimeter of the square.

39. Find the value of k such that $3x + 7y = 14$ and $ky - 7x = -3$ are perpendicular.

Copyright © 2012 Pearson Education, Inc.

Polynomials: Operations

Real-World Application

About 22,750,000 young people, ages 18–29, voted in the 2008 presidential election.
Convert the number 22,750,000 to scientific notation.

Source: Center for Information & Research on Civic Learning and Engagement, Tufts University

This problem appears as Exercise 64 in Section 10.2.

10.1

Integers as Exponents

OBJECTIVES

a Tell the meaning of exponential notation.

b Evaluate exponential expressions with exponents of 0 and 1.

c Evaluate algebraic expressions containing exponents.

d Use the product rule to multiply exponential expressions with like bases.

e Use the quotient rule to divide exponential expressions with like bases.

f Express an exponential expression involving negative exponents with positive exponents.

We introduced integer exponents of 2 and higher in Section 1.6. Here we consider 0 and 1, as well as negative integers, as exponents.

a Exponential Notation

An exponent of 2 or greater tells how many times the base is used as a factor. For example,

$$a \cdot a \cdot a \cdot a = a^4.$$

In this case, the **exponent** is 4 and the **base** is a. An expression for a power is called **exponential notation**.

$a^n \leftarrow$ This is the exponent.

↑
This is the base.

EXAMPLE 1 What is the meaning of 3^5? of n^4? of $(2n)^3$? of $50x^2$? of $(-n)^3$? of $-n^3$?

3^5 means $3 \cdot 3 \cdot 3 \cdot 3 \cdot 3$;	n^4 means $n \cdot n \cdot n \cdot n$;
$(2n)^3$ means $2n \cdot 2n \cdot 2n$;	$50x^2$ means $50 \cdot x \cdot x$;
$(-n)^3$ means $(-n) \cdot (-n) \cdot (-n)$;	$-n^3$ means $-1 \cdot n \cdot n \cdot n$

Do Margin Exercises 1–6.

We read exponential notation as follows: a^n is read the **nth power of a**, or simply **a to the nth**, or **a to the n**. We often read x^2 as "**x-squared**." The reason for this is that the area of a square of side x is $x \cdot x$, or x^2. We often read x^3 as "**x-cubed**." The reason for this is that the volume of a cube with length, width, and height x is $x \cdot x \cdot x$, or x^3.

SKILL TO REVIEW
Objective 7.1a: Evaluate algebraic expressions by substitution.

1. Evaluate $6y$ when $y = 4$.

2. Evaluate $\dfrac{m}{n}$ when $m = 48$ and $n = 8$.

What is the meaning of each of the following?

1. 5^4 **2.** x^5

3. $(3t)^2$ **4.** $3t^2$

5. $(-x)^4$ **6.** $-y^3$

Answers

Skill to Review:
1. 24   2. 6

Margin Exercises:
1. $5 \cdot 5 \cdot 5 \cdot 5$ 2. $x \cdot x \cdot x \cdot x \cdot x$
3. $3t \cdot 3t$ 4. $3 \cdot t \cdot t$
5. $(-x) \cdot (-x) \cdot (-x) \cdot (-x)$
6. $-1 \cdot y \cdot y \cdot y$

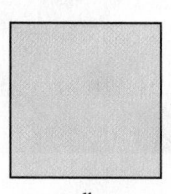
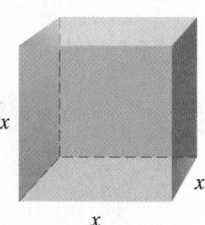

b One and Zero as Exponents

Look for a pattern in the following:

On each side, we **divide** by 8 at each step.	$8 \cdot 8 \cdot 8 \cdot 8 = 8^4$	On this side, the exponents **decrease** by 1 at each step.
	$8 \cdot 8 \cdot 8 = 8^3$	
	$8 \cdot 8 = 8^2$	
	$8 = 8^?$	
	$1 = 8^?$	

To continue the pattern, we would say that

$$8 = 8^1 \quad \text{and} \quad 1 = 8^0.$$

We make the following definition.

> ### EXPONENTS OF 0 AND 1
> $a^1 = a$, for any number a;
> $a^0 = 1$, for any nonzero number a

We consider 0^0 to be not defined. We will explain why later in this section.

EXAMPLE 2 Evaluate 5^1, $(-8)^1$, 3^0, $(-7.3)^0$, and $(186{,}892{,}046)^0$.

$5^1 = 5;$ $(-8)^1 = -8;$ $3^0 = 1;$
$(-7.3)^0 = 1;$ $(186{,}892{,}046)^0 = 1$

Do Exercises 7–12.

Do Exercises 7–12.

c Evaluating Algebraic Expressions

Algebraic expressions can involve exponential notation. For example, the following are algebraic expressions:

$$x^4, \quad (3x)^3 - 2, \quad a^2 + 2ab + b^2.$$

We evaluate algebraic expressions by replacing variables with numbers and following the rules for order of operations.

EXAMPLE 3 Evaluate $1000 - x^4$ when $x = 5$.

$$\begin{aligned}
1000 - x^4 &= 1000 - 5^4 &&\text{Substituting}\\
&= 1000 - 5 \cdot 5 \cdot 5 \cdot 5\\
&= 1000 - 625\\
&= 375
\end{aligned}$$

EXAMPLE 4 *Area of a Compact Disc.* The standard compact disc used for software and music has a radius of 6 cm. Find the area of such a CD (ignoring the hole in the middle).

$$\begin{aligned}
A &= \pi r^2\\
&= \pi \cdot (6\,\text{cm})^2\\
&= \pi \cdot 6\,\text{cm} \cdot 6\,\text{cm}\\
&\approx 3.14 \times 36\,\text{cm}^2\\
&= 113.04\,\text{cm}^2
\end{aligned}$$

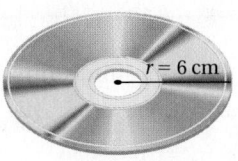

$r = 6$ cm

In Example 4, "cm^2" means "square centimeters" and "$\approx$" means "is approximately equal to."

EXAMPLE 5 Evaluate $(5x)^3$ when $x = -2$.

When we evaluate with a negative number, we often use extra parentheses to show the substitution.

$$\begin{aligned}
(5x)^3 &= [5 \cdot (-2)]^3 &&\text{Substituting}\\
&= [-10]^3 &&\text{Multiplying within brackets first}\\
&= [-10] \cdot [-10] \cdot [-10]\\
&= -1000 &&\text{Evaluating the power}
\end{aligned}$$

Evaluate.

7. 6^1 **8.** 7^0

9. $(8.4)^1$ **10.** 8654^0

11. $(-1.4)^1$ **12.** 0^1

STUDY TIPS

HELPING OTHERS HELPS YOU

When you are confident in your command of a topic, don't hesitate to help classmates who are having trouble understanding it. You will find that your understanding and retention of a concept will deepen when you explain it to someone else.

Answers

7. 6   **8.** 1   **9.** 8.4   **10.** 1
11. −1.4   **12.** 0

13. Evaluate t^3 when $t = 5$.

14. Evaluate $-5x^5$ when $x = -2$.

15. Find the area of a circle when $r = 32$ cm. Use 3.14 for π.

16. Evaluate $200 - a^4$ when $a = 3$.

17. Evaluate $t^1 - 4$ and $t^0 - 4$ when $t = 7$.

18. a) Evaluate $(4t)^2$ when $t = -3$.
   b) Evaluate $4t^2$ when $t = -3$.
   c) Determine whether $(4t)^2$ and $4t^2$ are equivalent.

EXAMPLE 6   Evaluate $5x^3$ when $x = -2$.

$$5x^3 = 5 \cdot (-2)^3 \qquad \text{Substituting}$$
$$= 5 \cdot (-2) \cdot (-2) \cdot (-2) \qquad \text{Evaluating the power first}$$
$$= 5(-8) \qquad (-2)(-2)(-2) = -8$$
$$= -40$$

Recall that two expressions are equivalent if they have the same value for all meaningful replacements. Note that Examples 5 and 6 show that $(5x)^3$ and $5x^3$ are *not* equivalent—that is, $(5x)^3 \neq 5x^3$.

Do Exercises 13–18.

(d) Multiplying Powers with Like Bases

There are several rules for manipulating exponential notation to obtain equivalent expressions. We first consider multiplying powers with like bases:

$$a^3 \cdot a^2 = \underbrace{(a \cdot a \cdot a)}_{\text{3 factors}}\underbrace{(a \cdot a)}_{\text{2 factors}} = \underbrace{a \cdot a \cdot a \cdot a \cdot a}_{\text{5 factors}} = a^5.$$

Since an integer exponent greater than 1 tells how many times we use a base as a factor, then $(a \cdot a \cdot a)(a \cdot a) = a \cdot a \cdot a \cdot a \cdot a = a^5$ by the associative law. Note that the exponent in a^5 is the sum of those in $a^3 \cdot a^2$. That is, $3 + 2 = 5$. Likewise,

$$b^4 \cdot b^3 = (b \cdot b \cdot b \cdot b)(b \cdot b \cdot b) = b^7, \quad \text{where} \quad 4 + 3 = 7.$$

Adding the exponents gives the correct result.

THE PRODUCT RULE

For any number a and any positive integers m and n,

$$a^m \cdot a^n = a^{m+n}.$$

(When multiplying with exponential notation, if the bases are the same, keep the base and add the exponents.)

EXAMPLES   Multiply and simplify.

7. $5^6 \cdot 5^2 = 5^{6+2}$ Adding exponents: $a^m \cdot a^n = a^{m+n}$
$$= 5^8$$

8. $m^5 m^{10} m^3 = m^{5+10+3} = m^{18}$

9. $x \cdot x^8 = x^1 \cdot x^8$ Writing x as x^1
$$= x^{1+8}$$
$$= x^9$$

10. $(a^3 b^2)(a^3 b^5) = (a^3 a^3)(b^2 b^5)$
$$= a^6 b^7$$

11. $(4y)^6 (4y)^3 = (4y)^{6+3} = (4y)^9$

Do Exercises 19–23.

Multiply and simplify.

19. $3^5 \cdot 3^5$

20. $x^4 \cdot x^6$

21. $p^4 p^{12} p^8$

22. $x \cdot x^4$

23. $(a^2 b^3)(a^7 b^5)$

Answers

13. 125   **14.** 160   **15.** 3215.36 cm^2
16. 119   **17.** 3; -3 **18. (a)** 144; **(b)** 36;
(c) no   **19.** 3^{10} **20.** x^{10} **21.** p^{24}
22. x^5 **23.** $a^9 b^8$

(e) Dividing Powers with Like Bases

The following suggests a rule for dividing powers with like bases, such as a^5/a^2:

$$\frac{a^5}{a^2} = \frac{a \cdot a \cdot a \cdot a \cdot a}{a \cdot a} = \frac{a \cdot a \cdot a \cdot a \cdot a}{1 \cdot a \cdot a} = \frac{a \cdot a \cdot a}{1} \cdot \frac{a \cdot a}{a \cdot a}$$

$$= \frac{a \cdot a \cdot a}{1} \cdot 1 = a \cdot a \cdot a = a^3.$$

Note that the exponent in a^3 is the difference of those in $a^5 \div a^2$. That is, $5 - 2 = 3$. In a similar way, we have

$$\frac{t^9}{t^4} = \frac{t \cdot t \cdot t \cdot t \cdot t \cdot t \cdot t \cdot t \cdot t}{t \cdot t \cdot t \cdot t} = t^5, \quad \text{where} \quad 9 - 4 = 5.$$

Subtracting exponents gives the correct answer.

THE QUOTIENT RULE

For any nonzero number a and any positive integers m and n,

$$\frac{a^m}{a^n} = a^{m-n}.$$

(When dividing with exponential notation, if the bases are the same, keep the base and subtract the exponent of the denominator from the exponent of the numerator.)

EXAMPLES Divide and simplify.

12. $\dfrac{6^5}{6^3} = 6^{5-3}$ Subtracting exponents

$\qquad = 6^2$

13. $\dfrac{x^8}{x^1} = x^{8-1}$

$\qquad = x^7$

14. $\dfrac{(3t)^{12}}{(3t)^2} = (3t)^{12-2}$

$\qquad = (3t)^{10}$

15. $\dfrac{p^5 q^7}{p^2 q^5} = \dfrac{p^5}{p^2} \cdot \dfrac{q^7}{q^5} = p^{5-2} q^{7-5}$

$\qquad = p^3 q^2$

The quotient rule can also be used to explain the definition of 0 as an exponent. Consider the expression a^4/a^4, where a is nonzero:

$$\frac{a^4}{a^4} = \frac{a \cdot a \cdot a \cdot a}{a \cdot a \cdot a \cdot a} = 1.$$

This is true because the numerator and the denominator are the same. Now suppose we apply the rule for dividing powers with the same base:

$$\frac{a^4}{a^4} = a^{4-4} = a^0.$$

Since $a^4/a^4 = 1$ and $a^4/a^4 = a^0$, it follows that $a^0 = 1$, when $a \neq 0$.

We can explain why we do not define 0^0 using the quotient rule. We know that 0^0 is 0^{1-1}. But 0^{1-1} is also equal to $0^1/0^1$, or $0/0$. We have already seen that division by 0 is not defined, so 0^0 is also not defined.

Do Exercises 24–27.

Divide and simplify.

24. $\dfrac{4^5}{4^2}$

25. $\dfrac{y^6}{y^2}$

26. $\dfrac{p^{10}}{p}$

27. $\dfrac{a^7 b^6}{a^3 b^4}$

Answers

24. 4^3 **25.** y^4 **26.** p^9 **27.** $a^4 b^2$

f Negative Integers as Exponents

We can use the rule for dividing powers with like bases to lead us to a definition of exponential notation when the exponent is a negative integer. Consider $5^3/5^7$ and first simplify it using procedures we have learned for working with fractions:

$$\frac{5^3}{5^7} = \frac{5 \cdot 5 \cdot 5}{5 \cdot 5 \cdot 5 \cdot 5 \cdot 5 \cdot 5 \cdot 5} = \frac{5 \cdot 5 \cdot 5 \cdot 1}{5 \cdot 5 \cdot 5 \cdot 5 \cdot 5 \cdot 5 \cdot 5}$$

$$= \frac{5 \cdot 5 \cdot 5}{5 \cdot 5 \cdot 5} \cdot \frac{1}{5 \cdot 5 \cdot 5 \cdot 5} = \frac{1}{5^4}.$$

Now we apply the rule for dividing exponential expressions with the same bases. Then

$$\frac{5^3}{5^7} = 5^{3-7} = 5^{-4}.$$

From these two expressions for $5^3/5^7$, it follows that

$$5^{-4} = \frac{1}{5^4}.$$

This leads to our definition of negative exponents.

NEGATIVE EXPONENT

For any real number a that is nonzero and any integer n,

$$a^{-n} = \frac{1}{a^n}.$$

In fact, the numbers a^n and a^{-n} are reciprocals because

$$a^n \cdot a^{-n} = a^n \cdot \frac{1}{a^n} = \frac{a^n}{a^n} = 1.$$

The following is another way to arrive at the definition of negative exponents.

On each side, we **divide** by 5 at each step.		On this side, the exponents **decrease** by 1 at each step.
	$5 \cdot 5 \cdot 5 \cdot 5 = 5^4$	
	$5 \cdot 5 \cdot 5 = 5^3$	
	$5 \cdot 5 = 5^2$	
	$5 = 5^1$	
	$1 = 5^0$	
	$\dfrac{1}{5} = 5^?$	
	$\dfrac{1}{25} = 5^?$	

To continue the pattern, it should follow that

$$\frac{1}{5} = \frac{1}{5^1} = 5^{-1} \quad \text{and} \quad \frac{1}{25} = \frac{1}{5^2} = 5^{-2}.$$

EXAMPLES Express using positive exponents. Then simplify.

16. $4^{-2} = \dfrac{1}{4^2} = \dfrac{1}{16}$

17. $(-3)^{-2} = \dfrac{1}{(-3)^2} = \dfrac{1}{(-3)(-3)} = \dfrac{1}{9}$

18. $m^{-3} = \dfrac{1}{m^3}$

19. $ab^{-1} = a\left(\dfrac{1}{b^1}\right) = a\left(\dfrac{1}{b}\right) = \dfrac{a}{b}$

20. $\dfrac{1}{x^{-3}} = x^{-(-3)} = x^3$

21. $3c^{-5} = 3\left(\dfrac{1}{c^5}\right) = \dfrac{3}{c^5}$

Example 20 might also be done as follows:

$$\dfrac{1}{x^{-3}} = \dfrac{1}{\dfrac{1}{x^3}} = 1 \cdot \dfrac{x^3}{1} = x^3.$$

------- *Caution!* -------

As shown in Examples 16 and 17, a negative exponent does not necessarily mean that an expression is negative.

> Do Exercises 28–33.

The rules for multiplying and dividing powers with like bases hold when exponents are 0 or negative.

EXAMPLES Simplify. Write the result using positive exponents.

22. $7^{-3} \cdot 7^6 = 7^{-3+6}$ Adding exponents

      $= 7^3$

23. $x^4 \cdot x^{-3} = x^{4+(-3)} = x^1 = x$

24. $\dfrac{5^4}{5^{-2}} = 5^{4-(-2)}$ Subtracting exponents

      $= 5^{4+2} = 5^6$

25. $\dfrac{x}{x^7} = x^{1-7} = x^{-6} = \dfrac{1}{x^6}$

26. $\dfrac{b^{-4}}{b^{-5}} = b^{-4-(-5)}$

      $= b^{-4+5} = b^1 = b$

27. $y^{-4} \cdot y^{-8} = y^{-4+(-8)}$

      $= y^{-12} = \dfrac{1}{y^{12}}$

> Do Exercises 34–38.

The following is a summary of the definitions and rules for exponents that we have considered in this section.

DEFINITIONS AND RULES FOR EXPONENTS

1 as an exponent:	$a^1 = a$
0 as an exponent:	$a^0 = 1, a \neq 0$
Negative integers as exponents:	$a^{-n} = \dfrac{1}{a^n}, \dfrac{1}{a^{-n}} = a^n; a \neq 0$
Product Rule:	$a^m \cdot a^n = a^{m+n}$
Quotient Rule:	$\dfrac{a^m}{a^n} = a^{m-n}, a \neq 0$

Express with positive exponents. Then simplify.

28. 4^{-3} **29.** 5^{-2}

30. 2^{-4} **31.** $(-2)^{-3}$

32. $4p^{-3}$ **33.** $\dfrac{1}{x^{-2}}$

Simplify.

34. $5^{-2} \cdot 5^4$

35. $x^{-3} \cdot x^{-4}$

36. $\dfrac{7^{-2}}{7^3}$

37. $\dfrac{b^{-2}}{b^{-3}}$

38. $\dfrac{t}{t^{-5}}$

Answers

28. $\dfrac{1}{4^3} = \dfrac{1}{64}$ **29.** $\dfrac{1}{5^2} = \dfrac{1}{25}$ **30.** $\dfrac{1}{2^4} = \dfrac{1}{16}$
31. $\dfrac{1}{(-2)^3} = -\dfrac{1}{8}$ **32.** $\dfrac{4}{p^3}$ **33.** x^2
34. 5^2 **35.** $\dfrac{1}{x^7}$ **36.** $\dfrac{1}{7^5}$ **37.** b **38.** t^6

10.1
Exercise Set

For Extra Help
MyMathLab

Math XL
PRACTICE   WATCH   DOWNLOAD   READ   REVIEW

ⓐ What is the meaning of each of the following?

1. 3^4 **2.** 4^3 **3.** $(-1.1)^5$ **4.** $(87.2)^6$ **5.** $\left(\dfrac{2}{3}\right)^4$ **6.** $\left(-\dfrac{5}{8}\right)^3$

7. $(7p)^2$ **8.** $(11c)^3$ **9.** $8k^3$ **10.** $17x^2$ **11.** $-6y^4$ **12.** $-q^5$

ⓑ Evaluate.

13. $a^0, a \neq 0$ **14.** $t^0, t \neq 0$ **15.** b^1 **16.** c^1 **17.** $\left(\dfrac{2}{3}\right)^0$

18. $\left(-\dfrac{5}{8}\right)^0$ **19.** $(-7.03)^1$ **20.** $\left(\dfrac{4}{5}\right)^1$ **21.** 8.38^0 **22.** 8.38^1

23. $(ab)^1$ **24.** $(ab)^0, a, b \neq 0$ **25.** ab^0 **26.** ab^1

ⓒ Evaluate.

27. m^3, when $m = 3$ **28.** x^6, when $x = 2$ **29.** p^1, when $p = 19$ **30.** x^{19}, when $x = 0$

31. $-x^4$, when $x = -3$ **32.** $-2y^7$, when $x = 2$ **33.** x^4, when $x = 4$ **34.** y^{15}, when $y = 1$

35. $y^2 - 7$, when $y = -10$ **36.** $z^5 + 5$, when $z = -2$ **37.** $161 - b^2$, when $b = 5$ **38.** $325 - v^3$, when $v = -3$

39. $x^1 + 3$ and $x^0 + 3$, when $x = 7$ **40.** $y^0 - 8$ and $y^1 - 8$, when $y = -3$

41. Find the area of a circle when $r = 34$ ft. Use 3.14 for π.

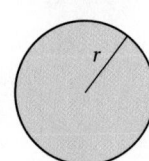

42. The area A of a square with sides of length s is given by $A = s^2$. Find the area of a square with sides of length 24 m.

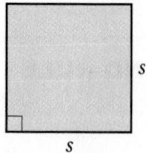

ⓕ Express using positive exponents. Then simplify.

43. 3^{-2} **44.** 2^{-3} **45.** 10^{-3} **46.** 5^{-4} **47.** a^{-3}

Copyright © 2012 Pearson Education, Inc.

48. x^{-2}

49. $\dfrac{1}{8^{-2}}$

50. $\dfrac{1}{2^{-5}}$

51. $\dfrac{1}{y^{-4}}$

52. $\dfrac{1}{t^{-7}}$

53. $5z^{-4}$

54. $6n^{-5}$

55. xy^{-2}

56. ab^{-3}

Express using negative exponents.

57. $\dfrac{1}{4^3}$

58. $\dfrac{1}{5^2}$

59. $\dfrac{1}{x^3}$

60. $\dfrac{1}{y^2}$

61. $\dfrac{1}{a^5}$

62. $\dfrac{1}{b^7}$

(d), (f) Multiply and simplify.

63. $2^4 \cdot 2^3$

64. $3^5 \cdot 3^2$

65. $8^5 \cdot 8^9$

66. $n^3 \cdot n^{20}$

67. $x^4 \cdot x$

68. $y \cdot y^9$

69. $9^{17} \cdot 9^{21}$

70. $t^0 \cdot t^{16}$

71. $(3y)^4(3y)^8$

72. $(2t)^8(2t)^{17}$

73. $(7y)^1(7y)^{16}$

74. $(8x)^0(8x)^1$

75. $3^{-5} \cdot 3^8$

76. $5^{-8} \cdot 5^9$

77. $x^{-2} \cdot x^2$

78. $x \cdot x^{-1}$

79. $x^{14} \cdot x^3$

80. $x^9 \cdot x^4$

81. $x^{-7} \cdot x^{-6}$

82. $y^{-5} \cdot y^{-8}$

83. $a^{11} \cdot a^{-3} \cdot a^{-18}$

84. $a^{-11} \cdot a^{-3} \cdot a^{-7}$

85. $(s^2t^3)(st^4)$

86. $(m^4n)(m^2n^7)$

e , **f**   Divide and simplify.

87. $\dfrac{7^5}{7^2}$ **88.** $\dfrac{5^8}{5^6}$ **89.** $\dfrac{y^9}{y}$ **90.** $\dfrac{x^{11}}{x}$

91. $\dfrac{16^2}{16^8}$ **92.** $\dfrac{7^2}{7^9}$ **93.** $\dfrac{m^6}{m^{12}}$ **94.** $\dfrac{a^3}{a^4}$

95. $\dfrac{(8x)^6}{(8x)^{10}}$ **96.** $\dfrac{(8t)^4}{(8t)^{11}}$ **97.** $\dfrac{(2y)^9}{(2y)^9}$ **98.** $\dfrac{(6y)^7}{(6y)^7}$

99. $\dfrac{x}{x^{-1}}$ **100.** $\dfrac{y^8}{y}$ **101.** $\dfrac{x^7}{x^{-2}}$ **102.** $\dfrac{t^8}{t^{-3}}$

103. $\dfrac{z^{-6}}{z^{-2}}$ **104.** $\dfrac{x^{-9}}{x^{-3}}$ **105.** $\dfrac{x^{-5}}{x^{-8}}$ **106.** $\dfrac{y^{-2}}{y^{-9}}$

107. $\dfrac{m^{-9}}{m^{-9}}$ **108.** $\dfrac{x^{-7}}{x^{-7}}$ **109.** $\dfrac{a^5 b^3}{a^2 b}$ **110.** $\dfrac{s^8 t^4}{s t^3}$

Matching.   In Exercises 111 and 112, match each item in the first column with the appropriate item in the second column by drawing connecting lines. Items in the second column may be used more than once.

111. 5^2 $-\dfrac{1}{10}$

      5^{-2} $\dfrac{1}{10}$

      $\left(\dfrac{1}{5}\right)^2$ $-\dfrac{1}{25}$

      $\left(\dfrac{1}{5}\right)^{-2}$ 10

      -5^2 25

      $(-5)^2$ -25

      $-\left(-\dfrac{1}{5}\right)^2$ $\dfrac{1}{25}$

      $\left(-\dfrac{1}{5}\right)^{-2}$ -10

112. $-\left(\dfrac{1}{8}\right)^2$ 16

      $\left(\dfrac{1}{8}\right)^{-2}$ -16

      8^{-2} 64

      8^2 -64

      -8^2 $\dfrac{1}{64}$

      $(-8)^2$ $-\dfrac{1}{64}$

      $\left(-\dfrac{1}{8}\right)^{-2}$ $-\dfrac{1}{16}$

      $\left(-\dfrac{1}{8}\right)^2$ $\dfrac{1}{16}$

Copyright © 2012 Pearson Education, Inc.

Skill Maintenance

Solve. [8.6a]

113. *Cutting a Submarine Sandwich.* A 12-in. submarine sandwich is cut into two pieces. One piece is twice as long as the other. How long are the pieces?

114. *Book Pages.* The sum of the page numbers on the facing pages of a book is 457. Find the page numbers.

115. The perimeter of a rectangle is 640 ft. The length is 15 ft more than the width. Find the area of the rectangle.

116. The first angle of a triangle is 24° more than the second. The third angle is twice the first. Find the measures of the angles of the triangle.

Solve. [8.3c]

117. $-6(2 - x) + 10(5x - 7) = 10$

118. $-10(x - 4) = 5(2x + 5) - 7$

Factor. [7.7d]

119. $4x - 12 + 24y$

120. $256 - 2a - 4b$

Synthesis

Determine whether each of the following is correct.

121. $(x + 1)^2 = x^2 + 1$

122. $(x - 1)^2 = x^2 - 2x + 1$

123. $(5x)^0 = 5x^0$

124. $\dfrac{x^3}{x^5} = x^2$

Simplify.

125. $(y^{2x})(y^{3x})$

126. $a^{5k} \div a^{3k}$

127. $\dfrac{a^{6t}(a^{7t})}{a^{9t}}$

128. $\dfrac{\left(\frac{1}{2}\right)^4}{\left(\frac{1}{2}\right)^5}$

129. $\dfrac{(0.8)^5}{(0.8)^3(0.8)^2}$

130. $\dfrac{(x - 3)^5}{x - 3}$

Use $>$, $<$, or $=$ for $\square$ to write a true sentence.

131. $3^5 \;\square\; 3^4$

132. $4^2 \;\square\; 4^3$

133. $4^3 \;\square\; 5^3$

134. $4^3 \;\square\; 3^4$

Evaluate.

135. $\dfrac{1}{-z^4}$, when $z = -10$

136. $\dfrac{1}{-z^5}$, when $z = -0.1$

137. Determine whether $(a + b)^2$ and $a^2 + b^2$ are equivalent. (*Hint*: Choose values for a and b and evaluate.)

10.2

Exponents and Scientific Notation

OBJECTIVES

a Use the power rule to raise powers to powers.

b Raise a product to a power and a quotient to a power.

c Convert between scientific notation and decimal notation.

d Multiply and divide using scientific notation.

e Solve applied problems using scientific notation.

We now add to our ability to work with exponential expressions by considering three more rules. The rules are also applied to a new way to name numbers called *scientific notation*.

a Raising Powers to Powers

Consider an expression like $(3^2)^4$. We are raising 3^2 to the fourth power:

$$(3^2)^4 = (3^2)(3^2)(3^2)(3^2)$$
$$= (3 \cdot 3)(3 \cdot 3)(3 \cdot 3)(3 \cdot 3)$$
$$= 3 \cdot 3 \cdot 3 \cdot 3 \cdot 3 \cdot 3 \cdot 3 \cdot 3$$
$$= 3^8.$$

Note that in this case we could have multiplied the exponents:

$$(3^2)^4 = 3^{2 \cdot 4} = 3^8.$$

Likewise, $(y^8)^3 = (y^8)(y^8)(y^8) = y^{24}$. Once again, we get the same result if we multiply the exponents:

$$(y^8)^3 = y^{8 \cdot 3} = y^{24}.$$

THE POWER RULE

For any real number a and any integers m and n,

$$(a^m)^n = a^{mn}.$$

(To raise a power to a power, multiply the exponents.)

EXAMPLES Simplify. Express the answers using positive exponents.

1. $(3^5)^4 = 3^{5 \cdot 4}$ Multiplying
$= 3^{20}$ exponents

2. $(2^2)^5 = 2^{2 \cdot 5} = 2^{10}$

3. $(y^{-5})^7 = y^{-5 \cdot 7} = y^{-35} = \dfrac{1}{y^{35}}$

4. $(x^4)^{-2} = x^{4(-2)} = x^{-8} = \dfrac{1}{x^8}$

5. $(a^{-4})^{-6} = a^{(-4)(-6)} = a^{24}$

Do Exercises 1–4.

b Raising a Product or a Quotient to a Power

When an expression inside parentheses is raised to a power, the inside expression is the base. Let's compare $2a^3$ and $(2a)^3$:

$$2a^3 = 2 \cdot a \cdot a \cdot a; \quad \text{The base is } a.$$

$$(2a)^3 = (2a)(2a)(2a) \qquad \text{The base is } 2a.$$
$$= (2 \cdot 2 \cdot 2)(a \cdot a \cdot a) \qquad \text{Using the associative and commutative}$$
$$= 2^3 a^3 \qquad \text{laws of multiplication to regroup}$$
$$\qquad\qquad\qquad\qquad \text{the factors}$$
$$= 8a^3.$$

Simplify. Express the answers using positive exponents.

1. $(3^4)^5$ **2.** $(x^{-3})^4$

3. $(y^{-5})^{-3}$ **4.** $(x^4)^{-8}$

Answers

1. 3^{20} 2. $\dfrac{1}{x^{12}}$ 3. y^{15} 4. $\dfrac{1}{x^{32}}$

We see that $2a^3$ and $(2a)^3$ are *not* equivalent. We also see that we can evaluate the power $(2a)^3$ by raising each factor to the power 3. This leads us to the following rule for raising a product to a power.

RAISING A PRODUCT TO A POWER

For any real numbers a and b and any integer n,

$$(ab)^n = a^n b^n.$$

(To raise a product to the nth power, raise each factor to the nth power.)

EXAMPLES Simplify.

6. $(4x^2)^3 = (4^1 x^2)^3$ Since $4 = 4^1$

       $= (4^1)^3 \cdot (x^2)^3$ Raising *each* factor to the third power

       $= 4^3 \cdot x^6 = 64x^6$

7. $(5x^3 y^5 z^2)^4 = 5^4(x^3)^4(y^5)^4(z^2)^4$ Raising *each* factor to the fourth power

       $= 625x^{12}y^{20}z^8$

8. $(-5x^4 y^3)^3 = (-5)^3(x^4)^3(y^3)^3$

       $= -125x^{12}y^9$

9. $[(-x)^{25}]^2 = (-x)^{50}$ Using the power rule

       $= (-1 \cdot x)^{50}$ Using the property of -1 (Section 7.8)

       $= (-1)^{50}x^{50}$

       $= 1 \cdot x^{50}$ The product of an even number of negative factors is positive.

       $= x^{50}$

10. $(5x^2 y^{-2})^3 = 5^3(x^2)^3(y^{-2})^3 = 125x^6 y^{-6}$ Be sure to raise *each* factor to the third power.

$$= \frac{125x^6}{y^6}$$

11. $(3x^3 y^{-5} z^2)^4 = 3^4(x^3)^4(y^{-5})^4(z^2)^4 = 81x^{12}y^{-20}z^8 = \dfrac{81x^{12}z^8}{y^{20}}$

12. $(-x^4)^{-3} = (-1 \cdot x^4)^{-3} = (-1)^{-3} \cdot x^{4(-3)} = (-1)^{-3} \cdot x^{-12}$

$$= \frac{1}{(-1)^3} \cdot \frac{1}{x^{12}} = \frac{1}{-1} \cdot \frac{1}{x^{12}} = -\frac{1}{x^{12}}$$

13. $(-2x^{-5}y^4)^{-4} = (-2)^{-4}(x^{-5})^{-4}(y^4)^{-4} = \dfrac{1}{(-2)^4} \cdot x^{20} \cdot y^{-16}$

$$= \frac{1}{16} \cdot x^{20} \cdot \frac{1}{y^{16}} = \frac{x^{20}}{16y^{16}}$$

Do Exercises 5–11.

Simplify.

5. $(2x^5 y^{-3})^4$

6. $(5x^5 y^{-6} z^{-3})^2$

7. $[(-x)^{37}]^2$

8. $(3y^{-2}x^{-5}z^8)^3$

9. $(-y^8)^{-3}$

10. $(-2x^4)^{-2}$

11. $(-3x^2 y^{-5})^{-3}$

Answers

5. $\dfrac{16x^{20}}{y^{12}}$ **6.** $\dfrac{25x^{10}}{y^{12}z^6}$ **7.** x^{74} **8.** $\dfrac{27z^{24}}{y^6 x^{15}}$

9. $-\dfrac{1}{y^{24}}$ **10.** $\dfrac{1}{4x^8}$ **11.** $-\dfrac{y^{15}}{27x^6}$

There is a similar rule for raising a quotient to a power.

RAISING A QUOTIENT TO A POWER

For any real numbers a and b, $b \neq 0$, and any integer n,

$$\left(\frac{a}{b}\right)^n = \frac{a^n}{b^n}.$$

(To raise a quotient to the nth power, raise both the numerator and the denominator to the nth power.) Also,

$$\left(\frac{a}{b}\right)^{-n} = \left(\frac{b}{a}\right)^n = \frac{b^n}{a^n}, \ a \neq 0.$$

EXAMPLES Simplify.

14. $\left(\dfrac{x^2}{4}\right)^3 = \dfrac{(x^2)^3}{4^3} = \dfrac{x^6}{64}$

15. $\left(\dfrac{3a^4}{b^3}\right)^2 = \dfrac{(3a^4)^2}{(b^3)^2} = \dfrac{3^2(a^4)^2}{b^{3\cdot2}} = \dfrac{9a^8}{b^6}$

16. $\left(\dfrac{y^2}{2z^{-5}}\right)^4 = \dfrac{(y^2)^4}{(2z^{-5})^4} = \dfrac{(y^2)^4}{2^4(z^{-5})^4} = \dfrac{y^8}{16z^{-20}} = \dfrac{y^8 z^{20}}{16}$

17. $\left(\dfrac{y^3}{5}\right)^{-2} = \dfrac{(y^3)^{-2}}{5^{-2}} = \dfrac{y^{-6}}{5^{-2}} = \dfrac{\frac{1}{y^6}}{\frac{1}{5^2}} = \dfrac{1}{y^6} \div \dfrac{1}{5^2} = \dfrac{1}{y^6} \cdot \dfrac{5^2}{1} = \dfrac{25}{y^6}$

Example 17 might also be done as follows:

$$\left(\frac{y^3}{5}\right)^{-2} = \left(\frac{5}{y^3}\right)^2 \qquad \left(\frac{a}{b}\right)^{-n} = \left(\frac{b}{a}\right)^n$$

$$= \frac{5^2}{(y^3)^2} = \frac{25}{y^6}.$$

Do Exercises 12–15.

(c) Scientific Notation

There are many kinds of symbols, or notation, for numbers. You are already familiar with fraction notation, decimal notation, and percent notation. Now we study another, **scientific notation**, which makes use of exponential notation. Scientific notation is especially useful when calculations involve very large or very small numbers. The following are examples of scientific notation.

① *Niagara Falls*: On the Canadian side, the amount of water that spills over the falls in 1 day during the summer is about

$$4.9793 \times 10^{10} \text{ gal} = 49{,}793{,}000{,}000 \text{ gal}.$$

Simplify.

12. $\left(\dfrac{x^6}{5}\right)^2$

13. $\left(\dfrac{2t^5}{w^4}\right)^3$

14. $\left(\dfrac{a^4}{3b^{-2}}\right)^3$

15. $\left(\dfrac{x^4}{3}\right)^{-2}$
   Do this two ways.

Answers

12. $\dfrac{x^{12}}{25}$ 13. $\dfrac{8t^{15}}{w^{12}}$ 14. $\dfrac{a^{12}b^6}{27}$ 15. $\dfrac{9}{x^8}$

② *The mass of the earth*:

6.615×10^{21} tons = 6,615,000,000,000,000,000,000 tons.

③ *The mass of a hydrogen atom*:

1.7×10^{-24} g = 0.0000000000000000000000017 g.

②

SCIENTIFIC NOTATION

Scientific notation for a number is an expression of the type

$$M \times 10^n,$$

where n is an integer, M is greater than or equal to 1 and less than 10 ($1 \le M < 10$), and M is expressed in decimal notation. 10^n is also considered to be scientific notation when $M = 1$.

You should try to make conversions to scientific notation mentally as much as possible. Here is a handy mental device.

A positive exponent in scientific notation indicates a large number (greater than or equal to 10) and a negative exponent indicates a small number (between 0 and 1).

③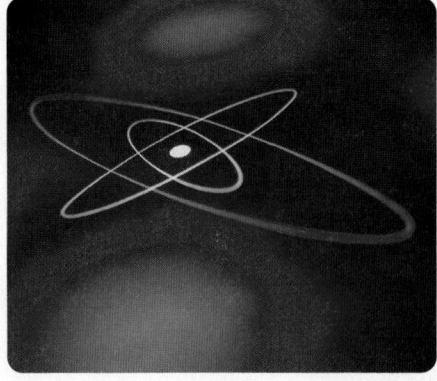

EXAMPLES Convert to scientific notation.

18. $78,000 = 7.8 \times 10^4$

7.8,000.

4 places

Large number, so the exponent is positive.

19. $0.0000057 = 5.7 \times 10^{-6}$

0.000005.7

6 places

Small number, so the exponent is negative.

Do Exercises 16 and 17.

EXAMPLES Convert mentally to decimal notation.

20. $7.893 \times 10^5 = 789,300$

7.89300.

5 places

Positive exponent, so the answer is a large number.

21. $4.7 \times 10^{-8} = 0.000000047$

.00000004.7

8 places

Negative exponent, so the answer is a small number.

Convert to scientific notation.
16. 0.000517

17. 523,000,000

--- *Caution!* ---

Each of the following is *not* scientific notation.

$$\underline{12.46} \times 10^7$$
↑

This number is greater than 10.

$$\underline{0.347} \times 10^{-5}$$
↑

This number is less than 1.

Answers
16. 5.17×10^{-4} **17.** 5.23×10^8

Do Exercises 18 and 19.

Convert to decimal notation.

18. 6.893×10^{11}

19. 5.67×10^{-5}

d Multiplying and Dividing Using Scientific Notation

Multiplying

Consider the product

$$400 \cdot 2000 = 800,000.$$

In scientific notation, this is

$$(4 \times 10^2) \cdot (2 \times 10^3) = (4 \cdot 2)(10^2 \cdot 10^3) = 8 \times 10^5.$$

By applying the commutative and associative laws, we can find this product by multiplying $4 \cdot 2$, to get 8, and $10^2 \cdot 10^3$, to get 10^5.

Multiply and write scientific notation for the result.

20. $(1.12 \times 10^{-8})(5 \times 10^{-7})$

21. $(9.1 \times 10^{-17})(8.2 \times 10^3)$

EXAMPLE 22 Multiply: $(1.8 \times 10^6) \cdot (2.3 \times 10^{-4})$.

We apply the commutative and associative laws to get

$$
\begin{aligned}
(1.8 \times 10^6) \cdot (2.3 \times 10^{-4}) &= (1.8 \cdot 2.3) \times (10^6 \cdot 10^{-4}) \\
&= 4.14 \times 10^{6+(-4)} \\
&= 4.14 \times 10^2.
\end{aligned}
$$

We get 4.14 by multiplying 1.8 and 2.3. We get 10^2 by adding the exponents 6 and -4.

EXAMPLE 23 Multiply: $(3.1 \times 10^5) \cdot (4.5 \times 10^{-3})$.

$$
\begin{aligned}
(3.1 \times 10^5) \cdot (4.5 \times 10^{-3}) &= (3.1 \times 4.5)(10^5 \cdot 10^{-3}) \\
&= 13.95 \times 10^2 \qquad \text{Not scientific notation;} \\
&\qquad\qquad\qquad\quad \text{13.95 is greater than 10.} \\
&= (1.395 \times 10^1) \times 10^2 \quad \text{Substituting } 1.395 \times 10^1 \\
&\qquad\qquad\qquad\qquad\quad \text{for 13.95} \\
&= 1.395 \times (10^1 \times 10^2) \quad \text{Associative law} \\
&= 1.395 \times 10^3 \qquad\quad \text{Adding exponents.} \\
&\qquad\qquad\qquad\qquad\quad \text{The answer is now in} \\
&\qquad\qquad\qquad\qquad\quad \text{scientific notation.}
\end{aligned}
$$

Do Exercises 20 and 21.

Dividing

Consider the quotient $800,000 \div 400 = 2000$. In scientific notation, this is

$$(8 \times 10^5) \div (4 \times 10^2) = \frac{8 \times 10^5}{4 \times 10^2} = \frac{8}{4} \times \frac{10^5}{10^2} = 2 \times 10^3.$$

We found this product by dividing 8 by 4, to get 2, and 10^5 by 10^2, to get 10^3.

EXAMPLE 24 Divide: $(3.41 \times 10^5) \div (1.1 \times 10^{-3})$.

$$
\begin{aligned}
(3.41 \times 10^5) \div (1.1 \times 10^{-3}) &= \frac{3.41 \times 10^5}{1.1 \times 10^{-3}} = \frac{3.41}{1.1} \times \frac{10^5}{10^{-3}} \\
&= 3.1 \times 10^{5-(-3)} \\
&= 3.1 \times 10^8
\end{aligned}
$$

Calculator Corner

To find the product in Example 22 and express the result in scientific notation on a graphing calculator, we first set the calculator in Scientific mode by pressing **MODE**, positioning the cursor over Sci on the first line, and pressing **ENTER**. Then we go to the home screen and enter the computation by pressing ① · ⑧ **2ND** **EE** ⑥ × ② · ③ **2ND** **EE** (−) ④ **ENTER**. (EE is the second operation associated with the **,** key.) The decimal portion of a number written in scientific notation appears before a small E and the exponent follows the E.

```
1.8E6*2.3E−4
               4.14E2
```

Exercises: Multiply or divide and express the answer in scientific notation.

1. $(3.15 \times 10^7)(4.3 \times 10^{-12})$

2. $(8 \times 10^9)(4 \times 10^{-5})$

3. $\dfrac{4.5 \times 10^6}{1.5 \times 10^{12}}$

4. $\dfrac{4 \times 10^{-9}}{5 \times 10^{16}}$

Answers

18. 689,300,000,000   **19.** 0.0000567
20. 5.6×10^{-15} **21.** 7.462×10^{-13}

EXAMPLE 25   Divide: $(6.4 \times 10^{-7}) \div (8.0 \times 10^{6})$.

$$(6.4 \times 10^{-7}) \div (8.0 \times 10^{6}) = \frac{6.4 \times 10^{-7}}{8.0 \times 10^{6}}$$

$$= \frac{6.4}{8.0} \times \frac{10^{-7}}{10^{6}}$$

$$= 0.8 \times 10^{-7-6}$$

$$= 0.8 \times 10^{-13} \qquad \text{Not scientific notation;}$$
$$\qquad\qquad\qquad\qquad \text{0.8 is less than 1.}$$

$$= (8.0 \times 10^{-1}) \times 10^{-13} \qquad \text{Substituting}$$
$$\qquad\qquad\qquad\qquad\qquad\qquad 8.0 \times 10^{-1} \text{ for 0.8}$$

$$= 8.0 \times (10^{-1} \times 10^{-13}) \qquad \text{Associative law}$$

$$= 8.0 \times 10^{-14} \qquad\qquad \text{Adding exponents}$$

Do Exercises 22 and 23.

Divide and write scientific notation for the result.

22. $\dfrac{4.2 \times 10^{5}}{2.1 \times 10^{2}}$

23. $\dfrac{1.1 \times 10^{-4}}{2.0 \times 10^{-7}}$

(e) Applications with Scientific Notation

EXAMPLE 26   *Distance from the Sun to Earth.*   Light from the sun traveling at a rate of 300,000 kilometers per second (km/s) reaches Earth in 499 sec. Find the distance, expressed in scientific notation, from the sun to Earth.

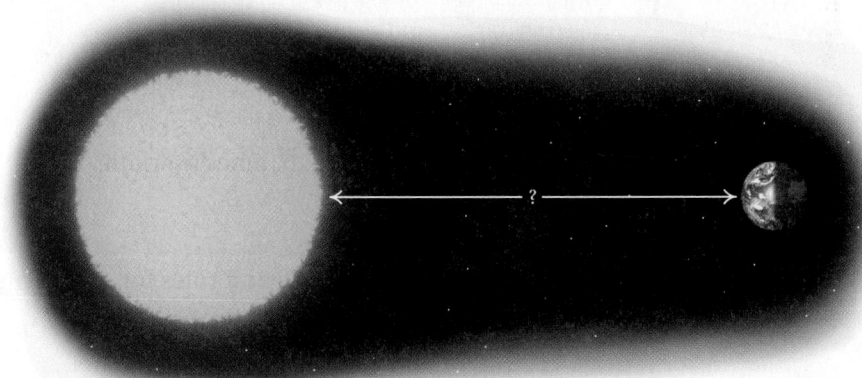

The time t that it takes for light to reach Earth from the sun is 4.99×10^{2} sec (s). The speed is 3.0×10^{5} km/s. Recall that distance can be expressed in terms of speed and time as

$$\text{Distance} = \text{Speed} \cdot \text{Time}$$
$$d = rt.$$

We substitute 3.0×10^{5} for r and 4.99×10^{2} for t:

$$d = rt$$
$$= (3.0 \times 10^{5})(4.99 \times 10^{2}) \qquad \text{Substituting}$$
$$= 14.97 \times 10^{7}$$
$$= (1.497 \times 10^{1}) \times 10^{7}$$
$$= 1.497 \times (10^{1} \times 10^{7})$$
$$= 1.497 \times 10^{8} \text{ km.} \qquad \text{Converting to scientific notation}$$

Thus the distance from the sun to Earth is 1.497×10^{8} km.

Do Exercise 24.

STUDY TIPS

WRITING ALL THE STEPS
Take the time to write all the steps when doing your homework. Doing so will help you organize your thinking and avoid computational errors. If you get a wrong answer, having all the steps allows easier checking of your work. It will also give you complete, step-by-step solutions of the exercises that can be used to study for an exam.

24. Niagara Falls Water Flow.   On the Canadian side, the amount of water that spills over Niagara Falls in 1 min during the summer is about

$$1.3088 \times 10^{8} \text{ L.}$$

How much water spills over the falls in one day? Express the answer in scientific notation.

Answers
22. 2.0×10^{3} **23.** 5.5×10^{2}
24. 1.884672×10^{11} L

EXAMPLE 27 *DNA.* A strand of DNA (deoxyribonucleic acid) is about 150 cm long and 1.3×10^{-10} cm wide. The length of a strand of DNA is how many times the width?

Source: Human Genome Project Information

25. Earth vs. Saturn. The mass of Earth is about 6×10^{21} metric tons. The mass of Saturn is about 5.7×10^{23} metric tons. About how many times the mass of Earth is the mass of Saturn? Express the answer in scientific notation.

To determine how many times longer DNA is than it is wide, we divide the length by the width:

$$\frac{150}{1.3 \times 10^{-10}} = \frac{150}{1.3} \times \frac{1}{10^{-10}}$$

$$\approx 115.385 \times 10^{10}$$

$$= (1.15385 \times 10^{2}) \times 10^{10}$$

$$= 1.15385 \times 10^{12}.$$

Thus the length of DNA is about 1.15385×10^{12} times its width.

Do Exercise 25.

The following is a summary of the definitions and rules for exponents that we have considered in this section and the preceding one.

DEFINITIONS AND RULES FOR EXPONENTS

Exponent of 1:	$a^1 = a$
Exponent of 0:	$a^0 = 1, a \neq 0$
Negative exponents:	$a^{-n} = \dfrac{1}{a^n}, \dfrac{1}{a^{-n}} = a^n, a \neq 0$
Product Rule:	$a^m \cdot a^n = a^{m+n}$
Quotient Rule:	$\dfrac{a^m}{a^n} = a^{m-n}, a \neq 0$
Power Rule:	$(a^m)^n = a^{mn}$
Raising a product to a power:	$(ab)^n = a^n b^n$
Raising a quotient to a power:	$\left(\dfrac{a}{b}\right)^n = \dfrac{a^n}{b^n}, b \neq 0;$
	$\left(\dfrac{a}{b}\right)^{-n} = \dfrac{b^n}{a^n}, b \neq 0, a \neq 0$
Scientific notation:	$M \times 10^n$, or 10^n, where $1 \leq M < 10$

Answer

25. The mass of Saturn is 9.5×10 times the mass of Earth.

For Extra Help
MyMathLab
Math XL PRACTICE
WATCH
DOWNLOAD
READ
REVIEW

a , **b**   Simplify.

1. $(2^3)^2$

2. $(5^2)^4$

3. $(5^2)^{-3}$

4. $(7^{-3})^5$

5. $(x^{-3})^{-4}$

6. $(a^{-5})^{-6}$

7. $(a^{-2})^9$

8. $(x^{-5})^6$

9. $(t^{-3})^{-6}$

10. $(a^{-4})^{-7}$

11. $(t^4)^{-3}$

12. $(t^5)^{-2}$

13. $(x^{-2})^{-4}$

14. $(t^{-6})^{-5}$

15. $(ab)^3$

16. $(xy)^2$

17. $(ab)^{-3}$

18. $(xy)^{-6}$

19. $(mn^2)^{-3}$

20. $(x^3y)^{-2}$

21. $(4x^3)^2$

22. $4(x^3)^2$

23. $(3x^{-4})^2$

24. $(2a^{-5})^3$

25. $(x^4y^5)^{-3}$

26. $(t^5x^3)^{-4}$

27. $(x^{-6}y^{-2})^{-4}$

28. $(x^{-2}y^{-7})^{-5}$

29. $(a^{-2}b^7)^{-5}$

30. $(q^5r^{-1})^{-3}$

31. $(5r^{-4}t^3)^2$

32. $(4x^5y^{-6})^3$

33. $(a^{-5}b^7c^{-2})^3$

34. $(x^{-4}y^{-2}z^9)^2$

35. $(3x^3y^{-8}z^{-3})^2$

36. $(2a^2y^{-4}z^{-5})^3$

37. $(-4x^3y^{-2})^2$

38. $(-8x^3y^{-2})^3$

39. $(-a^{-3}b^{-2})^{-4}$

40. $(-p^{-4}q^{-3})^{-2}$

41. $\left(\dfrac{y^3}{2}\right)^2$

42. $\left(\dfrac{a^5}{3}\right)^3$

43. $\left(\dfrac{a^2}{b^3}\right)^4$

44. $\left(\dfrac{x^3}{y^4}\right)^5$

45. $\left(\dfrac{y^2}{2}\right)^{-3}$

46. $\left(\dfrac{a^4}{3}\right)^{-2}$

47. $\left(\dfrac{7}{x^{-3}}\right)^2$

48. $\left(\dfrac{3}{a^{-2}}\right)^3$

49. $\left(\dfrac{x^2y}{z}\right)^3$

50. $\left(\dfrac{m}{n^4p}\right)^3$

51. $\left(\dfrac{a^2b}{cd^3}\right)^{-2}$

52. $\left(\dfrac{2a^2}{3b^4}\right)^{-3}$

c   Convert to scientific notation.

53. 28,000,000,000   **54.** 4,900,000,000,000   **55.** 907,000,000,000,000,000   **56.** 168,000,000,000,000

57. 0.00000304   **58.** 0.000000000865   **59.** 0.000000018   **60.** 0.00000000002

61. 100,000,000,000   **62.** 0.0000001

63. *Population of the United States.* It is estimated that the population of the United States will be 419,854,000 in 2050. Convert 419,854,000 to scientific notation.
Source: U.S. Census Bureau

64. *Young Voters.* About 22,750,000 young people, ages 18–29, voted in the 2008 presidential election. Convert 22,750,000 to scientific notation.
Source: Center for Information & Research on Civic Learning and Engagement, Tufts University

65. *Political Spending.* A record $2,400,000,000 was spent on campaigning, advertising, conventions, and other political activities in the 2008 presidential election. Convert $2,400,000,000 to scientific notation.
Source: Center for Responsive Politics

66. *Advertising Spending.* Coca-Cola spent $2,600,000,000 on advertising in a recent year. Convert $2,600,000,000 to scientific notation.
Source: Nielsen Media Research

Convert to decimal notation.

67. 8.74×10^7 **68.** 1.85×10^8 **69.** 5.704×10^{-8} **70.** 8.043×10^{-4}

71. 10^7 **72.** 10^6 **73.** 10^{-5} **74.** 10^{-8}

d   Multiply or divide and write scientific notation for the result.

75. $(3 \times 10^4)(2 \times 10^5)$ **76.** $(3.9 \times 10^8)(8.4 \times 10^{-3})$ **77.** $(5.2 \times 10^5)(6.5 \times 10^{-2})$

78. $(7.1 \times 10^{-7})(8.6 \times 10^{-5})$ **79.** $(9.9 \times 10^{-6})(8.23 \times 10^{-8})$ **80.** $(1.123 \times 10^4) \times 10^{-9}$

Copyright © 2012 Pearson Education, Inc.

81. $\dfrac{8.5 \times 10^8}{3.4 \times 10^{-5}}$

82. $\dfrac{5.6 \times 10^{-2}}{2.5 \times 10^5}$

83. $(3.0 \times 10^6) \div (6.0 \times 10^9)$

84. $(1.5 \times 10^{-3}) \div (1.6 \times 10^{-6})$

85. $\dfrac{7.5 \times 10^{-9}}{2.5 \times 10^{12}}$

86. $\dfrac{4.0 \times 10^{-3}}{8.0 \times 10^{20}}$

 Solve.

87. *River Discharge.* The average discharge at the mouths of the Amazon River is 4,200,000 cubic feet per second. How much water is discharged from the Amazon River in 1 yr? Express the answer in scientific notation.

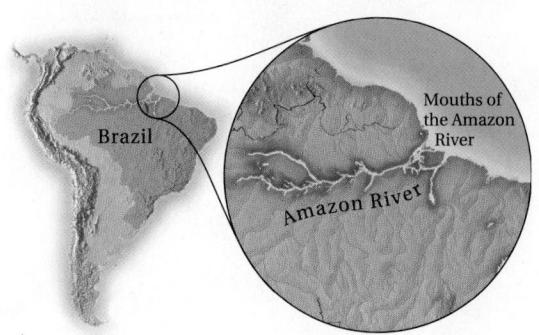

88. *Water Contamination.* Americans who change their own motor oil generate about 150 million gallons of used oil annually. If this oil is not disposed of properly, it can contaminate drinking water and soil. One gallon of used oil can contaminate one million gallons of drinking water. How many gallons of drinking water can 150 million gallons of oil contaminate? Express the answer in scientific notation. (1 million $= 10^6$).

Source: *New Car Buying Guide*

89. *Earth vs. Jupiter.* The mass of Earth is about 6×10^{21} metric tons. The mass of Jupiter is about 1.908×10^{24} metric tons. About how many times the mass of Earth is the mass of Jupiter? Express the answer in scientific notation.

90. *Computers.* A gigabyte is a measure of a computer's storage capacity. One gigabyte holds about one billion bytes of information. If a firm's computer network contains 2500 gigabytes of memory, how many bytes are in the network? Express the answer in scientific notation. (1 billion $= 10^9$)

91. Stars. It is estimated that there are 10 billion trillion stars in the known universe. Express the number of stars in scientific notation. (1 billion = 10^9; 1 trillion = 10^{12})

92. Closest Star. Excluding the sun, the closest star to Earth is Proxima Centauri, which is 4.3 light-years away. (One light-year = 5.88×10^{12} mi.) How far, in miles, is Proxima Centauri from Earth? Express the answer in scientific notation.

93. Red Light. The wavelength of light is given by the velocity divided by the frequency. The velocity of red light is 300,000,000 m/sec, and its frequency is 400,000,000,000,000 cycles per second. What is the wavelength of red light? Express the answer in scientific notation.

94. Earth vs. Sun. The mass of Earth is about 6×10^{21} metric tons. The mass of the sun is about 1.998×10^{27} metric tons. About how many times the mass of Earth is the mass of the sun? Express the answer in scientific notation.

Space Travel. Use the following information for Exercises 95 and 96.

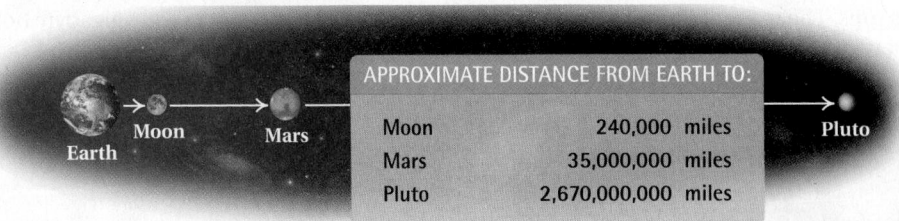

APPROXIMATE DISTANCE FROM EARTH TO:

Moon	240,000 miles
Mars	35,000,000 miles
Pluto	2,670,000,000 miles

95. Time to Reach Mars. Suppose that it takes about 3 days for a space vehicle to travel from Earth to the moon. About how long would it take the same space vehicle traveling at the same speed to reach Mars? Express the answer in scientific notation.

96. Time to Reach Pluto. Suppose that it takes about 3 days for a space vehicle to travel from Earth to the moon. About how long would it take the same space vehicle traveling at the same speed to reach the dwarf planet Pluto? Express the answer in scientific notation.

Copyright © 2012 Pearson Education, Inc.

Skill Maintenance

Factor. [7.7d]

97. $9x - 36$

98. $4x - 2y + 16$

99. $3s + 3t + 24$

100. $-7x - 14$

Solve. [8.3b]

101. $2x - 4 - 5x + 8 = x - 3$

102. $8x + 7 - 9x = 12 - 6x + 5$

Solve. [8.3c]

103. $8(2x + 3) - 2(x - 5) = 10$

104. $4(x - 3) + 5 = 6(x + 2) - 8$

Graph. [9.1d], [9.2a]

105. $y = x - 5$

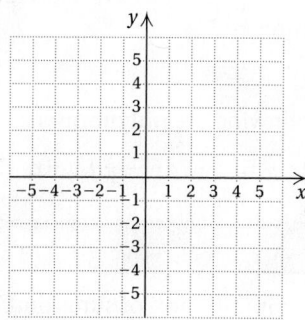

106. $2x + y = 4$

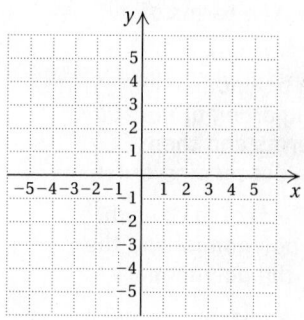

Synthesis

107. ▦ Carry out the indicated operations. Express the result in scientific notation.

$$\frac{(5.2 \times 10^6)(6.1 \times 10^{-11})}{1.28 \times 10^{-3}}$$

108. Find the reciprocal and express it in scientific notation.

$$6.25 \times 10^{-3}$$

Simplify.

109. $\dfrac{(5^{12})^2}{5^{25}}$

110. $\dfrac{a^{22}}{(a^2)^{11}}$

111. $\dfrac{(3^5)^4}{3^5 \cdot 3^4}$

112. $\left(\dfrac{5x^{-2}}{3y^{-2}z}\right)^0$

113. $\dfrac{49^{18}}{7^{35}}$

114. $\left(\dfrac{1}{a}\right)^{-n}$

115. $\dfrac{(0.4)^5}{[(0.4)^3]^2}$

116. $\left(\dfrac{4a^3b^{-2}}{5c^{-3}}\right)^1$

Determine whether each of the following is true for all pairs of integers m and n and all positive numbers x and y.

117. $x^m \cdot y^n = (xy)^{mn}$

118. $x^m \cdot y^m = (xy)^{2m}$

119. $(x - y)^m = x^m - y^m$

120. $-x^m = (-x)^m$

121. $(-x)^{2m} = x^{2m}$

122. $x^{-m} = \dfrac{-1}{x^m}$

10.3

Introduction to Polynomials

OBJECTIVES

a Evaluate a polynomial for a given value of the variable.

b Identify the terms of a polynomial.

c Identify the like terms of a polynomial.

d Identify the coefficients of a polynomial.

e Collect the like terms of a polynomial.

f Arrange a polynomial in descending order, or collect the like terms and then arrange in descending order.

g Identify the degree of each term of a polynomial and the degree of the polynomial.

h Identify the missing terms of a polynomial.

i Classify a polynomial as a monomial, a binomial, a trinomial, or none of these.

SKILL TO REVIEW
Objective 7.7e: Collect like terms.

Collect like terms.

1. $3x - 4y + 5x + y$

2. $2a - 7b + 6 - 3a + 4b - 1$

1. Write three polynomials.

Answers

Skill to Review:
1. $8x - 3y$ 2. $-a - 3b + 5$

Margin Exercise:
1. $4x^2 - 3x + \frac{5}{4}$; $15y^3$; $-7x^3 + 1.1$;

answers may vary

We have already learned to evaluate and to manipulate certain kinds of algebraic expressions. We will now consider algebraic expressions called *polynomials*.

The following are examples of *monomials in one variable*:

$$3x^2, \quad 2x, \quad -5, \quad 37p^4, \quad 0.$$

Each expression is a constant or a constant times some variable to a nonnegative integer power.

> **MONOMIAL**
>
> A **monomial** is an expression of the type ax^n, where a is a real-number constant and n is a nonnegative integer.

Algebraic expressions like the following are **polynomials**:

$$\tfrac{3}{4}y^5, \quad -2, \quad 5y + 3, \quad 3x^2 + 2x - 5, \quad -7a^3 + \tfrac{1}{2}a, \quad 6x, \quad 37p^4, \quad x, \quad 0.$$

> **POLYNOMIAL**
>
> A **polynomial** is a monomial or a combination of sums and/or differences of monomials.

The following algebraic expressions are *not* polynomials:

$$\textbf{(1)} \ \frac{x + 3}{x - 4}, \quad \textbf{(2)} \ 5x^3 - 2x^2 + \frac{1}{x}, \quad \textbf{(3)} \ \frac{1}{x^3 - 2}.$$

Expressions (1) and (3) are not polynomials because they represent quotients, not sums or differences. Expression (2) is not a polynomial because

$$\frac{1}{x} = x^{-1},$$

and this is not a monomial because the exponent is negative.

Do Margin Exercise 1.

a Evaluating Polynomials and Applications

When we replace the variable in a polynomial with a number, the polynomial then represents a number called a **value** of the polynomial. Finding that number, or value, is called **evaluating the polynomial**. We evaluate a polynomial using the rules for order of operations (Section 7.8).

EXAMPLE 1 Evaluate the polynomial when $x = 2$.

a) $3x + 5 = 3 \cdot 2 + 5$
   $= 6 + 5$
   $= 11$

b) $2x^2 - 7x + 3 = 2 \cdot 2^2 - 7 \cdot 2 + 3$
   $= 2 \cdot 4 - 7 \cdot 2 + 3$
   $= 8 - 14 + 3$
   $= -3$

EXAMPLE 2 Evaluate the polynomial when $x = -4$.

a) $2 - x^3 = 2 - (-4)^3 = 2 - (-64)$
$$= 2 + 64 = 66$$

b) $-x^2 - 3x + 1 = -(-4)^2 - 3(-4) + 1$
$$= -16 + 12 + 1 = -3$$

Do Exercises 2–5.

※ Algebraic-Graphical Connection

Recall from Chapter 9 that in order to plot points before graphing an equation, we choose values for x and compute the corresponding y-values. An equation like $y = 2x - 2$, which has a polynomial on one side and only y on the other, is called a **polynomial equation**. For such an equation, determining y is the same as evaluating the polynomial. Once the graph of such an equation has been drawn, we can evaluate the polynomial for a given x-value by finding the y-value that is paired with it on the graph.

EXAMPLE 3 Use *only* the given graph of $y = 2x - 2$ to evaluate the polynomial $2x - 2$ when $x = 3$.

First, we locate 3 on the x-axis. From there we move vertically to the graph of the equation and then horizontally to the y-axis. There we locate the y-value that is paired with 3. Although our drawing may not be precise, it appears that the y-value 4 is paired with 3. Thus the value of $2x - 2$ is 4 when $x = 3$.

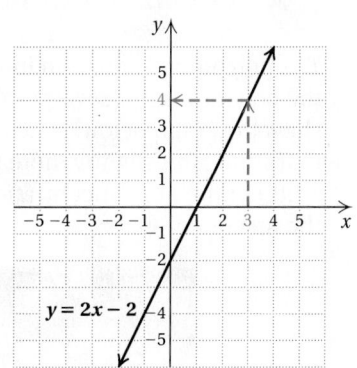

Do Exercise 6.

Polynomial equations can be used to model many real-world situations.

EXAMPLE 4 *Games in a Sports League.* In a sports league of x teams in which each team plays every other team twice, the total number of games N to be played is given by the polynomial equation

$$N = x^2 - x.$$

A women's slow-pitch softball league has 10 teams. What is the total number of games to be played?

We evaluate the polynomial when $x = 10$:

$$N = x^2 - x = 10^2 - 10 = 100 - 10 = 90.$$

The league plays 90 games.

Do Exercises 7 and 8.

Evaluate each polynomial when $x = 3$.

2. $-4x - 7$

3. $-5x^3 + 7x + 10$

Evaluate each polynomial when $x = -5$.

4. $5x + 7$

5. $2x^2 + 5x - 4$

6. Use *only* the graph shown in Example 3 to evaluate the polynomial $2x - 2$ when $x = 4$ and when $x = -1$.

7. Referring to Example 4, determine the total number of games to be played in a league of 12 teams.

8. Perimeter of a Baseball Diamond. The perimeter P of a square of side x is given by the polynomial equation $P = 4x$.

A baseball diamond is a square 90 ft on a side. Find the perimeter of a baseball diamond.

Answers

2. -19 **3.** -104 **4.** -18 **5.** 21
6. $6; -4$ **7.** 132 games   **8.** 360 ft

Calculator Corner

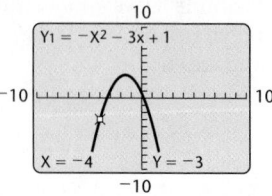

We can use the Value feature from the CALC menu to evaluate a polynomial on a graphing calculator. To evaluate the polynomial in Example 2(b), $-x^2 - 3x + 1$, when $x = -4$, we first graph $y_1 = -x^2 - 3x + 1$ in a window that includes the x-value -4. We will use the standard window. (See p. 666). Then we press **2ND** CALC 1 or **2ND** CALC **ENTER** to access the CALC menu and select item 1, Value. Now we supply the desired x-value by pressing (-) 4. We then press **ENTER** to see X $= -4$, Y $= -3$ at the bottom of the screen. Thus, when $x = -4$, the value of $-x^2 - 3x + 1$ is -3.

```
             10
  Y1 = -X2 - 3x + 1
-10 |_____| 10
  X = -4      Y = -3
            -10
```

Exercises: Use the Value feature to evaluate each polynomial for the given values of x.

1. $-x^2 - 3x + 1$, when $x = -2$, $x = -0.5$, and $x = 4$

2. $3x^2 - 5x + 2$, when $x = -3$, $x = 1$, and $x = 2.6$

9. Medical Dosage.

a) Referring to Example 5, determine the concentration after 3 hr by evaluating the polynomial when $t = 3$.

b) Use *only* the graph showing medical dosage to check the value found in part (a).

10. Medical Dosage. Referring to Example 5, use *only* the graph showing medical dosage to estimate the value of the polynomial when $t = 26$.

EXAMPLE 5 *Medical Dosage.* The concentration C, in parts per million, of a certain antibiotic in the bloodstream after t hours is given by the polynomial equation

$$C = -0.05t^2 + 2t + 2.$$

Find the concentration after 2 hr.

To find the concentration after 2 hr, we evaluate the polynomial when $t = 2$:

$$
\begin{aligned}
C &= -0.05t^2 + 2t + 2 \\
&= -0.05(2)^2 + 2(2) + 2 && \text{Substituting 2 for } t \\
&= -0.05(4) + 2(2) + 2 && \text{Carrying out the calculation using} \\
& && \text{the rules for order of operations} \\
&= -0.2 + 4 + 2 \\
&= 3.8 + 2 \\
&= 5.8.
\end{aligned}
$$

The concentration after 2 hr is 5.8 parts per million.

※ Algebraic–Graphical Connection

The polynomial equation in Example 5 can be graphed if we evaluate the polynomial for several values of t. We list the values in a table and show the graph below. Note that the concentration peaks at the 20-hr mark and after slightly more than 40 hr, the concentration is 0. Since neither time nor concentration can be negative, our graph uses only the first quadrant.

t	$C = -0.05t^2 + 2t + 2$
0	2
2	5.8 ← Example 5
10	17
20	22
30	17

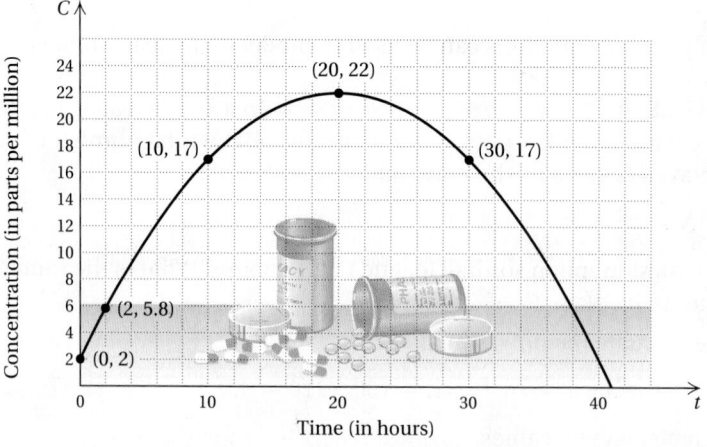

Do Exercises 9 and 10.

Answers

9. (a) 7.55 parts per million; **(b)** When $t = 3$, $C \approx 7.5$ so the value found in part (a) appears to be correct. **10.** 20 parts per million

b Identifying Terms

As we saw in Section 7.4, subtractions can be rewritten as additions. For any polynomial that has some subtractions, we can find an equivalent polynomial using only additions.

EXAMPLES Find an equivalent polynomial using only additions.

6. $-5x^2 - x = -5x^2 + (-x)$

7. $4x^5 - 2x^6 + 4x - 7 = 4x^5 + (-2x^6) + 4x + (-7)$

Do Exercises 11 and 12.

When a polynomial is written using only additions, the monomials being added are called **terms**. In Example 6, the terms are $-5x^2$ and $-x$. In Example 7, the terms are $4x^5$, $-2x^6$, $4x$, and -7.

EXAMPLE 8 Identify the terms of the polynomial

$$4x^7 + 3x + 12 + 8x^3 + 5x.$$

Terms: $4x^7$, $3x$, 12, $8x^3$, and $5x$.

If there are subtractions, you can *think* of them as additions without rewriting.

EXAMPLE 9 Identify the terms of the polynomial

$$3t^4 - 5t^6 - 4t + 2.$$

Terms: $3t^4$, $-5t^6$, $-4t$, and 2.

Do Exercises 13 and 14.

c Like Terms

When terms have the same variable and the same exponent power, we say that they are **like terms**.

EXAMPLES Identify the like terms in the polynomials.

10. $4x^3 + 5x - 4x^2 + 2x^3 + x^2$

Like terms: $4x^3$ and $2x^3$ Same variable and exponent

Like terms: $-4x^2$ and x^2 Same variable and exponent

11. $6 - 3a^2 - 8 - a - 5a$

Like terms: 6 and -8 Constant terms are like terms because $6 = 6x^0$ and $-8 = -8x^0$.

Like terms: $-a$ and $-5a$

Do Exercises 15–17.

d Coefficients

The coefficient of the term $5x^3$ is 5. In the following polynomial, the red numbers are the **coefficients**, 3, -2, 5, and 4:

$$3x^5 - 2x^3 + 5x + 4.$$

Find an equivalent polynomial using only additions.

11. $-9x^3 - 4x^5$

12. $-2y^3 + 3y^7 - 7y - 9$

Identify the terms of each polynomial.

13. $3x^2 + 6x + \dfrac{1}{2}$

14. $-4y^5 + 7y^2 - 3y - 2$

Identify the like terms in each polynomial.

15. $4x^3 - x^3 + 2$

16. $4t^4 - 9t^3 - 7t^4 + 10t^3$

17. $5x^2 + 3x - 10 + 7x^2 - 8x + 11$

Answers

11. $-9x^3 + (-4x^5)$
12. $-2y^3 + 3y^7 + (-7y) + (-9)$
13. $3x^2, 6x, \dfrac{1}{2}$ **14.** $-4y^5, 7y^2, -3y, -2$
15. $4x^3$ and $-x^3$ **16.** $4t^4$ and $-7t^4$; $-9t^3$ and $10t^3$ **17.** $5x^2$ and $7x^2$; $3x$ and $-8x$; -10 and 11

EXAMPLE 12 Identify the coefficient of each term in the polynomial

$$3x^4 - 4x^3 + \frac{1}{2}x^2 + x - 8.$$

The coefficient of the first term is 3.

The coefficient of the second term is -4.

The coefficient of the third term is $\frac{1}{2}$.

The coefficient of the fourth term is 1. $x = 1x$

The coefficient of the fifth term is -8.

Do Exercise 18.

(e) Collecting Like Terms

We can often simplify polynomials by **collecting like terms**, or **combining like terms**. To do this, we use the distributive laws. We factor out the variable expression and add or subtract the coefficients. We try to do this mentally as much as possible.

EXAMPLES Collect like terms.

13. $2x^3 - 6x^3 = (2 - 6)x^3$ Using a distributive law

$= -4x^3$

14. $5x^2 + 7 + 4x^4 + 2x^2 - 11 - 2x^4 = (5 + 2)x^2 + (4 - 2)x^4 + (7 - 11)$

$= 7x^2 + 2x^4 - 4$

Note that using the distributive laws in this manner allows us to collect like terms by adding or subtracting the coefficients. Often the middle step is omitted and we add or subtract mentally, writing just the answer. In collecting like terms, we may get 0.

EXAMPLE 15 Collect like terms: $3x^5 + 2x^2 - 3x^5 + 8$.

$3x^5 + 2x^2 - 3x^5 + 8 = (3 - 3)x^5 + 2x^2 + 8$

$= 0x^5 + 2x^2 + 8$

$= 2x^2 + 8$

Do Exercises 19–24.

Expressing a term like x^2 by showing 1 as a factor, $1 \cdot x^2$, may make it easier to understand how to factor or collect like terms.

EXAMPLES Collect like terms.

16. $5x^2 + x^2 = 5x^2 + 1x^2$ Replacing x^2 with $1x^2$

$= (5 + 1)x^2$ Using a distributive law

$= 6x^2$

---

18. Identify the coefficient of each term in the polynomial

$2x^4 - 7x^3 - 8.5x^2 - x - 4$.

Collect like terms.

19. $3x^2 + 5x^2$

20. $4x^3 - 2x^3 + 2 + 5$

21. $\frac{1}{2}x^5 - \frac{3}{4}x^5 + 4x^2 - 2x^2$

22. $24 - 4x^3 - 24$

23. $5x^3 - 8x^5 + 8x^5$

24. $-2x^4 + 16 + 2x^4 + 9 - 3x^5$

Answers

18. $2, -7, -8.5, -1, -4$ **19.** $8x^2$

20. $2x^3 + 7$ **21.** $-\frac{1}{4}x^5 + 2x^2$ **22.** $-4x^3$

23. $5x^3$ **24.** $25 - 3x^5$

17. $5x^8 - 6x^5 - x^8 = 5x^8 - 6x^5 - 1x^8$ $x^8 = 1x^8$

$$= (5 - 1)x^8 - 6x^5$$
$$= 4x^8 - 6x^5$$

18. $\frac{2}{3}x^4 - x^3 - \frac{1}{6}x^4 + \frac{2}{5}x^3 - \frac{3}{10}x^3$

$$= \left(\frac{2}{3} - \frac{1}{6}\right)x^4 + \left(-1 + \frac{2}{5} - \frac{3}{10}\right)x^3 \quad -x^3 = -1 \cdot x^3$$
$$= \left(\frac{4}{6} - \frac{1}{6}\right)x^4 + \left(-\frac{10}{10} + \frac{4}{10} - \frac{3}{10}\right)x^3$$
$$= \frac{3}{6}x^4 - \frac{9}{10}x^3$$
$$= \frac{1}{2}x^4 - \frac{9}{10}x^3$$

> Do Exercises 25–28.

Do Exercises 25–28.

Collect like terms.

25. $7x - x$

26. $5x^3 - x^3 + 4$

27. $\frac{3}{4}x^3 + 4x^2 - x^3 + 7$

28. $\frac{4}{5}x^4 - x^4 + x^5 - \frac{1}{5} - \frac{1}{4}x^4 + 10$

(f) Descending and Ascending Order

Note in the following polynomial that the exponents decrease from left to right. We say that the polynomial is arranged in **descending order**:

$$2x^4 - 8x^3 + 5x^2 - x + 3.$$

The term with the largest exponent is first. The term with the next largest exponent is second, and so on. The associative and commutative laws allow us to arrange the terms of a polynomial in descending order.

EXAMPLES   Arrange the polynomial in descending order.

19. $6x^5 + 4x^7 + x^2 + 2x^3 = 4x^7 + 6x^5 + 2x^3 + x^2$

20. $\frac{2}{3} + 4x^5 - 8x^2 + 5x - 3x^3 = 4x^5 - 3x^3 - 8x^2 + 5x + \frac{2}{3}$

> Do Exercises 29–31.

Do Exercises 29–31.

Arrange each polynomial in descending order.

29. $x + 3x^5 + 4x^3 + 5x^2 + 6x^7 - 2x^4$

30. $4x^2 - 3 + 7x^5 + 2x^3 - 5x^4$

31. $-14 + 7t^2 - 10t^5 + 14t^7$

EXAMPLE 21   Collect like terms and then arrange in descending order:

$$2x^2 - 4x^3 + 3 - x^2 - 2x^3.$$

$2x^2 - 4x^3 + 3 - x^2 - 2x^3 = x^2 - 6x^3 + 3$ Collecting like terms

$$= -6x^3 + x^2 + 3 \quad \text{Arranging in descending order}$$

> Do Exercises 32 and 33.

Do Exercises 32 and 33.

Collect like terms and then arrange in descending order.

32. $3x^2 - 2x + 3 - 5x^2 - 1 - x$

33. $-x + \frac{1}{2} + 14x^4 - 7x - 1 - 4x^4$

We usually arrange polynomials in descending order, but not always. The opposite order is called **ascending order**. Generally, if an exercise is written in a certain order, we give the answer in that same order.

(g) Degrees

The **degree** of a term is the exponent of the variable. The degree of the term $-5x^3$ is 3.

EXAMPLE 22   Identify the degree of each term of $8x^4 - 3x + 7$.

The degree of $8x^4$ is 4.

The degree of $-3x$ is 1.   Recall that $x = x^1$.

The degree of 7 is 0.   Think of 7 as $7x^0$. Recall that $x^0 = 1$.

Answers

25. $6x$ **26.** $4x^3 + 4$ **27.** $-\frac{1}{4}x^3 + 4x^2 + 7$

28. $x^5 - \frac{9}{20}x^4 + \frac{49}{5}$

29. $6x^7 + 3x^5 - 2x^4 + 4x^3 + 5x^2 + x$

30. $7x^5 - 5x^4 + 2x^3 + 4x^2 - 3$

31. $14t^7 - 10t^5 + 7t^2 - 14$

32. $-2x^2 - 3x + 2$ **33.** $10x^4 - 8x - \frac{1}{2}$

The **degree of a polynomial** is the largest of the degrees of the terms, unless it is the polynomial 0. The polynomial 0 is a special case. We agree that it has *no* degree either as a term or as a polynomial. This is because we can express 0 as $0 = 0x^5 = 0x^7$, and so on, using any exponent we wish.

EXAMPLE 23 Identify the degree of the polynomial $5x^3 - 6x^4 + 7$.

$$5x^3 - 6x^4 + 7. \qquad \text{The largest exponent is 4.}$$

The degree of the polynomial is 4.

Do Exercises 34 and 35.

Let's summarize the terminology that we have learned, using the polynomial $3x^4 - 8x^3 + x^2 + 7x - 6$.

TERM	COEFFICIENT	DEGREE OF THE TERM	DEGREE OF THE POLYNOMIAL
$3x^4$	3	4	
$-8x^3$	-8	3	
x^2	1	2	4
$7x$	7	1	
-6	-6	0	

(h) Missing Terms

If a coefficient is 0, we generally do not write the term. We say that we have a **missing term**.

EXAMPLE 24 Identify the missing terms in the polynomial

$$8x^5 - 2x^3 + 5x^2 + 7x + 8.$$

There is no term with x^4. We say that the x^4-term is missing.

Do Exercises 36–39.

For certain skills or manipulations, we can write missing terms with zero coefficients or leave space.

EXAMPLE 25 Write the polynomial $x^4 - 6x^3 + 2x - 1$ in two ways: with its missing term and by leaving space for it.

a) $x^4 - 6x^3 + 2x - 1 = x^4 - 6x^3 + 0x^2 + 2x - 1$ Writing with the missing x^2-term

b) $x^4 - 6x^3 + 2x - 1 = x^4 - 6x^3 \qquad + 2x - 1$ Leaving space for the missing x^2-term

EXAMPLE 26 Write the polynomial $y^5 - 1$ in two ways: with its missing terms and by leaving space for them.

a) $y^5 - 1 = y^5 + 0y^4 + 0y^3 + 0y^2 + 0y - 1$

b) $y^5 - 1 = y^5 \qquad\qquad\qquad - 1$

Do Exercises 40 and 41.

Identify the degree of each term and the degree of the polynomial.

34. $-6x^4 + 8x^2 - 2x + 9$

35. $4 - x^3 + \frac{1}{2}x^6 - x^5$

Identify the missing terms in each polynomial.

36. $2x^3 + 4x^2 - 2$

37. $-3x^4$

38. $x^3 + 1$

39. $x^4 - x^2 + 3x + 0.25$

Write each polynomial in two ways: with its missing terms and by leaving space for them.

40. $2x^3 + 4x^2 - 2$

41. $a^4 + 10$

Answers

34. $4, 2, 1, 0; 4$ **35.** $0, 3, 6, 5; 6$ **36.** x
37. x^3, x^2, x, x^0 **38.** x^2, x **39.** x^3
40. $2x^3 + 4x^2 + 0x - 2$;
     $2x^3 + 4x^2 \qquad - 2$
41. $a^4 + 0a^3 + 0a^2 + 0a + 10$;
     $a^4 \qquad\qquad\qquad + 10$

(i) Classifying Polynomials

Polynomials with just one term are called **monomials**. Polynomials with just two terms are called **binomials**. Those with just three terms are called **trinomials**. Those with more than three terms are generally not specified with a name.

EXAMPLE 27

MONOMIALS	BINOMIALS	TRINOMIALS	NONE OF THESE
$4x^2$	$2x + 4$	$3x^3 + 4x + 7$	$4x^3 - 5x^2 + x - 8$
9	$3x^5 + 6x$	$6x^7 - 7x^2 + 4$	$z^5 + 2z^4 - z^3 + 7z + 3$
$-23x^{19}$	$-9x^7 - 6$	$4x^2 - 6x - \frac{1}{2}$	$4x^6 - 3x^5 + x^4 - x^3 + 2x - 1$

Do Exercises 42–45.

Classify each polynomial as a monomial, a binomial, a trinomial, or none of these.

42. $3x^2 + x$　　　　**43.** $5x^4$

44. $4x^3 - 3x^2 + 4x + 2$

45. $3x^2 + 2x - 4$

Answers
42. Binomial　43. Monomial　44. None of these　45. Trinomial

10.3 Exercise Set

For Extra Help

 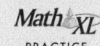

MyMathLab | Math XL PRACTICE | WATCH | DOWNLOAD | READ | REVIEW

(a) Evaluate each polynomial when $x = 4$ and when $x = -1$.

1. $-5x + 2$

2. $-8x + 1$

3. $2x^2 - 5x + 7$

4. $3x^2 + x - 7$

5. $x^3 - 5x^2 + x$

6. $7 - x + 3x^2$

Evaluate each polynomial when $x = -2$ and when $x = 0$.

7. $\frac{1}{3}x + 5$

8. $8 - \frac{1}{4}x$

9. $x^2 - 2x + 1$

10. $5x + 6 - x^2$

11. $-3x^3 + 7x^2 - 3x - 2$

12. $-2x^3 + 5x^2 - 4x + 3$

13. *Skydiving.* During the first 13 sec of a jump, the distance S, in feet, that a skydiver falls in t seconds can be approximated by the polynomial equation

$$S = 11.12t^2.$$

Approximately how far has a skydiver fallen 10 sec after having jumped from a plane?

14. *Skydiving.* For jumps that exceed 13 sec, the polynomial equation

$$S = 173t - 369$$

can be used to approximate the distance S, in feet, that a skydiver has fallen in t seconds. Approximately how far has a skydiver fallen 20 sec after having jumped from a plane?

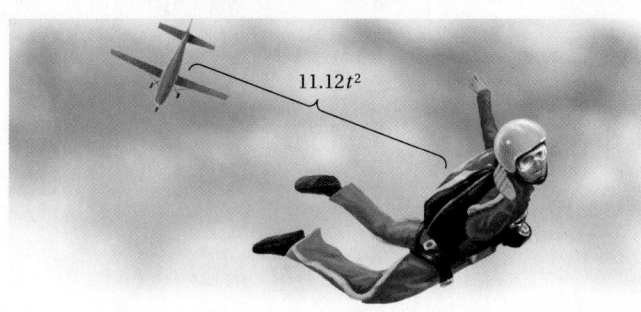

11.12t^2

15. *Total Revenue.* Hadley Electronics is marketing a new type of plasma TV. The firm determines that when it sells x TVs, its total revenue R (the total amount of money taken in) will be

$$R = 280x - 0.4x^2 \text{ dollars.}$$

What is the total revenue from the sale of 75 TVs? 100 TVs?

16. *Total Cost.* Hadley Electronics determines that the total cost C of producing x plasma TVs is given by

$$C = 5000 + 0.6x^2 \text{ dollars.}$$

What is the total cost of producing 500 TVs? 650 TVs?

17. The graph of the polynomial equation $y = 5 - x^2$ is shown below. Use *only* the graph to estimate the value of the polynomial when $x = -3$, $x = -1$, $x = 0$, $x = 1.5$, and $x = 2$.

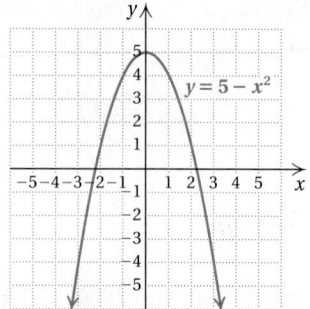

18. The graph of the polynomial equation $y = 6x^3 - 6x$ is shown below. Use *only* the graph to estimate the value of the polynomial when $x = -1$, $x = -0.5$, $x = 0.5$, $x = 1$, and $x = 1.1$.

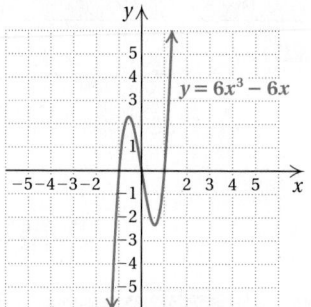

19. *Electricity Consumption.* The net consumption of electricity in China can be estimated by the polynomial equation

$$E = 158.68t + 2728.4,$$

where E is the consumption of electricity, in billions of kilowatt-hours, and t is the number of years after 2010. That is, $t = 0$ corresponds to 2010, $t = 5$ corresponds to 2015, and so on.

Source: Energy Information Administration

a) Use the equation to estimate the consumption of electricity, in billions of kilowatt-hours, in 2010, 2015, 2020, 2025, and 2030.

b) Check the results of part (a) using the graph below.

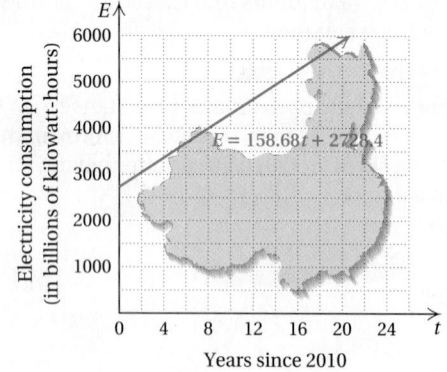

20. *Electricity Consumption.* The net consumption of electricity in the United States can be estimated by the polynomial equation

$$E = 72.9t + 4134.4,$$

where E is the consumption of electricity, in billions of kilowatt-hours, and t is the number of years after 2010. That is, $t = 0$ corresponds to 2010, $t = 5$ corresponds to 2015, and so on.

Source: Energy Information Administration

a) Use the equation to estimate the consumption of electricity, in billions of kilowatt-hours, in 2010, 2015, 2020, 2025, and 2030.

b) Check the results of part (a) using the graph below.

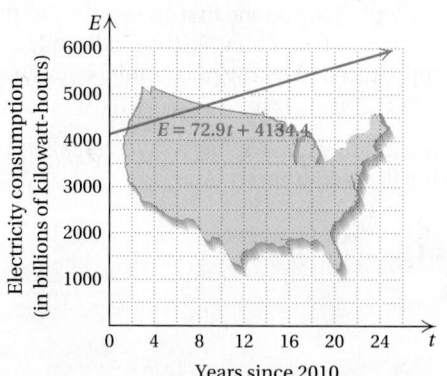

Copyright © 2012 Pearson Education, Inc.

Memorizing Words. Participants in a psychology experiment were able to memorize an average of M words in t minutes, where $M = -0.001t^3 + 0.1t^2$. Use the graph below for Exercises 21–26.

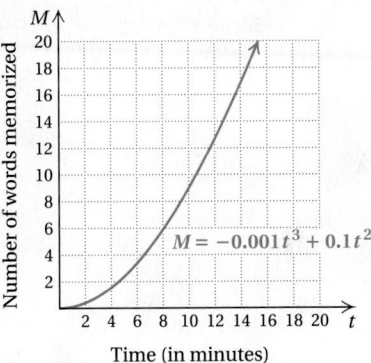

21. Estimate the number of words memorized after 10 min.

22. Estimate the number of words memorized after 14 min.

23. Find the approximate value of M for $t = 8$.

24. Find the approximate value of M for $t = 12$.

25. Estimate the value of M when t is 13.

26. Estimate the value of M when t is 7.

b Identify the terms of each polynomial.

27. $2 - 3x + x^2$

28. $2x^2 + 3x - 4$

29. $-2x^4 + \frac{1}{3}x^3 - x + 3$

30. $-\frac{2}{5}x^5 - x^3 + 6$

c Identify the like terms in each polynomial.

31. $5x^3 + 6x^2 - 3x^2$

32. $3x^2 + 4x^3 - 2x^2$

33. $2x^4 + 5x - 7x - 3x^4$

34. $-3t + t^3 - 2t - 5t^3$

35. $3x^5 - 7x + 8 + 14x^5 - 2x - 9$

36. $8x^3 + 7x^2 - 11 - 4x^3 - 8x^2 - 29$

d Identify the coefficient of each term of the polynomial.

37. $-3x + 6$

38. $2x - 4$

39. $5x^2 + \frac{3}{4}x + 3$

40. $\frac{2}{3}x^2 - 5x + 2$

41. $-5x^4 + 6x^3 - 2.7x^2 + x - 2$

42. $7x^3 - x^2 - 4.2x + 5$

e Collect like terms.

43. $2x - 5x$

44. $2x^2 + 8x^2$

45. $x - 9x$

46. $x - 5x$

47. $5x^3 + 6x^3 + 4$

48. $6x^4 - 2x^4 + 5$

49. $5x^3 + 6x - 4x^3 - 7x$

50. $3a^4 - 2a + 2a + a^4$

51. $6b^5 + 3b^2 - 2b^5 - 3b^2$

52. $2x^2 - 6x + 3x + 4x^2$

53. $\frac{1}{4}x^5 - 5 + \frac{1}{2}x^5 - 2x - 37$

54. $\frac{1}{3}x^3 + 2x - \frac{1}{6}x^3 + 4 - 16$

55. $6x^2 + 2x^4 - 2x^2 - x^4 - 4x^2$

56. $8x^2 + 2x^3 - 3x^3 - 4x^2 - 4x^2$

57. $\frac{1}{4}x^3 - x^2 - \frac{1}{6}x^2 + \frac{3}{8}x^3 + \frac{5}{16}x^3$

58. $\frac{1}{5}x^4 + \frac{1}{5} - 2x^2 + \frac{1}{10} - \frac{3}{15}x^4 + 2x^2 - \frac{3}{10}$

f   Arrange each polynomial in descending order.

59. $x^5 + x + 6x^3 + 1 + 2x^2$

60. $3 + 2x^2 - 5x^6 - 2x^3 + 3x$

61. $5y^3 + 15y^9 + y - y^2 + 7y^8$

62. $9p - 5 + 6p^3 - 5p^4 + p^5$

Collect like terms and then arrange in descending order.

63. $3x^4 - 5x^6 - 2x^4 + 6x^6$

64. $-1 + 5x^3 - 3 - 7x^3 + x^4 + 5$

65. $-2x + 4x^3 - 7x + 9x^3 + 8$

66. $-6x^2 + x - 5x + 7x^2 + 1$

67. $3x + 3x + 3x - x^2 - 4x^2$

68. $-2x - 2x - 2x + x^3 - 5x^3$

69. $-x + \frac{3}{4} + 15x^4 - x - \frac{1}{2} - 3x^4$

70. $2x - \frac{5}{6} + 4x^3 + x + \frac{1}{3} - 2x$

g   Identify the degree of each term of the polynomial and the degree of the polynomial.

71. $2x - 4$

72. $6 - 3x$

73. $3x^2 - 5x + 2$

74. $5x^3 - 2x^2 + 3$

75. $-7x^3 + 6x^2 + \frac{3}{5}x + 7$

76. $5x^4 + \frac{1}{4}x^2 - x + 2$

77. $x^2 - 3x + x^6 - 9x^4$

78. $8x - 3x^2 + 9 - 8x^3$

Copyright © 2012 Pearson Education, Inc.

79. Complete the following table for the polynomial $-7x^4 + 6x^3 - x^2 + 8x - 2$.

TERM	COEFFICIENT	DEGREE OF THE TERM	DEGREE OF THE POLYNOMIAL
$-7x^4$			
$6x^3$	6		
		2	
$8x$		1	
	-2		

80. Complete the following table for the polynomial $3x^2 + x^5 - 46x^3 + 6x - 2.4 - \frac{1}{2}x^4$.

TERM	COEFFICIENT	DEGREE OF THE TERM	DEGREE OF THE POLYNOMIAL
		5	
$-\frac{1}{2}x^4$		4	
	-46		
$3x^2$		2	
	6		
-2.4			

(h) Identify the missing terms in each polynomial.

81. $x^3 - 27$

82. $x^5 + x$

83. $x^4 - x$

84. $5x^4 - 7x + 2$

85. $2x^3 - 5x^2 + x - 3$

86. $-6x^3$

Write each polynomial in two ways: with its missing terms and by leaving space for them.

87. $x^3 - 27$

88. $x^5 + x$

89. $x^4 - x$

90. $5x^4 - 7x + 2$

91. $2x^3 - 5x^2 + x - 3$

92. $-6x^3$

(i) Classify each polynomial as a monomial, a binomial, a trinomial, or none of these.

93. $x^2 - 10x + 25$

94. $-6x^4$

95. $x^3 - 7x^2 + 2x - 4$

96. $x^2 - 9$

97. $4x^2 - 25$

98. $2x^4 - 7x^3 + x^2 + x - 6$

99. $40x$

100. $4x^2 + 12x + 9$

Skill Maintenance

101. Three tired hikers camped overnight. All they had to eat was a bag of apples. During the night, one awoke and ate one-third of the apples. Later, a second camper awoke and ate one-third of the apples that remained. Much later, the third camper awoke and ate one-third of those apples yet remaining after the other two had eaten. When they got up the next morning, 8 apples were left. How many apples did they begin with?   [8.6a]

Subtract.   [7.4a]

102. $1 - 20$

103. $\dfrac{1}{8} - \dfrac{5}{6}$

104. $\dfrac{3}{8} - \left(-\dfrac{1}{4}\right)$

105. $5.6 - 8.2$

106. Solve: $3(x + 2) = 5x - 9$.   [8.3c]

107. Solve $C = ab - r$ for b.   [8.4b]

108. A warehouse stores 1800 lb of peanuts, 1500 lb of cashews, and 700 lb of almonds. What percent of the total is peanuts? cashews? almonds?   [8.5a]

109. Factor: $3x - 15y + 63$.   [7.7d]

Synthesis

Collect like terms.

110. $6x^3 \cdot 7x^2 - (4x^3)^2 + (-3x^3)^2 - (-4x^2)(5x^3) - 10x^5 + 17x^6$

111. $(3x^2)^3 + 4x^2 \cdot 4x^4 - x^4(2x)^2 + ((2x)^2)^3 - 100x^2(x^2)^2$

112. Construct a polynomial in x (meaning that x is the variable) of degree 5 with four terms and coefficients that are integers.

113. What is the degree of $(5m^5)^2$?

114. A polynomial in x has degree 3. The coefficient of x^2 is 3 less than the coefficient of x^3. The coefficient of x is three times the coefficient of x^2. The remaining coefficient is 2 more than the coefficient of x^3. The sum of the coefficients is -4. Find the polynomial.

Use the CALC feature and choose VALUE on your graphing calculator to find the values in each of the following. (Refer to the Calculator Corner on p. 758.)

115. Exercise 17

116. Exercise 18

117. Exercise 21

118. Exercise 22

Copyright © 2012 Pearson Education, Inc.

10.4 Addition and Subtraction of Polynomials

a Addition of Polynomials

To add two polynomials, we can write a plus sign between them and then collect like terms. Depending on the situation, you may see polynomials written in descending order, ascending order, or neither. Generally, if an exercise is written in a particular order, we write the answer in that same order.

EXAMPLE 1 Add: $(-3x^3 + 2x - 4) + (4x^3 + 3x^2 + 2)$.

$(-3x^3 + 2x - 4) + (4x^3 + 3x^2 + 2)$
$= (-3 + 4)x^3 + 3x^2 + 2x + (-4 + 2)$ Collecting like terms
$= x^3 + 3x^2 + 2x - 2$

EXAMPLE 2 Add:

$\left(\frac{2}{3}x^4 + 3x^2 - 2x + \frac{1}{2}\right) + \left(-\frac{1}{3}x^4 + 5x^3 - 3x^2 + 3x - \frac{1}{2}\right).$

We have

$\left(\frac{2}{3}x^4 + 3x^2 - 2x + \frac{1}{2}\right) + \left(-\frac{1}{3}x^4 + 5x^3 - 3x^2 + 3x - \frac{1}{2}\right)$

$= \left(\frac{2}{3} - \frac{1}{3}\right)x^4 + 5x^3 + (3 - 3)x^2 + (-2 + 3)x + \left(\frac{1}{2} - \frac{1}{2}\right)$ Collecting like terms

$= \frac{1}{3}x^4 + 5x^3 + x.$

We can add polynomials as we do because they represent numbers. After some practice, you will be able to add mentally.

> Do Margin Exercises 1–4.

EXAMPLE 3 Add: $(3x^2 - 2x + 2) + (5x^3 - 2x^2 + 3x - 4)$.

$(3x^2 - 2x + 2) + (5x^3 - 2x^2 + 3x - 4)$
$= 5x^3 + (3 - 2)x^2 + (-2 + 3)x + (2 - 4)$ You might do this step mentally.
$= 5x^3 + x^2 + x - 2$ Then you would write only this.

> Do Exercises 5 and 6 on the following page.

We can also add polynomials by writing like terms in columns.

EXAMPLE 4 Add: $9x^5 - 2x^3 + 6x^2 + 3$ and $5x^4 - 7x^2 + 6$ and $3x^6 - 5x^5 + x^2 + 5$.

We arrange the polynomials with the like terms in columns.

$$
\begin{array}{l}
9x^5 \qquad\quad\ -\ 2x^3 + 6x^2 +\ \ 3 \\
\qquad\quad 5x^4 \qquad\quad\ -\ 7x^2 +\ \ 6 \quad\text{We leave spaces for missing terms.} \\
\underline{3x^6 - 5x^5 \qquad\qquad\quad +\ \ x^2 +\ \ 5} \\
3x^6 + 4x^5 + 5x^4 - 2x^3 \qquad\qquad +\ 14 \quad\text{Adding}
\end{array}
$$

We write the answer as $3x^6 + 4x^5 + 5x^4 - 2x^3 + 14$ without the space.

SKILL TO REVIEW
Objective 7.4a: Subtract real numbers and simplify combinations of additions and subtractions.

Simplify.
1. $-4 - (-8)$
2. $-5 - 6 + 4$

Add.

1. $(3x^2 + 2x - 2) + (-2x^2 + 5x + 5)$

2. $(-4x^5 + x^3 + 4) + (7x^4 + 2x^2)$

3. $(31x^4 + x^2 + 2x - 1) + (-7x^4 + 5x^3 - 2x + 2)$

4. $(17x^3 - x^2 + 3x + 4) + \left(-15x^3 + x^2 - 3x - \frac{2}{3}\right)$

Answers

Skill to Review:
1. 4   2. -7

Margin Exercises:
1. $x^2 + 7x + 3$
2. $-4x^5 + 7x^4 + x^3 + 2x^2 + 4$
3. $24x^4 + 5x^3 + x^2 + 1$
4. $2x^3 + \frac{10}{3}$

Add mentally. Try to write just the answer.

5. $(4x^2 - 5x + 3) +$
$(-2x^2 + 2x - 4)$

6. $(3x^3 - 4x^2 - 5x + 3) +$
$\left(5x^3 + 2x^2 - 3x - \dfrac{1}{2}\right)$

Add.

7.
$$\begin{array}{r} -2x^3 + 5x^2 - 2x + 4 \\ x^4 \qquad\quad + 6x^2 + 7x - 10 \\ -9x^4 + 6x^3 + \; x^2 \qquad\quad - 2 \\ \hline \end{array}$$

8. $-3x^3 + 5x + 2$ and
$x^3 + x^2 + 5$ and
$x^3 - 2x - 4$

Simplify.

9. $-(4x^3 - 6x + 3)$

10. $-(5x^4 + 3x^2 + 7x - 5)$

11. $-\left(14x^{10} - \frac{1}{2}x^5 + 5x^3 - x^2 + 3x\right)$

Subtract.

12. $(7x^3 + 2x + 4) - (5x^3 - 4)$

13. $(-3x^2 + 5x - 4) -$
$(-4x^2 + 11x - 2)$

Answers

5. $2x^2 - 3x - 1$ **6.** $8x^3 - 2x^2 - 8x + \dfrac{5}{2}$
7. $-8x^4 + 4x^3 + 12x^2 + 5x - 8$
8. $-x^3 + x^2 + 3x + 3$ **9.** $-4x^3 + 6x - 3$
10. $-5x^4 - 3x^2 - 7x + 5$
11. $-14x^{10} + \dfrac{1}{2}x^5 - 5x^3 + x^2 - 3x$
12. $2x^3 + 2x + 8$ **13.** $x^2 - 6x - 2$

Do Exercises 7 and 8.

(b) Opposites of Polynomials

In Section 7.8, we used the property of -1 to show that we can find the opposite of an expression. For example, the opposite of $x - 2y + 5$ can be written as

$$-(x - 2y + 5).$$

We find an equivalent expression by changing the sign of every term:

$$-(x - 2y + 5) = -x + 2y - 5.$$

We use this concept when we subtract polynomials.

> **OPPOSITES OF POLYNOMIALS**
>
> To find an equivalent polynomial for the **opposite**, or **additive inverse**, of a polynomial, change the sign of every term. This is the same as multiplying by -1.

EXAMPLE 5 Simplify: $-(x^2 - 3x + 4)$.
$$-(x^2 - 3x + 4) = -x^2 + 3x - 4$$

EXAMPLE 6 Simplify: $-(-t^3 - 6t^2 - t + 4)$.
$$-(-t^3 - 6t^2 - t + 4) = t^3 + 6t^2 + t - 4$$

EXAMPLE 7 Simplify: $-\left(-7x^4 - \frac{5}{9}x^3 + 8x^2 - x + 67\right)$.
$$-\left(-7x^4 - \tfrac{5}{9}x^3 + 8x^2 - x + 67\right) = 7x^4 + \tfrac{5}{9}x^3 - 8x^2 + x - 67$$

Do Exercises 9–11.

(c) Subtraction of Polynomials

Recall that we can subtract a real number by adding its opposite, or additive inverse: $a - b = a + (-b)$. This allows us to subtract polynomials.

EXAMPLE 8 Subtract:
$$(9x^5 + x^3 - 2x^2 + 4) - (2x^5 + x^4 - 4x^3 - 3x^2).$$

We have

$(9x^5 + x^3 - 2x^2 + 4) - (2x^5 + x^4 - 4x^3 - 3x^2)$

$= 9x^5 + x^3 - 2x^2 + 4 + [-(2x^5 + x^4 - 4x^3 - 3x^2)]$ Adding the opposite

$= 9x^5 + x^3 - 2x^2 + 4 - 2x^5 - x^4 + 4x^3 + 3x^2$ Finding the opposite by changing the sign of *each* term

$= 7x^5 - x^4 + 5x^3 + x^2 + 4.$ Adding (collecting like terms)

Do Exercises 12 and 13.

As with similar work in Section 7.8, we combine steps by changing the sign of each term of the polynomial being subtracted and collecting like terms. Try to do this mentally as much as possible.

EXAMPLE 9 Subtract: $(9x^5 + x^3 - 2x) - (-2x^5 + 5x^3 + 6)$.

$(9x^5 + x^3 - 2x) - (-2x^5 + 5x^3 + 6)$

$= 9x^5 + x^3 - 2x + 2x^5 - 5x^3 - 6$ Finding the opposite by changing the sign of each term

$= 11x^5 - 4x^3 - 2x - 6$ Adding (collecting like terms)

Do Exercises 14 and 15.

We can use columns to subtract. We replace coefficients with their opposites, as shown in Example 9.

EXAMPLE 10 Write in columns and subtract:

$(5x^2 - 3x + 6) - (9x^2 - 5x - 3)$.

a) $5x^2 - 3x + 6$ Writing like terms in columns
$\underline{-(9x^2 - 5x - 3)}$

b) $5x^2 - 3x + 6$
$\underline{-9x^2 + 5x + 3}$ Changing signs

c) $5x^2 - 3x + 6$
$\underline{-9x^2 + 5x + 3}$
$-4x^2 + 2x + 9$ Adding

If you can do so without error, you can arrange the polynomials in columns and write just the answer, remembering to change the signs and add.

EXAMPLE 11 Write in columns and subtract:

$(x^3 + x^2 + 2x - 12) - (-2x^3 + x^2 - 3x)$.

$x^3 + x^2 + 2x - 12$
$\underline{-(-2x^3 + x^2 - 3x \qquad)}$ Leaving space for the missing term
$3x^3 \qquad\quad + 5x - 12$ Changing the signs and adding

Do Exercises 16 and 17.

(d) Polynomials and Geometry

EXAMPLE 12 Find a polynomial for the sum of the areas of these rectangles.

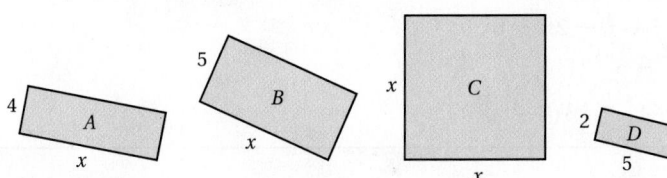

Recall that the area of a rectangle is the product of the length and the width. The sum of the areas is a sum of products. We find these products and then collect like terms.

Subtract.

14. $(-6x^4 + 3x^2 + 6) - (2x^4 + 5x^3 - 5x^2 + 7)$

15. $\left(\frac{3}{2}x^3 - \frac{1}{2}x^2 + 0.3\right) - \left(\frac{1}{2}x^3 + \frac{1}{2}x^2 + \frac{4}{3}x + 1.2\right)$

Write in columns and subtract.

16. $(4x^3 + 2x^2 - 2x - 3) - (2x^3 - 3x^2 + 2)$

17. $(2x^3 + x^2 - 6x + 2) - (x^5 + 4x^3 - 2x^2 - 4x)$

Answers

14. $-8x^4 - 5x^3 + 8x^2 - 1$

15. $x^3 - x^2 - \frac{4}{3}x - 0.9$

16. $2x^3 + 5x^2 - 2x - 5$

17. $-x^5 - 2x^3 + 3x^2 - 2x + 2$

18. Find a polynomial for the sums of the perimeters and of the areas of the rectangles.

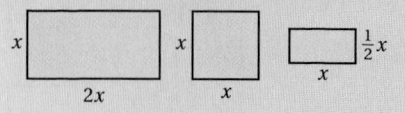

19. Lawn Area. An 8-ft by 8-ft shed is placed on a lawn x ft on a side. Find a polynomial for the remaining area.

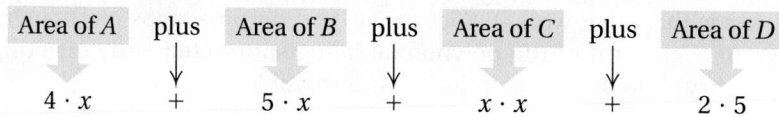

We collect like terms:

$$4x + 5x + x^2 + 10 = x^2 + 9x + 10.$$

Do Exercise 18.

EXAMPLE 13 *Lawn Area.* A water fountain with a 4-ft by 4-ft square base is placed in a park in a square grassy area that is x ft on a side. To determine the amount of grass seed needed for the lawn, find a polynomial for the grassy area.

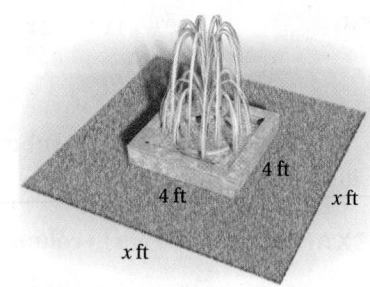

We make a drawing of the situation as shown here. We then reword the problem and write the polynomial as follows:

Area of grassy area $-$ Area of base of fountain $=$ Area left over

$$x \cdot x \quad - \quad 4 \cdot 4 \quad = \text{Area left over.}$$

Then $(x^2 - 16)$ ft^2 = Area left over.

Do Exercise 19.

Calculator Corner

Checking Addition and Subtraction of Polynomials   A table set in AUTO mode can be used to perform a partial check that polynomials have been added or subtracted correctly. To check Example 3, we enter $y_1 = (3x^2 - 2x + 2) + (5x^3 - 2x^2 + 3x - 4)$ and $y_2 = 5x^3 + x^2 + x - 2$. If the addition has been done correctly, the values of y_1 and y_2 will be the same regardless of the table settings used.

A graph can also be used to check addition and subtraction. See the Calculator Corner on p. 782 for the procedure.

X	Y₁	Y₂
-2	-40	-40
-1	-7	-7
0	-2	-2
1	5	5
2	44	44
3	145	145
4	338	338
X = -2		

Exercises: Use a table to determine whether the sum or the difference is correct.

1. $(-3x^3 + 2x - 4) + (4x^3 + 3x^2 + 2) = x^3 + 3x^2 + 2x - 2$

2. $(x^3 - 2x^2 + 3x - 7) + (3x^2 - 4x + 5) = x^3 + x^2 - x - 2$

3. $(5x^2 - 7x + 4) + (2x^2 + 3x - 6) = 7x^2 + 4x - 2$

4. $(9x^5 + x^3 - 2x) - (-2x^5 + 5x^3 + 6) = 11x^5 - 4x^3 - 2x - 6$

5. $(3x^4 - 2x^2 - 1) - (2x^4 - 3x^2 - 4) = x^4 + x^2 - 5$

6. $(-2x^3 + 3x^2 - 4x + 5) - (3x^2 + 2x + 8) = -2x^3 - 6x - 3$

Answers

18. Sum of perimeters: $13x$; sum of areas: $\frac{7}{2}x^2$

19. $(x^2 - 64)$ ft^2

a) Add.

1. $(3x + 2) + (-4x + 3)$

2. $(6x + 1) + (-7x + 2)$

3. $(-6x + 2) + \left(x^2 + \frac{1}{2}x - 3\right)$

4. $\left(x^2 - \frac{5}{3}x + 4\right) + (8x - 9)$

5. $(x^2 - 9) + (x^2 + 9)$

6. $(x^3 + x^2) + (2x^3 - 5x^2)$

7. $(3x^2 - 5x + 10) + (2x^2 + 8x - 40)$

8. $(6x^4 + 3x^3 - 1) + (4x^2 - 3x + 3)$

9. $(1.2x^3 + 4.5x^2 - 3.8x) + (-3.4x^3 - 4.7x^2 + 23)$

10. $(0.5x^4 - 0.6x^2 + 0.7) + (2.3x^4 + 1.8x - 3.9)$

11. $(1 + 4x + 6x^2 + 7x^3) + (5 - 4x + 6x^2 - 7x^3)$

12. $(3x^4 - 6x - 5x^2 + 5) + (6x^2 - 4x^3 - 1 + 7x)$

13. $\left(\frac{1}{4}x^4 + \frac{2}{3}x^3 + \frac{5}{8}x^2 + 7\right) + \left(-\frac{3}{4}x^4 + \frac{3}{8}x^2 - 7\right)$

14. $\left(\frac{1}{3}x^9 + \frac{1}{5}x^5 - \frac{1}{2}x^2 + 7\right) + \left(-\frac{1}{5}x^9 + \frac{1}{4}x^4 - \frac{3}{5}x^5 + \frac{3}{4}x^2 + \frac{1}{2}\right)$

15. $(0.02x^5 - 0.2x^3 + x + 0.08) + (-0.01x^5 + x^4 - 0.8x - 0.02)$

16. $(0.03x^6 + 0.05x^3 + 0.22x + 0.05) + \left(\frac{7}{100}x^6 - \frac{3}{100}x^3 + 0.5\right)$

17. $(9x^8 - 7x^4 + 2x^2 + 5) + (8x^7 + 4x^4 - 2x) + (-3x^4 + 6x^2 + 2x - 1)$

18. $(4x^5 - 6x^3 - 9x + 1) + (6x^3 + 9x^2 + 9x) + (-4x^3 + 8x^2 + 3x - 2)$

19.
$$
\begin{array}{r}
0.15x^4 + 0.10x^3 - 0.9x^2 \\
- 0.01x^3 + 0.01x^2 + x \\
1.25x^4 \qquad\quad + 0.11x^2 \qquad + 0.01 \\
0.27x^3 \qquad\qquad\qquad + 0.99 \\
\hline
-0.35x^4 \qquad\qquad\quad + 15x^2 - 0.03
\end{array}
$$

20.
$$
\begin{array}{r}
0.05x^4 + 0.12x^3 - 0.5x^2 \\
- 0.02x^3 + 0.02x^2 + 2x \\
1.5x^4 \qquad\quad + 0.01x^2 \qquad + 0.15 \\
0.25x^3 \qquad\qquad\qquad + 0.85 \\
\hline
-0.25x^4 \qquad\qquad\quad + 10x^2 - 0.04
\end{array}
$$

b Simplify.

21. $-(-5x)$

22. $-(x^2 - 3x)$

23. $-\left(-x^2 + \frac{3}{2}x - 2\right)$

24. $-\left(-4x^3 - x^2 - \frac{1}{4}x\right)$

25. $-(12x^4 - 3x^3 + 3)$

26. $-(4x^3 - 6x^2 - 8x + 1)$

27. $-(3x - 7)$

28. $-(-2x + 4)$

29. $-(4x^2 - 3x + 2)$

30. $-(-6a^3 + 2a^2 - 9a + 1)$

31. $-\left(-4x^4 + 6x^2 + \frac{3}{4}x - 8\right)$

32. $-(-5x^4 + 4x^3 - x^2 + 0.9)$

c Subtract.

33. $(3x + 2) - (-4x + 3)$

34. $(6x + 1) - (-7x + 2)$

35. $(-6x + 2) - (x^2 + x - 3)$

36. $(x^2 - 5x + 4) - (8x - 9)$

37. $(x^2 - 9) - (x^2 + 9)$

38. $(x^3 + x^2) - (2x^3 - 5x^2)$

39. $(6x^4 + 3x^3 - 1) - (4x^2 - 3x + 3)$

40. $(-4x^2 + 2x) - (3x^3 - 5x^2 + 3)$

41. $(1.2x^3 + 4.5x^2 - 3.8x) - (-3.4x^3 - 4.7x^2 + 23)$

42. $(0.5x^4 - 0.6x^2 + 0.7) - (2.3x^4 + 1.8x - 3.9)$

43. $\left(\frac{5}{8}x^3 - \frac{1}{4}x - \frac{1}{3}\right) - \left(-\frac{1}{8}x^3 + \frac{1}{4}x - \frac{1}{3}\right)$

44. $\left(\frac{1}{5}x^3 + 2x^2 - 0.1\right) - \left(-\frac{2}{5}x^3 + 2x^2 + 0.01\right)$

45. $(0.08x^3 - 0.02x^2 + 0.01x) - (0.02x^3 + 0.03x^2 - 1)$

46. $(0.8x^4 + 0.2x - 1) - \left(\frac{7}{10}x^4 + \frac{1}{5}x - 0.1\right)$

Copyright © 2012 Pearson Education, Inc.

Subtract.

47. $x^2 + 5x + 6$
$-(x^2 + 2x)$

48. $x^3 + 1$
$-(x^3 + x^2)$

49. $5x^4 + 6x^3 - 9x^2$
$-(-6x^4 - 6x^3 + 8x + 9)$

50. $5x^4 + 6x^2 - 3x + 6$
$-(6x^3 + 7x^2 - 8x - 9)$

51. $x^5 - 1$
$-(x^5 - x^4 + x^3 - x^2 + x - 1)$

52. $x^5 + x^4 - x^3 + x^2 - x + 2$
$-(x^5 - x^4 + x^3 - x^2 - x + 2)$

 Solve.

Find a polynomial for the perimeter of each figure.

53.

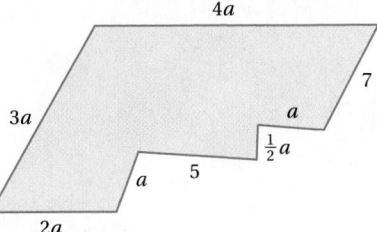

54.

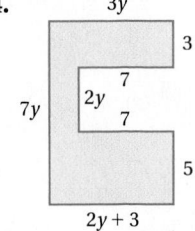

55. Find a polynomial for the sum of the areas of these rectangles.

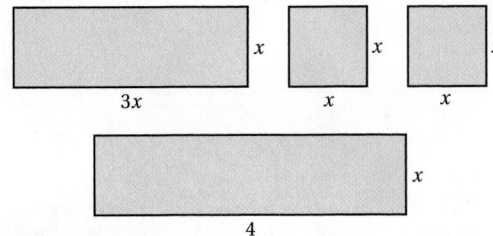

56. Find a polynomial for the sum of the areas of these circles.

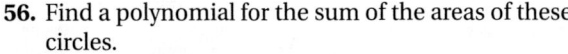
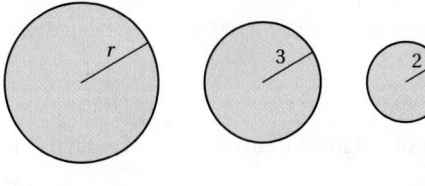

Find two algebraic expressions for the area of each figure. First, regard the figure as one large rectangle, and then regard the figure as a sum of four smaller rectangles.

57.

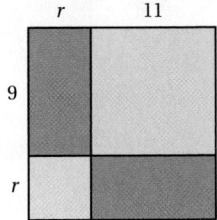

58.

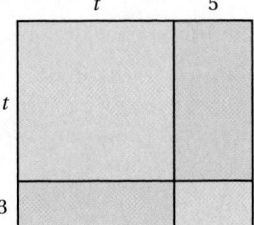

59.

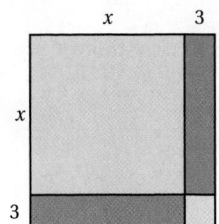

60.

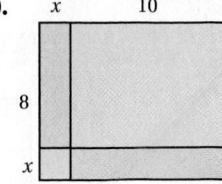

Find a polynomial for the shaded area of each figure.

61.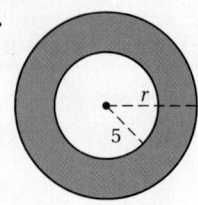

62.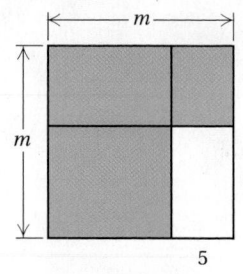

63.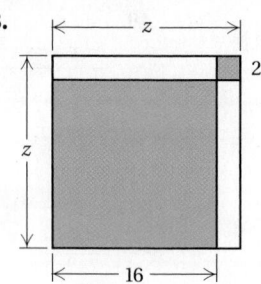

64.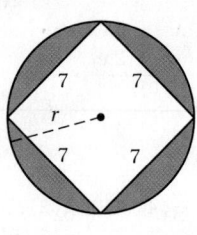

Skill Maintenance

Solve.   [8.3b]

65. $8x + 3x = 66$

66. $5x - 7x = 38$

67. $\frac{3}{8}x + \frac{1}{4} - \frac{3}{4}x = \frac{11}{16} + x$

68. $5x - 4 = 26 - x$

69. $1.5x - 2.7x = 22 - 5.6x$

70. $3x - 3 = -4x + 4$

Solve.   [8.3c]

71. $6(y - 3) - 8 = 4(y + 2) + 5$

72. $8(5x + 2) = 7(6x - 3)$

Solve.   [8.7e]

73. $3x - 7 \leq 5x + 13$

74. $2(x - 4) > 5(x - 3) + 7$

Synthesis

Find a polynomial for the surface area of each right rectangular solid.

75.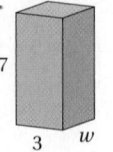

76.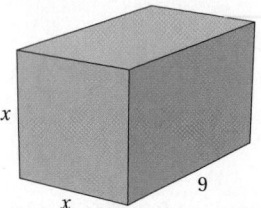

77.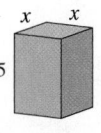

78.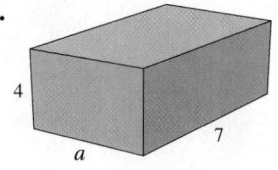

79. Find $(y - 2)^2$ using the four parts of this square.

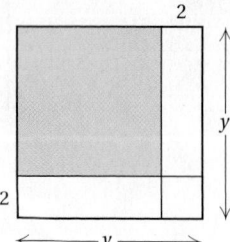

Simplify.

80. $(3x^2 - 4x + 6) - (-2x^2 + 4) + (-5x - 3)$

81. $(7y^2 - 5y + 6) - (3y^2 + 8y - 12) + (8y^2 - 10y + 3)$

82. $(-4 + x^2 + 2x^3) - (-6 - x + 3x^3) - (-x^2 - 5x^3)$

83. $(-y^4 - 7y^3 + y^2) + (-2y^4 + 5y - 2) - (-6y^3 + y^2)$

Copyright © 2012 Pearson Education, Inc.

Mid-Chapter Review

Concept Reinforcement

Determine whether each statement is true or false.

_____ **1.** a^n and a^{-n} are reciprocals. [10.1f]

_____ **2.** $x^2 \cdot x^3 = x^6$ [10.1d]

_____ **3.** $-5y^4$ and $-5y^2$ are like terms. [10.3c]

_____ **4.** $4920^0 = 1$ [10.1b]

Guided Solutions

Fill in each blank with the number or variable that creates a correct statement or solution.

5. Collect like terms: $4w^3 + 6w - 8w^3 - 3w$. [10.3e]

$$4w^3 + 6w - 8w^3 - 3w = (4 - 8)\,\square + (6 - 3)\,\square$$
$$= \square\, w^3 + \square\, w$$

6. Subtract: $(3y^4 - y^2 + 11) - (y^4 - 4y^2 + 5)$. [10.4c]

$$(3y^4 - y^2 + 11) - (y^4 - 4y^2 + 5) = 3y^4 - y^2 + 11\,\square\,y^4\,\square\,4y^2\,\square\,5$$
$$= \square\,y^4 + \square\,y^2 + \square$$

Mixed Review

Evaluate. [10.1b, c]

7. z^1

8. 4.56^0

9. a^5, when $a = -2$

10. $-x^3$, when $x = -1$

Multiply and simplify. [10.1d, f]

11. $5^3 \cdot 5^4$

12. $(3a)^2 (3a)^7$

13. $x^{-8} \cdot x^5$

14. $t^4 \cdot t^{-4}$

Divide and simplify. [10.1e, f]

15. $\dfrac{7^8}{7^4}$

16. $\dfrac{x}{x^3}$

17. $\dfrac{w^5}{w^{-3}}$

18. $\dfrac{y^{-6}}{y^{-2}}$

Simplify. [10.2a, b]

19. $(3^5)^3$

20. $(x^{-3}y^2)^{-6}$

21. $\left(\dfrac{a^4}{5}\right)^6$

22. $\left(\dfrac{2y^3}{xz^2}\right)^{-2}$

Convert to scientific notation. [10.2c]

23. 25,430,000

24. 0.00012

Convert to decimal notation. [10.2c]

25. 3.6×10^{-5}

26. 1.44×10^8

Multiply or divide and write scientific notation for the result.   [10.2d]

27. $(3 \times 10^6)(2 \times 10^{-3})$

28. $\dfrac{1.2 \times 10^{-4}}{2.4 \times 10^2}$

Evaluate the polynomial when $x = -3$ and when $x = 2$.   [10.3a]

29. $-3x + 7$

30. $x^3 - 2x + 5$

Collect like terms and then arrange in descending order.   [10.3f]

31. $3x - 2x^5 + x - 5x^2 + 2$

32. $4x^3 - 9x^2 - 2x^3 + x^2 + 8x^6$

Identify the degree of each term of the polynomial and the degree of the polynomial.   [10.3g]

33. $5x^3 - x + 4$

34. $2x - x^4 + 3x^6$

Classify the polynomial as a monomial, a binomial, a trinomial, or none of these.   [10.3i]

35. $x - 9$

36. $x^5 - 2x^3 + 6x^2$

Add or subtract.   [10.4a, c]

37. $(3x^2 - 1) + (5x^2 + 6)$

38. $(x^3 + 2x - 5) + (4x^3 - 2x^2 - 6)$

39. $(5x - 8) - (9x + 2)$

40. $(0.1x^2 - 2.4x + 3.6) - (0.5x^2 + x - 5.4)$

41. Find a polynomial for the sum of the areas of these rectangles.   [10.4d]

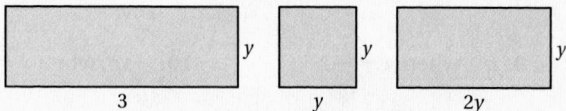

Understanding Through Discussion and Writing

42. Suppose that the length of a side of a square is three times the length of a side of a second square. How do the areas of the squares compare? Why?   [10.1d]

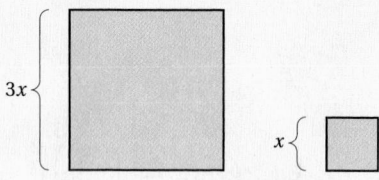

43. Suppose that the length of a side of a cube is twice the length of a side of a second cube. How do the volumes of the cubes compare? Why?   [10.1d]

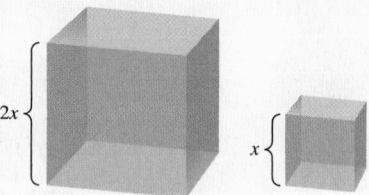

44. Explain in your own words when exponents should be added and when they should be multiplied.   [10.1d], [10.2a]

45. Without performing actual computations, explain why 3^{-29} is smaller than 2^{-29}.   [10.1f]

46. Is it better to evaluate a polynomial before or after like terms have been collected? Why?   [10.3a, e]

47. Is the sum of two binomials ever a trinomial? Why or why not?   [10.3i], [10.4a]

Copyright © 2012 Pearson Education, Inc.

10.5 Multiplication of Polynomials

We now multiply polynomials using techniques based, for the most part, on the distributive laws, but also on the associative and commutative laws. As we proceed in this chapter, we will develop special ways to find certain products.

a Multiplying Monomials

Consider $(3x)(4x)$. We multiply as follows:

$$
\begin{aligned}
(3x)(4x) &= 3 \cdot x \cdot 4 \cdot x && \text{By the associative law of multiplication} \\
&= 3 \cdot 4 \cdot x \cdot x && \text{By the commutative law of multiplication} \\
&= (3 \cdot 4)(x \cdot x) && \text{By the associative law} \\
&= 12x^2. && \text{Using the product rule for exponents}
\end{aligned}
$$

> **MULTIPLYING MONOMIALS**
>
> To find an equivalent expression for the product of two monomials, multiply the coefficients and then multiply the variables using the product rule for exponents.

EXAMPLES Multiply.

1. $5x \cdot 6x = (5 \cdot 6)(x \cdot x)$ By the associative and commutative laws
$ = 30x^2$ Multiplying the coefficients and multiplying the variables

2. $(3x)(-x) = (3x)(-1x)$
$ = (3)(-1)(x \cdot x) = -3x^2$

3. $(-7x^5)(4x^3) = (-7 \cdot 4)(x^5 \cdot x^3)$
$ = -28x^{5+3}$ Adding the exponents
$ = -28x^8$ Simplifying

After some practice, you will be able to multiply mentally. Multiply the coefficients and then the variables by keeping the base and adding the exponents. Write only the answer.

Do Margin Exercises 1–8.

b Multiplying a Monomial and Any Polynomial

To find an equivalent expression for the product of a monomial, such as $2x$, and a binomial, such as $5x + 3$, we use a distributive law and multiply each term of $5x + 3$ by $2x$.

EXAMPLE 4 Multiply: $2x(5x + 3)$.

$$
\begin{aligned}
2x(5x + 3) &= (2x)(5x) + (2x)(3) && \text{Using a distributive law} \\
&= 10x^2 + 6x && \text{Multiplying the monomials}
\end{aligned}
$$

SKILL TO REVIEW
Objective 7.7c: Use the distributive laws to multiply expressions like 8 and $x - y$.

Multiply.

1. $3(x - 5)$

2. $2(3y + 4z - 1)$

Multiply.

1. $(3x)(-5)$ **2.** $(-x) \cdot x$

3. $(-x)(-x)$ **4.** $(-x^2)(x^3)$

5. $3x^5 \cdot 4x^2$ **6.** $(4y^5)(-2y^6)$

7. $(-7y^4)(-y)$ **8.** $7x^5 \cdot 0$

Answers

Skill to Review:
1. $3x - 15$ 2. $6y + 8z - 2$

Margin Exercises:
1. $-15x$ 2. $-x^2$ 3. x^2 4. $-x^5$
5. $12x^7$ 6. $-8y^{11}$ 7. $7y^5$ 8. 0

EXAMPLE 5 Multiply: $5x(2x^2 - 3x + 4)$.

$$5x(2x^2 - 3x + 4) = (5x)(2x^2) - (5x)(3x) + (5x)(4)$$
$$= 10x^3 - 15x^2 + 20x$$

> **MULTIPLYING A MONOMIAL AND A POLYNOMIAL**
>
> To multiply a monomial and a polynomial, multiply each term of the polynomial by the monomial.

EXAMPLE 6 Multiply: $-2x^2(x^3 - 7x^2 + 10x - 4)$.

$$-2x^2(x^3 - 7x^2 + 10x - 4)$$
$$= (-2x^2)(x^3) - (-2x^2)(7x^2) + (-2x^2)(10x) - (-2x^2)(4)$$
$$= -2x^5 + 14x^4 - 20x^3 + 8x^2$$

Do Exercises 9–11.

Multiply.

9. $4x(2x + 4)$

10. $3t^2(-5t + 2)$

11. $-5x^3(x^3 + 5x^2 - 6x + 8)$

c Multiplying Two Binomials

To find an equivalent expression for the product of two binomials, we use the distributive laws more than once. In Example 7, we use a distributive law three times.

EXAMPLE 7 Multiply: $(x + 5)(x + 4)$.

$$(x + 5)(x + 4) = x(x + 4) + 5(x + 4) \qquad \text{Using a distributive law}$$
$$= x \cdot x + x \cdot 4 + 5 \cdot x + 5 \cdot 4 \qquad \text{Using a distributive law on each part}$$
$$= x^2 + 4x + 5x + 20 \qquad \text{Multiplying the monomials}$$
$$= x^2 + 9x + 20 \qquad \text{Collecting like terms}$$

To visualize the product in Example 7, consider a rectangle of length $x + 5$ and width $x + 4$.

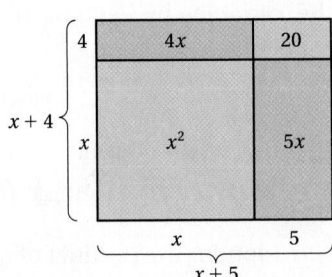

The total area can be expressed as $(x + 5)(x + 4)$ or, by adding the four smaller areas, $x^2 + 4x + 5x + 20$, or $x^2 + 9x + 20$.

Do Exercises 12–14.

12. Multiply: $(y + 2)(y + 7)$.

a) Fill in the blanks in the steps of the solution below.

$(y + 2)(y + 7)$

$= y \cdot \underline{\hspace{1cm}} + 2 \cdot \underline{\hspace{1cm}}$

$= y \cdot \underline{\hspace{1cm}} + y \cdot \underline{\hspace{1cm}}$

$\quad + 2 \cdot \underline{\hspace{1cm}} + 2 \cdot \underline{\hspace{1cm}}$

$= \underline{\hspace{1cm}} + \underline{\hspace{1cm}}$

$\quad + \underline{\hspace{1cm}} + \underline{\hspace{1cm}}$

$= y^2 + \underline{\hspace{1cm}} + 14$

b) Write an algebraic expression that represents the total area of the four smaller rectangles in the figure shown here.

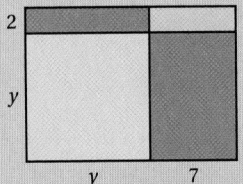

Multiply.

13. $(x + 8)(x + 5)$

14. $(x + 5)(x - 4)$

Answers

9. $8x^2 + 16x$ **10.** $-15t^3 + 6t^2$
11. $-5x^6 - 25x^5 + 30x^4 - 40x^3$
12. (a) $(y + 2)(y + 7)$
$\quad = y \cdot (y + 7) + 2 \cdot (y + 7)$
$\quad = y \cdot y + y \cdot 7$
$\quad\quad + 2 \cdot y + 2 \cdot 7$
$\quad = y^2 + 7y$
$\quad\quad + 2y + 14$
$\quad = y^2 + 9y + 14$
(b) $(y + 2)(y + 7)$, or $y^2 + 2y + 7y + 14$, or
$y^2 + 9y + 14$ **13.** $x^2 + 13x + 40$
14. $x^2 + x - 20$

EXAMPLE 8 Multiply: $(4x + 3)(x - 2)$.

$(4x + 3)(x - 2) = 4x(x - 2) + 3(x - 2)$ Using a distributive law

$= 4x \cdot x - 4x \cdot 2 + 3 \cdot x - 3 \cdot 2$ Using a distributive law on each part

$= 4x^2 - 8x + 3x - 6$ Multiplying the monomials

$= 4x^2 - 5x - 6$ Collecting like terms

Do Exercises 15 and 16.

Multiply.

15. $(5x + 3)(x - 4)$

16. $(2x - 3)(3x - 5)$

(d) Multiplying Any Two Polynomials

Let's consider the product of a binomial and a trinomial. We use a distributive law four times. You may see ways to skip some steps and do the work mentally.

EXAMPLE 9 Multiply: $(x^2 + 2x - 3)(x^2 + 4)$.

$(x^2 + 2x - 3)(x^2 + 4) = x^2(x^2 + 4) + 2x(x^2 + 4) - 3(x^2 + 4)$

$= x^2 \cdot x^2 + x^2 \cdot 4 + 2x \cdot x^2 + 2x \cdot 4 - 3 \cdot x^2 - 3 \cdot 4$

$= x^4 + 4x^2 + 2x^3 + 8x - 3x^2 - 12$

$= x^4 + 2x^3 + x^2 + 8x - 12$

Do Exercises 17 and 18.

Multiply.

17. $(x^2 + 3x - 4)(x^2 + 5)$

18. $(3y^2 - 7)(2y^3 - 2y + 5)$

> **PRODUCT OF TWO POLYNOMIALS**
>
> To multiply two polynomials P and Q, select one of the polynomials—say, P. Then multiply each term of P by every term of Q and collect like terms.

To use columns for long multiplication, multiply each term in the top row by every term in the bottom row. We write like terms in columns, and then add the results. Such multiplication is like multiplying with whole numbers.

$$
\begin{array}{r}
3\ 2\ 1 \\
\times\ \ 1\ 2 \\
\hline
6\ 4\ 2 \\
3\ 2\ 1 \\
\hline
3\ 8\ 5\ 2
\end{array}
\qquad
\begin{array}{r}
300 + 20 + 1 \\
\times \quad\quad 10 + 2 \\
\hline
600 + 40 + 2 \\
3000 + 200 + 10 \\
\hline
3000 + 800 + 50 + 2
\end{array}
$$

Multiplying the top row by 2
Multiplying the top row by 10
Adding

EXAMPLE 10 Multiply: $(4x^3 - 2x^2 + 3x)(x^2 + 2x)$.

$$
\begin{array}{r}
4x^3 - 2x^2 + 3x \\
x^2 + 2x \\
\hline
8x^4 - 4x^3 + 6x^2 \\
4x^5 - 2x^4 + 3x^3 \\
\hline
4x^5 + 6x^4 - x^3 + 6x^2
\end{array}
$$

Multiplying the top row by $2x$
Multiplying the top row by x^2
Collecting like terms
Line up like terms in columns.

Answers

15. $5x^2 - 17x - 12$ **16.** $6x^2 - 19x + 15$
17. $x^4 + 3x^3 + x^2 + 15x - 20$
18. $6y^5 - 20y^3 + 15y^2 + 14y - 35$

EXAMPLE 11 Multiply: $(2x^2 + 3x - 4)(2x^2 - x + 3)$.

$$
\begin{array}{r}
2x^2 + 3x - 4 \\
2x^2 - x + 3 \\
\hline
6x^2 + 9x - 12 \\
-2x^3 - 3x^2 + 4x \\
4x^4 + 6x^3 - 8x^2 \\
\hline
4x^4 + 4x^3 - 5x^2 + 13x - 12
\end{array}
$$

Multiplying by 3
Multiplying by $-x$
Multiplying by $2x^2$
Collecting like terms

19. Multiply.

$$
\begin{array}{r}
3x^2 - 2x - 5 \\
2x^2 + x - 2 \\
\hline
\end{array}
$$

Do Exercise 19.

EXAMPLE 12 Multiply: $(5x^3 - 3x + 4)(-2x^2 - 3)$.

When missing terms occur, it helps to leave spaces for them and align like terms as we multiply.

$$
\begin{array}{r}
5x^3 - 3x + 4 \\
-2x^2 - 3 \\
\hline
-15x^3 + 9x - 12 \\
-10x^5 + 6x^3 - 8x^2 \\
\hline
-10x^5 - 9x^3 - 8x^2 + 9x - 12
\end{array}
$$

Multiplying by -3
Multiplying by $-2x^2$
Collecting like terms

Multiply.

20. $3x^2 - 2x + 4$
$x + 5$

21. $-5x^2 + 4x + 2$
$-4x^2 - 8$

Do Exercises 20 and 21.

Calculator Corner

Checking Multiplication of Polynomials A partial check of multiplication of polynomials can be performed graphically. Consider the product $(x + 3)(x - 2) = x^2 + x - 6$. We will use two graph styles to determine whether this product is correct. First, we press **MODE** to determine whether SEQUENTIAL mode is selected. If it is not, we position the blinking cursor over SEQUENTIAL and then press **ENTER**. Next, on the Y= screen, we enter $y_1 = (x + 3)(x - 2)$ and $y_2 = x^2 + x - 6$. We will select the line-graph style for y_1 and the path style for y_2. To select these graph styles, we use ◁ to position the cursor over the icon to the left of the equation and press **ENTER** repeatedly until the desired style of icon appears, as shown below. Then we graph the equations.

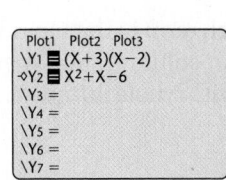
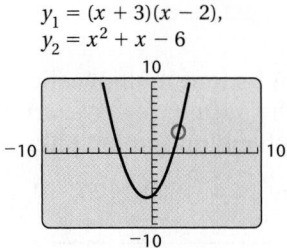

$y_1 = (x + 3)(x - 2),$
$y_2 = x^2 + x - 6$

The graphing calculator will graph y_1 first as a solid line. Then it will graph y_2 as the circular cursor traces the leading edge of the graph, allowing us to determine visually whether the graphs coincide. In this case, the graphs appear to coincide, so the factorization is probably correct.

A table can also be used to perform a partial check of a product. See the Calculator Corner on p. 772 for the procedure.

Exercises Determine graphically whether each product is correct.

1. $(x + 5)(x + 4) = x^2 + 9x + 20$

2. $(4x + 3)(x - 2) = 4x^2 - 5x - 6$

3. $(5x + 3)(x - 4) = 5x^2 + 17x - 12$

4. $(2x - 3)(3x - 5) = 6x^2 - 19x - 15$

Answers

19. $6x^4 - x^3 - 18x^2 - x + 10$
20. $3x^3 + 13x^2 - 6x + 20$
21. $20x^4 - 16x^3 + 32x^2 - 32x - 16$

a Multiply.

1. $(8x^2)(5)$

2. $(4x^2)(-2)$

3. $(-x^2)(-x)$

4. $(-x^3)(x^2)$

5. $(8x^5)(4x^3)$

6. $(10a^2)(2a^2)$

7. $(0.1x^6)(0.3x^5)$

8. $(0.3x^4)(-0.8x^6)$

9. $\left(-\frac{1}{5}x^3\right)\left(-\frac{1}{3}x\right)$

10. $\left(-\frac{1}{4}x^4\right)\left(\frac{1}{5}x^8\right)$

11. $(-4x^2)(0)$

12. $(-4m^5)(-1)$

13. $(3x^2)(-4x^3)(2x^6)$

14. $(-2y^5)(10y^4)(-3y^3)$

b Multiply.

15. $2x(-x + 5)$

16. $3x(4x - 6)$

17. $-5x(x - 1)$

18. $-3x(-x - 1)$

19. $x^2(x^3 + 1)$

20. $-2x^3(x^2 - 1)$

21. $3x(2x^2 - 6x + 1)$

22. $-4x(2x^3 - 6x^2 - 5x + 1)$

23. $(-6x^2)(x^2 + x)$

24. $(-4x^2)(x^2 - x)$

25. $(3y^2)(6y^4 + 8y^3)$

26. $(4y^4)(y^3 - 6y^2)$

c Multiply.

27. $(x + 6)(x + 3)$

28. $(x + 5)(x + 2)$

29. $(x + 5)(x - 2)$

30. $(x + 6)(x - 2)$

31. $(x - 1)(x + 4)$

32. $(x - 8)(x + 7)$

33. $(x - 4)(x - 3)$

34. $(x - 7)(x - 3)$

35. $(x + 3)(x - 3)$

36. $(x + 6)(x - 6)$

37. $(x - 4)(x + 4)$

38. $(x - 9)(x + 9)$

39. $(3x + 5)(x + 2)$

40. $(2x + 6)(x + 3)$

41. $(5 - x)(5 - 2x)$

42. $(3 - 4x)(2 - x)$

43. $(2x + 5)(2x + 5)$

44. $(3x + 4)(3x + 4)$

45. $(x - 3)(x - 3)$

46. $(x - 6)(x - 6)$

47. $\left(x - \frac{5}{2}\right)\left(x + \frac{2}{5}\right)$

48. $\left(x + \frac{4}{3}\right)\left(x + \frac{3}{2}\right)$

49. $(x - 2.3)(x + 4.7)$

50. $(2x + 0.13)(2x - 0.13)$

Write an algebraic expression that represents the total area of the four smaller rectangles.

51.
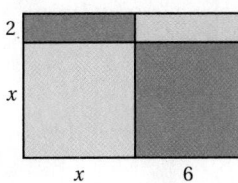

52.
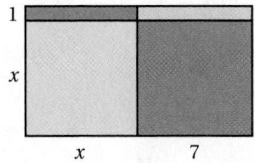

53.
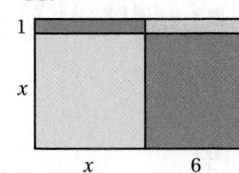

54.
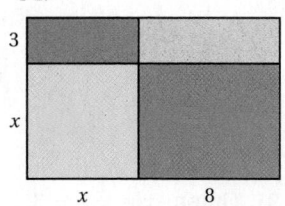

Draw and label rectangles similar to the one following Example 7 to illustrate each product.

55. $x(x + 5)$ **56.** $x(x + 2)$ **57.** $(x + 1)(x + 2)$

58. $(x + 3)(x + 1)$ **59.** $(x + 5)(x + 3)$ **60.** $(x + 4)(x + 6)$

d   Multiply.

61. $(x^2 + x + 1)(x - 1)$ **62.** $(x^2 + x - 2)(x + 2)$ **63.** $(2x + 1)(2x^2 + 6x + 1)$

64. $(3x - 1)(4x^2 - 2x - 1)$ **65.** $(y^2 - 3)(3y^2 - 6y + 2)$ **66.** $(3y^2 - 3)(y^2 + 6y + 1)$

67. $(x^3 + x^2)(x^3 + x^2 - x)$ **68.** $(x^3 - x^2)(x^3 - x^2 + x)$ **69.** $(-5x^3 - 7x^2 + 1)(2x^2 - x)$

70. $(-4x^3 + 5x^2 - 2)(5x^2 + 1)$ **71.** $(1 + x + x^2)(-1 - x + x^2)$ **72.** $(1 - x + x^2)(1 - x + x^2)$

73. $(2t^2 - t - 4)(3t^2 + 2t - 1)$ **74.** $(3a^2 - 5a + 2)(2a^2 - 3a + 4)$ **75.** $(x - x^3 + x^5)(x^2 - 1 + x^4)$

76. $(x - x^3 + x^5)(3x^2 + 3x^6 + 3x^4)$ **77.** $(x^3 + x^2 + x + 1)(x - 1)$ **78.** $(x + 2)(x^3 - x^2 + x - 2)$

79. $(x + 1)(x^3 + 7x^2 + 5x + 4)$ **80.** $(x + 2)(x^3 + 5x^2 + 9x + 3)$

81. $\left(x - \frac{1}{2}\right)\left(2x^3 - 4x^2 + 3x - \frac{2}{5}\right)$ **82.** $\left(x + \frac{1}{3}\right)\left(6x^3 - 12x^2 - 5x + \frac{1}{2}\right)$

Skill Maintenance

Simplify.

83. $-\frac{1}{4} - \frac{1}{2}$ [7.4a]   **84.** $-3.8 - (-10.2)$ [7.4a]   **85.** $(10 - 2)(10 + 2)$ [7.8d]   **86.** $10 - 2 + (-6)^2 \div 3 \cdot 2$ [7.8d]

Factor. [7.7d]

87. $15x - 18y + 12$ **88.** $16x - 24y + 36$ **89.** $-9x - 45y + 15$ **90.** $100x - 100y + 1000a$

91. Graph: $y = \frac{1}{2}x - 3$. [9.5a]   **92.** Solve: $4(x - 3) = 5(2 - 3x) + 1$. [8.3c]

Copyright © 2012 Pearson Education, Inc.

Synthesis

Find a polynomial for the shaded area of each figure.

93.

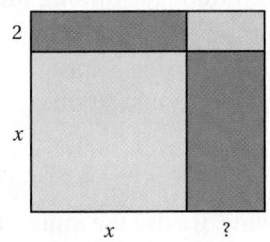

14y − 5
3y
6y   3y + 5

94.

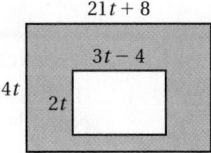

21t + 8
3t − 4
4t   2t

95. A box with a square bottom is to be made from a 12-in.-square piece of cardboard. Squares with side x are cut out of the corners and the sides are folded up. Find the polynomials for the volume and the outside surface area of the box.

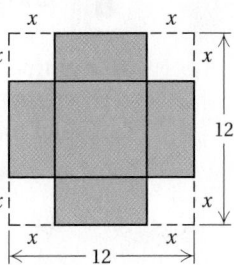

For each figure, determine what the missing number must be in order for the figure to have the given area.

96. Area $= x^2 + 7x + 10$

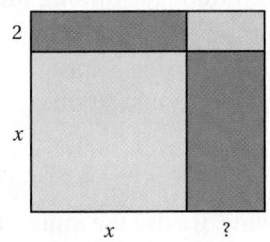

2

x

x   ?

97. Area $= x^2 + 8x + 15$

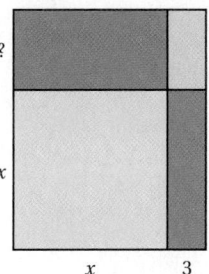

?

x

x   3

98. An open wooden box is a cube with side x cm. The box, including its bottom, is made of wood that is 1 cm thick. Find a polynomial for the interior volume of the cube.

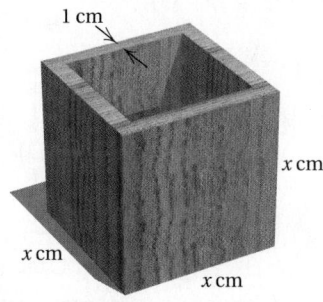

1 cm

x cm

x cm

x cm

99. Find a polynomial for the volume of the solid shown below.

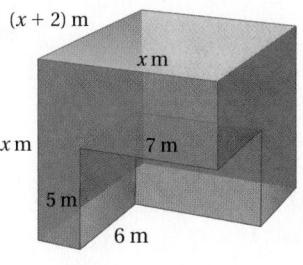

(x + 2) m

x m

x m   7 m

5 m

6 m

Compute and simplify.

100. $(x + 3)(x + 6) + (x + 3)(x + 6)$

101. $(x − 2)(x − 7) − (x − 7)(x − 2)$

102. $(x + 5)^2 − (x − 3)^2$

103. Extend the pattern and simplify:
$$(x − a)(x − b)(x − c)(x − d) \cdots (x − z).$$

104. Use a graphing calculator to check your answers to Exercises 15, 29, and 61. Use graphs, tables, or both, as directed by your instructor.

10.6

Special Products

OBJECTIVES

a Multiply two binomials mentally using the FOIL method.

b Multiply the sum and the difference of two terms mentally.

c Square a binomial mentally.

d Find special products when polynomial products are mixed together.

We encounter certain products so often that it is helpful to have faster methods of computing. Such techniques are called *special products*. We now consider special ways of multiplying any two binomials.

a Products of Two Binomials Using FOIL

To multiply two binomials, we can select one binomial and multiply each term of that binomial by every term of the other. Then we collect like terms. Consider the product $(x + 3)(x + 7)$:

$$(x + 3)(x + 7) = x(x + 7) + 3(x + 7)$$
$$= x \cdot x + x \cdot 7 + 3 \cdot x + 3 \cdot 7$$
$$= x^2 + 7x + 3x + 21$$
$$= x^2 + 10x + 21.$$

This example illustrates a special technique for finding the product of two binomials:

$$\underbrace{\text{First}}_{\text{terms}} \quad \underbrace{\text{Outside}}_{\text{terms}} \quad \underbrace{\text{Inside}}_{\text{terms}} \quad \underbrace{\text{Last}}_{\text{terms}}$$

$$(x + 3)(x + 7) = x \cdot x + 7 \cdot x + 3 \cdot x + 3 \cdot 7.$$

To remember this method of multiplying, we use the initials **FOIL**.

THE FOIL METHOD

To multiply two binomials, $A + B$ and $C + D$, multiply the First terms AC, the Outside terms AD, the Inside terms BC, and then the Last terms BD. Then collect like terms, if possible.

$$(A + B)(C + D) = AC + AD + BC + BD$$

1. Multiply First terms: AC.
2. Multiply Outside terms: AD.
3. Multiply Inside terms: BC.
4. Multiply Last terms: BD.

FOIL

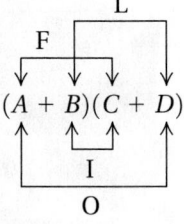

STUDY TIPS

MEMORIZING FORMULAS

Memorizing can be a very helpful tool in the study of mathematics. Don't underestimate its power as you consider the special products. Consider putting the rules, in words and in math symbols, on index cards and reviewing them many times.

 EXAMPLE 1 Multiply: $(x + 8)(x^2 - 5)$.

We have

$$\begin{array}{cccc} \text{F} & \text{O} & \text{I} & \text{L} \end{array}$$
$$(x + 8)(x^2 - 5) = x \cdot x^2 + x \cdot (-5) + 8 \cdot x^2 + 8(-5)$$
$$= x^3 - 5x + 8x^2 - 40$$
$$= x^3 + 8x^2 - 5x - 40.$$

Since each of the original binomials is in descending order, we write the product in descending order, as is customary, but this is not a "must."

Often we can collect like terms after we have multiplied.

EXAMPLES   Multiply.

2. $(x + 6)(x - 6) = x^2 - 6x + 6x - 36$ Using FOIL
$$= x^2 - 36 \qquad \text{Collecting like terms}$$

3. $(x + 7)(x + 4) = x^2 + 4x + 7x + 28$
$$= x^2 + 11x + 28$$

4. $(y - 3)(y - 2) = y^2 - 2y - 3y + 6$
$$= y^2 - 5y + 6$$

5. $(x^3 - 5)(x^3 + 5) = x^6 + 5x^3 - 5x^3 - 25$
$$= x^6 - 25$$

6. $(4t^3 + 5)(3t^2 - 2) = 12t^5 - 8t^3 + 15t^2 - 10$

> Do Exercises 1-8.

EXAMPLES   Multiply.

7. $\left(x - \frac{2}{3}\right)\left(x + \frac{2}{3}\right) = x^2 + \frac{2}{3}x - \frac{2}{3}x - \frac{4}{9}$
$$= x^2 - \frac{4}{9}$$

8. $(x^2 - 0.3)(x^2 - 0.3) = x^4 - 0.3x^2 - 0.3x^2 + 0.09$
$$= x^4 - 0.6x^2 + 0.09$$

9. $(3 - 4x)(7 - 5x^3) = 21 - 15x^3 - 28x + 20x^4$
$$= 21 - 28x - 15x^3 + 20x^4$$

(*Note*: If the original polynomials are in ascending order, it is natural to write the product in ascending order, but this is not a "must.")

10. $(5x^4 + 2x^3)(3x^2 - 7x) = 15x^6 - 35x^5 + 6x^5 - 14x^4$
$$= 15x^6 - 29x^5 - 14x^4$$

> Do Exercises 9-12.

We can show the FOIL method geometrically as follows.

The area of the large rectangle is $(A + B)(C + D)$.

The area of rectangle ① is AC.

The area of rectangle ② is AD.

The area of rectangle ③ is BC.

The area of rectangle ④ is BD.

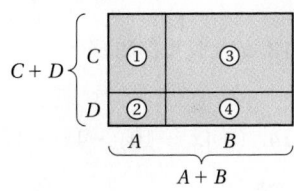

The area of the large rectangle is the sum of the areas of the smaller rectangles. Thus,

$$(A + B)(C + D) = AC + AD + BC + BD.$$

(b) Multiplying Sums and Differences of Two Terms

Consider the product of the sum and the difference of the same two terms, such as

$$(x + 2)(x - 2).$$

Multiply mentally, if possible. If you need extra steps, be sure to use them.

1. $(x + 3)(x + 4)$

2. $(x + 3)(x - 5)$

3. $(2x - 1)(x - 4)$

4. $(2x^2 - 3)(x - 2)$

5. $(6x^2 + 5)(2x^3 + 1)$

6. $(y^3 + 7)(y^3 - 7)$

7. $(t + 2)(t + 3)$

8. $(2x^4 + x^2)(-x^3 + x)$

Multiply.

9. $\left(x + \frac{4}{5}\right)\left(x - \frac{4}{5}\right)$

10. $(x^3 - 0.5)(x^2 + 0.5)$

11. $(2 + 3x^2)(4 - 5x^2)$

12. $(6x^3 - 3x^2)(5x^2 - 2x)$

Answers

1. $x^2 + 7x + 12$ 2. $x^2 - 2x - 15$
3. $2x^2 - 9x + 4$ 4. $2x^3 - 4x^2 - 3x + 6$
5. $12x^5 + 10x^3 + 6x^2 + 5$ 6. $y^6 - 49$
7. $t^2 + 5t + 6$ 8. $-2x^7 + x^5 + x^3$
9. $x^2 - \dfrac{16}{25}$ 10. $x^5 + 0.5x^3 - 0.5x^2 - 0.25$
11. $8 + 2x^2 - 15x^4$ 12. $30x^5 - 27x^4 + 6x^3$

Since this is the product of two binomials, we can use FOIL. This type of product occurs so often, however, that it would be valuable if we could use an even faster method. To find a faster way to compute such a product, look for a pattern in the following:

a) $(x + 2)(x - 2) = x^2 - 2x + 2x - 4$ Using FOIL
$$= x^2 - 4;$$

b) $(3x - 5)(3x + 5) = 9x^2 + 15x - 15x - 25$
$$= 9x^2 - 25.$$

Do Exercises 13 and 14.

Perhaps you discovered in each case that when you multiply the two binomials, two terms are opposites, or additive inverses, which add to 0 and "drop out."

> **PRODUCT OF THE SUM AND THE DIFFERENCE OF TWO TERMS**
>
> The product of the sum and the difference of the same two terms is the square of the first term minus the square of the second term:
> $$(A + B)(A - B) = A^2 - B^2.$$

It is helpful to memorize this rule in both words and symbols. (If you do forget it, you can, of course, use FOIL.)

EXAMPLES   Multiply. (Carry out the rule and say the words as you go.)

$$(A + B)(A - B) = A^2 - B^2$$

11. $(x + 4)(x - 4) = x^2 - 4^2$ "The square of the first term, x^2, minus the square of the second, 4^2"
$$= x^2 - 16$$ Simplifying

12. $(5 + 2w)(5 - 2w) = 5^2 - (2w)^2$
$$= 25 - 4w^2$$

13. $(3x^2 - 7)(3x^2 + 7) = (3x^2)^2 - 7^2$
$$= 9x^4 - 49$$

14. $(-4x - 10)(-4x + 10) = (-4x)^2 - 10^2$
$$= 16x^2 - 100$$

15. $\left(x + \dfrac{3}{8}\right)\left(x - \dfrac{3}{8}\right) = x^2 - \left(\dfrac{3}{8}\right)^2 = x^2 - \dfrac{9}{64}$

Do Exercises 15–19.

c   Squaring Binomials

Consider the square of a binomial, such as $(x + 3)^2$. This can be expressed as $(x + 3)(x + 3)$. Since this is the product of two binomials, we can use FOIL. But again, this type of product occurs so often that we would like to use an even faster method. Look for a pattern in the following.

Multiply.

13. $(x + 5)(x - 5)$

14. $(2x - 3)(2x + 3)$

Multiply.

15. $(x + 8)(x - 8)$

16. $(x - 7)(x + 7)$

17. $(6 - 4y)(6 + 4y)$

18. $(2x^3 - 1)(2x^3 + 1)$

19. $\left(x - \dfrac{2}{5}\right)\left(x + \dfrac{2}{5}\right)$

Answers

13. $x^2 - 25$ **14.** $4x^2 - 9$ **15.** $x^2 - 64$
16. $x^2 - 49$ **17.** $36 - 16y^2$ **18.** $4x^6 - 1$
19. $x^2 - \dfrac{4}{25}$

a) $(x + 3)^2 = (x + 3)(x + 3)$
$\qquad = x^2 + 3x + 3x + 9$
$\qquad = x^2 + 6x + 9;$

b) $(x - 3)^2 = (x - 3)(x - 3)$
$\qquad = x^2 - 3x - 3x + 9$
$\qquad = x^2 - 6x + 9;$

c) $(5 + 3p)^2 = (5 + 3p)(5 + 3p)$
$\qquad = 25 + 15p + 15p + 9p^2$
$\qquad = 25 + 30p + 9p^2;$

d) $(3x - 5)^2 = (3x - 5)(3x - 5)$
$\qquad = 9x^2 - 15x - 15x + 25$
$\qquad = 9x^2 - 30x + 25$

> Do Exercises 20 and 21.

Do Exercises 20 and 21.

Multiply.

20. $(x + 8)(x + 8)$

21. $(x - 5)(x - 5)$

When squaring a binomial, we multiply a binomial by itself. Perhaps you noticed that two terms are the same and when added give twice the product of the terms in the binomial. The other two terms are squares.

SQUARE OF A BINOMIAL

The square of a sum or a difference of two terms is the square of the first term, plus twice the product of the two terms, plus the square of the last term:

$$(A + B)^2 = A^2 + 2AB + B^2; \qquad (A - B)^2 = A^2 - 2AB + B^2.$$

It is helpful to memorize this rule in both words and symbols.

EXAMPLES Multiply. (Carry out the rule and say the words as you go.)

$(A + B)^2 = A^2 + 2 \cdot A \cdot B + B^2$

16. $(x + 3)^2 = x^2 + 2 \cdot x \cdot 3 + 3^2$ "x^2 plus 2 times x times 3 plus 3^2"
$\qquad = x^2 + 6x + 9$

$(A - B)^2 = A^2 - 2 \cdot A \cdot B + B^2$

17. $(t - 5)^2 = t^2 - 2 \cdot t \cdot 5 + 5^2$
$\qquad = t^2 - 10t + 25$

18. $(2x + 7)^2 = (2x)^2 + 2 \cdot 2x \cdot 7 + 7^2 = 4x^2 + 28x + 49$

19. $(5x - 3x^2)^2 = (5x)^2 - 2 \cdot 5x \cdot 3x^2 + (3x^2)^2 = 25x^2 - 30x^3 + 9x^4$

20. $(2.3 - 5.4m)^2 = 2.3^2 - 2(2.3)(5.4m) + (5.4m)^2$
$\qquad = 5.29 - 24.84m + 29.16m^2$

> Do Exercises 22–27.

Do Exercises 22–27.

Multiply.

22. $(x + 2)^2$

23. $(a - 4)^2$

24. $(2x + 5)^2$

25. $(4x^2 - 3x)^2$

26. $(7.8 + 1.2y)(7.8 + 1.2y)$

27. $(3x^2 - 5)(3x^2 - 5)$

-------- *Caution!* --------

Although the square of a product is the product of the squares, the square of a sum is *not* the sum of the squares. That is, $(AB)^2 = A^2B^2$, but

The term $2AB$ is missing.

$$(A + B)^2 \neq A^2 + B^2.$$

To illustrate this inequality, note, using the rules for order of operations, that

$$(7 + 5)^2 = 12^2 = 144,$$

whereas

$$7^2 + 5^2 = 49 + 25 = 74, \quad \text{and} \quad 74 \neq 144.$$

Answers

20. $x^2 + 16x + 64$ **21.** $x^2 - 10x + 25$
22. $x^2 + 4x + 4$ **23.** $a^2 - 8a + 16$
24. $4x^2 + 20x + 25$ **25.** $16x^4 - 24x^3 + 9x^2$
26. $60.84 + 18.72y + 1.44y^2$
27. $9x^4 - 30x^2 + 25$

We can look at the rule for finding $(A + B)^2$ geometrically as follows. The area of the large square is

$$(A + B)(A + B) = (A + B)^2.$$

This is equal to the sum of the areas of the smaller rectangles:

$$A^2 + AB + AB + B^2 = A^2 + 2AB + B^2.$$

Thus, $(A + B)^2 = A^2 + 2AB + B^2$.

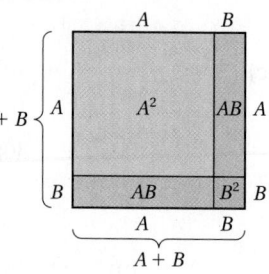

Do Exercise 28.

Do Exercise 28.

28. In the figure at right, describe in terms of area the sum $A^2 + B^2$. How can the figure be used to verify that $(A + B)^2 \neq A^2 + B^2$?

d Multiplication of Various Types

Let's now try several types of multiplications mixed together so that we can learn to sort them out. When you multiply, first see what kind of multiplication you have. Then use the best method.

MULTIPLYING TWO POLYNOMIALS

1. Is it the product of a monomial and a polynomial? If so, multiply each term of the polynomial by the monomial.

   Example: $5x(x + 7) = 5x \cdot x + 5x \cdot 7 = 5x^2 + 35x$

2. Is it the product of the sum and the difference of the *same* two terms? If so, use the following:

   $$(A + B)(A - B) = A^2 - B^2.$$

   The product of the sum and the difference of the same two terms is the difference of the squares. [The answer has 2 terms.]

   Example: $(x + 7)(x - 7) = x^2 - 7^2 = x^2 - 49$

3. Is it the product the square of a binomial? If so, use the following:

   $$(A + B)(A + B) = (A + B)^2 = A^2 + 2AB + B^2,$$

   or $(A - B)(A - B) = (A - B)^2 = A^2 - 2AB + B^2.$

   The square of a binomial is the square of the first term, plus *twice* the product of the two terms, plus the square of the last term. [The answer has 3 terms.]

   Example: $(x + 7)(x + 7) = (x + 7)^2$
   $$= x^2 + 2 \cdot x \cdot 7 + 7^2 = x^2 + 14x + 49$$

4. Is it the product of two binomials other than those above? If so, use FOIL. [The answer will have 3 or 4 terms.]

   Example: $(x + 7)(x - 4) = x^2 - 4x + 7x - 28 = x^2 + 3x - 28$

5. Is it the product of two polynomials other than those above? If so, multiply each term of one by every term of the other. Use columns if you wish. [The answer will have 2 or more terms, usually more than 2 terms.]

   Example:

   $$(x^2 - 3x + 2)(x + 7) = x^2(x + 7) - 3x(x + 7) + 2(x + 7)$$
   $$= x^2 \cdot x + x^2 \cdot 7 - 3x \cdot x - 3x \cdot 7$$
   $$+ 2 \cdot x + 2 \cdot 7$$
   $$= x^3 + 7x^2 - 3x^2 - 21x + 2x + 14$$
   $$= x^3 + 4x^2 - 19x + 14$$

STUDY TIPS

CHECKLIST

The foundation of all your study skills is TIME!

- Are you taking the time to include all the steps when doing your homework and taking tests?

- Are you using the time-management suggestions we have given so that you have the proper amount of time to study mathematics?

- Have you been using the supplements for the text such as the *Student's Solutions Manual*?

- Have you memorized the rules for special products of polynomials and for manipulating expressions with exponents?

Answer

28. $(A + B)^2$ represents the area of the large square. This includes all four sections. $A^2 + B^2$ represents the area of only two of the sections.

Remember that FOIL will *always* work for two binomials. You can use it instead of either of rules 2 and 3, but those rules will make your work go faster.

EXAMPLE 21 Multiply: $(x + 3)(x - 3)$.

$$(x + 3)(x - 3) = x^2 - 9 \qquad \text{Using method 2 (the product of the sum and the difference of two terms)}$$

EXAMPLE 22 Multiply: $(t + 7)(t - 5)$.

$$(t + 7)(t - 5) = t^2 + 2t - 35 \qquad \text{Using method 4, FOIL (the product of two binomials, but neither the square of a binomial nor the product of the sum and the difference of two terms)}$$

EXAMPLE 23 Multiply: $(x + 6)(x + 6)$.

$$(x + 6)(x + 6) = x^2 + 2(6)x + 36 \qquad \text{Using method 3 (the square of a binomial sum)}$$

$$= x^2 + 12x + 36$$

EXAMPLE 24 Multiply: $2x^3(9x^2 + x - 7)$.

$$2x^3(9x^2 + x - 7) = 18x^5 + 2x^4 - 14x^3 \qquad \text{Using method 1 (the product of a monomial and a trinomial; multiplying each term of the trinomial by the monomial)}$$

EXAMPLE 25 Multiply: $(5x^3 - 7x)^2$.

$$(5x^3 - 7x)^2 = 25x^6 - 2(5x^3)(7x) + 49x^2 \qquad \text{Using method 3 (the square of a binomial)}$$

$$= 25x^6 - 70x^4 + 49x^2$$

EXAMPLE 26 Multiply: $\left(3x + \frac{1}{4}\right)^2$.

$$\left(3x + \frac{1}{4}\right)^2 = 9x^2 + 2(3x)\left(\frac{1}{4}\right) + \frac{1}{16} \qquad \text{Using method 3 (the square of a binomial. To get the middle term, we find twice the product of } 3x \text{ and } \frac{1}{4}\text{.)}$$

$$= 9x^2 + \frac{3}{2}x + \frac{1}{16}$$

EXAMPLE 27 Multiply: $\left(4x - \frac{3}{4}\right)^2$.

$$\left(4x - \frac{3}{4}\right)^2 = 16x^2 - 2(4x)\left(\frac{3}{4}\right) + \frac{9}{16} \qquad \text{Using method 3 (the square of a binomial)}$$

$$= 16x^2 - 6x + \frac{9}{16}$$

EXAMPLE 28 Multiply: $(p + 3)(p^2 + 2p - 1)$.

$$\begin{array}{r} p^2 + 2p - 1 \\ p + 3 \\ \hline 3p^2 + 6p - 3 \\ p^3 + 2p^2 - p \quad\;\; \\ \hline p^3 + 5p^2 + 5p - 3 \end{array}$$

Using method 5 (the product of two polynomials)

Multiplying by 3

Multiplying by p

Do Exercises 29–36.

Multiply.

29. $(x + 5)(x + 6)$

30. $(t - 4)(t + 4)$

31. $4x^2(-2x^3 + 5x^2 + 10)$

32. $(9x^2 + 1)^2$

33. $(2a - 5)(2a + 8)$

34. $\left(5x + \frac{1}{2}\right)^2$

35. $\left(2x - \frac{1}{2}\right)^2$

36. $(x^2 - x + 4)(x - 2)$

Answers

29. $x^2 + 11x + 30$ **30.** $t^2 - 16$
31. $-8x^5 + 20x^4 + 40x^2$ **32.** $81x^4 + 18x^2 + 1$
33. $4a^2 + 6a - 40$ **34.** $25x^2 + 5x + \frac{1}{4}$
35. $4x^2 - 2x + \frac{1}{4}$ **36.** $x^3 - 3x^2 + 6x - 8$

Visualizing for Success

1

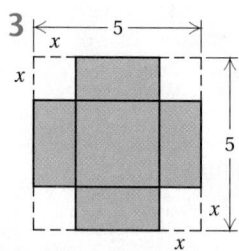

In each of Exercises 1–10, find two algebraic expressions for the shaded area of the figure from the list below.

A. $9 - 4x^2$

B. $x^2 - (x - 6)^2$

C. $(x + 3)(x - 3)$

D. $10^2 + 2^2$

E. $x^2 + 8x + 15$

F. $(x + 5)(x + 3)$

G. $x^2 - 6x + 9$

H. $(3 - 2x)^2 + 4x(3 - 2x)$

I. $(x + 3)^2$

J. $(5x + 3)^2$

K. $(5 - 2x)^2 + 4x(5 - 2x)$

L. $x^2 - 9$

M. 104

N. $x^2 - 15$

O. $12x - 36$

P. $25x^2 + 30x + 9$

Q. $(x - 5)(x - 3)$
$\quad + 3(x - 5) + 5(x - 3)$

R. $(x - 3)^2$

S. $25 - 4x^2$

T. $x^2 + 6x + 9$

Answers on page A-23

2

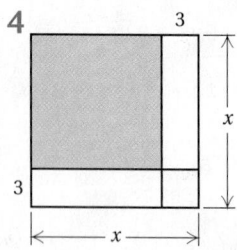

3

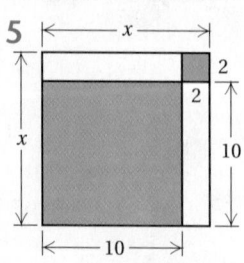

4

5

6

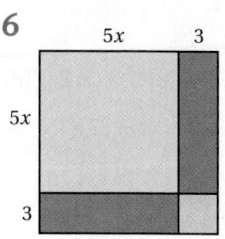

7

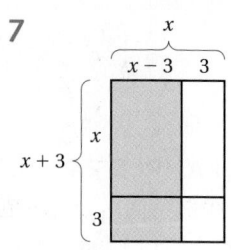

8

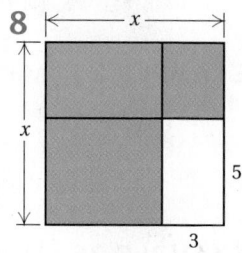

9

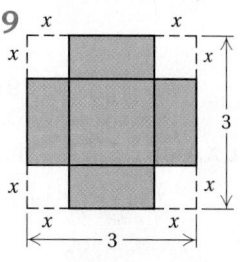

10

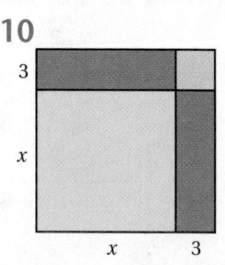

a   Multiply. Try to write only the answer. If you need more steps, be sure to use them.

1. $(x + 1)(x^2 + 3)$

2. $(x^2 - 3)(x - 1)$

3. $(x^3 + 2)(x + 1)$

4. $(x^4 + 2)(x + 10)$

5. $(y + 2)(y - 3)$

6. $(a + 2)(a + 3)$

7. $(3x + 2)(3x + 2)$

8. $(4x + 1)(4x + 1)$

9. $(5x - 6)(x + 2)$

10. $(x - 8)(x + 8)$

11. $(3t - 1)(3t + 1)$

12. $(2m + 3)(2m + 3)$

13. $(4x - 2)(x - 1)$

14. $(2x - 1)(3x + 1)$

15. $\left(p - \frac{1}{4}\right)\left(p + \frac{1}{4}\right)$

16. $\left(q + \frac{3}{4}\right)\left(q + \frac{3}{4}\right)$

17. $(x - 0.1)(x + 0.1)$

18. $(x + 0.3)(x - 0.4)$

19. $(2x^2 + 6)(x + 1)$

20. $(2x^2 + 3)(2x - 1)$

21. $(-2x + 1)(x + 6)$

22. $(3x + 4)(2x - 4)$

23. $(a + 7)(a + 7)$

24. $(2y + 5)(2y + 5)$

25. $(1 + 2x)(1 - 3x)$

26. $(-3x - 2)(x + 1)$

27. $\left(\frac{3}{8}y - \frac{5}{6}\right)\left(\frac{3}{8}y - \frac{5}{6}\right)$

28. $\left(\frac{1}{5}x - \frac{2}{7}\right)\left(\frac{1}{5}x + \frac{2}{7}\right)$

29. $(x^2 + 3)(x^3 - 1)$

30. $(x^4 - 3)(2x + 1)$

31. $(3x^2 - 2)(x^4 - 2)$

32. $(x^{10} + 3)(x^{10} - 3)$

33. $(2.8x - 1.5)(4.7x + 9.3)$

34. $\left(x - \frac{3}{8}\right)\left(x + \frac{4}{7}\right)$

35. $(3x^5 + 2)(2x^2 + 6)$ **36.** $(1 - 2x)(1 + 3x^2)$ **37.** $(8x^3 + 1)(x^3 + 8)$ **38.** $(4 - 2x)(5 - 2x^2)$

39. $(4x^2 + 3)(x - 3)$ **40.** $(7x - 2)(2x - 7)$

41. $(4y^4 + y^2)(y^2 + y)$ **42.** $(5y^6 + 3y^3)(2y^6 + 2y^3)$

b Multiply mentally, if possible. If you need extra steps, be sure to use them.

43. $(x + 4)(x - 4)$ **44.** $(x + 1)(x - 1)$ **45.** $(2x + 1)(2x - 1)$ **46.** $(x^2 + 1)(x^2 - 1)$

47. $(5m - 2)(5m + 2)$ **48.** $(3x^4 + 2)(3x^4 - 2)$ **49.** $(2x^2 + 3)(2x^2 - 3)$ **50.** $(6x^5 - 5)(6x^5 + 5)$

51. $(3x^4 - 4)(3x^4 + 4)$ **52.** $(t^2 - 0.2)(t^2 + 0.2)$

53. $(x^6 - x^2)(x^6 + x^2)$ **54.** $(2x^3 - 0.3)(2x^3 + 0.3)$

55. $(x^4 + 3x)(x^4 - 3x)$ **56.** $\left(\frac{3}{4} + 2x^3\right)\left(\frac{3}{4} - 2x^3\right)$ **57.** $(x^{12} - 3)(x^{12} + 3)$ **58.** $(12 - 3x^2)(12 + 3x^2)$

59. $(2y^8 + 3)(2y^8 - 3)$ **60.** $\left(m - \frac{2}{3}\right)\left(m + \frac{2}{3}\right)$

61. $\left(\frac{5}{8}x - 4.3\right)\left(\frac{5}{8}x + 4.3\right)$ **62.** $(10.7 - x^3)(10.7 + x^3)$

c Multiply mentally, if possible. If you need extra steps, be sure to use them.

63. $(x + 2)^2$ **64.** $(2x - 1)^2$ **65.** $(3x^2 + 1)^2$ **66.** $\left(3x + \frac{3}{4}\right)^2$

67. $\left(a - \frac{1}{2}\right)^2$ **68.** $\left(2a - \frac{1}{5}\right)^2$ **69.** $(3 + x)^2$ **70.** $(x^3 - 1)^2$

Copyright © 2012 Pearson Education, Inc.

71. $(x^2 + 1)^2$

72. $(8x - x^2)^2$

73. $(2 - 3x^4)^2$

74. $(6x^3 - 2)^2$

75. $(5 + 6t^2)^2$

76. $(3p^2 - p)^2$

77. $\left(x - \frac{5}{8}\right)^2$

78. $(0.3y + 2.4)^2$

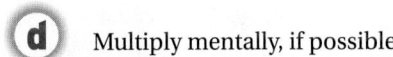 Multiply mentally, if possible.

79. $(3 - 2x^3)^2$

80. $(x - 4x^3)^2$

81. $4x(x^2 + 6x - 3)$

82. $8x(-x^5 + 6x^2 + 9)$

83. $\left(2x^2 - \frac{1}{2}\right)\left(2x^2 - \frac{1}{2}\right)$

84. $(-x^2 + 1)^2$

85. $(-1 + 3p)(1 + 3p)$

86. $(-3q + 2)(3q + 2)$

87. $3t^2(5t^3 - t^2 + t)$

88. $-6x^2(x^3 + 8x - 9)$

89. $(6x^4 + 4)^2$

90. $(8a + 5)^2$

91. $(3x + 2)(4x^2 + 5)$

92. $(2x^2 - 7)(3x^2 + 9)$

93. $(8 - 6x^4)^2$

94. $\left(\frac{1}{5}x^2 + 9\right)\left(\frac{3}{5}x^2 - 7\right)$

95. $(t - 1)(t^2 + t + 1)$

96. $(y + 5)(y^2 - 5y + 25)$

Compute each of the following and compare.

97. $3^2 + 4^2;\ (3 + 4)^2$

98. $6^2 + 7^2;\ (6 + 7)^2$

99. $9^2 - 5^2;\ (9 - 5)^2$

100. $11^2 - 4^2;\ (11 - 4)^2$

Find the total area of all the shaded rectangles.

101.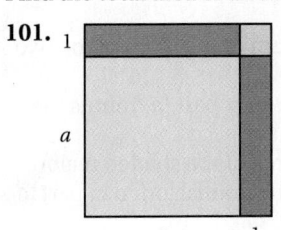

102.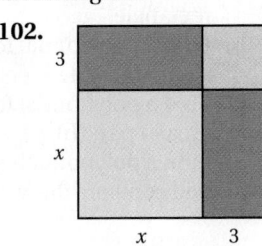

103.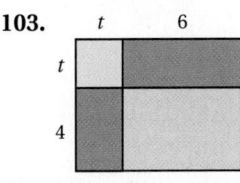

104.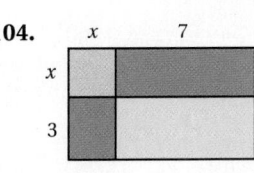

Skill Maintenance

105. *Electricity Usage.* In apartment 3B, lamps, an air conditioner, and a television set are all operating at the same time. The lamps use 10 times as many watts of electricity as the television set, and the air conditioner uses 40 times as many watts as the television set. The total wattage used in the apartment is 2550. How many watts are used by each appliance? [8.6a]

Solve. [8.3c]

106. $3x - 8x = 4(7 - 8x)$ **107.** $3(x - 2) = 5(2x + 7)$ **108.** $5(2x - 3) - 2(3x - 4) = 20$

Solve. [8.4b]

109. $3x - 2y = 12$, for y **110.** $3a - 5d = 4$, for a

Synthesis

Multiply.

111. $5x(3x - 1)(2x + 3)$ **112.** $[(2x - 3)(2x + 3)](4x^2 + 9)$ **113.** $[(a - 5)(a + 5)]^2$

114. $(a - 3)^2(a + 3)^2$
(*Hint*: Examine Exercise 113.)

115. $(3t^4 - 2)^2(3t^4 + 2)^2$
(*Hint*: Examine Exercise 113.)

116. $[3a - (2a - 3)][3a + (2a - 3)]$

Solve.

117. $(x + 2)(x - 5) = (x + 1)(x - 3)$ **118.** $(2x + 5)(x - 4) = (x + 5)(2x - 4)$

119. *Factors and Sums.* To *factor* a number is to express it as a product. Since $12 = 4 \cdot 3$, we say that 12 is *factored* and that 4 and 3 are *factors* of 12. In the table below, the top number has been factored in such a way that the sum of the factors is the bottom number. For example, in the first column, 40 has been factored as $5 \cdot 8$, and $5 + 8 = 13$, the bottom number. Such thinking is important in algebra when we factor trinomials of the type $x^2 + bx + c$. Find the missing numbers in the table.

PRODUCT	40	63	36	72	−140	−96	48	168	110			
FACTOR	5									−9	−24	−3
FACTOR	8									−10	18	
SUM	13	16	−20	−38	−4	4	−14	−29	−21			18

120. Consider the rectangle below.

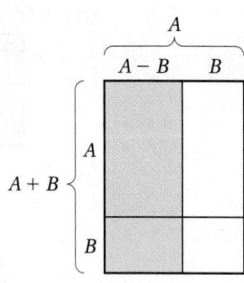

a) Find a polynomial for the area of the entire rectangle.
b) Find a polynomial for the sum of the areas of the two small unshaded rectangles.
c) Find a polynomial for the area in part (a) minus the area in part (b).
d) Find a polynomial for the area of the shaded region and compare this with the polynomial found in part (c).

Use the TABLE or GRAPH feature to check whether each of the following is correct.

121. $(x - 1)^2 = x^2 - 2x + 1$ **122.** $(x - 2)^2 = x^2 - 4x - 4$

123. $(x - 3)(x + 3) = x^2 - 6$ **124.** $(x - 3)(x + 2) = x^2 - x - 6$

Copyright © 2012 Pearson Education, Inc.

10.7 Operations with Polynomials in Several Variables

The polynomials that we have been studying have only one variable. A **polynomial in several variables** is an expression like those you have already seen, but with more than one variable. Here are two examples:

$$3x + xy^2 + 5y + 4, \qquad 8xy^2z - 2x^3z - 13x^4y^2 + 15.$$

(a) Evaluating Polynomials

EXAMPLE 1 Evaluate the polynomial $4 + 3x + xy^2 + 8x^3y^3$ when $x = -2$ and $y = 5$.

We replace x with -2 and y with 5:

$$
\begin{aligned}
4 + 3x + xy^2 + 8x^3y^3 &= 4 + 3(-2) + (-2) \cdot 5^2 + 8(-2)^3 \cdot 5^3 \\
&= 4 + 3(-2) + (-2) \cdot 25 + 8(-8)(125) \\
&= 4 - 6 - 50 - 8000 \\
&= -8052.
\end{aligned}
$$

EXAMPLE 2 *Male Caloric Needs.* The number of calories needed each day by a moderately active man who weighs w kilograms, is h centimeters tall, and is a years old can be estimated by the polynomial

$$19.18w + 7h - 9.52a + 92.4.$$

Steve is moderately active, weighs 82 kg, is 185 cm tall, and is 67 yr old. What are his daily caloric needs?

Source: Parker, M., *She Does Math.* Mathematical Association of America

Breakfast
Oatmeal with skim milk–231 calories
Cinnamon raisin bagel–350 calories
Orange juice–83 calories

Dinner
Chicken breast–142 calories
Wild rice–166 calories
Broccoli–42 calories
Cranberry sauce–209 calories

Lunch
Peanut butter and jelly sandwich–1018 calories
Apple–81 calories

We evaluate the polynomial for $w = 82$, $h = 185$, and $a = 67$:

$$
\begin{aligned}
&19.18w + 7h - 9.52a + 92.4 \\
&= 19.18(82) + 7(185) - 9.52(67) + 92.4 \qquad \text{Substituting} \\
&= 2322.32.
\end{aligned}
$$

Steve's daily caloric need is about 2322 calories.

Do Exercises 1–3.

OBJECTIVES

a Evaluate a polynomial in several variables for given values of the variables.

b Identify the coefficients and the degrees of the terms of a polynomial and the degree of a polynomial.

c Collect like terms of a polynomial.

d Add polynomials.

e Subtract polynomials.

f Multiply polynomials.

---

1. Evaluate the polynomial
$$4 + 3x + xy^2 + 8x^3y^3$$
when $x = 2$ and $y = -5$.

2. Evaluate the polynomial
$$8xy^2 - 2x^3z - 13x^4y^2 + 5$$
when $x = -1$, $y = 3$, and $z = 4$.

3. Female Caloric Needs. The number of calories needed each day by a moderately active woman who weighs w pounds, is h inches tall, and is a years old can be estimated by the polynomial
$$917 + 6w + 6h - 6a.$$
Christine is moderately active, weighs 125 lb, is 64 in. tall, and is 27 yr old. What are her daily caloric needs?

Source: Parker, M., *She Does Math.* Mathematical Association of America

Answers
1. -7940 **2.** -176 **3.** 1889 calories

b Coefficients and Degrees

The **degree** of a term is the sum of the exponents of the variables. The **degree of a polynomial** is the degree of the term of highest degree.

EXAMPLE 3 Identify the coefficient and the degree of each term and the degree of the polynomial

$$9x^2y^3 - 14xy^2z^3 + xy + 4y + 5x^2 + 7.$$

TERM	COEFFICIENT	DEGREE	DEGREE OF THE POLYNOMIAL
$9x^2y^3$	9	5	
$-14xy^2z^3$	-14	6	6
xy	1	2	
$4y$	4	1	
$5x^2$	5	2	
7	7	0	

Think: $4y = 4y^1$.

Think: $7 = 7x^0$, or $7x^0y^0z^0$.

Do Exercises 4 and 5.

4. Identify the coefficient of each term:

$$-3xy^2 + 3x^2y - 2y^3 + xy + 2.$$

5. Identify the degree of each term and the degree of the polynomial

$$4xy^2 + 7x^2y^3z^2 - 5x + 2y + 4.$$

c Collecting Like Terms

Like terms have exactly the same variables with exactly the same exponents. For example,

$$3x^2y^3 \text{ and } -7x^2y^3 \text{ are like terms;}$$
$$9x^4z^7 \text{ and } 12x^4z^7 \text{ are like terms.}$$

But

$$13xy^5 \text{ and } -2x^2y^5 \text{ are } not \text{ like terms, because the } x\text{-factors have different exponents;}$$

and

$$3xyz^2 \text{ and } 4xy \text{ are } not \text{ like terms, because there is no factor of } z^2 \text{ in the second expression.}$$

Collecting like terms is based on the distributive laws.

EXAMPLES Collect like terms.

4. $5x^2y + 3xy^2 - 5x^2y - xy^2 = (5 - 5)x^2y + (3 - 1)xy^2 = 2xy^2$

5. $8a^2 - 2ab + 7b^2 + 4a^2 - 9ab - 17b^2 = 12a^2 - 11ab - 10b^2$

6. $7xy - 5xy^2 + 3xy^2 - 7 + 6x^3 + 9xy - 11x^3 + y - 1$
$= 16xy - 2xy^2 - 5x^3 + y - 8$

Do Exercises 6 and 7.

Collect like terms.

6. $4x^2y + 3xy - 2x^2y$

7. $-3pq - 5pqr^3 - 12 + 8pq + 5pqr^3 + 4$

Answers

4. $-3, 3, -2, 1, 2$ **5.** $3, 7, 1, 1, 0; 7$
6. $2x^2y + 3xy$ **7.** $5pq - 8$

d Addition

We can find the sum of two polynomials in several variables by writing a plus sign between them and then collecting like terms.

EXAMPLE 7 Add: $(-5x^3 + 3y - 5y^2) + (8x^3 + 4x^2 + 7y^2)$.

$$(-5x^3 + 3y - 5y^2) + (8x^3 + 4x^2 + 7y^2)$$
$$= (-5 + 8)x^3 + 4x^2 + 3y + (-5 + 7)y^2$$
$$= 3x^3 + 4x^2 + 3y + 2y^2$$

EXAMPLE 8 Add:

$$(5xy^2 - 4x^2y + 5x^3 + 2) + (3xy^2 - 2x^2y + 3x^3y - 5).$$

We have

$$(5xy^2 - 4x^2y + 5x^3 + 2) + (3xy^2 - 2x^2y + 3x^3y - 5)$$
$$= (5 + 3)xy^2 + (-4 - 2)x^2y + 5x^3 + 3x^3y + (2 - 5)$$
$$= 8xy^2 - 6x^2y + 5x^3 + 3x^3y - 3.$$

> Do Exercises 8-10.

e Subtraction

We subtract a polynomial by adding its opposite, or additive inverse. The opposite of the polynomial $4x^2y - 6x^3y^2 + x^2y^2 - 5y$ is

$$-(4x^2y - 6x^3y^2 + x^2y^2 - 5y) = -4x^2y + 6x^3y^2 - x^2y^2 + 5y.$$

EXAMPLE 9 Subtract:

$$(4x^2y + x^3y^2 + 3x^2y^3 + 6y + 10) - (4x^2y - 6x^3y^2 + x^2y^2 - 5y - 8).$$

We have

$$(4x^2y + x^3y^2 + 3x^2y^3 + 6y + 10) - (4x^2y - 6x^3y^2 + x^2y^2 - 5y - 8)$$
$$= 4x^2y + x^3y^2 + 3x^2y^3 + 6y + 10 - 4x^2y + 6x^3y^2 - x^2y^2 + 5y + 8$$

Finding the opposite by changing the sign of each term

$$= 7x^3y^2 + 3x^2y^3 - x^2y^2 + 11y + 18.$$ Collecting like terms. (Try to write just the answer!)

Caution!

Do *not* add exponents when collecting like terms—that is,

$$7x^3 + 8x^3 \neq 15x^6; \longleftarrow \text{Wrong}$$
$$7x^3 + 8x^3 = 15x^3. \longleftarrow \text{Correct}$$

> Do Exercises 11 and 12.

Add.

8. $(4x^3 + 4x^2 - 8y - 3) + (-8x^3 - 2x^2 + 4y + 5)$

9. $(13x^3y + 3x^2y - 5y) + (x^3y + 4x^2y - 3xy + 3y)$

10. $(-5p^2q^4 + 2p^2q^2 + 3q) + (6pq^2 + 3p^2q + 5)$

Subtract.

11. $(-4s^4t + s^3t^2 + 2s^2t^3) - (4s^4t - 5s^3t^2 + s^2t^2)$

12. $(-5p^4q + 5p^3q^2 - 3p^2q^3 - 7q^4 - 2) - (4p^4q - 4p^3q^2 + p^2q^3 + 2q^4 - 7)$

Answers

8. $-4x^3 + 2x^2 - 4y + 2$
9. $14x^3y + 7x^2y - 3xy - 2y$
10. $-5p^2q^4 + 2p^2q^2 + 3p^2q + 6pq^2 + 3q + 5$
11. $-8s^4t + 6s^3t^2 + 2s^2t^3 - s^2t^2$
12. $-9p^4q + 9p^3q^2 - 4p^2q^3 - 9q^4 + 5$

(f) Multiplication

To multiply polynomials in several variables, we can multiply each term of one by every term of the other. We can use columns for long multiplications as with polynomials in one variable. We multiply each term at the top by every term at the bottom. We write like terms in columns, and then we add.

EXAMPLE 10 Multiply: $(3x^2y - 2xy + 3y)(xy + 2y)$.

$$
\begin{array}{r}
3x^2y - 2xy + 3y \\
xy + 2y \\
\hline
6x^2y^2 - 4xy^2 + 6y^2 \\
3x^3y^2 - 2x^2y^2 + 3xy^2 \\
\hline
3x^3y^2 + 4x^2y^2 - \;\; xy^2 + 6y^2
\end{array}
$$

Multiplying by $2y$
Multiplying by xy
Adding

Do Exercises 13 and 14.

Where appropriate, we use the special products that we have learned.

EXAMPLES Multiply.

11. $(x^2y + 2x)(xy^2 + y^2) = x^3y^3 + x^2y^3 + 2x^2y^2 + 2xy^2$ Using FOIL

12. $(p + 5q)(2p - 3q) = 2p^2 - 3pq + 10pq - 15q^2$ Using FOIL
$$= 2p^2 + 7pq - 15q^2$$

$$(A + B)^2 = A^2 + 2 \cdot A \cdot B + B^2$$

13. $(3x + 2y)^2 = (3x)^2 + 2(3x)(2y) + (2y)^2 = 9x^2 + 12xy + 4y^2$

$$(A - B)^2 = A^2 - 2 \cdot A \cdot B + B^2$$

14. $(2y^2 - 5x^2y)^2 = (2y^2)^2 - 2(2y^2)(5x^2y) + (5x^2y)^2$
$$= 4y^4 - 20x^2y^3 + 25x^4y^2$$

$$(A + B)(A - B) = A^2 - B^2$$

15. $(3x^2y + 2y)(3x^2y - 2y) = (3x^2y)^2 - (2y)^2 = 9x^4y^2 - 4y^2$

16. $(-2x^3y^2 + 5t)(2x^3y^2 + 5t) = (5t - 2x^3y^2)(5t + 2x^3y^2)$

The sum and the difference of the same two terms

$$= (5t)^2 - (2x^3y^2)^2 = 25t^2 - 4x^6y^4$$

$$(A - B)(A + B) = A^2 - B^2$$

17. $(2x + 3 - 2y)(2x + 3 + 2y) = (2x + 3)^2 - (2y)^2$
$$= 4x^2 + 12x + 9 - 4y^2$$

Remember that FOIL will always work when you are multiplying binomials. You can use it instead of the rules for special products, but those rules will make your work go faster.

Do Exercises 15–22.

Multiply.

13. $(x^2y^3 + 2x)(x^3y^2 + 3x)$

14. $(p^4q - 2p^3q^2 + 3q^3)(p + 2q)$

Multiply.

15. $(3xy + 2x)(x^2 + 2xy^2)$

16. $(x - 3y)(2x - 5y)$

17. $(4x + 5y)^2$

18. $(3x^2 - 2xy^2)^2$

19. $(2xy^2 + 3x)(2xy^2 - 3x)$

20. $(3xy^2 + 4y)(-3xy^2 + 4y)$

21. $(3y + 4 - 3x)(3y + 4 + 3x)$

22. $(2a + 5b + c)(2a - 5b - c)$

Answers

13. $x^5y^5 + 2x^4y^2 + 3x^3y^3 + 6x^2$
14. $p^5q - 4p^3q^3 + 3pq^3 + 6q^4$
15. $3x^3y + 6x^2y^3 + 2x^3 + 4x^2y^2$
16. $2x^2 - 11xy + 15y^2$
17. $16x^2 + 40xy + 25y^2$
18. $9x^4 - 12x^3y^2 + 4x^2y^4$
19. $4x^2y^4 - 9x^2$ **20.** $16y^2 - 9x^2y^4$
21. $9y^2 + 24y + 16 - 9x^2$
22. $4a^2 - 25b^2 - 10bc - c^2$

a Evaluate the polynomial when $x = 3$, $y = -2$, and $z = -5$.

1. $x^2 - y^2 + xy$

2. $x^2 + y^2 - xy$

3. $x^2 - 3y^2 + 2xy$

4. $x^2 - 4xy + 5y^2$

5. $8xyz$

6. $-3xyz^2$

7. $xyz^2 - z$

8. $xy - xz + yz$

Lung Capacity. The polynomial equation
$$C = 0.041h - 0.018A - 2.69$$
can be used to estimate the lung capacity C, in liters, of a person of height h, in centimeters, and age A, in years. Use this formula for Exercises 9 and 10.

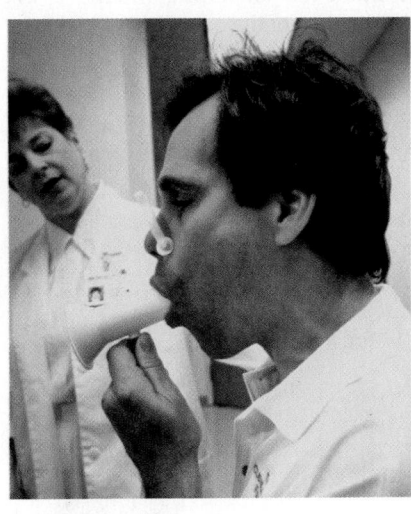

9. Find the lung capacity of a 20-year-old person who is 165 cm tall.

10. Find the lung capacity of a 50-year-old person who is 160 cm tall.

Altitude of a Launched Object. The altitude h, in meters, of a launched object is given by the polynomial equation
$$h = h_0 + vt - 4.9t^2,$$
where h_0 is the height, in meters, from which the launch occurs, v is the initial upward speed (or velocity), in meters per second (m/s), and t is the number of seconds for which the object is airborne. Use this formula for Exercises 11 and 12.

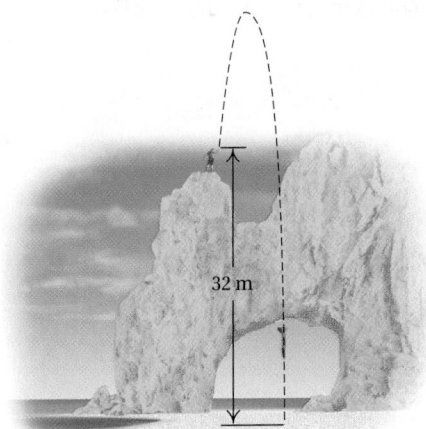

32 m

11. A golf ball is thrown upward with an initial speed of 30 m/s from the top of the Washington Monument, which is 160 m above the ground. How high above the ground will the ball be after 3 sec?

12. A model rocket is launched from the top of the Lands End Arch, near San Lucas, Baja, Mexico, 32 m above the ground. The upward speed is 40 m/s. How high will the rocket be 2 sec after the blastoff?

Surface Area of a Right Circular Cylinder. The surface area S of a right circular cylinder is given by the polynomial equation

$$S = 2\pi rh + 2\pi r^2,$$

where h is the height and r is the radius of the base. Use this formula for Exercises 13 and 14.

13. A 12-oz beverage can has a height of 4.7 in. and a radius of 1.2 in. Evaluate the polynomial when $h = 4.7$ and $r = 1.2$ to find the area of the can. Use 3.14 for π.

14. A 26-oz coffee can has a height of 6.5 in. and a radius of 2.5 in. Evaluate the polynomial when $h = 6.5$ and $r = 2.5$ to find the area of the can. Use 3.14 for π.

Surface Area of a Silo. A silo is a structure that is shaped like a right circular cylinder with a half sphere on top. The surface area S of a silo of height h and radius r (including the area of the base) is given by the polynomial equation $S = 2\pi rh + \pi r^2$. Note that h is the height of the entire silo.

15. A container of tennis balls is silo-shaped, with a height of $7\frac{1}{2}$ in. and a radius of $1\frac{1}{4}$ in. Find the surface area of the container. Use 3.14 for π.

16. A $1\frac{1}{2}$-oz bottle of roll-on deodorant has a height of 4 in. and a radius of $\frac{3}{4}$ in. Find the surface area of the bottle if the bottle is shaped like a silo. Use 3.14 for π.

b Identify the coefficient and the degree of each term of the polynomial. Then find the degree of the polynomial.

17. $x^3y - 2xy + 3x^2 - 5$

18. $5x^2y^2 - y^2 + 15xy + 1$

19. $17x^2y^3 - 3x^3yz - 7$

20. $6 - xy + 8x^2y^2 - y^5$

c Collect like terms.

21. $a + b - 2a - 3b$

22. $xy^2 - 1 + y - 6 - xy^2$

23. $3x^2y - 2xy^2 + x^2$

24. $m^3 + 2m^2n - 3m^2 + 3mn^2$

25. $6au + 3av + 14au + 7av$

26. $3x^2y - 2z^2y + 3xy^2 + 5z^2y$

27. $2u^2v - 3uv^2 + 6u^2v - 2uv^2$

28. $3x^2 + 6xy + 3y^2 - 5x^2 - 10xy - 5y^2$

Copyright © 2012 Pearson Education, Inc.

d Add.

29. $(2x^2 - xy + y^2) + (-x^2 - 3xy + 2y^2)$

30. $(2zt - z^2 + 5t^2) + (z^2 - 3zt + t^2)$

31. $(r - 2s + 3) + (2r + s) + (s + 4)$

32. $(ab - 2a + 3b) + (5a - 4b) + (3a + 7ab - 8b)$

33. $(b^3a^2 - 2b^2a^3 + 3ba + 4) + (b^2a^3 - 4b^3a^2 + 2ba - 1)$

34. $(2x^2 - 3xy + y^2) + (-4x^2 - 6xy - y^2)$
$\quad\ + (x^2 + xy - y^2)$

e Subtract.

35. $(a^3 + b^3) - (a^2b - ab^2 + b^3 + a^3)$

36. $(x^3 - y^3) - (-2x^3 + x^2y - xy^2 + 2y^3)$

37. $(xy - ab - 8) - (xy - 3ab - 6)$

38. $(3y^4x^2 + 2y^3x - 3y - 7)$
$\quad\ - (2y^4x^2 + 2y^3x - 4y - 2x + 5)$

39. $(-2a + 7b - c) - (-3b + 4c - 8d)$

40. Subtract $5a + 2b$ from the sum of $2a + b$ and $3a - b$.

f Multiply.

41. $(3z - u)(2z + 3u)$

42. $(a - b)(a^2 + b^2 + 2ab)$

43. $(a^2b - 2)(a^2b - 5)$

44. $(xy + 7)(xy - 4)$

45. $(a^3 + bc)(a^3 - bc)$

46. $(m^2 + n^2 - mn)(m^2 + mn + n^2)$

47. $(y^4x + y^2 + 1)(y^2 + 1)$

48. $(a - b)(a^2 + ab + b^2)$

49. $(3xy - 1)(4xy + 2)$

50. $(m^3n + 8)(m^3n - 6)$

51. $(3 - c^2d^2)(4 + c^2d^2)$

52. $(6x - 2y)(5x - 3y)$

53. $(m^2 - n^2)(m + n)$

54. $(pq + 0.2)(0.4pq - 0.1)$

55. $(xy + x^5y^5)(x^4y^4 - xy)$

56. $(x - y^3)(2y^3 + x)$

57. $(x + h)^2$

58. $(y - a)^2$

59. $(3a + 2b)^2$

60. $(2ab - cd)^2$

61. $(r^3t^2 - 4)^2$

62. $(3a^2b - b^2)^2$

63. $(p^4 + m^2n^2)^2$

64. $\left(2a^3 - \frac{1}{2}b^3\right)^2$

65. $3a(a - 2b)^2$

66. $-3x(x + 8y)^2$

67. $(m + n - 3)^2$

68. $(a^2 + b + 2)^2$

69. $(a + b)(a - b)$

70. $(x - y)(x + y)$

71. $(2a - b)(2a + b)$

72. $(w + 3z)(w - 3z)$

73. $(c^2 - d)(c^2 + d)$

74. $(p^3 - 5q)(p^3 + 5q)$

75. $(ab + cd^2)(ab - cd^2)$

76. $(xy + pq)(xy - pq)$

77. $(x + y - 3)(x + y + 3)$

78. $(p + q + 4)(p + q - 4)$

79. $[x + y + z][x - (y + z)]$

80. $[a + b + c][a - (b + c)]$

81. $(a + b + c)(a + b - c)$

82. $(3x + 2 - 5y)(3x + 2 + 5y)$

83. $(x^2 - 4y + 2)(3x^2 + 5y - 3)$

84. $(2x^2 - 7y + 4)(x^2 + y - 3)$

Copyright © 2012 Pearson Education, Inc.

Skill Maintenance

In which quadrant is each point located? [9.1a]

85. $(2, -5)$

86. $(-8, -9)$

87. $(16, 23)$

88. $(-3, 2)$

Graph. [9.2b]

89. $2x = -10$

90. $y = -4$

91. $8y - 16 = 0$

92. $x = 4$

Synthesis

Find a polynomial for each shaded area. (Leave results in terms of π where appropriate.)

93.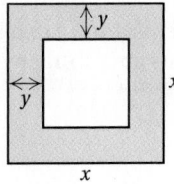

94.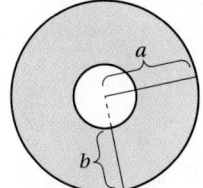

95.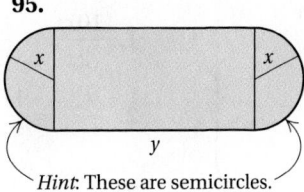

Hint: These are semicircles.

96.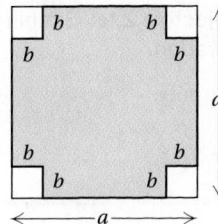

Find a formula for the surface area of each solid object. Leave results in terms of π.

97.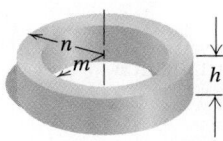

98.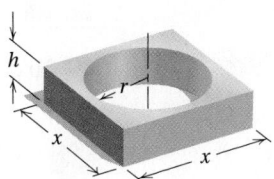

99. *Observatory Paint Costs.* The observatory at Danville University is shaped like a silo that is 40 ft high and 30 ft wide (see Exercise 15). The Heavenly Bodies Astronomy Club is to paint the exterior of the observatory using paint that covers 250 ft² per gallon. How many gallons should they purchase?

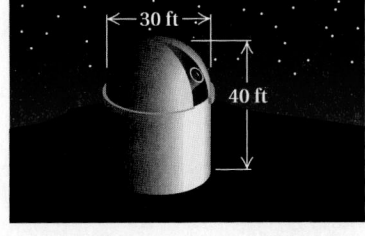

100. *Interest Compounded Annually.* An amount of money P that is invested at the yearly interest rate r grows to the amount

$$P(1 + r)^t$$

after t years. Find a polynomial that can be used to determine the amount to which P will grow after 2 yr.

101. Suppose that $10,400 is invested at 3.5%, compounded annually. How much is in the account at the end of 5 yr? (See Exercise 100.)

102. Multiply: $(x + a)(x - b)(x - a)(x + b)$.

10.8

Division of Polynomials

OBJECTIVES

a Divide a polynomial by a monomial.

b Divide a polynomial by a divisor that is a binomial.

SKILL TO REVIEW

Objective 2.1e: Simplify fraction notation.

Simplify.

1. $\dfrac{20}{4}$ 2. $\dfrac{-30}{5}$

Divide.

1. $\dfrac{20x^3}{5x}$ 2. $\dfrac{-28x^{14}}{4x^3}$

3. $\dfrac{-56p^5q^7}{2p^2q^6}$ 4. $\dfrac{x^5}{4x}$

In this section, we consider division of polynomials. You will see that such division is similar to what is done in arithmetic.

a Dividing by a Monomial

We first consider division by a monomial. When dividing a monomial by a monomial, we use the quotient rule of Section 10.1 to subtract exponents when the bases are the same. We also divide the coefficients.

EXAMPLES Divide.

1. $\dfrac{10x^2}{2x} = \dfrac{10}{2} \cdot \dfrac{x^2}{x} = 5x^{2-1} = 5x$

2. $\dfrac{x^9}{3x^2} = \dfrac{1x^9}{3x^2} = \dfrac{1}{3} \cdot \dfrac{x^9}{x^2} = \dfrac{1}{3}x^{9-2} = \dfrac{1}{3}x^7$

3. $\dfrac{-18x^{10}}{3x^3} = \dfrac{-18}{3} \cdot \dfrac{x^{10}}{x^3} = -6x^{10-3} = -6x^7$

4. $\dfrac{42a^2b^5}{-3ab^2} = \dfrac{42}{-3} \cdot \dfrac{a^2}{a} \cdot \dfrac{b^5}{b^2} = -14a^{2-1}b^{5-2} = -14ab^3$

---------- *Caution!* ----------

The coefficients are divided but the exponents are subtracted.

Do Margin Exercises 1–4.

To divide a polynomial by a monomial, we note that since

$$\frac{A}{C} + \frac{B}{C} = \frac{A+B}{C},$$

it follows that

$$\frac{A+B}{C} = \frac{A}{C} + \frac{B}{C}.$$ Switching the left and right sides of the equation

This is actually the procedure we use when performing divisions like $86 \div 2$. Although we might write

$$\frac{86}{2} = 43,$$

we could also calculate as follows:

$$\frac{86}{2} = \frac{80+6}{2} = \frac{80}{2} + \frac{6}{2} = 40 + 3 = 43.$$

Similarly, to divide a polynomial by a monomial, we divide each term by the monomial.

EXAMPLE 5 Divide: $(9x^8 + 12x^6) \div (3x^2)$.

We have

$$(9x^8 + 12x^6) \div (3x^2) = \frac{9x^8 + 12x^6}{3x^2}$$

$$= \frac{9x^8}{3x^2} + \frac{12x^6}{3x^2}.$$ To see this, add and get the original expression.

Answers

Skill to Review:

1. 5   2. −6

Margin Exercises:

1. $4x^2$ 2. $-7x^{11}$ 3. $-28p^3q$ 4. $\dfrac{1}{4}x^4$

We now perform the separate divisions:

$$\frac{9x^8}{3x^2} + \frac{12x^6}{3x^2} = \frac{9}{3} \cdot \frac{x^8}{x^2} + \frac{12}{3} \cdot \frac{x^6}{x^2}$$

$$= 3x^{8-2} + 4x^{6-2}$$

$$= 3x^6 + 4x^4.$$

------------ *Caution!* ------------

The coefficients are *divided*, but the exponents are *subtracted*.

To check, we multiply the quotient, $3x^6 + 4x^4$, by the divisor, $3x^2$:

$$3x^2(3x^6 + 4x^4) = (3x^2)(3x^6) + (3x^2)(4x^4) = 9x^8 + 12x^6.$$

This is the polynomial that was being divided, so our answer is $3x^6 + 4x^4$.

Do Exercises 5-7.

Do Exercises 5-7.

Divide. Check the result.

5. $(28x^7 + 32x^5) \div (4x^3)$

6. $(2x^3 + 6x^2 + 4x) \div (2x)$

7. $(6x^2 + 3x - 2) \div 3$

EXAMPLE 6 Divide and check: $(10a^5b^4 - 2a^3b^2 + 6a^2b) \div (2a^2b)$.

$$\frac{10a^5b^4 - 2a^3b^2 + 6a^2b}{2a^2b} = \frac{10a^5b^4}{2a^2b} - \frac{2a^3b^2}{2a^2b} + \frac{6a^2b}{2a^2b}$$

$$= \frac{10}{2}a^{5-2}b^{4-1} - \frac{2}{2}a^{3-2}b^{2-1} + \frac{6}{2}$$

$$= 5a^3b^3 - ab + 3$$

Check: $2a^2b(5a^3b^3 - ab + 3) = 2a^2b \cdot 5a^3b^3 - 2a^2b \cdot ab + 2a^2b \cdot 3$

$$= 10a^5b^4 - 2a^3b^2 + 6a^2b$$

Our answer, $5a^3b^3 - ab + 3$, checks.

To divide a polynomial by a monomial, divide each term of the polynomial by the monomial.

Do Exercises 8 and 9.

Do Exercises 8 and 9.

Divide and check.

8. $(8x^2 - 3x + 1) \div 2$

9. $\dfrac{2x^4y^6 - 3x^3y^4 + 5x^2y^3}{x^2y^2}$

(b) Dividing by a Binomial

Let's first consider long division as it is performed in arithmetic. When we divide, we repeat the procedure at right.

We review this by considering the division $3711 \div 8$.

$$\begin{array}{r} 4 \\ 8\overline{)3\ 7\ 1\ 1} \\ 3\ 2 \\ \hline 5\ 1 \end{array}$$

① Divide: $37 \div 8 \approx 4$.

② Multiply: $4 \times 8 = 32$.

③ Subtract: $37 - 32 = 5$.

④ Bring down the 1.

$$\begin{array}{r} 4\ 6\ 3 \\ 8\ \overline{)\ 3\ 7\ 1\ 1} \\ 3\ 2 \\ \hline 5\ 1 \\ 4\ 8 \\ \hline 3\ 1 \\ 2\ 4 \\ \hline 7 \end{array}$$

To carry out long division:

1. Divide,
2. Multiply,
3. Subtract, and
4. Bring down the next term.

Answers

5. $7x^4 + 8x^2$ 6. $x^2 + 3x + 2$

7. $2x^2 + x - \dfrac{2}{3}$ 8. $4x^2 - \dfrac{3}{2}x + \dfrac{1}{2}$

9. $2x^2y^4 - 3xy^2 + 5y$

Next, we repeat the process two more times. We obtain the complete division as shown on the right above. The quotient is 463. The remainder is 7, expressed as R = 7. We write the answer as

$$463 \text{ R } 7 \quad \text{or} \quad 463 + \frac{7}{8} = 463\frac{7}{8}.$$

We check by multiplying the quotient, 463, by the divisor, 8, and adding the remainder, 7:

$$8 \cdot 463 + 7 = 3704 + 7 = 3711.$$

Now let's look at long division with polynomials. We use this procedure when the divisor is not a monomial. We write polynomials in descending order and then write in missing terms.

EXAMPLE 7 Divide $x^2 + 5x + 6$ by $x + 2$.

$$
\begin{array}{r}
x \\
x + 2 \overline{)\, x^2 + 5x + 6} \\
x^2 + 2x \\
\hline
3x
\end{array}
$$

      Divide the first term by the first term: $x^2/x = x$. Ignore the term 2.

      Multiply x above by the divisor, $x + 2$.

      Subtract: $(x^2 + 5x) - (x^2 + 2x) = x^2 + 5x - x^2 - 2x = 3x$.

We now "bring down" the next term of the dividend—in this case, 6.

$$
\begin{array}{r}
x + 3 \\
x + 2 \overline{)\, x^2 + 5x + 6} \\
x^2 + 2x \\
\hline
3x + 6 \\
3x + 6 \\
\hline
0
\end{array}
$$

      Divide the first term by the first term: $3x/x = 3$.

      The 6 has been "brought down."

      Multiply 3 by the divisor, $x + 2$.

      Subtract: $(3x + 6) - (3x + 6) = 3x + 6 - 3x - 6 = 0$.

The quotient is $x + 3$. The remainder is 0, expressed as R = 0. A remainder of 0 is generally not included in an answer.

To check, we multiply the quotient by the divisor and add the remainder, if any, to see if we get the dividend:

Divisor	Quotient	Remainder		Dividend	
$(x + 2) \cdot$	$(x + 3) +$	0	$=$	$x^2 + 5x + 6$.	The division checks.

10. Divide and check:
$(x^2 + x - 6) \div (x + 3)$.

Do Exercise 10.

EXAMPLE 8 Divide and check: $(x^2 + 2x - 12) \div (x - 3)$.

$$
\begin{array}{r}
x \\
x - 3 \overline{)\, x^2 + 2x - 12} \\
x^2 - 3x \\
\hline
5x
\end{array}
$$

      Divide the first term by the first term: $x^2/x = x$.

      Multiply x above by the divisor, $x - 3$.

      Subtract: $(x^2 + 2x) - (x^2 - 3x) = x^2 + 2x - x^2 + 3x = 5x$.

We now "bring down" the next term of the dividend—in this case, -12.

$$
\begin{array}{r}
x + 5 \\
x - 3 \overline{)\, x^2 + 2x - 12} \\
x^2 - 3x \\
\hline
5x - 12 \\
5x - 15 \\
\hline
3
\end{array}
$$

      Divide the first term by the first term: $5x/x = 5$.

      Bring down the -12.

      Multiply 5 above by the divisor, $x - 3$.

      Subtract: $(5x - 12) - (5x - 15) = 5x - 12 - 5x + 15 = 3$.

Answer

10. $x - 2$

The answer is $x + 5$ with R = 3, or

$$\underbrace{x + 5}_{\text{Quotient}} + \underbrace{\dfrac{3}{x - 3}}_{}.$$

3 → Remainder
$x - 3$ → Divisor

(This is the way answers will be given at the back of the book.)

Check: We can check by multiplying the divisor by the quotient and adding the remainder, as follows:

$$(x - 3)(x + 5) + 3 = x^2 + 2x - 15 + 3$$
$$= x^2 + 2x - 12.$$

When dividing, an answer may "come out even" (that is, have a remainder of 0, as in Example 7), or it may not (as in Example 8). **If a remainder is not 0, we continue dividing until the degree of the remainder is less than the degree of the divisor.** Check this in each of Examples 7 and 8.

> Do Exercises 11 and 12.

Divide and check.

11. $x - 2\overline{)x^2 + 2x - 8}$

12. $x + 3\overline{)x^2 + 7x + 10}$

EXAMPLE 9   Divide and check: $(x^3 + 1) \div (x + 1)$.

$$
\begin{array}{r}
x^2 - x + 1 \\
x + 1\overline{)x^3 + 0x^2 + 0x + 1} \\
\underline{x^3 + x^2} \\
-x^2 + 0x \\
\underline{-x^2 - x} \\
x + 1 \\
\underline{x + 1} \\
0
\end{array}
$$

← Fill in the missing terms. (See Section 4.3.)
Subtract: $x^3 - (x^3 + x^2) = -x^2$.
Subtract: $-x^2 - (-x^2 - x) = x$.
Subtract: $(x + 1) - (x + 1) = 0$.

The answer is $x^2 - x + 1$. The check is left to the student.

EXAMPLE 10   Divide and check: $(9x^4 - 7x^2 - 4x + 13) \div (3x - 1)$.

$$
\begin{array}{r}
3x^3 + x^2 - 2x - 2 \\
3x - 1\overline{)9x^4 + 0x^3 - 7x^2 - 4x + 13} \\
\underline{9x^4 - 3x^3} \\
3x^3 - 7x^2 \\
\underline{3x^3 - x^2} \\
-6x^2 - 4x \\
\underline{-6x^2 + 2x} \\
-6x + 13 \\
\underline{-6x + 2} \\
11
\end{array}
$$

← Fill in the missing term.
Subtract: $9x^4 - (9x^4 - 3x^3) = 3x^3$.
Subtract: $(3x^3 - 7x^2) - (3x^3 - x^2) = -6x^2$.
Subtract: $(-6x^2 - 4x) - (-6x^2 + 2x) = -6x$.
Subtract: $(-6x + 13) - (-6x + 2) = 11$.

The answer is $3x^3 + x^2 - 2x - 2$ with R = 11, or

$$3x^3 + x^2 - 2x - 2 + \dfrac{11}{3x - 1}.$$

Check: $(3x - 1)(3x^3 + x^2 - 2x - 2) + 11$
$$= 9x^4 + 3x^3 - 6x^2 - 6x - 3x^3 - x^2 + 2x + 2 + 11$$
$$= 9x^4 - 7x^2 - 4x + 13$$

> Do Exercises 13 and 14.

Divide and check.

13. $(x^3 - 1) \div (x - 1)$

14. $(8x^4 + 10x^2 + 2x + 9) \div (4x + 2)$

Answers

11. $x + 4$ **12.** $x + 4$ with R = -2, or

$x + 4 + \dfrac{-2}{x + 3}$ **13.** $x^2 + x + 1$

14. $2x^3 - x^2 + 3x - 1$ with R = 11, or

$2x^3 - x^2 + 3x - 1 + \dfrac{11}{4x + 2}$

a   Divide and check.

1. $\dfrac{24x^4}{8}$

2. $\dfrac{-2u^2}{u}$

3. $\dfrac{25x^3}{5x^2}$

4. $\dfrac{16x^7}{-2x^2}$

5. $\dfrac{-54x^{11}}{-3x^8}$

6. $\dfrac{-75a^{10}}{3a^2}$

7. $\dfrac{64a^5b^4}{16a^2b^3}$

8. $\dfrac{-34p^{10}q^{11}}{-17pq^9}$

9. $\dfrac{24x^4 - 4x^3 + x^2 - 16}{8}$

10. $\dfrac{12a^4 - 3a^2 + a - 6}{6}$

11. $\dfrac{u - 2u^2 - u^5}{u}$

12. $\dfrac{50x^5 - 7x^4 + x^2}{x}$

13. $(15t^3 + 24t^2 - 6t) \div (3t)$

14. $(25t^3 + 15t^2 - 30t) \div (5t)$

15. $(20x^6 - 20x^4 - 5x^2) \div (-5x^2)$

16. $(24x^6 + 32x^5 - 8x^2) \div (-8x^2)$

17. $(24x^5 - 40x^4 + 6x^3) \div (4x^3)$

18. $(18x^6 - 27x^5 - 3x^3) \div (9x^3)$

19. $\dfrac{18x^2 - 5x + 2}{2}$

20. $\dfrac{15x^2 - 30x + 6}{3}$

21. $\dfrac{12x^3 + 26x^2 + 8x}{2x}$

22. $\dfrac{2x^4 - 3x^3 + 5x^2}{x^2}$

23. $\dfrac{9r^2s^2 + 3r^2s - 6rs^2}{3rs}$

24. $\dfrac{4x^4y - 8x^6y^2 + 12x^8y^6}{4x^4y}$

Copyright © 2012 Pearson Education, Inc.

b Divide.

25. $(x^2 + 4x + 4) \div (x + 2)$

26. $(x^2 - 6x + 9) \div (x - 3)$

27. $(x^2 - 10x - 25) \div (x - 5)$

28. $(x^2 + 8x - 16) \div (x + 4)$

29. $(x^2 + 4x - 14) \div (x + 6)$

30. $(x^2 + 5x - 9) \div (x - 2)$

31. $\dfrac{x^2 - 9}{x + 3}$

32. $\dfrac{x^2 - 25}{x - 5}$

33. $\dfrac{x^5 + 1}{x + 1}$

34. $\dfrac{x^4 - 81}{x - 3}$

35. $\dfrac{8x^3 - 22x^2 - 5x + 12}{4x + 3}$

36. $\dfrac{2x^3 - 9x^2 + 11x - 3}{2x - 3}$

37. $(x^6 - 13x^3 + 42) \div (x^3 - 7)$

38. $(x^6 + 5x^3 - 24) \div (x^3 - 3)$

39. $(t^3 - t^2 + t - 1) \div (t - 1)$

40. $(y^3 + 3y^2 - 5y - 15) \div (y + 3)$

41. $(y^3 - y^2 - 5y - 3) \div (y + 2)$

42. $(t^3 - t^2 + t - 1) \div (t + 1)$

43. $(15x^3 + 8x^2 + 11x + 12) \div (5x + 1)$

44. $(20x^4 - 2x^3 + 5x + 3) \div (2x - 3)$

45. $(12y^3 + 42y^2 - 10y - 41) \div (2y + 7)$

46. $(15y^3 - 27y^2 - 35y + 60) \div (5y - 9)$

Skill Maintenance

In each of Exercises 47–54, fill in the blank with the correct term from the given list. Some of the choices may not be used.

47. The _____ rule asserts that when multiplying with exponential notation, if the bases are the same, we keep the base and add the exponents. [10.1d]

48. A(n) _____ is an expression of the type ax^n, where a is a real-number constant and n is a nonnegative integer. [10.3a, i]

49. The _____ principle asserts that when we multiply or divide by the same nonzero number on each side of an equation, we get _____ equations. [8.2a]

50. Vertical lines are graphs of equations of the type _____. [9.2b]

51. A(n) _____ is a polynomial with three terms, such as $5x^4 - 7x^2 + 4$. [10.3i]

52. The _____ rule asserts that when dividing with exponential notation, if the bases are the same, we keep the base and subtract the exponent of the denominator from the exponent of the numerator. [10.1e]

53. The _____ of a number is its distance from zero on the number line. [7.2e]

54. The _____ of the line $y = mx + b$ is m. [9.4a]

$x = a$

$y = b$

slope

y-intercept

opposite

absolute value

equivalent

inverse

quotient

product

monomial

binomial

trinomial

addition

multiplication

Synthesis

Divide.

55. $(x^4 + 9x^2 + 20) \div (x^2 + 4)$

56. $(y^4 + a^2) \div (y + a)$

57. $(5a^3 + 8a^2 - 23a - 1) \div (5a^2 - 7a - 2)$

58. $(15y^3 - 30y + 7 - 19y^2) \div (3y^2 - 2 - 5y)$

59. $(6x^5 - 13x^3 + 5x + 3 - 4x^2 + 3x^4) \div (3x^3 - 2x - 1)$

60. $(5x^7 - 3x^4 + 2x^2 - 10x + 2) \div (x^2 - x + 1)$

61. $(a^6 - b^6) \div (a - b)$

62. $(x^5 + y^5) \div (x + y)$

If the remainder is 0 when one polynomial is divided by another, the divisor is a *factor* of the dividend. Find the value(s) of c for which $x - 1$ is a factor of the polynomial.

63. $x^2 + 4x + c$

64. $2x^2 + 3cx - 8$

65. $c^2x^2 - 2cx + 1$

Copyright © 2012 Pearson Education, Inc.

Summary and Review

Key Terms and Properties

exponent, p. 734
base, p. 734
scientific notation, p. 746
polynomial, p. 756
monomial, pp. 756, 763

binomial, p. 763
trinomial, p. 763
like terms, p. 759
coefficients, p. 759
collecting like terms, p. 760

descending/ascending order, p. 761
degree of a term/polynomial,
  pp. 761, 762
opposite of a polynomial, p. 770
polynomial in several variables, p. 797

Definitions and Rules for Exponents: See p. 750

FOIL: $(A + B)(C + D) = AC + AD + BC + BD$

Square of a Sum: $(A + B)(A + B) = (A + B)^2 = A^2 + 2AB + B^2$

Square of a Difference: $(A - B)(A - B) = (A - B)^2 = A^2 - 2AB + B^2$

Product of a Sum and a Difference: $(A + B)(A - B) = A^2 - B^2$

Concept Reinforcement

Determine whether each statement is true or false.

_____ **1.** All trinomials are polynomials. [10.3i]

_____ **2.** $(x + y)^2 = x^2 + y^2$ [10.6c]

_____ **3.** The square of the difference of two expressions is the difference of the squares of the
two expressions. [10.6c]

_____ **4.** The product of the sum and the difference of two expressions is the difference of the
squares of the expressions. [10.6b]

Important Concepts

Objective 10.1d Use the product rule to multiply exponential expressions with like bases.

Example Multiply and simplify: $x^3 \cdot x^4$.
   $x^3 \cdot x^4 = x^{3+4} = x^7$

Practice Exercise
   1. Multiply and simplify: $z^5 \cdot z^3$.

Objective 10.1e Use the quotient rule to divide exponential expressions with like bases.

Example Divide and simplify: $\dfrac{x^6 y^5}{xy^3}$.

$\dfrac{x^6 y^5}{xy^3} = \dfrac{x^6}{x} \cdot \dfrac{y^5}{y^3}$

$= x^{6-1} y^{5-3}$

$= x^5 y^2$

Practice Exercise

   2. Divide and simplify: $\dfrac{a^4 b^7}{a^2 b}$.

Objective 10.1f   Express an exponential expression involving negative exponents with positive exponents.

Objective 10.2a   Use the power rule to raise powers to powers.

Objective 10.2b   Raise a product to a power and a quotient to a power.

Example   Simplify: $\left(\dfrac{2a^3b^{-2}}{c^4}\right)^5$.

$$\left(\dfrac{2a^3b^{-2}}{c^4}\right)^5 = \dfrac{(2a^3b^{-2})^5}{(c^4)^5}$$

$$= \dfrac{2^5(a^3)^5(b^{-2})^5}{(c^4)^5}$$

$$= \dfrac{32a^{3\cdot5}b^{-2\cdot5}}{c^{4\cdot5}}$$

$$= \dfrac{32a^{15}b^{-10}}{c^{20}}$$

$$= \dfrac{32a^{15}}{b^{10}c^{20}}$$

Practice Exercise

3. Simplify: $\left(\dfrac{x^{-4}y^2}{3z^3}\right)^3$.

Objective 10.2c   Convert between scientific notation and decimal notation.

Example   Convert 0.00095 to scientific notation.

0.0009.5

     4 places

The number is small, so the exponent is negative. (If the number were large, the exponent would be positive.)

$$0.00095 = 9.5 \times 10^{-4}$$

Example   Convert 3.409×10^6 to decimal notation.

3.409000.

     6 places

The exponent is positive, so the number is large. (If the exponent were negative, the number would be small.)

$$3.409 \times 10^6 = 3,409,000$$

Practice Exercises

4. Convert to scientific notation: 763,000.

5. Convert to decimal notation: 3×10^{-4}.

Objective 10.2d   Multiply and divide using scientific notation.

Example   Multiply and express the result in scientific notation: $(5.3 \times 10^9) \cdot (2.4 \times 10^{-5})$.

$$(5.3 \times 10^9) \cdot (2.4 \times 10^{-5}) = (5.3 \cdot 2.4) \times (10^9 \cdot 10^{-5})$$
$$= 12.72 \times 10^4$$

The answer at this stage is not in scientific notation, because 12.72 is not a number between 1 and 10. We convert 12.72 to scientific notation and simplify:

$$12.72 \times 10^4 = (1.272 \times 10) \times 10^4$$
$$= 1.272 \times (10 \times 10^4)$$
$$= 1.272 \times 10^5.$$

Practice Exercise

6. Divide and express the result in scientific notation:
$$\dfrac{3.6 \times 10^3}{6.0 \times 10^{-2}}.$$

Objective 10.3e   Collect the like terms of a polynomial.

Example Collect like terms: $4x^3 - 2x^2 + 5 + 3x^2 - 12$. $\quad 4x^3 - 2x^2 + 5 + 3x^2 - 12$ $\quad = 4x^3 + (-2 + 3)x^2 + (5 - 12)$ $\quad = 4x^3 + x^2 - 7$	**Practice Exercise** **7.** Collect like terms: $5x^4 - 6x^2 - 3x^4 + 2x^2 - 3$.

Objective 10.4a   Add polynomials.

Example Add: $(4x^3 + x^2 - 8) + (2x^3 - 5x + 1)$. $\quad (4x^3 + x^2 - 8) + (2x^3 - 5x + 1)$ $\quad = (4 + 2)x^3 + x^2 - 5x + (-8 + 1)$ $\quad = 6x^3 + x^2 - 5x - 7$	**Practice Exercise** **8.** Add: $(3x^4 - 5x^2 - 4) + (x^3 + 3x^2 + 6)$.

Objective 10.5d   Multiply any two polynomials.

Example Multiply: $(z^2 - 2z + 3)(z - 1)$. We use columns. First, we multiply the top row by -1 and then by z, placing like terms of the product in the same column. Finally, we collect like terms. $\quad\quad z^2 - 2z + 3$ $\quad\quad\quad\quad z - 1$ $\quad\overline{\quad -z^2 + 2z - 3\quad}$ $\quad z^3 - 2z^2 + 3z$ $\quad\overline{\quad z^3 - 3z^2 + 5z - 3\quad}$	**Practice Exercise** **9.** Multiply: $(x^4 - 3x^2 + 2)(x^2 - 3)$.

Objective 10.6a   Multiply two binomials mentally using the FOIL method.

Example Multiply: $(3x + 5)(x - 1)$. $\quad\quad\quad\quad\text{F}\quad\quad\text{O}\quad\quad\text{I}\quad\quad\text{L}$ $(3x + 5)(x - 1) = 3x \cdot x + 3x \cdot (-1) + 5 \cdot x + 5 \cdot (-1)$ $\quad\quad\quad\quad = 3x^2 - 3x + 5x - 5$ $\quad\quad\quad\quad = 3x^2 + 2x - 5$	**Practice Exercise** **10.** Multiply: $(y + 4)(2y + 3)$.

Objective 10.6b   Multiply the sum and the difference of two terms mentally.

Example Multiply: $(3y + 2)(3y - 2)$. $\quad (3y + 2)(3y - 2) = (3y)^2 - 2^2$ $\quad\quad\quad\quad\quad = 9y^2 - 4$	**Practice Exercise** **11.** Multiply: $(x + 5)(x - 5)$.

Objective 10.6c   Square a binomial mentally.

Example Multiply: $(2x - 3)^2$. $\quad (2x - 3)^2 = (2x)^2 - 2 \cdot 2x \cdot 3 + 3^2$ $\quad\quad\quad\quad = 4x^2 - 12x + 9$	**Practice Exercise** **12.** Multiply: $(3w + 4)^2$.

Objective 10.7e   Subtract polynomials.

Example   Subtract:

$(m^4n + 2m^3n^2 - m^2n^3) - (3m^4n + 2m^3n^2 - 4m^2n^2)$.

$(m^4n + 2m^3n^2 - m^2n^3) - (3m^4n + 2m^3n^2 - 4m^2n^2)$

$= m^4n + 2m^3n^2 - m^2n^3 - 3m^4n - 2m^3n^2 + 4m^2n^2$

$= -2m^4n - m^2n^3 + 4m^2n^2$

Practice Exercise

13. Subtract:

$(a^3b^2 - 5a^2b + 2ab) - (3a^3b^2 - ab^2 + 4ab)$.

Objective 10.8a   Divide a polynomial by a monomial.

Example   Divide: $(6x^3 - 8x^2 + 15x) \div (3x)$.

$\dfrac{6x^3 - 8x^2 + 15x}{3x} = \dfrac{6x^3}{3x} - \dfrac{8x^2}{3x} + \dfrac{15x}{3x}$

$= \dfrac{6}{3}x^{3-1} - \dfrac{8}{3}x^{2-1} + \dfrac{15}{3}x^{1-1}$

$= 2x^2 - \dfrac{8}{3}x + 5$

Practice Exercise

14. Divide: $(5y^2 - 20y + 8) \div 5$.

Objective 10.8b   Divide a polynomial by a divisor that is a binomial.

Example   Divide $x^2 - 3x + 7$ by $x + 1$.

$$
\begin{array}{r}
x - 4 \\
x + 1 \overline{\smash{)}\, x^2 - 3x + 7} \\
\underline{x^2 + x} \\
-4x + 7 \\
\underline{-4x - 4} \\
11
\end{array}
$$

The answer is $x - 4 + \dfrac{11}{x + 1}$.

Practice Exercise

15. Divide: $(x^2 - 4x + 3) \div (x + 5)$.

Review Exercises

Multiply and simplify.   [10.1d, f]

1. $7^2 \cdot 7^{-4}$

2. $y^7 \cdot y^3 \cdot y$

3. $(3x)^5 \cdot (3x)^9$

4. $t^8 \cdot t^0$

Divide and simplify.   [10.1e, f]

5. $\dfrac{4^5}{4^2}$

6. $\dfrac{a^5}{a^8}$

7. $\dfrac{(7x)^4}{(7x)^4}$

Simplify.

8. $(3t^4)^2$ [10.2a, b]

9. $(2x^3)^2(-3x)^2$
[10.1d], [10.2a, b]

10. $\left(\dfrac{2x}{y}\right)^{-3}$ [10.2b]

11. Express using a negative exponent: $\dfrac{1}{t^5}$.   [10.1f]

12. Express using a positive exponent: y^{-4}.   [10.1f]

13. Convert to scientific notation: 0.0000328.   [10.2c]

14. Convert to decimal notation: 8.3×10^6.   [10.2c]

Multiply or divide and write scientific notation for the result.   [10.2d]

15. $(3.8 \times 10^4)(5.5 \times 10^{-1})$

16. $\dfrac{1.28 \times 10^{-8}}{2.5 \times 10^{-4}}$

Copyright © 2012 Pearson Education, Inc.

17. *Pizza Consumption.* Each man, woman, and child in the United States eats an average of 46 slices of pizza per year. The U.S. population is projected to be about 335.8 million in 2020. At this rate, how many slices of pizza would be consumed in 2020? Express the answer in scientific notation. [10.2e]

Sources: Packaged Facts; U.S. Census Bureau

18. Evaluate the polynomial $x^2 - 3x + 6$ when $x = -1$. [10.3a]

19. Identify the terms of the polynomial $-4y^5 + 7y^2 - 3y - 2$. [10.3b]

20. Identify the missing terms in $x^3 + x$. [10.3h]

21. Identify the degree of each term and the degree of the polynomial $4x^3 + 6x^2 - 5x + \frac{5}{3}$. [10.3g]

Classify the polynomial as a monomial, a binomial, a trinomial, or none of these. [10.3i]

22. $4x^3 - 1$

23. $4 - 9t^3 - 7t^4 + 10t^2$

24. $7y^2$

Collect like terms and then arrange in descending order. [10.3f]

25. $3x^2 - 2x + 3 - 5x^2 - 1 - x$

26. $-x + \frac{1}{2} + 14x^4 - 7x^2 - 1 - 4x^4$

Add. [10.4a]

27. $(3x^4 - x^3 + x - 4) + (x^5 + 7x^3 - 3x^2 - 5) + (-5x^4 + 6x^2 - x)$

28. $(3x^5 - 4x^4 + x^3 - 3) + (3x^4 - 5x^3 + 3x^2) + (-5x^5 - 5x^2) + (-5x^4 + 2x^3 + 5)$

Subtract. [10.4c]

29. $(5x^2 - 4x + 1) - (3x^2 + 1)$

30. $(3x^5 - 4x^4 + 3x^2 + 3) - (2x^5 - 4x^4 + 3x^3 + 4x^2 - 5)$

31. Find a polynomial for the perimeter and for the area. [10.4d], [10.5b]

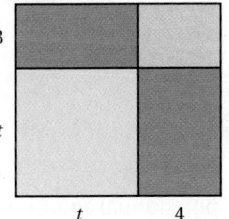

32. Find two algebraic expressions for the area of this figure. First, regard the figure as one large rectangle, and then regard the figure as a sum of four smaller rectangles. [10.4d]

Multiply.

33. $\left(x + \frac{2}{3}\right)\left(x + \frac{1}{2}\right)$ [10.6a]   **34.** $(7x + 1)^2$ [10.6c]

35. $(4x^2 - 5x + 1)(3x - 2)$ [10.5d]   **36.** $(3x^2 + 4)(3x^2 - 4)$ [10.6b]

37. $5x^4(3x^3 - 8x^2 + 10x + 2)$ [10.5b]

38. $(x + 4)(x - 7)$ [10.6a]

39. $(3y^2 - 2y)^2$ [10.6c]   **40.** $(2t^2 + 3)(t^2 - 7)$ [10.6a]

41. Evaluate the polynomial
$$2 - 5xy + y^2 - 4xy^3 + x^6$$
when $x = -1$ and $y = 2$. [10.7a]

42. Identify the coefficient and the degree of each term of the polynomial
$$x^5y - 7xy + 9x^2 - 8.$$
Then find the degree of the polynomial. [10.7b]

Collect like terms. [10.7c]

43. $y + w - 2y + 8w - 5$

44. $m^6 - 2m^2n + m^2n^2 + n^2m - 6m^3 + m^2n^2 + 7n^2m$

45. Add: [10.7d]
$$(5x^2 - 7xy + y^2) + (-6x^2 - 3xy - y^2) + (x^2 + xy - 2y^2).$$

46. Subtract: [10.7e]
$$(6x^3y^2 - 4x^2y - 6x) - (-5x^3y^2 + 4x^2y + 6x^2 - 6).$$

Multiply. [10.7f]

47. $(p - q)(p^2 + pq + q^2)$ **48.** $\left(3a^4 - \frac{1}{3}b^3\right)^2$

Divide.

49. $(10x^3 - x^2 + 6x) \div (2x)$ [10.8a]

50. $(6x^3 - 5x^2 - 13x + 13) \div (2x + 3)$ [10.8b]

51. The graph of the polynomial equation $y = 10x^3 - 10x$ is shown below. Use *only* the graph to estimate the value of the polynomial when $x = -1$, $x = -0.5$, $x = 0.5$, and $x = 1$.   [10.3a]

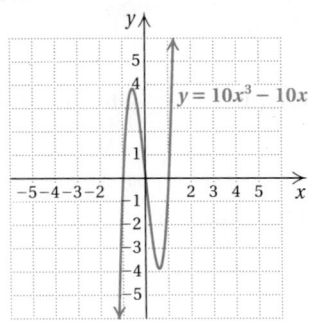

52. Subtract: $(2x^2 - 3x + 4) - (x^2 + 2x)$.   [10.4c]

   A. $x^2 - 3x - 2$ **B.** $x^2 - 5x + 4$
   C. $x^2 - x + 4$ **D.** $3x^2 - x + 4$

53. Multiply: $(x - 1)^2$.   [10.6c]

   A. $x^2 - 1$ **B.** $x^2 + 1$
   C. $x^2 - 2x - 1$ **D.** $x^2 - 2x + 1$

Synthesis

Find a polynomial for each shaded area.   [10.4d], [10.6b]

54.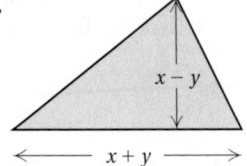

55.

56. Collect like terms: [10.1d], [10.2a], [10.3e]
$$-3x^5 \cdot 3x^3 - x^6(2x)^2 + (3x^4)^2 + (2x^2)^4 - 40x^2(x^3)^2.$$

57. Solve: [8.3b], [10.6a]
$$(x - 7)(x + 10) = (x - 4)(x - 6).$$

58. The product of two polynomials is $x^5 - 1$. One of the polynomials is $x - 1$. Find the other.   [10.8b]

59. A rectangular garden is twice as long as it is wide and is surrounded by a sidewalk that is 4 ft wide (see the figure below). The area of the sidewalk is 1024 ft^2. Find the dimensions of the garden.   [8.3b], [10.4d], [10.5a], [10.6a]

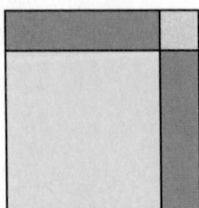

Understanding Through Discussion and Writing

1. Explain why the expression 578.6×10^{-7} is not in scientific notation.   [10.2c]

2. Explain why an understanding of the rules for order of operations is essential when evaluating polynomials.   [10.3a]

3. How can the following figure be used to show that $(x + 3)^2 \neq x^2 + 9$?   [10.5c]

4. On an assignment, Emma *incorrectly* writes
$$\frac{12x^3 - 6x}{3x} = 4x^2 - 6x.$$
What mistake do you think she is making and how might you convince her that a mistake has been made?   [10.8a]

5. Can the sum of two trinomials in several variables be a trinomial in one variable? Why or why not?   [10.7d]

6. Is it possible for a polynomial in four variables to have a degree less than 4? Why or why not?   [10.7b]

Copyright © 2012 Pearson Education, Inc.

Test

For Extra Help

CHAPTER
Test Prep
VIDEOS

Step-by-step test solutions are found on the Chapter Test Prep Videos available via the Video Resources on DVD, in *MyMathLab* , and on You Tube (search "BittingerDevMath" and click on "Channels").

Multiply and simplify.

1. $6^{-2} \cdot 6^{-3}$

2. $x^6 \cdot x^2 \cdot x$

3. $(4a)^3 \cdot (4a)^8$

Divide and simplify.

4. $\dfrac{3^5}{3^2}$

5. $\dfrac{x^3}{x^8}$

6. $\dfrac{(2x)^5}{(2x)^5}$

Simplify.

7. $(x^3)^2$

8. $(-3y^2)^3$

9. $(2a^3b)^4$

10. $\left(\dfrac{ab}{c}\right)^3$

11. $(3x^2)^3(-2x^5)^3$

12. $3(x^2)^3(-2x^5)^3$

13. $2x^2(-3x^2)^4$

14. $(2x)^2(-3x^2)^4$

15. Express using a positive exponent: 5^{-3}.

16. Express using a negative exponent: $\dfrac{1}{y^8}$.

17. Convert to scientific notation: 3,900,000,000.

18. Convert to decimal notation: 5×10^{-8}.

Multiply or divide and write scientific notation for the answer.

19. $\dfrac{5.6 \times 10^6}{3.2 \times 10^{-11}}$

20. $(2.4 \times 10^5)(5.4 \times 10^{16})$

21. *CD-ROM Memory.* A CD-ROM can contain about 600 million pieces of information (bytes). How many sound files, each containing 40,000 bytes, can a CD-ROM hold? Express the answer in scientific notation.

22. Evaluate the polynomial $x^5 + 5x - 1$ when $x = -2$.

23. Identify the coefficient of each term of the polynomial $\frac{1}{3}x^5 - x + 7$.

24. Identify the degree of each term and the degree of the polynomial $2x^3 - 4 + 5x + 3x^6$.

25. Classify the polynomial $7 - x$ as a monomial, a binomial, a trinomial, or none of these.

Collect like terms.

26. $4a^2 - 6 + a^2$

27. $y^2 - 3y - y + \dfrac{3}{4}y^2$

28. Collect like terms and then arrange in descending order:
$$3 - x^2 + 2x^3 + 5x^2 - 6x - 2x + x^5.$$

Add.

29. $(3x^5 + 5x^3 - 5x^2 - 3) +$
$(x^5 + x^4 - 3x^3 - 3x^2 + 2x - 4)$

30. $\left(x^4 + \dfrac{2}{3}x + 5\right) + \left(4x^4 + 5x^2 + \dfrac{1}{3}x\right)$

Subtract.

31. $(2x^4 + x^3 - 8x^2 - 6x - 3) - (6x^4 - 8x^2 + 2x)$

32. $(x^3 - 0.4x^2 - 12) - (x^5 + 0.3x^3 + 0.4x^2 + 9)$

Multiply.

33. $-3x^2(4x^2 - 3x - 5)$

34. $\left(x - \dfrac{1}{3}\right)^2$

35. $(3x + 10)(3x - 10)$

36. $(3b + 5)(b - 3)$

37. $(x^6 - 4)(x^8 + 4)$

38. $(8 - y)(6 + 5y)$

39. $(2x + 1)(3x^2 - 5x - 3)$

40. $(5t + 2)^2$

41. Collect like terms:
$$x^3y - y^3 + xy^3 + 8 - 6x^3y - x^2y^2 + 11.$$

42. Subtract:
$$(8a^2b^2 - ab + b^3) - (-6ab^2 - 7ab - ab^3 + 5b^3).$$

43. Multiply: $(3x^5 - 4y^5)(3x^5 + 4y^5)$.

Divide.

44. $(12x^4 + 9x^3 - 15x^2) \div (3x^2)$

45. $(6x^3 - 8x^2 - 14x + 13) \div (3x + 2)$

46. The graph of the polynomial equation $y = x^3 - 5x - 1$ is shown at right. Use *only* the graph to estimate the value of the polynomial when $x = -1$, $x = -0.5$, $x = 0.5$, $x = 1$, and $x = 1.1$.

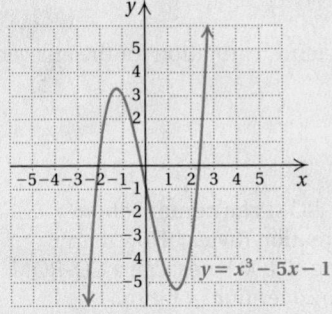

47. Find two algebraic expressions for the area of this figure. First, regard the figure as one large rectangle, and then regard the figure as a sum of four smaller rectangles.

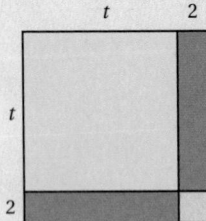

48. Find a polynomial for the surface area of this right rectangular solid.

A. $28a$

B. $28a + 90$

C. $14a + 45$

D. $45a$

Synthesis

49. The height of a box is 1 less than its length, and the length is 2 more than its width. Find the volume in terms of the length.

50. Solve: $(x - 5)(x + 5) = (x + 6)^2$.

Copyright © 2012 Pearson Education, Inc.

Polynomials: Factoring

Real-World Application

Dr. Benton wants to investigate the potential spread of germs by contact. She knows that the number of possible handshakes within a group of x people, assuming each person shakes every other person's hand only once, is given by $N = \frac{1}{2}(x^2 - x)$. There are 40 people at a meeting. How many handshakes are possible?

This problem appears as Exercise 14 in Section 11.8.

11.1

Introduction to Factoring

OBJECTIVES

a Find the greatest common factor, the GCF, of monomials.

b Factor polynomials when the terms have a common factor, factoring out the greatest common factor.

c Factor certain expressions with four terms using factoring by grouping.

SKILL TO REVIEW

Objectives 1.7a, d: Find all the factors of numbers and find prime factorizations of numbers.

Find the prime factorization of each number.

1. 60   2. 105

We introduce factoring with a review of factoring natural numbers. Consider the product $15 = 3 \cdot 5$. We say that 3 and 5 are **factors** of 15 and that $3 \cdot 5$ is a **factorization** of 15. Since $15 = 15 \cdot 1$, we also know that 15 and 1 are factors of 15 and that $15 \cdot 1$ is a factorization of 15.

a Finding the Greatest Common Factor

The numbers 20 and 30 have several factors in common, among them 2 and 5. The greatest of the common factors is called the **greatest common factor**, **GCF**. One way to find the GCF is by making a list of factors of each number.

List all the factors of 20:   <u>1</u>, <u>2</u>, 4, <u>5</u>, <u>10</u>, and 20.

List all the factors of 30:   <u>1</u>, <u>2</u>, 3, <u>5</u>, 6, <u>10</u>, 15, and 30.

We now list the numbers common to both lists, the common factors:

1, 2, 5, and 10.

The greatest common factor, the GCF, is 10, the largest number in the common list.

The preceding procedure gives meaning to the notion of a GCF, but the following method, using prime factorizations, is generally faster.

EXAMPLE 1 Find the GCF of 20 and 30.

We find the prime factorization of each number. Then we draw lines between the common factors.

$$20 = 2 \cdot 2 \cdot 5$$
$$30 = 2 \cdot 3 \cdot 5$$

The GCF $= 2 \cdot 5 = 10$.

EXAMPLE 2 Find the GCF of 180 and 420.

We find the prime factorization of each number. Then we draw lines between the common factors.

$$180 = 2 \cdot 2 \cdot 3 \cdot 3 \cdot 5 = 2^2 \cdot 3^2 \cdot 5^1$$
$$420 = 2 \cdot 2 \cdot 3 \cdot 5 \cdot 7 = 2^2 \cdot 3^1 \cdot 5^1 \cdot 7^1$$

The GCF $= 2 \cdot 2 \cdot 3 \cdot 5 = 2^2 \cdot 3^1 \cdot 5^1 = 60$. Note how we can use the exponents to determine the GCF. There are 2 lines for the 2's, 1 line for the 3, 1 line for the 5, and no line for the 7.

EXAMPLE 3 Find the GCF of 30 and 77.

We find the prime factorization of each number. Then we draw lines between the common factors, if any exist.

$$30 = 2 \cdot 3 \cdot 5 = 2^1 \cdot 3^1 \cdot 5^1$$

$$77 = 7 \cdot 11 = 7^1 \cdot 11^1$$

Since there is no common prime factor, the GCF is 1.

Answers

Skill to Review:
1. $2 \cdot 2 \cdot 3 \cdot 5$ 2. $3 \cdot 5 \cdot 7$

EXAMPLE 4 Find the GCF of 54, 90, and 252.

We find the prime factorization of each number. Then we draw lines between the common factors.

$$54 = 2 \cdot 3 \cdot 3 \cdot 3 = 2^1 \cdot 3^3,$$

$$90 = 2 \cdot 3 \cdot 3 \cdot 5 = 2^1 \cdot 3^2 \cdot 5^1,$$

$$252 = 2 \cdot 2 \cdot 3 \cdot 3 \cdot 7 = 2^2 \cdot 3^2 \cdot 7^1$$

The GCF $= 2^1 \cdot 3^2 = 18$.

Do Exercises 1–4.

Find the GCF.

1. 40, 100

2. 7, 21

3. 72, 360, 432

4. 3, 5, 22

Consider the product

$$12x^3(x^2 - 6x + 2) = 12x^5 - 72x^4 + 24x^3.$$

To factor the polynomial on the right, we reverse the process of multiplication:

$$12x^5 - 72x^4 + 24x^3 = \underbrace{12x^3(x^2 - 6x + 2)}.$$

This is a *factorization*. The *factors* are $(12x^3)$ and $(x^2 - 6x + 2)$.

FACTOR; FACTORIZATION

To **factor** a polynomial is to express it as a product.

A **factor** of a polynomial P is a polynomial that can be used to express P as a product.

A **factorization** of a polynomial is an expression that names that polynomial as a product.

In the factorization

$$12x^5 - 72x^4 + 24x^3 = 12x^3(x^2 - 6x + 2),$$

the monomial $12x^3$ is called the GCF of the terms, $12x^5$, $-72x^4$, and $24x^3$. The first step in factoring polynomials is to find the GCF of the terms.

Consider the monomials

$$x^3, \ x^4, \ x^6, \ \text{and} \ x^7.$$

The GCF of these monomials is x^3, found by noting that the smallest exponent of x is 3.

Consider

$$20x^2 \ \text{and} \ 30x^5.$$

The GCF of 20 and 30 is 10. The GCF of x^2 and x^5 is x^2. Then the GCF of $20x^2$ and $30x^5$ is the product of the individual GCFs, $10x^2$.

Answers

1. 20   **2.** 7   **3.** 72   **4.** 1

EXAMPLE 5 Find the GCF of $15x^5$, $-12x^4$, $27x^3$, and $-3x^2$.

First, we find a prime factorization of the coefficients, including a factor of -1 for the negative coefficients.

$$15x^5 = \qquad 3 \cdot 5 \cdot x^5,$$

$$-12x^4 = -1 \cdot 2 \cdot 2 \cdot 3 \cdot x^4,$$

$$27x^3 = \qquad 3 \cdot 3 \cdot 3 \cdot x^3,$$

$$-3x^2 = \qquad -1 \cdot 3 \cdot x^2$$

The greatest *positive* common factor of the coefficients is 3.

Next, we find the GCF of the powers of x. That GCF is x^2, because 2 is the smallest exponent of x. Thus the GCF of the set of monomials is $3x^2$.

What about the factors of -1 in Example 5? Strictly speaking, both 1 and -1 are factors of any number or expression. We see this as follows:

$$3x^2 = 1 \cdot 3x^2 = (-1)(-3x^2).$$

Because the coefficient -3 is less than the coefficient 3, we consider $3x^2$, and not $-3x^2$, the GCF.

EXAMPLE 6 Find the GCF of $14p^2y^3$, $-8py^2$, $2py$, and $4p^3$.

We have

$$14p^2y^3 = 2 \cdot 7 \cdot p^2 \cdot y^3,$$

$$-8py^2 = -1 \cdot 2 \cdot 2 \cdot 2 \cdot p \cdot y^2,$$

$$2py = 2 \cdot p \cdot y,$$

$$4p^3 = 2 \cdot 2 \cdot p^3.$$

The greatest positive common factor of the coefficients is 2, the GCF of the powers of p is p, and the GCF of the powers of y is 1 since there is no y-factor in the last monomial. Thus the GCF is $2p$.

> **TO FIND THE GCF OF TWO OR MORE MONOMIALS**
>
> 1. Find the prime factorization of the coefficients, including -1 as a factor if any coefficient is negative.
>
> 2. Determine any common prime factors of the coefficients. For each one that occurs, include it as a factor of the GCF. If none occurs, use 1 as a factor.
>
> 3. Examine each of the variables as factors. If any appear as a factor of all the monomials, include it as a factor, using the smallest exponent of the variable. If none occurs in all the monomials, use 1 as a factor.
>
> 4. The GCF is the product of the results of steps (2) and (3).

Find the GCF.

5. $12x^2$, $-16x^3$

6. $3y^6$, $-5y^3$, $2y^2$

7. $-24m^5n^6$, $12mn^3$, $-16m^2n^2$, $8m^4n^4$

8. $-35x^7$, $-49x^6$, $-14x^5$, $-63x^3$

Do Exercises 5–8.

Answers

5. $4x^2$　**6.** y^2　**7.** $4mn^2$　**8.** $7x^3$

(b) Factoring When Terms Have a Common Factor

The polynomials we consider most when factoring are those with more than one term. To multiply a monomial and a polynomial with more than one term, we multiply each term of the polynomial by the monomial using the distributive laws:

$$a(b + c) = ab + ac \quad \text{and} \quad a(b - c) = ab - ac.$$

To factor, we do the reverse. We express a polynomial as a product using the distributive laws in reverse:

$$ab + ac = a(b + c) \quad \text{and} \quad ab - ac = a(b - c).$$

Compare.

Multiply

$$3x(x^2 + 2x - 4)$$
$$= 3x \cdot x^2 + 3x \cdot 2x - 3x \cdot 4$$
$$= 3x^3 + 6x^2 - 12x$$

Factor

$$3x^3 + 6x^2 - 12x$$
$$= 3x \cdot x^2 + 3x \cdot 2x - 3x \cdot 4$$
$$= 3x(x^2 + 2x - 4)$$

---------------------- *Caution!* ----------------------

Consider the following:

$$3x^3 + 6x^2 - 12x = 3 \cdot x \cdot x \cdot x + 2 \cdot 3 \cdot x \cdot x - 2 \cdot 2 \cdot 3 \cdot x.$$

The terms of the polynomial, $3x^3$, $6x^2$, and $-12x$, have been factored but the polynomial itself has not been factored. This is not what we mean by a factorization of the polynomial. The *factorization* is

$$3x(x^2 + 2x - 4). \leftarrow \text{A product}$$

The expressions $3x$ and $x^2 + 2x - 4$ are *factors* of $3x^3 + 6x^2 - 12x$.

> Do Exercises 9 and 10.

9. a) Multiply: $3(x + 2)$.

b) Factor: $3x + 6$.

10. a) Multiply: $2x(x^2 + 5x + 4)$.

b) Factor: $2x^3 + 10x^2 + 8x$.

To factor, we first find the GCF of all terms. It may be 1.

EXAMPLE 7 Factor: $7x^2 + 14$.

We have

$$7x^2 + 14 = 7 \cdot x^2 + 7 \cdot 2 \qquad \text{Factoring each term}$$
$$= 7(x^2 + 2). \qquad \text{Factoring out the GCF, 7}$$

Check: We multiply to check:

$$7(x^2 + 2) = 7 \cdot x^2 + 7 \cdot 2 = 7x^2 + 14.$$

Answers

9. (a) $3x + 6$; (b) $3(x + 2)$
10. (a) $2x^3 + 10x^2 + 8x$; (b) $2x(x^2 + 5x + 4)$

EXAMPLE 8 Factor: $16x^3 + 20x^2$.

$$16x^3 + 20x^2 = (4x^2)(4x) + (4x^2)(5) \qquad \text{Factoring each term}$$
$$= 4x^2(4x + 5) \qquad \text{Factoring out the GCF, } 4x^2$$

Although it is always more efficient to begin by finding the GCF, suppose in Example 8 that you had not recognized the GCF and removed only part of it, as follows:

$$16x^3 + 20x^2 = (2x^2)(8x) + (2x^2)(10)$$
$$= 2x^2(8x + 10).$$

Note that $8x + 10$ still has a common factor of 2. You need not begin again. Just continue factoring out common factors, as follows, until finished:

$$= 2x^2(2 \cdot 4x + 2 \cdot 5)$$
$$= 2x^2[2(4x + 5)]$$
$$= (2x^2 \cdot 2)(4x + 5)$$
$$= 4x^2(4x + 5).$$

EXAMPLE 9 Factor: $15x^5 - 12x^4 + 27x^3 - 3x^2$.

$$15x^5 - 12x^4 + 27x^3 - 3x^2 = (3x^2)(5x^3) - (3x^2)(4x^2) + (3x^2)(9x) - (3x^2)(1)$$
$$= 3x^2(5x^3 - 4x^2 + 9x - 1) \qquad \text{Factoring out the GCF, } 3x^2$$

-------------- *Caution!* --------------

Don't forget the term -1.

Check: We multiply to check:

$$3x^2(5x^3 - 4x^2 + 9x - 1)$$
$$= (3x^2)(5x^3) - (3x^2)(4x^2) + (3x^2)(9x) - (3x^2)(1)$$
$$= 15x^5 - 12x^4 + 27x^3 - 3x^2.$$

As you become more familiar with factoring, you will be able to spot the GCF without factoring each term. Then you can write just the answer.

EXAMPLES Factor.

10. $24x^2 + 12x - 36 = 12(2x^2 + x - 3)$

11. $8m^3 - 16m = 8m(m^2 - 2)$

12. $14p^2y^3 - 8py^2 + 2py = 2py(7py^2 - 4y + 1)$

13. $\dfrac{4}{5}x^2 + \dfrac{1}{5}x + \dfrac{2}{5} = \dfrac{1}{5}(4x^2 + x + 2)$

Do Exercises 11–16.

Factor. Check by multiplying.

11. $x^2 + 3x$

12. $3y^6 - 5y^3 + 2y^2$

13. $9x^4y^2 - 15x^3y + 3x^2y$

14. $\dfrac{3}{4}t^3 + \dfrac{5}{4}t^2 + \dfrac{7}{4}t + \dfrac{1}{4}$

15. $35x^7 - 49x^6 + 14x^5 - 63x^3$

16. $84x^2 - 56x + 28$

Answers

11. $x(x + 3)$ **12.** $y^2(3y^4 - 5y + 2)$

13. $3x^2y(3x^2y - 5x + 1)$

14. $\dfrac{1}{4}(3t^3 + 5t^2 + 7t + 1)$

15. $7x^3(5x^4 - 7x^3 + 2x^2 - 9)$

16. $28(3x^2 - 2x + 1)$

There are two important points to keep in mind as we study this chapter.

> **TIPS FOR FACTORING**
> - Before doing any other kind of factoring, first try to factor out the GCF.
> - Always check the result of factoring by multiplying.

(c) Factoring by Grouping: Four Terms

Certain polynomials with four terms can be factored using a method called *factoring by grouping*.

EXAMPLE 14 Factor: $x^2(x + 1) + 2(x + 1)$.

The binomial $x + 1$ is a common factor. We factor it out:

$$x^2(x + 1) + 2(x + 1) = (x + 1)(x^2 + 2).$$

The factorization is $(x + 1)(x^2 + 2)$.

Do Exercises 17 and 18.

Consider the four-term polynomial

$$x^3 + x^2 + 2x + 2.$$

There is no factor other than 1 that is common to all the terms. We can, however, factor $x^3 + x^2$ and $2x + 2$ separately:

$$x^3 + x^2 = x^2(x + 1); \qquad \text{Factoring } x^3 + x^2$$
$$2x + 2 = 2(x + 1). \qquad \text{Factoring } 2x + 2$$

When we group the terms as shown above and factor each polynomial separately, we see that $(x + 1)$ appears in *both* factorizations. Thus we can factor out the common binomial factor as in Example 14:

$$x^3 + x^2 + 2x + 2 = (x^3 + x^2) + (2x + 2)$$
$$= x^2(x + 1) + 2(x + 1)$$
$$= (x + 1)(x^2 + 2).$$

This method of factoring is called **factoring by grouping**. We began with a polynomial with four terms. After grouping and removing common factors, we obtained a polynomial with two parts, each having the common factor $x + 1$, which we then factored out. Not all polynomials with four terms can be factored by this procedure, but it does give us a method to try.

Factor.

17. $x^2(x + 7) + 3(x + 7)$

18. $x^3(a + b) - 5(a + b)$

> ### STUDY TIPS
>
> #### CHECKLIST
>
> The foundation of all your study skills is TIME!
>
> - Are you staying on schedule, getting to class on time, and adapting your study time to your schedule?
> - Do you study the examples in the text carefully?
> - Are you asking questions at appropriate times in class and with your tutors?

Answers

17. $(x + 7)(x^2 + 3)$ **18.** $(a + b)(x^3 - 5)$

11.1 Introduction to Factoring **827**

EXAMPLES Factor by grouping.

15. $6x^3 - 9x^2 + 4x - 6$

$\quad = (6x^3 - 9x^2) + (4x - 6) \qquad$ Grouping the terms

$\quad = 3x^2(2x - 3) + 2(2x - 3) \qquad$ Factoring each binomial

$\quad = (2x - 3)(3x^2 + 2) \qquad$ Factoring out the common factor $2x - 3$

We think through this process as follows:

$$6x^3 - 9x^2 + 4x - 6 = \underline{3x^2(2x - 3)}\ \boxed{}\ (2x - 3)$$

(1) Factor the first two terms.

(2) The factor $2x - 3$ gives us a hint to the factorization of the last two terms.

(3) Now we ask ourselves, "What times $2x - 3$ is $4x - 6$?" The answer is $+ 2$.

---- *Caution!* ----

16. $x^3 + x^2 + x + 1 = (x^3 + x^2) + (x + 1) \qquad$ Don't forget the 1.

$\quad\quad\quad\quad\quad = x^2(x + 1) + 1(x + 1) \qquad$ Factoring each binomial

$\quad\quad\quad\quad\quad = (x + 1)(x^2 + 1) \qquad$ Factoring out the common factor $x + 1$

17. $2x^3 - 6x^2 - x + 3$

$\quad = (2x^3 - 6x^2) + (-x + 3) \qquad$ Grouping as two binomials

$\quad = 2x^2(x - 3) - 1(x - 3) \qquad$ *Check*: $-1(x - 3) = -x + 3$.

$\quad = (x - 3)(2x^2 - 1) \qquad$ Factoring out the common factor $x - 3$

We can think through this process as follows.

(1) Factor the first two terms: $2x^3 - 6x^2 = 2x^2(x - 3)$.

(2) The factor $x - 3$ gives us a hint for factoring the last two terms:

$$2x^3 - 6x^2 - x + 3 = 2x^2(x - 3)\ \boxed{}\ (x - 3).$$

(3) Now we ask ourselves, "What times $x - 3$ is $-x + 3$?" The answer is -1.

18. $12x^5 + 20x^2 - 21x^3 - 35 = 4x^2(3x^3 + 5) - 7(3x^3 + 5)$

$\quad\quad\quad\quad\quad\quad\quad\quad\quad = (3x^3 + 5)(4x^2 - 7)$

19. $x^3 + x^2 + 2x - 2 = x^2(x + 1) + 2(x - 1)$

This polynomial is not factorable using factoring by grouping. It may be factorable, but not by methods that we will consider in this text.

Do Exercises 19–24.

Factor by grouping.

19. $x^3 + 7x^2 + 3x + 21$

20. $8t^3 + 2t^2 + 12t + 3$

21. $3m^5 - 15m^3 + 2m^2 - 10$

22. $3x^3 - 6x^2 - x + 2$

23. $4x^3 - 6x^2 - 6x + 9$

24. $y^4 - 2y^3 - 2y - 10$

Answers

19. $(x + 7)(x^2 + 3)$ **20.** $(4t + 1)(2t^2 + 3)$
21. $(m^2 - 5)(3m^3 + 2)$
22. $(x - 2)(3x^2 - 1)$ **23.** $(2x - 3)(2x^2 - 3)$
24. Not factorable using factoring by grouping

a Find the GCF.

1. x^2, $-6x$

2. x^2, $5x$

3. $3x^4$, x^2

4. $8x^4$, $-24x^2$

5. $2x^2$, $2x$, -8

6. $8x^2$, $-4x$, -20

7. $-17x^5y^3$, $34x^3y^2$, $51xy$

8. $16p^6q^4$, $32p^3q^3$, $-48pq^2$

9. $-x^2$, $-5x$, $-20x^3$

10. $-x^2$, $-6x$, $-24x^5$

11. x^5y^5, x^4y^3, x^3y^3, $-x^2y^2$

12. $-x^9y^6$, $-x^7y^5$, x^4y^4, x^3y^3

b Factor. Check by multiplying.

13. $x^2 - 6x$

14. $x^2 + 5x$

15. $2x^2 + 6x$

16. $8y^2 - 8y$

17. $x^3 + 6x^2$

18. $3x^4 - x^2$

19. $8x^4 - 24x^2$

20. $5x^5 + 10x^3$

21. $2x^2 + 2x - 8$

22. $8x^2 - 4x - 20$

23. $17x^5y^3 + 34x^3y^2 + 51xy$

24. $16p^6q^4 + 32p^5q^3 - 48pq^2$

25. $6x^4 - 10x^3 + 3x^2$

26. $5x^5 + 10x^2 - 8x$

27. $x^5y^5 + x^4y^3 + x^3y^3 - x^2y^2$

28. $x^9y^6 - x^7y^5 + x^4y^4 + x^3y^3$

29. $2x^7 - 2x^6 - 64x^5 + 4x^3$

30. $8y^3 - 20y^2 + 12y - 16$

31. $1.6x^4 - 2.4x^3 + 3.2x^2 + 6.4x$

32. $2.5x^6 - 0.5x^4 + 5x^3 + 10x^2$

33. $\dfrac{5}{3}x^6 + \dfrac{4}{3}x^5 + \dfrac{1}{3}x^4 + \dfrac{1}{3}x^3$

34. $\dfrac{5}{9}x^7 + \dfrac{2}{9}x^5 - \dfrac{4}{9}x^3 - \dfrac{1}{9}x$

c Factor.

35. $x^2(x + 3) + 2(x + 3)$

36. $y^2(y + 4) + 6(y + 4)$

37. $4z^2(3z - 1) + 7(3z - 1)$

38. $2x^2(4x - 3) + 5(4x - 3)$

39. $2x^2(3x + 2) + (3x + 2)$ **40.** $3z^2(2z + 7) + (2z + 7)$

41. $5a^3(2a - 7) - (2a - 7)$ **42.** $m^4(8 - 3m) - 3(8 - 3m)$

Factor by grouping.

43. $x^3 + 3x^2 + 2x + 6$ **44.** $6z^3 + 3z^2 + 2z + 1$ **45.** $2x^3 + 6x^2 + x + 3$

46. $3x^3 + 2x^2 + 3x + 2$ **47.** $8x^3 - 12x^2 + 6x - 9$ **48.** $10x^3 - 25x^2 + 4x - 10$

49. $12p^3 - 16p^2 + 3p - 4$ **50.** $18x^3 - 21x^2 + 30x - 35$ **51.** $5x^3 - 5x^2 - x + 1$

52. $7x^3 - 14x^2 - x + 2$ **53.** $x^3 + 8x^2 - 3x - 24$ **54.** $2x^3 + 12x^2 - 5x - 30$

55. $2x^3 - 8x^2 - 9x + 36$ **56.** $20g^3 - 4g^2 - 25g + 5$

Skill Maintenance

Solve.

57. $-2x < 48$ [8.7d]   **58.** $4x - 8x + 16 \geq 6(x - 2)$ [8.7e]

59. Divide: $\dfrac{-108}{-4}$.   [7.6a]   **60.** Solve $A = \dfrac{p + q}{2}$ for p.   [8.4b]

Multiply.   [10.6d]

61. $(y + 5)(y + 7)$ **62.** $(y + 7)^2$ **63.** $(y + 7)(y - 7)$ **64.** $(y - 7)^2$

Find the intercepts of each equation. Then graph the equation.   [9.2a]

65. $x + y = 4$ **66.** $x - y = 3$ **67.** $5x - 3y = 15$ **68.** $y - 3x = 6$

Synthesis

Factor.

69. $4x^5 + 6x^3 + 6x^2 + 9$ **70.** $x^6 + x^4 + x^2 + 1$ **71.** $x^{12} + x^7 + x^5 + 1$

72. $x^3 - x^2 - 2x + 5$ **73.** $p^3 + p^2 - 3p + 10$

Copyright © 2012 Pearson Education, Inc.

11.2

Factoring Trinomials of the Type $x^2 + bx + c$

(a) Factoring $x^2 + bx + c$

We now begin a study of the factoring of trinomials. We first factor trinomials like

$$x^2 + 5x + 6 \quad \text{and} \quad x^2 + 3x - 10$$

by a refined *trial-and-error process*. In this section, we restrict our attention to trinomials of the type $ax^2 + bx + c$, where $a = 1$. The coefficient a is called the **leading coefficient**.

To understand the factoring that follows, compare the following multiplications:

$$
\begin{array}{cccc}
\text{F} & \text{O} & \text{I} & \text{L} \\
\downarrow & \downarrow & \downarrow & \downarrow
\end{array}
$$

$$(x + 2)(x + 5) = x^2 + 5x + 2x + 2 \cdot 5$$
$$= x^2 + 7x + 10;$$

$$(x - 2)(x - 5) = x^2 - 5x - 2x + (-2)(-5)$$
$$= x^2 - 7x + 10;$$

$$(x + 3)(x - 7) = x^2 - 7x + 3x + 3(-7)$$
$$= x^2 - 4x - 21;$$

$$(x - 3)(x + 7) = x^2 + 7x - 3x + (-3)7$$
$$= x^2 + 4x - 21.$$

Note that for all four products:

- The product of the two binomials is a trinomial.
- The coefficient of x in the trinomial is the sum of the constant terms in the binomials.
- The constant term in the trinomial is the product of the constant terms in the binomials.

These observations lead to a method for factoring certain trinomials. The first type we consider has a positive constant term, just as in the first two multiplications above.

Constant Term Positive

To factor $x^2 + 7x + 10$, we think of FOIL in reverse. We multiplied x times x to get the first term of the trinomial, so we know that the first term of each binomial factor is x. Next, we look for numbers p and q such that

$$x^2 + 7x + 10 = (x + p)(x + q).$$

To get the middle term and the last term of the trinomial, we look for two numbers p and q whose product is 10 and whose sum is 7. Those numbers are 2 and 5. Thus the factorization is

$$(x + 2)(x + 5).$$

Check: $(x + 2)(x + 5) = x^2 + 5x + 2x + 10$
$$= x^2 + 7x + 10.$$

OBJECTIVE

 Factor trinomials of the type $x^2 + bx + c$ by examining the constant term c.

SKILL TO REVIEW
Objective 10.6a: Multiply two binomials mentally using the FOIL method.

Multiply.
1. $(x + 3)(x + 4)$
2. $(x - 1)(x + 2)$

Answers

Skill to Review:
1. $x^2 + 7x + 12$ 2. $x^2 + x - 2$

1. Consider the trinomial $x^2 + 7x + 12$.

a) Complete the following table.

PAIRS OF FACTORS	SUMS OF FACTORS
1, 12	13
−1, −12	
2, 6	
−2, −6	
3, 4	
−3, −4	

b) Explain why you need to consider only the positive factors in the table above.

c) Factor: $x^2 + 7x + 12$.

2. Factor: $x^2 + 13x + 36$.

3. Explain why you would *not* consider the pairs of factors listed below in factoring $y^2 - 8y + 12$.

PAIRS OF FACTORS	SUMS OF FACTORS
1, 12	
2, 6	
3, 4	

Factor.

4. $x^2 - 8x + 15$

5. $t^2 - 9t + 20$

Answers

1. (a) −13, 8, −8, 7, −7; **(b)** Both 7 and 12 are positive. **(c)** $(x + 3)(x + 4)$
2. $(x + 4)(x + 9)$ **3.** The coefficient of the middle term, −8, is negative.
4. $(x - 5)(x - 3)$
5. $(t - 5)(t - 4)$

EXAMPLE 1 Factor: $x^2 + 5x + 6$.

Think of FOIL in reverse. The first term of each factor is x: $(x + \boxed{})(x + \boxed{})$. Next, we look for two numbers whose product is 6 and whose sum is 5. All the pairs of factors of 6 are shown in the table on the left below. Since both the product, 6, and the sum, 5, of the pair of numbers must be positive, we need consider only the positive factors, listed in the table on the right.

PAIRS OF FACTORS	SUMS OF FACTORS
1, 6	7
−1, −6	−7
2, 3	5
−2, −3	−5

PAIRS OF FACTORS	SUMS OF FACTORS
1, 6	7
2, 3	5

↑
The numbers we need
are 2 and 3.

The factorization is $(x + 2)(x + 3)$. We can check by multiplying to see whether we get the original trinomial.

Check: $(x + 2)(x + 3) = x^2 + 3x + 2x + 6 = x^2 + 5x + 6$.

Do Exercises 1 and 2.

Compare these multiplications:

$$(x - 2)(x - 5) = x^2 - 5x - 2x + 10 = x^2 - 7x + 10;$$
$$(x + 2)(x + 5) = x^2 + 5x + 2x + 10 = x^2 + 7x + 10.$$

TO FACTOR $x^2 + bx + c$ WHEN c IS POSITIVE

When the constant term of a trinomial is positive, look for two numbers with the same sign. The sign is that of the middle term:

$$x^2 - 7x + 10 = (x - 2)(x - 5);$$

$$x^2 + 7x + 10 = (x + 2)(x + 5).$$

EXAMPLE 2 Factor: $y^2 - 8y + 12$.

Since the constant term, 12, is positive and the coefficient of the middle term, −8, is negative, we look for a factorization of 12 in which both factors are negative. Their sum must be −8.

PAIRS OF FACTORS	SUMS OF FACTORS
−1, −12	−13
−2, −6	−8 ←
−3, −4	−7

The numbers we need
are −2 and −6.

The factorization is $(y - 2)(y - 6)$. The student should check by multiplying.

Do Exercises 3–5.

Constant Term Negative

As we saw in two of the multiplications earlier in this section, the product of two binomials can have a negative constant term:

$$(x + 3)(x - 7) = x^2 - 4x - 21$$

and

$$(x - 3)(x + 7) = x^2 + 4x - 21.$$

Note that when the signs of the constants in the binomials are reversed, only the sign of the middle term in the product changes.

EXAMPLE 3 Factor: $x^2 - 8x - 20$.

The constant term, -20, must be expressed as the product of a negative number and a positive number. Since the sum of these two numbers must be negative (specifically, -8), the negative number must have the greater absolute value.

PAIRS OF FACTORS	SUMS OF FACTORS
1, −20	−19
2, −10	−8 ←
4, −5	−1
5, −4	1
10, −2	8
20, −1	19

The numbers we need are 2 and −10.

Because these sums are all positive, for this problem all the corresponding pairs can be disregarded. Note that in all three pairs, the positive number has the greater absolute value.

The numbers that we are looking for are 2 and -10. The factorization is $(x + 2)(x - 10)$.

Check: $(x + 2)(x - 10) = x^2 - 10x + 2x - 20$
$$= x^2 - 8x - 20.$$

TO FACTOR $x^2 + bx + c$ WHEN c IS NEGATIVE

When the constant term of a trinomial is negative, look for two numbers whose product is negative. One must be positive and the other negative:

$$x^2 - 4x - 21 = (x + 3)(x - 7);$$

$$x^2 + 4x - 21 = (x - 3)(x + 7).$$

Consider pairs of numbers for which the number with the larger absolute value has the same sign as b, the coefficient of the middle term.

Do Exercises 6 and 7. (Exercise 7 is on the following page.)

6. Consider $x^2 - 5x - 24$.

a) Explain why you would *not* consider the pairs of factors listed below in factoring $x^2 - 5x - 24$.

PAIRS OF FACTORS	SUMS OF FACTORS
−1, 24	
−2, 12	
−3, 8	
−4, 6	

b) Explain why you *would* consider the pairs of factors listed below in factoring $x^2 - 5x - 24$.

PAIRS OF FACTORS	SUMS OF FACTORS
1, −24	
2, −12	
3, −8	
4, −6	

c) Factor: $x^2 - 5x - 24$.

Answers

6. (a) The positive factor has the larger absolute value. (b) The negative factor has the larger absolute value. (c) $(x + 3)(x - 8)$

7. Consider $x^2 + 10x - 24$.

a) Explain why you would *not* consider the pairs of factors listed below in factoring $x^2 + 10x - 24$.

PAIRS OF FACTORS	SUMS OF FACTORS
1, −24	
2, −12	
3, −8	
4, −6	

b) Explain why you *would* consider the pairs of factors listed below in factoring $x^2 + 10x - 24$.

PAIRS OF FACTORS	SUMS OF FACTORS
−1, 24	
−2, 12	
−3, 8	
−4, 6	

c) Factor: $x^2 + 10x - 24$.

Factor.

8. $a^2 - 40 + 3a$

9. $-18 - 3t + t^2$

EXAMPLE 4 Factor: $t^2 - 24 + 5t$.

It helps to first write the trinomial in descending order: $t^2 + 5t - 24$. Since the constant term, -24, is negative, we look for a factorization of -24 in which one factor is positive and one factor is negative. Their sum must be 5, so we consider only pairs of factors in which the positive factor has the larger absolute value.

PAIRS OF FACTORS	SUMS OF FACTORS	
−1, 24	23	
−2, 12	10	
−3, 8	5	← The numbers we need are −3 and 8.
−4, 6	2	

The factorization is $(t - 3)(t + 8)$. The check is left to the student.

> Do Exercises 8 and 9.

EXAMPLE 5 Factor: $x^4 - x^2 - 110$.

Consider this trinomial as $(x^2)^2 - x^2 - 110$. We look for numbers p and q such that

$$x^4 - x^2 - 110 = (x^2 + p)(x^2 + q).$$

Since the constant term, -110, is negative, we look for a factorization of -110 in which one factor is positive and one factor is negative. Their sum must be -1. The middle-term coefficient, -1, is small compared to -110. This tells us that the desired factors are close to each other in absolute value. The numbers we want are 10 and -11. The factorization is

$$(x^2 + 10)(x^2 - 11).$$

EXAMPLE 6 Factor: $a^2 + 4ab - 21b^2$.

We consider the trinomial in the equivalent form

$$a^2 + 4ba - 21b^2.$$

This way we think of $-21b^2$ as the "constant" term and $4b$ as the "coefficient" of the middle term. Then we try to express $-21b^2$ as a product of two factors whose sum is $4b$. Those factors are $-3b$ and $7b$. The factorization is $(a - 3b)(a + 7b)$.

Check: $(a - 3b)(a + 7b) = a^2 + 7ab - 3ba - 21b^2$
$$= a^2 + 4ab - 21b^2.$$

There are polynomials that are not factorable.

EXAMPLE 7 Factor: $x^2 - x + 5$.

Since 5 has very few factors, we can easily check all possibilities.

PAIRS OF FACTORS	SUMS OF FACTORS
5, 1	6
−5, −1	−6

Answers

7. **(a)** The negative factor has the larger absolute value. **(b)** The positive factor has the larger absolute value. **(c)** $(x - 2)(x + 12)$
8. $(a - 5)(a + 8)$ **9.** $(t - 6)(t + 3)$

There are no factors whose sum is -1. Thus the polynomial is *not* factorable into factors that are polynomials with rational-number coefficients.

In this text, a polynomial like $x^2 - x + 5$ that cannot be factored further is said to be **prime**. In more advanced courses, polynomials like $x^2 - x + 5$ can be factored and are not considered prime.

Do Exercises 10-12.

Often factoring requires two or more steps. In general, when told to factor, we should *factor completely*. This means that the final factorization should not contain any factors that can be factored further.

EXAMPLE 8 Factor: $2x^3 - 20x^2 + 50x$.

Always look first for a common factor. This time there is one, $2x$, which we factor out first:

$$2x^3 - 20x^2 + 50x = 2x(x^2 - 10x + 25).$$

Now consider $x^2 - 10x + 25$. Since the constant term is positive and the coefficient of the middle term is negative, we look for a factorization of 25 in which both factors are negative. Their sum must be -10.

PAIRS OF FACTORS	SUMS OF FACTORS
$-25, -1$	-26
$-5, -5$	-10

The numbers we need are -5 and -5.

The factorization of $x^2 - 10x + 25$ is $(x - 5)(x - 5)$, or $(x - 5)^2$. The final factorization is $2x(x - 5)^2$. We check by multiplying:

$$\begin{aligned} 2x(x - 5)^2 &= 2x(x^2 - 10x + 25) \\ &= (2x)(x^2) - (2x)(10x) + (2x)(25) \\ &= 2x^3 - 20x^2 + 50x. \end{aligned}$$

Do Exercises 13-15.

Once any common factors have been factored out, the following summary can be used to factor $x^2 + bx + c$.

> **TO FACTOR $x^2 + bx + c$**
>
> 1. First arrange in descending order.
> 2. Use a trial-and-error process that looks for factors of c whose sum is b.
> 3. If c is positive, the signs of the factors are the same as the sign of b.
> 4. If c is negative, one factor is positive and the other is negative. If the sum of two factors is the opposite of b, changing the sign of each factor will give the desired factors whose sum is b.
> 5. Check by multiplying.

Factor.

10. $y^2 - 12 - 4y$

11. $t^4 + 5t^2 - 14$

12. $x^2 + 2x + 7$

Factor.

13. $x^3 + 4x^2 - 12x$

14. $p^2 - pq - 3pq^2$

15. $3x^3 + 24x^2 + 48x$

Answers

10. $(y - 6)(y + 2)$ **11.** $(t^2 + 7)(t^2 - 2)$
12. Prime   **13.** $x(x + 6)(x - 2)$
14. $p(p - q - 3q^2)$ **15.** $3x(x + 4)^2$

Leading Coefficient −1

EXAMPLE 9 Factor: $10 - 3x - x^2$.

Note that the polynomial is written in ascending order. When we write it in descending order, we get

$$-x^2 - 3x + 10,$$

which has a leading coefficient of -1. Before factoring in such a case, we can factor out a -1, as follows:

$$-x^2 - 3x + 10 = -1 \cdot x^2 + (-1)(3x) + (-1)(-10)$$
$$= -1(x^2 + 3x - 10).$$

Then we proceed to factor $x^2 + 3x - 10$. We get

$$-x^2 - 3x + 10 = -1(x^2 + 3x - 10) = -1(x + 5)(x - 2).$$

We can also express this answer in two other ways by multiplying either binomial by -1. Thus each of the following is a correct answer:

$$-x^2 - 3x + 10 = -1(x + 5)(x - 2)$$
$$= (-x - 5)(x - 2) \qquad \text{Multiplying } x + 5 \text{ by } -1$$
$$= (x + 5)(-x + 2). \qquad \text{Multiplying } x - 2 \text{ by } -1$$

Factor.

16. $14 + 5x - x^2$

17. $-x^2 + 3x + 18$

Do Exercises 16 and 17.

STUDY TIPS

TIME MANAGEMENT

- **Are you a morning or an evening person?** If you are an evening person, it might be best to avoid scheduling early-morning classes. If you are a morning person, you will probably want to schedule morning classes if your work schedule and family obligations will allow it. Nothing can drain your study time and effectiveness like fatigue.

- **Keep on schedule.** Your course syllabus provides a plan for the semester's schedule. Read the entire syllabus at the beginning of the semester. Use a write-on calendar, daily planner, PDA, or laptop computer to outline your time for the semester. Be sure to note deadlines involving writing assignments and exams so you can begin a big task early, breaking it down into smaller segments that will not overwhelm you.

Answers

16. $-1(x + 2)(x - 7)$, or $(-x - 2)(x - 7)$, or $(x + 2)(-x + 7)$

17. $-1(x + 3)(x - 6)$, or $(-x - 3)(x - 6)$, or $(x + 3)(-x + 6)$

11.2 **Exercise Set**

For Extra Help

Math **MyMathLab**

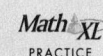
PRACTICE

WATCH

DOWNLOAD

READ

REVIEW

a Factor. Remember that you can check by multiplying.

1. $x^2 + 8x + 15$

PAIRS OF FACTORS	SUMS OF FACTORS

2. $x^2 + 5x + 6$

PAIRS OF FACTORS	SUMS OF FACTORS

3. $x^2 + 7x + 12$

PAIRS OF FACTORS	SUMS OF FACTORS

4. $x^2 + 9x + 8$

PAIRS OF FACTORS	SUMS OF FACTORS

5. $x^2 - 6x + 9$

PAIRS OF FACTORS	SUMS OF FACTORS

6. $y^2 - 11y + 28$

PAIRS OF FACTORS	SUMS OF FACTORS

7. $x^2 - 5x - 14$

PAIRS OF FACTORS	SUMS OF FACTORS

8. $a^2 + 7a - 30$

PAIRS OF FACTORS	SUMS OF FACTORS

9. $b^2 + 5b + 4$

PAIRS OF FACTORS	SUMS OF FACTORS

10. $z^2 - 8z + 7$

PAIRS OF FACTORS	SUMS OF FACTORS

11. $x^2 + \dfrac{2}{3}x + \dfrac{1}{9}$

PAIRS OF FACTORS	SUMS OF FACTORS

12. $x^2 - \dfrac{2}{5}x + \dfrac{1}{25}$

PAIRS OF FACTORS	SUMS OF FACTORS

13. $d^2 - 7d + 10$ **14.** $t^2 - 12t + 35$ **15.** $y^2 - 11y + 10$ **16.** $x^2 - 4x - 21$

17. $x^2 + x + 1$ **18.** $x^2 + 5x + 3$ **19.** $x^2 - 7x - 18$ **20.** $y^2 - 3y - 28$

21. $x^3 - 6x^2 - 16x$ **22.** $x^3 - x^2 - 42x$ **23.** $y^3 - 4y^2 - 45y$ **24.** $x^3 - 7x^2 - 60x$

25. $-2x - 99 + x^2$ **26.** $x^2 - 72 + 6x$ **27.** $c^4 + c^2 - 56$ **28.** $b^4 + 5b^2 - 24$

29. $a^4 + 2a^2 - 35$ **30.** $x^4 - x^2 - 6$ **31.** $x^2 + x - 42$ **32.** $x^2 + 2x - 15$

33. $7 - 2p + p^2$ **34.** $11 - 3w + w^2$ **35.** $x^2 + 20x + 100$ **36.** $a^2 + 19a + 88$

37. $2z^3 - 2z^2 - 24z$ **38.** $5w^4 - 20w^3 - 25w^2$ **39.** $3t^4 + 3t^3 + 3t^2$ **40.** $4y^5 - 4y^4 - 4y^3$

Copyright © 2012 Pearson Education, Inc.

41. $x^4 - 21x^3 - 100x^2$

42. $x^4 - 20x^3 + 96x^2$

43. $x^2 - 21x - 72$

44. $4x^2 + 40x + 100$

45. $x^2 - 25x + 144$

46. $y^2 - 21y + 108$

47. $a^2 + a - 132$

48. $a^2 + 9a - 90$

49. $3t^2 + 6t + 3$

50. $2y^2 + 24y + 72$

51. $w^4 - 8w^3 + 16w^2$

52. $z^5 - 6z^4 + 9z^3$

53. $30 + 7x - x^2$

54. $45 + 4x - x^2$

55. $24 - a^2 - 10a$

56. $-z^2 + 36 - 9z$

57. $120 - 23x + x^2$

58. $96 + 22d + d^2$

59. $108 - 3x - x^2$

60. $112 + 9y - y^2$

61. $y^2 - 0.2y - 0.08$

62. $t^2 - 0.3t - 0.10$

63. $p^2 + 3pq - 10q^2$

64. $a^2 + 2ab - 3b^2$

65. $84 - 8t - t^2$

66. $72 - 6m - m^2$

67. $m^2 + 5mn + 4n^2$

68. $x^2 + 11xy + 24y^2$

69. $s^2 - 2st - 15t^2$

70. $p^2 + 5pq - 24q^2$

71. $6a^{10} - 30a^9 - 84a^8$

72. $7x^9 - 28x^8 - 35x^7$

Skill Maintenance

Multiply.   [10.5b], [10.6d]

73. $8x(2x^2 - 6x + 1)$

74. $(7w + 6)(4w - 11)$

75. $(7w + 6)^2$

76. $(4w - 11)^2$

77. $(4w - 11)(4w + 11)$

78. $-y(-y^2 + 3y - 5)$

79. $(3x - 5y)(2x + 7y)$

80. Simplify: $(3x^4)^3$.   [10.2a, b]

Solve.   [8.3a]

81. $3x - 8 = 0$

82. $2x + 7 = 0$

Solve.

83. *Arrests for Counterfeiting.*   In 2008, the U.S. Secret Service made 2231 arrests for counterfeiting. This was an increase of 28% over the number of arrests in 2007. How many arrests for counterfeiting were made in 2007?   [8.5a]
Source: U.S. Secret Service

84. The first angle of a triangle is four times as large as the second. The measure of the third angle is 30° greater than that of the second. Find the angle measures. [8.6a]

Synthesis

85. Find all integers m for which $y^2 + my + 50$ can be factored.

86. Find all integers b for which $a^2 + ba - 50$ can be factored.

Factor completely.

87. $x^2 - \frac{1}{2}x - \frac{3}{16}$

88. $x^2 - \frac{1}{4}x - \frac{1}{8}$

89. $x^2 + \frac{30}{7}x - \frac{25}{7}$

90. $\frac{1}{3}x^3 + \frac{1}{3}x^2 - 2x$

91. $b^{2n} + 7b^n + 10$

92. $a^{2m} - 11a^m + 28$

Find a polynomial in factored form for the shaded area in each figure. (Leave answers in terms of π.)

93.

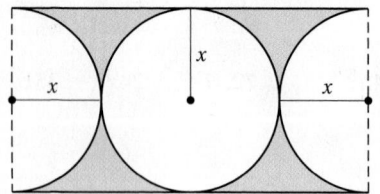

94.

Copyright © 2012 Pearson Education, Inc.

11.3 Factoring $ax^2 + bx + c$, $a \neq 1$: The FOIL Method

In Section 11.2, we learned a trial-and-error method to factor trinomials of the type $x^2 + bx + c$. In this section, we factor trinomials in which the coefficient of the leading term x^2 is not 1. Again, the procedure we use is a refined trial-and-error method.

a The FOIL Method

We want to factor trinomials of the type $ax^2 + bx + c$. Consider the following multiplication:

$$
\begin{array}{ccccc}
 & \text{F} & \text{O} & \text{I} & \text{L} \\
(2x + 5)(3x + 4) = & 6x^2 & + 8x & + 15x & + 20
\end{array}
$$

$$
= 6x^2 + 23x + 20
$$

F	O + I	L
$2 \cdot 3$	$2 \cdot 4$ $5 \cdot 3$	$5 \cdot 4$

To factor $6x^2 + 23x + 20$, we reverse the above multiplication, using what we might call an "unFOIL" process. We look for two binomials $rx + p$ and $sx + q$ whose product is $(rx + p)(sx + q) = 6x^2 + 23x + 20$. The product of the First terms must be $6x^2$. The product of the Outside terms plus the product of the Inside terms must be $23x$. The product of the Last terms must be 20. We know from the preceding discussion that the answer is $(2x + 5)(3x + 4)$. Generally, however, finding such an answer is a refined trial-and-error process. It turns out that $(-2x - 5)(-3x - 4)$ is also a correct answer, but we generally choose an answer in which the first coefficients are positive.

We will use the following trial-and-error method.

THE FOIL METHOD

To factor $ax^2 + bx + c$, $a \neq 1$, using the FOIL method:

1. Factor out the largest common factor, if one exists.

2. Find two First terms whose product is ax^2.

$$(\boxed{}x + \,)(\boxed{}x + \,) = ax^2 + bx + c.$$
$$\underbrace{}_{\text{FOIL}}$$

3. Find two Last terms whose product is c:

$$(x + \boxed{})(x + \boxed{}) = ax^2 + bx + c.$$
$$\underbrace{}_{\text{FOIL}}$$

4. Look for Outer and Inner products resulting from steps (2) and (3) for which the sum is bx:

$$(\boxed{}x + \boxed{})(\boxed{}x + \boxed{}) = ax^2 + bx + c.$$
$$\underbrace{}_{\text{I}} \quad \underbrace{}_{\text{FOIL}}$$
$$\underbrace{}_{\text{O}}$$

5. Always check by multiplying.

OBJECTIVE

 Factor trinomials of the type $ax^2 + bx + c$, $a \neq 1$, using the FOIL method.

SKILL TO REVIEW
Objective 10.6a: Multiply two binomials mentally using the FOIL method.

Multiply.

1. $(2x + 3)(x + 1)$
2. $(3x - 4)(2x - 1)$

The ac-method in Section 11.4

To the student: In Section 11.4, we will consider an alternative method for the same kind of factoring. It involves factoring by grouping and is called the *ac*-method.

To the instructor: We present two ways to factor general trinomials in Sections 11.3 and 11.4: the FOIL method in Section 11.3 and the *ac*-method in Section 11.4. You can teach both methods and let the student use the one that he or she prefers or you can select just one.

Answers

Skill to Review:
1. $2x^2 + 5x + 3$ 2. $6x^2 - 11x + 4$

Calculator Corner

A partial check of a factorization can be performed using a table or a graph. To check the factorization
$6x^3 - 9x^2 + 4x - 6 =$
$(2x - 3)(3x^2 + 2)$, for example, we enter $y_1 = 6x^3 - 9x^2 + 4x - 6$ and $y_2 = (2x - 3)(3x^2 + 2)$ on the equation-editor screen. Then we set up a table in AUTO mode. If the factorization is correct, the values of y_1 and y_2 will be the same regardless of the table settings used.

X	Y1	Y2
-3	-261	-261
-2	-98	-98
-1	-25	-25
0	-6	-6
1	-5	-5
2	14	14
3	87	87
X = -3		

We can also graph $y_1 = 6x^3 - 9x^2 + 4x - 6$ and $y_2 = (2x - 3)(3x^2 + 2)$. If the graphs appear to coincide, the factorization is probably correct.

$$y_1 = 6x^3 - 9x^2 + 4x - 6,$$
$$y_2 = (2x - 3)(3x^2 + 2)$$

Yscl = 2

Keep in mind that these procedures provide only a partial check since we cannot view all possible values of x in a table or see the entire graph.

Exercises: Use a table or a graph to determine whether each factorization is correct.

1. $24x^2 - 76x + 40 = 4(3x - 2)(2x - 5)$
2. $4x^2 - 5x - 6 = (4x + 3)(x - 2)$
3. $5x^2 + 17x - 12 = (5x + 3)(x - 4)$
4. $10x^2 + 37x + 7 = (5x - 1)(2x + 7)$

EXAMPLE 1 Factor: $3x^2 - 10x - 8$.

1) First, we check for a common factor. Here there is none (other than 1 or -1).

2) Find two **First** terms whose product is $3x^2$.

   The only possibilities for the **First** terms are $3x$ and x, so any factorization must be of the form

   $(3x + \square)(x + \square)$.

3) Find two **Last** terms whose product is -8.

   Possible factorizations of -8 are

   $(-8) \cdot 1, \quad 8 \cdot (-1), \quad (-2) \cdot 4, \quad \text{and} \quad 2 \cdot (-4).$

   Since the First terms are not identical, we must also consider

   $1 \cdot (-8), \quad (-1) \cdot 8, \quad 4 \cdot (-2), \quad \text{and} \quad (-4) \cdot 2.$

4) Inspect the **O**utside and **I**nside products resulting from steps (2) and (3). Look for a combination in which the sum of the products is the middle term, $-10x$:

Trial	*Product*	
$(3x - 8)(x + 1)$	$3x^2 + 3x - 8x - 8$ $= 3x^2 - 5x - 8$	← Wrong middle term
$(3x + 8)(x - 1)$	$3x^2 - 3x + 8x - 8$ $= 3x^2 + 5x - 8$	← Wrong middle term
$(3x - 2)(x + 4)$	$3x^2 + 12x - 2x - 8$ $= 3x^2 + 10x - 8$	← Wrong middle term
$(3x + 2)(x - 4)$	$3x^2 - 12x + 2x - 8$ $= 3x^2 - 10x - 8$	← **Correct middle term!**
$(3x + 1)(x - 8)$	$3x^2 - 24x + x - 8$ $= 3x^2 - 23x - 8$	← Wrong middle term
$(3x - 1)(x + 8)$	$3x^2 + 24x - x - 8$ $= 3x^2 + 23x - 8$	← Wrong middle term
$(3x + 4)(x - 2)$	$3x^2 - 6x + 4x - 8$ $= 3x^2 - 2x - 8$	← Wrong middle term
$(3x - 4)(x + 2)$	$3x^2 + 6x - 4x - 8$ $= 3x^2 + 2x - 8$	← Wrong middle term

The correct factorization is $(3x + 2)(x - 4)$.

5) Check: $(3x + 2)(x - 4) = 3x^2 - 10x - 8$.

Two observations can be made from Example 1. First, we listed all possible trials even though we could have stopped after having found the correct factorization. We did this to show that each trial differs only in the middle term of the product. **Second, note that as in Section 11.2, only the sign of the middle term changes when the signs in the binomials are reversed:**

Plus   Minus

$(3x + 4)(x - 2) = 3x^2 - 2x - 8$

Minus   Plus

$(3x - 4)(x + 2) = 3x^2 + 2x - 8$.

—— Middle term changes sign

Factor.
1. $2x^2 - x - 15$

2. $12x^2 - 17x - 5$

EXAMPLE 2 Factor: $24x^2 - 76x + 40$.

1) First, we factor out the largest common factor, 4:

$4(6x^2 - 19x + 10)$.

Now we factor the trinomial $6x^2 - 19x + 10$.

2) Because $6x^2$ can be factored as $3x \cdot 2x$ or $6x \cdot x$, we have these possibilities for factorizations:

$(3x + \boxed{})(2x + \boxed{})$ or $(6x + \boxed{})(x + \boxed{})$.

3) There are four pairs of factors of 10 and each pair can be listed in two ways:

$10, 1 \quad -10, -1 \quad 5, 2 \quad -5, -2$

and

$1, 10 \quad -1, -10 \quad 2, 5 \quad -2, -5$.

4) The two possibilities from step (2) and the eight possibilities from step (3) give $2 \cdot 8$, or 16 possibilities for factorizations. We look for **O**utside and **I**nside products resulting from steps (2) and (3) for which the sum is the middle term, $-19x$. Since the sign of the middle term is negative, but the sign of the last term, 10, is positive, both factors of 10 must be negative. This means only four pairings from step (3) need be considered. We first try these factors with

$(3x + \boxed{})(2x + \boxed{})$.

If none gives the correct factorization, we will consider

$(6x + \boxed{})(x + \boxed{})$.

Trial	*Product*
$(3x - 10)(2x - 1)$	$6x^2 - 3x - 20x + 10$
	$= 6x^2 - 23x + 10$ ← Wrong middle term
$(3x - 1)(2x - 10)$	$6x^2 - 30x - 2x + 10$
	$= 6x^2 - 32x + 10$ ← Wrong middle term
$(3x - 5)(2x - 2)$	$6x^2 - 6x - 10x + 10$
	$= 6x^2 - 16x + 10$ ← Wrong middle term
$(3x - 2)(2x - 5)$	$6x^2 - 15x - 4x + 10$
	$= 6x^2 - 19x + 10$ ← **Correct middle term!**

Since we have a correct factorization, we need not consider

$(6x + \boxed{})(x + \boxed{})$.

The factorization of $6x^2 - 19x + 10$ is $(3x - 2)(2x - 5)$, but *do not forget the common factor!* We must include it in order to factor the original trinomial:

$24x^2 - 76x + 40 = 4(6x^2 - 19x + 10)$

$= 4(3x - 2)(2x - 5)$.

5) Check: $4(3x - 2)(2x - 5) = 4(6x^2 - 19x + 10) = 24x^2 - 76x + 40$.

--------- *Caution!* ---------

When factoring any polynomial, always look for a common factor first. Failure to do so is such a common error that this caution bears repeating.

Answers
1. $(2x + 5)(x - 3)$ 2. $(4x + 1)(3x - 5)$

In Example 2, look again at the possibility $(3x - 5)(2x - 2)$. Without multiplying, we can reject such a possibility. To see why, consider the following:

$$(3x - 5)(2x - 2) = (3x - 5)(2)(x - 1) = 2(3x - 5)(x - 1).$$

The expression $2x - 2$ has a common factor, 2. But we removed the *largest* common factor in the first step. If $2x - 2$ were one of the factors, then 2 would have to be a common factor in addition to the original 4. Thus, $(2x - 2)$ cannot be part of the factorization of the original trinomial.

> Given that the largest common factor is factored out at the outset, we need not consider factorizations that have a common factor.

Do Exercises 3 and 4.

EXAMPLE 3 Factor: $10x^2 + 37x + 7$.

1) There is no common factor (other than 1 or -1).

2) Because $10x^2$ factors as $10x \cdot x$ or $5x \cdot 2x$, we have these possibilities for factorizations:

$$(10x + \boxed{})(x + \boxed{}) \quad \text{or} \quad (5x + \boxed{})(2x + \boxed{}).$$

3) There are two pairs of factors of 7 and each pair can be listed in two ways:

$$1, 7 \quad -1, -7 \qquad \text{and} \qquad 7, 1 \quad -7, -1.$$

4) From steps (2) and (3), we see that there are 8 possibilities for factorizations. Look for **O**uter and **I**nner products for which the sum is the middle term. Because all coefficients in $10x^2 + 37x + 7$ are positive, we need consider only positive factors of 7. The possibilities are

$$(10x + 1)(x + 7) = 10x^2 + 71x + 7,$$
$$(10x + 7)(x + 1) = 10x^2 + 17x + 7,$$
$$(5x + 7)(2x + 1) = 10x^2 + 19x + 7,$$
$$(5x + 1)(2x + 7) = 10x^2 + 37x + 7. \quad \leftarrow \textbf{Correct middle term}$$

The factorization is $(5x + 1)(2x + 7)$.

5) Check: $(5x + 1)(2x + 7) = 10x^2 + 37x + 7$.

Do Exercise 5.

Factor.

3. $3x^2 - 19x + 20$

4. $20x^2 - 46x + 24$

5. Factor: $6x^2 + 7x + 2$.

> **TIPS FOR FACTORING** $ax^2 + bx + c$, $a \neq 1$
>
> - Always factor out the largest common factor first, if one exists.
> - Once the common factor has been factored out of the original trinomial, no binomial factor can contain a common factor (other than 1 or -1).
> - If c is positive, then the signs in both binomial factors must match the sign of b. (This assumes that $a > 0$.)
> - Reversing the signs in the binomials reverses the sign of the middle term of their product.
> - Organize your work so that you can keep track of which possibilities have or have not been checked.
> - Always check by multiplying.

Answers

3. $(3x - 4)(x - 5)$ **4.** $2(5x - 4)(2x - 3)$
5. $(2x + 1)(3x + 2)$

EXAMPLE 4   Factor: $10x + 8 - 3x^2$.

An important problem-solving strategy is to find a way to make new problems look like problems we already know how to solve. (See Example 9 in Section 11.2.) The factoring tips on the preceding page apply only to trinomials of the form $ax^2 + bx + c$, with $a > 0$. This leads us to rewrite $10x + 8 - 3x^2$ in descending order:

$$10x + 8 - 3x^2 = -3x^2 + 10x + 8. \quad \text{Writing in descending order}$$

Although $-3x^2 + 10x + 8$ looks similar to the trinomials we have factored, the factoring tips require a positive leading coefficient. This can be attained by factoring out -1:

$$-3x^2 + 10x + 8 = -1(3x^2 - 10x - 8) \quad \begin{array}{l}\text{Factoring out } -1 \text{ changes}\\\text{the signs of the coefficients.}\end{array}$$

$$= -1(3x + 2)(x - 4). \quad \begin{array}{l}\text{Using the result from}\\\text{Example 1}\end{array}$$

The factorization of $10x + 8 - 3x^2$ is $-1(3x + 2)(x - 4)$. Other correct answers are

$$10x + 8 - 3x^2 = (3x + 2)(-x + 4) \quad \text{Multiplying } x - 4 \text{ by } -1$$

$$= (-3x - 2)(x - 4). \quad \text{Multiplying } 3x + 2 \text{ by } -1$$

Do Exercises 6 and 7.

STUDY TIPS

READING EXAMPLES

A careful study of the examples in these sections on factoring is critical. *Read them carefully* to ensure success!

Factor.

6. $2 - x - 6x^2$

7. $2x + 8 - 6x^2$

EXAMPLE 5   Factor: $6p^2 - 13pq - 28q^2$.

1) Factor out a common factor, if any.

There is none (other than 1 or -1).

2) Factor the first term, $6p^2$.

Possibilities are $2p, 3p$ and $6p, p$. We have these as possibilities for factorizations:

$$(2p + \square)(3p + \square) \quad \text{or} \quad (6p + \square)(p + \square).$$

3) Factor the last term, $-28q^2$, which has a negative coefficient.

There are six pairs of factors and each can be listed in two ways:

$$-28q, q \quad 28q, -q \quad -14q, 2q \quad 14q, -2q \quad -7q, 4q \quad 7q, -4q$$

and

$$q, -28q \quad -q, 28q \quad 2q, -14q \quad -2q, 14q \quad 4q, -7q \quad -4q, 7q.$$

4) The coefficient of the middle term is negative, so we look for combinations of factors from steps (2) and (3) such that the sum of their products has a negative coefficient. We try some possibilities:

$$(2p + q)(3p - 28q) = 6p^2 - 53pq - 28q^2,$$

$$(2p - 7q)(3p + 4q) = 6p^2 - 13pq - 28q^2. \quad \leftarrow \textbf{Correct middle term}$$

The factorization of $6p^2 - 13pq - 28q^2$ is $(2p - 7q)(3p + 4q)$.

5) The check is left to the student.

Do Exercises 8 and 9.

Factor.

8. $6a^2 - 5ab + b^2$

9. $6x^2 + 15xy + 9y^2$

Answers

6. $-1(2x - 1)(3x + 2)$, or $(2x - 1)(-3x - 2)$, or $(-2x + 1)(3x + 2)$ **7.** $-2(3x - 4)(x + 1)$, or $2(3x - 4)(-x - 1)$, or $2(-3x + 4)(x + 1)$
8. $(2a - b)(3a - b)$ **9.** $3(2x + 3y)(x + y)$

a Factor.

1. $2x^2 - 7x - 4$

2. $3x^2 - x - 4$

3. $5x^2 - x - 18$

4. $4x^2 - 17x + 15$

5. $6x^2 + 23x + 7$

6. $6x^2 - 23x + 7$

7. $3x^2 + 4x + 1$

8. $7x^2 + 15x + 2$

9. $4x^2 + 4x - 15$

10. $9x^2 + 6x - 8$

11. $2x^2 - x - 1$

12. $15x^2 - 19x - 10$

13. $9x^2 + 18x - 16$

14. $2x^2 + 5x + 2$

15. $3x^2 - 5x - 2$

16. $18x^2 - 3x - 10$

17. $12x^2 + 31x + 20$

18. $15x^2 + 19x - 10$

19. $14x^2 + 19x - 3$

20. $35x^2 + 34x + 8$

21. $9x^2 + 18x + 8$

22. $6 - 13x + 6x^2$

23. $49 - 42x + 9x^2$

24. $16 + 36x^2 + 48x$

25. $24x^2 + 47x - 2$

26. $16p^2 - 78p + 27$

27. $35x^2 - 57x - 44$

28. $9a^2 + 12a - 5$

29. $20 + 6x - 2x^2$

30. $15 + x - 2x^2$

31. $12x^2 + 28x - 24$

32. $6x^2 + 33x + 15$

Copyright © 2012 Pearson Education, Inc.

33. $30x^2 - 24x - 54$

34. $18t^2 - 24t + 6$

35. $4y + 6y^2 - 10$

36. $-9 + 18x^2 - 21x$

37. $3x^2 - 4x + 1$

38. $6t^2 + 13t + 6$

39. $12x^2 - 28x - 24$

40. $6x^2 - 33x + 15$

41. $-1 + 2x^2 - x$

42. $-19x + 15x^2 + 6$

43. $9x^2 - 18x - 16$

44. $14y^2 + 35y + 14$

45. $15x^2 - 25x - 10$

46. $18x^2 + 3x - 10$

47. $12p^3 + 31p^2 + 20p$

48. $15x^3 + 19x^2 - 10x$

49. $16 + 18x - 9x^2$

50. $33t - 15 - 6t^2$

51. $-15x^2 + 19x - 6$

52. $1 + p - 2p^2$

53. $14x^4 + 19x^3 - 3x^2$

54. $70x^4 + 68x^3 + 16x^2$

55. $168x^3 - 45x^2 + 3x$

56. $144x^5 + 168x^4 + 48x^3$

57. $15x^4 - 19x^2 + 6$

58. $9x^4 + 18x^2 + 8$

59. $25t^2 + 80t + 64$

60. $9x^2 - 42x + 49$

61. $6x^3 + 4x^2 - 10x$

62. $18x^3 - 21x^2 - 9x$

63. $25x^2 + 79x + 64$

64. $9y^2 + 42y + 47$

65. $6x^2 - 19x - 5$ **66.** $2x^2 + 11x - 9$ **67.** $12m^2 - mn - 20n^2$ **68.** $12a^2 - 17ab + 6b^2$

69. $6a^2 - ab - 15b^2$ **70.** $3p^2 - 16pq - 12q^2$ **71.** $9a^2 + 18ab + 8b^2$ **72.** $10s^2 + 4st - 6t^2$

73. $35p^2 + 34pq + 8q^2$ **74.** $30a^2 + 87ab + 30b^2$ **75.** $18x^2 - 6xy - 24y^2$ **76.** $15a^2 - 5ab - 20b^2$

Skill Maintenance

Solve. [8.4b]

77. $A = pq - 7$, for q **78.** $y = mx + b$, for x **79.** $3x + 2y = 6$, for y **80.** $p - q + r = 2$, for q

Solve. [8.7e]

81. $5 - 4x < -11$ **82.** $2x - 4(x + 3x) \geq 6x - 8 - 9x$

83. Graph: $y = \dfrac{2}{5}x - 1$. [9.1d]   **84.** Divide: $\dfrac{y^{12}}{y^4}$. [10.1e]

Find the intercepts of each equation. [9.2a]

85. $4x - 16y = 64$ **86.** $4x + 16y = 64$ **87.** $x - 1.3y = 6.5$

88. $\frac{2}{3}x + \frac{5}{8}y = \frac{5}{12}$ **89.** $y = 4 - 5x$ **90.** $y = 2x - 5$

Synthesis

Factor.

91. $20x^{2n} + 16x^n + 3$ **92.** $-15x^{2m} + 26x^m - 8$

93. $3x^{6a} - 2x^{3a} - 1$ **94.** $x^{2n+1} - 2x^{n+1} + x$

95.–104. 📈 Use the TABLE feature to check the factoring in Exercises 15–24. (See the Calculator Corner on p. 842.)

Copyright © 2012 Pearson Education, Inc.

11.4 Factoring $ax^2 + bx + c$, $a \neq 1$: The ac-Method

a The ac-Method

OBJECTIVE

a Factor trinomials of the type $ax^2 + bx + c$, $a \neq 1$, using the ac-method.

Another method for factoring trinomials of the type $ax^2 + bx + c$, $a \neq 1$, involves the product, ac, of the leading coefficient a and the last term c. It is called the **ac-method**. Because it uses factoring by grouping, it is also referred to as the **grouping method**.

We know how to factor the trinomial $x^2 + 5x + 6$. We look for factors of the constant term, 6, whose sum is the coefficient of the middle term, 5. What happens when the leading coefficient is not 1? To factor a trinomial like $3x^2 - 10x - 8$, we can use a method similar to the one that we used for $x^2 + 5x + 6$. That method is outlined as follows.

> **THE ac-METHOD**
>
> To factor $ax^2 + bx + c$, $a \neq 1$, using the ac-method:
>
> 1. Factor out a common factor, if any.
> 2. Multiply the leading coefficient a and the constant c.
> 3. Try to factor the product ac so that the sum of the factors is b. That is, find integers p and q such that $pq = ac$ and $p + q = b$.
> 4. Split the middle term, writing it as a sum using the factors found in step (3).
> 5. Factor by grouping.
> 6. Check by multiplying.

EXAMPLE 1   Factor: $3x^2 - 10x - 8$.

1) First, we factor out a common factor, if any. There is none (other than 1 or -1).

2) We multiply the leading coefficient, 3, and the constant, -8:
$$3(-8) = -24.$$

3) Then we look for a factorization of -24 in which the sum of the factors is the coefficient of the middle term, -10.

PAIRS OF FACTORS	SUMS OF FACTORS	
-1, 24	23	
$1, -24$	-23	
-2, 12	10	
$2, -12$	-10 ←	$2 + (-12) = -10$
-3, 8	5	
$3, -8$	-5	
-4, 6	2	
$4, -6$	-2	

4) Next, we split the middle term as a sum or a difference using the factors found in step (3): $-10x = 2x - 12x$.

5) Finally, we factor by grouping, as follows:

$$3x^2 - 10x - 8 = 3x^2 + 2x - 12x - 8 \qquad \text{Substituting } 2x - 12x \\ \text{for } -10x$$

$$= (3x^2 + 2x) + (-12x - 8)$$

$$= x(3x + 2) - 4(3x + 2) \qquad \text{Factoring by grouping}$$

$$= (3x + 2)(x - 4).$$

We can also split the middle term as $-12x + 2x$. We still get the same factorization, although the factors may be in a different order. Note the following:

$$3x^2 - 10x - 8 = 3x^2 - 12x + 2x - 8 \qquad \text{Substituting } -12x + 2x \\ \text{for } -10x$$

$$= (3x^2 - 12x) + (2x - 8)$$

$$= 3x(x - 4) + 2(x - 4) \qquad \text{Factoring by grouping}$$

$$= (x - 4)(3x + 2).$$

6) Check: $(3x + 2)(x - 4) = 3x^2 - 10x - 8.$

Do Exercises 1 and 2.

EXAMPLE 2 Factor: $8x^2 + 8x - 6.$

1) First, we factor out a common factor, if any. The number 2 is common to all three terms, so we factor it out: $2(4x^2 + 4x - 3).$

2) Next, we factor the trinomial $4x^2 + 4x - 3$. We multiply the leading coefficient and the constant, 4 and -3: $4(-3) = -12.$

3) We try to factor -12 so that the sum of the factors is 4.

PAIRS OF FACTORS	SUMS OF FACTORS	
$-1, \quad 12$	11	
$1, -12$	-11	
$-2, \quad 6$	4 ←	$-2 + 6 = 4$
$2, \quad -6$	-4	
$-3, \quad 4$	1	
$3, \quad -4$	-1	

4) Then we split the middle term, $4x$, as follows: $4x = -2x + 6x.$

5) Finally, we factor by grouping:

$$4x^2 + 4x - 3 = 4x^2 - 2x + 6x - 3 \qquad \text{Substituting } -2x + 6x \\ \text{for } 4x$$

$$= (4x^2 - 2x) + (6x - 3)$$

$$= 2x(2x - 1) + 3(2x - 1) \qquad \text{Factoring by grouping}$$

$$= (2x - 1)(2x + 3).$$

The factorization of $4x^2 + 4x - 3$ is $(2x - 1)(2x + 3)$. But don't forget the common factor! We must include it to get a factorization of the original trinomial: $8x^2 + 8x - 6 = 2(2x - 1)(2x + 3).$

6) Check: $2(2x - 1)(2x + 3) = 2(4x^2 + 4x - 3) = 8x^2 + 8x - 6.$

Do Exercises 3 and 4.

Factor.

1. $6x^2 + 7x + 2$

2. $12x^2 - 17x - 5$

Factor.

3. $6x^2 + 15x + 9$

4. $20x^2 - 46x + 24$

Answers

1. $(2x + 1)(3x + 2)$ **2.** $(4x + 1)(3x - 5)$
3. $3(2x + 3)(x + 1)$ **4.** $2(5x - 4)(2x - 3)$

a Factor. Note that the middle term has already been split.

1. $x^2 + 2x + 7x + 14$

2. $x^2 + 3x + x + 3$

3. $x^2 - 4x - x + 4$

4. $a^2 + 5a - 2a - 10$

5. $6x^2 + 4x + 9x + 6$

6. $3x^2 - 2x + 3x - 2$

7. $3x^2 - 4x - 12x + 16$

8. $24 - 18y - 20y + 15y^2$

9. $35x^2 - 40x + 21x - 24$

10. $8x^2 - 6x - 28x + 21$

11. $4x^2 + 6x - 6x - 9$

12. $2x^4 - 6x^2 - 5x^2 + 15$

13. $2x^4 + 6x^2 + 5x^2 + 15$

14. $9x^4 - 6x^2 - 6x^2 + 4$

Factor using the *ac*-method.

15. $2x^2 + 7x - 4$

16. $5x^2 + x - 18$

17. $3x^2 - 4x - 15$

18. $3x^2 + x - 4$

19. $6x^2 + 23x + 7$

20. $6x^2 + 13x + 6$

21. $3x^2 - 4x + 1$

22. $7x^2 - 15x + 2$

23. $4x^2 - 4x - 15$

24. $9x^2 - 6x - 8$

25. $2x^2 + x - 1$

26. $15x^2 + 19x - 10$

27. $9x^2 - 18x - 16$ **28.** $2x^2 - 5x + 2$ **29.** $3x^2 + 5x - 2$ **30.** $18x^2 + 3x - 10$

31. $12x^2 - 31x + 20$ **32.** $15x^2 - 19x - 10$ **33.** $14x^2 - 19x - 3$ **34.** $35x^2 - 34x + 8$

35. $9x^2 + 18x + 8$ **36.** $6 - 13x + 6x^2$ **37.** $49 - 42x + 9x^2$ **38.** $25x^2 + 40x + 16$

39. $24x^2 - 47x - 2$ **40.** $16a^2 + 78a + 27$ **41.** $5 - 9a^2 - 12a$ **42.** $17x - 4x^2 + 15$

43. $20 + 6x - 2x^2$ **44.** $15 + x - 2x^2$ **45.** $12x^2 + 28x - 24$ **46.** $6x^2 + 33x + 15$

47. $30x^2 - 24x - 54$ **48.** $18t^2 - 24t + 6$ **49.** $4y + 6y^2 - 10$ **50.** $-9 + 18x^2 - 21x$

51. $3x^2 - 4x + 1$ **52.** $6t^2 + t - 15$ **53.** $12x^2 - 28x - 24$ **54.** $6x^2 - 33x + 15$

55. $-1 + 2x^2 - x$ **56.** $-19x + 15x^2 + 6$ **57.** $9x^2 + 18x - 16$ **58.** $14y^2 + 35y + 14$

Copyright © 2012 Pearson Education, Inc.

59. $15x^2 - 25x - 10$

60. $18x^2 + 3x - 10$

61. $12p^3 + 31p^2 + 20p$

62. $15x^3 + 19x^2 - 10x$

63. $4 - x - 5x^2$

64. $1 - p - 2p^2$

65. $33t - 15 - 6t^2$

66. $-15x^2 - 19x - 6$

67. $14x^4 + 19x^3 - 3x^2$

68. $70x^4 + 68x^3 + 16x^2$

69. $168x^3 - 45x^2 + 3x$

70. $144x^5 + 168x^4 + 48x^3$

71. $15x^4 - 19x^2 + 6$

72. $9x^4 + 18x^2 + 8$

73. $25t^2 + 80t + 64$

74. $9x^2 - 42x + 49$

75. $6x^3 + 4x^2 - 10x$

76. $18x^3 - 21x^2 - 9x$

77. $25x^2 + 79x + 64$

78. $9y^2 + 42y + 47$

79. $6x^2 - 19x - 5$

80. $2x^2 + 11x - 9$

81. $12m^2 - mn - 20n^2$

82. $12a^2 - 17ab + 6b^2$

83. $6a^2 - ab - 15b^2$

84. $3p^2 - 16pq - 12q^2$

85. $9a^2 - 18ab + 8b^2$

86. $10s^2 + 4st - 6t^2$

87. $35p^2 + 34pq + 8q^2$ **88.** $30a^2 + 87ab + 30b^2$ **89.** $18x^2 - 6xy - 24y^2$ **90.** $15a^2 - 5ab - 20b^2$

91. $60x + 18x^2 - 6x^3$ **92.** $60x + 4x^2 - 8x^3$ **93.** $35x^5 - 57x^4 - 44x^3$ **94.** $15x^3 + 33x^4 + 6x^5$

Skill Maintenance

Solve.   [8.7d, e]

95. $-10x > 1000$ **96.** $-3.8x \leq -824.6$ **97.** $6 - 3x \geq -18$

98. $3 - 2x - 4x > -9$ **99.** $\frac{1}{2}x - 6x + 10 \leq x - 5x$ **100.** $-2(x + 7) > -4(x - 5)$

101. $3x - 6x + 2(x - 4) > 2(9 - 4x)$ **102.** $-6(x - 4) + 8(4 - x) \leq 3(x - 7)$

Solve.   [8.6a]

103. The earth is a sphere (or ball) that is about 40,000 km in circumference. Find the radius of the earth, in kilometers and in miles. Use 3.14 for π. (*Hint*: 1 km $\approx$ 0.62 mi.)

104. The second angle of a triangle is 10° less than twice the first. The third angle is 15° more than four times the first. Find the measure of the second angle.

Synthesis

Factor.

105. $9x^{10} - 12x^5 + 4$ **106.** $24x^{2n} + 22x^n + 3$

107. $16x^{10} + 8x^5 + 1$ **108.** $(a + 4)^2 - 2(a + 4) + 1$

109.–118. Use graphs to check the factoring in Exercises 15–24. (See the Calculator Corner on p. 842.)

Copyright © 2012 Pearson Education, Inc.

Mid-Chapter Review

Concept Reinforcement

Determine whether each statement is true or false.

_____ 1. The greatest common factor (GCF) of a set of natural numbers is at least 1 and always less than or equal to the smallest number in the set. [11.1a]

_____ 2. To factor $x^2 + bx + c$, we use a trial-and-error process that looks for factors of b whose sum is c. [11.2a]

_____ 3. A prime polynomial has no common factor other than 1 and -1. [11.2a]

_____ 4. When factoring $x^2 - 14x + 45$, we need consider only positive pairs of factors of 45. [11.2a]

Guided Solutions

Fill in each blank with the number, variable, or expression that creates a correct statement or solution.

5. Factor: $10y^3 - 18y^2 + 12y$. [11.1b]

$$10y^3 - 18y^2 + 12y = \square \cdot 5y^2 - \square \cdot 9y + \square \cdot 6$$
$$= 2y(\square)$$

6. Factor $2x^2 - x - 6$ using the *ac*-method. [11.4a]

$a \cdot c = \square \cdot \square = -12;$ Multiplying the leading coefficient and the constant

$-x = \square + 3x;$ Splitting the middle term

$2x^2 - x - 6 = 2x^2 - 4x + \square - 6$
$= \square(x - 2) + \square(x - 2)$
$= (x - 2)(\square)$

Mixed Review

Find the GCF. [11.1a]

7. x^3, $3x$

8. $5x^4$, x^2

9. $6x^5$, $-12x^3$

10. $-8x$, -12, $16x^2$

11. $15x^3y^2$, $5x^2y$, $40x^4y^3$

12. x^2y^4, $-x^3y^3$, x^3y^2, x^5y^4

Factor completely. [11.1b, c], [11.2a], [11.3a], [11.4a]

13. $x^3 - 8x$

14. $3x^2 + 12x$

15. $2y^2 + 8y - 4$

16. $3t^6 - 5t^4 - 2t^3$

17. $x^2 + 4x + 3$

18. $z^2 - 4z + 4$

19. $x^3 + 4x^2 + 3x + 12$

20. $8y^5 - 48y^3$

21. $6x^3y + 24x^2y^2 - 42xy^3$

22. $6 - 11t - 4t^2$

23. $z^2 + 4z - 5$

24. $2z^3 + 8z^2 + 5z + 20$

25. $3p^3 - 2p^2 - 9p + 6$

26. $10x^8 - 25x^6 - 15x^5 + 35x^3$

27. $2w^3 + 3w^2 - 6w - 9$

28. $4x^4 - 5x^3 + 3x^2$

29. $6y^2 + 7y - 10$

30. $3x^2 - 3x - 18$

31. $6x^3 + 4x^2 + 3x + 2$

32. $15 - 8w + w^2$

33. $8x^3 + 20x^2 + 2x + 5$

34. $10z^2 - 21z - 10$

35. $6x^2 + 7x + 2$

36. $x^2 - 10xy + 24y^2$

37. $6z^3 + 3z^2 + 2z + 1$

38. $a^3b^7 + a^4b^5 - a^2b^3 + a^5b^6$

39. $4y^2 - 7yz - 15z^2$

40. $3x^3 + 21x^2 + 30x$

41. $x^3 - 3x^2 - 2x + 6$

42. $9y^2 + 6y + 1$

43. $y^2 + 6y + 8$

44. $6y^2 + 33y + 45$

45. $x^3 - 7x^2 + 4x - 28$

46. $4 + 3y - y^2$

47. $16x^2 - 16x - 60$

48. $10a^2 - 11ab + 3b^2$

49. $6w^3 - 15w^2 - 10w + 25$

50. $y^3 + 9y^2 + 18y$

51. $4x^2 + 11xy + 6y^2$

52. $6 - 5z - 6z^2$

53. $12t^3 + 8t^2 - 9t - 6$

54. $y^2 + yz - 20z^2$

55. $9x^2 - 6xy - 8y^2$

56. $-3 + 8z + 3z^2$

57. $m^2 - 6mn - 16n^2$

58. $2w^2 - 12w + 18$

59. $18t^3 - 18t^2 + 4t$

60. $5z^3 + 15z^2 + z + 3$

61. $-14 + 5t + t^2$

62. $4t^2 - 20t + 25$

63. $t^2 + 4t - 12$

64. $12 + 5z - 2z^2$

65. $12 + 4y - y^2$

Understanding Through Discussion and Writing

66. Explain how one could construct a polynomial with four terms that can be factored by grouping.   [11.1a], [11.4a]

67. When searching for a factorization, why do we list pairs of numbers with the correct *product* instead of pairs of numbers with the correct *sum*?   [11.2a]

68. Without multiplying $(x - 17)(x - 18)$, explain why it cannot possibly be a factorization of $x^2 + 35x + 306$. [11.2a]

69. A student presents the following work:
$$4x^2 + 28x + 48 = (2x + 6)(2x + 8)$$
$$= 2(x + 3)(x + 4).$$
Is it correct? Explain.   [11.3a], [11.4a]

Copyright © 2012 Pearson Education, Inc.

11.5 Factoring Trinomial Squares and Differences of Squares

In this section, we first learn to factor trinomials that are squares of binomials. Then we factor binomials that are differences of squares.

a Recognizing Trinomial Squares

Some trinomials are squares of binomials. For example, the trinomial $x^2 + 10x + 25$ is the square of the binomial $x + 5$. To see this, we can calculate $(x + 5)^2$. It is $x^2 + 2 \cdot x \cdot 5 + 5^2$, or $x^2 + 10x + 25$. A trinomial that is the square of a binomial is called a **trinomial square**, or a **perfect-square trinomial**.

In Chapter 10, we considered squaring binomials as special-product rules:

$$(A + B)^2 = A^2 + 2AB + B^2;$$
$$(A - B)^2 = A^2 - 2AB + B^2.$$

We can use these equations in reverse to factor trinomial squares.

> **TRINOMIAL SQUARES**
>
> $A^2 + 2AB + B^2 = (A + B)^2;$
> $A^2 - 2AB + B^2 = (A - B)^2$

How can we recognize when an expression to be factored is a trinomial square? Look at $A^2 + 2AB + B^2$ and $A^2 - 2AB + B^2$. In order for an expression to be a trinomial square:

a) The two expressions A^2 and B^2 must be squares, such as

$$4, \quad x^2, \quad 25x^4, \quad 16t^2.$$

When the coefficient is a perfect square and the power(s) of the variable(s) is (are) even, then the expression is a perfect square.

b) There must be no minus sign before A^2 or B^2.

c) If we multiply A and B and double the result, $2 \cdot AB$, we get either the remaining term or its opposite.

EXAMPLE 1 Determine whether $x^2 + 6x + 9$ is a trinomial square.

a) We know that x^2 and 9 are squares.

b) There is no minus sign before x^2 or 9.

c) If we multiply the square roots, x and 3, and double the product, we get the remaining term: $2 \cdot x \cdot 3 = 6x$.

Thus, $x^2 + 6x + 9$ is the square of a binomial. In fact, $x^2 + 6x + 9 = (x + 3)^2$.

EXAMPLE 2 Determine whether $x^2 + 6x + 11$ is a trinomial square.

The answer is no, because only one term, x^2, is a square.

OBJECTIVES

a Recognize trinomial squares.

b Factor trinomial squares.

c Recognize differences of squares.

d Factor differences of squares, being careful to factor completely.

It would be helpful to memorize this table of perfect squares.

NUMBER, N	PERFECT SQUARE, N^2
1	1
2	4
3	9
4	16
5	25
6	36
7	49
8	64
9	81
10	100
11	121
12	144
13	169
14	196
15	225
16	256
17	289
18	324
19	361
20	400
21	441
22	484
23	529
24	576
25	625

Determine whether each is a
trinomial square. Write "yes" or "no."

1. $x^2 + 8x + 16$

2. $25 - x^2 + 10x$

3. $t^2 - 12t + 4$

4. $25 + 20y + 4y^2$

5. $5x^2 + 16 - 14x$

6. $16x^2 + 40x + 25$

7. $p^2 + 6p - 9$

8. $25a^2 + 9 - 30a$

EXAMPLE 3 Determine whether $16x^2 + 49 - 56x$ is a trinomial square.

It helps to first write the trinomial in descending order:

$$16x^2 - 56x + 49.$$

a) We know that $16x^2$ and 49 are squares.

b) There is no minus sign before $16x^2$ or 49.

c) If we multiply the square roots, $4x$ and 7, and double the product, we get the opposite of the remaining term: $2 \cdot 4x \cdot 7 = 56x$; $56x$ is the opposite of $-56x$.

Thus, $16x^2 + 49 - 56x$ is a trinomial square. In fact, $16x^2 - 56x + 49 = (4x - 7)^2$.

Do Exercises 1–8.

b Factoring Trinomial Squares

We can use the factoring methods from Sections 11.2–11.4 to factor trinomial squares, but there is a faster method using the following equations.

> **FACTORING TRINOMIAL SQUARES**
> $A^2 + 2AB + B^2 = (A + B)^2$;
> $A^2 - 2AB + B^2 = (A - B)^2$

We consider 3 to be a square root of 9 because $3^2 = 9$. Similarly, A is a square root of A^2. We use square roots of the squared terms and the sign of the remaining term to factor a trinomial square.

EXAMPLE 4 Factor: $x^2 + 6x + 9$.

$$x^2 + 6x + 9 = x^2 + 2 \cdot x \cdot 3 + 3^2 = (x + 3)^2$$

The sign of the middle term is positive.

$$A^2 + 2 \ A \ B + B^2 = (A + B)^2$$

EXAMPLE 5 Factor: $x^2 + 49 - 14x$.

$$x^2 + 49 - 14x = x^2 - 14x + 49 \qquad \text{Changing to descending order}$$
$$= x^2 - 2 \cdot x \cdot 7 + 7^2 \qquad \text{The sign of the middle term is negative.}$$
$$= (x - 7)^2$$

EXAMPLE 6 Factor: $16x^2 - 40x + 25$.

$$16x^2 - 40x + 25 = (4x)^2 - 2 \cdot 4x \cdot 5 + 5^2 = (4x - 5)^2$$

$$A^2 - 2 \ A \ B + B^2 = (A - B)^2$$

Do Exercises 9–13.

Factor.

9. $x^2 + 2x + 1$

10. $1 - 2x + x^2$

11. $4 + t^2 + 4t$

12. $25x^2 - 70x + 49$

13. $49 - 56y + 16y^2$

Answers

1. Yes   2. No   3. No   4. Yes
5. No   6. Yes   7. No   8. Yes
9. $(x + 1)^2$ 10. $(x - 1)^2$, or $(1 - x)^2$
11. $(t + 2)^2$ 12. $(5x - 7)^2$
13. $(4y - 7)^2$, or $(7 - 4y)^2$

EXAMPLE 7 Factor: $t^4 + 20t^2 + 100$.

$$t^4 + 20t^2 + 100 = (t^2)^2 + 2(t^2)(10) + 10^2$$
$$= (t^2 + 10)^2$$

EXAMPLE 8 Factor: $75m^3 + 210m^2 + 147m$.

Always look first for a common factor. This time there is one, $3m$:

$$75m^3 + 210m^2 + 147m = 3m(25m^2 + 70m + 49)$$
$$= 3m[(5m)^2 + 2(5m)(7) + 7^2]$$
$$= 3m(5m + 7)^2.$$

EXAMPLE 9 Factor: $4p^2 - 12pq + 9q^2$.

$$4p^2 - 12pq + 9q^2 = (2p)^2 - 2(2p)(3q) + (3q)^2$$
$$= (2p - 3q)^2$$

Do Exercises 14-17.

Factor.

14. $48m^2 + 75 + 120m$

15. $p^4 + 18p^2 + 81$

16. $4z^5 - 20z^4 + 25z^3$

17. $9a^2 + 30ab + 25b^2$

c Recognizing Differences of Squares

The following polynomials are *differences of squares*:

$$x^2 - 9, \quad 4t^2 - 49, \quad a^2 - 25b^2.$$

To factor a difference of squares such as $x^2 - 9$, think about the formula we used in Chapter 10:

$$(A + B)(A - B) = A^2 - B^2.$$

Equations are reversible, so we also know the following.

DIFFERENCE OF SQUARES

$$A^2 - B^2 = (A + B)(A - B)$$

Thus,

$$x^2 - 9 = (x + 3)(x - 3).$$

To use this formula, we must be able to recognize when it applies. A **difference of squares** is an expression like the following:

$$A^2 - B^2.$$

How can we recognize such expressions? Look at $A^2 - B^2$. In order for a binomial to be a difference of squares:

a) There must be two expressions, both squares, such as

$$4x^2, \quad 9, \quad 25t^4, \quad 1, \quad x^6, \quad 49y^8.$$

b) The terms must have different signs.

Answers

14. $3(4m + 5)^2$ **15.** $(p^2 + 9)^2$
16. $z^3(2z - 5)^2$ **17.** $(3a + 5b)^2$

11.5   Factoring Trinomial Squares and Differences of Squares   **859**

EXAMPLE 10 Is $9x^2 - 64$ a difference of squares?

a) The first expression is a square: $9x^2 = (3x)^2$.
The second expression is a square: $64 = 8^2$.

b) The terms have different signs, $+9x^2$ and -64.

Thus we have a difference of squares, $(3x)^2 - 8^2$.

EXAMPLE 11 Is $25 - t^3$ a difference of squares?

a) The expression t^3 is not a square.

The expression is not a difference of squares.

EXAMPLE 12 Is $-4x^2 + 16$ a difference of squares?

a) The expressions $4x^2$ and 16 are squares: $4x^2 = (2x)^2$ and $16 = 4^2$.

b) The terms have different signs, $-4x^2$ and $+16$.

Thus we have a difference of squares. We can also see this by rewriting in the equivalent form: $16 - 4x^2$.

Do Exercises 18–24.

Determine whether each is a difference of squares. Write "yes" or "no."

18. $x^2 - 25$

19. $t^2 - 24$

20. $y^2 + 36$

21. $4x^2 - 15$

22. $16x^4 - 49$

23. $9w^6 - 1$

24. $-49 + 25t^2$

(d) Factoring Differences of Squares

To factor a difference of squares, we use the following equation.

> **FACTORING A DIFFERENCE OF SQUARES**
> $A^2 - B^2 = (A + B)(A - B)$

To factor a difference of squares $A^2 - B^2$, we find A and B, which are square roots of the expressions A^2 and B^2. We then use A and B to form two factors. One is the sum $A + B$, and the other is the difference $A - B$.

EXAMPLE 13 Factor: $x^2 - 4$.

$$x^2 - 4 = x^2 - 2^2 = (x + 2)(x - 2)$$
$$A^2 - B^2 = (A + B)(A - B)$$

EXAMPLE 14 Factor: $9 - 16t^4$.

$$9 - 16t^4 = 3^2 - (4t^2)^2 = (3 + 4t^2)(3 - 4t^2)$$
$$A^2 - B^2 = (A + B)(A - B)$$

Answers

18. Yes   **19.** No   **20.** No   **21.** No
22. Yes   **23.** Yes   **24.** Yes

EXAMPLE 15 Factor: $m^2 - 4p^2$.

$$m^2 - 4p^2 = m^2 - (2p)^2 = (m + 2p)(m - 2p)$$

EXAMPLE 16 Factor: $x^2 - \dfrac{1}{9}$.

$$x^2 - \frac{1}{9} = x^2 - \left(\frac{1}{3}\right)^2 = \left(x + \frac{1}{3}\right)\left(x - \frac{1}{3}\right)$$

EXAMPLE 17 Factor: $18x^2 - 50x^6$.

Always look first for a factor common to all terms. This time there is one, $2x^2$.

$$\begin{aligned}
18x^2 - 50x^6 &= 2x^2(9 - 25x^4) \\
&= 2x^2[3^2 - (5x^2)^2] \\
&= 2x^2(3 + 5x^2)(3 - 5x^2)
\end{aligned}$$

EXAMPLE 18 Factor: $49x^4 - 9x^6$.

$$\begin{aligned}
49x^4 - 9x^6 &= x^4(49 - 9x^2) \\
&= x^4[7^2 - (3x)^2] \\
&= x^4(7 + 3x)(7 - 3x)
\end{aligned}$$

Do Exercises 25–29.

Factor.

25. $x^2 - 9$

26. $4t^2 - 64$

27. $a^2 - 25b^2$

28. $64x^4 - 25x^6$

29. $5 - 20t^6$
[*Hint:* $1 = 1^2, t^6 = (t^3)^2$.]

Caution!

Note carefully in these examples that a difference of squares is *not* the square of the difference; that is,

$$A^2 - B^2 \neq (A - B)^2.$$

For example,

$$(45 - 5)^2 = 40^2 = 1600,$$

but

$$45^2 - 5^2 = 2025 - 25 = 2000.$$

Similarly,

$$A^2 - 2AB + B^2 \neq (A - B)(A + B).$$

For example,

$$(10 - 3)(10 + 3) = 7 \cdot 13 = 91,$$

but

$$\begin{aligned}
10^2 - 2 \cdot 10 \cdot 3 + 3^2 &= 100 - 2 \cdot 10 \cdot 3 + 9 \\
&= 100 - 60 + 9 \\
&= 49.
\end{aligned}$$

Answers

25. $(x + 3)(x - 3)$
26. $4(t + 4)(t - 4)$
27. $(a + 5b)(a - 5b)$
28. $x^4(8 + 5x)(8 - 5x)$
29. $5(1 + 2t^3)(1 - 2t^3)$

Factoring Completely

If a factor with more than one term can still be factored, you should do so. When no factor can be factored further, you have **factored completely**. Always factor completely whenever told to factor.

EXAMPLE 19 Factor: $p^4 - 16$.

$$p^4 - 16 = (p^2)^2 - 4^2$$
$$= (p^2 + 4)(p^2 - 4) \qquad \text{Factoring a difference of squares}$$
$$= (p^2 + 4)(p + 2)(p - 2) \qquad \text{Factoring further; } p^2 - 4 \text{ is a difference of squares.}$$

The polynomial $p^2 + 4$ cannot be factored further into polynomials with real coefficients.

-- *Caution!* --

Apart from possibly removing a common factor, you cannot factor a sum of squares as a product of binomials. In particular,

$$A^2 + B^2 \neq (A + B)^2.$$

Consider $25x^2 + 100$. Here a sum of squares has a common factor, 25. Factoring, we get $25(x^2 + 4)$, where $x^2 + 4$ is prime. For example,

$$x^2 + 4 \neq (x + 2)^2.$$

EXAMPLE 20 Factor: $y^4 - 16x^{12}$.

$$y^4 - 16x^{12} = (y^2 + 4x^6)(y^2 - 4x^6) \qquad \text{Factoring a difference of squares}$$
$$= (y^2 + 4x^6)(y + 2x^3)(y - 2x^3) \qquad \text{Factoring further. The factor } y^2 - 4x^6 \text{ is a difference of squares.}$$

The polynomial $y^2 + 4x^6$ cannot be factored further into polynomials with real coefficients.

EXAMPLE 21 Factor: $\dfrac{1}{16}x^8 - 81$.

$$\frac{1}{16}x^8 - 81 = \left(\frac{1}{4}x^4 + 9\right)\left(\frac{1}{4}x^4 - 9\right) \qquad \text{Factoring a difference of squares}$$
$$= \left(\frac{1}{4}x^4 + 9\right)\left(\frac{1}{2}x^2 + 3\right)\left(\frac{1}{2}x^2 - 3\right) \qquad \text{Factoring further. The factor } \frac{1}{4}x^4 - 9 \text{ is a difference of squares.}$$

Factor completely.

30. $81x^4 - 1$

31. $16 - \dfrac{1}{81}y^8$

32. $49p^4 - 25q^6$

> **TIPS FOR FACTORING**
> - Always look first for a common factor. If there is one, factor it out.
> - Be alert for trinomial squares and differences of squares. Once recognized, they can be factored without trial and error.
> - Always factor completely.
> - Check by multiplying.

Answers

30. $(9x^2 + 1)(3x + 1)(3x - 1)$

31. $\left(4 + \dfrac{1}{9}y^4\right)\left(2 + \dfrac{1}{3}y^2\right)\left(2 - \dfrac{1}{3}y^2\right)$

32. $(7p^2 + 5q^3)(7p^2 - 5q^3)$

Do Exercises 30–32.

a   Determine whether each of the following is a trinomial square. Answer "yes" or "no."

1. $x^2 - 14x + 49$

2. $x^2 - 16x + 64$

3. $x^2 + 16x - 64$

4. $x^2 - 14x - 49$

5. $x^2 - 2x + 4$

6. $x^2 + 3x + 9$

7. $9x^2 - 24x + 16$

8. $25x^2 + 30x + 9$

b   Factor completely. Remember to look first for a common factor and to check by multiplying.

9. $x^2 - 14x + 49$

10. $x^2 - 20x + 100$

11. $x^2 + 16x + 64$

12. $x^2 + 20x + 100$

13. $x^2 - 2x + 1$

14. $x^2 + 2x + 1$

15. $4 + 4x + x^2$

16. $4 + x^2 - 4x$

17. $y^2 + 12y + 36$

18. $y^2 + 18y + 81$

19. $16 + t^2 - 8t$

20. $9 + t^2 - 6t$

21. $q^4 - 6q^2 + 9$

22. $64 + 16a^2 + a^4$

23. $49 + 56y + 16y^2$

24. $75 + 48a^2 - 120a$

25. $2x^2 - 4x + 2$

26. $2x^2 - 40x + 200$

27. $x^3 - 18x^2 + 81x$

28. $x^3 + 24x^2 + 144x$

29. $12q^2 - 36q + 27$

30. $20p^2 + 100p + 125$

31. $49 - 42x + 9x^2$

32. $64 - 112x + 49x^2$

33. $5y^4 + 10y^2 + 5$

34. $a^4 + 14a^2 + 49$

35. $1 + 4x^4 + 4x^2$

36. $1 - 2a^5 + a^{10}$

37. $4p^2 + 12pq + 9q^2$

38. $25m^2 + 20mn + 4n^2$

39. $a^2 - 6ab + 9b^2$

40. $x^2 - 14xy + 49y^2$

41. $81a^2 - 18ab + b^2$

42. $64p^2 + 16pq + q^2$

43. $36a^2 + 96ab + 64b^2$

44. $16m^2 - 40mn + 25n^2$

---

c Determine whether each of the following is a difference of squares. Answer "yes" or "no."

45. $x^2 - 4$

46. $x^2 - 36$

47. $x^2 + 25$

48. $x^2 + 9$

49. $x^2 - 45$

50. $x^2 - 80y^2$

51. $-25y^2 + 16x^2$

52. $-1 + 36x^2$

---

d Factor completely. Remember to look first for a common factor.

53. $y^2 - 4$

54. $q^2 - 1$

55. $p^2 - 9$

56. $x^2 - 36$

57. $-49 + t^2$

58. $-64 + m^2$

59. $a^2 - b^2$

60. $p^2 - q^2$

61. $25t^2 - m^2$

62. $w^2 - 49z^2$

63. $100 - k^2$

64. $81 - w^2$

65. $16a^2 - 9$

66. $25x^2 - 4$

67. $4x^2 - 25y^2$

68. $9a^2 - 16b^2$

Copyright © 2012 Pearson Education, Inc.

69. $8x^2 - 98$

70. $24x^2 - 54$

71. $36x - 49x^3$

72. $16x - 81x^3$

73. $\dfrac{1}{16} - 49x^8$

74. $\dfrac{1}{625}x^8 - 49$

75. $0.09y^2 - 0.0004$

76. $0.16p^2 - 0.0025$

77. $49a^4 - 81$

78. $25a^4 - 9$

79. $a^4 - 16$

80. $y^4 - 1$

81. $5x^4 - 405$

82. $4x^4 - 64$

83. $1 - y^8$

84. $x^8 - 1$

85. $x^{12} - 16$

86. $x^8 - 81$

87. $y^2 - \dfrac{1}{16}$

88. $x^2 - \dfrac{1}{25}$

89. $25 - \dfrac{1}{49}x^2$

90. $\dfrac{1}{4} - 9q^2$

91. $16m^4 - t^4$

92. $p^4q^4 - 1$

Skill Maintenance

Divide.   [7.6a, c]

93. $(-110) \div 10$

94. $-1000 \div (-2.5)$

95. $\left(-\dfrac{2}{3}\right) \div \dfrac{4}{5}$

96. $8.1 \div (-9)$

97. $-64 \div (-32)$

98. $-256 \div 1.6$

Find a polynomial for the shaded area in each figure. (Leave results in terms of π where appropriate.)   [10.4d]

99.

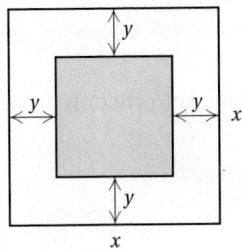

100.

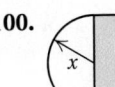

Simplify.

101. $y^5 \cdot y^7$ [10.1d]

102. $(5a^2b^3)^2$ [10.2a, b]

Find the intercepts. Then graph each equation.   [9.2a]

103. $y - 6x = 6$

104. $3x - 5y = 15$

Synthesis

Factor completely, if possible.

105. $49x^2 - 216$

106. $27x^3 - 13x$

107. $x^2 + 22x + 121$

108. $x^2 - 5x + 25$

109. $18x^3 + 12x^2 + 2x$

110. $162x^2 - 82$

111. $x^8 - 2^8$

112. $4x^4 - 4x^2$

113. $3x^5 - 12x^3$

114. $3x^2 - \frac{1}{3}$

115. $18x^3 - \frac{8}{25}x$

116. $x^2 - 2.25$

117. $0.49p - p^3$

118. $3.24x^2 - 0.81$

119. $0.64x^2 - 1.21$

120. $1.28x^2 - 2$

121. $(x + 3)^2 - 9$

122. $(y - 5)^2 - 36q^2$

123. $x^2 - \left(\frac{1}{x}\right)^2$

124. $a^{2n} - 49b^{2n}$

125. $81 - b^{4k}$

126. $9x^{18} + 48x^9 + 64$

127. $9b^{2n} + 12b^n + 4$

128. $(x + 7)^2 - 4x - 24$

129. $(y + 3)^2 + 2(y + 3) + 1$

130. $49(x + 1)^2 - 42(x + 1) + 9$

Find c such that the polynomial is the square of a binomial.

131. $cy^2 + 6y + 1$

132. $cy^2 - 24y + 9$

Use the TABLE feature or graphs to determine whether each factorization is correct. (See the Calculator Corner on p. 842.)

133. $x^2 + 9 = (x + 3)(x + 3)$

134. $x^2 - 49 = (x - 7)(x + 7)$

135. $x^2 + 9 = (x + 3)^2$

136. $x^2 - 49 = (x - 7)^2$

Copyright © 2012 Pearson Education, Inc.

11.6 Factoring: A General Strategy

OBJECTIVE

a Factor polynomials completely using any of the methods considered in this chapter.

We now combine all of our factoring techniques and consider a general strategy for factoring polynomials. Here we will encounter polynomials of all the types we have considered, in random order, so you will have the opportunity to determine which method to use.

FACTORING STRATEGY

To factor a polynomial:

a) Always look first for a common factor. If there is one, factor out the largest common factor.

b) Then look at the number of terms.

Two terms: Determine whether you have a difference of squares, $A^2 - B^2$. Do not try to factor a sum of squares: $A^2 + B^2$.

Three terms: Determine whether the trinomial is a square. If it is, you know how to factor. If not, try trial and error, using FOIL or the *ac*-method.

Four terms: Try factoring by grouping.

c) *Always factor completely.* If a factor with more than one term can still be factored, you should factor it. When no factor can be factored further, you have finished.

d) Check by multiplying.

EXAMPLE 1 Factor: $5t^4 - 80$.

a) We look for a common factor. There is one, 5.

$$5t^4 - 80 = 5(t^4 - 16)$$

b) The factor $t^4 - 16$ has only two terms. It is a difference of squares: $(t^2)^2 - 4^2$. We factor $t^4 - 16$ and then include the common factor:

$$5(t^2 + 4)(t^2 - 4).$$

c) We see that one of the factors, $t^2 - 4$, is again a difference of squares. We factor it:

$$5(t^2 + 4)(t + 2)(t - 2).$$

This is a sum of squares. It cannot be factored.

We have factored completely because no factor with more than one term can be factored further.

d) Check: $5(t^2 + 4)(t + 2)(t - 2) = 5(t^2 + 4)(t^2 - 4)$
$$= 5(t^4 - 16)$$
$$= 5t^4 - 80.$$

STUDY TIPS

LEARN FROM YOUR MISTAKES

When your instructor returns a graded homework assignment, quiz, or test, take time to review it and understand the mistakes you made. Be sure to ask your instructor for help if you can't see what your mistakes are. We often learn much more from our mistakes than from the things we do correctly.

EXAMPLE 2 Factor: $2x^3 + 10x^2 + x + 5$.

a) We look for a common factor. There isn't one.

b) There are four terms. We try factoring by grouping:

$$2x^3 + 10x^2 + x + 5$$
$$= (2x^3 + 10x^2) + (x + 5) \qquad \text{Separating into two binomials}$$
$$= 2x^2(x + 5) + 1(x + 5) \qquad \text{Factoring each binomial}$$
$$= (x + 5)(2x^2 + 1). \qquad \text{Factoring out the common factor } x + 5$$

c) None of these factors can be factored further, so we have factored completely.

d) Check: $(x + 5)(2x^2 + 1) = x \cdot 2x^2 + x \cdot 1 + 5 \cdot 2x^2 + 5 \cdot 1$
$$= 2x^3 + x + 10x^2 + 5, \text{ or}$$
$$2x^3 + 10x^2 + x + 5.$$

EXAMPLE 3 Factor: $x^5 - 2x^4 - 35x^3$.

a) We look first for a common factor. This time there is one, x^3:

$$x^5 - 2x^4 - 35x^3 = x^3(x^2 - 2x - 35).$$

b) The factor $x^2 - 2x - 35$ has three terms, but it is not a trinomial square. We factor it using trial and error:

$$x^5 - 2x^4 - 35x^3 = x^3(x^2 - 2x - 35) = x^3(x - 7)(x + 5).$$

> Don't forget to include the common factor in the final answer!

c) No factor with more than one term can be factored further, so we have factored completely.

d) Check: $x^3(x - 7)(x + 5) = x^3(x^2 - 2x - 35) = x^5 - 2x^4 - 35x^3$.

EXAMPLE 4 Factor: $x^4 - 10x^2 + 25$.

a) We look first for a common factor. There isn't one.

b) There are three terms. We see that this polynomial is a trinomial square. We factor it:

$$x^4 - 10x^2 + 25 = (x^2)^2 - 2 \cdot x^2 \cdot 5 + 5^2 = (x^2 - 5)^2.$$

We could use trial and error if we have not recognized that we have a trinomial square.

c) Since $x^2 - 5$ cannot be factored further, we have factored completely.

d) Check: $(x^2 - 5)^2 = (x^2)^2 - 2(x^2)(5) + 5^2 = x^4 - 10x^2 + 25$.

Do Exercises 1–5.

EXAMPLE 5 Factor: $6x^2y^4 - 21x^3y^5 + 3x^2y^6$.

a) We look first for a common factor:

$$6x^2y^4 - 21x^3y^5 + 3x^2y^6 = 3x^2y^4(2 - 7xy + y^2).$$

Factor.

1. $3m^4 - 3$

2. $x^6 + 8x^3 + 16$

3. $2x^4 + 8x^3 + 6x^2$

4. $3x^3 + 12x^2 - 2x - 8$

5. $8x^3 - 200x$

Answers

1. $3(m^2 + 1)(m + 1)(m - 1)$
2. $(x^3 + 4)^2$ 3. $2x^2(x + 1)(x + 3)$
4. $(x + 4)(3x^2 - 2)$
5. $8x(x - 5)(x + 5)$

b) There are three terms in $2 - 7xy + y^2$. We determine whether the trinomial is a square. Since only y^2 is a square, we do not have a trinomial square. Can the trinomial be factored by trial and error? A key to the answer is that x is only in the term $-7xy$. The polynomial might be in a form like $(1 - y)(2 + y)$, but there would be no x in the middle term. Thus, $2 - 7xy + y^2$ cannot be factored.

c) Have we factored completely? Yes, because no factor with more than one term can be factored further.

d) The check is left to the student.

EXAMPLE 6 Factor: $(p + q)(x + 2) + (p + q)(x + y)$.

a) We look for a common factor:
$$(p + q)(x + 2) + (p + q)(x + y) = (p + q)[(x + 2) + (x + y)]$$
$$= (p + q)(2x + y + 2).$$

b) There are three terms in $2x + y + 2$, but this trinomial cannot be factored further.

c) Neither factor can be factored further, so we have factored completely.

d) The check is left to the student.

EXAMPLE 7 Factor: $px + py + qx + qy$.

a) We look first for a common factor. There isn't one.

b) There are four terms. We try factoring by grouping:
$$px + py + qx + qy = p(x + y) + q(x + y)$$
$$= (x + y)(p + q).$$

c) Have we factored completely? Since neither factor can be factored further, we have factored completely.

d) Check: $(x + y)(p + q) = px + qx + py + qy$, or
$$px + py + qx + qy.$$

EXAMPLE 8 Factor: $25x^2 + 20xy + 4y^2$.

a) We look first for a common factor. There isn't one.

b) There are three terms. We determine whether the trinomial is a square. The first term and the last term are squares:
$$25x^2 = (5x)^2 \quad \text{and} \quad 4y^2 = (2y)^2.$$

Since twice the product of $5x$ and $2y$ is the other term,
$$2 \cdot 5x \cdot 2y = 20xy,$$

the trinomial is a perfect square.

We factor by writing the square roots of the square terms and the sign of the middle term:
$$25x^2 + 20xy + 4y^2 = (5x + 2y)^2.$$

c) Since $5x + 2y$ cannot be factored further, we have factored completely.

d) Check: $(5x + 2y)^2 = (5x)^2 + 2(5x)(2y) + (2y)^2$
$$= 25x^2 + 20xy + 4y^2.$$

STUDY TIPS

TIME MANAGEMENT

Here are some additional tips to help you with time management. (See also the Study Tips on time management in Sections 8.2 and 11.2.)

- **Avoid distractions.** Don't allow yourself to be distracted from your studies by electronic "time robbers" such as video games, the Internet, and television. Be disciplined and *study first*. Then reward yourself with a leisure activity if there is enough time in your day.

- **Don't be overwhelmed.** Don't let the idea of starting your homework or studying for a test overwhelm you. Begin by choosing a few homework problems to do or focus on a single topic to review for a test. Often, getting started is the most difficult part of an assignment. Once you have cleared this mental hurdle, your task will seem less overwhelming.

EXAMPLE 9 Factor: $p^2q^2 + 7pq + 12$.

a) We look first for a common factor. There isn't one.

b) There are three terms. We determine whether the trinomial is a square. The first term is a square, but neither of the other terms is a square, so we do not have a trinomial square. We factor, thinking of the product pq as a single variable. We consider this possibility for factorization:

$$(pq + \boxed{})(pq + \boxed{}).$$

We factor the last term, 12. All the signs are positive, so we consider only positive factors. Possibilities are 1, 12 and 2, 6 and 3, 4. The pair 3, 4 gives a sum of 7 for the coefficient of the middle term. Thus,

$$p^2q^2 + 7pq + 12 = (pq + 3)(pq + 4).$$

c) No factor with more than one term can be factored further, so we have factored completely.

d) Check: $(pq + 3)(pq + 4) = (pq)(pq) + 4 \cdot pq + 3 \cdot pq + 3 \cdot 4$
$$= p^2q^2 + 7pq + 12.$$

EXAMPLE 10 Factor: $8x^4 - 20x^2y - 12y^2$.

a) We look first for a common factor:

$$8x^4 - 20x^2y - 12y^2 = 4(2x^4 - 5x^2y - 3y^2).$$

b) There are three terms in $2x^4 - 5x^2y - 3y^2$. We determine whether the trinomial is a square. Since none of the terms is a square, we do not have a trinomial square. We factor $2x^4$. Possibilities are $2x^2$, x^2 and $2x$, x^3 and others. We also factor the last term, $-3y^2$. Possibilities are $3y$, $-y$ and $-3y$, y and others. We look for factors such that the sum of their products is the middle term. The x^2 in the middle term, $-5x^2y$, should lead us to try $(2x^2)(x^2)$. We try some possibilities:

$$(2x^2 - y)(x^2 + 3y) = 2x^4 + 5x^2y - 3y^2,$$
$$(2x^2 + y)(x^2 - 3y) = 2x^4 - 5x^2y - 3y^2.$$

c) No factor with more than one term can be factored further, so we have factored completely. The factorization, including the common factor, is

$$4(2x^2 + y)(x^2 - 3y).$$

d) Check: $4(2x^2 + y)(x^2 - 3y) = 4[(2x^2)(x^2) + 2x^2(-3y) + yx^2 + y(-3y)]$
$$= 4[2x^4 - 6x^2y + x^2y - 3y^2]$$
$$= 4(2x^4 - 5x^2y - 3y^2)$$
$$= 8x^4 - 20x^2y - 12y^2.$$

EXAMPLE 11 Factor: $a^4 - 16b^4$.

a) We look first for a common factor. There isn't one.

b) There are two terms. Since $a^4 = (a^2)^2$ and $16b^4 = (4b^2)^2$, we see that we do have a difference of squares. Thus,

$$a^4 - 16b^4 = (a^2 + 4b^2)(a^2 - 4b^2).$$

c) The last factor can be factored further. It is also a difference of squares.

$$a^4 - 16b^4 = (a^2 + 4b^2)(a + 2b)(a - 2b)$$

d) Check: $(a^2 + 4b^2)(a + 2b)(a - 2b) = (a^2 + 4b^2)(a^2 - 4b^2)$
$$= a^4 - 16b^4.$$

Do Exercises 6-12.

Factor.

6. $15x^4 + 5x^2y - 10y^2$

7. $10p^6q^2 + 4p^5q^3 + 2p^4q^4$

8. $(a - b)(x + 5) + (a - b)(x + y^2)$

9. $ax^2 + ay + bx^2 + by$

10. $x^4 + 2x^2y^2 + y^4$

11. $x^2y^2 + 5xy + 4$

12. $p^4 - 81q^4$

Answers

6. $5(3x^2 - 2y)(x^2 + y)$
7. $2p^4q^2(5p^2 + 2pq + q^2)$
8. $(a - b)(2x + 5 + y^2)$
9. $(x^2 + y)(a + b)$ 10. $(x^2 + y^2)^2$
11. $(xy + 1)(xy + 4)$
12. $(p^2 + 9q^2)(p + 3q)(p - 3q)$

a   Factor completely.

1. $3x^2 - 192$

2. $2t^2 - 18$

3. $a^2 + 25 - 10a$

4. $y^2 + 49 + 14y$

5. $2x^2 - 11x + 12$

6. $8y^2 - 18y - 5$

7. $x^3 + 24x^2 + 144x$

8. $x^3 - 18x^2 + 81x$

9. $x^3 + 3x^2 - 4x - 12$

10. $x^3 - 5x^2 - 25x + 125$

11. $48x^2 - 3$

12. $50x^2 - 32$

13. $9x^3 + 12x^2 - 45x$

14. $20x^3 - 4x^2 - 72x$

15. $x^2 + 4$

16. $t^2 + 25$

17. $x^4 + 7x^2 - 3x^3 - 21x$

18. $m^4 + 8m^3 + 8m^2 + 64m$

19. $x^5 - 14x^4 + 49x^3$

20. $2x^6 + 8x^5 + 8x^4$

21. $20 - 6x - 2x^2$

22. $45 - 3x - 6x^2$

23. $x^2 - 6x + 1$

24. $x^2 + 8x + 5$

25. $4x^4 - 64$

26. $5x^5 - 80x$

27. $1 - y^8$

28. $t^8 - 1$

29. $x^5 - 4x^4 + 3x^3$

30. $x^6 - 2x^5 + 7x^4$

31. $\dfrac{1}{81}x^6 - \dfrac{8}{27}x^3 + \dfrac{16}{9}$

32. $36a^2 - 15a + \dfrac{25}{16}$

33. $mx^2 + my^2$

34. $12p^2 + 24q^3$

35. $9x^2y^2 - 36xy$

36. $x^2y - xy^2$

37. $2\pi rh + 2\pi r^2$

38. $10p^4q^4 + 35p^3q^3 + 10p^2q^2$

39. $(a + b)(x - 3) + (a + b)(x + 4)$

40. $5c(a^3 + b) - (a^3 + b)$

41. $(x - 1)(x + 1) - y(x + 1)$

42. $3(p - q) - q^2(p - q)$

43. $n^2 + 2n + np + 2p$

44. $a^2 - 3a + ay - 3y$

45. $6q^2 - 3q + 2pq - p$

46. $2x^2 - 4x + xy - 2y$

47. $4b^2 + a^2 - 4ab$

48. $x^2 + y^2 - 2xy$

49. $16x^2 + 24xy + 9y^2$

50. $9c^2 + 6cd + d^2$

51. $49m^4 - 112m^2n + 64n^2$

52. $4x^2y^2 + 12xyz + 9z^2$

53. $y^4 + 10y^2z^2 + 25z^4$

54. $0.01x^4 - 0.1x^2y^2 + 0.25y^4$

Copyright © 2012 Pearson Education, Inc.

55. $\frac{1}{4}a^2 + \frac{1}{3}ab + \frac{1}{9}b^2$

56. $4p^2q + pq^2 + 4p^3$

57. $a^2 - ab - 2b^2$

58. $3b^2 - 17ab - 6a^2$

59. $2mn - 360n^2 + m^2$

60. $15 + x^2y^2 + 8xy$

61. $m^2n^2 - 4mn - 32$

62. $p^2q^2 + 7pq + 6$

63. $r^5s^2 - 10r^4s + 16r^3$

64. $p^5q^2 + 3p^4q - 10p^3$

65. $a^5 + 4a^4b - 5a^3b^2$

66. $2s^6t^2 + 10s^3t^3 + 12t^4$

67. $a^2 - \frac{1}{25}b^2$

68. $p^2 - \frac{1}{49}b^2$

69. $x^2 - y^2$

70. $p^2q^2 - r^2$

71. $16 - p^4q^4$

72. $15a^4 - 15b^4$

73. $1 - 16x^{12}y^{12}$

74. $81a^4 - b^4$

75. $q^3 + 8q^2 - q - 8$

76. $m^3 - 7m^2 - 4m + 28$

77. $6a^3b^3 - a^2b^2 - 2ab$

78. $4ab^5 - 32b^4 + a^2b^6$

79. $m^4 - 5m^2 + 4$

80. $8x^3y^3 - 6x^2y^2 - 5xy$

81. $t^4 - 2t^2 + 1$

Skill Maintenance

Find an equation of a line containing the given point and having the given slope.   [9.4b]

82. $(0, -4); m = 8$

83. $(-4, 0); m = -3$

84. $(3, -2); m = -0.28$

85. $(-4, 5); m = -\dfrac{2}{3}$

86. Multiply: $(5x - t)^2$.   [10.6d]

87. Divide: $\dfrac{7}{5} \div \left(-\dfrac{11}{10}\right)$.   [7.6c]

88. Solve: $4(x - 9) - 2(x + 7) < 14$.   [8.7e]

89. Solve $A = aX + bX - 7$ for X.   [8.4b]

Synthesis

Factor completely.

90. $x^4 + 9$

91. $x^3 + 20 - (5x^2 + 4x)$

92. $\dfrac{1}{5}x^2 - x + \dfrac{4}{5}$

93. $12.25x^2 - 7x + 1$

94. $x^3 - (x - 3x^2) - 3$

95. $5x^2 + 13x + 7.2$

96. $-(x^4 - 7x^2 - 18)$

97. $18 + y^3 - 9y - 2y^2$

98. $x^3 + x^2 - (4x + 4)$

99. $x^3 - x^2 - 4x + 4$

100. $3x^4 - 15x^2 + 12$

101. $a^3 - 4a^2 - a - 4$

102. $y^2(y + 1) - 4y(y + 1) - 21(y + 1)$

103. $y^2(y - 1) - 2y(y - 1) + (y - 1)$

104. $6(x - 1)^2 + 7y(x - 1) - 3y^2$

105. $(y + 4)^2 + 2x(y + 4) + x^2$

Copyright © 2012 Pearson Education, Inc.

11.7 Solving Quadratic Equations by Factoring

Second-degree equations like $x^2 + x - 156 = 0$ and $9 - x^2 = 0$ are examples of *quadratic equations*.

QUADRATIC EQUATION

A **quadratic equation** is an equation equivalent to an equation of the type

$$ax^2 + bx + c = 0, \ a \neq 0.$$

In order to solve quadratic equations, we need a new equation-solving principle.

a The Principle of Zero Products

The product of two numbers is 0 if one or both of the numbers is 0. Furthermore, *if any product is 0, then a factor must be 0.* For example:

If $7x = 0$, then we know that $x = 0$.

If $x(2x - 9) = 0$, then we know that $x = 0$ or $2x - 9 = 0$.

If $(x + 3)(x - 2) = 0$, then we know that $x + 3 = 0$ or $x - 2 = 0$.

Caution!

In a product such as $ab = 24$, we cannot conclude with certainty that a is 24 or that b is 24, but if $ab = 0$, we can conclude that $a = 0$ or $b = 0$.

EXAMPLE 1 Solve: $(x + 3)(x - 2) = 0$.

We have a product of 0. This equation will be true when either factor is 0. Thus it is true when

$$x + 3 = 0 \quad or \quad x - 2 = 0.$$

Here we have two simple equations that we know how to solve:

$$x = -3 \quad or \quad x = 2.$$

Each of the numbers -3 and 2 is a solution of the original equation, as we can see in the following checks.

Check: For -3:

$$\frac{(x + 3)(x - 2) = 0}{(-3 + 3)(-3 - 2) \ ? \ 0}$$
$$0(-5) \ \Big|$$
$$0 \ \Big| \quad \text{TRUE}$$

For 2:

$$\frac{(x + 3)(x - 2) = 0}{(2 + 3)(2 - 2) \ ? \ 0}$$
$$5(0) \ \Big|$$
$$0 \ \Big| \quad \text{TRUE}$$

OBJECTIVES

a Solve equations (already factored) using the principle of zero products.

b Solve quadratic equations by factoring and then using the principle of zero products.

SKILL TO REVIEW
Objective 8.3a: Solve equations using both the addition principle and the multiplication principle.

Solve.

1. $3x - 7 = 2$

2. $4y + 5 = 1$

STUDY TIPS

WORKING WITH A CLASSMATE

If you are finding it difficult to master a particular topic or concept, try talking about it with a classmate. Verbalizing your questions about the material might help clarify it. If your classmate is also finding the material difficult, it is possible that the majority of the people in your class are confused and you can ask your instructor to explain the concept again.

Answers

Skill to Review:
1. 3   2. -1

We now have a principle to help in solving quadratic equations.

> ### THE PRINCIPLE OF ZERO PRODUCTS
>
> An equation $ab = 0$ is true if and only if $a = 0$ is true or $b = 0$ is true, or both are true. (A product is 0 if and only if one or both of the factors is 0.)

EXAMPLE 2 Solve: $(5x + 1)(x - 7) = 0$.

We have

$$(5x + 1)(x - 7) = 0$$

$$5x + 1 = 0 \quad or \quad x - 7 = 0 \qquad \text{Using the principle of zero products}$$

$$5x = -1 \quad or \qquad x = 7 \qquad \text{Solving the two equations separately}$$

$$x = -\tfrac{1}{5} \quad or \qquad x = 7.$$

Check: For $-\tfrac{1}{5}$:

$$\frac{(5x + 1)(x - 7) = 0}{\left(5\left(-\tfrac{1}{5}\right) + 1\right)\left(-\tfrac{1}{5} - 7\right) \overset{?}{} 0}$$
$$(-1 + 1)\left(-7\tfrac{1}{5}\right)$$
$$0\left(-7\tfrac{1}{5}\right)$$
$$0 \quad \text{TRUE}$$

For 7:

$$\frac{(5x + 1)(x - 7) = 0}{(5(7) + 1)(7 - 7) \overset{?}{} 0}$$
$$(35 + 1) \cdot 0$$
$$36 \cdot 0$$
$$0 \quad \text{TRUE}$$

The solutions are $-\tfrac{1}{5}$ and 7.

When you solve an equation using the principle of zero products, a check by substitution, as in Examples 1 and 2, will detect errors in solving.

> Do Exercises 1–3.

When some factors have only one term, you can still use the principle of zero products.

EXAMPLE 3 Solve: $x(2x - 9) = 0$.

We have

$$x(2x - 9) = 0$$

$$x = 0 \quad or \quad 2x - 9 = 0 \qquad \text{Using the principle of zero products}$$

$$x = 0 \quad or \qquad 2x = 9$$

$$x = 0 \quad or \qquad x = \frac{9}{2}.$$

Check: For 0:

$$\frac{x(2x - 9) = 0}{0 \cdot (2 \cdot 0 - 9) \overset{?}{} 0}$$
$$0 \cdot (-9)$$
$$0 \quad \text{TRUE}$$

For $\frac{9}{2}$:

$$\frac{x(2x - 9) = 0}{\tfrac{9}{2} \cdot \left(2 \cdot \tfrac{9}{2} - 9\right) \overset{?}{} 0}$$
$$\tfrac{9}{2} \cdot (9 - 9)$$
$$\tfrac{9}{2} \cdot 0$$
$$0 \quad \text{TRUE}$$

> Do Exercise 4.

Solve using the principle of zero products.

1. $(x - 3)(x + 4) = 0$

2. $(x - 7)(x - 3) = 0$

3. $(4t + 1)(3t - 2) = 0$

4. Solve: $y(3y - 17) = 0$.

Answers

1. $3, -4$ 2. $7, 3$ 3. $-\dfrac{1}{4}, \dfrac{2}{3}$ 4. $0, \dfrac{17}{3}$

(b) Using Factoring to Solve Equations

Using factoring and the principle of zero products, we can solve some new kinds of equations. Thus we have extended our equation-solving abilities.

EXAMPLE 4 Solve: $x^2 + 5x + 6 = 0$.

There are no like terms to collect, and we have a squared term. We first factor the polynomial. Then we use the principle of zero products.

$$x^2 + 5x + 6 = 0$$
$$(x + 2)(x + 3) = 0 \qquad \text{Factoring}$$
$$x + 2 = 0 \quad or \quad x + 3 = 0 \qquad \text{Using the principle of zero products}$$
$$x = -2 \quad or \qquad x = -3$$

Check: For -2:

$$\begin{array}{c} x^2 + 5x + 6 = 0 \\ \hline (-2)^2 + 5(-2) + 6 \ \overset{?}{\vert} \ 0 \\ 4 - 10 + 6 \\ -6 + 6 \\ 0 \ \vert \quad \text{TRUE} \end{array}$$

For -3:

$$\begin{array}{c} x^2 + 5x + 6 = 0 \\ \hline (-3)^2 + 5(-3) + 6 \ \overset{?}{\vert} \ 0 \\ 9 - 15 + 6 \\ -6 + 6 \\ 0 \ \vert \quad \text{TRUE} \end{array}$$

The solutions are -2 and -3.

------------------------------ *Caution!* ------------------------------

Keep in mind that you *must* have 0 on one side of the equation before you can use the principle of zero products. Get all nonzero terms on one side and 0 on the other.

Do Exercise 5.

5. Solve: $x^2 - x - 6 = 0$.

EXAMPLE 5 Solve: $x^2 - 8x = -16$.

We first add 16 to get a 0 on one side:

$$x^2 - 8x = -16$$
$$x^2 - 8x + 16 = 0 \qquad \text{Adding 16}$$
$$(x - 4)(x - 4) = 0 \qquad \text{Factoring}$$
$$x - 4 = 0 \quad or \quad x - 4 = 0 \qquad \text{Using the principle of zero products}$$
$$x = 4 \quad or \qquad x = 4. \qquad \text{Solving each equation}$$

There is only one solution, 4. The check is left to the student.

Do Exercises 6 and 7.

Solve.

6. $x^2 - 3x = 28$

7. $x^2 = 6x - 9$

EXAMPLE 6 Solve: $x^2 + 5x = 0$.

$$x^2 + 5x = 0$$
$$x(x + 5) = 0 \qquad \text{Factoring out a common factor}$$
$$x = 0 \quad or \quad x + 5 = 0 \qquad \text{Using the principle of zero products}$$
$$x = 0 \quad or \qquad x = -5$$

The solutions are 0 and -5. The check is left to the student.

Answers
5. $-2, 3$ **6.** $-4, 7$ **7.** 3

EXAMPLE 7 Solve: $4x^2 = 25$.

$$4x^2 = 25$$

$$4x^2 - 25 = 0 \qquad \text{Subtracting 25 on both sides to get 0 on one side}$$

$$(2x - 5)(2x + 5) = 0 \qquad \text{Factoring a difference of squares}$$

$$2x - 5 = 0 \quad or \quad 2x + 5 = 0 \qquad \text{Using the principle of zero products}$$

$$2x = 5 \quad or \qquad 2x = -5 \qquad \text{Solving each equation}$$

$$x = \frac{5}{2} \quad or \qquad x = -\frac{5}{2}$$

The solutions are $\frac{5}{2}$ and $-\frac{5}{2}$. The check is left to the student.

Do Exercises 8 and 9.

Solve.

8. $x^2 - 4x = 0$

9. $9x^2 = 16$

EXAMPLE 8 Solve: $-5x^2 + 2x + 3 = 0$.

In this case, the leading coefficient of the trinomial is negative. Thus we first multiply by -1 and then proceed as we have in Examples 4–7.

$$-5x^2 + 2x + 3 = 0$$

$$-1(-5x^2 + 2x + 3) = -1 \cdot 0 \qquad \text{Multiplying by } -1$$

$$5x^2 - 2x - 3 = 0 \qquad \text{Simplifying}$$

$$(5x + 3)(x - 1) = 0 \qquad \text{Factoring}$$

$$5x + 3 = 0 \quad or \quad x - 1 = 0 \qquad \text{Using the principle of zero products}$$

$$5x = -3 \quad or \qquad x = 1$$

$$x = -\frac{3}{5} \quad or \qquad x = 1$$

The solutions are $-\frac{3}{5}$ and 1. The check is left to the student.

Do Exercises 10 and 11.

Solve.

10. $-2x^2 + 13x - 21 = 0$

11. $10 - 3x - x^2 = 0$

EXAMPLE 9 Solve: $(x + 2)(x - 2) = 5$.

Be careful with an equation like this one! It might be tempting to set each factor equal to 5. **Remember: We must have a 0 on one side**. We first carry out the multiplication on the left. Next, we subtract 5 on both sides to get 0 on one side. Then we proceed with the principle of zero products.

$$(x + 2)(x - 2) = 5$$

$$x^2 - 4 = 5 \qquad \text{Multiplying on the left}$$

$$x^2 - 4 - 5 = 5 - 5 \qquad \text{Subtracting 5}$$

$$x^2 - 9 = 0 \qquad \text{Simplifying}$$

$$(x + 3)(x - 3) = 0 \qquad \text{Factoring}$$

$$x + 3 = 0 \quad or \quad x - 3 = 0 \qquad \text{Using the principle of zero products}$$

$$x = -3 \quad or \qquad x = 3$$

The solutions are -3 and 3. The check is left to the student.

Do Exercise 12.

12. Solve: $(x + 1)(x - 1) = 8$.

Answers

8. $0, 4$ **9.** $-\frac{4}{3}, \frac{4}{3}$ **10.** $-3, \frac{7}{2}$ **11.** $-5, 2$
12. $-3, 3$

❋ Algebraic-Graphical Connection

In Chapter 9, we graphed linear equations of the type $y = mx + b$ and $Ax + By = C$. Recall that to find the x-intercept, we replaced y with 0 and solved for x. This procedure can also be used to find the x-intercepts when an equation of the form $y = ax^2 + bx + c, a \neq 0$, is to be graphed. Although the details of creating such graphs will be left to Chapter 15, we consider them briefly here from the standpoint of finding the x-intercepts. The graph of $y = ax^2 + bx + c, a \neq 0$, is shaped like one of the following curves. Note that each x-intercept represents a solution of $ax^2 + bx + c = 0$.

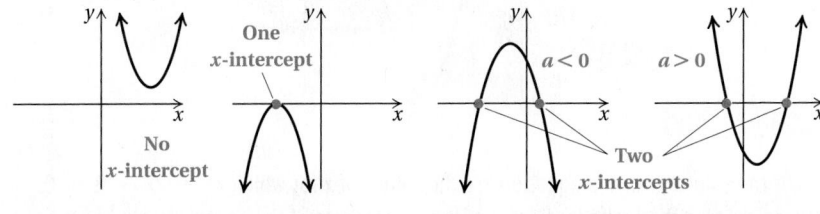

EXAMPLE 10 Find the x-intercepts of the graph of $y = x^2 - 4x - 5$ shown at right. (The grid is intentionally not included.)

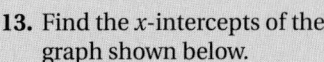

To find the x-intercepts, we let $y = 0$ and solve for x:

$$y = x^2 - 4x - 5$$
$$0 = x^2 - 4x - 5 \qquad \text{Substituting 0 for } y$$
$$0 = (x - 5)(x + 1) \qquad \text{Factoring}$$
$$x - 5 = 0 \quad or \quad x + 1 = 0 \qquad \text{Using the principle of zero products}$$
$$x = 5 \quad or \qquad x = -1.$$

The solutions of the equation $0 = x^2 - 4x - 5$ are 5 and -1. Thus the x-intercepts of the graph of $y = x^2 - 4x - 5$ are $(5, 0)$ and $(-1, 0)$. We can now label them on the graph.

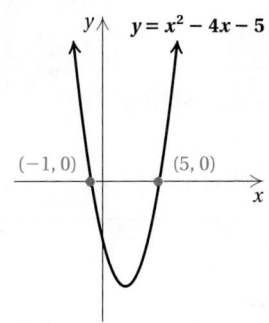

Do Exercises 13 and 14.

13. Find the x-intercepts of the graph shown below.

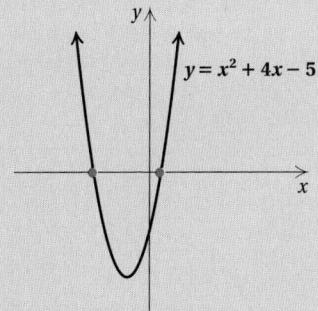

14. Use *only* the graph shown below to solve $3x - x^2 = 0$.

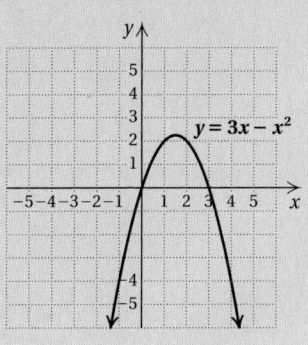

Answers
13. $(-5, 0), (1, 0)$ **14.** $0, 3$

Solving Quadratic Equations   We can solve quadratic equations graphically. Consider the equation $x^2 + 2x = 8$. First, we must write the equation with 0 on one side. To do this, we subtract 8 on both sides of the equation; we get $x^2 + 2x - 8 = 0$. Next, we graph $y = x^2 + 2x - 8$ in a window that shows the x-intercepts. The standard window works well in this case.

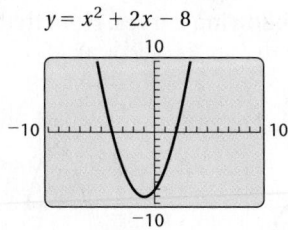

$y = x^2 + 2x - 8$

The solutions of the equation are the values of x for which $x^2 + 2x - 8 = 0$. These are also the first coordinates of the x-intercepts of the graph. We use the ZERO feature from the CALC menu to find these numbers. To find the solution corresponding to the leftmost x-intercept, we first press **2ND** (CALC) (2) to select the ZERO feature. The prompt "Left Bound?" appears. Next, we use the (◁) or the (▷) key to move the cursor to the left of the intercept and press **ENTER**. Now the prompt "Right Bound?" appears. Then we move the cursor to the right of the intercept and press **ENTER**. The prompt "Guess?" appears. We move the cursor close to the intercept and press **ENTER** again. We now see the cursor positioned at the leftmost x-intercept and the coordinates of that point, $x = -4$, $y = 0$, are displayed. Thus, $x^2 + 2x - 8 = 0$ when $x = -4$. This is one solution of the equation.

We can repeat this procedure to find the first coordinate of the other x-intercept. We see that $x = 2$ at that point. Thus the solutions of the equation $x^2 + 2x - 8 = 0$ are -4 and 2. Note that the x-intercepts of the graph of $y = x^2 + 2x - 8$ are $(-4, 0)$ and $(2, 0)$.

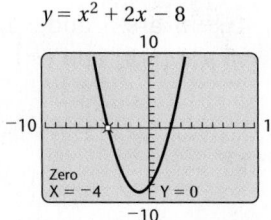

$y = x^2 + 2x - 8$

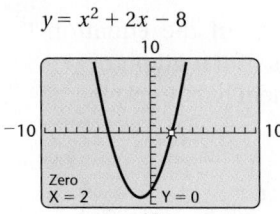

$y = x^2 + 2x - 8$

Exercises:

1. Solve each of the equations in Examples 4–8 graphically.

ⓐ Solve using the principle of zero products.

1. $(x + 4)(x + 9) = 0$

2. $(x + 2)(x - 7) = 0$

3. $(x + 3)(x - 8) = 0$

4. $(x + 6)(x - 8) = 0$

5. $(x + 12)(x - 11) = 0$

6. $(x - 13)(x + 53) = 0$

7. $x(x + 3) = 0$

8. $y(y + 5) = 0$

9. $0 = y(y + 18)$

10. $0 = x(x - 19)$

11. $(2x + 5)(x + 4) = 0$

12. $(2x + 9)(x + 8) = 0$

13. $(5x + 1)(4x - 12) = 0$

14. $(4x + 9)(14x - 7) = 0$

15. $(7x - 28)(28x - 7) = 0$

16. $(13x + 14)(6x - 5) = 0$

17. $2x(3x - 2) = 0$

18. $55x(8x - 9) = 0$

19. $\left(\frac{1}{5} + 2x\right)\left(\frac{1}{9} - 3x\right) = 0$

20. $\left(\frac{7}{4}x - \frac{1}{16}\right)\left(\frac{2}{3}x - \frac{16}{15}\right) = 0$

21. $(0.3x - 0.1)(0.05x + 1) = 0$

22. $(0.1x + 0.3)(0.4x - 20) = 0$

23. $9x(3x - 2)(2x - 1) = 0$

24. $(x + 5)(x - 75)(5x - 1) = 0$

ⓑ Solve by factoring and using the principle of zero products. Remember to check.

25. $x^2 + 6x + 5 = 0$

26. $x^2 + 7x + 6 = 0$

27. $x^2 + 7x - 18 = 0$

28. $x^2 + 4x - 21 = 0$

29. $x^2 - 8x + 15 = 0$

30. $x^2 - 9x + 14 = 0$

31. $x^2 - 8x = 0$

32. $x^2 - 3x = 0$

33. $x^2 + 18x = 0$

34. $x^2 + 16x = 0$

35. $x^2 = 16$

36. $100 = x^2$

37. $9x^2 - 4 = 0$

38. $4x^2 - 9 = 0$

39. $0 = 6x + x^2 + 9$

40. $0 = 25 + x^2 + 10x$

41. $x^2 + 16 = 8x$

42. $1 + x^2 = 2x$

43. $5x^2 = 6x$

44. $7x^2 = 8x$

45. $6x^2 - 4x = 10$

46. $3x^2 - 7x = 20$

47. $12y^2 - 5y = 2$

48. $2y^2 + 12y = -10$

49. $t(3t + 1) = 2$ **50.** $x(x - 5) = 14$ **51.** $100y^2 = 49$ **52.** $64a^2 = 81$

53. $x^2 - 5x = 18 + 2x$ **54.** $3x^2 + 8x = 9 + 2x$ **55.** $10x^2 - 23x + 12 = 0$ **56.** $12x^2 + 17x - 5 = 0$

Find the *x*-intercepts of the graph of each equation. (The grids are intentionally not included.)

57.
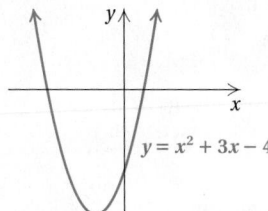
$y = x^2 + 3x - 4$

58.
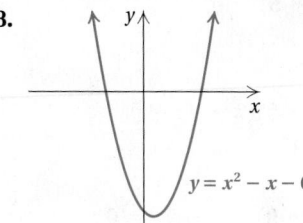
$y = x^2 - x - 6$

59.
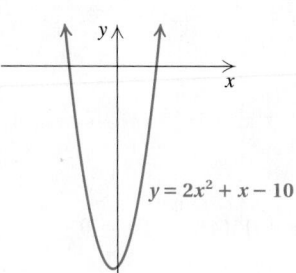
$y = 2x^2 + x - 10$

60.
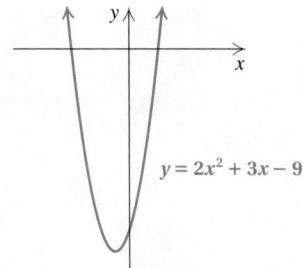
$y = 2x^2 + 3x - 9$

61.
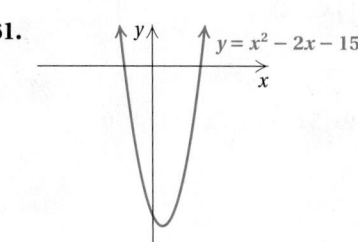
$y = x^2 - 2x - 15$

62.
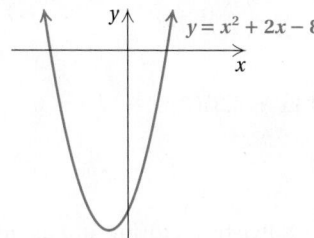
$y = x^2 + 2x - 8$

63. Use the following graph to solve $x^2 - 3x - 4 = 0$.

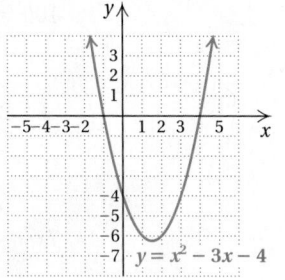
$y = x^2 - 3x - 4$

64. Use the following graph to solve $x^2 + x - 6 = 0$.

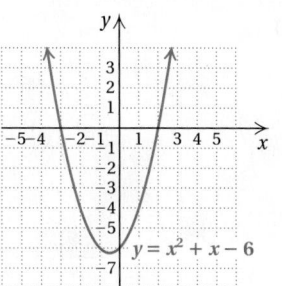
$y = x^2 + x - 6$

Copyright © 2012 Pearson Education, Inc.

65. Use the following graph to solve $-x^2 + 2x + 3 = 0$.

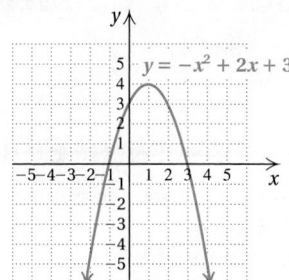

66. Use the following graph to solve $-x^2 - x + 6 = 0$.

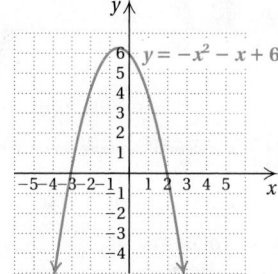

Skill Maintenance

Translate to an algebraic expression.   [7.1b]

67. The square of the sum of a and b

68. The sum of the squares of a and b

Divide.   [7.6a, c]

69. $144 \div (-9)$

70. $-24.3 \div 5.4$

71. $-\frac{5}{8} \div \frac{3}{16}$

72. $-\frac{3}{16} \div \left(-\frac{5}{8}\right)$

Synthesis

Solve.

73. $b(b + 9) = 4(5 + 2b)$

74. $y(y + 8) = 16(y - 1)$

75. $(t - 3)^2 = 36$

76. $(t - 5)^2 = 2(5 - t)$

77. $x^2 - \frac{1}{64} = 0$

78. $x^2 - \frac{25}{36} = 0$

79. $\frac{5}{16}x^2 = 5$

80. $\frac{27}{25}x^2 = \frac{1}{3}$

81. Find an equation that has the given numbers as solutions. For example, 3 and -2 are solutions of $x^2 - x - 6 = 0$.

  a) $-3, 4$ **b)** $-3, -4$ **c)** $\frac{1}{2}, \frac{1}{2}$

  d) $5, -5$ **e)** $0, 0.1, \frac{1}{4}$

82. *Matching.* Match each equation in the first column with the equivalent equation in the second column.

$x^2 + 10x - 2 = 0$	$4x^2 + 8x + 36 = 0$
$(x - 6)(x + 3) = 0$	$(2x + 8)(2x - 5) = 0$
$5x^2 - 5 = 0$	$9x^2 - 12x + 24 = 0$
$(2x - 5)(x + 4) = 0$	$(x + 1)(5x - 5) = 0$
$x^2 + 2x + 9 = 0$	$x^2 - 3x - 18 = 0$
$3x^2 - 4x + 8 = 0$	$2x^2 + 20x - 4 = 0$

Use a graphing calculator to find the solutions of each equation. Round solutions to the nearest hundredth.

83. $x^2 - 9.10x + 15.77 = 0$

84. $-x^2 + 0.63x + 0.22 = 0$

85. $0.84x^2 - 2.30x = 0$

86. $6.4x^2 - 8.45x - 94.06 = 0$

11.8

Applications of Quadratic Equations

OBJECTIVE

a Solve applied problems involving quadratic equations that can be solved by factoring.

a Applied Problems, Quadratic Equations, and Factoring

We can solve problems that translate to quadratic equations using the five steps for solving problems.

EXAMPLE 1 *Kitchen Island.* Lisa buys a kitchen island with a butcher-block top as part of a remodeling project. The top of the island is a rectangle that is twice as long as it is wide and that has an area of 800 in². What are the dimensions of the top of the island?

1. **Familiarize.** We first make a drawing. Recall that the area of a rectangle is Length · Width. We let $x =$ the width of the top, in inches. The length is then $2x$.

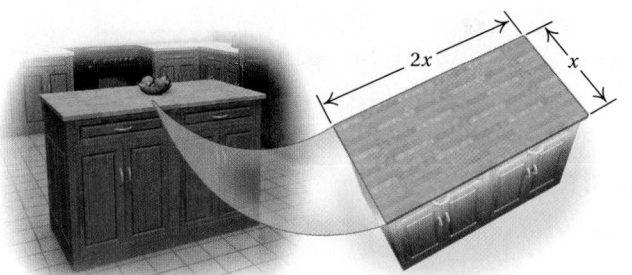

2. **Translate.** We reword and translate as follows:

   Rewording: The area of the rectangle is 800 in².

   Translating: $2x \cdot x = 800$

3. **Solve.** We solve the equation as follows:

$$2x \cdot x = 800$$
$$2x^2 = 800$$
$$2x^2 - 800 = 0 \qquad \text{Subtracting 800 to get 0 on one side}$$
$$2(x^2 - 400) = 0 \qquad \text{Removing a common factor of 2}$$
$$2(x - 20)(x + 20) = 0 \qquad \text{Factoring a difference of squares}$$
$$(x - 20)(x + 20) = 0 \qquad \text{Dividing by 2}$$
$$x - 20 = 0 \quad or \quad x + 20 = 0 \qquad \text{Using the principle of zero products}$$
$$x = 20 \quad or \quad x = -20. \qquad \text{Solving each equation}$$

4. **Check.** The solutions of the equation are 20 and −20. Since the width must be positive, −20 cannot be a solution. To check 20 in., we note that if the width is 20 in., then the length is 2 · 20 in., or 40 in., and the area is 20 in. · 40 in., or 800 in². Thus the solution 20 checks.

5. **State.** The top is 20 in. wide and 40 in. long.

1. Dimensions of Picture. A rectangular picture is twice as long as it is wide. If the area of the picture is 288 in², what are its dimensions?

$2w$

Do Exercise 1.

Answer

1. Length: 24 in.; width: 12 in.

EXAMPLE 2 *Racing Sailboat.* The height of a triangular sail on a racing sailboat is 9 ft more than the base. The area of the triangle is 110 ft². Find the height and the base of the sail.

Source: Whitney Gladstone, North Graphics, San Diego, CA

1. **Familiarize.** We first make a drawing. If you don't remember the formula for the area of a triangle, look it up in the list of formulas at the back of this book or in a geometry book. The area is $\frac{1}{2}$(base)(height).
   We let b = the base of the triangle, in feet. Then $b + 9$ = the height.

2. **Translate.** It helps to reword this problem before translating:

Rewording: $\frac{1}{2}$ times Base times Height is 110

↓ ↓ ↓ ↓ ↓ ↓ ↓

Translating: $\frac{1}{2}$ · b · $(b + 9)$ = 110.

3. **Solve.** We solve the equation as follows:

$$\frac{1}{2} \cdot b \cdot (b + 9) = 110$$

$$\frac{1}{2}(b^2 + 9b) = 110 \qquad \text{Multiplying}$$

$$2 \cdot \frac{1}{2}(b^2 + 9b) = 2 \cdot 110 \qquad \text{Multiplying by 2}$$

$$b^2 + 9b = 220 \qquad \text{Simplifying}$$

$$b^2 + 9b - 220 = 220 - 220 \qquad \text{Subtracting 220 to get 0 on one side}$$

$$b^2 + 9b - 220 = 0$$

$$(b - 11)(b + 20) = 0 \qquad \text{Factoring}$$

$$b - 11 = 0 \quad or \quad b + 20 = 0 \qquad \text{Using the principle of zero products}$$

$$b = 11 \quad or \qquad b = -20.$$

4. **Check.** The base of a triangle cannot have a negative length, so -20 cannot be a solution. Suppose the base is 11 ft. The height is 9 ft more than the base, so the height is 11 ft + 9 ft, or 20 ft, and the area is $\frac{1}{2}(11)(20)$, or 110 ft². These numbers check in the original problem.

5. **State.** The height is 20 ft and the base is 11 ft.

Do Exercise 2.

2. Dimensions of a Sail. The triangular mainsail on Stacey's lightning-styled sailboat has an area of 125 ft². The height of the sail is 15 ft more than the base. Find the height and the base of the sail.

Answer

2. Height: 25 ft; base: 10 ft

EXAMPLE 3 *Games in a Sports League.* In a sports league of x teams in which each team plays every other team twice, the total number N of games to be played is given by

$$x^2 - x = N.$$

Maggie's basketball league plays a total of 240 games. How many teams are in the league?

1., 2. Familiarize and Translate. We are given that x is the number of teams in a league and N is the number of games. To familiarize yourself with this problem, reread Example 4 in Section 10.3 where we first considered it. To find the number of teams x in a league in which 240 games are played, we substitute 240 for N in the equation:

$$x^2 - x = 240. \qquad \text{Substituting 240 for } N$$

3. Solve. We solve the equation as follows:

$$x^2 - x = 240$$
$$x^2 - x - 240 = 240 - 240 \qquad \text{Subtracting 240 to get 0 on one side}$$
$$x^2 - x - 240 = 0$$
$$(x - 16)(x + 15) = 0 \qquad \text{Factoring}$$
$$x - 16 = 0 \quad or \quad x + 15 = 0 \qquad \text{Using the principle of zero products}$$
$$x = 16 \quad or \qquad x = -15.$$

4. Check. The solutions of the equation are 16 and -15. Since the number of teams cannot be negative, -15 cannot be a solution. But 16 checks, since $16^2 - 16 = 256 - 16 = 240$.

5. State. There are 16 teams in the league.

> Do Exercise 3.

---

3. Use $N = x^2 - x$ for each of the following.

   a) **Volleyball League.** Amy's volleyball league has 19 teams. What is the total number of games to be played if each team plays every other team twice?

   b) **Softball League.** Barry's slow-pitch softball league plays a total of 72 games. How many teams are in the league if each team plays every other team twice?

STUDY TIPS

FIVE STEPS FOR PROBLEM SOLVING

Recall the five steps for problem solving that were developed in Section 8.6.

1. **Familiarize** yourself with the situation.

   a) Carefully read and reread until you understand *what* you are being asked to find.

   b) Draw a diagram or see if there is a formula that applies.

   c) Assign a letter, or *variable,* to the unknown.

2. **Translate** the problem to an equation using the letter or variable.

3. **Solve** the equation.

4. **Check** the answer in the original wording of the problem.

5. **State** the answer to the problem clearly with appropriate units.

Answer

3. (a) 342 games; (b) 9 teams

EXAMPLE 4 *Marathoners' Numbers.* The product of the numbers of two consecutive entrants in a marathon race is 156. Find the numbers.

1. **Familiarize.** The numbers are consecutive integers. Recall that consecutive integers are one unit apart, like 49 and 50, or -6 and -5. Let $x =$ the smaller integer; then $x + 1 =$ the larger integer.

2. **Translate.** It helps to reword the problem before translating:

   Rewording: First integer times Second integer is 156

   Translating: x $\cdot$ $(x + 1)$ $=$ 156.

3. **Solve.** We solve the equation as follows:

$$x(x + 1) = 156$$
$$x^2 + x = 156 \qquad \text{Multiplying}$$
$$x^2 + x - 156 = 156 - 156 \qquad \text{Subtracting 156 to get 0 on one side}$$
$$x^2 + x - 156 = 0 \qquad \text{Simplifying}$$
$$(x - 12)(x + 13) = 0 \qquad \text{Factoring}$$
$$x - 12 = 0 \quad or \quad x + 13 = 0 \qquad \text{Using the principle of zero products}$$
$$x = 12 \quad or \quad x = -13.$$

4. **Check.** The solutions of the equation are 12 and -13. When x is 12, then $x + 1$ is 13, and $12 \cdot 13 = 156$. The numbers 12 and 13 are consecutive integers that are solutions to the problem. When x is -13, then $x + 1$ is -12, and $(-13)(-12) = 156$. The numbers -13 and -12 are consecutive integers, but they are not solutions of the problem because negative numbers are not used as entry numbers.

5. **State.** The entry numbers are 12 and 13.

Do Exercise 4.

4. **Page Numbers.** The product of the page numbers on two facing pages of a book is 506. Find the page numbers.

The Pythagorean Theorem

The problems that follow involve the Pythagorean theorem, which states a relationship involving the lengths of the sides of a *right* triangle. A triangle is a **right triangle** if it has a 90°, or *right*, angle. The side opposite the 90° angle is called the **hypotenuse**. The other sides are called **legs**.

Answer

4. 22 and 23

THE PYTHAGOREAN THEOREM

In any right triangle, if a and b are the lengths of the legs and c is the length of the hypotenuse, then

$$a^2 + b^2 = c^2.$$

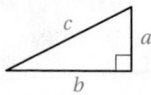

The symbol $\llcorner$ denotes a 90° angle.

EXAMPLE 5 *Wood Scaffold.* Jonah is building a wood scaffold to use for a home improvement project. He designs the scaffold with diagonal braces that are 5 ft long and that span a distance of 3 ft. How high does each brace reach vertically?

1. **Familiarize.** We make a drawing as shown above and let h = the height, in feet, to which each brace rises vertically.

2. **Translate.** A right triangle is formed, so we can use the Pythagorean theorem:

$$a^2 + b^2 = c^2$$
$$3^2 + h^2 = 5^2.$$ Substituting 3 and h for the lengths of the legs and 5 for the length of the hypotenuse

3. **Solve.** We solve the equation as follows:

$$3^2 + h^2 = 5^2$$
$$9 + h^2 = 25 \qquad \text{Squaring 3 and 5}$$
$$9 + h^2 - 25 = 25 - 25 \qquad \text{Subtracting 25 to get 0 on one side}$$
$$h^2 - 16 = 0 \qquad \text{Simplifying}$$
$$(h - 4)(h + 4) = 0 \qquad \text{Factoring}$$
$$h - 4 = 0 \quad or \quad h + 4 = 0 \qquad \text{Using the principle of zero products}$$
$$h = 4 \quad or \qquad h = -4.$$

4. **Check.** Since height cannot be negative, -4 cannot be a solution. If the height is 4 ft, we have $3^2 + 4^2 = 9 + 16 = 25$, which is 5^2. Thus, 4 checks and is the solution.

5. **State.** Each brace reaches a height of 4 ft.

Do Exercise 5.

5. Reach of a Ladder. Twila has a 26-ft ladder leaning against her house. If the bottom of the ladder is 10 ft from the base of the house, how high does the ladder reach?

Answer

5. 24 ft

EXAMPLE 6 *Ladder Settings.* A ladder of length 13 ft is placed against a building in such a way that the distance from the top of the ladder to the ground is 7 ft more than the distance from the bottom of the ladder to the building. Find both distances.

1. **Familiarize.** We first make a drawing. The ladder and the missing distances form the hypotenuse and the legs of a right triangle. We let x = the length of the side (leg) across the bottom, in feet. Then $x + 7$ = the length of the other side (leg). The hypotenuse has length 13 ft.

2. **Translate.** Since a right triangle is formed, we can use the Pythagorean theorem:

$$a^2 + b^2 = c^2$$
$$x^2 + (x + 7)^2 = 13^2. \quad \text{Substituting}$$

3. **Solve.** We solve the equation as follows:

$x^2 + (x^2 + 14x + 49) = 169$	Squaring the binomial and 13
$2x^2 + 14x + 49 = 169$	Collecting like terms
$2x^2 + 14x + 49 - 169 = 169 - 169$	Subtracting 169 to get 0 on one side
$2x^2 + 14x - 120 = 0$	Simplifying
$2(x^2 + 7x - 60) = 0$	Factoring out a common factor
$x^2 + 7x - 60 = 0$	Dividing by 2
$(x + 12)(x - 5) = 0$	Factoring
$x + 12 = 0 \quad or \quad x - 5 = 0$	Using the principle of zero products
$x = -12 \quad or \quad x = 5.$	

4. **Check.** The negative integer -12 cannot be the length of a side. When $x = 5$, $x + 7 = 12$, and $5^2 + 12^2 = 13^2$. Thus, 5 and 12 check.

5. **State.** The distance from the top of the ladder to the ground is 12 ft. The distance from the bottom of the ladder to the building is 5 ft.

Do Exercise 6.

6. Right-Triangle Geometry.
The length of one leg of a right triangle is 1 m longer than the other. The length of the hypotenuse is 5 m. Find the lengths of the legs.

Answer

6. 3 m, 4 m

Translating
for Success

1. **Angle Measures.** The measures of the angles of a triangle are three consecutive integers. Find the measures of the angles.

2. **Rectangle Dimensions.** The area of a rectangle is 3599 ft². The length is 2 ft longer than the width. Find the dimensions of the rectangle.

3. **Sales Tax.** Claire paid $40,704 for a new SUV. This included 6% for sales tax. How much did the SUV cost before tax?

4. **Wire Cutting.** A 180-m wire is cut into three pieces. The third piece is 2 m longer than the first. The second is two-thirds as long as the first. How long is each piece?

5. **Perimeter.** The perimeter of a rectangle is 240 ft. The length is 2 ft greater than the width. Find the length and the width.

The goal of these matching questions is to practice step (2), *Translate*, of the five-step problem-solving process. Translate each word problem to an equation and select a correct translation from equations A–O.

A. $2x \cdot x = 288$

B. $x(x + 60) = 7021$

C. $59 = x \cdot 60$

D. $x^2 + (x + 2)^2 = 3599$

E. $x^2 + (x + 70)^2 = 130^2$

F. $6\% \cdot x = 40,704$

G. $2(x + 2) + 2x = 240$

H. $\frac{1}{2}x(x - 1) = 1770$

I. $x + \frac{2}{3}x + (x + 2) = 180$

J. $59\% \cdot x = 60$

K. $x + 6\% \cdot x = 40,704$

L. $2x^2 + x = 288$

M. $x(x + 2) = 3599$

N. $x^2 + 60 = 7021$

O. $x + (x + 1) + (x + 2) = 180$

Answers on page A-27

---

6. **Cell-Phone Tower.** A guy wire on a cell-phone tower is 130 ft long and is attached to the top of the tower. The height of the tower is 70 ft longer than the distance from the point on the ground where the wire is attached to the bottom of the tower. Find the height of the tower.

7. **Sales Meeting Attendance.** PTQ Corporation holds a sales meeting in Tucson. Of the 60 employees, 59 of them attend the meeting. What percent attend the meeting?

8. **Dimensions of a Pool.** A rectangular swimming pool is twice as long as it is wide. The area of the surface is 288 ft². Find the dimensions of the pool.

9. **Dimensions of a Triangle.** The height of a triangle is 1 cm less than the length of the base. The area of the triangle is 1770 cm². Find the height and the length of the base.

10. **Width of a Rectangle.** The length of a rectangle is 60 ft longer than the width. Find the width if the area of the rectangle is 7021 ft².

Solve.

1. *Dimensions of a Painting.* A rectangular painting is three times as long as it is wide. The area of the picture is 588 in². Find the dimensions of the painting.

2. *Area of a Garden.* The length of a rectangular garden is 4 m greater than the width. The area of the garden is 96 m². Find the length and the width.

3. *Furnishings.* A rectangular table in Arlo's House of Tunes is six times as long as it is wide. The area of the table is 24 ft². Find the length and the width of the table.

4. *Design.* The screen of the TI-84 Plus graphing calculator is nearly rectangular. The length of the rectangle is 2 cm more than the width. If the area of the rectangle is 24 cm², find the length and the width.

5. *Dimensions of a Triangle.* A triangle is 10 cm wider than it is tall. The area is 28 cm². Find the height and the base.

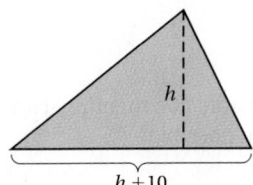

6. *Dimensions of a Triangle.* The height of a triangle is 3 cm less than the length of the base. The area of the triangle is 35 cm². Find the height and the length of the base.

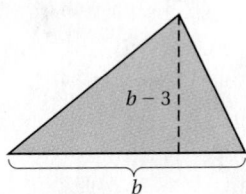

7. *Road Design.* A triangular traffic island has a base half as long as its height. The island has an area of 64 m². Find the base and the height.

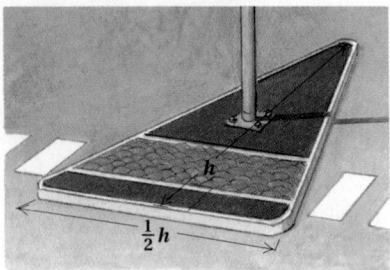

8. *Dimensions of a Sail.* The height of the jib sail on a Lightning sailboat is 5 ft greater than the length of its "foot." The area of the sail is 42 ft². Find the length of the foot and the height of the sail.

Games in a League. Use $x^2 - x = N$ for Exercises 9–12.

9. A chess league has 14 teams. What is the total number of games to be played if each team plays every other team twice?

10. A women's volleyball league has 23 teams. What is the total number of games to be played if each team plays every other team twice?

11. A slow-pitch softball league plays a total of 132 games. How many teams are in the league if each team plays every other team twice?

12. A basketball league plays a total of 90 games. How many teams are in the league if each team plays every other team twice?

Handshakes. Dr. Benton wants to investigate the potential spread of germs by contact. She knows that the number of possible handshakes within a group of x people, assuming each person shakes every other person's hand only once, is given by

$$N = \tfrac{1}{2}(x^2 - x).$$

Use this formula for Exercises 13–16.

13. There are 100 people at a party. How many handshakes are possible?

14. There are 40 people at a meeting. How many handshakes are possible?

Copyright © 2012 Pearson Education, Inc.

15. Everyone at a meeting shook hands with each other. There were 300 handshakes in all. How many people were at the meeting?

16. Everyone at a party shook hands with each other. There were 153 handshakes in all. How many people were at the party?

17. *Toasting.* During a toast at the party celebrating James's fourth birthday, there were 190 "clicks" of paper cups. How many people took part in the toast?

18. *High-Fives.* After the Wildcats won the city baseball championship, all the teammates exchanged "high-fives." Altogether there were 66 high-fives. How many players were there?

19. *Consecutive Page Numbers.* The product of the page numbers on two facing pages of a book is 210. Find the page numbers.

20. *Consecutive Page Numbers.* The product of the page numbers on two facing pages of a book is 420. Find the page numbers.

21. The product of two consecutive even integers is 168. Find the integers. (See Section 8.6.)

22. The product of two consecutive even integers is 224. Find the integers. (See Section 8.6.)

23. The product of two consecutive odd integers is 255. Find the integers. (See Section 8.6.)

24. The product of two consecutive odd integers is 143. Find the integers. (See Section 8.6.)

25. *Right-Triangle Geometry.* The length of one leg of a right triangle is 8 ft. The length of the hypotenuse is 2 ft longer than the other leg. Find the length of the hypotenuse and the other leg.

26. *Right-Triangle Geometry.* The length of one leg of a right triangle is 24 ft. The length of the other leg is 16 ft shorter than the hypotenuse. Find the length of the hypotenuse and the other leg.

27. *Roadway Design.* Elliott Street is 24 ft wide when it ends at Main Street in Brattleboro, Vermont. A 40-ft long diagonal crosswalk allows pedestrians to cross Main Street to or from either corner of Elliott Street (see the figure). Determine the width of Main Street.

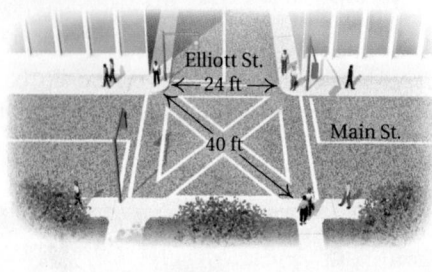

28. *Sailing.* The mainsail of a Lightning sailboat is a right triangle in which the hypotenuse is called the leech. If a 24-ft tall mainsail has a leech length of 26 ft and if Dacron® sailcloth costs $10 per square foot, find the cost of a new mainsail.

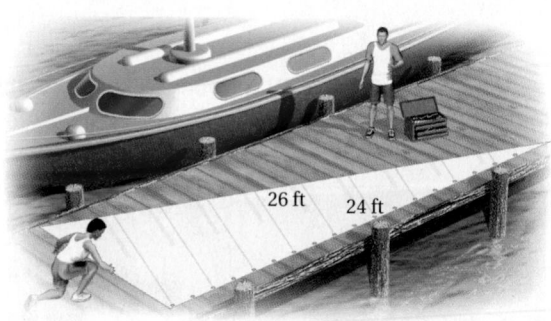

29. *Lookout Tower.* The diagonal braces in a lookout tower are 15 ft long and span a distance of 12 ft. How high does each brace reach vertically?

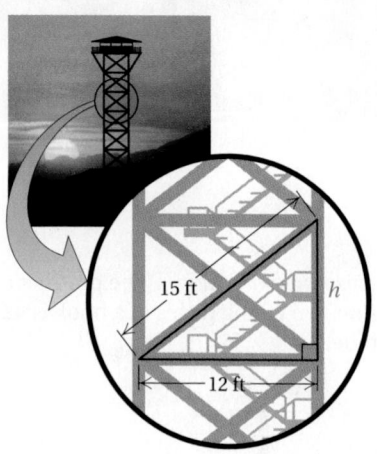

30. *Aviation.* Engine failure forced Geraldine to pilot her Cessna 150 to an emergency landing. To land, Geraldine's plane glided 17,000 ft over a 15,000-ft stretch of deserted highway. From what altitude did the descent begin?

31. *Architecture.* An architect has allocated a rectangular space of 264 ft² for a square dining room and a 10-ft wide kitchen, as shown in the figure. Find the dimensions of each room.

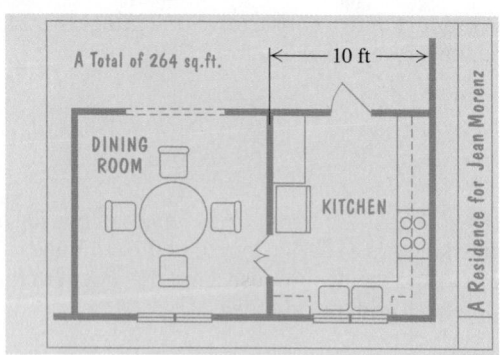

32. *Guy Wire.* The guy wire on a TV antenna is 1 m longer than the height of the antenna. If the guy wire is anchored 3 m from the foot of the antenna, how tall is the antenna?

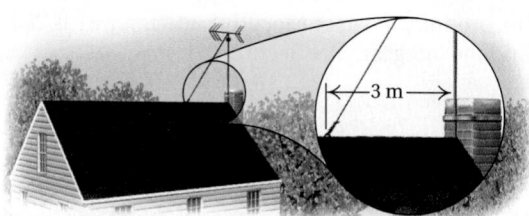

Copyright © 2012 Pearson Education, Inc.

Rocket Launch. A model rocket is launched with an initial velocity of 180 ft/sec. Its height h, in feet, after t seconds is given by the formula

$$h = 180t - 16t^2.$$

Use this formula for Exercises 33 and 34.

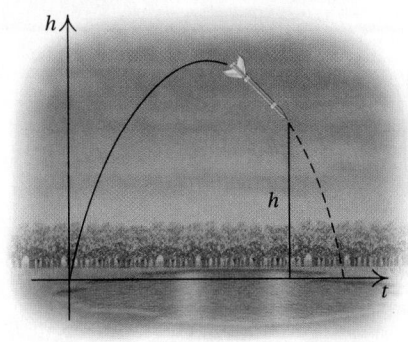

33. After how many seconds will the rocket first reach a height of 464 ft?

34. After how many seconds from launching will the rocket again be at that same height of 464 ft? (See Exercise 33.)

35. The sum of the squares of two consecutive odd positive integers is 74. Find the integers.

36. The sum of the squares of two consecutive odd positive integers is 130. Find the integers.

Skill Maintenance

In each of Exercises 37–44, fill in the blank with the correct term from the given list. Some of the choices may not be used and some may be used more than once.

37. To _____ a polynomial is to express it as a product. [11.1b]

38. A(n) _____ of a polynomial P is a polynomial that can be used to express P as a product. [11.1b]

39. A factorization of a polynomial is an expression that names that polynomial as a(n) _____ . [11.1b]

40. When factoring, always look first for a(n) _____ . [11.1b]

41. The expression $-5x^2 + 8x - 7$ is an example of a(n) _____ . [10.3i]

42. The _____ asserts that when dividing with exponential notation, if the bases are the same, keep the base and subtract the exponent of the denominator from the exponent of the numerator. [10.1e]

43. For the graph of the equation $4x - 3y = 12$, the pair $(0, -4)$ is known as the _____ . [9.2a]

44. For the graph of the equation $4x - 3y = 12$, the _____ is $\frac{4}{3}$. [9.3b]

quotient rule
product rule
slope
common factor
common multiple
factor
x-intercept
y-intercept
binomial
trinomial
quotient
product

Synthesis

45. *Telephone Service.* Use the information in the figure below to determine the height of the telephone pole.

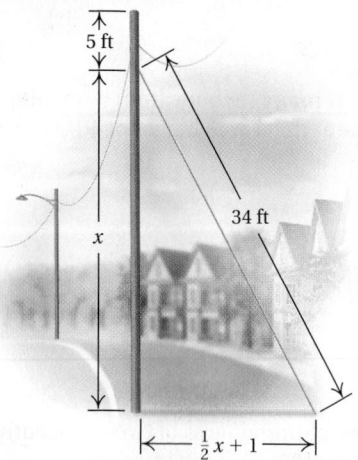

46. *Roofing.* A *square* of shingles covers 100 ft² of surface area. How many squares will be needed to reshingle the roof of the house shown?

47. *Pool Sidewalk.* A cement walk of constant width is built around a 20-ft by 40-ft rectangular pool. The total area of the pool and the walk is 1500 ft². Find the width of the walk.

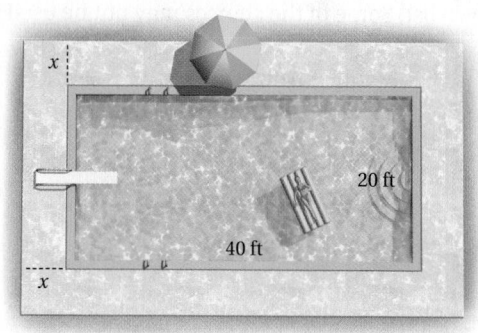

48. *Rain-Gutter Design.* An open rectangular gutter is made by turning up the sides of a piece of metal 20 in. wide. The area of the cross-section of the gutter is 50 in². Find the depth of the gutter.

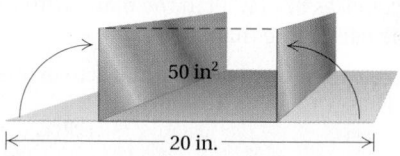

49. *Dimensions of an Open Box.* A rectangular piece of cardboard is twice as long as it is wide. A 4-cm square is cut out of each corner, and the sides are turned up to make a box with an open top. The volume of the box is 616 cm³. Find the original dimensions of the cardboard.

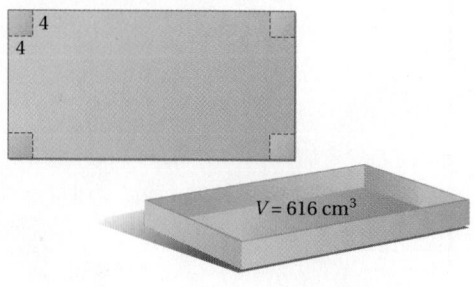

50. Solve for x.

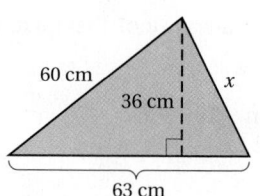

51. *Dimensions of a Closed Box.* The total surface area of a closed box is 350 in². The box is 9 in. high and has a square base and lid. Find the length of a side of the base.

52. The ones digit of a number less than 100 is 4 greater than the tens digit. The sum of the number and the product of the digits is 58. Find the number.

Copyright © 2012 Pearson Education, Inc.

Summary and Review

Key Terms and Properties

greatest common factor (GCF), p. 822
factor, p. 823
factorization, p. 823
factoring by grouping, p. 827

leading coefficient, p. 831
FOIL method, p. 841
ac-method, p. 849
trinomial square, or perfect-square trinomial, p. 857

difference of squares, p. 859
quadratic equation, p. 875
right triangle, p. 887
hypotenuse, p. 887
legs of a right triangle, p. 887

Factoring Formulas:

$$A^2 - B^2 = (A + B)(A - B),$$
$$A^2 + 2AB + B^2 = (A + B)^2,$$
$$A^2 - 2AB + B^2 = (A - B)^2$$

The Principle of Zero Products: An equation $ab = 0$ is true if and only if $a = 0$ is true or $b = 0$ is true, or both are true.

The Pythagorean Theorem: $a^2 + b^2 = c^2$

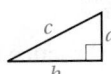

Concept Reinforcement

Determine whether each statement is true or false.

_____ **1.** Every polynomial with four terms can be factored by grouping.   [11.1c]

_____ **2.** When factoring $x^2 + 5x + 6$, we need consider only positive pairs of factors of 6.   [11.2a]

_____ **3.** A product is 0 if and only if all the factors are 0.   [11.7a]

_____ **4.** If the principle of zero products is to be used, one side of the equation must be 0.   [11.7b]

Important Concepts

Objective 11.1a   Find the greatest common factor, the GCF, of monomials.

Example   Find the GCF of $15x^4y^2$, $-18x$, and $12x^3y$.

$$15x^4y^2 = 3 \cdot 5 \cdot x^4 \cdot y^2;$$
$$-18x = -1 \cdot 2 \cdot 3 \cdot 3 \cdot x;$$
$$12x^3y = 2 \cdot 2 \cdot 3 \cdot x^3 \cdot y$$

Each coefficient has a factor of 3. There are no other common prime factors. The GCF of the powers of x is x because 1 is the smallest exponent of x. The GCF of the powers of y is 1 because $18x$ has no y-factor. Thus the GCF is $3 \cdot x \cdot 1$, or $3x$.

Practice Exercise

1. Find the GCF of $8x^3y^2$, $-20xy^3$, and $32x^2y$.

Objective 11.1b Factor polynomials when the terms have a common factor, factoring out the greatest common factor.

Example Factor: $16y^4 + 8y^3 - 24y^2$.

The *largest* common factor is $8y^2$.

$$16y^4 + 8y^3 - 24y^2 = (8y^2)(2y^2) + (8y^2)(y) - (8y^2)(3)$$
$$= 8y^2(2y^2 + y - 3)$$

Practice Exercise

2. Factor $27x^5 - 9x^3 + 18x^2$, factoring out the largest common factor.

Objective 11.1c Factor certain expressions with four terms using factoring by grouping.

Example Factor $6x^3 + 4x^2 - 15x - 10$ by grouping.

$$6x^3 + 4x^2 - 15x - 10 = (6x^3 + 4x^2) + (-15x - 10)$$
$$= 2x^2(3x + 2) - 5(3x + 2)$$
$$= (3x + 2)(2x^2 - 5)$$

Practice Exercise

3. Factor $z^3 - 3z^2 + 4z - 12$ by grouping.

Objective 11.2a Factor trinomials of the type $x^2 + bx + c$ by examining the constant term c.

Example Factor: $x^2 - x - 12$.

Since the constant term, -12, is negative, we look for a factorization of -12 in which one factor is positive and one factor is negative. The sum of the factors must be the coefficient of the middle term, -1, so the negative factor must have the larger absolute value. The possible pairs of factors that meet these criteria are 1, -12 and 2, -6 and 3, -4. The numbers we need are 3 and -4:

$$x^2 - x - 12 = (x + 3)(x - 4).$$

Practice Exercise

4. Factor: $x^2 + 6x + 8$.

Objective 11.3a Factor trinomials of the type $ax^2 + bx + c$, $a \neq 1$, using the FOIL method.

Example Factor $2y^3 + 5y^2 - 3y$.

1) Factor out the largest common factor, y:

$y(2y^2 + 5y - 3)$.

Now we factor $2y^2 + 5y - 3$.

2) Because $2y^2$ factors as $2y \cdot y$, we have this possibility for a factorization:

$(2y + \quad)(y + \quad)$.

3) There are two pairs of factors of -3 and each can be written in two ways:

$$3, -1 \qquad -3, 1$$
$$\text{and} \quad -1, 3 \qquad 1, -3.$$

4) From steps (2) and (3), we see that there are 4 possibilities for factorizations. We look for **O**utside and **I**nside products for which the sum is the middle term, $5y$. We try some possibilities and find that the factorization of $2y^2 + 5y - 3$ is $(2y - 1)(y + 3)$.

We must include the common factor to get a factorization of the original trinomial:

$$2y^3 + 5y^2 - 3y = y(2y - 1)(y + 3).$$

Practice Exercise

5. Factor: $6z^2 - 21z - 12$.

Objective 11.4a Factor trinomials of the type $ax^2 + bx + c, a \neq 1$, using the ac-method.

Example   Factor $5x^2 + 7x - 6$ using the ac-method.

1) There is no common factor (other than 1 or −1).

2) Multiply the leading coefficient 5 and the constant, −6:
$$5(-6) = -30.$$

3) Look for a factorization of −30 in which the sum of the factors is the coefficient of the middle term, 7. One number will be positive and the other will be negative. Since their sum, 7, is positive, the positive number will have the larger absolute value. The numbers we need are 10 and −3.

4) Split the middle term, writing it as a sum or a difference using the factors found in step (3):
$$7x = 10x - 3x.$$

5) Factor by grouping:
$$5x^2 + 7x - 6 = 5x^2 + 10x - 3x - 6$$
$$= 5x(x + 2) - 3(x + 2)$$
$$= (x + 2)(5x - 3).$$

6) Check: $(x + 2)(5x - 3) = 5x^2 + 7x - 6.$

Practice Exercise

6. Factor $6y^2 + 7y - 3$ using the ac-method.

Objective 11.5b   Factor trinomial squares.

Example   Factor: $9x^2 - 12x + 4.$
$$9x^2 - 12x + 4 = (3x)^2 - 2 \cdot 3x \cdot 2 + 2^2$$
$$= (3x - 2)^2$$

Practice Exercise

7. Factor: $4x^2 + 4x + 1.$

Objective 11.5d   Factor differences of squares, being careful to factor completely.

Example   Factor: $b^6 - b^2.$
$$b^6 - b^2 = b^2(b^4 - 1)$$
$$= b^2(b^2 + 1)(b^2 - 1)$$
$$= b^2(b^2 + 1)(b + 1)(b - 1)$$

Practice Exercise

8. Factor $18x^2 - 8$ completely.

Objective 11.7b   Solve quadratic equations by factoring and then using the principle of zero products.

Example   Solve: $x^2 - 3x = 28.$
$$x^2 - 3x = 28$$
$$x^2 - 3x - 28 = 28 - 28$$
$$x^2 - 3x - 28 = 0$$
$$(x + 4)(x - 7) = 0$$
$$x + 4 = 0 \quad or \quad x - 7 = 0$$
$$x = -4 \quad or \qquad x = 7$$
The solutions are −4 and 7.

Practice Exercise

9. Solve: $x^2 + 4x = 5.$

Review Exercises

Find the GCF. [11.1a]

1. $-15y^2,\ 25y^6$

2. $12x^3,\ -60x^2y,\ 36xy$

Factor completely. [11.6a]

3. $5 - 20x^6$

4. $x^2 - 3x$

5. $9x^2 - 4$

6. $x^2 + 4x - 12$

7. $x^2 + 14x + 49$

8. $6x^3 + 12x^2 + 3x$

9. $x^3 + x^2 + 3x + 3$

10. $6x^2 - 5x + 1$

11. $x^4 - 81$

12. $9x^3 + 12x^2 - 45x$

13. $2x^2 - 50$

14. $x^4 + 4x^3 - 2x - 8$

15. $16x^4 - 1$

16. $8x^6 - 32x^5 + 4x^4$

17. $75 + 12x^2 + 60x$

18. $x^2 + 9$

19. $x^3 - x^2 - 30x$

20. $4x^2 - 25$

21. $9x^2 + 25 - 30x$

22. $6x^2 - 28x - 48$

23. $x^2 - 6x + 9$

24. $2x^2 - 7x - 4$

25. $18x^2 - 12x + 2$

26. $3x^2 - 27$

27. $15 - 8x + x^2$

28. $25x^2 - 20x + 4$

29. $49b^{10} + 4a^8 - 28a^4b^5$

30. $x^2y^2 + xy - 12$

31. $12a^2 + 84ab + 147b^2$

32. $m^2 + 5m + mt + 5t$

33. $32x^4 - 128y^4z^4$

Solve. [11.7a, b]

34. $(x - 1)(x + 3) = 0$

35. $x^2 + 2x - 35 = 0$

36. $x^2 + 4x = 0$

37. $3x^2 + 2 = 5x$

38. $x^2 = 64$

39. $16 = x(x - 6)$

Copyright © 2012 Pearson Education, Inc.

Find the *x*-intercepts of the graph of each equation.   [11.7b]

40. $y = x^2 + 9x + 20$

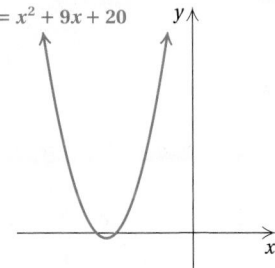

41. $y = 2x^2 - 7x - 15$

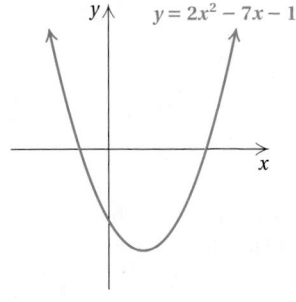

Solve.   [11.8a]

42. *Sharks' Teeth.*   Sharks' teeth are shaped like triangles. The height of a tooth of a great white shark is 1 cm longer than the base. The area is 15 cm². Find the height and the base.

43. The product of two consecutive even integers is 288. Find the integers.

44. The product of two consecutive odd integers is 323. Find the integers.

45. *Tree Supports.*   A duckbill-anchor system is used to support a newly planted Bradford pear tree. Each cable is 5 ft long. The distance from the base of the tree to the point on the ground where each cable is anchored is 1 ft more than the distance from the base of the tree to the point where the cable is attached to the tree. Find both distances.

5 ft

46. If the sides of a square are lengthened by 3 km, the area increases to 81 km². Find the length of a side of the original square.

47. Factor: $x^2 - 9x + 8$. Which of the following is one factor?   [11.2a], [11.6a]

  A. $(x + 1)$ **B.** $(x - 1)$
  C. $(x + 8)$ **D.** $(x - 4)$

48. Factor $15x^2 + 5x - 20$ completely. Which of the following is one factor?   [11.3a], [11.4a], [11.6a]

  A. $(3x + 4)$ **B.** $(3x - 4)$
  C. $(5x - 5)$ **D.** $(15x + 20)$

Synthesis

Solve. [11.8a]

49. The pages of a book measure 15 cm by 20 cm. Margins of equal width surround the printing on each page and constitute one-half of the area of the page. Find the width of the margins.

15 cm

20 cm

50. The cube of a number is the same as twice the square of the number. Find all such numbers.

51. The length of a rectangle is two times its width. When the length is increased by 20 in. and the width is decreased by 1 in., the area is 160 in^2. Find the original length and width.

Solve. [11.7b]

52. $x^2 + 25 = 0$

53. $(x - 2)(x + 3)(2x - 5) = 0$

54. $(x - 3)4x^2 + 3x(x - 3) - (x - 3)10 = 0$

55. Find a polynomial in factored form for the shaded area in the figure below. Leave the answer in terms of π. [11.1b]

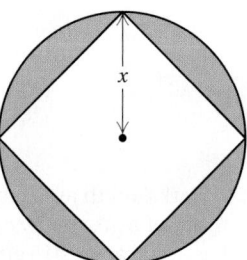

x

Understanding Through Discussion and Writing

1. Gwen factors $x^3 - 8x^2 + 15x$ as $(x^2 - 5x)(x - 3)$. Is she wrong? Why or why not? What advice would you offer? [11.2a]

2. After a test, Josh told a classmate that he was sure he had not written any incorrect factorizations. How could he be certain? [11.6a]

3. Kelly factored $16 - 8x + x^2$ as $(x - 4)^2$, while Tony factored it as $(4 - x)^2$. Evaluate each expression for several values of x. Then explain why both answers are correct. [11.5b]

4. What is wrong with the following? Explain the correct method of solution. [11.7b]

$$(x - 3)(x + 4) = 8$$
$$x - 3 = 8 \quad or \quad x + 4 = 8$$
$$x = 11 \quad or \quad x = 4$$

5. What is incorrect about solving $x^2 = 3x$ by dividing by x on both sides? [11.7b]

6. An archaeologist has measuring sticks of 3 ft, 4 ft, and 5 ft. Explain how she could draw a 7-ft by 9-ft rectangle on a piece of land being excavated. [11.8a]

Copyright © 2012 Pearson Education, Inc.

CHAPTER

11

Test

For Extra Help

CHAPTER
Test Prep
VIDEOS

Step-by-step test solutions are found on the Chapter Test Prep Videos available via the Video Resources on DVD, in *MyMathLab*, and on You Tube (search "BittingerDevMath" and click on "Channels").

1. Find the GCF: $28x^3, 48x^7$.

Factor completely.

2. $x^2 - 7x + 10$

3. $x^2 + 25 - 10x$

4. $6y^2 - 8y^3 + 4y^4$

5. $x^3 + x^2 + 2x + 2$

6. $x^2 - 5x$

7. $x^3 + 2x^2 - 3x$

8. $28x - 48 + 10x^2$

9. $4x^2 - 9$

10. $x^2 - x - 12$

11. $6m^3 + 9m^2 + 3m$

12. $3w^2 - 75$

13. $60x + 45x^2 + 20$

14. $3x^4 - 48$

15. $49x^2 - 84x + 36$

16. $5x^2 - 26x + 5$

17. $x^4 + 2x^3 - 3x - 6$

18. $80 - 5x^4$

19. $6t^3 + 9t^2 - 15t$

Solve.

20. $x^2 - 3x = 0$

21. $2x^2 = 32$

22. $x^2 - x - 20 = 0$

23. $2x^2 + 7x = 15$

24. $x(x - 3) = 28$

Find the *x*-intercepts of the graph of each equation.

25.

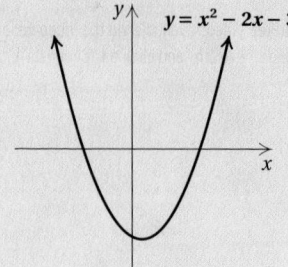

$y = x^2 - 2x - 35$

26.

$y = 3x^2 - 5x + 2$

Solve.

27. The length of a rectangle is 2 m more than the width. The area of the rectangle is 48 m². Find the length and the width.

28. The base of a triangle is 6 cm greater than twice the height. The area is 28 cm². Find the height and the base.

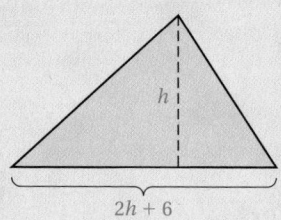

h

$2h + 6$

29. *Masonry Corner.* A mason wants to be sure he has a right angle corner of a building's foundation. He marks a point 3 ft from the corner along one wall and another point 4 ft from the corner along the other wall. If the corner is a right angle, what should the distance be between the two marked points?

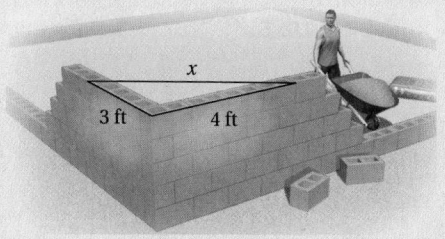

x

3 ft   4 ft

30. Factor $2y^4 - 32$ completely. Which of the following is one factor?

A. $(y + 2)$ **B.** $(y + 4)$
C. $(y^2 - 4)$ **D.** $(2y^2 + 8)$

Synthesis

31. The length of a rectangle is five times its width. When the length is decreased by 3 m and the width is increased by 2 m, the area of the new rectangle is 60 m². Find the original length and width.

32. Factor: $(a + 3)^2 - 2(a + 3) - 35$.

33. Solve: $20x(x + 2)(x - 1) = 5x^3 - 24x - 14x^2$.

34. If $x + y = 4$ and $x - y = 6$, then $x^2 - y^2 =$ which of the following?

A. 2   **B.** 10
C. 34   **D.** 24

Copyright © 2012 Pearson Education, Inc.

Rational Expressions and Equations

Real-World Application

A company that prepares and sells gift boxes and baskets of fruit must order quantities of fruit larger than what they need to allow for selecting fruit that meets their quality standards. The packing-room supervisor keeps records and notes that approximately 87 pears from a shipment of 1000 do not meet the company standards. Over the holidays, a shipment of 3200 pears is ordered. How many pears can the company expect will not meet the quality required?

This problem appears as Example 5 in Section 12.7.

12.1

Multiplying and Simplifying Rational Expressions

OBJECTIVES

a Find all numbers for which a rational expression is not defined.

b Multiply a rational expression by 1, using an expression such as A/A.

c Simplify rational expressions by factoring the numerator and the denominator and removing factors of 1.

d Multiply rational expressions and simplify.

a Rational Expressions and Replacements

Rational numbers are quotients of integers. Some examples are

$$\frac{2}{3}, \quad \frac{4}{-5}, \quad \frac{-8}{17}, \quad \frac{563}{1}.$$

The following are called **rational expressions** or **fraction expressions**. They are quotients, or ratios, of polynomials:

$$\frac{3}{4}, \quad \frac{z}{6}, \quad \frac{5}{x+2}, \quad \frac{t^2 + 3t - 10}{7t^2 - 4}.$$

A rational expression is also a division. For example,

$$\frac{3}{4} \quad \text{means} \quad 3 \div 4 \quad \text{and} \quad \frac{x-8}{x+2} \quad \text{means} \quad (x-8) \div (x+2).$$

Because rational expressions indicate division, we must be careful to avoid denominators of zero. When a variable is replaced with a number that produces a denominator equal to zero, the rational expression is not defined. For example, in the expression

$$\frac{x-8}{x+2},$$

when x is replaced with -2, the denominator is 0, and the expression is *not* defined:

$$\frac{x-8}{x+2} = \frac{-2-8}{-2+2} = \frac{-10}{0}. \leftarrow \text{Division by 0 is not defined.}$$

When x is replaced with a number other than -2, such as 3, the expression *is* defined because the denominator is nonzero:

$$\frac{x-8}{x+2} = \frac{3-8}{3+2} = \frac{-5}{5} = -1.$$

EXAMPLE 1 Find all numbers for which the rational expression

$$\frac{x+4}{x^2 - 3x - 10}$$

is not defined.

The value of the numerator has no bearing on whether or not a rational expression is defined. To determine which numbers make the rational expression not defined, we set the *denominator* equal to 0 and solve:

$$x^2 - 3x - 10 = 0$$
$$(x-5)(x+2) = 0 \qquad \text{Factoring}$$
$$x - 5 = 0 \quad or \quad x + 2 = 0 \qquad \text{Using the principle of zero products (See Section 11.7.)}$$
$$x = 5 \quad or \qquad x = -2.$$

The rational expression is not defined for the replacement numbers 5 and -2.

Do Margin Exercises 1–3.

SKILL TO REVIEW
Objective 2.1e: Simplify fraction notation.

Simplify.

1. $\dfrac{360}{140}$ **2.** $\dfrac{189}{252}$

Find all numbers for which the rational expression is not defined.

1. $\dfrac{16}{x-3}$

2. $\dfrac{2x-7}{x^2 + 5x - 24}$

3. $\dfrac{x+5}{8}$

Answers

Skill to Review:
1. $\dfrac{18}{7}$ 2. $\dfrac{3}{4}$

Margin Exercises:
1. 3 2. $-8, 3$ 3. None

(b) Multiplying by 1

We multiply rational expressions in the same way that we multiply fraction notation in arithmetic. For a review, see Section 2.1. We saw there that

$$\frac{3}{7} \cdot \frac{2}{5} = \frac{3 \cdot 2}{7 \cdot 5} = \frac{6}{35}.$$

MULTIPLYING RATIONAL EXPRESSIONS

To multiply rational expressions, multiply numerators and multiply denominators:

$$\frac{A}{B} \cdot \frac{C}{D} = \frac{AC}{BD}.$$

For example,

$$\frac{x-2}{3} \cdot \frac{x+2}{x+7} = \frac{(x-2)(x+2)}{3(x+7)}.$$ Multiplying the numerators and the denominators

Note that we leave the numerator, $(x-2)(x+2)$, and the denominator, $3(x+7)$, in factored form because it is easier to simplify if we do not multiply. In order to learn to simplify, we first need to consider multiplying the rational expression by 1.

Any rational expression with the same numerator and denominator is a symbol for 1:

$$\frac{19}{19} = 1, \qquad \frac{x+8}{x+8} = 1, \qquad \frac{3x^2-4}{3x^2-4} = 1, \qquad \frac{-1}{-1} = 1.$$

EQUIVALENT EXPRESSIONS

Expressions that have the same value for all allowable (or meaningful) replacements are called **equivalent expressions**.

We can multiply by 1 to obtain an *equivalent expression*. At this point, we select expressions for 1 arbitrarily. Later, we will have a system for our choices when we add and subtract.

EXAMPLES   Multiply.

2. $\dfrac{3x+2}{x+1} \cdot 1 = \dfrac{3x+2}{x+1} \cdot \dfrac{2x}{2x} = \dfrac{(3x+2)2x}{(x+1)2x}$ Using the identity property of 1. We arbitrarily choose $2x/2x$ as a symbol for 1.

3. $\dfrac{x+2}{x-7} \cdot \dfrac{x+3}{x+3} = \dfrac{(x+2)(x+3)}{(x-7)(x+3)}$ We arbitrarily choose $(x+3)/(x+3)$ as a symbol for 1.

4. $\dfrac{2+x}{2-x} \cdot \dfrac{-1}{-1} = \dfrac{(2+x)(-1)}{(2-x)(-1)}$ Using $(-1)/(-1)$ as a symbol for 1

Do Exercises 4–6.

Multiply.

4. $\dfrac{2x+1}{3x-2} \cdot \dfrac{x}{x}$

5. $\dfrac{x+1}{x-2} \cdot \dfrac{x+2}{x+2}$

6. $\dfrac{x-8}{x-y} \cdot \dfrac{-1}{-1}$

Answers

4. $\dfrac{(2x+1)x}{(3x-2)x}$ **5.** $\dfrac{(x+1)(x+2)}{(x-2)(x+2)}$

6. $\dfrac{(x-8)(-1)}{(x-y)(-1)}$

c Simplifying Rational Expressions

Simplifying rational expressions is similar to simplifying fraction expressions in arithmetic. For a review, see Section 2.1. We saw there, for example, that an expression like $\frac{15}{40}$ can be simplified as follows:

$$\frac{15}{40} = \frac{3 \cdot 5}{8 \cdot 5} \qquad \text{Factoring the numerator and the denominator.}$$
Note the common factor, 5.

$$= \frac{3}{8} \cdot \frac{5}{5} \qquad \text{Factoring the fraction expression}$$

$$= \frac{3}{8} \cdot 1 \qquad \frac{5}{5} = 1$$

$$= \frac{3}{8}. \qquad \text{Using the identity property of 1,}$$
or "removing a factor of 1"

Similar steps are followed when simplifying rational expressions: We factor and remove a factor of 1, using the fact that

$$\frac{ab}{cb} = \frac{a}{c} \cdot \frac{b}{b} = \frac{a}{c} \cdot 1 = \frac{a}{c}.$$

In algebra, instead of simplifying

$$\frac{15}{40},$$

we may need to simplify an expression like

$$\frac{x^2 - 16}{x + 4}.$$

Just as factoring is important in simplifying in arithmetic, so too is it important in simplifying rational expressions. The factoring we use most is the factoring of polynomials, which we studied in Chapter 11.

To simplify, we can do the reverse of multiplying. We factor the numerator and the denominator and "remove" a factor of 1.

EXAMPLE 5 Simplify: $\frac{8x^2}{24x}$.

$$\frac{8x^2}{24x} = \frac{8 \cdot x \cdot x}{3 \cdot 8 \cdot x} \qquad \text{Factoring the numerator and the denominator.}$$
Note the common factor, $8x$.

$$= \frac{8x}{8x} \cdot \frac{x}{3} \qquad \text{Factoring the rational expression}$$

$$= 1 \cdot \frac{x}{3} \qquad \frac{8x}{8x} = 1$$

$$= \frac{x}{3} \qquad \text{We removed a factor of 1.}$$

Do Exercises 7 and 8.

Simplify.

7. $\frac{5y}{y}$ 8. $\frac{9x^2}{36x}$

Answers

7. 5   8. $\frac{x}{4}$

EXAMPLES Simplify.

6. $\dfrac{5a + 15}{10} = \dfrac{5(a + 3)}{5 \cdot 2}$ Factoring the numerator and the denominator

$\qquad = \dfrac{5}{5} \cdot \dfrac{a + 3}{2}$ Factoring the rational expression

$\qquad = 1 \cdot \dfrac{a + 3}{2}$ $\dfrac{5}{5} = 1$

$\qquad = \dfrac{a + 3}{2}$ Removing a factor of 1

7. $\dfrac{6a + 12}{7a + 14} = \dfrac{6(a + 2)}{7(a + 2)}$ Factoring the numerator and the denominator

$\qquad = \dfrac{6}{7} \cdot \dfrac{a + 2}{a + 2}$ Factoring the rational expression

$\qquad = \dfrac{6}{7} \cdot 1$ $\dfrac{a + 2}{a + 2} = 1$

$\qquad = \dfrac{6}{7}$ Removing a factor of 1

8. $\dfrac{6x^2 + 4x}{2x^2 + 2x} = \dfrac{2x(3x + 2)}{2x(x + 1)}$ Factoring the numerator and the denominator

$\qquad = \dfrac{2x}{2x} \cdot \dfrac{3x + 2}{x + 1}$ Factoring the rational expression

$\qquad = 1 \cdot \dfrac{3x + 2}{x + 1}$ $\dfrac{2x}{2x} = 1$

$\qquad = \dfrac{3x + 2}{x + 1}$ Removing a factor of 1

Caution!

Note that you *cannot* simplify further by removing the x's because x is not a *factor* of the entire numerator, $3x + 2$, and the entire denominator, $x + 1$.

---

9. $\dfrac{x^2 + 3x + 2}{x^2 - 1} = \dfrac{(x + 2)(x + 1)}{(x + 1)(x - 1)}$ Factoring the numerator and the denominator

$\qquad = \dfrac{x + 1}{x + 1} \cdot \dfrac{x + 2}{x - 1}$ Factoring the rational expression

$\qquad = 1 \cdot \dfrac{x + 2}{x - 1}$ $\dfrac{x + 1}{x + 1} = 1$

$\qquad = \dfrac{x + 2}{x - 1}$ Removing a factor of 1

Canceling

You may have encountered canceling when working with rational expressions. With great concern, we mention it as a possible way to speed up your work. Our concern is that canceling be done with care and understanding. Example 9 might have been done faster as follows:

$$\frac{x^2 + 3x + 2}{x^2 - 1} = \frac{(x + 2)(x + 1)}{(x + 1)(x - 1)}$$ Factoring the numerator and the denominator

$$= \frac{(x + 2)\cancel{(x + 1)}}{\cancel{(x + 1)}(x - 1)}$$ When a factor of 1 is noted, it is canceled, as shown: $\dfrac{x + 1}{x + 1} = 1$.

$$= \frac{x + 2}{x - 1}.$$ Simplifying

--------------- *Caution!* ---------------

The difficulty with canceling is that it is often applied incorrectly, as in the following situations:

$$\frac{\cancel{x} + 3}{\cancel{x}} = 3; \qquad \frac{\cancel{4} + 1}{\cancel{4} + 2} = \frac{1}{2}; \qquad \frac{1\cancel{5}}{5\cancel{4}} = \frac{1}{4}.$$

Wrong! Wrong! Wrong!

In each of these situations, the expressions canceled were *not* factors of 1. Factors are parts of products. For example, in $2 \cdot 3$, 2 and 3 are factors, but in $2 + 3$, 2 and 3 are *not* factors. If you can't factor, you can't cancel. If in doubt, don't cancel!

Do Exercises 9–12.

Opposites in Rational Expressions

Expressions of the form $a - b$ and $b - a$ are **opposites** of each other. When either of these binomials is multiplied by -1, the result is the other binomial:

$$\left.\begin{array}{l} -1(a - b) = -a + b = b + (-a) = b - a; \\ -1(b - a) = -b + a = a + (-b) = a - b. \end{array}\right\}$$ Multiplication by -1 reverses the order in which subtraction occurs.

Consider, for example,

$$\frac{x - 4}{4 - x}.$$

At first glance, it appears as though the numerator and the denominator do not have any common factors other than 1. But $x - 4$ and $4 - x$ are opposites, or additive inverses, of each other. Thus we can rewrite one as the opposite of the other by factoring out a -1.

EXAMPLE 10 Simplify: $\dfrac{x - 4}{4 - x}$.

$$\frac{x - 4}{4 - x} = \frac{x - 4}{-(x - 4)} = \frac{1(x - 4)}{-1(x - 4)}$$ $4 - x = -(x - 4); 4 - x$ and $x - 4$ are opposites.

$$= -1 \cdot \frac{x - 4}{x - 4}$$ $1/-1 = -1$

$$= -1 \cdot 1$$

$$= -1$$

Do Exercises 13–15.

Simplify.

9. $\dfrac{2x^2 + x}{3x^2 + 2x}$

10. $\dfrac{x^2 - 1}{2x^2 - x - 1}$

11. $\dfrac{7x + 14}{7}$

12. $\dfrac{12y + 24}{48}$

Simplify.

13. $\dfrac{x - 8}{8 - x}$

14. $\dfrac{c - d}{d - c}$

15. $\dfrac{-x - 7}{x + 7}$

Answers

9. $\dfrac{2x + 1}{3x + 2}$ **10.** $\dfrac{x + 1}{2x + 1}$ **11.** $x + 2$

12. $\dfrac{y + 2}{4}$ **13.** -1 **14.** -1 **15.** -1

(d) Multiplying and Simplifying

We try to simplify after we multiply. That is why we leave the numerator and the denominator in factored form.

EXAMPLE 11 Multiply and simplify: $\dfrac{5a^3}{4} \cdot \dfrac{2}{5a}$.

$$\frac{5a^3}{4} \cdot \frac{2}{5a} = \frac{5a^3(2)}{4(5a)} \qquad \text{Multiplying the numerators and the denominators}$$

$$= \frac{5 \cdot a \cdot a \cdot a \cdot 2}{2 \cdot 2 \cdot 5 \cdot a} \qquad \text{Factoring the numerator and the denominator}$$

$$= \frac{5 \cdot \cancel{a} \cdot a \cdot a \cdot 2}{2 \cdot 2 \cdot \cancel{5} \cdot \cancel{a}} \qquad \text{Removing a factor of 1: } \frac{2 \cdot 5 \cdot a}{2 \cdot 5 \cdot a} = 1$$

$$= \frac{a^2}{2} \qquad \text{Simplifying}$$

EXAMPLE 12 Multiply and simplify: $\dfrac{x^2 + 6x + 9}{x^2 - 4} \cdot \dfrac{x - 2}{x + 3}$.

$$\frac{x^2 + 6x + 9}{x^2 - 4} \cdot \frac{x - 2}{x + 3} = \frac{(x^2 + 6x + 9)(x - 2)}{(x^2 - 4)(x + 3)} \qquad \text{Multiplying the numerators and the denominators}$$

$$= \frac{(x + 3)(x + 3)(x - 2)}{(x + 2)(x - 2)(x + 3)} \qquad \text{Factoring the numerator and the denominator}$$

$$= \frac{\cancel{(x + 3)}(x + 3)\cancel{(x - 2)}}{(x + 2)\cancel{(x - 2)}\cancel{(x + 3)}} \qquad \text{Removing a factor of 1:}$$
$$\frac{(x + 3)(x - 2)}{(x + 3)(x - 2)} = 1$$

$$= \frac{x + 3}{x + 2} \qquad \text{Simplifying}$$

Do Exercise 16.

16. Multiply and simplify:
$$\frac{a^2 - 4a + 4}{a^2 - 9} \cdot \frac{a + 3}{a - 2}.$$

EXAMPLE 13 Multiply and simplify: $\dfrac{x^2 + x - 2}{15} \cdot \dfrac{5}{2x^2 - 3x + 1}$.

$$\frac{x^2 + x - 2}{15} \cdot \frac{5}{2x^2 - 3x + 1} = \frac{(x^2 + x - 2)5}{15(2x^2 - 3x + 1)} \qquad \text{Multiplying the numerators and the denominators}$$

$$= \frac{(x + 2)(x - 1)5}{5(3)(x - 1)(2x - 1)} \qquad \text{Factoring the numerator and the denominator}$$

$$= \frac{(x + 2)\cancel{(x - 1)}\cancel{5}}{\cancel{5}(3)\cancel{(x - 1)}(2x - 1)} \qquad \text{Removing a factor of 1: } \frac{(x - 1)5}{(x - 1)5} = 1$$

$$= \frac{x + 2}{3(2x - 1)} \qquad \text{Simplifying}$$

You need not carry out this multiplication.

Do Exercise 17.

17. Multiply and simplify:
$$\frac{x^2 - 25}{6} \cdot \frac{3}{x + 5}.$$

Answers

16. $\dfrac{a - 2}{a - 3}$ **17.** $\dfrac{x - 5}{2}$

a Find all numbers for which the rational expression is not defined.

1. $\dfrac{-3}{2x}$

2. $\dfrac{24}{-8y}$

3. $\dfrac{5}{x-8}$

4. $\dfrac{y-4}{y+6}$

5. $\dfrac{3}{2y+5}$

6. $\dfrac{x^2-9}{4x-15}$

7. $\dfrac{x^2+11}{x^2-3x-28}$

8. $\dfrac{p^2-9}{p^2-7p+10}$

9. $\dfrac{m^3-2m}{m^2-25}$

10. $\dfrac{7-3x+x^2}{49-x^2}$

11. $\dfrac{x-4}{3}$

12. $\dfrac{x^2-25}{14}$

b Multiply. Do not simplify. Note that in each case you are multiplying by 1.

13. $\dfrac{4x}{4x}\cdot\dfrac{3x^2}{5y}$

14. $\dfrac{5x^2}{5x^2}\cdot\dfrac{6y^3}{3z^4}$

15. $\dfrac{2x}{2x}\cdot\dfrac{x-1}{x+4}$

16. $\dfrac{2a-3}{5a+2}\cdot\dfrac{a}{a}$

17. $\dfrac{3-x}{4-x}\cdot\dfrac{-1}{-1}$

18. $\dfrac{x-5}{5-x}\cdot\dfrac{-1}{-1}$

19. $\dfrac{y+6}{y+6}\cdot\dfrac{y-7}{y+2}$

20. $\dfrac{x^2+1}{x^3-2}\cdot\dfrac{x-4}{x-4}$

c Simplify.

21. $\dfrac{8x^3}{32x}$

22. $\dfrac{4x^2}{20x}$

23. $\dfrac{48p^7q^5}{18p^5q^4}$

24. $\dfrac{-76x^8y^3}{-24x^4y^3}$

25. $\dfrac{4x-12}{4x}$

26. $\dfrac{5a-40}{5}$

Copyright © 2012 Pearson Education, Inc.

27. $\dfrac{3m^2 + 3m}{6m^2 + 9m}$

28. $\dfrac{4y^2 - 2y}{5y^2 - 5y}$

29. $\dfrac{a^2 - 9}{a^2 + 5a + 6}$

30. $\dfrac{t^2 - 25}{t^2 + t - 20}$

31. $\dfrac{a^2 - 10a + 21}{a^2 - 11a + 28}$

32. $\dfrac{x^2 - 2x - 8}{x^2 - x - 6}$

33. $\dfrac{x^2 - 25}{x^2 - 10x + 25}$

34. $\dfrac{x^2 + 8x + 16}{x^2 - 16}$

35. $\dfrac{a^2 - 1}{a - 1}$

36. $\dfrac{t^2 - 1}{t + 1}$

37. $\dfrac{x^2 + 1}{x + 1}$

38. $\dfrac{m^2 + 9}{m + 3}$

39. $\dfrac{6x^2 - 54}{4x^2 - 36}$

40. $\dfrac{8x^2 - 32}{4x^2 - 16}$

41. $\dfrac{6t + 12}{t^2 - t - 6}$

42. $\dfrac{4x + 32}{x^2 + 9x + 8}$

43. $\dfrac{2t^2 + 6t + 4}{4t^2 - 12t - 16}$

44. $\dfrac{3a^2 - 9a - 12}{6a^2 + 30a + 24}$

45. $\dfrac{t^2 - 4}{(t + 2)^2}$

46. $\dfrac{m^2 - 36}{(m - 6)^2}$

47. $\dfrac{6 - x}{x - 6}$

48. $\dfrac{t - 3}{3 - t}$

49. $\dfrac{a - b}{b - a}$

50. $\dfrac{y - x}{-x + y}$

51. $\dfrac{6t - 12}{2 - t}$

52. $\dfrac{5a - 15}{3 - a}$

53. $\dfrac{x^2 - 1}{1 - x}$

54. $\dfrac{a^2 - b^2}{b^2 - a^2}$

d Multiply and simplify.

55. $\dfrac{4x^3}{3x} \cdot \dfrac{14}{x}$

56. $\dfrac{18}{x^3} \cdot \dfrac{5x^2}{6}$

57. $\dfrac{3c}{d^2} \cdot \dfrac{4d}{6c^3}$

58. $\dfrac{3x^2y}{2} \cdot \dfrac{4}{xy^3}$

59. $\dfrac{x + 4}{x} \cdot \dfrac{x^2 - 3x}{x^2 + x - 12}$

60. $\dfrac{t^2}{t^2 - 4} \cdot \dfrac{t^2 - 5t + 6}{t^2 - 3t}$

61. $\dfrac{a^2 - 9}{a^2} \cdot \dfrac{a^2 - 3a}{a^2 + a - 12}$

62. $\dfrac{x^2 + 10x - 11}{x^2 - 1} \cdot \dfrac{x + 1}{x + 11}$

63. $\dfrac{4a^2}{3a^2 - 12a + 12} \cdot \dfrac{3a - 6}{2a}$

64. $\dfrac{5v + 5}{v - 2} \cdot \dfrac{v^2 - 4v + 4}{v^2 - 1}$

65. $\dfrac{t^4 - 16}{t^4 - 1} \cdot \dfrac{t^2 + 1}{t^2 + 4}$

66. $\dfrac{x^4 - 1}{x^4 - 81} \cdot \dfrac{x^2 + 9}{x^2 + 1}$

Copyright © 2012 Pearson Education, Inc.

67. $\dfrac{(x+4)^3}{(x+2)^3} \cdot \dfrac{x^2+4x+4}{x^2+8x+16}$

68. $\dfrac{(t-2)^3}{(t-1)^3} \cdot \dfrac{t^2-2t+1}{t^2-4t+4}$

69. $\dfrac{5a^2-180}{10a^2-10} \cdot \dfrac{20a+20}{2a-12}$

70. $\dfrac{2t^2-98}{4t^2-4} \cdot \dfrac{8t+8}{16t-112}$

Skill Maintenance

Graph.

71. $x+y=-1$ [9.2a]

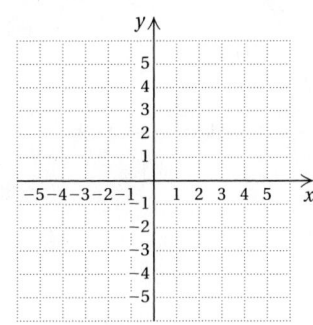

72. $y=-\dfrac{7}{2}$ [9.2b]

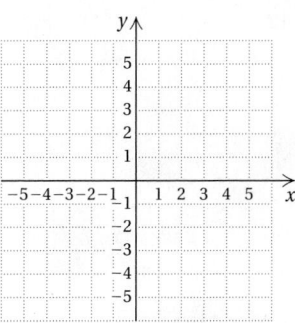

Solve.

73. *Consecutive Even Integers.* The product of two consecutive even integers is 360. Find the integers. [11.8a]

74. *Chemistry.* About 5 L of oxygen can be dissolved in 100 L of water at 0°C. This is 1.6 times the amount that can be dissolved in the same volume of water at 20°C. How much oxygen can be dissolved in 100 L at 20°C? [8.6a]

Factor. [11.6a]

75. x^2-x-56

76. $a^2-16a+64$

77. $x^5-2x^4-35x^3$

78. $2y^3-10y^2+y-5$

79. $16-t^4$

80. $10x^2+80x+70$

81. $x^2-9x+14$

82. x^2+x+7

83. $16x^2-40xy+25y^2$

84. $a^2-9ab+14b^2$

Synthesis

Simplify.

85. $\dfrac{x^4-16y^4}{(x^2+4y^2)(x-2y)}$

86. $\dfrac{(a-b)^2}{b^2-a^2}$

87. $\dfrac{t^4-1}{t^4-81} \cdot \dfrac{t^2-9}{t^2+1} \cdot \dfrac{(t-9)^2}{(t+1)^2}$

88. $\dfrac{(t+2)^3}{(t+1)^3} \cdot \dfrac{t^2+2t+1}{t^2+4t+4} \cdot \dfrac{t+1}{t+2}$

89. $\dfrac{x^2-y^2}{(x-y)^2} \cdot \dfrac{x^2-2xy+y^2}{x^2-4xy-5y^2}$

90. $\dfrac{x-1}{x^2+1} \cdot \dfrac{x^4-1}{(x-1)^2} \cdot \dfrac{x^2-1}{x^4-2x^2+1}$

91. Select any number x, multiply by 2, add 5, multiply by 5, subtract 25, and divide by 10. What do you get? Explain how this procedure can be used for a number trick.

12.2

Division and Reciprocals

OBJECTIVES

a Find the reciprocal of a rational expression.

b Divide rational expressions and simplify.

SKILL TO REVIEW
Objective 11.6a: Factor polynomials.

Factor.
1. $x^2 - 2x$
2. $5y^2 - 11y - 12$

Find the reciprocal.

1. $\dfrac{7}{2}$ 2. $\dfrac{x^2 + 5}{2x^3 - 1}$

3. $x - 5$ 4. $\dfrac{1}{x^2 - 3}$

5. Divide: $\dfrac{3}{5} \div \dfrac{7}{10}$.

Answers

Skill to Review:
1. $x(x - 2)$ 2. $(5y + 4)(y - 3)$

Margin Exercises:
1. $\dfrac{2}{7}$ 2. $\dfrac{2x^3 - 1}{x^2 + 5}$ 3. $\dfrac{1}{x - 5}$

4. $x^2 - 3$ 5. $\dfrac{6}{7}$

There is a similarity between what we do with rational expressions and what we do with rational numbers. In fact, after variables have been replaced with rational numbers, a rational expression represents a rational number.

a Finding Reciprocals

Two expressions are **reciprocals** of each other if their product is 1. The reciprocal of a rational expression is found by interchanging the numerator and the denominator.

EXAMPLES

1. The reciprocal of $\dfrac{2}{5}$ is $\dfrac{5}{2}$. $\left(\text{This is because } \dfrac{2}{5} \cdot \dfrac{5}{2} = \dfrac{10}{10} = 1.\right)$

2. The reciprocal of $\dfrac{2x^2 - 3}{x + 4}$ is $\dfrac{x + 4}{2x^2 - 3}$.

3. The reciprocal of $x + 2$ is $\dfrac{1}{x + 2}$. $\left(\text{Think of } x + 2 \text{ as } \dfrac{x + 2}{1}.\right)$

Do Margin Exercises 1–4.

b Division

We divide rational expressions in the same way that we divide fraction notation in arithmetic. For a review, see Section 2.2.

> **DIVIDING RATIONAL EXPRESSIONS**
>
> To divide by a rational expression, multiply by its reciprocal:
>
> $$\frac{A}{B} \div \frac{C}{D} = \frac{A}{B} \cdot \frac{D}{C} = \frac{AD}{BC}.$$
>
> Then factor and, if possible, simplify.

EXAMPLE 4 Divide: $\dfrac{3}{4} \div \dfrac{9}{5}$.

$\dfrac{3}{4} \div \dfrac{9}{5} = \dfrac{3}{4} \cdot \dfrac{5}{9}$ — Multiplying by the reciprocal of the divisor

$= \dfrac{3 \cdot 5}{4 \cdot 9} = \dfrac{3 \cdot 5}{2 \cdot 2 \cdot 3 \cdot 3}$ — Factoring

$= \dfrac{3 \cdot 5}{2 \cdot 2 \cdot 3 \cdot 3}$ — Removing a factor of 1: $\dfrac{3}{3} = 1$

$= \dfrac{5}{12}$ — Simplifying

Do Exercise 5.

EXAMPLE 5 Divide: $\dfrac{2}{x} \div \dfrac{3}{x}$.

$$\dfrac{2}{x} \div \dfrac{3}{x} = \dfrac{2}{x} \cdot \dfrac{x}{3} \qquad \text{Multiplying by the reciprocal of the divisor}$$

$$= \dfrac{2 \cdot x}{x \cdot 3} = \dfrac{2 \cdot \cancel{x}}{\cancel{x} \cdot 3} \qquad \text{Removing a factor of 1: } \dfrac{x}{x} = 1$$

$$= \dfrac{2}{3}$$

Do Exercise 6.

6. Divide: $\dfrac{x}{8} \div \dfrac{x}{5}$.

EXAMPLE 6 Divide: $\dfrac{x+1}{x+2} \div \dfrac{x-1}{x+3}$.

$$\dfrac{x+1}{x+2} \div \dfrac{x-1}{x+3} = \dfrac{x+1}{x+2} \cdot \dfrac{x+3}{x-1} \qquad \text{Multiplying by the reciprocal of the divisor}$$

$$= \dfrac{(x+1)(x+3)}{(x+2)(x-1)}$$

We usually do not carry out the multiplication in the numerator or the denominator. It is not wrong to do so, but the factored form is often more useful.

Do Exercise 7.

7. Divide:

$$\dfrac{x-3}{x+5} \div \dfrac{x+5}{x-2}.$$

EXAMPLE 7 Divide: $\dfrac{4}{x^2 - 7x} \div \dfrac{28x}{x^2 - 49}$.

$$\dfrac{4}{x^2 - 7x} \div \dfrac{28x}{x^2 - 49} = \dfrac{4}{x^2 - 7x} \cdot \dfrac{x^2 - 49}{28x} \qquad \text{Multiplying by the reciprocal}$$

$$= \dfrac{4(x^2 - 49)}{(x^2 - 7x)(28x)}$$

$$= \dfrac{2 \cdot 2 \cdot (x - 7)(x + 7)}{x(x - 7) \cdot 2 \cdot 2 \cdot 7 \cdot x} \qquad \begin{array}{l}\text{Factoring the numerator}\\\text{and the denominator}\end{array}$$

$$= \dfrac{2 \cdot 2 \cdot (\cancel{x - 7})(x + 7)}{x(\cancel{x - 7}) \cdot 2 \cdot 2 \cdot 7 \cdot x} \qquad \begin{array}{l}\text{Removing a factor of 1:}\\ \dfrac{2 \cdot 2 \cdot (x - 7)}{2 \cdot 2 \cdot (x - 7)} = 1\end{array}$$

$$= \dfrac{x + 7}{7x^2}$$

Do Exercise 8.

8. Divide:

$$\dfrac{a^2 + 5a}{6} \div \dfrac{a^2 - 25}{18a}.$$

Answers

6. $\dfrac{5}{8}$ 7. $\dfrac{(x-3)(x-2)}{(x+5)(x+5)}$ 8. $\dfrac{3a^2}{a-5}$

STUDY TIPS

STUDYING THE EXAMPLES

The examples in each section prepare you for success with the exercise set. Study the step-by-step solutions. The time you spend studying the examples will save you valuable time when you do your homework.

EXAMPLE 8 Divide and simplify: $\dfrac{x+1}{x^2-1} \div \dfrac{x+1}{x^2-2x+1}$.

$$\dfrac{x+1}{x^2-1} \div \dfrac{x+1}{x^2-2x+1}$$

$$= \dfrac{x+1}{x^2-1} \cdot \dfrac{x^2-2x+1}{x+1} \qquad \text{Multiplying by the reciprocal}$$

$$= \dfrac{(x+1)(x^2-2x+1)}{(x^2-1)(x+1)}$$

$$= \dfrac{(x+1)(x-1)(x-1)}{(x-1)(x+1)(x+1)} \qquad \begin{array}{l}\text{Factoring the numerator}\\ \text{and the denominator}\end{array}$$

$$= \dfrac{\cancel{(x+1)}\cancel{(x-1)}(x-1)}{\cancel{(x-1)}\cancel{(x+1)}(x+1)} \qquad \text{Removing a factor of 1: } \dfrac{(x+1)(x-1)}{(x+1)(x-1)} = 1$$

$$= \dfrac{x-1}{x+1}$$

EXAMPLE 9 Divide and simplify: $\dfrac{x^2-2x-3}{x^2-4} \div \dfrac{x+1}{x+5}$.

$$\dfrac{x^2-2x-3}{x^2-4} \div \dfrac{x+1}{x+5}$$

$$= \dfrac{x^2-2x-3}{x^2-4} \cdot \dfrac{x+5}{x+1} \qquad \text{Multiplying by the reciprocal}$$

$$= \dfrac{(x^2-2x-3)(x+5)}{(x^2-4)(x+1)}$$

$$= \dfrac{(x-3)(x+1)(x+5)}{(x-2)(x+2)(x+1)} \qquad \begin{array}{l}\text{Factoring the numerator and}\\ \text{the denominator}\end{array}$$

$$= \dfrac{(x-3)\cancel{(x+1)}(x+5)}{(x-2)(x+2)\cancel{(x+1)}} \qquad \text{Removing a factor of 1: } \dfrac{x+1}{x+1} = 1$$

$$= \dfrac{(x-3)(x+5)}{(x-2)(x+2)} \quad \left.\begin{array}{c}\\ \\ \\ \end{array}\right\} \leftarrow \boxed{\begin{array}{l}\text{You need not carry out the}\\ \text{multiplications in the numerator}\\ \text{and the denominator.}\end{array}}$$

Divide and simplify.

9. $\dfrac{x-3}{x+5} \div \dfrac{x+2}{x+5}$

10. $\dfrac{x^2-5x+6}{x+5} \div \dfrac{x+2}{x+5}$

11. $\dfrac{y^2-1}{y+1} \div \dfrac{y^2-2y+1}{y+1}$

Do Exercises 9–11.

Answers

9. $\dfrac{x-3}{x+2}$ 10. $\dfrac{(x-3)(x-2)}{x+2}$ 11. $\dfrac{y+1}{y-1}$

12.2

Exercise Set

For Extra Help

MyMathLab

Math XL
PRACTICE   WATCH   DOWNLOAD   READ   REVIEW

a Find the reciprocal.

1. $\dfrac{4}{x}$

2. $\dfrac{a+3}{a-1}$

3. $x^2 - y^2$

4. $x^2 - 5x + 7$

5. $\dfrac{1}{a+b}$

6. $\dfrac{x^2}{x^2-3}$

7. $\dfrac{x^2+2x-5}{x^2-4x+7}$

8. $\dfrac{(a-b)(a+b)}{(a+4)(a-5)}$

b Divide and simplify.

9. $\dfrac{2}{5} \div \dfrac{4}{3}$

10. $\dfrac{3}{10} \div \dfrac{3}{2}$

11. $\dfrac{2}{x} \div \dfrac{8}{x}$

12. $\dfrac{t}{3} \div \dfrac{t}{15}$

13. $\dfrac{a}{b^2} \div \dfrac{a^2}{b^3}$

14. $\dfrac{x^2}{y} \div \dfrac{x^3}{y^3}$

15. $\dfrac{a+2}{a-3} \div \dfrac{a-1}{a+3}$

16. $\dfrac{x-8}{x+9} \div \dfrac{x+2}{x-1}$

17. $\dfrac{x^2-1}{x} \div \dfrac{x+1}{x-1}$

18. $\dfrac{4y-8}{y+2} \div \dfrac{y-2}{y^2-4}$

19. $\dfrac{x+1}{6} \div \dfrac{x+1}{3}$

20. $\dfrac{a}{a-b} \div \dfrac{b}{a-b}$

21. $\dfrac{5x-5}{16} \div \dfrac{x-1}{6}$

22. $\dfrac{4y-12}{12} \div \dfrac{y-3}{3}$

23. $\dfrac{-6+3x}{5} \div \dfrac{4x-8}{25}$

24. $\dfrac{-12+4x}{4} \div \dfrac{-6+2x}{6}$

25. $\dfrac{a+2}{a-1} \div \dfrac{3a+6}{a-5}$

26. $\dfrac{t-3}{t+2} \div \dfrac{4t-12}{t+1}$

27. $\dfrac{x^2-4}{x} \div \dfrac{x-2}{x+2}$

28. $\dfrac{x+y}{x-y} \div \dfrac{x^2+y}{x^2-y^2}$

29. $\dfrac{x^2-9}{4x+12} \div \dfrac{x-3}{6}$

30. $\dfrac{a-b}{2a} \div \dfrac{a^2-b^2}{8a^3}$

31. $\dfrac{c^2+3c}{c^2+2c-3} \div \dfrac{c}{c+1}$

32. $\dfrac{y+5}{2y} \div \dfrac{y^2-25}{4y^2}$

33. $\dfrac{2y^2 - 7y + 3}{2y^2 + 3y - 2} \div \dfrac{6y^2 - 5y + 1}{3y^2 + 5y - 2}$

34. $\dfrac{x^2 + x - 20}{x^2 - 7x + 12} \div \dfrac{x^2 + 10x + 25}{x^2 - 6x + 9}$

35. $\dfrac{x^2 - 1}{4x + 4} \div \dfrac{2x^2 - 4x + 2}{8x + 8}$

36. $\dfrac{5t^2 + 5t - 30}{10t + 30} \div \dfrac{2t^2 - 8}{6t^2 + 36t + 54}$

Skill Maintenance

Solve.

37. Bonnie is taking an astronomy course. In order to receive an A, she must average at least 90 after four exams. Bonnie scored 96, 98, and 89 on the first three tests. Determine (in terms of an inequality) what scores on the last test will earn her an A.   [8.8b]

38. *Triangle Dimensions.*   The base of a triangle is 4 in. less than twice the height. The area is 35 in^2. Find the height and the base.   [11.8a]

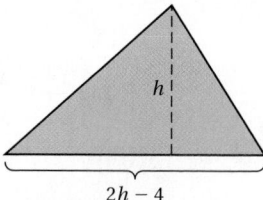

$2h - 4$

Subtract.   [10.4c]

39. $(8x^3 - 3x^2 + 7) - (8x^2 + 3x - 5)$

40. $(3p^2 - 6pq + 7q^2) - (5p^2 - 10pq + 11q^2)$

Simplify.   [10.2a, b]

41. $(2x^{-3}y^4)^2$

42. $(5x^6y^{-4})^3$

43. $\left(\dfrac{2x^3}{y^5}\right)^2$

44. $\left(\dfrac{a^{-3}}{b^4}\right)^5$

Synthesis

Simplify.

45. $\dfrac{3a^2 - 5ab - 12b^2}{3ab + 4b^2} \div (3b^2 - ab)$

46. $\dfrac{3x + 3y + 3}{9x} \div \dfrac{x^2 + 2xy + y^2 - 1}{x^4 + x^2}$

47. $\dfrac{a^2b^2 + 3ab^2 + 2b^2}{a^2b^4 + 4b^4} \div (5a^2 + 10a)$

48. The volume of this rectangular solid is $x - 3$. What is its height?

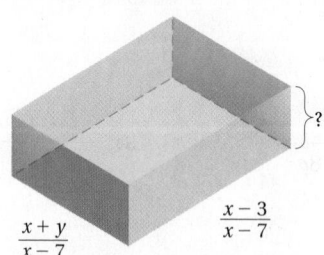

$\dfrac{x + y}{x - 7}$

$\dfrac{x - 3}{x - 7}$

Copyright © 2012 Pearson Education, Inc.

12.3

Least Common Multiples and Denominators

a) Least Common Multiples

To add when denominators are different, we first find a common denominator. For a review, see Section 2.3. We saw there, for example, that to add $\frac{5}{12}$ and $\frac{7}{30}$, we first look for the **least common multiple, LCM,** of 12 and 30. That number becomes the **least common denominator, LCD.** To find the LCM of 12 and 30, we factor:

$$12 = 2 \cdot 2 \cdot 3;$$
$$30 = 2 \cdot 3 \cdot 5.$$

The LCM is the number that has 2 as a factor twice, 3 as a factor once, and 5 as a factor once:

                          ——— 12 is a factor of the LCM.

$$\text{LCM} = 2 \cdot 2 \cdot 3 \cdot 5 = 60.$$

                          ——— 30 is a factor of the LCM.

> **FINDING LCMS**
>
> To find the LCM, use each factor the greatest number of times that it appears in any one factorization.

EXAMPLE 1 Find the LCM of 24 and 36.

$$\left.\begin{array}{l} 24 = 2 \cdot 2 \cdot 2 \cdot 3 \\ 36 = 2 \cdot 2 \cdot 3 \cdot 3 \end{array}\right\} \quad \text{LCM} = 2 \cdot 2 \cdot 2 \cdot 3 \cdot 3, \text{ or } 72$$

Do Margin Exercises 1–4.

b) Adding Using the LCD

Let's finish adding $\frac{5}{12}$ and $\frac{7}{30}$:

$$\frac{5}{12} + \frac{7}{30} = \frac{5}{2 \cdot 2 \cdot 3} + \frac{7}{2 \cdot 3 \cdot 5}.$$

The least common denominator, LCD, is $2 \cdot 2 \cdot 3 \cdot 5$. To get the LCD in the first denominator, we need a 5. To get the LCD in the second denominator, we need another 2. We get these numbers by multiplying by forms of 1:

$$\frac{5}{12} + \frac{7}{30} = \frac{5}{2 \cdot 2 \cdot 3} \cdot \frac{5}{5} + \frac{7}{2 \cdot 3 \cdot 5} \cdot \frac{2}{2} \qquad \text{Multiplying by 1}$$

$$= \frac{25}{2 \cdot 2 \cdot 3 \cdot 5} + \frac{14}{2 \cdot 3 \cdot 5 \cdot 2} \qquad \begin{array}{l}\text{Each denominator is} \\ \text{now the LCD.}\end{array}$$

$$= \frac{39}{2 \cdot 2 \cdot 3 \cdot 5} \qquad \begin{array}{l}\text{Adding the numerators} \\ \text{and keeping the LCD}\end{array}$$

$$= \frac{3 \cdot 13}{2 \cdot 2 \cdot 3 \cdot 5} \qquad \begin{array}{l}\text{Factoring the numerator and} \\ \text{removing a factor of 1: } \frac{3}{3} = 1\end{array}$$

$$= \frac{13}{20}. \qquad \text{Simplifying}$$

SKILL TO REVIEW

Objectives 1.7a, d: Find all the factors of numbers and find prime factorizations of numbers.

Find the prime factorization of each number.

1. 750   **2.** 364

Find the LCM by factoring.

1. 16, 18

2. 6, 12

3. 2, 5

4. 24, 30, 20

Answers

Skill to Review:
1. $2 \cdot 3 \cdot 5 \cdot 5 \cdot 5$, or $2 \cdot 3 \cdot 5^3$
2. $2 \cdot 2 \cdot 7 \cdot 13$, or $2^2 \cdot 7 \cdot 13$

Margin Exercises:
1. 144   **2.** 12   **3.** 10   **4.** 120

Add, first finding the LCD. Simplify if possible.

5. $\dfrac{3}{16} + \dfrac{1}{18}$

6. $\dfrac{1}{6} + \dfrac{1}{12}$

7. $\dfrac{1}{2} + \dfrac{3}{5}$

8. $\dfrac{1}{24} + \dfrac{1}{30} + \dfrac{3}{20}$

EXAMPLE 2 Add: $\dfrac{5}{12} + \dfrac{11}{18}$.

$$\left.\begin{array}{l} 12 = 2 \cdot 2 \cdot 3 \\ 18 = 2 \cdot 3 \cdot 3 \end{array}\right\} \quad \text{LCD} = 2 \cdot 2 \cdot 3 \cdot 3, \text{ or } 36$$

$$\dfrac{5}{12} + \dfrac{11}{18} = \dfrac{5}{2 \cdot 2 \cdot 3} \cdot \dfrac{3}{3} + \dfrac{11}{2 \cdot 3 \cdot 3} \cdot \dfrac{2}{2} = \dfrac{15 + 22}{2 \cdot 2 \cdot 3 \cdot 3} = \dfrac{37}{36}$$

Do Exercises 5–8.

(c) LCMs of Algebraic Expressions

To find the LCM of two or more algebraic expressions, we factor them. Then we use each factor the greatest number of times that it occurs in any one expression. In Section 12.4, each LCM will become an LCD used to add rational expressions.

EXAMPLE 3 Find the LCM of $12x$, $16y$, and $8xyz$.

$$\left.\begin{array}{l} 12x = 2 \cdot 2 \cdot 3 \cdot x \\ 16y = 2 \cdot 2 \cdot 2 \cdot 2 \cdot y \\ 8xyz = 2 \cdot 2 \cdot 2 \cdot x \cdot y \cdot z \end{array}\right\} \quad \begin{array}{l} \text{LCM} = 2 \cdot 2 \cdot 2 \cdot 2 \cdot 3 \cdot x \cdot y \cdot z \\ \qquad\;\; = 48xyz \end{array}$$

EXAMPLE 4 Find the LCM of $x^2 + 5x - 6$ and $x^2 - 1$.

$$\left.\begin{array}{l} x^2 + 5x - 6 = (x + 6)(x - 1) \\ x^2 - 1 = (x + 1)(x - 1) \end{array}\right\} \quad \text{LCM} = (x + 6)(x - 1)(x + 1)$$

EXAMPLE 5 Find the LCM of $x^2 + 4$, $x + 1$, and 5.

These expressions do not share a common factor other than 1, so the LCM is their product:

$$5(x^2 + 4)(x + 1).$$

EXAMPLE 6 Find the LCM of $x^2 - 25$ and $2x - 10$.

$$\left.\begin{array}{l} x^2 - 25 = (x + 5)(x - 5) \\ 2x - 10 = 2(x - 5) \end{array}\right\} \quad \text{LCM} = 2(x + 5)(x - 5)$$

Find the LCM.

9. $12xy^2$, $15x^3y$

10. $y^2 + 5y + 4$, $y^2 + 2y + 1$

11. $t^2 + 16$, $t - 2$, 7

12. $x^2 + 2x + 1$, $3x^2 - 3x$, $x^2 - 1$

EXAMPLE 7 Find the LCM of $x^2 - 4y^2$, $x^2 - 4xy + 4y^2$, and $x - 2y$.

$$\left.\begin{array}{l} x^2 - 4y^2 = (x - 2y)(x + 2y) \\ x^2 - 4xy + 4y^2 = (x - 2y)(x - 2y) \\ x - 2y = x - 2y \end{array}\right\} \quad \begin{array}{l} \text{LCM} = (x + 2y)(x - 2y)(x - 2y) \\ \qquad\;\; = (x + 2y)(x - 2y)^2 \end{array}$$

Do Exercises 9–12.

Answers

5. $\dfrac{35}{144}$ 6. $\dfrac{1}{4}$ 7. $\dfrac{11}{10}$ 8. $\dfrac{9}{40}$ 9. $60x^3y^2$
10. $(y + 1)^2(y + 4)$ 11. $7(t^2 + 16)(t - 2)$
12. $3x(x + 1)^2(x - 1)$

a Find the LCM.

1. 12, 27

2. 10, 15

3. 8, 9

4. 12, 18

5. 6, 9, 21

6. 8, 36, 40

7. 24, 36, 40

8. 4, 5, 20

9. 10, 100, 500

10. 28, 42, 60

b Add, first finding the LCD. Simplify if possible.

11. $\dfrac{7}{24} + \dfrac{11}{18}$

12. $\dfrac{7}{60} + \dfrac{2}{25}$

13. $\dfrac{1}{6} + \dfrac{3}{40}$

14. $\dfrac{5}{24} + \dfrac{3}{20}$

15. $\dfrac{1}{20} + \dfrac{1}{30} + \dfrac{2}{45}$

16. $\dfrac{2}{15} + \dfrac{5}{9} + \dfrac{3}{20}$

c Find the LCM.

17. $6x^2,\ 12x^3$

18. $2a^2b,\ 8ab^3$

19. $2x^2,\ 6xy,\ 18y^2$

20. $p^3q,\ p^2q,\ pq^2$

21. $2(y-3),\ 6(y-3)$

22. $5(m+2),\ 15(m+2)$

23. $t,\ t+2,\ t-2$

24. $y,\ y-5,\ y+5$

25. $x^2-4,\ x^2+5x+6$

26. $x^2-4,\ x^2-x-2$

27. $t^3+4t^2+4t,\ t^2-4t$

28. $m^4-m^2,\ m^3-m^2$

29. $a+1,\ (a-1)^2,\ a^2-1$

30. $a^2-2ab+b^2,\ a^2-b^2,\ 3a+3b$

31. $m^2-5m+6,\ m^2-4m+4$

32. $2x^2+5x+2,\ 2x^2-x-1$

33. $2+3x,\ 4-9x^2,\ 2-3x$

34. $9-4x^2,\ 3+2x,\ 3-2x$

35. $10v^2+30v,\ 5v^2+35v+60$

36. $12a^2+24a,\ 4a^2+20a+24$

37. $9x^3 - 9x^2 - 18x$, $6x^5 - 24x^4 + 24x^3$

38. $x^5 - 4x^3$, $x^3 + 4x^2 + 4x$

39. $x^5 + 4x^4 + 4x^3$, $3x^2 - 12$, $2x + 4$

40. $x^5 + 2x^4 + x^3$, $2x^3 - 2x$, $5x - 5$

41. $24w^4$, w^2, $10w^3$, w^6

42. t, $6t^4$, t^2, $15t^{15}$, $2t^3$

Skill Maintenance

Factor.　[11.6a]

43. $x^2 - 6x + 9$

44. $6x^2 + 4x$

45. $x^2 - 9$

46. $x^2 + 4x - 21$

47. $x^2 + 6x + 9$

48. $x^2 - 4x - 21$

Complete the table below, finding the LCM, the GCF, and the product of each pair of expressions.　[10.5a], [11.1a], [12.3a]

	EXPRESSIONS	LCM	GCF	PRODUCT
	$12x^3$, $8x^2$	$24x^3$	$4x^2$	$96x^5$
49.	$40x^3$, $24x^4$			
50.	$16x^5$, $48x^6$			
51.	$20x^2$, $10x$			
52.	$12ab$, $16ab^3$			
53.	$10x^2$, $24x^3$			
54.	a^5, a^{15}			

Synthesis

55. Look for a pattern in Exercises 49–54. See if you can discover a formula connecting the LCM and the GCF.

56. *Running.* Pedro and Maria leave the starting point of a fitness loop at the same time. Pedro jogs a lap in 6 min and Maria jogs one in 8 min. Assuming they continue to run at the same pace, when will they next meet at the starting place?

Copyright © 2012 Pearson Education, Inc.

12.4 Adding Rational Expressions

a Adding Rational Expressions

We add rational expressions as we do rational numbers.

> **ADDING RATIONAL EXPRESSIONS WITH LIKE DENOMINATORS**
>
> To add when the denominators are the same, add the numerators and keep the same denominator. Then simplify if possible.

EXAMPLES Add.

1. $\dfrac{x}{x+1} + \dfrac{2}{x+1} = \dfrac{x+2}{x+1}$

2. $\dfrac{2x^2 + 3x - 7}{2x+1} + \dfrac{x^2 + x - 8}{2x+1} = \dfrac{(2x^2 + 3x - 7) + (x^2 + x - 8)}{2x+1}$

$\qquad = \dfrac{3x^2 + 4x - 15}{2x+1}$

$\qquad = \dfrac{(x+3)(3x-5)}{2x+1}$ Factoring the numerator to determine whether we can simplify

3. $\dfrac{x-5}{x^2-9} + \dfrac{2}{x^2-9} = \dfrac{(x-5)+2}{x^2-9} = \dfrac{x-3}{x^2-9}$

$\qquad = \dfrac{x-3}{(x-3)(x+3)}$ Factoring

$\qquad = \dfrac{1(x-3)}{(x-3)(x+3)}$ Removing a factor of 1: $\dfrac{x-3}{x-3} = 1$

$\qquad = \dfrac{1}{x+3}$ Simplifying

Do Margin Exercises 1–3.

When denominators are different, we find the least common denominator, LCD. The procedure we use follows.

> **ADDING RATIONAL EXPRESSIONS WITH DIFFERENT DENOMINATORS**
>
> To add rational expressions with different denominators:
>
> **1.** Find the LCM of the denominators. This is the least common denominator (LCD).
>
> **2.** For each rational expression, find an equivalent expression with the LCD. Multiply by 1 using an expression for 1 made up of factors of the LCD that are missing from the original denominator.
>
> **3.** Add the numerators. Write the sum over the LCD.
>
> **4.** Simplify if possible.

OBJECTIVE

a Add rational expressions.

SKILL TO REVIEW
Objective 2.3a: Add using fraction notation.

Add and simplify.

1. $\dfrac{7}{10} + \dfrac{11}{15}$ **2.** $\dfrac{11}{42} + \dfrac{5}{14}$

Add.

1. $\dfrac{5}{9} + \dfrac{2}{9}$

2. $\dfrac{3}{x-2} + \dfrac{x}{x-2}$

3. $\dfrac{4x+5}{x-1} + \dfrac{2x-1}{x-1}$

Answers

Skill to Review:
1. $\dfrac{43}{30}$ **2.** $\dfrac{13}{21}$

Margin Exercises:
1. $\dfrac{7}{9}$ **2.** $\dfrac{3+x}{x-2}$ **3.** $\dfrac{6x+4}{x-1}$

STUDY TIPS

WORKING WITH RATIONAL EXPRESSIONS

The procedures covered in this chapter are by their nature rather long. It may help to write out lots of steps as you do the problems. If you have difficulty, consider taking a clean sheet of paper and starting over. Don't squeeze your work into a small amount of space. When using lined paper, consider using two spaces at a time, with the paper's line representing the fraction bar.

EXAMPLE 4 Add: $\dfrac{5x^2}{8} + \dfrac{7x}{12}$.

First, we find the LCD:

$$\left.\begin{array}{l} 8 = 2 \cdot 2 \cdot 2 \\ 12 = 2 \cdot 2 \cdot 3 \end{array}\right\} \quad \text{LCD} = 2 \cdot 2 \cdot 2 \cdot 3, \text{ or } 24.$$

Compare the factorization $8 = 2 \cdot 2 \cdot 2$ with the factorization of the LCD, $24 = 2 \cdot 2 \cdot 2 \cdot 3$. The factor of 24 that is missing from 8 is 3. Compare $12 = 2 \cdot 2 \cdot 3$ and $24 = 2 \cdot 2 \cdot 2 \cdot 3$. The factor of 24 that is missing from 12 is 2.

We multiply each term by a symbol for 1 to get the LCD in each expression, and then add and, if possible, simplify:

$$\begin{aligned} \frac{5x^2}{8} + \frac{7x}{12} &= \frac{5x^2}{2 \cdot 2 \cdot 2} + \frac{7x}{2 \cdot 2 \cdot 3} \\ &= \frac{5x^2}{2 \cdot 2 \cdot 2} \cdot \frac{3}{3} + \frac{7x}{2 \cdot 2 \cdot 3} \cdot \frac{2}{2} \qquad \text{Multiplying by 1 to get} \\ &\qquad\qquad\qquad\qquad\qquad\qquad\qquad\quad \text{the same denominators} \\ &= \frac{15x^2}{24} + \frac{14x}{24} = \frac{15x^2 + 14x}{24} = \frac{x(15x + 14)}{24}. \end{aligned}$$

EXAMPLE 5 Add: $\dfrac{3}{8x} + \dfrac{5}{12x^2}$.

First, we find the LCD:

$$\left.\begin{array}{l} 8x = 2 \cdot 2 \cdot 2 \cdot x \\ 12x^2 = 2 \cdot 2 \cdot 3 \cdot x \cdot x \end{array}\right\} \quad \text{LCD} = 2 \cdot 2 \cdot 2 \cdot 3 \cdot x \cdot x, \text{ or } 24x^2.$$

The factors of the LCD missing from $8x$ are 3 and x. The factor of the LCD missing from $12x^2$ is 2. We multiply each term by 1 to get the LCD in each expression, and then add and, if possible, simplify:

$$\begin{aligned} \frac{3}{8x} + \frac{5}{12x^2} &= \frac{3}{8x} \cdot \frac{3 \cdot x}{3 \cdot x} + \frac{5}{12x^2} \cdot \frac{2}{2} \\ &= \frac{9x}{24x^2} + \frac{10}{24x^2} = \frac{9x + 10}{24x^2}. \end{aligned}$$

Do Exercises 4 and 5.

EXAMPLE 6 Add: $\dfrac{2a}{a^2 - 1} + \dfrac{1}{a^2 + a}$.

First, we find the LCD:

$$\left.\begin{array}{l} a^2 - 1 = (a - 1)(a + 1) \\ a^2 + a = a(a + 1) \end{array}\right\} \quad \text{LCD} = a(a - 1)(a + 1).$$

We multiply each term by 1 to get the LCD in each expression, and then add and simplify:

$$\begin{aligned} \frac{2a}{(a - 1)(a + 1)} &\cdot \frac{a}{a} + \frac{1}{a(a + 1)} \cdot \frac{a - 1}{a - 1} \\ &= \frac{2a^2}{a(a - 1)(a + 1)} + \frac{a - 1}{a(a - 1)(a + 1)} \\ &= \frac{2a^2 + a - 1}{a(a - 1)(a + 1)} \\ &= \frac{(a + 1)(2a - 1)}{a(a - 1)(a + 1)}. \qquad \text{Factoring the numerator} \\ &\qquad\qquad\qquad\qquad\qquad \text{in order to simplify} \end{aligned}$$

Add.

4. $\dfrac{3x}{16} + \dfrac{5x^2}{24}$

5. $\dfrac{3}{16x} + \dfrac{5}{24x^2}$

Answers

4. $\dfrac{x(10x + 9)}{48}$ **5.** $\dfrac{9x + 10}{48x^2}$

Then

$$= \frac{\cancel{(a+1)}(2a-1)}{a(a-1)\cancel{(a+1)}} \qquad \text{Removing a factor of 1: } \frac{a+1}{a+1} = 1$$

$$= \frac{2a-1}{a(a-1)}.$$

Do Exercise 6.

6. Add:

$$\frac{3}{x^3 - x} + \frac{4}{x^2 + 2x + 1}.$$

EXAMPLE 7 Add: $\dfrac{x+4}{x-2} + \dfrac{x-7}{x+5}$.

First, we find the LCD. It is just the product of the denominators:

$$\text{LCD} = (x-2)(x+5).$$

We multiply by 1 to get the LCD in each expression, and then add and simplify:

$$\frac{x+4}{x-2} \cdot \frac{x+5}{x+5} + \frac{x-7}{x+5} \cdot \frac{x-2}{x-2}$$

$$= \frac{(x+4)(x+5)}{(x-2)(x+5)} + \frac{(x-7)(x-2)}{(x-2)(x+5)}$$

$$= \frac{x^2 + 9x + 20}{(x-2)(x+5)} + \frac{x^2 - 9x + 14}{(x-2)(x+5)}$$

$$= \frac{x^2 + 9x + 20 + x^2 - 9x + 14}{(x-2)(x+5)} = \frac{2x^2 + 34}{(x-2)(x+5)} = \frac{2(x^2 + 17)}{(x-2)(x+5)}.$$

Do Exercise 7.

7. Add:

$$\frac{x-2}{x+3} + \frac{x+7}{x+8}.$$

EXAMPLE 8 Add: $\dfrac{x}{x^2 + 11x + 30} + \dfrac{-5}{x^2 + 9x + 20}$.

$$\frac{x}{x^2 + 11x + 30} + \frac{-5}{x^2 + 9x + 20}$$

$$= \frac{x}{(x+5)(x+6)} + \frac{-5}{(x+5)(x+4)} \qquad \begin{array}{l}\text{Factoring the denominators in} \\ \text{order to find the LCD. The LCD is} \\ (x+4)(x+5)(x+6).\end{array}$$

$$= \frac{x}{(x+5)(x+6)} \cdot \frac{x+4}{x+4} + \frac{-5}{(x+5)(x+4)} \cdot \frac{x+6}{x+6} \qquad \text{Multiplying by 1}$$

$$= \frac{x(x+4) + (-5)(x+6)}{(x+4)(x+5)(x+6)} = \frac{x^2 + 4x - 5x - 30}{(x+4)(x+5)(x+6)}$$

$$= \frac{x^2 - x - 30}{(x+4)(x+5)(x+6)}$$

$$= \frac{(x-6)\cancel{(x+5)}}{(x+4)\cancel{(x+5)}(x+6)} \qquad \begin{array}{l}\text{Always simplify at the end if} \\ \text{possible: } \dfrac{x+5}{x+5} = 1.\end{array}$$

$$= \frac{x-6}{(x+4)(x+6)}$$

Do Exercise 8.

8. Add:

$$\frac{5}{x^2 + 17x + 16} + \frac{3}{x^2 + 9x + 8}.$$

Denominators That Are Opposites

When one denominator is the opposite of the other, we can first multiply either expression by 1 using $-1/-1$.

Answers

6. $\dfrac{4x^2 - x + 3}{x(x-1)(x+1)^2}$ **7.** $\dfrac{2x^2 + 16x + 5}{(x+3)(x+8)}$

8. $\dfrac{8(x+11)}{(x+16)(x+1)(x+8)}$

9. $\dfrac{x}{2} + \dfrac{3}{-2} = \dfrac{x}{2} + \dfrac{3}{-2} \cdot \dfrac{-1}{-1}$ Multiplying by 1 using $\dfrac{-1}{-1}$

$\phantom{9.\ \dfrac{x}{2} + \dfrac{3}{-2}} = \dfrac{x}{2} + \dfrac{-3}{2}$ The denominators are now the same.

$\phantom{9.\ \dfrac{x}{2} + \dfrac{3}{-2}} = \dfrac{x + (-3)}{2} = \dfrac{x - 3}{2}$

10. $\dfrac{3x + 4}{x - 2} + \dfrac{x - 7}{2 - x} = \dfrac{3x + 4}{x - 2} + \dfrac{x - 7}{2 - x} \cdot \dfrac{-1}{-1}$

> We could have chosen to multiply this expression by $-1/-1$. We multiply only one expression, *not* both.

$\phantom{10.\ \dfrac{3x + 4}{x - 2}} = \dfrac{3x + 4}{x - 2} + \dfrac{-x + 7}{x - 2}$ *Note:* $(2 - x)(-1) = -2 + x$
$\phantom{10.\ \dfrac{3x + 4}{x - 2} = \dfrac{3x + 4}{x - 2} + \dfrac{-x + 7}{x - 2}\ \ Note:\ } = x - 2.$

$\phantom{10.\ \dfrac{3x + 4}{x - 2}} = \dfrac{(3x + 4) + (-x + 7)}{x - 2} = \dfrac{2x + 11}{x - 2}$

Do Exercises 9 and 10.

Factors That Are Opposites

Suppose that when we factor to find the LCD, we find factors that are opposites. The easiest way to handle this is to first go back and multiply by $-1/-1$ appropriately to change factors so that they are not opposites.

EXAMPLE 11 Add: $\dfrac{x}{x^2 - 25} + \dfrac{3}{10 - 2x}$.

First, we factor to find the LCD:

$$x^2 - 25 = (x - 5)(x + 5);$$
$$10 - 2x = 2(5 - x).$$

We note that $x - 5$ is one factor of $x^2 - 25$ and $5 - x$ is one factor of $10 - 2x$. If the denominator of the second expression were $2x - 10$, then $x - 5$ would be a factor of both denominators. To rewrite the second expression with a denominator of $2x - 10$, we multiply by 1 using $-1/-1$, and then continue as before:

$$\frac{x}{x^2 - 25} + \frac{3}{10 - 2x} = \frac{x}{(x - 5)(x + 5)} + \frac{3}{10 - 2x} \cdot \frac{-1}{-1}$$

$$= \frac{x}{(x - 5)(x + 5)} + \frac{-3}{2x - 10}$$

$$= \frac{x}{(x - 5)(x + 5)} + \frac{-3}{2(x - 5)}   \qquad \text{LCD} = 2(x - 5)(x + 5)$$

$$= \frac{x}{(x - 5)(x + 5)} \cdot \frac{2}{2} + \frac{-3}{2(x - 5)} \cdot \frac{x + 5}{x + 5}$$

$$= \frac{2x}{2(x - 5)(x + 5)} + \frac{-3(x + 5)}{2(x - 5)(x + 5)}$$

$$= \frac{2x - 3(x + 5)}{2(x - 5)(x + 5)} = \frac{2x - 3x - 15}{2(x - 5)(x + 5)}$$

$$= \frac{-x - 15}{2(x - 5)(x + 5)}. \qquad \text{Collecting like terms}$$

Do Exercise 11.

Add.

9. $\dfrac{x}{4} + \dfrac{5}{-4}$

10. $\dfrac{2x + 1}{x - 3} + \dfrac{x + 2}{3 - x}$

11. Add:

$$\dfrac{x + 3}{x^2 - 16} + \dfrac{5}{12 - 3x}.$$

Answers

9. $\dfrac{x - 5}{4}$ **10.** $\dfrac{x - 1}{x - 3}$ **11.** $\dfrac{-2x - 11}{3(x + 4)(x - 4)}$

a   Add. Simplify if possible.

1. $\dfrac{5}{8} + \dfrac{3}{8}$

2. $\dfrac{3}{16} + \dfrac{5}{16}$

3. $\dfrac{1}{3+x} + \dfrac{5}{3+x}$

4. $\dfrac{x^2 + 7x}{x^2 - 5x} + \dfrac{x^2 - 4x}{x^2 - 5x}$

5. $\dfrac{4x + 6}{2x - 1} + \dfrac{5 - 8x}{-1 + 2x}$

6. $\dfrac{4}{x + y} + \dfrac{9}{y + x}$

7. $\dfrac{2}{x} + \dfrac{5}{x^2}$

8. $\dfrac{3}{y^2} + \dfrac{6}{y}$

9. $\dfrac{5}{6r} + \dfrac{7}{8r}$

10. $\dfrac{13}{18x} + \dfrac{7}{24x}$

11. $\dfrac{4}{xy^2} + \dfrac{6}{x^2 y}$

12. $\dfrac{8}{ab^3} + \dfrac{3}{a^2 b}$

13. $\dfrac{2}{9t^3} + \dfrac{1}{6t^2}$

14. $\dfrac{5}{c^2 d^3} + \dfrac{-4}{7cd^2}$

15. $\dfrac{x + y}{xy^2} + \dfrac{3x + y}{x^2 y}$

16. $\dfrac{2c - d}{c^2 d} + \dfrac{c + d}{cd^2}$

17. $\dfrac{3}{x - 2} + \dfrac{3}{x + 2}$

18. $\dfrac{2}{y + 1} + \dfrac{2}{y - 1}$

19. $\dfrac{3}{x + 1} + \dfrac{2}{3x}$

20. $\dfrac{4}{5y} + \dfrac{7}{y - 2}$

21. $\dfrac{2x}{x^2 - 16} + \dfrac{x}{x - 4}$

22. $\dfrac{4x}{x^2 - 25} + \dfrac{x}{x + 5}$

23. $\dfrac{5}{z + 4} + \dfrac{3}{3z + 12}$

24. $\dfrac{t}{t - 3} + \dfrac{5}{4t - 12}$

25. $\dfrac{3}{x - 1} + \dfrac{2}{(x - 1)^2}$

26. $\dfrac{8}{(y + 3)^2} + \dfrac{5}{y + 3}$

27. $\dfrac{4a}{5a - 10} + \dfrac{3a}{10a - 20}$

28. $\dfrac{9x}{6x - 30} + \dfrac{3x}{4x - 20}$

29. $\dfrac{x + 4}{x} + \dfrac{x}{x + 4}$

30. $\dfrac{a}{a - 3} + \dfrac{a - 3}{a}$

31. $\dfrac{4}{a^2 - a - 2} + \dfrac{3}{a^2 + 4a + 3}$

32. $\dfrac{a}{a^2 - 2a + 1} + \dfrac{1}{a^2 - 5a + 4}$

33. $\dfrac{x + 3}{x - 5} + \dfrac{x - 5}{x + 3}$

34. $\dfrac{3x}{2y - 3} + \dfrac{2x}{3y - 2}$

35. $\dfrac{a}{a^2 - 1} + \dfrac{2a}{a^2 - a}$

36. $\dfrac{3x + 2}{3x + 6} + \dfrac{x - 2}{x^2 - 4}$

37. $\dfrac{7}{8} + \dfrac{5}{-8}$

38. $\dfrac{5}{-3} + \dfrac{11}{3}$

39. $\dfrac{3}{t} + \dfrac{4}{-t}$

40. $\dfrac{5}{-a} + \dfrac{8}{a}$

41. $\dfrac{2x + 7}{x - 6} + \dfrac{3x}{6 - x}$

42. $\dfrac{2x - 7}{5x - 8} + \dfrac{6 + 10x}{8 - 5x}$

Copyright © 2012 Pearson Education, Inc.

43. $\dfrac{y^2}{y-3} + \dfrac{9}{3-y}$

44. $\dfrac{t^2}{t-2} + \dfrac{4}{2-t}$

45. $\dfrac{b-7}{b^2-16} + \dfrac{7-b}{16-b^2}$

46. $\dfrac{a-3}{a^2-25} + \dfrac{a-3}{25-a^2}$

47. $\dfrac{a^2}{a-b} + \dfrac{b^2}{b-a}$

48. $\dfrac{x^2}{x-7} + \dfrac{49}{7-x}$

49. $\dfrac{x+3}{x-5} + \dfrac{2x-1}{5-x} + \dfrac{2(3x-1)}{x-5}$

50. $\dfrac{3(x-2)}{2x-3} + \dfrac{5(2x+1)}{2x-3} + \dfrac{3(x+1)}{3-2x}$

51. $\dfrac{2(4x+1)}{5x-7} + \dfrac{3(x-2)}{7-5x} + \dfrac{-10x-1}{5x-7}$

52. $\dfrac{5(x-2)}{3x-4} + \dfrac{2(x-3)}{4-3x} + \dfrac{3(5x+1)}{4-3x}$

53. $\dfrac{x+1}{(x+3)(x-3)} + \dfrac{4(x-3)}{(x-3)(x+3)} + \dfrac{(x-1)(x-3)}{(3-x)(x+3)}$

54. $\dfrac{2(x+5)}{(2x-3)(x-1)} + \dfrac{3x+4}{(2x-3)(1-x)} + \dfrac{x-5}{(3-2x)(x-1)}$

55. $\dfrac{6}{x-y} + \dfrac{4x}{y^2-x^2}$

56. $\dfrac{a-2}{3-a} + \dfrac{4-a^2}{a^2-9}$

57. $\dfrac{4-a}{25-a^2} + \dfrac{a+1}{a-5}$

58. $\dfrac{x+2}{x-7} + \dfrac{3-x}{49-x^2}$

59. $\dfrac{2}{t^2+t-6} + \dfrac{3}{t^2-9}$

60. $\dfrac{10}{a^2-a-6} + \dfrac{3a}{a^2+4a+4}$

Skill Maintenance

Subtract. [10.4c]

61. $(x^2 + x) - (x + 1)$

62. $(4y^3 - 5y^2 + 7y - 24) - (-9y^3 + 9y^2 - 5y + 49)$

Simplify. [10.2a, b]

63. $(2x^4y^3)^{-3}$

64. $\left(\dfrac{x^3}{5y}\right)^2$

65. $\left(\dfrac{x^{-4}}{y^7}\right)^3$

66. $(5x^{-2}y^{-3})^2$

Graph.

67. $y = \dfrac{1}{2}x - 5$ [9.1d]

68. $2y + x + 10 = 0$ [9.1d]

69. $y = 3$ [9.2b]

70. $x = -5$ [9.2b]

Solve.

71. $3x - 7 = 5x + 9$ [8.3b]

72. $2a + 8 = 13 - 4a$ [8.3b]

73. $x^2 - 8x + 15 = 0$ [11.7b]

74. $x^2 - 7x = 18$ [11.7b]

Synthesis

Find the perimeter and the area of each figure.

75.

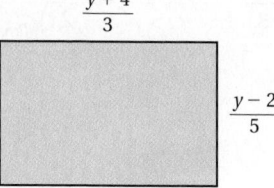

$\dfrac{y+4}{3}$

$\dfrac{y-2}{5}$

76.

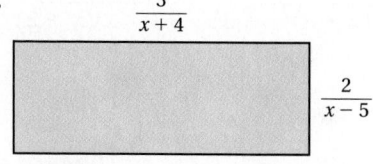

$\dfrac{3}{x+4}$

$\dfrac{2}{x-5}$

Add. Simplify if possible.

77. $\dfrac{5}{z+2} + \dfrac{4z}{z^2-4} + 2$

78. $\dfrac{-2}{y^2-9} + \dfrac{4y}{(y-3)^2} + \dfrac{6}{3-y}$

79. $\dfrac{3z^2}{z^4-4} + \dfrac{5z^2-3}{2z^4+z^2-6}$

80. Find an expression equivalent to

$$\dfrac{a-3b}{a-b}$$

that is a sum of two rational expressions. Answers may vary.

Copyright © 2012 Pearson Education, Inc.

12.5 Subtracting Rational Expressions

a Subtracting Rational Expressions

We subtract rational expressions as we do rational numbers.

> ### SUBTRACTING RATIONAL EXPRESSIONS WITH LIKE DENOMINATORS
>
> To subtract when the denominators are the same, subtract the numerators and keep the same denominator. Then simplify if possible.

EXAMPLE 1 Subtract: $\dfrac{8}{x} - \dfrac{3}{x}$.

$$\frac{8}{x} - \frac{3}{x} = \frac{8 - 3}{x} = \frac{5}{x}$$

EXAMPLE 2 Subtract: $\dfrac{3x}{x + 2} - \dfrac{x - 2}{x + 2}$.

Caution!

The parentheses are important to make sure that you subtract the entire numerator.

$$\frac{3x}{x + 2} - \frac{x - 2}{x + 2} = \frac{3x - (x - 2)}{x + 2}$$

$$= \frac{3x - x + 2}{x + 2} \qquad \text{Removing parentheses}$$

$$= \frac{2x + 2}{x + 2} = \frac{2(x + 1)}{x + 2}$$

Do Margin Exercises 1–3.

To subtract rational expressions with different denominators, we use a procedure similar to what we used for addition, except that we subtract numerators and write the difference over the LCD.

> ### SUBTRACTING RATIONAL EXPRESSIONS WITH DIFFERENT DENOMINATORS
>
> To subtract rational expressions with different denominators:
>
> 1. Find the LCM of the denominators. This is the least common denominator (LCD).
> 2. For each rational expression, find an equivalent expression with the LCD. To do so, multiply by 1 using a symbol for 1 made up of factors of the LCD that are missing from the original denominator.
> 3. Subtract the numerators. Write the difference over the LCD.
> 4. Simplify if possible.

OBJECTIVES

a Subtract rational expressions.

b Simplify combined additions and subtractions of rational expressions.

SKILL TO REVIEW
Objective 7.8a: Find an equivalent expression for an opposite without parentheses, where an expression has several terms.

Find an expression without parentheses.

1. $-(3x - 11)$
2. $-(-x + 8)$

Subtract.

1. $\dfrac{7}{11} - \dfrac{3}{11}$

2. $\dfrac{7}{y} - \dfrac{2}{y}$

3. $\dfrac{2x^2 + 3x - 7}{2x + 1} - \dfrac{x^2 + x - 8}{2x + 1}$

Answers

Skill to Review:
1. $-3x + 11$ 2. $x - 8$

Margin Exercises:
1. $\dfrac{4}{11}$ 2. $\dfrac{5}{y}$ 3. $\dfrac{(x + 1)^2}{2x + 1}$

EXAMPLE 3 Subtract: $\dfrac{x+2}{x-4} - \dfrac{x+1}{x+4}$.

The LCD $= (x-4)(x+4)$.

$\dfrac{x+2}{x-4} \cdot \dfrac{x+4}{x+4} - \dfrac{x+1}{x+4} \cdot \dfrac{x-4}{x-4}$ Multiplying by 1

$= \dfrac{(x+2)(x+4)}{(x-4)(x+4)} - \dfrac{(x+1)(x-4)}{(x-4)(x+4)}$

$= \dfrac{x^2+6x+8}{(x-4)(x+4)} - \dfrac{x^2-3x-4}{(x-4)(x+4)}$

Subtracting this numerator.
Don't forget the parentheses.

$= \dfrac{x^2+6x+8 - (x^2-3x-4)}{(x-4)(x+4)}$

$= \dfrac{x^2+6x+8 - x^2+3x+4}{(x-4)(x+4)}$ Removing parentheses

$= \dfrac{9x+12}{(x-4)(x+4)} = \dfrac{3(3x+4)}{(x-4)(x+4)}$

4. Subtract:

$\dfrac{x-2}{3x} - \dfrac{2x-1}{5x}$.

Do Exercise 4.

EXAMPLE 4 Subtract: $\dfrac{x}{x^2+5x+6} - \dfrac{2}{x^2+3x+2}$.

$\dfrac{x}{x^2+5x+6} - \dfrac{2}{x^2+3x+2}$

$= \dfrac{x}{(x+2)(x+3)} - \dfrac{2}{(x+2)(x+1)}$ LCD $= (x+1)(x+2)(x+3)$

$= \dfrac{x}{(x+2)(x+3)} \cdot \dfrac{x+1}{x+1} - \dfrac{2}{(x+2)(x+1)} \cdot \dfrac{x+3}{x+3}$

$= \dfrac{x^2+x}{(x+1)(x+2)(x+3)} - \dfrac{2x+6}{(x+1)(x+2)(x+3)}$

Subtracting this numerator.
Don't forget the parentheses.

$= \dfrac{x^2+x - (2x+6)}{(x+1)(x+2)(x+3)}$

$= \dfrac{x^2+x-2x-6}{(x+1)(x+2)(x+3)} = \dfrac{x^2-x-6}{(x+1)(x+2)(x+3)}$

$= \dfrac{(x+2)(x-3)}{(x+1)(x+2)(x+3)}$

$= \dfrac{\cancel{(x+2)}(x-3)}{(x+1)\cancel{(x+2)}(x+3)}$ Simplifying by removing a factor
of 1: $\dfrac{x+2}{x+2} = 1$

$= \dfrac{x-3}{(x+1)(x+3)}$

5. Subtract:

$\dfrac{x}{x^2+15x+56} - \dfrac{6}{x^2+13x+42}$.

Do Exercise 5.

Denominators That Are Opposites

When one denominator is the opposite of the other, we can first multiply one expression by $-1/-1$ to obtain a common denominator.

Answers

4. $\dfrac{-x-7}{15x}$ **5.** $\dfrac{x^2-48}{(x+7)(x+8)(x+6)}$

EXAMPLE 5 Subtract: $\dfrac{x}{5} - \dfrac{3x-4}{-5}$.

$$\dfrac{x}{5} - \dfrac{3x-4}{-5} = \dfrac{x}{5} - \dfrac{3x-4}{-5} \cdot \dfrac{-1}{-1} \qquad \text{Multiplying by 1 using } \dfrac{-1}{-1}$$

> This is equal to 1 (not −1).

$$= \dfrac{x}{5} - \dfrac{(3x-4)(-1)}{(-5)(-1)}$$

$$= \dfrac{x}{5} - \dfrac{4-3x}{5}$$

$$= \dfrac{x-(4-3x)}{5} \qquad \text{Remember the parentheses!}$$

$$= \dfrac{x-4+3x}{5} = \dfrac{4x-4}{5} = \dfrac{4(x-1)}{5}$$

EXAMPLE 6 Subtract: $\dfrac{5y}{y-5} - \dfrac{2y-3}{5-y}$.

$$\dfrac{5y}{y-5} - \dfrac{2y-3}{5-y} = \dfrac{5y}{y-5} - \dfrac{2y-3}{5-y} \cdot \dfrac{-1}{-1}$$

$$= \dfrac{5y}{y-5} - \dfrac{(2y-3)(-1)}{(5-y)(-1)}$$

$$= \dfrac{5y}{y-5} - \dfrac{3-2y}{y-5}$$

$$= \dfrac{5y-(3-2y)}{y-5} \qquad \text{Remember the parentheses!}$$

$$= \dfrac{5y-3+2y}{y-5} = \dfrac{7y-3}{y-5}$$

> Do Exercises 6 and 7.

Do Exercises 6 and 7.

Subtract.

6. $\dfrac{x}{3} - \dfrac{2x-1}{-3}$

7. $\dfrac{3x}{x-2} - \dfrac{x-3}{2-x}$

Factors That Are Opposites

Suppose that when we factor to find the LCD, we find factors that are opposites. Then we multiply by $-1/-1$ appropriately to change factors so that they are not opposites.

EXAMPLE 7 Subtract: $\dfrac{p}{64-p^2} - \dfrac{5}{p-8}$.

Factoring $64 - p^2$, we get $(8-p)(8+p)$. Note that the factors $8-p$ in the first denominator and $p-8$ in the second denominator are opposites. We multiply the first expression by $-1/-1$ to avoid this situation. Then we proceed as before.

$$\dfrac{p}{64-p^2} - \dfrac{5}{p-8} = \dfrac{p}{64-p^2} \cdot \dfrac{-1}{-1} - \dfrac{5}{p-8}$$

$$= \dfrac{-p}{p^2-64} - \dfrac{5}{p-8}$$

$$= \dfrac{-p}{(p-8)(p+8)} - \dfrac{5}{p-8} \qquad \text{LCD} = (p-8)(p+8)$$

$$= \dfrac{-p}{(p-8)(p+8)} - \dfrac{5}{p-8} \cdot \dfrac{p+8}{p+8}$$

Answers

6. $\dfrac{3x-1}{3}$ 7. $\dfrac{4x-3}{x-2}$

Multiplying, we have

$$\frac{-p}{(p-8)(p+8)} - \frac{5p+40}{(p-8)(p+8)}$$

Subtracting this numerator.
Don't forget the parentheses.

$$= \frac{-p - (5p+40)}{(p-8)(p+8)}$$

$$= \frac{-p-5p-40}{(p-8)(p+8)} = \frac{-6p-40}{(p-8)(p+8)} = \frac{-2(3p+20)}{(p-8)(p+8)}.$$

Do Exercise 8.

8. Subtract:

$$\frac{y}{16-y^2} - \frac{7}{y-4}.$$

(b) Combined Additions and Subtractions

Now let's look at some combined additions and subtractions.

EXAMPLE 8 Perform the indicated operations and simplify:

$$\frac{x+9}{x^2-4} + \frac{5-x}{4-x^2} - \frac{2+x}{x^2-4}.$$

$$\frac{x+9}{x^2-4} + \frac{5-x}{4-x^2} - \frac{2+x}{x^2-4}$$

$$= \frac{x+9}{x^2-4} + \frac{5-x}{4-x^2} \cdot \frac{-1}{-1} - \frac{2+x}{x^2-4}$$

$$= \frac{x+9}{x^2-4} + \frac{x-5}{x^2-4} - \frac{2+x}{x^2-4} = \frac{(x+9)+(x-5)-(2+x)}{x^2-4}$$

$$= \frac{x+9+x-5-2-x}{x^2-4} = \frac{x+2}{x^2-4} = \frac{(x+2)\cdot 1}{(x+2)(x-2)} = \frac{1}{x-2}$$

Do Exercise 9.

9. Perform the indicated operations and simplify:

$$\frac{x+2}{x^2-9} - \frac{x-7}{9-x^2} + \frac{-8-x}{x^2-9}.$$

EXAMPLE 9 Perform the indicated operations and simplify:

$$\frac{1}{x} - \frac{1}{x^2} + \frac{2}{x+1}.$$

The LCD $= x \cdot x(x+1)$, or $x^2(x+1)$.

$$\frac{1}{x} \cdot \frac{x(x+1)}{x(x+1)} - \frac{1}{x^2} \cdot \frac{(x+1)}{(x+1)} + \frac{2}{x+1} \cdot \frac{x^2}{x^2}$$

$$= \frac{x(x+1)}{x^2(x+1)} - \frac{x+1}{x^2(x+1)} + \frac{2x^2}{x^2(x+1)}$$

Subtracting this numerator.
Don't forget the parentheses.

$$= \frac{x(x+1) - (x+1) + 2x^2}{x^2(x+1)}$$

$$= \frac{x^2 + x - x - 1 + 2x^2}{x^2(x+1)}$$ Removing parentheses

$$= \frac{3x^2 - 1}{x^2(x+1)}$$

Do Exercise 10.

10. Perform the indicated operations and simplify:

$$\frac{1}{x} - \frac{5}{3x} + \frac{2x}{x+1}.$$

Answers

8. $\dfrac{-4(2y+7)}{(y+4)(y-4)}$ **9.** $\dfrac{x-13}{(x+3)(x-3)}$

10. $\dfrac{2(3x^2-x-1)}{3x(x+1)}$

12.5

Exercise Set

For Extra Help

MyMathLab

Math XL
PRACTICE

WATCH

DOWNLOAD

READ

REVIEW

a Subtract. Simplify if possible.

1. $\dfrac{7}{x} - \dfrac{3}{x}$

2. $\dfrac{5}{a} - \dfrac{8}{a}$

3. $\dfrac{y}{y-4} - \dfrac{4}{y-4}$

4. $\dfrac{t^2}{t+5} - \dfrac{25}{t+5}$

5. $\dfrac{2x-3}{x^2+3x-4} - \dfrac{x-7}{x^2+3x-4}$

6. $\dfrac{x+1}{x^2-2x+1} - \dfrac{5-3x}{x^2-2x+1}$

7. $\dfrac{a-2}{10} - \dfrac{a+1}{5}$

8. $\dfrac{y+3}{2} - \dfrac{y-4}{4}$

9. $\dfrac{4z-9}{3z} - \dfrac{3z-8}{4z}$

10. $\dfrac{a-1}{4a} - \dfrac{2a+3}{a}$

11. $\dfrac{4x+2t}{3xt^2} - \dfrac{5x-3t}{x^2t}$

12. $\dfrac{5x+3y}{2x^2y} - \dfrac{3x+4y}{xy^2}$

13. $\dfrac{5}{x+5} - \dfrac{3}{x-5}$

14. $\dfrac{3t}{t-1} - \dfrac{8t}{t+1}$

15. $\dfrac{3}{2t^2-2t} - \dfrac{5}{2t-2}$

16. $\dfrac{11}{x^2-4} - \dfrac{8}{x+2}$

17. $\dfrac{2s}{t^2-s^2} - \dfrac{s}{t-s}$

18. $\dfrac{3}{12+x-x^2} - \dfrac{2}{x^2-9}$

19. $\dfrac{y-5}{y} - \dfrac{3y-1}{4y}$

20. $\dfrac{3x-2}{4x} - \dfrac{3x+1}{6x}$

21. $\dfrac{a}{x+a} - \dfrac{a}{x-a}$

22. $\dfrac{a}{a-b} - \dfrac{a}{a+b}$

23. $\dfrac{11}{6} - \dfrac{5}{-6}$

24. $\dfrac{5}{9} - \dfrac{7}{-9}$

25. $\dfrac{5}{a} - \dfrac{8}{-a}$

26. $\dfrac{8}{x} - \dfrac{3}{-x}$

27. $\dfrac{4}{y-1} - \dfrac{4}{1-y}$

28. $\dfrac{5}{a-2} - \dfrac{3}{2-a}$

29. $\dfrac{3-x}{x-7} - \dfrac{2x-5}{7-x}$

30. $\dfrac{t^2}{t-2} - \dfrac{4}{2-t}$

31. $\dfrac{a-2}{a^2-25} - \dfrac{6-a}{25-a^2}$

32. $\dfrac{x-8}{x^2-16} - \dfrac{x-8}{16-x^2}$

33. $\dfrac{4-x}{x-9} - \dfrac{3x-8}{9-x}$

34. $\dfrac{4x-6}{x-5} - \dfrac{7-2x}{5-x}$

35. $\dfrac{5x}{x^2-9} - \dfrac{4}{3-x}$

36. $\dfrac{8x}{16-x^2} - \dfrac{5}{x-4}$

Copyright © 2012 Pearson Education, Inc.

37. $\dfrac{t^2}{2t^2 - 2t} - \dfrac{1}{2t - 2}$

38. $\dfrac{4}{5a^2 - 5a} - \dfrac{2}{5a - 5}$

39. $\dfrac{x}{x^2 + 5x + 6} - \dfrac{2}{x^2 + 3x + 2}$

40. $\dfrac{a}{a^2 + 11a + 30} - \dfrac{5}{a^2 + 9a + 20}$

ⓑ Perform the indicated operations and simplify.

41. $\dfrac{3(2x + 5)}{x - 1} - \dfrac{3(2x - 3)}{1 - x} + \dfrac{6x - 1}{x - 1}$

42. $\dfrac{a - 2b}{b - a} - \dfrac{3a - 3b}{a - b} + \dfrac{2a - b}{a - b}$

43. $\dfrac{x - y}{x^2 - y^2} + \dfrac{x + y}{x^2 - y^2} - \dfrac{2x}{x^2 - y^2}$

44. $\dfrac{x - 3y}{2(y - x)} + \dfrac{x + y}{2(x - y)} - \dfrac{2x - 2y}{2(x - y)}$

45. $\dfrac{2(x - 1)}{2x - 3} - \dfrac{3(x + 2)}{2x - 3} - \dfrac{x - 1}{3 - 2x}$

46. $\dfrac{5(2y + 1)}{2y - 3} - \dfrac{3(y - 1)}{3 - 2y} - \dfrac{3(y - 2)}{2y - 3}$

47. $\dfrac{10}{2y - 1} - \dfrac{6}{1 - 2y} + \dfrac{y}{2y - 1} + \dfrac{y - 4}{1 - 2y}$

48. $\dfrac{(x + 1)(2x - 1)}{(2x - 3)(x - 3)} - \dfrac{(x - 3)(x + 1)}{(3 - x)(3 - 2x)} + \dfrac{(2x + 1)(x + 3)}{(3 - 2x)(x - 3)}$

49. $\dfrac{a + 6}{4 - a^2} - \dfrac{a + 3}{a + 2} + \dfrac{a - 3}{2 - a}$

50. $\dfrac{4t}{t^2 - 1} - \dfrac{2}{t} - \dfrac{2}{t + 1}$

51. $\dfrac{2z}{1 - 2z} + \dfrac{3z}{2z + 1} - \dfrac{3}{4z^2 - 1}$

52. $\dfrac{1}{x - y} - \dfrac{2x}{x^2 - y^2} + \dfrac{1}{x + y}$

53. $\dfrac{1}{x + y} - \dfrac{1}{x - y} + \dfrac{2x}{x^2 - y^2}$

54. $\dfrac{2b}{a^2 - b^2} - \dfrac{1}{a + b} + \dfrac{1}{a - b}$

Skill Maintenance

Simplify.

55. $\dfrac{x^8}{x^3}$ [10.1e]

56. $3x^4 \cdot 10x^8$ [10.1d]

57. $(a^2 b^{-5})^{-4}$ [10.2a, b]

58. $\dfrac{54x^{10}}{3x^7}$ [10.1e]

59. $\dfrac{66x^2}{11x^5}$ [10.1e]

60. $5x^{-7} \cdot 2x^4$ [10.1d]

Solve. [8.3b]

61. $\dfrac{4}{7} + 3x = \dfrac{1}{2}x - \dfrac{3}{14}$

62. $2.5x + 15.5 = 0.5 + 4x$

Find a polynomial for the shaded area of each figure. [10.4d]

63.

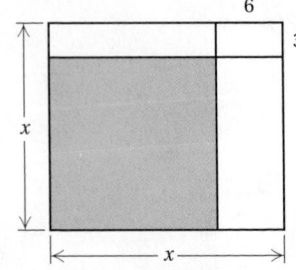

64.

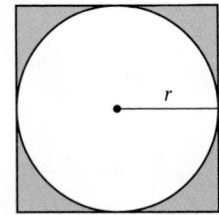

Synthesis

Perform the indicated operations and simplify.

65. $\dfrac{2x + 11}{x - 3} \cdot \dfrac{3}{x + 4} + \dfrac{2x + 1}{4 + x} \cdot \dfrac{3}{3 - x}$

66. $\dfrac{x^2}{3x^2 - 5x - 2} - \dfrac{2x}{3x + 1} \cdot \dfrac{1}{x - 2}$

67. $\dfrac{x}{x^4 - y^4} - \left(\dfrac{1}{x + y}\right)^2$

68. $\left(\dfrac{a}{a - b} + \dfrac{b}{a + b}\right)\left(\dfrac{1}{3a + b} + \dfrac{2a + 6b}{9a^2 - b^2}\right)$

angle is $2a + 5$.

the area.

$\dfrac{6}{6}$

Copyright © 2012 Pearson Education, Inc.

Mid-Chapter Review

Concept Reinforcement

Determine whether each statement is true or false.

_____ 1. The reciprocal of $\dfrac{3-w}{w+2}$ is $\dfrac{w-3}{w+2}$. [12.2a]

_____ 2. The value of the numerator has no bearing on whether or not a rational expression is defined. [12.1a]

_____ 3. To add or subtract rational expressions when the denominators are the same, add or subtract the numerators and keep the same denominator. [12.4a], [12.5a]

_____ 4. For the rational expression $\dfrac{x(x-2)}{x+3}$, x is a factor of the numerator and a factor of the denominator. [12.1c]

_____ 5. To find the LCM, use each factor the greatest number of times that it appears in any one factorization. [12.3a, c]

Guided Solutions

Fill in each blank with the number or expression that creates a correct solution.

6. Subtract: $\dfrac{x-1}{x-2} - \dfrac{x+1}{x+2} - \dfrac{x-6}{4-x^2}$. [12.5b]

$$\dfrac{x-1}{x-2} - \dfrac{x+1}{x+2} - \dfrac{x-6}{4-x^2} = \dfrac{x-1}{x-2} - \dfrac{x+1}{x+2} - \dfrac{x-6}{4-x^2} \cdot \dfrac{\square}{\square}$$

$$= \dfrac{x-1}{x-2} - \dfrac{x+1}{x+2} - \dfrac{6-\square}{\square-4}$$

$$= \dfrac{x-1}{x-2} - \dfrac{x+1}{x+2} - \dfrac{6-x}{(x-\square)(\square+2)}$$

$$= \dfrac{x-1}{x-2} \cdot \dfrac{\square}{\square} - \dfrac{x+1}{x+2} \cdot \dfrac{\square}{\square} - \dfrac{6-x}{(x-2)(x+2)}$$

$$= \dfrac{x^2+\square-2}{(x-2)(x+2)} - \dfrac{\square-x-2}{(x-2)(x+2)} - \dfrac{6-x}{(x-2)(x+2)}$$

$$= \dfrac{x^2+x-\square-x^2+\square+2-\square+x}{(x-2)(x+2)}$$

$$= \dfrac{\square-\square}{(x-2)(x+2)}$$

$$= \dfrac{3(\square-\square)}{(x-2)(x+2)} = \dfrac{\square}{\square} \cdot \dfrac{\square}{x+2} = \dfrac{3}{\square}$$

Mixed Review

Find all numbers for which the rational expression is not defined. [12.1a]

7. $\dfrac{t^2-16}{3}$

8. $\dfrac{x-8}{x^2-11x+24}$

9. $\dfrac{7}{2w-7}$

Simplify. [12.1c]

10. $\dfrac{x^2+2x-3}{x^2-9}$

11. $\dfrac{6y^2+12y-48}{3y^2-9y+6}$

12. $\dfrac{r-s}{s-r}$

13. Find the reciprocal of $-x + 3$.   [12.2a]

14. Find the LCM of
$$x^2 - 100, 10x^3, \text{ and } x^2 - 20x + 100.$$ [12.3c]

Add, subtract, multiply, or divide and simplify if possible.

15. $\dfrac{a^2 - a - 2}{a^2 - a - 6} \div \dfrac{a^2 - 2a}{2a + a^2}$ [12.2b]

16. $\dfrac{3y}{y^2 - 7y + 10} - \dfrac{2y}{y^2 - 8y + 15}$ [12.5a]

17. $\dfrac{x^2}{x - 11} + \dfrac{121}{11 - x}$ [12.4a]

18. $\dfrac{x^2 - y^2}{(x - y)^2} \cdot \dfrac{1}{x + y}$ [12.1d]

19. $\dfrac{3a - b}{a^2 b} + \dfrac{a + 2b}{ab^2}$ [12.4a]

20. $\dfrac{5x}{x^2 - 4} - \dfrac{3}{x} + \dfrac{4}{x + 2}$ [12.5b]

Matching.   Perform the indicated operation and simplify. Then select the correct answer from selections A–G listed in the second column.   [12.1d], [12.2b], [12.4a], [12.5a]

21. $\dfrac{2}{x - 2} \div \dfrac{1}{x + 3}$

A. $\dfrac{-x - 8}{(x - 2)(x + 3)}$

22. $\dfrac{1}{x + 3} - \dfrac{2}{x - 2}$

B. $\dfrac{x - 2}{2(x + 3)}$

23. $\dfrac{2}{x - 2} - \dfrac{1}{x + 3}$

C. $\dfrac{2}{(x - 2)(x + 3)}$

24. $\dfrac{1}{x + 3} \div \dfrac{2}{x - 2}$

D. $\dfrac{x + 8}{(x - 2)(x + 3)}$

25. $\dfrac{2}{x - 2} + \dfrac{1}{x + 3}$

E. $\dfrac{2(x + 3)}{x - 2}$

26. $\dfrac{2}{x - 2} \cdot \dfrac{1}{x + 3}$

F. $\dfrac{3x + 4}{(x - 2)(x + 3)}$

G. $\dfrac{x + 3}{x - 2}$

Understanding Through Discussion and Writing

27. Explain why the product of two numbers is not always their least common multiple.   [12.3a]

28. Is the reciprocal of a product the product of the reciprocals? Why or why not?   [12.2a]

29. A student insists on finding a common denominator by always multiplying the denominators of the expressions being added. How could this approach be improved?   [12.4a]

30. Explain why the expressions
$$\dfrac{1}{3 - x} \quad \text{and} \quad \dfrac{1}{x - 3}$$
are opposites.   [12.4a]

31. Explain why 5, -1, and 7 are *not* allowable replacements in the division
$$\dfrac{x + 3}{x - 5} \div \dfrac{x - 7}{x + 1}.$$ [12.1a], [12.2a, b]

32. If the LCM of a binomial and a trinomial is the trinomial, what relationship exists between the two expressions?   [12.3c]

Copyright © 2012 Pearson Education, Inc.

12.7

Applications Using Rational Equations and Proportions

OBJECTIVES

a Solve applied problems using rational equations.

b Solve proportion problems.

In many areas of study, applications involving rates, proportions, or reciprocals translate to rational equations. By using the five steps for problem solving and the skills of Sections 12.1–12.6, we can now solve such problems.

a Solving Applied Problems

Problems Involving Work

EXAMPLE 1 *Sodding a Yard.* Charlie's Lawn Care has two three-person crews who lay sod. Crew A can lay 7 skids of sod in 4 hr, while crew B requires 6 hr to do the same job. How long would it take the two crews working together to lay 7 skids of sod?

1. **Familiarize.** We familiarize ourselves with the problem by considering two *incorrect* ways of translating the problem to mathematical language.

   a) A common *incorrect* way to translate the problem is to add the two times: $4\,\text{hr} + 6\,\text{hr} = 10\,\text{hr}$. Let's think about this. Crew A can do the job in 4 hr. If crew A and crew B work together, the time it takes them should be *less* than 4 hr. Thus we reject 10 hr as a solution, but we do have a partial check on any answer we get. The answer should be less than 4 hr.

   b) Another *incorrect* way to translate the problem is as follows. Suppose the two crews split up the sodding job in such a way that crew A does half the sodding and crew B does the other half. Then

   $$\text{crew A lays } \frac{1}{2} \text{ the skids of sod in } \frac{1}{2}\,(4\,\text{hr}), \text{ or } 2\,\text{hr},$$

   and $\quad$ crew B lays $\frac{1}{2}$ the skids of sod in $\frac{1}{2}\,(6\,\text{hr})$, or 3 hr.

   But time is wasted since crew A would finish 1 hr earlier than crew B. In effect, they have not worked together to get the job done as fast as possible. If crew A helps crew B after completing their half, the entire job could be done in a time somewhere between 2 hr and 3 hr.

   We proceed to a translation by considering how much of the job is finished in 1 hr, 2 hr, 3 hr, and so on. It takes crew A 4 hr to do the sodding job alone. Then, in 1 hr, crew A can do $\frac{1}{4}$ of the job. It takes crew B 6 hr to do the job alone. Then, in 1 hr, crew B can do $\frac{1}{6}$ of the job. Working together, the crews can do

   $$\frac{1}{4} + \frac{1}{6}, \text{ or } \frac{3}{12} + \frac{2}{12}, \text{ or } \frac{5}{12} \text{ of the job in 1 hr.} \quad \text{(See Fig. 1.)}$$

   In 2 hr, crew A can do $2\left(\frac{1}{4}\right)$ of the job and crew B can do $2\left(\frac{1}{6}\right)$ of the job. Working together, they can do

   $$2\left(\frac{1}{4}\right) + 2\left(\frac{1}{6}\right), \text{ or } \frac{6}{12} + \frac{4}{12}, \text{ or } \frac{10}{12}, \text{ or } \frac{5}{6} \text{ of the job in 2 hr.}$$

   (See Fig. 2.)

In one hour:
Crew A $\quad$ Crew B

FIGURE 1

In two hours:
Crew A $\quad$ Crew B

FIGURE 2

Continuing this reasoning, we can create a table like the following one.

| TIME | FRACTION OF THE JOB COMPLETED | | |
	CREW A	CREW B	TOGETHER
1 hr	$\dfrac{1}{4}$	$\dfrac{1}{6}$	$\dfrac{1}{4} + \dfrac{1}{6}$, or $\dfrac{5}{12}$
2 hr	$2\left(\dfrac{1}{4}\right)$	$2\left(\dfrac{1}{6}\right)$	$2\left(\dfrac{1}{4}\right) + 2\left(\dfrac{1}{6}\right)$, or $\dfrac{5}{6}$
3 hr	$3\left(\dfrac{1}{4}\right)$	$3\left(\dfrac{1}{6}\right)$	$3\left(\dfrac{1}{4}\right) + 3\left(\dfrac{1}{6}\right)$, or $1\dfrac{1}{4}$
t hr	$t\left(\dfrac{1}{4}\right)$	$t\left(\dfrac{1}{6}\right)$	$t\left(\dfrac{1}{4}\right) + t\left(\dfrac{1}{6}\right)$

From the table, we see that if the crews work together for 3 hr, the fraction of the job completed is $1\frac{1}{4}$, which is more of the job than needs to be done. We see again that the answer is somewhere between 2 hr and 3 hr. What we want is a number t such that the fraction of the job that gets completed is 1; that is, the job is just completed.

2. **Translate.** From the table, we see that the time we want is some number t for which

$$t\left(\dfrac{1}{4}\right) + t\left(\dfrac{1}{6}\right) = 1, \quad \text{or} \quad \dfrac{t}{4} + \dfrac{t}{6} = 1,$$

where 1 represents the idea that the entire job is completed in time t.

3. **Solve.** We solve the equation:

$$12\left(\dfrac{t}{4} + \dfrac{t}{6}\right) = 12 \cdot 1 \qquad \text{Multiplying by the LCM, which is } 2 \cdot 2 \cdot 3, \text{ or } 12$$

$$12 \cdot \dfrac{t}{4} + 12 \cdot \dfrac{t}{6} = 12$$

$$3t + 2t = 12$$

$$5t = 12$$

$$t = \dfrac{12}{5}, \text{ or } 2\dfrac{2}{5} \text{ hr.}$$

4. **Check.** In $\frac{12}{5}$ hr, crew A does $\frac{12}{5} \cdot \frac{1}{4}$, or $\frac{3}{5}$, of the job and crew B does $\frac{12}{5} \cdot \frac{1}{6}$, or $\frac{2}{5}$, of the job. Together, they do $\frac{3}{5} + \frac{2}{5}$, or 1 entire job.

We also have another check in what we learned from the *Familiarize* step. The answer, $2\frac{2}{5}$ hr, is between 2 hr and 3 hr (see the table), and it is less than 4 hr, the time it takes crew A working alone.

5. **State.** It takes $2\frac{2}{5}$ hr for crew A and crew B working together to lay 7 skids of sod.

1. Work Recycling. Emma and Evan work as volunteers at a community recycling center. Emma can sort a morning's accumulation of recyclable objects in 3 hr, while Evan requires 5 hr to do the same job. How long would it take them, working together, to sort the recyclable material?

THE WORK PRINCIPLE

Suppose a = the time it takes A to do a job, b = the time it takes B to do the same job, and t = the time it takes them to do the job working together. Then

$$\frac{t}{a} + \frac{t}{b} = 1.$$

Do Exercise 1.

Problems Involving Motion

Problems that deal with distance, speed (or rate), and time are called **motion problems**. Translation of these problems involves the distance formula, $d = r \cdot t$, and/or the equivalent formulas $r = d/t$ and $t = d/r$.

MOTION FORMULAS

The following are the formulas for motion problems:

$d = rt;$ Distance = Rate · Time (basic formula)

$r = \dfrac{d}{t};$ Rate = Distance/Time

$t = \dfrac{d}{r}.$ Time = Distance/Rate

EXAMPLE 2 *Animal Speeds.* A zebra can run 15 mph faster than an elephant. A zebra can 8 mi in the same time that an elephant can run 5 mi. Find the speed of each animal.

Source: *The World Almanac*, 2008, p. 279

1. **Familiarize.** We first make a drawing. We let r = the speed of the elephant. Then $r + 15$ = the speed of the zebra.

5 mi, r mph

8 mi, $r + 15$ mph

Recall that sometimes we need to find a formula in order to solve an application. As we see above, a formula that relates the notions of distance, speed, and time is $d = rt$, or

Distance = Speed · Time.

(Indeed, you may need to look up such a formula.)

Answer

1. $1\frac{7}{8}$ hr

Since each animal travels for the same length of time, we can use just t for time. We organize the information in a chart, as follows.

$$d \quad = \quad r \quad \cdot \quad t$$

	DISTANCE	SPEED	TIME	
Elephant	5	r	t	$\rightarrow 5 = rt$
Zebra	8	$r + 15$	t	$\rightarrow 8 = (r + 15)t$

2. **Translate.** We can apply the formula $d = rt$ along the rows of the table to obtain two equations:

$$5 = rt, \quad \textbf{(1)}$$
$$8 = (r + 15)t. \quad \textbf{(2)}$$

We know that the animals travel for the same length of time. Thus if we solve each equation for t and set the results equal to each other, we get an equation in terms of r.

Solving $5 = rt$ for t: $\qquad t = \dfrac{5}{r}$

Solving $8 = (r + 15)t$ for t: $\qquad t = \dfrac{8}{r + 15}$

Since the times are the same, we have the following equation:

$$\frac{5}{r} = \frac{8}{r + 15}.$$

3. **Solve.** To solve the equation, we first multiply on both sides by the LCM, which is $r(r + 15)$:

$$r(r + 15) \cdot \frac{5}{r} = r(r + 15) \cdot \frac{8}{r + 15} \qquad \text{Multiplying on both sides by the LCM, which is } r(r + 15)$$
$$5(r + 15) = 8r \qquad \text{Simplifying}$$
$$5r + 75 = 8r \qquad \text{Removing parentheses}$$
$$75 = 3r$$
$$25 = r.$$

We now have a possible solution. The speed of the elephant is 25 mph, and the speed of the zebra is $r + 15 = 25 + 15$, or 40 mph.

4. **Check.** We first reread the problem to see what we were to find. We check the speeds of 25 for the elephant and 40 for the zebra. The zebra does travel 15 mph faster than the elephant and will travel farther than the elephant, which runs at a slower speed. If the zebra runs 8 mi at 40 mph, the time it has traveled is $\frac{8}{40}$, or $\frac{1}{5}$ hr. If the elephant runs 5 mi at 25 mph, the time it has traveled is $\frac{5}{25}$, or $\frac{1}{5}$ hr. Since the times are the same, the speeds check.

5. **State.** The speed of the elephant is 25 mph and the speed of the zebra is 40 mph.

Do Exercise 2.

2. **Driving Speed.** Nancy drives 20 mph faster than her father, Greg. In the same time that Nancy travels 180 mi, her father travels 120 mi. Find their speeds.

Nancy's car
180 mi, $r + 20$ mph

Greg's car
120 mi, r mph

Answer

2. Greg: 40 mph; Nancy: 60 mph

3. Find the ratio of 145 km to 2.5 liters (L).

4. Batting Average. Recently, a baseball player got 7 hits in 25 times at bat. What was the rate, or batting average, in hits per times at bat?

5. Impulses in nerve fibers travel 310 km in 2.5 hr. What is the rate, or speed, in kilometers per hour?

6. A lake of area 550 yd^2 contains 1320 fish. What is the population density of the lake, in number of fish per square yard?

b Applications Involving Proportions

We now consider applications with proportions. A **proportion** involves ratios. A **ratio** of two quantities is their quotient. For example, 73% is the ratio of 73 to 100, $\frac{73}{100}$. The ratio of two different kinds of measure is called a **rate**. Suppose an animal travels 720 ft in 2.5 hr. Its **rate**, or **speed**, is then

$$\frac{720 \text{ ft}}{2.5 \text{ hr}} = 288 \ \frac{\text{ft}}{\text{hr}}.$$

Do Exercises 3–6.

PROPORTION

An equality of ratios, $A/B = C/D$, is called a **proportion**. The numbers within a proportion are said to be **proportional** to each other.

EXAMPLE 3 *Mileage.* A 2009 Chevrolet Cobalt SS can travel 176 mi in city driving on 8 gal of gas. Find the amount of gas required for 242 mi of city driving.
Source: *Road & Track*, November 2008

1. **Familiarize.** We know that the Chevrolet can travel 176 mi on 8 gal of gas. Thus we can set up a proportion, letting $x =$ the amount of gas required to drive 242 mi.

2. **Translate.** We assume that the car uses gas at the same rate in all city driving. Thus the ratios are the same and we can write a proportion. Note that the units of *mileage* are in the numerators and the units of *gasoline* are in the denominators.

$$\begin{array}{ll} \text{Miles} \rightarrow \\ \text{Gas} \rightarrow \end{array} \frac{176}{8} = \frac{242}{x} \begin{array}{ll} \leftarrow \text{Miles} \\ \leftarrow \text{Gas} \end{array}$$

3. **Solve.** To solve for x, we multiply on both sides by the LCM, which is $8x$:

$$8x \cdot \frac{176}{8} = 8x \cdot \frac{242}{x} \qquad \text{Multiplying by } 8x$$

$$176x = 1936 \qquad \text{Simplifying}$$

$$\frac{176x}{176} = \frac{1936}{176} \qquad \text{Dividing by 176}$$

$$x = 11. \qquad \text{Simplifying}$$

We can also use cross products to solve the proportion:

$$\frac{176}{8} = \frac{242}{x} \qquad 176 \cdot x \text{ and } 8 \cdot 242 \text{ are cross products.}$$

$$176 \cdot x = 8 \cdot 242 \qquad \text{Equating cross products}$$

$$\frac{176 \cdot x}{176} = \frac{8 \cdot 242}{176} \qquad \text{Dividing by 176}$$

$$x = 11.$$

4. **Check.** The check is left to the student.

5. **State.** The Chevrolet Cobalt will require 11 gal of gas for 242 mi of city driving.

7. Mileage. In highway driving, a 2009 Toyota Venza can travel 261 mi on 9 gal of gas. How much gas will be required for an 820-mi trip?
Source: *Car and Driver*, January 2009

Do Exercise 7.

Answers

3. 58 km/L   4. 0.28 hits per times at bat
5. 124 km/h   6. 2.4 fish/yd^2
7. About 28.3 gal

EXAMPLE 4 *Environmental Science.* The Fish and Wildlife Division of the Indiana Department of Natural Resources recently completed a study that determined the number of largemouth bass in Lake Monroe, near Bloomington, Indiana. For this project, anglers caught 300 largemouth bass, tagged them, and threw them back into the lake. Later, they caught 85 largemouth bass and found that 15 of them were tagged. Estimate how many largemouth bass are in the lake.

Source: Department of Natural Resources, Fish and Wildlife Division, Kevin Hoffman

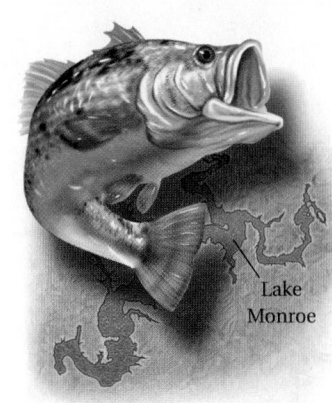
Lake
Monroe

1. **Familiarize.** The ratio of the number of largemouth bass tagged to the total number of fish in the lake, F, is $300/F$. Of the 85 largemouth bass caught later, 15 fish were tagged. The ratio of fish tagged to fish caught is $\frac{15}{85}$.

2. **Translate.** Assuming that the two ratios are the same, we can translate to a proportion.

$$\text{Fish tagged originally} \rightarrow \frac{300}{F} = \frac{15}{85} \leftarrow \text{Tagged fish caught later}$$
$$\text{Fish in lake} \rightarrow \quad\quad\quad\quad \leftarrow \text{Fish caught later}$$

3. **Solve.** We solve the proportion. We multiply by the LCM, which is $85F$.

$$85F \cdot \frac{300}{F} = 85F \cdot \frac{15}{85} \quad \text{Multiplying by } 85F$$

$$85 \cdot 300 = F \cdot 15$$

$$\frac{85 \cdot 300}{15} = F \quad\quad \text{Dividing by 15}$$

$$1700 = F$$

4. **Check.** The check is left to the student.

5. **State.** We estimate that there are about 1700 largemouth bass in the lake.

Do Exercise 8.

8. Environmental Science.
To determine the number of humpback whales in a pod, a marine biologist, using tail markings, identifies 27 members of the pod. Several weeks later, 40 whales from the pod are randomly sighted. Of the 40 sighted, 12 are from the 27 originally identified. Estimate the number of whales in the pod.

EXAMPLE 5 *Fruit Quality.* A company that prepares and sells gift boxes and baskets of fruit must order quantities of fruit larger than what they need to allow for selecting fruit that meets their quality standards. The packing-room supervisor keeps records and notes that approximately 87 pears from a shipment of 1000 do not meet the company standards. Over the holidays, a shipment of 3200 pears is ordered. How many pears can the company expect will not meet the quality required?

Answer

8. 90 whales

1. **Familiarize.** The ratio of the number of pears P that do not meet the standards to the total order of 3200 is $P/3200$. The ratio of the average number of pears that do not meet the standard in an order of 1000 pears is $\frac{87}{1000}$.

2. **Translate.** Assuming that the two ratios are the same, we can translate to a proportion:

$$\frac{P}{3200} = \frac{87}{1000}.$$

3. **Solve.** We solve the proportion. We multiply by the LCM, which is 16,000.

$$16{,}000 \cdot \frac{P}{3200} = 16{,}000 \cdot \frac{87}{1000}$$

$$5 \cdot P = 16 \cdot 87$$

$$P = \frac{16 \cdot 87}{5}$$

$$P \approx 278.4$$

4. **Check.** The check is left to the student.

5. **State.** We estimate that there are about 278 pears in an order of 3200 that do not meet the quality standards.

> Do Exercise 9.

Similar Triangles

Proportions arise in geometry when we are studying *similar triangles*. If two triangles are **similar**, then their corresponding angles have the same measure and their corresponding sides are proportional. To illustrate, if triangle *ABC* is similar to triangle *RST*, then angles *A* and *R* have the same measure, angles *B* and *S* have the same measure, angles *C* and *T* have the same measure, and

$$\frac{a}{r} = \frac{b}{s} = \frac{c}{t}.$$

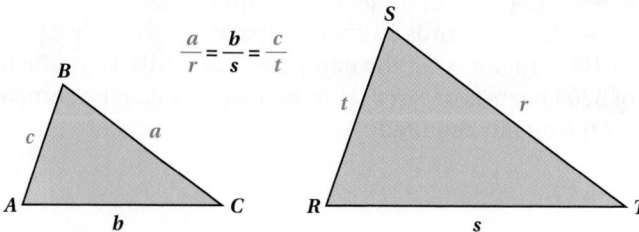

9. XYZ Pools and Spas, Inc., adds 2 gal of chlorine per 8000 gal of water in a newly constructed pool. How much chlorine is needed for a pool requiring 20,500 gal of water? Round the answer to the nearest tenth of a gallon.

Answer

9. 5.1 gal

SIMILAR TRIANGLES

In **similar triangles**, corresponding angles have the same measure and the lengths of corresponding sides are proportional.

EXAMPLE 6 *Similar Triangles.* Triangles *ABC* and *XYZ* below are similar triangles. Solve for *z* if $a = 8$, $c = 5$, and $x = 10$.

We make a drawing, write a proportion, and then solve. Note that side *a* is always opposite angle *A*, side *x* is always opposite angle *X*, and so on.

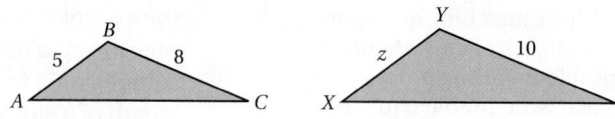

We have

$$\frac{z}{5} = \frac{10}{8} \qquad \text{The proportion } \frac{5}{z} = \frac{8}{10} \text{ could also be used.}$$

$$40 \cdot \frac{z}{5} = 40 \cdot \frac{10}{8} \qquad \text{Multiplying by 40}$$

$$8z = 50$$

$$z = \frac{50}{8} \qquad \text{Dividing by 8}$$

$$z = \frac{25}{4}, \text{ or } 6.25.$$

Do Exercise 10.

EXAMPLE 7 *Rafters of a House.* Carpenters use similar triangles to determine the lengths of rafters for a house. They first choose the pitch of the roof, or the ratio of the rise over the run. Then using a triangle with that ratio, they calculate the length of the rafter needed for the house. Loren is constructing rafters for a roof with a 6/12 pitch on a house that is 30 ft wide. Using a rafter guide (see the figure at right), Loren knows that the rafter length corresponding to a 6-unit rise and a 12-unit run is 13.4. Find the length *x* of the rafter of the house.

We have the proportion

Length of rafter
in 6/12 triangle → $\dfrac{13.4}{x} = \dfrac{12}{15}$ ← Run in 6/12 triangle
Length of rafter →   ← Run in similar
on the house   triangle on the house

Solve: $13.4 \cdot 15 = x \cdot 12$ Equating cross products

$$\frac{13.4 \cdot 15}{12} = \frac{x \cdot 12}{12} \qquad \text{Dividing by 12 on both sides}$$

$$\frac{13.4 \cdot 15}{12} = x$$

$$16.75 \text{ ft} = x$$

The length of the rafter *x* of the house is about 16.75 ft, or 16 ft 9 in.

Do Exercise 11.

10. Height of a Flagpole. How high is a flagpole that casts a 45-ft shadow at the same time that a 5.5-ft woman casts a 10-ft shadow?

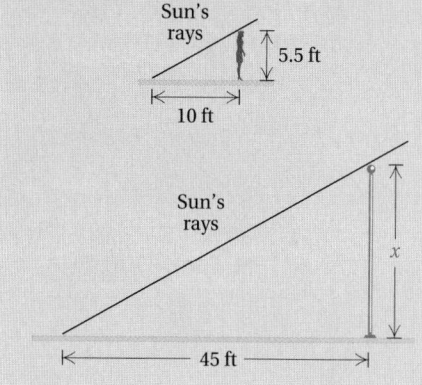

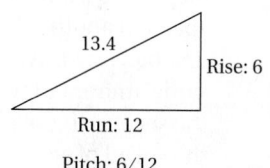

Pitch: 6/12

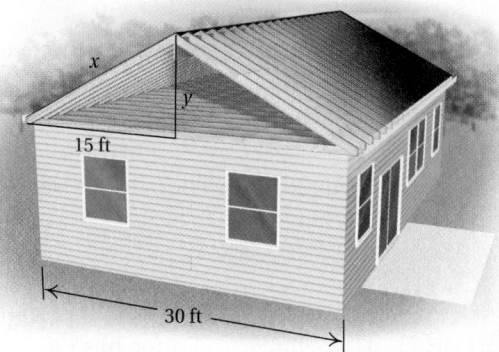

11. Rafters of a House. Referring to Example 7, find the length *y* in the rafter of the house.

Answers

10. 24.75 ft   **11.** 7.5 ft

Translating for Success

1. *Search Engine Ads.* In 2009, it was estimated that $3.6 billion was spent in advertising on Internet search engines. This was a 25% increase over the amount spent in 2008. How much was spent in 2008?

2. *Cycling Distance.* A bicyclist traveled 197 mi in 7 days. At this rate, how many miles could the cyclist travel in 30 days?

3. *Bicycling.* The speed of one bicyclist is 2 km/h faster than the speed of another bicyclist. The first bicyclist travels 60 km in the same amount of time that it takes the second to travel 50 km. Find the speed of each bicyclist.

4. *Filling Time.* A swimming pool can be filled in 5 hr by hose A alone and in 6 hr by hose B alone. How long would it take to fill the tank if both hoses were working?

5. *Office Budget.* Emma has $36 budgeted for office stationery. Engraved stationery costs $20 for the first 25 sheets and $0.08 for each additional sheet. How many engraved sheets of stationery can Emma order and still stay within her budget?

The goal of these matching questions is to practice step (2), *Translate*, of the five-step problem-solving process. Translate each word problem to an equation and select a correct translation from equations A–O.

A. $2x + 2(x + 1) = 613$

B. $x^2 + (x + 1)^2 = 613$

C. $\dfrac{60}{x + 2} = \dfrac{50}{x}$

D. $20 + 0.08(x - 25) = 36$

E. $\dfrac{197}{7} = \dfrac{x}{30}$

F. $x + (x + 1) = 613$

G. $\dfrac{7}{197} = \dfrac{x}{30}$

H. $x^2 + (x + 2)^2 = 612$

I. $x^2 + (x + 1)^2 = 612$

J. $\dfrac{50}{x + 2} = \dfrac{60}{x}$

K. $x + 25\% \cdot x = 3.6$

L. $t + 5 = 7$

M. $x^2 + (x + 1)^2 = 452$

N. $\dfrac{1}{5} + \dfrac{1}{6} = \dfrac{1}{t}$

O. $x^2 + (x + 2)^2 = 452$

Answers on page A-30

---

6. *Sides of a Square.* If the sides of a square are increased by 2 ft, the area of the original square plus the area of the enlarged square is 452 ft^2. Find the length of a side of the original square.

7. *Consecutive Integers.* The sum of two consecutive integers is 613. Find the integers.

8. *Sums of Squares.* The sum of the squares of two consecutive odd integers is 612. Find the integers.

9. *Sums of Squares.* The sum of the squares of two consecutive integers is 613. Find the integers.

10. *Rectangle Dimensions.* The length of a rectangle is 1 ft longer than its width. Find the dimensions of the rectangle such that the perimeter of the rectangle is 613 ft.

 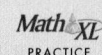
a Solve.

1. *Construction.* It takes Mandy 4 hr to put up paneling in a room. Omar takes 5 hr to do the same job. How long would it take them, working together, to panel the room?

2. *Carpentry.* By checking work records, a carpenter finds that Juanita can build a small shed in 12 hr. Anton can do the same job in 16 hr. How long would it take if they worked together?

3. *Shoveling.* Vern can shovel the snow from his driveway in 45 min. Nina can do the same job in 60 min. How long would it take Nina and Vern to shovel the driveway if they worked together?

4. *Raking.* Zoë can rake her yard in 4 hr. Steffi does the same job in 3 hr. How long would it take the two of them, working together, to rake the yard?

5. *Wiring.* By checking work records, a contractor finds that Peggy Ann can wire a room addition in 9 hr. It takes Matthew 7 hr to wire the same room. How long would it take if they worked together?

6. *Plumbing.* By checking work records, a plumber finds that Raul can plumb a house in 48 hr. Mira can do the same job in 36 hr. How long would it take if they worked together?

7. *Gardening.* Nicole can weed her vegetable garden in 50 min. Glen can weed the same garden in 40 min. How long would it take if they worked together?

8. *Harvesting.* Bobbi can pick a quart of raspberries in 20 min. Blanche can pick a quart in 25 min. How long would it take if Bobbi and Blanche worked together?

9. *Office Printers.* The HP Officejet 4215 All-In-One printer, fax, scanner, and copier can print in black one copy of a company's year-end report in 10 min. The HP Officejet 7410 All-In-One can print the same report in 6 min. How long would it take the two printers, working together, to print one copy of the report?

HP Officejet 4215   HP Officejet 7410

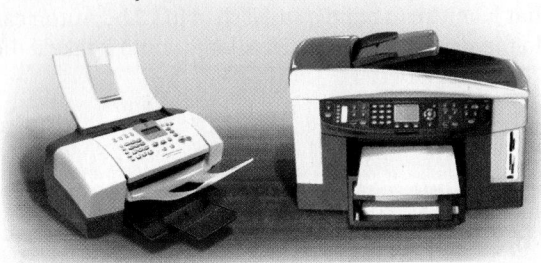

10. *Office Copiers.* The HP Officejet 7410 All-In-One printer, fax, scanner, and copier can copy in color a staff training manual in 9 min. The HP Officejet 4215 All-In-One can copy the same report in 15 min. How long would it take the two copiers, working together, to make one copy of the manual?

11. *Car Speed.* Rick drives his four-wheel-drive truck 40 km/h faster than Sarah drives her Saturn. While Sarah travels 150 km, Rick travels 350 km. Find their speeds.

Complete this table and the equations as part of the *Familiarize* step.

$$d = r \cdot t$$

	DISTANCE	SPEED	TIME	
Car	150	r		$\rightarrow 150 = r(\quad)$
Truck	350		t	$\rightarrow 350 = (\quad)t$

Sarah's car
150 km, r km/h

Rick's truck
350 km, $r + 40$ km/h

12. *Car Speed.* A passenger car travels 30 km/h faster than a delivery truck. While the car goes 400 km, the truck goes 250 km. Find their speeds.

13. *Train Speed.* The speed of a B & M freight train is 14 mph slower than the speed of an Amtrak passenger train. The freight train travels 330 mi in the same time that it takes the passenger train to travel 400 mi. Find the speed of each train.

Complete this table and the equations as part of the *Familiarize* step.

$$d = r \cdot t$$

	DISTANCE	SPEED	TIME	
B & M	330		t	$\rightarrow 330 = (\quad)t$
Amtrak	400	r		$\rightarrow 400 = r(\quad)$

Copyright © 2012 Pearson Education, Inc.

14. *Train Speed.*   The speed of a freight train is 15 mph slower than the speed of a passenger train. The freight train travels 390 mi in the same time that it takes the passenger train to travel 480 mi. Find the speed of each train.

15. *Trucking Speed.*   A long-distance trucker traveled 120 mi in one direction during a snowstorm. The return trip in rainy weather was accomplished at double the speed and took 3 hr less time. Find the speed going.

16. *Car Speed.*   After driving 126 mi, Syd found that the drive would have taken 1 hr less time by increasing the speed by 8 mph. What was the actual speed?

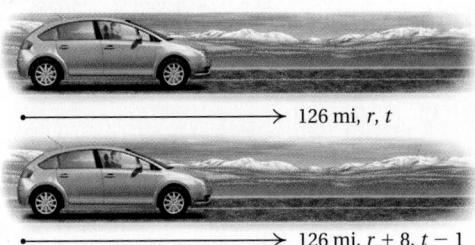

17. *Bicycle Speed.*   Hank bicycles 5 km/h slower than Kelly. In the time that it takes Hank to bicycle 42 km, Kelly can bicycle 57 km. How fast does each bicyclist travel?

18. *Driving Speed.*   Kaylee's Lexus travels 30 mph faster than Gavin's Harley. In the same time that Gavin travels 75 mi, Kaylee travels 120 mi. Find their speeds.

19. *Walking Speed.*   Bonnie power walks 3 km/h faster than Ralph. In the time that it takes Ralph to walk 7.5 km, Bonnie walks 12 km. Find their speeds.

20. *Cross-Country Skiing.*   Gerard cross-country skis 4 km/h faster than Sally. In the time that it takes Sally to ski 18 km, Gerard skis 24 km. Find their speeds.

21. *Tractor Speed.*   Hobart's tractor is just as fast as Evan's. It takes Hobart 1 hr more than it takes Evan to drive to town. If Hobart is 20 mi from town and Evan is 15 mi from town, how long does it take Evan to drive to town?

22. *Boat Speed.*   Tory and Emilio's motorboats travel at the same speed. Tory pilots her boat 40 km before docking. Emilio continues for another 2 hr, traveling a total of 100 km before docking. How long did it take Tory to navigate the 40 km?

b Find the ratio of each of the following. Simplify if possible.

23. 60 students, 18 teachers

24. 800 mi, 50 gal

25. *Speed of Black Racer.* A black racer snake travels 4.6 km in 2 hr. What is the speed, in kilometers per hour?

26. *Speed of Light.* Light travels 558,000 mi in 3 sec. What is the speed, in miles per second?

Solve.

27. *Protein Needs.* A 120-lb person should eat a minimum of 44 g of protein each day. How much protein should a 180-lb person eat each day?

28. *Coffee Beans.* The coffee beans from 14 trees are required to produce 7.7 kg of coffee. (This is the average amount that each person in the United States drinks each year.) How many trees are required to produce 320 kg of coffee?

29. *Hemoglobin.* A normal 10-cc specimen of human blood contains 1.2 g of hemoglobin. How much hemoglobin would 16 cc of the same blood contain?

30. *Walking Speed.* Wanda walked 234 km in 14 days. At this rate, how far would she walk in 42 days?

31. *Honey Bees.* Making 1 lb of honey requires 20,000 trips by bees to flowers to gather nectar. How many pounds of honey would 35,000 trips produce?

Source: Tom Turpin, Professor of Entomology, Purdue University

32. *Cockroaches and Horses.* A cockroach can run about 2 mi/hr (mph). The average body length of a cockroach is 1 in. The average body length of a horse is 8 ft (96 in.). If a horse's speed-to-length ratio were the same as that of a cockroach, how fast would a horse run?

Source: Tom Turpin, Professor of Entomology, Purdue University

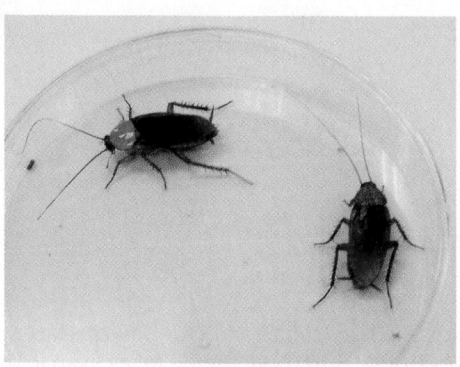

Professor Turpin founded the annual cockroach race at Purdue University.

Copyright © 2012 Pearson Education, Inc.

33. Money. The ratio of the weight of copper to the weight of zinc in a U.S. penny is $\frac{1}{39}$. If 50 kg of zinc is being turned into pennies, how much copper is needed?

34. Baking. In a potato bread recipe, the ratio of milk to flour is $\frac{3}{13}$. If 5 cups of milk are used, how many cups of flour are used?

35. Ryan Howard. In the 2009 Major League Baseball season, Ryan Howard, playing for the Philadelphia Phillies of the National League, collected 118 hits in 439 at-bats in his first 114 games.

   a) The ratio of number of hits to number of at-bats, rounded to the nearest thousandth, is a player's *batting average*. What was Howard's batting average in his first 114 games?

   b) Based on the ratio of number of hits to number of games, how many hits would he get in the 162-game season?

   c) Based on the ratio of number of hits to number of at-bats and assuming he bats 700 times in 2009, how many hits would he get?

36. Evan Longoria. In the 2009 Major League Baseball season, Evan Longoria, playing for the Tampa Bay Rays of the American League, collected 116 hits in 416 at-bats in his first 112 games.

   a) The ratio of number of hits to number of at-bats, rounded to the nearest thousandth, is a player's *batting average*. What was Longoria's batting average in his first 112 games?

   b) Based on the ratio of number of hits to number of games, how many hits would he get in the 162-game season?

   c) Based on the ratio of number of hits to number of at-bats and assuming he bats 620 times in 2009, how many hits would he get?

Hat Sizes. Hat sizes are determined by measuring the circumference of one's head in either inches or centimeters. Use ratio and proportion to complete the missing parts of the following table.

	HAT SIZE	HEAD CIRCUMFERENCE (in inches)	HEAD CIRCUMFERENCE (in centimeters)
	$6\frac{3}{4}$	$21\frac{1}{5}$ in.	53.8 cm
37.	7		
38.			56.8 cm
39.		$22\frac{4}{5}$ in.	
40.	$7\frac{3}{8}$		
41.			59.8 cm
42.		24 in.	

43. Estimating Trout Population. To determine the number of trout in a lake, a conservationist catches 112 trout, tags them, and throws them back into the lake. Later, 82 trout are caught; 32 of them are tagged. Estimate the number of trout in the lake.

44. Grass Seed. It takes 60 oz of grass seed to seed 3000 ft² of lawn. At this rate, how much would be needed to seed 5000 ft² of lawn?

45. Quality Control. A sample of 144 firecrackers contained 9 "duds." How many duds would you expect in a sample of 3200 firecrackers?

46. Frog Population. To estimate how many frogs there are in a rain forest, a research team tags 600 frogs and then releases them. Later, the team catches 300 frogs and notes that 25 of them have been tagged. Estimate the total frog population in the rain forest.

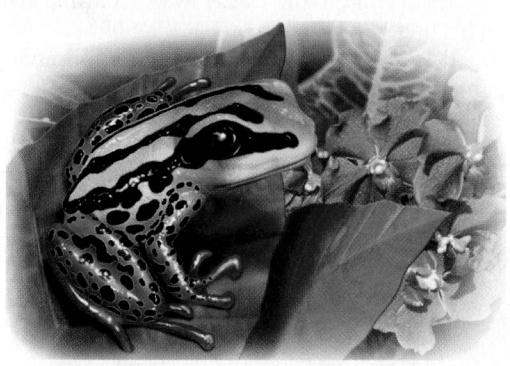

47. Weight on Mars. The ratio of the weight of an object on Mars to the weight of the same object on Earth is 0.4 to 1.

a) How much would a 12-ton rocket weigh on Mars?
b) How much would a 120-lb astronaut weigh on Mars?

48. Weight on Moon. The ratio of the weight of an object on the moon to the weight of the same object on Earth is 0.16 to 1.

a) How much would a 12-ton rocket weigh on the moon?
b) How much would a 180-lb astronaut weigh on the moon?

Geometry. For each pair of similar triangles, find the length of the indicated side.

49. b: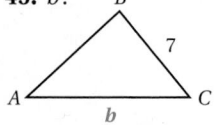

50. a: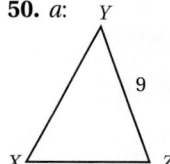

51. f: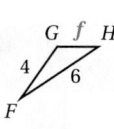

52. r: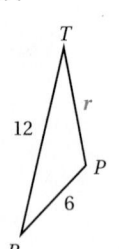

53. h: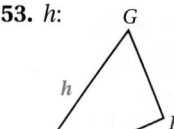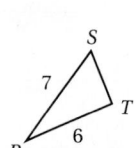

54. n: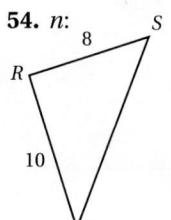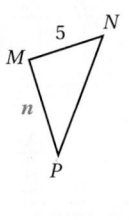

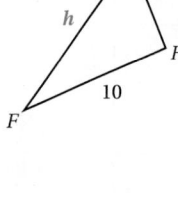

Copyright © 2012 Pearson Education, Inc.

55. l:

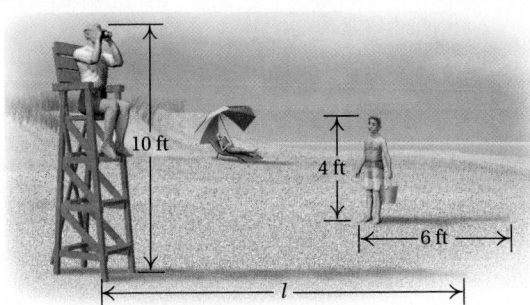

56. h:

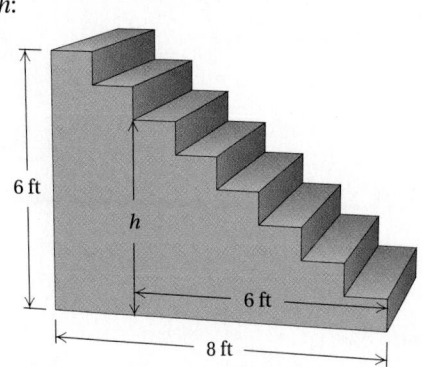

Skill Maintenance

57. Find an equation of the line containing $\left(\frac{1}{2}, \frac{3}{4}\right)$ whose slope is -2. [9.4b]

58. Find an equation of the line containing $(-7, 4)$ and $(3, 8)$. [9.4c]

Simplify. [10.1d]

59. $x^5 \cdot x^6$

60. $x^{-5} \cdot x^6$

61. $x^{-5} \cdot x^{-6}$

62. $x^5 \cdot x^{-6}$

Graph. [9.1d]

63. $y = 2x - 6$

64. $y = -2x + 6$

65. $3x + 2y = 12$

66. $x - 3y = 6$

67. $y = -\frac{3}{4}x + 2$

68. $y = \frac{2}{5}x - 4$

Synthesis

69. Ann and Betty work together and complete a sales report in 4 hr. It would take Betty 6 hr longer, working alone, to do the job than it would Ann. How long would it take each of them to do the job working alone?

70. Express 100 as the sum of two numbers for which the ratio of one number, increased by 5, to the other number, decreased by 5, is 4.

71. How soon, in minutes, after 5 o'clock will the hands on a clock first be together?

72. Rachel allows herself 1 hr to reach a sales appointment 50 mi away. After she has driven 30 mi, she realizes that she must increase her speed by 15 mph in order to arrive on time. What was her speed for the first 30 mi?

73. Solve $\dfrac{t}{a} + \dfrac{t}{b} = 1$ for t.

Summary and Review

Key Terms

Concept Reinforcement

Determine whether each statement is true or false.

_____ **1.** To determine the numbers for which a rational expression is not defined, we set the denominator equal to 0 and solve. [12.1a]

_____ **2.** When a situation translates to an equation described by $y = k/x$, with k a positive constant, y varies directly as x. [12.9a]

_____ **3.** The opposite of $2 - x$ is $x - 2$. [12.4a]

_____ **4.** When clearing an equation of fractions, we multiply by the LCM of all the denominators on both sides of the equation. [12.6a]

_____ **5.** The expressions $y + 5$ and $y - 5$ are opposites of each other. [12.1c]

Important Concepts

Objective 12.1c Simplify rational expressions by factoring the numerator and the denominator and removing factors of 1.

Example Simplify: $\dfrac{6y - 12}{2y^2 + y - 10}$.

$$\frac{6y - 12}{2y^2 + y - 10} = \frac{6(y - 2)}{(2y + 5)(y - 2)}$$

$$= \frac{y - 2}{y - 2} \cdot \frac{6}{2y + 5} = 1 \cdot \frac{6}{2y + 5} = \frac{6}{2y + 5}$$

Practice Exercise

1. Simplify:

$$\frac{2x^2 - 2}{4x^2 + 24x + 20}.$$

Objective 12.1d Multiply rational expressions and simplify.

Example Multiply and simplify: $\dfrac{x^2 + 14x + 49}{x^2 - 25} \cdot \dfrac{x + 5}{x + 7}$.

$$\frac{x^2 + 14x + 49}{x^2 - 25} \cdot \frac{x + 5}{x + 7} = \frac{(x^2 + 14x + 49)(x + 5)}{(x^2 - 25)(x + 7)}$$

$$= \frac{(x + 7)(x + 7)(x + 5)}{(x + 5)(x - 5)(x + 7)}$$

$$= \frac{x + 7}{x - 5}$$

Practice Exercise

2. Multiply and simplify:

$$\frac{2y^2 + 7y - 15}{5y^2 - 45} \cdot \frac{y - 3}{2y - 3}.$$

Objective 12.2b Divide rational expressions and simplify.

Example Divide and simplify: $\dfrac{a^2 - 9a}{a^2 - a - 6} \div \dfrac{a}{a + 2}$.

$$\dfrac{a^2 - 9a}{a^2 - a - 6} \div \dfrac{a}{a + 2} = \dfrac{a^2 - 9a}{a^2 - a - 6} \cdot \dfrac{a + 2}{a}$$

$$= \dfrac{(a^2 - 9a)(a + 2)}{(a^2 - a - 6)a}$$

$$= \dfrac{a(a - 9)(a + 2)}{(a + 2)(a - 3)a}$$

$$= \dfrac{a - 9}{a - 3}$$

Practice Exercise

3. Divide and simplify:

$$\dfrac{b^2 + 3b - 28}{b^2 + 5b - 24} \div \dfrac{b - 4}{b - 3}.$$

Objective 12.4a Add rational expressions.

Example Add and simplify: $\dfrac{6x - 5}{x - 1} + \dfrac{x}{1 - x}$.

$$\dfrac{6x - 5}{x - 1} + \dfrac{x}{1 - x} = \dfrac{6x - 5}{x - 1} + \dfrac{x}{1 - x} \cdot \dfrac{-1}{-1}$$

$$= \dfrac{6x - 5}{x - 1} + \dfrac{-x}{x - 1}$$

$$= \dfrac{6x - 5 - x}{x - 1}$$

$$= \dfrac{5x - 5}{x - 1}$$

$$= \dfrac{5(x - 1)}{x - 1} = 5$$

Practice Exercise

4. Add and simplify:

$$\dfrac{x}{x - 4} + \dfrac{2x - 4}{4 - x}.$$

Objective 12.5a Subtract rational expressions.

Example Subtract: $\dfrac{3}{x^2 - 1} - \dfrac{2x - 1}{x^2 + x - 2}$.

$$\dfrac{3}{x^2 - 1} - \dfrac{2x - 1}{x^2 + x - 2}$$

$$= \dfrac{3}{(x + 1)(x - 1)} - \dfrac{2x - 1}{(x + 2)(x - 1)}$$

The LCM is $(x + 1)(x - 1)(x + 2)$.

$$= \dfrac{3}{(x + 1)(x - 1)} \cdot \dfrac{x + 2}{x + 2} - \dfrac{2x - 1}{(x + 2)(x - 1)} \cdot \dfrac{x + 1}{x + 1}$$

$$= \dfrac{3(x + 2)}{(x + 1)(x - 1)(x + 2)} - \dfrac{(2x - 1)(x + 1)}{(x + 2)(x - 1)(x + 1)}$$

$$= \dfrac{3x + 6 - (2x^2 + x - 1)}{(x + 1)(x - 1)(x + 2)}$$

$$= \dfrac{3x + 6 - 2x^2 - x + 1}{(x + 1)(x - 1)(x + 2)}$$

$$= \dfrac{-2x^2 + 2x + 7}{(x + 1)(x - 1)(x + 2)}$$

Practice Exercise

5. Subtract:

$$\dfrac{x}{x^2 + x - 2} - \dfrac{5}{x^2 - 1}.$$

Review Exercises

Find all numbers for which the rational expression is not defined. [12.1a]

1. $\dfrac{3}{x}$

2. $\dfrac{4}{x-6}$

3. $\dfrac{x+5}{x^2-36}$

4. $\dfrac{x^2-3x+2}{x^2+x-30}$

5. $\dfrac{-4}{(x+2)^2}$

6. $\dfrac{x-5}{5}$

Simplify. [12.1c]

7. $\dfrac{4x^2-8x}{4x^2+4x}$

8. $\dfrac{14x^2-x-3}{2x^2-7x+3}$

9. $\dfrac{(y-5)^2}{y^2-25}$

Multiply and simplify. [12.1d]

10. $\dfrac{a^2-36}{10a}\cdot\dfrac{2a}{a+6}$

11. $\dfrac{6t-6}{2t^2+t-1}\cdot\dfrac{t^2-1}{t^2-2t+1}$

Divide and simplify. [12.2b]

12. $\dfrac{10-5t}{3}\div\dfrac{t-2}{12t}$

13. $\dfrac{4x^4}{x^2-1}\div\dfrac{2x^3}{x^2-2x+1}$

Find the LCM. [12.3c]

14. $3x^2,\ 10xy,\ 15y^2$

15. $a-2,\ 4a-8$

16. $y^2-y-2,\ y^2-4$

Add and simplify. [12.4a]

17. $\dfrac{x+8}{x+7}+\dfrac{10-4x}{x+7}$

18. $\dfrac{3}{3x-9}+\dfrac{x-2}{3-x}$

19. $\dfrac{2a}{a+1}+\dfrac{4a}{a^2-1}$

20. $\dfrac{d^2}{d-c}+\dfrac{c^2}{c-d}$

Copyright © 2012 Pearson Education, Inc.

Subtract and simplify. [12.5a]

21. $\dfrac{6x - 3}{x^2 - x - 12} - \dfrac{2x - 15}{x^2 - x - 12}$

22. $\dfrac{3x - 1}{2x} - \dfrac{x - 3}{x}$

23. $\dfrac{x + 3}{x - 2} - \dfrac{x}{2 - x}$

24. $\dfrac{1}{x^2 - 25} - \dfrac{x - 5}{x^2 - 4x - 5}$

25. Perform the indicated operations and simplify: [12.5b]

$$\dfrac{3x}{x + 2} - \dfrac{x}{x - 2} + \dfrac{8}{x^2 - 4}.$$

Simplify. [12.8a]

26. $\dfrac{\dfrac{1}{z} + 1}{\dfrac{1}{z^2} - 1}$

27. $\dfrac{\dfrac{c}{d} - \dfrac{d}{c}}{\dfrac{1}{c} + \dfrac{1}{d}}$

Solve. [12.6a]

28. $\dfrac{3}{y} - \dfrac{1}{4} = \dfrac{1}{y}$

29. $\dfrac{15}{x} - \dfrac{15}{x + 2} = 2$

Solve. [12.7a]

30. *Highway Work.* In checking records, a contractor finds that crew A can pave a certain length of highway in 9 hr, while crew B can do the same job in 12 hr. How long would it take if they worked together?

31. *Airplane Speed.* One plane travels 80 mph faster than another. While one travels 1750 mi, the other travels 950 mi. Find the speed of each plane.

32. *Train Speed.* A manufacturer is testing two high-speed trains. One train travels 40 km/h faster than the other. While one train travels 70 km, the other travels 60 km. Find the speed of each train.

70 km, $r + 1$

60 km, r

Solve. [12.7b]

33. *Quality Control.* A sample of 250 calculators contained 8 defective calculators. How many defective calculators would you expect to find in a sample of 5000?

34. *Pizza Proportions.* At Finnelli's Pizzeria, the following ratios are used: 5 parts sausage to 7 parts cheese, 6 parts onion to 13 parts green pepper, and 9 parts pepperoni to 14 parts cheese.

a) Finnelli's makes several pizzas with green pepper and onion. They use 2 cups of green pepper. How much onion would they use?

b) Finnelli's makes several pizzas with sausage and cheese. They use 3 cups of sausage. How much cheese would they use?

c) Finnelli's makes several pizzas with pepperoni and cheese. They use 6 cups of pepperoni. How much cheese would they use?

35. *Estimating Whale Population.* To determine the number of blue whales in the world's oceans, marine biologists tag 500 blue whales in various parts of the world. Later, 400 blue whales are checked, and it is found that 20 of them are tagged. Estimate the blue whale population.

36. Triangles *ABC* and *XYZ* below are similar. Find the value of *x*.

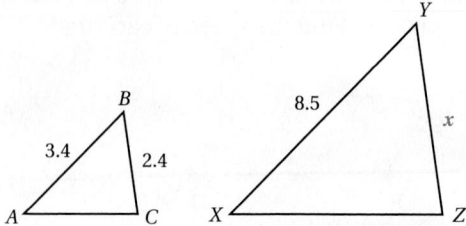

Find an equation of variation in which *y* varies directly as *x* and the following are true. Then find the value of *y* when *x* = 20.   [12.9a]

37. *y* = 12 when *x* = 4

38. *y* = 0.4 when *x* = 0.5

Find an equation of variation in which *y* varies inversely as *x* and the following are true. Then find the value of *y* when *x* = 5.   [12.9c]

39. *y* = 5 when *x* = 6

40. *y* = 0.5 when *x* = 2

41. *y* = 1.3 when *x* = 0.5

Solve.

42. *Wages.*   A person's paycheck *P* varies directly as the number *H* of hours worked. The pay is $165.00 for working 20 hr. Find the pay for 35 hr of work.   [12.9b]

43. *Washing Time.*   It takes 5 hr for 2 washing machines to wash a fixed amount of laundry. How long would it take 10 washing machines to do the same job? (The number of hours varies inversely as the number of washing machines.)   [12.9d]

44. Find all numbers for which

$$\frac{3x^2 - 2x - 1}{3x^2 + x}$$

is not defined.   [12.1a]

A. $1, -\dfrac{1}{3}$ **B.** $-\dfrac{1}{3}$

C. $0, -\dfrac{1}{3}$ **D.** $0, \dfrac{1}{3}$

45. Subtract: $\dfrac{1}{x - 5} - \dfrac{1}{x + 5}$.   [12.5a]

A. $\dfrac{10}{(x - 5)(x + 5)}$ **B.** 0

C. $\dfrac{5}{x - 5}$ **D.** $\dfrac{10}{x + 5}$

Synthesis

46. Simplify: [12.1d], [12.2b]

$$\frac{2a^2 + 5a - 3}{a^2} \cdot \frac{5a^3 + 30a^2}{2a^2 + 7a - 4} \div \frac{a^2 + 6a}{a^2 + 7a + 12}.$$

47. Compare

$$\frac{A + B}{B} = \frac{C + D}{D}$$

with the proportion

$$\frac{A}{B} = \frac{C}{D}.$$

[12.7b]

Understanding Through Discussion and Writing

1. Are parentheses as important when adding rational expressions as they are when subtracting? Why or why not?   [12.4a], [12.5a]

2. How can a graph be used to determine how many solutions an equation has?   [12.6a]

3. How is the process of canceling related to the identity property of 1?   [12.1c]

4. Determine whether the situation represents direct variation, inverse variation, or neither. Give a reason for your answer.   [12.9a, c]
The number of plays that it takes to go 80 yd for a touchdown and the average gain per play

5. Explain how a rational expression can be formed for which −3 and 4 are not allowable replacements.   [12.1a]

6. Why is it especially important to check the possible solutions to a rational equation?   [12.6a]

Copyright © 2012 Pearson Education, Inc.

CHAPTER

12

Test For Extra Help

CHAPTER Test Prep VIDEOS

Step-by-step test solutions are found on the Chapter Test Prep Videos available via the Video Resources on DVD, in *MyMathLab* , and on You Tube (search "BittingerDevMath" and click on "Channels").

Find all numbers for which the rational expression is not defined.

1. $\dfrac{8}{2x}$

2. $\dfrac{5}{x+8}$

3. $\dfrac{x-7}{x^2-49}$

4. $\dfrac{x^2+x-30}{x^2-3x+2}$

5. $\dfrac{11}{(x-1)^2}$

6. $\dfrac{x+2}{2}$

7. Simplify:
$$\frac{6x^2+17x+7}{2x^2+7x+3}.$$

8. Multiply and simplify:
$$\frac{a^2-25}{6a}\cdot\frac{3a}{a-5}.$$

9. Divide and simplify:
$$\frac{25x^2-1}{9x^2-6x}\div\frac{5x^2+9x-2}{3x^2+x-2}.$$

10. Find the LCM:
$$y^2-9,\ y^2+10y+21,\ y^2+4y-21.$$

Add or subtract. Simplify if possible.

11. $\dfrac{16+x}{x^3}+\dfrac{7-4x}{x^3}$

12. $\dfrac{5-t}{t^2+1}-\dfrac{t-3}{t^2+1}$

13. $\dfrac{x-4}{x-3}+\dfrac{x-1}{3-x}$

14. $\dfrac{x-4}{x-3}-\dfrac{x-1}{3-x}$

15. $\dfrac{5}{t-1}+\dfrac{3}{t}$

16. $\dfrac{1}{x^2-16}-\dfrac{x+4}{x^2-3x-4}$

17. $\dfrac{1}{x-1}+\dfrac{4}{x^2-1}-\dfrac{2}{x^2-2x+1}$

18. Simplify: $\dfrac{9-\dfrac{1}{y^2}}{3-\dfrac{1}{y}}.$

Solve.

19. $\dfrac{7}{y}-\dfrac{1}{3}=\dfrac{1}{4}$

20. $\dfrac{15}{x}-\dfrac{15}{x-2}=-2$

Find an equation of variation in which y varies directly as x and the following are true. Then find the value of y when $x=25$.

21. $y=6$ when $x=3$

22. $y=1.5$ when $x=3$

Find an equation of variation in which y varies inversely as x and the following are true. Then find the value of y when $x = 100$.

23. $y = 6$ when $x = 3$

24. $y = 11$ when $x = 2$

Solve.

25. *Train Travel.*   The distance d traveled by a train varies directly as the time t that it travels. The train travels 60 km in $\frac{1}{2}$ hr. How far will it travel in 2 hr?

26. *Concrete Work.*   It takes 3 hr for 2 concrete mixers to mix a fixed amount of concrete. The number of hours varies inversely as the number of concrete mixers used. How long would it take 5 concrete mixers to do the same job?

27. *Quality Control.*   A sample of 125 spark plugs contained 4 defective spark plugs. How many defective spark plugs would you expect to find in a sample of 500?

28. *Zebra Population.*   A game warden catches, tags, and then releases 15 zebras. A month later, a sample of 20 zebras is collected and 6 of them have tags. Use this information to estimate the size of the zebra population in that area.

29. *Copying Time.*   Kopy Kwik has 2 copiers. One can copy a year-end report in 20 min. The other can copy the same document in 30 min. How long would it take both machines, working together, to copy the report?

30. *Driving Speed.*   Craig drives 20 km/h faster than Marilyn. In the same time that Marilyn drives 225 km, Craig drives 325 km. Find the speed of each car.

31. This pair of triangles is similar. Find the missing length x.

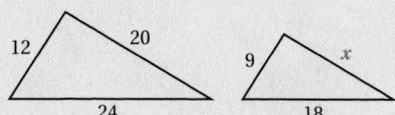

32. Solve: $\dfrac{2}{x-4} + \dfrac{2x}{x^2-16} = \dfrac{1}{x+4}$.

   A. -4 **B.** 4

   C. $4, -4$ **D.** No solution

Synthesis

33. Reggie and Rema work together to mulch the flower beds around an office complex in $2\frac{6}{7}$ hr. Working alone, it would take Reggie 6 hr more than it would take Rema. How long would it take each of them to complete the landscaping working alone?

34. Simplify: $1 + \dfrac{1}{1 + \dfrac{1}{1 + \dfrac{1}{a}}}$.

Copyright © 2012 Pearson Education, Inc.

Radical Expressions and Equations

Real-World Application

Ramps.com of America sells Landwave ramps and decks that can be combined to create a skateboard ramp as high or as wide as one wants. The dimensions of the basic ramp unit are 28 in. wide, 38.5 in. long, and 12 in. high. **(a)** What is the length of the skating surface of one ramp unit? **(b)** How many ramp units are needed for a 10-ft long skating surface?

Source: www.ramps.com

This problem appears as Example 5 in Section 14.6.

14.1

Introduction to Radical Expressions

OBJECTIVES

a Find the principal square roots and their opposites of the whole numbers from 0^2 to 25^2.

b Approximate square roots of real numbers using a calculator.

c Solve applied problems involving square roots.

d Identify radicands of radical expressions.

e Determine whether a radical expression represents a real number.

f Simplify a radical expression with a perfect-square radicand.

SKILL TO REVIEW

Objective 1.6b: Evaluate exponential expressions.

Evaluate.

1. 7^2　　　**2.** $\left(\dfrac{1}{2}\right)^2$

Find the square roots.

1. 36　　　　　**2.** 64

3. 121　　　　**4.** 144

Find the following.

5. $\sqrt{16}$　　　　**6.** $\sqrt{49}$

7. $\sqrt{100}$　　　**8.** $\sqrt{441}$

9. $-\sqrt{49}$　　　**10.** $-\sqrt{169}$

a　Square Roots

When we raise a number to the second power, we have squared the number. Sometimes we may need to find the number that was squared. We call this process finding a square root of a number.

> **SQUARE ROOT**
>
> The number c is a **square root** of a if $c^2 = a$.

Every positive number has two square roots. For example, the square roots of 25 are 5 and -5 because $5^2 = 25$ and $(-5)^2 = 25$. The positive square root is also called the **principal square root**. The symbol $\sqrt{}$ is called a **radical*** (or **square root**) symbol. The radical symbol represents only the principal square root. Thus, $\sqrt{25} = 5$. To name the negative square root of a number, we use $-\sqrt{}$. The number 0 has only one square root, 0.

EXAMPLE 1　Find the square roots of 81.

The square roots are 9 and -9.

EXAMPLE 2　Find $\sqrt{225}$.

There are two square roots of 225, 15 and -15. We want the principal, or positive, square root since this is what $\sqrt{}$ represents. Thus, $\sqrt{225} = 15$.

EXAMPLE 3　Find $-\sqrt{64}$.

The symbol $\sqrt{64}$ represents the positive square root. Then $-\sqrt{64}$ represents the negative square root. That is, $\sqrt{64} = 8$, so $-\sqrt{64} = -8$.

Do Margin Exercises 1–10.

We can think of the processes of "squaring" and "finding square roots" as inverses of each other. We square a number and get one answer. When we find the square roots of the answer, we get the original number *and* its opposite.

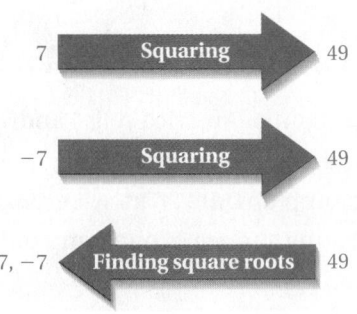

Answers

Skill to Review:

1. 49　2. $\dfrac{1}{4}$

Margin Exercises:

1. 6, -6　2. 8, -8　3. 11, -11
4. 12, -12　5. 4　6. 7　7. 10
8. 21　9. -7　10. -13

---

*Radicals can be other than square roots, but we will consider only square-root radicals in Chapter 14. See Appendix J for other types of radicals.

b Approximating Square Roots

We often need to use rational numbers to *approximate* square roots that are irrational. Such approximations can be found using a calculator with a square-root key $\sqrt{\ }$.

EXAMPLES Use a calculator to approximate each of the following.

Number	Using a calculator with a 10-digit readout	Rounded to three decimal places
4. $\sqrt{10}$	3.162277660	3.162
5. $-\sqrt{583.8}$	-24.16195356	-24.162
6. $\sqrt{\dfrac{48}{55}}$	0.934198733	0.934

Do Exercises 11–16.

Use a calculator to approximate each of the following square roots to three decimal places.

11. $\sqrt{15}$ **12.** $\sqrt{30}$

13. $\sqrt{980}$ **14.** $-\sqrt{667.8}$

15. $\sqrt{\dfrac{2}{3}}$ **16.** $-\sqrt{\dfrac{203.4}{67.82}}$

c Applications of Square Roots

We now consider an application involving a formula with a radical expression.

EXAMPLE 7 *Speed of a Skidding Car.* After an accident, how do police determine the speed at which the car had been traveling? The formula $r = 2\sqrt{5L}$ can be used to approximate the speed r, in miles per hour, of a car that has left a skid mark of length L, in feet. What was the speed of a car that left skid marks of length **(a)** 30 ft? **(b)** 150 ft?

a) We substitute 30 for L and find an approximation:

$$r = 2\sqrt{5L} = 2\sqrt{5 \cdot 30} = 2\sqrt{150} \approx 24.495.$$

The speed of the car was about 24.5 mph.

b) We substitute 150 for L and find an approximation:

$$r = 2\sqrt{5L} = 2\sqrt{5 \cdot 150} \approx 54.772.$$

The speed of the car was about 54.8 mph.

Do Exercise 17.

17. Speed of a Skidding Car. Referring to Example 7, determine the speed of a car that left skid marks of length **(a)** 40 ft; **(b)** 123 ft.

Calculator Corner

Approximating Square Roots To approximate $\sqrt{18}$, we press **2ND** $\sqrt{\ }$ **1** **8** **)** **ENTER**. ($\sqrt{\ }$ is the second operation associated with the **x²** key.) Although it is not necessary for this example to include the right parenthesis, we do so here in order to close the set of parentheses that are opened when the graphing calculator displays the radical sign. To approximate $-\sqrt{8.65}$, we press **(-)** **2ND** $\sqrt{\ }$ **8** **.** **6** **5** **)** **ENTER**. We see that $\sqrt{18} \approx 4.243$ and $-\sqrt{8.65} \approx -2.941$.

```
√(18)
          4.242640687
-√(8.65)
         -2.941088234
```

Exercises: Use a graphing calculator to approximate each of the following to three decimal places.

1. $\sqrt{43}$ **2.** $\sqrt{101}$ **3.** $\sqrt{10{,}467}$

4. $\sqrt{\dfrac{2}{5}}$ **5.** $-\sqrt{9406}$ **6.** $-\sqrt{\dfrac{11}{17}}$

Answers

11. 3.873   **12.** 5.477   **13.** 31.305
14. -25.842 **15.** 0.816   **16.** -1.732
17. (a) About 28.3 mph; **(b)** about 49.6 mph

(d) Radicands and Radical Expressions

When an expression is written under a radical, we have a **radical expression**. Here are some examples:

$$\sqrt{14}, \qquad \sqrt{x}, \qquad 8\sqrt{x^2 + 4}, \qquad \sqrt{\frac{x^2 - 5}{2}}.$$

The expression written under the radical is called the **radicand**.

EXAMPLES   Identify the radicand in each expression.

8. $-\sqrt{105}$ The radicand is 105.

9. $\sqrt{x} + 2$ The radicand is x.

10. $\sqrt{x + 2}$ The radicand is $x + 2$.

11. $6\sqrt{y^2 - 5}$ The radicand is $y^2 - 5$.

12. $\sqrt{\dfrac{a - b}{a + b}}$ The radicand is $\dfrac{a - b}{a + b}$.

Do Exercises 18–21.

Identify the radicand.

18. $\sqrt{227}$

19. $-\sqrt{45 + x}$

20. $\sqrt{\dfrac{x}{x + 2}}$

21. $8\sqrt{x^2 + 4}$

(e) Expressions That Are Meaningful as Real Numbers

The square of any nonzero number is always positive. For example, $8^2 = 64$ and $(-11)^2 = 121$. There are no real numbers that when squared yield negative numbers. Thus, $\sqrt{-100}$ does not represent a real number because there is no real number that when squared yields -100. We can try to square 10 and -10, but we know that $10^2 = 100$ and $(-10)^2 = 100$. Neither square is -100. Thus the following expressions do not represent real numbers (they are meaningless as real numbers):

$$\sqrt{-100}, \qquad \sqrt{-49}, \qquad -\sqrt{-3}.$$

> **EXCLUDING NEGATIVE RADICANDS**
>
> Radical expressions with negative radicands do not represent real numbers.

Later in your study of mathematics, you may encounter a number system called the **complex numbers** in which negative numbers have defined square roots.

Do Exercises 22–25.

Determine whether each expression represents a real number. Write "yes" or "no."

22. $-\sqrt{25}$ **23.** $\sqrt{-25}$

24. $-\sqrt{-36}$ **25.** $-\sqrt{36}$

Answers

18. 227   **19.** $45 + x$ **20.** $\dfrac{x}{x + 2}$
21. $x^2 + 4$ **22.** Yes   **23.** No
24. No   **25.** Yes

Perfect-Square Radicands

The expression $\sqrt{x^2}$, with a perfect-square radicand, x^2, can be troublesome to simplify. Recall that $\sqrt{}$ denotes the principal square root. That is, the answer is nonnegative (either positive or zero). If x represents a nonnegative number, $\sqrt{x^2}$ simplifies to x. If x represents a negative number, $\sqrt{x^2}$ simplifies to $-x$ (the opposite of x), which is positive.

Suppose that $x = 3$. Then

$$\sqrt{x^2} = \sqrt{3^2} = \sqrt{9} = 3.$$

Suppose that $x = -3$. Then

$$\sqrt{x^2} = \sqrt{(-3)^2} = \sqrt{9} = 3, \quad \text{the } \textit{opposite} \text{ of } -3.$$

Note that 3 is the *absolute value* of both 3 and -3. In general, when replacements for x are considered to be *any* real numbers, it follows that

$$\sqrt{x^2} = |x|,$$

and when $x = 3$ or $x = -3$,

$$\sqrt{x^2} = \sqrt{3^2} = |3| = 3 \quad \text{and} \quad \sqrt{x^2} = \sqrt{(-3)^2} = |-3| = 3.$$

PRINCIPAL SQUARE ROOT OF A^2

For any real number A,

$$\sqrt{A^2} = |A|.$$

(That is, for any real number A, the principal square root of A^2 is the absolute value of A.)

EXAMPLES Simplify. Assume that expressions under radicals represent any real number.

13. $\sqrt{10^2} = |10| = 10$

14. $\sqrt{(-7)^2} = |-7| = 7$

15. $\sqrt{(3x)^2} = |3x| = 3|x|$ Absolute-value notation is necessary.

16. $\sqrt{a^2b^2} = \sqrt{(ab)^2} = |ab|$

17. $\sqrt{x^2 + 2x + 1} = \sqrt{(x + 1)^2} = |x + 1|$

Do Exercises 26–31.

Fortunately, in many cases, it can be assumed that radicands that are variable expressions do not represent the square of a negative number. When this assumption is made, the need for absolute-value symbols disappears. Then

$$\text{for } x \geq 0, \quad \sqrt{x^2} = x,$$

since x is nonnegative.

PRINCIPAL SQUARE ROOT OF A^2

For any *nonnegative* real number A,

$$\sqrt{A^2} = A.$$

(That is, for any *nonnegative* real number A, the principal square root of A^2 is A.)

Simplify. Assume that expressions under radicals represent any real number.

26. $\sqrt{(-13)^2}$ **27.** $\sqrt{(7w)^2}$

28. $\sqrt{(xy)^2}$ **29.** $\sqrt{x^2y^2}$

30. $\sqrt{(x - 11)^2}$

31. $\sqrt{x^2 + 8x + 16}$

Answers
26. 13   **27.** $7|w|$ **28.** $|xy|$
29. $|xy|$ **30.** $|x - 11|$ **31.** $|x + 4|$

Simplify. Assume that radicands do not represent the square of a negative number.

32. $\sqrt{(xy)^2}$ **33.** $\sqrt{x^2y^2}$

34. $\sqrt{25y^2}$ **35.** $\sqrt{\frac{1}{4}t^2}$

36. $\sqrt{(x-11)^2}$

37. $\sqrt{x^2 + 8x + 16}$

▌**EXAMPLES** Simplify. Assume that radicands do not represent the square of a negative number.

18. $\sqrt{(3x)^2} = 3x$ Since $3x$ is assumed to be nonnegative, $|3x| = 3x$.

19. $\sqrt{a^2b^2} = \sqrt{(ab)^2} = ab$ Since ab is assumed to be nonnegative, $|ab| = ab$.

20. $\sqrt{x^2 + 2x + 1} = \sqrt{(x+1)^2} = x + 1$ Since $x + 1$ is assumed to be nonnegative

Do Exercises 32–37.

RADICALS AND ABSOLUTE VALUE

Henceforth, in this text we will assume that no radicands are formed by raising negative quantities to even powers.

We make this assumption in order to eliminate some confusion and because it is valid in many applications. As you study further in mathematics, however, you will frequently have to make a determination about expressions under radicals being nonnegative or positive. This will often be necessary in calculus.

STUDY TIPS

BEGINNING TO STUDY FOR THE FINAL EXAM

The best scenario for preparing for a final exam is to do so over a period of at least two weeks. Work in a diligent, disciplined manner, doing some final-exam preparation each day. Here is a detailed plan that many find useful.

1. **Begin by browsing through each chapter, reviewing the highlighted or boxed information regarding important formulas in both the text and the Summary and Review.** There may be some formulas that you will need to memorize.

2. **Retake each chapter test that you took in class, assuming your instructor has returned it. Otherwise, use the chapter tests in the book.** Restudy the objectives in the text that correspond to each question you missed.

3. **If you are still missing questions, use the supplements for extra review.** For example, you might check out the *Student's Solutions Manual.* See the Preface for more information on this and other supplements.

4. **For remaining difficulties, see your instructor, go to a tutoring session, or participate in a study group.**

5. **Then work the Cumulative Review following Chapter 9 during the last day or two before your final exam.** This review covers material from all chapters in the text. Be careful to avoid any questions corresponding to objectives not covered. Again, restudy the objectives in the text that correspond to each question you missed.

Answers

32. xy **33.** xy **34.** $5y$

35. $\frac{1}{2}t$ **36.** $x - 11$ **37.** $x + 4$

a Find the square roots.

1. 4   **2.** 1   **3.** 9   **4.** 16   **5.** 100

6. 121   **7.** 169   **8.** 144   **9.** 256   **10.** 625

Simplify.

11. $\sqrt{4}$ **12.** $\sqrt{1}$ **13.** $-\sqrt{9}$ **14.** $-\sqrt{25}$ **15.** $-\sqrt{36}$

16. $-\sqrt{81}$ **17.** $-\sqrt{225}$ **18.** $\sqrt{400}$ **19.** $\sqrt{361}$ **20.** $-\sqrt{441}$

b Use a calculator to approximate each square root. Round to three decimal places.

21. $\sqrt{5}$ **22.** $\sqrt{8}$ **23.** $\sqrt{432}$ **24.** $-\sqrt{8196}$ **25.** $-\sqrt{347.7}$

26. $-\sqrt{204.788}$ **27.** $\sqrt{\dfrac{278}{36}}$ **28.** $-\sqrt{\dfrac{567}{788}}$ **29.** $-5\sqrt{189 \cdot 6}$ **30.** $2\sqrt{18 \cdot 3}$

c Solve.

31. *Water Flow of Fire Hose.*   The number of gallons per minute discharged from a fire hose depends on the diameter of the hose and the nozzle pressure. For a 2-in. diameter solid bore nozzle, the water flow W, in gallons per minute (GPM), is given by $W = 118.8\sqrt{P}$, where P is the nozzle pressure, in pounds per square inch (psi). Find the water flow, in GPM, when the pressure is **(a)** 650 psi; **(b)** 1500 psi.

Source: www.firetactics.com

32. *Parking-Lot Arrival Spaces.*   The attendants at a parking lot park cars in temporary spaces before the cars are taken to long-term parking spaces. The number N of such spaces needed is approximated by the formula $N = 2.5\sqrt{A}$, where A is the average number of arrivals during peak hours. Find the number of spaces needed when the average number of arrivals is **(a)** 25; **(b)** 62.

Hang Time. An athlete's *hang time* (the time airborne for a jump) T, in seconds, is given by $T = 0.144\sqrt{V}$, where V is the athlete's vertical leap, in inches.

Source: Peter Brancazio

46 in.

33. Jason Richardson of the Phoenix Suns can jump 46 in. vertically. Find his hang time.

34. Vince Carter of the Orlando Magic can jump 43 in. vertically. Find his hang time.

35. Paul Pierce of the Boston Celtics can jump 38 in. vertically. Find his hang time.

36. Shawn Marion of the Dallas Mavericks can jump 41 in. vertically. Find his hang time.

d Identify the radicand.

37. $\sqrt{200}$

38. $\sqrt{16z}$

39. $\sqrt{x} - 4$

40. $\sqrt{3t + 10} + 8$

41. $5\sqrt{t^2 + 1}$

42. $-9\sqrt{x^2 + 16}$

43. $x^2 y\sqrt{\dfrac{3}{x + 2}}$

44. $ab^2\sqrt{\dfrac{a}{a + b}}$

e Determine whether each expression represents a real number. Write "yes" or "no."

45. $\sqrt{-16}$

46. $\sqrt{-81}$

47. $-\sqrt{81}$

48. $-\sqrt{64}$

49. $-\sqrt{-25}$

50. $\sqrt{-(-49)}$

f Simplify. Remember that we have assumed that radicands do not represent the square of a negative number.

51. $\sqrt{c^2}$

52. $\sqrt{x^2}$

53. $\sqrt{9x^2}$

54. $\sqrt{16y^2}$

55. $\sqrt{(8p)^2}$

56. $\sqrt{(7pq)^2}$

57. $\sqrt{(ab)^2}$

58. $\sqrt{(6y)^2}$

Copyright © 2012 Pearson Education, Inc.

59. $\sqrt{(34d)^2}$ **60.** $\sqrt{(53b)^2}$ **61.** $\sqrt{(x+3)^2}$ **62.** $\sqrt{(d-3)^2}$

63. $\sqrt{a^2 - 10a + 25}$ **64.** $\sqrt{x^2 + 2x + 1}$ **65.** $\sqrt{4a^2 - 20a + 25}$ **66.** $\sqrt{9p^2 + 12p + 4}$

67. $\sqrt{121y^2 - 198y + 81}$ **68.** $\sqrt{49b^2 + 140b + 100}$

Skill Maintenance

Solve. [13.4a]

69. *Supplementary Angles.* Two angles are supplementary. One angle is 3° less than twice the other. Find the measures of the angles.

70. *Complementary Angles.* Two angles are complementary. The sum of the measure of the first angle and half the measure of the second is 64°. Find the measures of the angles.

71. *Food Expenses.* The amount F that a family spends on food varies directly as its income I. A family making \$39,200 a year will spend \$10,192 on food. At this rate, how much would a family making \$41,000 spend on food? [12.9b]

Divide and simplify. [12.2b]

72. $\dfrac{x-3}{x+4} \div \dfrac{x^2-9}{x+4}$ **73.** $\dfrac{x^2 + 10x - 11}{x^2 - 1} \div \dfrac{x+11}{x+1}$ **74.** $\dfrac{x^4 - 16}{x^4 - 1} \div \dfrac{x^2 + 4}{x^2 + 1}$

Synthesis

75. Use only the graph of $y = \sqrt{x}$, shown below, to approximate $\sqrt{3}$, $\sqrt{5}$, and $\sqrt{7}$. Answers may vary.

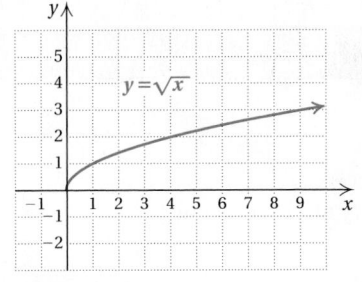

76. *Wind Chill Temperature.* When the temperature is T degrees Celsius and the wind speed is V meters per second, the *wind chill temperature*, T_W, is the temperature that it feels like. Here is a formula for finding wind chill temperature:

$$T_W = 13.112 + 0.6215T - 11.37V^{0.16} + 0.3965TV^{0.16}.$$

Estimate the wind chill temperature (to the nearest tenth of a degree) for the given actual temperatures and wind speeds.

a) $T = 7°C$, $V = 8\,\text{m/sec}$
b) $T = -5°C$, $V = 14\,\text{m/sec}$

Solve.

77. $\sqrt{x^2} = 16$ **78.** $\sqrt{y^2} = -7$ **79.** $t^2 = 49$

80. Suppose that the area of a square is 3. Find the length of a side.

14.2

Multiplying and Simplifying with Radical Expressions

OBJECTIVES

a Simplify radical expressions.

b Simplify radical expressions where radicands are powers.

c Multiply radical expressions and, if possible, simplify.

SKILL TO REVIEW
Objective 11.5b: Factor trinomial squares.

Factor.

1. $x^2 - 12x + 36$

2. $64x^2 + 48x + 9$

1. Simplify.

  a) $\sqrt{25} \cdot \sqrt{16}$

  b) $\sqrt{25 \cdot 16}$

Multiply.

2. $\sqrt{3}\sqrt{11}$ **3.** $\sqrt{5}\sqrt{5}$

4. $\sqrt{\dfrac{5}{11}}\sqrt{\dfrac{6}{7}}$ **5.** $\sqrt{x}\sqrt{x+1}$

6. $\sqrt{x+2}\sqrt{x-2}$

a Simplifying by Factoring

To see how to multiply with radical notation, consider the following.

a) $\sqrt{9} \cdot \sqrt{4} = 3 \cdot 2 = 6$ This is a product of square roots.

b) $\sqrt{9 \cdot 4} = \sqrt{36} = 6$ This is the square root of a product.

Note that
$$\sqrt{9} \cdot \sqrt{4} = \sqrt{9 \cdot 4}.$$

Do Margin Exercise 1.

We can multiply radical expressions by multiplying the radicands.

> **THE PRODUCT RULE FOR RADICALS**
>
> For any nonnegative radicands A and B,
> $$\sqrt{A} \cdot \sqrt{B} = \sqrt{A \cdot B}.$$
>
> (The product of square roots is the square root of the product of the radicands.)

EXAMPLES Multiply.

1. $\sqrt{5}\sqrt{7} = \sqrt{5 \cdot 7} = \sqrt{35}$

2. $\sqrt{8}\sqrt{8} = \sqrt{8 \cdot 8} = \sqrt{64} = 8$

3. $\sqrt{\dfrac{2}{3}}\sqrt{\dfrac{4}{5}} = \sqrt{\dfrac{2}{3} \cdot \dfrac{4}{5}} = \sqrt{\dfrac{8}{15}}$

4. $\sqrt{2x}\sqrt{3x-1} = \sqrt{2x(3x-1)} = \sqrt{6x^2 - 2x}$

Do Exercises 2–6.

To factor radical expressions, we can use the product rule for radicals in reverse.

> **FACTORING RADICAL EXPRESSIONS**
> $$\sqrt{AB} = \sqrt{A}\sqrt{B}$$

In some cases, we can simplify after factoring.

> A square-root radical expression is simplified when its radicand has no factors that are perfect squares.

Answers

Skill to Review:
1. $(x-6)^2$ **2.** $(8x+3)^2$

Margin Exercises:
1. (a) 20; (b) 20   **2.** $\sqrt{33}$ **3.** 5
4. $\sqrt{\dfrac{30}{77}}$ **5.** $\sqrt{x^2 + x}$ **6.** $\sqrt{x^2 - 4}$

When simplifying a square-root radical expression, we first determine whether the radicand is a perfect square. Then we determine whether it has perfect-square factors. The radicand is then factored and the radical expression simplified using the preceding rule.

Compare the following:

$$\sqrt{50} = \sqrt{10 \cdot 5} = \sqrt{10}\,\sqrt{5};$$
$$\sqrt{50} = \sqrt{25 \cdot 2} = \sqrt{25}\,\sqrt{2} = 5\sqrt{2}.$$

In the second case, the radicand is written using the perfect-square factor 25. If you do not recognize perfect-square factors, try factoring the radicand into its prime factors. For example,

$$\sqrt{50} = \sqrt{2 \cdot \underbrace{5 \cdot 5}} = 5\sqrt{2}.$$

Perfect square (a pair of the same factors)

Square-root radical expressions in which the radicand has no perfect-square factors, such as $5\sqrt{2}$, are considered to be in simplest form.

STUDY TIPS

TAKE THE TIME!

The foundation of all your study skills is making time to study! If you invest your time, you increase your likelihood of succeeding.

EXAMPLES   Simplify by factoring.

5. $\sqrt{18} = \sqrt{9 \cdot 2}$ Identifying a perfect-square factor and factoring the radicand. The factor 9 is a perfect square.

$= \sqrt{9} \cdot \sqrt{2}$ Factoring into a product of radicals

$= 3\sqrt{2}$ Simplifying $\sqrt{9}$

The radicand has no factors that are perfect squares.

6. $\sqrt{48t} = \sqrt{16 \cdot 3 \cdot t}$ Identifying a perfect-square factor and factoring the radicand. The factor 16 is a perfect square.

$= \sqrt{16}\,\sqrt{3t}$ Factoring into a product of radicals

$= 4\sqrt{3t}$ Taking a square root

7. $\sqrt{20t^2} = \sqrt{4 \cdot 5 \cdot t^2}$ Identifying perfect-square factors and factoring the radicand. The factors 4 and t^2 are perfect squares.

$= \sqrt{4}\,\sqrt{t^2}\,\sqrt{5}$ Factoring into a product of several radicals

$= 2t\sqrt{5}$ Taking square roots. No absolute-value signs are necessary since we have assumed that expressions under radicals do not represent the square of a negative number.

8. $\sqrt{x^2 - 6x + 9} = \sqrt{(x-3)^2} = x - 3$ No absolute-value signs are necessary since we have assumed that expressions under radicals do not represent the square of a negative number.

9. $\sqrt{36x^2} = \sqrt{36}\,\sqrt{x^2} = 6x$, or $\sqrt{36x^2} = \sqrt{(6x)^2} = 6x$

10. $\sqrt{3x^2 + 6x + 3} = \sqrt{3(x^2 + 2x + 1)}$ Factoring the radicand

$= \sqrt{3(x+1)^2}$ Factoring further

$= \sqrt{3}\,\sqrt{(x+1)^2}$ Factoring into a product of radicals

$= \sqrt{3}(x+1)$, or $(x+1)\sqrt{3}$ Taking the square root

Do Exercises 7–14.

Simplify by factoring.

7. $\sqrt{32}$ **8.** $\sqrt{92}$

9. $\sqrt{128t}$ **10.** $\sqrt{363q}$

11. $\sqrt{63x^2}$ **12.** $\sqrt{81m^2}$

13. $\sqrt{x^2 + 14x + 49}$

14. $\sqrt{3x^2 - 60x + 300}$

Answers

7. $4\sqrt{2}$ **8.** $2\sqrt{23}$ **9.** $8\sqrt{2t}$ **10.** $11\sqrt{3q}$
11. $3x\sqrt{7}$ **12.** $9m$ **13.** $x + 7$
14. $\sqrt{3}(x - 10)$, or $(x - 10)\sqrt{3}$

b) Simplifying Square Roots of Powers

To take the square root of an even power such as x^{10}, we note that $x^{10} = (x^5)^2$. Then

$$\sqrt{x^{10}} = \sqrt{(x^5)^2} = x^5.$$

We can find the answer by taking half the exponent. That is,

$$\sqrt{x^{10}} = x^5. \longleftarrow \tfrac{1}{2}(10) = 5$$

EXAMPLES Simplify.

11. $\sqrt{x^6} = \sqrt{(x^3)^2} = x^3 \qquad \tfrac{1}{2}(6) = 3$

12. $\sqrt{x^8} = x^4$

13. $\sqrt{t^{22}} = t^{11}$

Do Exercises 15–18.

Simplify.

15. $\sqrt{t^4}$ **16.** $\sqrt{t^{20}}$

17. $\sqrt{h^{46}}$ **18.** $\sqrt{x^{100}}$

If an odd power occurs, we express the power in terms of the largest even power. Then we simplify the even power as in Examples 11–13.

EXAMPLE 14 Simplify by factoring: $\sqrt{x^9}$.

$$\begin{aligned}
\sqrt{x^9} &= \sqrt{x^8 \cdot x} \\
&= \sqrt{x^8}\sqrt{x} \qquad \text{------ } \textit{Caution!} \text{ ------} \\
&= x^4\sqrt{x} \longleftarrow \text{Note that } \sqrt{x^9} \neq x^3.
\end{aligned}$$

EXAMPLE 15 Simplify by factoring: $\sqrt{32x^{15}}$.

$$\sqrt{32x^{15}} = \sqrt{16 \cdot 2 \cdot x^{14} \cdot x}$$
We factor the radicand, looking for perfect-square factors. The largest even power of x is 14.

$$= \sqrt{16}\sqrt{x^{14}}\sqrt{2x}$$
Factoring into a product of radicals. Perfect-square factors are usually listed first.

$$= 4x^7\sqrt{2x}$$
Simplifying

Do Exercises 19 and 20.

Simplify by factoring.

19. $\sqrt{x^7}$ **20.** $\sqrt{24x^{11}}$

c) Multiplying and Simplifying

Sometimes we can simplify after multiplying. We leave the radicand in factored form and factor further to determine perfect-square factors. Then we simplify the perfect-square factors.

EXAMPLE 16 Multiply and then simplify by factoring: $\sqrt{2}\sqrt{14}$.

$$\begin{aligned}
\sqrt{2}\sqrt{14} &= \sqrt{2 \cdot 14} \qquad \text{Multiplying} \\
&= \sqrt{2 \cdot 2 \cdot 7} \qquad \text{Factoring} \\
&= \sqrt{2 \cdot 2}\sqrt{7} \qquad \text{Looking for perfect-square factors, pairs of factors} \\
&= 2\sqrt{7}
\end{aligned}$$

Do Exercises 21 and 22.

Multiply and simplify.

21. $\sqrt{3}\sqrt{6}$ **22.** $\sqrt{2}\sqrt{50}$

Answers

15. t^2 **16.** t^{10} **17.** h^{23} **18.** x^{50}
19. $x^3\sqrt{x}$ **20.** $2x^5\sqrt{6x}$ **21.** $3\sqrt{2}$
22. 10

EXAMPLE 17 Multiply and then simplify by factoring: $\sqrt{3x^2}\,\sqrt{9x^3}$.

$$\sqrt{3x^2}\,\sqrt{9x^3} = \sqrt{3x^2 \cdot 9x^3} \qquad \text{Multiplying}$$

$$= \sqrt{3 \cdot x^2 \cdot 9 \cdot x^2 \cdot x} \qquad \begin{array}{l}\text{Looking for perfect-square} \\ \text{factors or largest even powers}\end{array}$$

$$= \sqrt{9 \cdot x^2 \cdot x^2 \cdot 3x}$$

           Perfect-square factors are usually listed first.

$$= \sqrt{9}\,\sqrt{x^2}\,\sqrt{x^2}\,\sqrt{3x}$$

$$= 3 \cdot x \cdot x \cdot \sqrt{3x}$$

$$= 3x^2\sqrt{3x}$$

In doing an example like the preceding one, it might be helpful to do more factoring, as follows:

$$\sqrt{3x^2} \cdot \sqrt{9x^3} = \sqrt{3 \cdot \underline{x \cdot x} \cdot 3 \cdot 3 \cdot \underline{x \cdot x} \cdot x}.$$

Then we look for pairs of factors, as shown, and simplify perfect-square factors:

$$= 3 \cdot x \cdot x\sqrt{3x}$$

$$= 3x^2\sqrt{3x}.$$

EXAMPLE 18 Simplify: $\sqrt{20cd^2}\,\sqrt{35cd^5}$.

$$\sqrt{20cd^2}\,\sqrt{35cd^5}$$

$$= \sqrt{20cd^2 \cdot 35cd^5} \qquad \text{Multiplying}$$

$$= \sqrt{2 \cdot 2 \cdot 5 \cdot c \cdot d \cdot d \cdot 5 \cdot 7 \cdot c \cdot d \cdot d \cdot d \cdot d \cdot d} \qquad \begin{array}{l}\text{Looking for} \\ \text{pairs of factors}\end{array}$$

$$= \sqrt{2 \cdot 2 \cdot 5 \cdot 5 \cdot c \cdot c \cdot d \cdot d \cdot d \cdot d \cdot d \cdot d \cdot 7d}$$

$$= 2 \cdot 5 \cdot c \cdot d \cdot d \cdot d\sqrt{7d}$$

$$= 10cd^3\sqrt{7d}$$

Do Exercises 23–25.

We know that $\sqrt{AB} = \sqrt{A}\,\sqrt{B}$. That is, the square root of a product is the product of the square roots. What about the square root of a sum? That is, is the square root of a sum equal to the sum of the square roots? To check, consider $\sqrt{A+B}$ and $\sqrt{A} + \sqrt{B}$ when $A = 16$ and $B = 9$:

$$\sqrt{A+B} = \sqrt{16+9} = \sqrt{25} = 5;$$

and

$$\sqrt{A} + \sqrt{B} = \sqrt{16} + \sqrt{9} = 4 + 3 = 7.$$

Thus we see the following.

------------------------------ *Caution!* ------------------------------

The square root of a sum is not the sum of the square roots.

$$\sqrt{A+B} \neq \sqrt{A} + \sqrt{B}$$

Multiply and simplify.

23. $\sqrt{2x^3}\,\sqrt{8x^3y^4}$

24. $\sqrt{10xy^2}\,\sqrt{5x^2y^3}$

25. $\sqrt{28q^2r} \cdot \sqrt{21q^3r^7}$

Calculator Corner

Simplifying Radical Expressions

Exercises: Use a table or a graph to determine whether each of the following is true.

1. $\sqrt{x+4} = \sqrt{x} + 2$

2. $\sqrt{3+x} = \sqrt{3} + x$

3. $\sqrt{x-2} = \sqrt{x} - \sqrt{2}$

4. $\sqrt{9x} = 3\sqrt{x}$

Answers

23. $4x^3y^2$ **24.** $5xy^2\sqrt{2xy}$ **25.** $14q^2r^4\sqrt{3q}$

14.2 **Exercise Set**

For Extra Help

MathXL
MyMathLab

Math XL
PRACTICE   WATCH   DOWNLOAD   READ   REVIEW

a Simplify by factoring.

1. $\sqrt{12}$

2. $\sqrt{8}$

3. $\sqrt{75}$

4. $\sqrt{50}$

5. $\sqrt{20}$

6. $\sqrt{45}$

7. $\sqrt{600}$

8. $\sqrt{300}$

9. $\sqrt{486}$

10. $\sqrt{567}$

11. $\sqrt{9x}$

12. $\sqrt{4y}$

13. $\sqrt{48x}$

14. $\sqrt{40m}$

15. $\sqrt{16a}$

16. $\sqrt{49b}$

17. $\sqrt{64y^2}$

18. $\sqrt{9x^2}$

19. $\sqrt{13x^2}$

20. $\sqrt{23s^2}$

21. $\sqrt{8t^2}$

22. $\sqrt{125a^2}$

23. $\sqrt{180}$

24. $\sqrt{320}$

25. $\sqrt{288y}$

26. $\sqrt{363p}$

27. $\sqrt{28x^2}$

28. $\sqrt{20x^2}$

29. $\sqrt{x^2 - 6x + 9}$

30. $\sqrt{t^2 + 22t + 121}$

31. $\sqrt{8x^2 + 8x + 2}$

32. $\sqrt{20x^2 - 20x + 5}$

33. $\sqrt{36y + 12y^2 + y^3}$

34. $\sqrt{x - 2x^2 + x^3}$

Copyright © 2012 Pearson Education, Inc.

b Simplify by factoring.

35. $\sqrt{t^6}$

36. $\sqrt{x^{18}}$

37. $\sqrt{x^{12}}$

38. $\sqrt{x^{16}}$

39. $\sqrt{x^5}$

40. $\sqrt{x^3}$

41. $\sqrt{t^{19}}$

42. $\sqrt{p^{17}}$

43. $\sqrt{(y-2)^8}$

44. $\sqrt{(x+3)^6}$

45. $\sqrt{4(x+5)^{10}}$

46. $\sqrt{16(a-7)^4}$

47. $\sqrt{36m^3}$

48. $\sqrt{250y^3}$

49. $\sqrt{8a^5}$

50. $\sqrt{12b^7}$

51. $\sqrt{104p^{17}}$

52. $\sqrt{284m^{23}}$

53. $\sqrt{448x^6y^3}$

54. $\sqrt{243x^5y^4}$

c Multiply and then, if possible, simplify by factoring.

55. $\sqrt{3}\,\sqrt{18}$

56. $\sqrt{5}\,\sqrt{10}$

57. $\sqrt{15}\,\sqrt{6}$

58. $\sqrt{3}\,\sqrt{27}$

59. $\sqrt{18}\,\sqrt{14x}$

60. $\sqrt{12}\,\sqrt{18x}$

61. $\sqrt{3x}\,\sqrt{12y}$

62. $\sqrt{7x}\,\sqrt{21y}$

63. $\sqrt{13}\,\sqrt{13}$

64. $\sqrt{11}\,\sqrt{11x}$

65. $\sqrt{5b}\,\sqrt{15b}$

66. $\sqrt{6a}\,\sqrt{18a}$

67. $\sqrt{2t}\,\sqrt{2t}$

68. $\sqrt{7a}\,\sqrt{7a}$

69. $\sqrt{ab}\,\sqrt{ac}$

70. $\sqrt{xy}\,\sqrt{xz}$

71. $\sqrt{2x^2y}\,\sqrt{4xy^2}$

72. $\sqrt{15mn^2}\,\sqrt{5m^2n}$

73. $\sqrt{18}\,\sqrt{18}$

74. $\sqrt{16}\,\sqrt{16}$

75. $\sqrt{5}\,\sqrt{2x-1}$

76. $\sqrt{3}\,\sqrt{4x+2}$

77. $\sqrt{x+2}\,\sqrt{x+2}$

78. $\sqrt{x-9}\,\sqrt{x-9}$

79. $\sqrt{18x^2y^3}\,\sqrt{6xy^4}$

80. $\sqrt{12x^3y^2}\,\sqrt{8xy}$

81. $\sqrt{50x^4y^6}\,\sqrt{10xy}$

82. $\sqrt{10xy^2}\,\sqrt{5x^2y^3}$

83. $\sqrt{99p^4q^3}\,\sqrt{22p^5q^2}$

84. $\sqrt{75m^8n^9}\,\sqrt{50m^5n^7}$

85. $\sqrt{24a^2b^3c^4}\,\sqrt{32a^5b^4c^7}$

86. $\sqrt{18p^5q^2r^{11}}\,\sqrt{108p^3q^6r^9}$

Copyright © 2012 Pearson Education, Inc.

Skill Maintenance

Solve. [13.3a, b]

87. $x - y = -6,$
$x + y = 2$

88. $3x + 5y = 6,$
$5x + 3y = 4$

89. $3x - 2y = 4,$
$2x + 5y = 9$

90. $4a - 5b = 25,$
$a - b = 7$

Solve.

91. *Canoe Travel.* Greg and Beth paddled to a picnic spot downriver in 2 hr. It took them 3 hr to return against the current. If the speed of the current was 2 mph, at what speed were they paddling the canoe? [13.5a]

92. *Storage Area Dimensions.* The perimeter of a rectangular storage area is 84 ft. The length is 18 ft greater than the width. Find the area of the rectangle. [13.4a]

93. *Fund-Raiser Attendance.* As part of a fund-raiser, 382 people attended a dinner and tour of a space museum. Tickets were $24 each for adults and $9 each for children, and receipts totalled $6603. How many adults and how many children attended? [13.4a]

94. *Insecticide Mixtures.* A solution containing 30% insecticide is to be mixed with a solution containing 50% insecticide in order to make 200 L of a solution containing 42% insecticide. How much of each solution should be used? [13.4a]

Synthesis

Factor.

95. $\sqrt{5x - 5}$

96. $\sqrt{x^2 - x - 2}$

97. $\sqrt{x^2 - 36}$

98. $\sqrt{2x^2 - 5x - 12}$

99. $\sqrt{x^3 - 2x^2}$

100. $\sqrt{a^2 - b^2}$

Simplify.

101. $\sqrt{0.25}$

102. $\sqrt{0.01}$

103. $\sqrt{\sqrt{\sqrt{256}}}$

Multiply and then simplify by factoring.

104. $(\sqrt{2y})(\sqrt{3})(\sqrt{8y})$

105. $\sqrt{18(x - 2)}\,\sqrt{20(x - 2)^3}$

106. $\sqrt{27(x + 1)}\,\sqrt{12y(x + 1)^2}$

107. $\sqrt{2^{109}}\,\sqrt{x^{306}}\,\sqrt{x^{11}}$

108. $\sqrt{x}\,\sqrt{2x}\,\sqrt{10x^5}$

109. $\sqrt{a}(\sqrt{a^3} - 5)$

14.3

Quotients Involving Radical Expressions

OBJECTIVES

a Divide radical expressions.

b Simplify square roots of quotients.

c Rationalize the denominator of a radical expression.

SKILL TO REVIEW

Objective 12.1c: Simplify rational expressions by factoring the numerator and the denominator and removing factors of 1.

Simplify.

1. $\dfrac{10x^8}{15x^3}$ 2. $\dfrac{64a^5b}{24a^2b^6}$

Divide and simplify.

1. $\dfrac{\sqrt{96}}{\sqrt{6}}$ 2. $\dfrac{\sqrt{75}}{\sqrt{3}}$

3. $\dfrac{\sqrt{x^{14}}}{\sqrt{x^3}}$ 4. $\dfrac{\sqrt{42x^5}}{\sqrt{7x^2}}$

a Dividing Radical Expressions

Consider the expressions

$$\frac{\sqrt{25}}{\sqrt{16}} \quad \text{and} \quad \sqrt{\frac{25}{16}}.$$

Let's evaluate them separately:

a) $\dfrac{\sqrt{25}}{\sqrt{16}} = \dfrac{5}{4}$ because $\sqrt{25} = 5$ and $\sqrt{16} = 4$;

b) $\sqrt{\dfrac{25}{16}} = \dfrac{5}{4}$ because $\dfrac{5}{4} \cdot \dfrac{5}{4} = \dfrac{25}{16}$.

We see that both expressions represent the same number. This suggests that the quotient of two square roots is the square root of the quotient of the radicands.

> **THE QUOTIENT RULE FOR RADICALS**
>
> For any nonnegative number A and any positive number B,
> $$\frac{\sqrt{A}}{\sqrt{B}} = \sqrt{\frac{A}{B}}.$$
>
> (The quotient of two square roots is the square root of the quotient of the radicands.)

EXAMPLES Divide and simplify.

1. $\dfrac{\sqrt{27}}{\sqrt{3}} = \sqrt{\dfrac{27}{3}} = \sqrt{9} = 3$

2. $\dfrac{\sqrt{30a^5}}{\sqrt{6a^2}} = \sqrt{\dfrac{30a^5}{6a^2}} = \sqrt{5a^3} = \sqrt{5 \cdot a^2 \cdot a} = \sqrt{a^2} \cdot \sqrt{5a} = a\sqrt{5a}$

Do Margin Exercises 1–4.

b Square Roots of Quotients

To find the square root of certain quotients, we can reverse the quotient rule for radicals. We can take the square root of a quotient by taking the square roots of the numerator and the denominator separately.

> **SQUARE ROOTS OF QUOTIENTS**
>
> For any nonnegative number A and any positive number B,
> $$\sqrt{\frac{A}{B}} = \frac{\sqrt{A}}{\sqrt{B}}.$$
>
> (We can take the square roots of the numerator and the denominator separately.)

Answers

Skill to Review:

1. $\dfrac{2x^5}{3}$ 2. $\dfrac{8a^3}{3b^5}$

Margin Exercises:

1. 4 2. 5 3. $x^5\sqrt{x}$ 4. $x\sqrt{6x}$

EXAMPLES Simplify by taking the square roots of the numerator and the denominator separately.

3. $\sqrt{\dfrac{25}{9}} = \dfrac{\sqrt{25}}{\sqrt{9}} = \dfrac{5}{3}$ Taking the square root of the numerator and the square root of the denominator

4. $\sqrt{\dfrac{1}{16}} = \dfrac{\sqrt{1}}{\sqrt{16}} = \dfrac{1}{4}$ Taking the square root of the numerator and the square root of the denominator

5. $\sqrt{\dfrac{49}{t^2}} = \dfrac{\sqrt{49}}{\sqrt{t^2}} = \dfrac{7}{t}$

Do Exercises 5–8.

Simplify.

5. $\sqrt{\dfrac{16}{9}}$ **6.** $\sqrt{\dfrac{1}{25}}$

7. $\sqrt{\dfrac{36}{x^2}}$ **8.** $\sqrt{\dfrac{b^2}{121}}$

We are assuming that expressions for numerators are nonnegative and expressions for denominators are positive. Thus we need not be concerned about absolute-value signs or zero denominators.

Sometimes a rational expression can be simplified to one that has a perfect-square numerator and a perfect-square denominator.

EXAMPLES Simplify.

6. $\sqrt{\dfrac{18}{50}} = \sqrt{\dfrac{9 \cdot 2}{25 \cdot 2}} = \sqrt{\dfrac{9}{25} \cdot \dfrac{2}{2}} = \sqrt{\dfrac{9}{25} \cdot 1}$

$= \sqrt{\dfrac{9}{25}} = \dfrac{\sqrt{9}}{\sqrt{25}} = \dfrac{3}{5}$

7. $\sqrt{\dfrac{2560}{2890}} = \sqrt{\dfrac{256 \cdot 10}{289 \cdot 10}} = \sqrt{\dfrac{256}{289} \cdot \dfrac{10}{10}} = \sqrt{\dfrac{256}{289} \cdot 1}$

$= \sqrt{\dfrac{256}{289}} = \dfrac{\sqrt{256}}{\sqrt{289}} = \dfrac{16}{17}$

8. $\dfrac{\sqrt{48x^3}}{\sqrt{3x^7}} = \sqrt{\dfrac{48x^3}{3x^7}} = \sqrt{\dfrac{16}{x^4}}$ Simplifying the radicand

$= \dfrac{\sqrt{16}}{\sqrt{x^4}} = \dfrac{4}{x^2}$

Do Exercises 9–12.

Simplify.

9. $\sqrt{\dfrac{18}{32}}$ **10.** $\sqrt{\dfrac{2250}{2560}}$

11. $\dfrac{\sqrt{98y}}{\sqrt{2y^{11}}}$ **12.** $\sqrt{\dfrac{108a^{11}}{3a^{37}}}$

(c) Rationalizing Denominators

Sometimes in mathematics it is useful to find an equivalent expression without a radical in the denominator. This provides a standard notation for expressing results. The procedure for finding such an expression is called **rationalizing the denominator**. We carry this out by multiplying by 1 in either of two ways.

To rationalize a denominator:

Method 1. Multiply by 1 under the radical to make the denominator of the radicand a perfect square.

Method 2. Multiply by 1 outside the radical to make the radicand in the denominator a perfect square.

Answers

5. $\dfrac{4}{3}$ 6. $\dfrac{1}{5}$ 7. $\dfrac{6}{x}$ 8. $\dfrac{b}{11}$ 9. $\dfrac{3}{4}$

10. $\dfrac{15}{16}$ 11. $\dfrac{7}{y^5}$ 12. $\dfrac{6}{a^{13}}$

EXAMPLE 9   Rationalize the denominator: $\sqrt{\dfrac{2}{3}}$.

METHOD 1:   We multiply by 1, choosing $\frac{3}{3}$ for 1. This makes the denominator of the radicand a perfect square:

$$\sqrt{\dfrac{2}{3}} = \sqrt{\dfrac{2}{3} \cdot \dfrac{3}{3}} \qquad \text{Multiplying by 1}$$

$$= \sqrt{\dfrac{6}{9}} = \dfrac{\sqrt{6}}{\sqrt{9}} \qquad \text{The radicand in the denominator, 9, is a perfect square.}$$

$$= \dfrac{\sqrt{6}}{3}.$$

METHOD 2:   We can also rationalize by first taking the square roots of the numerator and the denominator. Then we multiply by 1, using $\sqrt{3}/\sqrt{3}$:

$$\sqrt{\dfrac{2}{3}} = \dfrac{\sqrt{2}}{\sqrt{3}}$$

$$= \dfrac{\sqrt{2}}{\sqrt{3}} \cdot \dfrac{\sqrt{3}}{\sqrt{3}} \qquad \text{Multiplying by 1}$$

$$= \dfrac{\sqrt{2} \cdot \sqrt{3}}{\sqrt{3} \cdot \sqrt{3}} = \dfrac{\sqrt{6}}{\sqrt{9}} \qquad \text{The radicand, 9, in the denominator is a perfect square.}$$

$$= \dfrac{\sqrt{6}}{3}.$$

13. Rationalize the denominator:

$$\sqrt{\dfrac{3}{5}}.$$

a) Use method 1.

b) Use method 2.

Do Exercise 13.

We can always multiply by 1 to make a denominator a perfect square. Then we can take the square root of the denominator.

EXAMPLE 10   Rationalize the denominator: $\sqrt{\dfrac{5}{18}}$.

The denominator, 18, is not a perfect square. Factoring, we get $18 = 3 \cdot 3 \cdot 2$. If we had another factor of 2, however, we would have a perfect square, 36. Thus we multiply by 1, choosing $\frac{2}{2}$. This makes the denominator a perfect square.

$$\sqrt{\dfrac{5}{18}} = \sqrt{\dfrac{5}{3 \cdot 3 \cdot 2}} = \sqrt{\dfrac{5}{3 \cdot 3 \cdot 2} \cdot \dfrac{2}{2}} = \sqrt{\dfrac{10}{36}} = \dfrac{\sqrt{10}}{\sqrt{36}} = \dfrac{\sqrt{10}}{6}$$

EXAMPLE 11   Rationalize the denominator: $\dfrac{8}{\sqrt{7}}$.

This time we obtain an expression without a radical in the denominator by multiplying by 1, choosing $\sqrt{7}/\sqrt{7}$:

---- *Caution!* ----

$$\dfrac{8}{\sqrt{7}} = \dfrac{8}{\sqrt{7}} \cdot \dfrac{\sqrt{7}}{\sqrt{7}} = \dfrac{8\sqrt{7}}{\sqrt{49}} = \dfrac{8\sqrt{7}}{7}. \longleftarrow \quad 8\sqrt{7} \neq \sqrt{56}.$$

Rationalize the denominator.

14. $\sqrt{\dfrac{5}{8}}$

$\left(\textit{Hint}: \text{Multiply the radicand by } \frac{2}{2}. \right)$

15. $\dfrac{10}{\sqrt{3}}$

Do Exercises 14 and 15.

Answers

13. (a) $\dfrac{\sqrt{15}}{5}$; (b) $\dfrac{\sqrt{15}}{5}$ 14. $\dfrac{\sqrt{10}}{4}$ 15. $\dfrac{10\sqrt{3}}{3}$

EXAMPLE 12 Rationalize the denominator: $\dfrac{\sqrt{3}}{\sqrt{2}}$.

We look at the denominator. It is $\sqrt{2}$. We multiply by 1, choosing $\sqrt{2}/\sqrt{2}$:

$$\frac{\sqrt{3}}{\sqrt{2}} = \frac{\sqrt{3}}{\sqrt{2}} \cdot \frac{\sqrt{2}}{\sqrt{2}} = \frac{\sqrt{3} \cdot \sqrt{2}}{\sqrt{2} \cdot \sqrt{2}} = \frac{\sqrt{6}}{\sqrt{4}} = \frac{\sqrt{6}}{2}, \text{ or } \frac{1}{2}\sqrt{6}.$$

EXAMPLES Rationalize the denominator.

13. $\dfrac{\sqrt{5}}{\sqrt{x}} = \dfrac{\sqrt{5}}{\sqrt{x}} \cdot \dfrac{\sqrt{x}}{\sqrt{x}}$ Multiplying by 1

$\quad = \dfrac{\sqrt{5}\sqrt{x}}{\sqrt{x}\sqrt{x}}$

$\quad = \dfrac{\sqrt{5x}}{x}$ $\sqrt{x} \cdot \sqrt{x} = x$ by the definition of square root

14. $\dfrac{\sqrt{49a^5}}{\sqrt{12}} = \dfrac{\sqrt{49a^5}}{\sqrt{12}} \cdot \dfrac{\sqrt{3}}{\sqrt{3}}$ Factoring 12, we get $2 \cdot 2 \cdot 3$, so we need another factor of 3 in order for the radicand in the denominator to be a perfect square. We multiply by $\sqrt{3}/\sqrt{3}$.

$\quad = \dfrac{\sqrt{49a^5}\sqrt{3}}{\sqrt{12}\sqrt{3}}$

$\quad = \dfrac{\sqrt{49 \cdot a^4 \cdot a \cdot 3}}{\sqrt{36}} = \dfrac{\sqrt{49}\sqrt{a^4}\sqrt{3a}}{\sqrt{36}}$

$\quad = \dfrac{7a^2\sqrt{3a}}{6}$

Do Exercises 16–19.

Rationalize the denominator.

16. $\dfrac{\sqrt{3}}{\sqrt{7}}$ **17.** $\dfrac{\sqrt{5}}{\sqrt{r}}$

18. $\dfrac{\sqrt{64y^2}}{\sqrt{7}}$ **19.** $\dfrac{\sqrt{64x^9}}{\sqrt{15}}$

Answers

16. $\dfrac{\sqrt{21}}{7}$ **17.** $\dfrac{\sqrt{5r}}{r}$ **18.** $\dfrac{8y\sqrt{7}}{7}$

19. $\dfrac{8x^4\sqrt{15x}}{15}$

14.3 **Exercise Set**

For Extra Help
MyMathLab Math XL PRACTICE   WATCH   DOWNLOAD   READ   REVIEW

a Divide and simplify.

1. $\dfrac{\sqrt{18}}{\sqrt{2}}$ **2.** $\dfrac{\sqrt{20}}{\sqrt{5}}$ **3.** $\dfrac{\sqrt{108}}{\sqrt{3}}$ **4.** $\dfrac{\sqrt{60}}{\sqrt{15}}$ **5.** $\dfrac{\sqrt{65}}{\sqrt{13}}$

6. $\dfrac{\sqrt{45}}{\sqrt{15}}$ **7.** $\dfrac{\sqrt{3}}{\sqrt{75}}$ **8.** $\dfrac{\sqrt{3}}{\sqrt{48}}$ **9.** $\dfrac{\sqrt{12}}{\sqrt{75}}$ **10.** $\dfrac{\sqrt{18}}{\sqrt{32}}$

11. $\dfrac{\sqrt{8x}}{\sqrt{2x}}$ **12.** $\dfrac{\sqrt{18b}}{\sqrt{2b}}$ **13.** $\dfrac{\sqrt{63y^3}}{\sqrt{7y}}$ **14.** $\dfrac{\sqrt{48x^3}}{\sqrt{3x}}$

b Simplify.

15. $\sqrt{\dfrac{16}{49}}$

16. $\sqrt{\dfrac{9}{49}}$

17. $\sqrt{\dfrac{1}{36}}$

18. $\sqrt{\dfrac{1}{4}}$

19. $-\sqrt{\dfrac{16}{81}}$

20. $-\sqrt{\dfrac{25}{49}}$

21. $\sqrt{\dfrac{64}{289}}$

22. $\sqrt{\dfrac{81}{361}}$

23. $\sqrt{\dfrac{1690}{1960}}$

24. $\sqrt{\dfrac{1210}{6250}}$

25. $\sqrt{\dfrac{25}{x^2}}$

26. $\sqrt{\dfrac{36}{a^2}}$

27. $\sqrt{\dfrac{9a^2}{625}}$

28. $\sqrt{\dfrac{x^2y^2}{256}}$

29. $\dfrac{\sqrt{50y^{15}}}{\sqrt{2y^{25}}}$

30. $\dfrac{\sqrt{3t^{15}}}{\sqrt{12t}}$

31. $\dfrac{\sqrt{7x^{23}}}{\sqrt{343x^5}}$

32. $\dfrac{\sqrt{125q^3}}{\sqrt{5q^{19}}}$

c Rationalize the denominator.

33. $\sqrt{\dfrac{2}{5}}$

34. $\sqrt{\dfrac{2}{7}}$

35. $\sqrt{\dfrac{7}{8}}$

36. $\sqrt{\dfrac{3}{8}}$

37. $\sqrt{\dfrac{1}{12}}$

38. $\sqrt{\dfrac{7}{12}}$

39. $\sqrt{\dfrac{5}{18}}$

40. $\sqrt{\dfrac{1}{18}}$

41. $\dfrac{3}{\sqrt{5}}$

42. $\dfrac{4}{\sqrt{3}}$

43. $\sqrt{\dfrac{8}{3}}$

44. $\sqrt{\dfrac{12}{5}}$

45. $\sqrt{\dfrac{3}{x}}$

46. $\sqrt{\dfrac{2}{x}}$

47. $\sqrt{\dfrac{x}{y}}$

Copyright © 2012 Pearson Education, Inc.

48. $\sqrt{\dfrac{a}{b}}$

49. $\sqrt{\dfrac{x^2}{20}}$

50. $\sqrt{\dfrac{x^2}{18}}$

51. $\dfrac{1}{\sqrt{3}}$

52. $\dfrac{1}{\sqrt{2}}$

53. $\dfrac{\sqrt{9}}{\sqrt{8}}$

54. $\dfrac{\sqrt{4}}{\sqrt{27}}$

55. $\dfrac{\sqrt{11}}{\sqrt{5}}$

56. $\dfrac{\sqrt{2}}{\sqrt{5}}$

57. $\dfrac{2}{\sqrt{2}}$

58. $\dfrac{3}{\sqrt{3}}$

59. $\dfrac{\sqrt{5}}{\sqrt{11}}$

60. $\dfrac{\sqrt{7}}{\sqrt{27}}$

61. $\dfrac{\sqrt{7}}{\sqrt{12}}$

62. $\dfrac{\sqrt{5}}{\sqrt{18}}$

63. $\dfrac{\sqrt{48}}{\sqrt{32}}$

64. $\dfrac{\sqrt{56}}{\sqrt{40}}$

65. $\dfrac{\sqrt{450}}{\sqrt{18}}$

66. $\dfrac{\sqrt{224}}{\sqrt{14}}$

67. $\dfrac{\sqrt{3}}{\sqrt{x}}$

68. $\dfrac{\sqrt{2}}{\sqrt{y}}$

69. $\dfrac{4y}{\sqrt{5}}$

70. $\dfrac{8x}{\sqrt{3}}$

71. $\dfrac{\sqrt{a^3}}{\sqrt{8}}$

72. $\dfrac{\sqrt{x^3}}{\sqrt{27}}$

73. $\dfrac{\sqrt{56}}{\sqrt{12x}}$

74. $\dfrac{\sqrt{45}}{\sqrt{8a}}$

75. $\dfrac{\sqrt{27c}}{\sqrt{32c^3}}$

76. $\dfrac{\sqrt{7x^3}}{\sqrt{12x}}$

77. $\dfrac{\sqrt{y^5}}{\sqrt{xy^2}}$

78. $\dfrac{\sqrt{x^3}}{\sqrt{xy}}$

79. $\dfrac{\sqrt{45mn^2}}{\sqrt{32m}}$

80. $\dfrac{\sqrt{16a^4b^6}}{\sqrt{128a^6b^6}}$

Skill Maintenance

Solve. [13.3a, b]

81. $x = y + 2,$
$\quad x + y = 6$

82. $4x - y = 10,$
$\quad 4x + y = 70$

83. $2x - 3y = 7,$
$\quad 2x - 3y = 9$

84. $2x - 3y = 7,$
$\quad -4x + 6y = -14$

85. $x + y = -7,$
$\quad x - y = 2$

86. $2x + 3y = 8,$
$\quad 5x - 4y = -2$

Divide and simplify. [12.2b]

87. $\dfrac{x^2 - 49}{x + 8} \div \dfrac{x^2 - 14x + 49}{x^2 + 15x + 56}$

88. $\dfrac{x - 2}{x - 3} \div \dfrac{x - 4}{x - 5}$

89. $\dfrac{a^2 - 25}{6} \div \dfrac{a + 5}{3}$

90. $\dfrac{x - 2}{x + 3} \div \dfrac{x^2 - 4x + 4}{x^2 - 9}$

Multiply.

91. $(3x - 7)(3x + 7)$ [10.6b]

92. $(4a - 5b)(4a + 5b)$ [10.7f]

Synthesis

Periods of Pendulums. The period T of a pendulum is the time it takes the pendulum to move from one side to the other and back. A formula for the period is

$$T = 2\pi \sqrt{\dfrac{L}{32}},$$

where T is in seconds and L is the length of the pendulum, in feet. Use 3.14 for π.

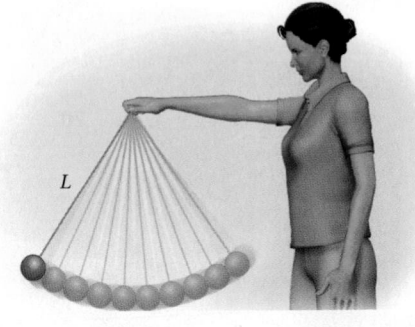

L

93. Find the periods of pendulums of lengths 2 ft, 8 ft, and 10 in.

94. The pendulum of a grandfather clock is $(32/\pi^2)$ ft long. How long does it take to swing from one side to the other?

Rationalize the denominator.

95. $\sqrt{\dfrac{5}{1600}}$

96. $\sqrt{\dfrac{3a}{b}}$

97. $\sqrt{\dfrac{3x^2 y}{a^2 x^5}}$

98. $\sqrt{0.009}$

Simplify.

99. $\sqrt{\dfrac{1}{x^2} - \dfrac{2}{xy} + \dfrac{1}{y^2}}$

100. $\sqrt{2 - \dfrac{4}{z^2} + \dfrac{2}{z^4}}$

Copyright © 2012 Pearson Education, Inc.

Mid-Chapter Review

Concept Reinforcement

Determine whether each statement is true or false.

_____ **1.** The radical symbol $\sqrt{}$ represents only the principal square root. [14.1a]

_____ **2.** For any nonnegative real number A, the principal square root of A^2 is $-A$. [14.1f]

_____ **3.** Every nonnegative number has two square roots. [14.1a]

_____ **4.** There are no real numbers that when squared yield negative numbers. [14.1e]

Guided Solutions

Fill in each blank with the number or expression that creates a correct solution.

5. Simplify by factoring: $\sqrt{3x^2 - 48x + 192}$. [14.2a]

$$\begin{aligned}
\sqrt{3x^2 - 48x + 192} &= \sqrt{\square(x^2 - 16x + 64)} \\
&= \sqrt{3(\square)^2} \\
&= \sqrt{\square}\,\sqrt{(x-8)^2} \\
&= \sqrt{3}(x - \square)
\end{aligned}$$

6. Multiply and simplify by factoring: $\sqrt{30}\,\sqrt{40y}$. [14.2c]

$$\begin{aligned}
\sqrt{30}\,\sqrt{40y} &= \sqrt{30 \cdot \square\, y} \\
&= \sqrt{\square\, y} \\
&= \sqrt{100 \cdot \square \cdot y} \\
&= \sqrt{100 \cdot \square \cdot 3 \cdot y} \\
&= \sqrt{100}\,\sqrt{4}\,\sqrt{\square} \\
&= 10 \cdot \square\,\sqrt{3y} \\
&= \square\,\sqrt{3y}
\end{aligned}$$

7. Multiply and simplify by factoring:
$\sqrt{18ab^2}\,\sqrt{14a^2b^4}$. [14.2c]

$$\begin{aligned}
\sqrt{18ab^2}\,\sqrt{14a^2b^4} &= \sqrt{18ab^2 \cdot 14\,\square\,b^4} \\
&= \sqrt{2 \cdot 3 \cdot 3 \cdot 2 \cdot 7 \cdot \square \cdot b^6} \\
&= \sqrt{2^2 \cdot 3^2 \cdot 7 \cdot a^2 \cdot \square \cdot b^6} \\
&= \sqrt{2^2}\,\sqrt{3^2}\,\sqrt{a^2}\,\sqrt{b^6}\,\sqrt{\square} \\
&= 2 \cdot 3 \cdot a \cdot \square\,\sqrt{7a} \\
&= 6\,\square\,b^3\,\sqrt{7a}
\end{aligned}$$

8. Rationalize the denominator: $\sqrt{\dfrac{3y^2}{44}}$. [14.3c]

$$\begin{aligned}
\sqrt{\frac{3y^2}{44}} &= \sqrt{\frac{3y^2}{2 \cdot \square \cdot 11}} \\
&= \sqrt{\frac{3y^2}{2 \cdot 2 \cdot 11} \cdot \frac{\square}{\square}} \\
&= \sqrt{\frac{33y^2}{\square^2 \cdot 11^2}} \\
&= \frac{\square\,\sqrt{33}}{2 \cdot 11} = \frac{y\sqrt{33}}{\square}
\end{aligned}$$

Mixed Review

9. Find the square roots of 121. [14.1a]

10. Identify the radicand: $2x\sqrt{\dfrac{x-3}{7}}$. [14.1d]

11. Determine whether each expression represents a real number. Write "yes" or "no." [14.1e]

a) $\sqrt{-100}$ **b)** $-\sqrt{9}$

Simplify.

12. $\sqrt{128r^7s^6}$ [14.2b]

13. $\sqrt{25(x-3)^2}$ [14.2b]

14. $\sqrt{\dfrac{1}{100}}$ [14.3b]

15. $-\sqrt{36}$ [14.1a]

16. $-\sqrt{\dfrac{6250}{490}}$ [14.3b]

17. $\sqrt{225}$ [14.1a]

18. $\sqrt{(10y)^2}$ [14.1f]

19. $\sqrt{4x^2 - 4x + 1}$ [14.2a]

20. $\sqrt{800x}$ [14.2a]

21. $\dfrac{\sqrt{6}}{\sqrt{96}}$ [14.3a]

22. $\sqrt{32q^{11}}$ [14.2b]

23. $\sqrt{\dfrac{81}{z^2}}$ [14.3b]

Multiply or divide and, if possible, simplify.

24. $\sqrt{25}\,\sqrt{25}$ [14.2c]

25. $\dfrac{\sqrt{18}}{\sqrt{98}}$ [14.3a]

26. $\dfrac{\sqrt{192x}}{\sqrt{3x}}$ [14.3a]

27. $\sqrt{40c^2d^7}\,\sqrt{15c^3d^3}$ [14.2c]

28. $\sqrt{24x^5y^8z^2}\,\sqrt{60xy^3z}$ [14.2c]

29. $\sqrt{2x}\,\sqrt{30y}$ [14.2c]

30. $\sqrt{21a}\,\sqrt{35a}$ [14.2c]

31. $\dfrac{\sqrt{3y^{29}}}{\sqrt{75y^5}}$ [14.3a]

32. Rationalize the denominator and simplify. Match each expression in the first column with an equivalent expression in the second column by drawing connecting lines.   [14.3c]

$\dfrac{x}{\sqrt{3}}$ $\dfrac{3\sqrt{x}}{x}$

$\sqrt{\dfrac{3}{x}}$ $\dfrac{\sqrt{3x}}{3}$

$\dfrac{3}{\sqrt{x}}$ $\dfrac{x\sqrt{3}}{3}$

$\dfrac{3x}{\sqrt{3}}$ $\sqrt{3}$

$\dfrac{3}{\sqrt{3}}$ $\dfrac{\sqrt{3x}}{x}$

$\sqrt{\dfrac{x}{3}}$ $x\sqrt{3}$

Understanding Through Discussion and Writing

33. What is the difference between "**the** square root of 100" and "**a** square root of 100"?   [14.1a]

34. Explain why the following is incorrect: [14.3b]
$$\sqrt{\dfrac{9 + 100}{25}} = \dfrac{3 + 10}{3}.$$

35. Explain the error(s) in the following: [14.2a]
$$\sqrt{x^2 - 25} = \sqrt{x^2} - \sqrt{25} = x - 5.$$

36. Describe a method that could be used to rationalize the *numerator* of a radical expression.   [14.3c]

Radical Expressions and Equations

Copyright © 2012 Pearson Education, Inc.

14.4 Addition, Subtraction, and More Multiplication

(a) Addition and Subtraction

We can add any two real numbers. The sum of 5 and $\sqrt{2}$ can be expressed as $5 + \sqrt{2}$. We cannot simplify this unless we use rational approximations such as $5 + \sqrt{2} \approx 5 + 1.414 = 6.414$. However, when we have *like radicals*, a sum can be simplified using the distributive laws and collecting like terms. **Like radicals** have the same radicands.

EXAMPLE 1   Add: $3\sqrt{5} + 4\sqrt{5}$.

Suppose we were considering $3x + 4x$. Recall that to add, we use a distributive law as follows:

$$3x + 4x = (3 + 4)x = 7x.$$

The situation is similar in this example, but we let $x = \sqrt{5}$:

$$3\sqrt{5} + 4\sqrt{5} = (3 + 4)\sqrt{5} \qquad \text{Using a distributive law to factor out } \sqrt{5}$$
$$= 7\sqrt{5}.$$

If we wish to add or subtract as we did in Example 1, the radicands must be the same. Sometimes after simplifying the radical terms, we discover that we have like radicals.

EXAMPLES   Add or subtract. Simplify, if possible, by collecting like radical terms.

2. $5\sqrt{2} - \sqrt{18} = 5\sqrt{2} - \sqrt{9 \cdot 2}$ Factoring 18
$$= 5\sqrt{2} - \sqrt{9}\sqrt{2}$$
$$= 5\sqrt{2} - 3\sqrt{2}$$
$$= (5 - 3)\sqrt{2} \qquad \text{Using a distributive law to factor out the common factor, } \sqrt{2}$$
$$= 2\sqrt{2}$$

3. $\sqrt{4x^3} + 7\sqrt{x} = \sqrt{4 \cdot x^2 \cdot x} + 7\sqrt{x}$
$$= 2x\sqrt{x} + 7\sqrt{x}$$
$$= (2x + 7)\sqrt{x} \qquad \text{Using a distributive law to factor out } \sqrt{x}$$

Don't forget the parentheses!

4. $\sqrt{x^3 - x^2} + \sqrt{4x - 4} = \sqrt{x^2(x - 1)} + \sqrt{4(x - 1)}$ Factoring radicands
$$= \sqrt{x^2}\sqrt{x - 1} + \sqrt{4}\sqrt{x - 1}$$
$$= x\sqrt{x - 1} + 2\sqrt{x - 1}$$
$$= (x + 2)\sqrt{x - 1} \qquad \text{Using a distributive law to factor out the common factor, } \sqrt{x - 1}. \text{ Don't forget the parentheses!}$$

Do Margin Exercises 1–5.

OBJECTIVES

(a) Add or subtract with radical notation, using the distributive laws to simplify.

(b) Multiply expressions involving radicals, where some of the expressions contain more than one term.

(c) Rationalize denominators having two terms.

SKILL TO REVIEW
Objective 10.6d: Find special products when polynomial products are mixed together.

Multiply.

1. $(3x - 7)(3x + 7)$

2. $\left(4x - \dfrac{1}{2}\right)^2$

Add or subtract and simplify by collecting like radical terms, if possible.

1. $3\sqrt{2} + 9\sqrt{2}$

2. $8\sqrt{5} - 3\sqrt{5}$

3. $2\sqrt{10} - 7\sqrt{40}$

4. $\sqrt{24} + \sqrt{54}$

5. $\sqrt{9x + 9} - \sqrt{4x + 4}$

Answers

Skill to Review:

1. $9x^2 - 49$ **2.** $16x^2 - 4x + \dfrac{1}{4}$

Margin Exercises:
1. $12\sqrt{2}$ **2.** $5\sqrt{5}$ **3.** $-12\sqrt{10}$ **4.** $5\sqrt{6}$
5. $\sqrt{x + 1}$

Sometimes rationalizing denominators enables us to combine like radicals.

EXAMPLE 5 Add: $\sqrt{3} + \sqrt{\dfrac{1}{3}}$.

$\sqrt{3} + \sqrt{\dfrac{1}{3}} = \sqrt{3} + \sqrt{\dfrac{1}{3} \cdot \dfrac{3}{3}}$ Multiplying by 1 in order to rationalize the denominator

$= \sqrt{3} + \sqrt{\dfrac{3}{9}}$

$= \sqrt{3} + \dfrac{\sqrt{3}}{\sqrt{9}}$

$= \sqrt{3} + \dfrac{\sqrt{3}}{3}$

$= 1 \cdot \sqrt{3} + \dfrac{1}{3}\sqrt{3}$

$= \left(1 + \dfrac{1}{3}\right)\sqrt{3}$ Factoring out the common factor, $\sqrt{3}$

$= \dfrac{4}{3}\sqrt{3}$, or $\dfrac{4\sqrt{3}}{3}$

Add or subtract.

6. $\sqrt{2} + \sqrt{\dfrac{1}{2}}$

7. $\sqrt{\dfrac{5}{3}} + \sqrt{\dfrac{3}{5}}$

Do Exercises 6 and 7.

(b) Multiplication

Now let's multiply where some of the expressions may contain more than one term. To do this, we use procedures already studied in this chapter as well as the distributive laws and special products for multiplying with polynomials.

EXAMPLE 6 Multiply: $\sqrt{2}(\sqrt{3} + \sqrt{7})$.

$\sqrt{2}(\sqrt{3} + \sqrt{7}) = \sqrt{2}\sqrt{3} + \sqrt{2}\sqrt{7}$ Multiplying using a distributive law

$= \sqrt{6} + \sqrt{14}$ Using the rule for multiplying with radicals

EXAMPLE 7 Multiply: $(2 + \sqrt{3})(5 - 4\sqrt{3})$.

$(2 + \sqrt{3})(5 - 4\sqrt{3}) = 2 \cdot 5 - 2 \cdot 4\sqrt{3} + \sqrt{3} \cdot 5 - \sqrt{3} \cdot 4\sqrt{3}$ Using FOIL

$= 10 - 8\sqrt{3} + 5\sqrt{3} - 4 \cdot 3$

$= 10 - 8\sqrt{3} + 5\sqrt{3} - 12$

$= -2 - 3\sqrt{3}$

STUDY TIPS

AVOID DISTRACTIONS

Don't allow yourself to be distracted from your studies by electronic "time robbers" such as video games, the Internet, and television. Be disciplined and *study first*. Then reward yourself with a leisure activity if there is enough time in your day.

Answers

6. $\dfrac{3}{2}\sqrt{2}$ **7.** $\dfrac{8\sqrt{15}}{15}$

EXAMPLE 8 Multiply: $(\sqrt{3} - \sqrt{x})(\sqrt{3} + \sqrt{x})$.

$$(\sqrt{3} - \sqrt{x})(\sqrt{3} + \sqrt{x}) = (\sqrt{3})^2 - (\sqrt{x})^2 \qquad \text{Using } (A - B)(A + B) = A^2 - B^2$$
$$= 3 - x$$

EXAMPLE 9 Multiply: $(3 - \sqrt{p})^2$.

$$(3 - \sqrt{p})^2 = 3^2 - 2 \cdot 3 \cdot \sqrt{p} + (\sqrt{p})^2 \qquad \text{Using } (A - B)^2 = A^2 - 2AB + B^2$$
$$= 9 - 6\sqrt{p} + p$$

EXAMPLE 10 Multiply: $(2 + \sqrt{5})^2$.

$$(2 + \sqrt{5})^2 = 2^2 + 2 \cdot 2\sqrt{5} + (\sqrt{5})^2 \qquad \text{Using } (A + B)^2 = A^2 + 2AB + B^2$$
$$= 4 + 4\sqrt{5} + 5$$
$$= 9 + 4\sqrt{5}$$

Do Exercises 8-12.

Multiply.

8. $\sqrt{3}(\sqrt{5} + \sqrt{2})$

9. $(1 - \sqrt{2})(4 + 3\sqrt{5})$

10. $(\sqrt{2} + \sqrt{a})(\sqrt{2} - \sqrt{a})$

11. $(5 + \sqrt{x})^2$

12. $(3 - \sqrt{7})(3 + \sqrt{7})$

(c) More on Rationalizing Denominators

Note in Example 8 that the result has no radicals. This will happen whenever we multiply expressions such as $\sqrt{a} - \sqrt{b}$ and $\sqrt{a} + \sqrt{b}$. We see this in the following:

$$(\sqrt{a} + \sqrt{b})(\sqrt{a} - \sqrt{b}) = (\sqrt{a})^2 - (\sqrt{b})^2 = a - b.$$

Expressions such as $\sqrt{3} - \sqrt{x}$ and $\sqrt{3} + \sqrt{x}$ are known as **conjugates**; so too are $2 + \sqrt{5}$ and $2 - \sqrt{5}$. We can use conjugates to rationalize a denominator that involves a sum or a difference of two terms, where one or both are radicals. To do so, we multiply by 1 using the conjugate to form the expression for 1.

Do Exercises 13-15.

Find the conjugate of each expression.

13. $7 + \sqrt{5}$

14. $\sqrt{5} - \sqrt{2}$

15. $1 - \sqrt{x}$

EXAMPLE 11 Rationalize the denominator: $\dfrac{3}{2 + \sqrt{5}}$.

We multiply by 1 using the conjugate of $2 + \sqrt{5}$, which is $2 - \sqrt{5}$, as the numerator and the denominator of the expression for 1:

$$\frac{3}{2 + \sqrt{5}} = \frac{3}{2 + \sqrt{5}} \cdot \frac{2 - \sqrt{5}}{2 - \sqrt{5}} \qquad \text{Multiplying by 1}$$

$$= \frac{3(2 - \sqrt{5})}{(2 + \sqrt{5})(2 - \sqrt{5})} \qquad \text{Multiplying}$$

$$= \frac{6 - 3\sqrt{5}}{2^2 - (\sqrt{5})^2} \qquad \text{Using } (A + B)(A - B) = A^2 - B^2$$

$$= \frac{6 - 3\sqrt{5}}{4 - 5}$$

$$= \frac{6 - 3\sqrt{5}}{-1}$$

$$= -6 + 3\sqrt{5}, \text{ or } 3\sqrt{5} - 6.$$

Answers

8. $\sqrt{15} + \sqrt{6}$ **9.** $4 + 3\sqrt{5} - 4\sqrt{2} - 3\sqrt{10}$
10. $2 - a$ **11.** $25 + 10\sqrt{x} + x$ **12.** 2
13. $7 - \sqrt{5}$ **14.** $\sqrt{5} + \sqrt{2}$ **15.** $1 + \sqrt{x}$

EXAMPLE 12   Rationalize the denominator: $\dfrac{\sqrt{3} + \sqrt{5}}{\sqrt{3} - \sqrt{5}}$.

We multiply by 1 using the conjugate of $\sqrt{3} - \sqrt{5}$, which is $\sqrt{3} + \sqrt{5}$, as the numerator and the denominator of the expression for 1:

$$\dfrac{\sqrt{3} + \sqrt{5}}{\sqrt{3} - \sqrt{5}} = \dfrac{\sqrt{3} + \sqrt{5}}{\sqrt{3} - \sqrt{5}} \cdot \dfrac{\sqrt{3} + \sqrt{5}}{\sqrt{3} + \sqrt{5}} \qquad \text{Multiplying by 1}$$

$$= \dfrac{(\sqrt{3} + \sqrt{5})^2}{(\sqrt{3} - \sqrt{5})(\sqrt{3} + \sqrt{5})}$$

$$= \dfrac{(\sqrt{3})^2 + 2\sqrt{3}\sqrt{5} + (\sqrt{5})^2}{(\sqrt{3})^2 - (\sqrt{5})^2} \qquad \begin{array}{l}\text{Using } (A + B)^2 = A^2 + 2AB + B^2 \\ \text{and } (A + B)(A - B) = A^2 - B^2\end{array}$$

$$= \dfrac{3 + 2\sqrt{15} + 5}{3 - 5}$$

$$= \dfrac{8 + 2\sqrt{15}}{-2}$$

$$= \dfrac{2(4 + \sqrt{15})}{2(-1)} \qquad \text{Factoring in order to simplify}$$

$$= \dfrac{2}{2} \cdot \dfrac{4 + \sqrt{15}}{-1}$$

$$= \dfrac{4 + \sqrt{15}}{-1}$$

$$= -4 - \sqrt{15}.$$

Do Exercises 16 and 17.

Rationalize the denominator.

16. $\dfrac{3}{7 + \sqrt{5}}$

17. $\dfrac{\sqrt{5} + \sqrt{7}}{\sqrt{5} - \sqrt{7}}$

EXAMPLE 13   Rationalize the denominator: $\dfrac{5}{2 + \sqrt{x}}$.

We multiply by 1 using the conjugate of $2 + \sqrt{x}$, which is $2 - \sqrt{x}$, as the numerator and the denominator of the expression for 1:

$$\dfrac{5}{2 + \sqrt{x}} = \dfrac{5}{2 + \sqrt{x}} \cdot \dfrac{2 - \sqrt{x}}{2 - \sqrt{x}} \qquad \text{Multiplying by 1}$$

$$= \dfrac{5(2 - \sqrt{x})}{(2 + \sqrt{x})(2 - \sqrt{x})}$$

$$= \dfrac{5 \cdot 2 - 5 \cdot \sqrt{x}}{2^2 - (\sqrt{x})^2} \qquad \text{Using } (A + B)(A - B) = A^2 - B^2$$

$$= \dfrac{10 - 5\sqrt{x}}{4 - x}.$$

Do Exercise 18.

18. Rationalize the denominator:

$$\dfrac{7}{1 - \sqrt{x}}.$$

Answers

16. $\dfrac{21 - 3\sqrt{5}}{44}$ **17.** $-6 - \sqrt{35}$

18. $\dfrac{7 + 7\sqrt{x}}{1 - x}$

a Add or subtract. Simplify by collecting like radical terms, if possible.

1. $7\sqrt{3} + 9\sqrt{3}$

2. $6\sqrt{2} + 8\sqrt{2}$

3. $7\sqrt{5} - 3\sqrt{5}$

4. $8\sqrt{2} - 5\sqrt{2}$

5. $6\sqrt{x} + 7\sqrt{x}$

6. $9\sqrt{y} + 3\sqrt{y}$

7. $4\sqrt{d} - 13\sqrt{d}$

8. $2\sqrt{a} - 17\sqrt{a}$

9. $5\sqrt{8} + 15\sqrt{2}$

10. $3\sqrt{12} + 2\sqrt{3}$

11. $\sqrt{27} - 2\sqrt{3}$

12. $7\sqrt{50} - 3\sqrt{2}$

13. $\sqrt{45} - \sqrt{20}$

14. $\sqrt{27} - \sqrt{12}$

15. $\sqrt{72} + \sqrt{98}$

16. $\sqrt{45} + \sqrt{80}$

17. $2\sqrt{12} + \sqrt{27} - \sqrt{48}$

18. $9\sqrt{8} - \sqrt{72} + \sqrt{98}$

19. $\sqrt{18} - 3\sqrt{8} + \sqrt{50}$

20. $3\sqrt{18} - 2\sqrt{32} - 5\sqrt{50}$

21. $2\sqrt{27} - 3\sqrt{48} + 3\sqrt{12}$

22. $3\sqrt{48} - 2\sqrt{27} - 3\sqrt{12}$

23. $\sqrt{4x} + \sqrt{81x^3}$

24. $\sqrt{12x^2} + \sqrt{27}$

25. $\sqrt{27} - \sqrt{12x^2}$

26. $\sqrt{81x^3} - \sqrt{4x}$

27. $\sqrt{8x + 8} + \sqrt{2x + 2}$

28. $\sqrt{12x + 12} + \sqrt{3x + 3}$

29. $\sqrt{x^5 - x^2} + \sqrt{9x^3 - 9}$

30. $\sqrt{16x - 16} + \sqrt{25x^3 - 25x^2}$

31. $4a\sqrt{a^2b} + a\sqrt{a^2b^3} - 5\sqrt{b^3}$

32. $3x\sqrt{y^3x} - x\sqrt{yx^3} + y\sqrt{y^3x}$

33. $\sqrt{3} - \sqrt{\dfrac{1}{3}}$

34. $\sqrt{2} - \sqrt{\dfrac{1}{2}}$

35. $5\sqrt{2} + 3\sqrt{\dfrac{1}{2}}$

36. $4\sqrt{3} + 2\sqrt{\dfrac{1}{3}}$

37. $\sqrt{\dfrac{2}{3}} - \sqrt{\dfrac{1}{6}}$

38. $\sqrt{\dfrac{1}{2}} - \sqrt{\dfrac{1}{8}}$

ⓑ Multiply.

39. $\sqrt{3}(\sqrt{5} - 1)$

40. $\sqrt{2}(\sqrt{2} + \sqrt{3})$

41. $(2 + \sqrt{3})(5 - \sqrt{7})$

42. $(\sqrt{5} + \sqrt{7})(2\sqrt{5} - 3\sqrt{7})$

43. $(2 - \sqrt{5})^2$

44. $(\sqrt{3} + \sqrt{10})^2$

45. $(\sqrt{2} + 8)(\sqrt{2} - 8)$

46. $(1 + \sqrt{7})(1 - \sqrt{7})$

47. $(\sqrt{6} - \sqrt{5})(\sqrt{6} + \sqrt{5})$

Copyright © 2012 Pearson Education, Inc.

48. $(\sqrt{3} + \sqrt{10})(\sqrt{3} - \sqrt{10})$ **49.** $(3\sqrt{5} - 2)(\sqrt{5} + 1)$ **50.** $(\sqrt{5} - 2\sqrt{2})(\sqrt{10} - 1)$

51. $(\sqrt{x} - \sqrt{y})^2$ **52.** $(\sqrt{w} + 11)^2$

c   Rationalize the denominator.

53. $\dfrac{2}{\sqrt{3} - \sqrt{5}}$ **54.** $\dfrac{5}{3 + \sqrt{7}}$ **55.** $\dfrac{\sqrt{3} - \sqrt{2}}{\sqrt{3} + \sqrt{2}}$ **56.** $\dfrac{2 - \sqrt{7}}{\sqrt{3} - \sqrt{2}}$

57. $\dfrac{4}{\sqrt{10} + 1}$ **58.** $\dfrac{6}{\sqrt{11} - 3}$ **59.** $\dfrac{1 - \sqrt{7}}{3 + \sqrt{7}}$ **60.** $\dfrac{2 + \sqrt{8}}{1 - \sqrt{5}}$

61. $\dfrac{3}{4 + \sqrt{x}}$ **62.** $\dfrac{8}{2 - \sqrt{x}}$ **63.** $\dfrac{3 + \sqrt{2}}{8 - \sqrt{x}}$ **64.** $\dfrac{4 - \sqrt{3}}{6 + \sqrt{y}}$

65. $\dfrac{\sqrt{a} - 1}{1 + \sqrt{a}}$ **66.** $\dfrac{12 + \sqrt{w}}{\sqrt{w} - 12}$ **67.** $\dfrac{4 + \sqrt{3}}{\sqrt{a} - \sqrt{t}}$ **68.** $\dfrac{\sqrt{2} - 1}{\sqrt{w} + \sqrt{b}}$

Skill Maintenance

Solve.

69. $3x + 5 + 2(x - 3) = 4 - 6x$ [8.3c]   **70.** $3(x - 4) - 2 = 8(2x + 3)$ [8.3c]

71. $x^2 - 5x = 6$ [11.7b]   **72.** $x^2 + 10 = 7x$ [11.7b]

Multiply and simplify.   [12.1d]

73. $\dfrac{7x^9}{27} \cdot \dfrac{9}{7x^3}$ **74.** $\dfrac{3}{x^2 - 9} \cdot \dfrac{x^2 - 6x + 9}{12}$

75. Continental Divide. The Continental Divide in the Americas divides the flow of water between the Pacific Ocean and the Atlantic Ocean. The Continental Divide National Scenic Trail in the United States runs through five states: Montana, Idaho, Wyoming, Colorado, and New Mexico. The Trail's highest altitude is 9990 ft higher than its lowest altitude of 4280 ft. What is the highest altitude of the Trail?   [8.6a]

Source: www.continental-divide.net

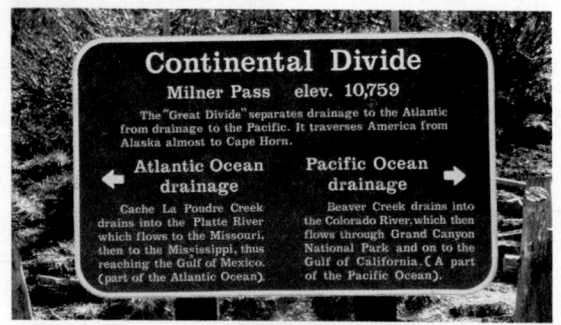

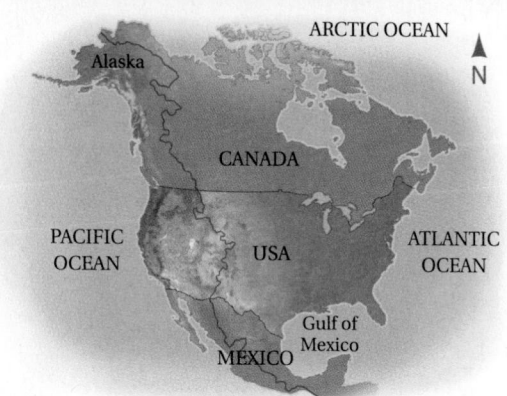

76. The graph of the polynomial equation

$$y = x^3 - 5x^2 + x - 2$$

is shown below. Use either the graph or the equation to estimate or find the value of the polynomial when $x = -1$, $x = 0$, $x = 1$, $x = 3$, and $x = 4.85$.   [10.3a]

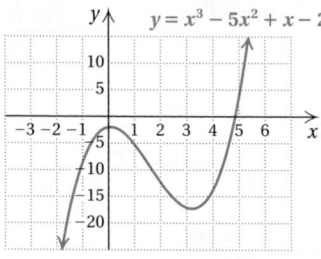

Synthesis

77. Evaluate $\sqrt{a^2 + b^2}$ and $\sqrt{a^2} + \sqrt{b^2}$ when $a = 2$ and $b = 3$.

78. On the basis of Exercise 77, determine whether $\sqrt{a^2 + b^2}$ and $\sqrt{a^2} + \sqrt{b^2}$ are equivalent.

Use the TABLE feature to determine whether each of the following is correct.

79. $\sqrt{9x^3} + \sqrt{x} = \sqrt{9x^3 + x}$

80. $\sqrt{x^2 + 4} = x + 2$

Add or subtract as indicated.

81. $\frac{3}{5}\sqrt{24} + \frac{2}{5}\sqrt{150} - \sqrt{96}$

82. $\frac{1}{3}\sqrt{27} + \sqrt{8} + \sqrt{300} - \sqrt{18} - \sqrt{162}$

Determine whether each of the following is true. Show why or why not.

83. $(3\sqrt{x + 2})^2 = 9(x + 2)$

84. $(\sqrt{x + 2})^2 = x + 2$

Copyright © 2012 Pearson Education, Inc.

Translating
for Success

1. *Coin Mixture.* A collection of nickels and quarters is worth $9.35. There are 59 coins in all. How many of each coin are there?

2. *Diagonal of a Square.* Find the length of a diagonal of a square whose sides are 8 ft long.

3. *Shoveling Time.* It takes Mark 55 min to shovel 4 in. of snow from his driveway. It takes Eric 75 min to do the same job. How long would it take if they worked together?

4. *Angles of a Triangle.* The second angle of a triangle is three times as large as the first. The third is 17° less than the sum of the other angles. Find the measures of the angles.

5. *Perimeter.* The perimeter of a rectangle is 568 ft. The length is 26 ft greater than the width. Find the length and the width.

The goal of these matching questions is to practice step (2), *Translate*, of the five-step problem-solving process. Translate each word problem to an equation or a system of equations and select a correct translation from equations A–O.

A. $5x + 25y = 9.35,$
$x + y = 59$

B. $4^2 + x^2 = 8^2$

C. $x(x + 26) = 568$

D. $8 = x \cdot 24$

E. $\dfrac{75}{x} = \dfrac{105}{x + 5}$

F. $\dfrac{75}{x} = \dfrac{55}{x + 5}$

G. $2x + 2(x + 26) = 568$

H. $x + 3x + (x + 3x - 17) = 180$

I. $x + 3x + (3x - 17) = 180$

J. $0.05x + 0.25y = 9.35,$
$x + y = 59$

K. $8^2 + 8^2 = x^2$

L. $x^2 + (x + 26)^2 = 568$

M. $x - 5\% \cdot x = 8568$

N. $\dfrac{1}{55} + \dfrac{1}{75} = \dfrac{1}{x}$

O. $x + 5\% \cdot x = 8568$

Answers on page A-34

---

6. *Car Travel.* One horse travels 75 km in the same time that a horse traveling 5 km/h faster travels 105 km. Find the speed of each horse.

7. *Money Borrowed.* Emma borrows some money at 5% simple interest. After 1 year, $8568 pays off her loan. How much did she originally borrow?

8. *TV Time.* The average amount of time per day that TV sets in the United States are turned on is 8 hr. What percent of the time are our TV sets on?
Source: Nielsen Media Research

9. *Ladder Height.* An 8-ft plank is leaning against a shed. The bottom of the plank is 4 ft from the building. How high is the top of the plank?

10. *Lengths of a Rectangle.* The area of a rectangle is 568 ft². The length is 26 ft greater than the width. Find the length and the width.

Summary and Review

Key Terms and Formulas

square root, p. 1046
principal square root, p. 1046
radical symbol, p. 1046
square root symbol, p. 1046
radical expression, p. 1048

radicand, p. 1048
complex numbers, p. 1048
rationalizing the denominator, p. 1063
like radicals, p. 1071

conjugates, p. 1073
right triangle, p. 1087
hypotenuse, p. 1087
leg, p. 1087

Product Rule for Radicals: $\sqrt{A}\sqrt{B} = \sqrt{AB}$

Quotient Rule for Radicals: $\dfrac{\sqrt{A}}{\sqrt{B}} = \sqrt{\dfrac{A}{B}}$

Principle of Squaring: If an equation $a = b$ is true, then the equation $a^2 = b^2$ is true.

Pythagorean Equation: $a^2 + b^2 = c^2$, where a and b are the lengths of the legs of a right triangle and c is the length of the hypotenuse.

Concept Reinforcement

Determine whether each statement is true or false.

_____ 1. When both sides of an equation are squared, the new equation may have solutions that the first equation does not.   [14.5a]

_____ 2. The square root of a sum is not the sum of the square roots.   [14.2c]

_____ 3. If an equation $a = b$ is true, then the equation $a^2 = b^2$ is true.   [14.5a]

_____ 4. If an equation $a^2 = b^2$ is true, then the equation $a = b$ is true.   [14.5a]

Important Concepts

Objective 14.1d   Identify radicands of radical expressions.

Example   Identify the radicand in each expression.

a) $\sqrt{a} + \dfrac{1}{4}$ b) $2x\sqrt{\dfrac{x-1}{x+4}}$

a) The radicand in $\sqrt{a} + \dfrac{1}{4}$ is a.

b) The radicand in $2x\sqrt{\dfrac{x-1}{x+4}}$ is $\dfrac{x-1}{x+4}$.

Practice Exercise

1. Identify the radicand in the radical expression $10y + \sqrt{y^2 - 3}$.

Objective 14.1e   Determine whether a radical expression represents a real number.

Example   Determine whether each expression represents a real number.

a) $\sqrt{-11}$ b) $-\sqrt{134}$

a) The radicand, -11, is negative; $\sqrt{-11}$ *is not* a real number.

b) The radicand, 134, is positive; $-\sqrt{134}$ *is* a real number.

Practice Exercise

2. Determine whether each expression represents a real number. Write "yes" or "no."

a) $-\sqrt{-(-3)}$ b) $\sqrt{-200}$

Objective 14.2a Simplify radical expressions.

Example Simplify by factoring: $\sqrt{162x^2}$.
$$\sqrt{162x^2} = \sqrt{81 \cdot 2 \cdot x^2}$$
$$= \sqrt{81}\sqrt{x^2}\sqrt{2} = 9x\sqrt{2}$$

Practice Exercise

3. Simplify by factoring: $\sqrt{1200y^2}$.

Objective 14.2b Simplify radical expressions where radicands are powers.

Example Simplify by factoring: $\sqrt{98x^7y^8}$.
$$\sqrt{98x^7y^8} = \sqrt{49 \cdot 2 \cdot x^6 \cdot x \cdot y^8}$$
$$= \sqrt{49}\sqrt{x^6}\sqrt{y^8}\sqrt{2x} = 7x^3y^4\sqrt{2x}$$

Practice Exercise

4. Simplify by factoring: $\sqrt{175a^{12}b^9}$.

Objective 14.2c Multiply radical expressions and, if possible, simplify.

Example Multiply and then, if possible, simplify:
$\sqrt{6cd^3}\sqrt{30c^3d^2}$.
$$\sqrt{6cd^3}\sqrt{30c^3d^2} = \sqrt{6cd^3 \cdot 30c^3d^2}$$
$$= \sqrt{2 \cdot 3 \cdot 2 \cdot 3 \cdot 5 \cdot c^4 \cdot d^4 \cdot d}$$
$$= \sqrt{4}\sqrt{9}\sqrt{c^4}\sqrt{d^4}\sqrt{5d}$$
$$= 2 \cdot 3 \cdot c^2 \cdot d^2 \cdot \sqrt{5d}$$
$$= 6c^2d^2\sqrt{5d}$$

Practice Exercise

5. Multiply and then, if possible, simplify:
$\sqrt{8x^3y}\sqrt{12x^4y^3}$.

Objective 14.3a Divide radical expressions.

Example Divide and simplify: $\dfrac{\sqrt{108y^5}}{\sqrt{3y^2}}$.

$$\frac{\sqrt{108y^5}}{\sqrt{3y^2}} = \sqrt{\frac{108y^5}{3y^2}} = \sqrt{36y^3}$$
$$= \sqrt{36 \cdot y^2 \cdot y} = \sqrt{36}\sqrt{y^2}\sqrt{y} = 6y\sqrt{y}$$

Practice Exercise

6. Divide and simplify: $\dfrac{\sqrt{15b^7}}{\sqrt{5b^4}}$.

Objective 14.3b Simplify square roots of quotients.

Example Simplify: $\sqrt{\dfrac{320}{500}}$.

$$\sqrt{\frac{320}{500}} = \sqrt{\frac{16 \cdot 20}{25 \cdot 20}} = \sqrt{\frac{16}{25} \cdot \frac{20}{20}}$$
$$= \sqrt{\frac{16}{25} \cdot 1} = \sqrt{\frac{16}{25}} = \frac{\sqrt{16}}{\sqrt{25}} = \frac{4}{5}$$

Practice Exercise

7. Simplify: $\sqrt{\dfrac{50}{162}}$.

Objective 14.3c Rationalize the denominator of a radical expression.

Example Rationalize the denominator: $\dfrac{7x}{\sqrt{18}}$.

$$\frac{7x}{\sqrt{18}} = \frac{7x}{\sqrt{2 \cdot 3 \cdot 3}} \cdot \frac{\sqrt{2}}{\sqrt{2}}$$
$$= \frac{7x \cdot \sqrt{2}}{\sqrt{2 \cdot 3 \cdot 3} \cdot \sqrt{2}} = \frac{7x\sqrt{2}}{\sqrt{2 \cdot 3 \cdot 3 \cdot 2}}$$
$$= \frac{7x\sqrt{2}}{\sqrt{36}} = \frac{7x\sqrt{2}}{6}$$

Practice Exercise

8. Rationalize the denominator: $\dfrac{2a}{\sqrt{50}}$.

Objective 14.4a Add or subtract with radical notation, using the distributive laws to simplify.

Example Add and, if possible, simplify.
$$\sqrt{9x - 18} + \sqrt{16x^3 - 32x^2}.$$

$\sqrt{9x - 18} + \sqrt{16x^3 - 32x^2}$
$= \sqrt{9(x - 2)} + \sqrt{16x^2(x - 2)}$
$= \sqrt{9}\sqrt{x - 2} + \sqrt{16x^2}\sqrt{x - 2}$
$= 3\sqrt{x - 2} + 4x\sqrt{x - 2}$
$= (3 + 4x)\sqrt{x - 2}$

Practice Exercise

9. Add and, if possible, simplify:
$$\sqrt{x^3 - x^2} + \sqrt{36x - 36}.$$

Objective 14.4b Multiply expressions involving radicals, where some of the expressions contain more than one term.

Example Multiply: $(\sqrt{3} + 4\sqrt{5})(\sqrt{3} - \sqrt{5})$.
$(\sqrt{3} + 4\sqrt{5})(\sqrt{3} - \sqrt{5})$
$= \sqrt{3} \cdot \sqrt{3} - \sqrt{3} \cdot \sqrt{5} + 4\sqrt{5} \cdot \sqrt{3} - 4\sqrt{5} \cdot \sqrt{5}$
$= 3 - \sqrt{15} + 4\sqrt{15} - 4 \cdot 5$
$= 3 - \sqrt{15} + 4\sqrt{15} - 20 = 3\sqrt{15} - 17$

Practice Exercise

10. Multiply: $(\sqrt{13} - \sqrt{2})(\sqrt{13} + 2\sqrt{2})$.

Objective 14.4c Rationalize denominators having two terms.

Example Rationalize the denominator: $\dfrac{1 + \sqrt{3}}{5 - \sqrt{3}}$.

$\dfrac{1 + \sqrt{3}}{5 - \sqrt{3}} = \dfrac{1 + \sqrt{3}}{5 - \sqrt{3}} \cdot \dfrac{5 + \sqrt{3}}{5 + \sqrt{3}}$

$= \dfrac{(1 + \sqrt{3})(5 + \sqrt{3})}{(5 - \sqrt{3})(5 + \sqrt{3})}$

$= \dfrac{1 \cdot 5 + 1 \cdot \sqrt{3} + 5 \cdot \sqrt{3} + (\sqrt{3})^2}{5^2 - (\sqrt{3})^2}$

$= \dfrac{5 + \sqrt{3} + 5\sqrt{3} + 3}{25 - 3} = \dfrac{8 + 6\sqrt{3}}{22}$

$= \dfrac{2(4 + 3\sqrt{3})}{2 \cdot 11} = \dfrac{4 + 3\sqrt{3}}{11}$

Practice Exercise

11. Rationalize the denominator: $\dfrac{5 - \sqrt{2}}{9 + \sqrt{2}}$.

Review Exercises

Find the square roots. [14.1a]

1. 64

2. 400

Simplify. [14.1a]

3. $\sqrt{36}$

4. $-\sqrt{169}$

Use a calculator to approximate each of the following square roots to three decimal places. [14.1b]

5. $\sqrt{3}$

6. $\sqrt{99}$

7. $-\sqrt{320.12}$

8. $\sqrt{\dfrac{11}{20}}$

9. $-\sqrt{\dfrac{47.3}{11.2}}$

10. $18\sqrt{11 \cdot 43.7}$

Identify the radicand. [14.1d]

11. $\sqrt{x^2 + 4}$

12. $\sqrt{x} + 2$

13. $3\sqrt{4 - x}$

14. $\sqrt{\dfrac{2}{y - 7}}$

Determine whether the expression represents a real number Write " yes" or "no." [14.1e]

15. $-\sqrt{49}$

16. $-\sqrt{-4}$

17. $\sqrt{-36}$

18. $\sqrt{(-3)(-27)}$

Simplify. [14.1f]

19. $\sqrt{m^2}$

20. $\sqrt{(x - 4)^2}$

21. $\sqrt{16x^2}$

22. $\sqrt{4p^2 - 12p + 9}$

Simplify by factoring. [14.2a]

23. $\sqrt{48}$

24. $\sqrt{32t^2}$

25. $\sqrt{t^2 - 14t + 49}$

26. $\sqrt{x^2 + 16x + 64}$

Copyright © 2012 Pearson Education, Inc.

Simplify by factoring. [14.2b]

27. $\sqrt{x^8}$

28. $\sqrt{75a^7}$

Multiply. [14.2c]

29. $\sqrt{3}\sqrt{7}$

30. $\sqrt{x-3}\sqrt{x+3}$

Multiply and simplify. [14.2c]

31. $\sqrt{6}\sqrt{10}$

32. $\sqrt{5x}\sqrt{8x}$

33. $\sqrt{5x}\sqrt{10xy^2}$

34. $\sqrt{20a^3b}\sqrt{5a^2b^2}$

Simplify. [14.3b]

35. $\sqrt{\dfrac{25}{64}}$

36. $\sqrt{\dfrac{49}{t^2}}$

37. $\dfrac{\sqrt{2c^9}}{\sqrt{32c}}$

Rationalize the denominator. [14.3c]

38. $\sqrt{\dfrac{1}{2}}$

39. $\dfrac{\sqrt{x^3}}{\sqrt{15}}$

40. $\sqrt{\dfrac{5}{y}}$

41. $\dfrac{\sqrt{b^9}}{\sqrt{ab^2}}$

42. $\dfrac{\sqrt{27}}{\sqrt{45}}$

43. $\dfrac{\sqrt{45x^2y}}{\sqrt{54y}}$

Simplify. [14.4a]

44. $10\sqrt{5} + 3\sqrt{5}$

45. $\sqrt{80} - \sqrt{45}$

46. $3\sqrt{2} - 5\sqrt{\dfrac{1}{2}}$

Simplify. [14.4b]

47. $(2 + \sqrt{3})^2$

48. $(2 + \sqrt{3})(2 - \sqrt{3})$

49. Rationalize the denominator: [14.4c]

$$\dfrac{4}{2 + \sqrt{3}}.$$

Solve. [14.5a]

50. $\sqrt{x-3} = 7$

51. $\sqrt{5x+3} = \sqrt{2x-1}$

52. $1 + x = \sqrt{1+5x}$

53. Solve: $\sqrt{x} = \sqrt{x-5} + 1$. [14.5b]

Solve. [14.1c], [14.5c]

54. *Speed of a Skidding Car.* The formula $r = 2\sqrt{5L}$ can be used to approximate the speed r, in miles per hour, of a car that has left a skid mark of length L, in feet.

a) What was the speed of a car that left skid marks of length 200 ft?

b) How far will a car skid at 90 mph?

In a right triangle, find the length of the side not given. Give an exact answer and an approximation to three decimal places where appropriate. Standard lettering has been used. [14.6a]

55. $a = 15$, $c = 25$

56. $a = 1$, $b = \sqrt{2}$

Solve. [14.6b]

57. *Airplane Descent.* A pilot is instructed to descend from 30,000 ft to 20,000 ft over a horizontal distance of 50,000 ft. What distance will the plane travel during this descent?

30,000 ft
20,000 ft
50,000 ft

58. *Lookout Tower.* The diagonal braces in a lookout tower are 15 ft long and span a distance of 12 ft. How high does each brace reach vertically?

12 ft

15 ft

59. Solve: $x - 2 = \sqrt{4 - 9x}$. [14.5a]

   A. -5 **B.** No solution

   C. 0 **D.** $0, -5$

60. Simplify: $(2\sqrt{7} + \sqrt{2})(\sqrt{7} - \sqrt{2})$. [14.4b]

   A. $12 - \sqrt{7}$ **B.** 12

   C. $12 - \sqrt{14}$ **D.** $3\sqrt{7} - 2$

Synthesis

61. *Distance Driven.* Two cars leave a service station at the same time. One car travels east at a speed of 50 mph, and the other travels south at a speed of 60 mph. After one-half hour, how far apart are they? [14.6b]

50 mph

60 mph

62. Solve $A = \sqrt{a^2 + b^2}$ for b. [14.5a]

63. Find x. [14.6a]

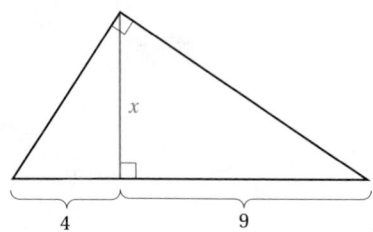

x

4   9

Understanding Through Discussion and Writing

1. Explain why it is necessary for the signs within a pair of conjugates to differ. [14.4c]

2. Determine whether the statement below is true or false and explain your answer. [14.1a], [14.5a]

    The solution of $\sqrt{11 - 2x} = -3$ is 1.

3. Why are the rules for manipulating expressions with exponents important when simplifying radical expressions? [14.2b]

4. Can a carpenter use a 28-ft ladder to repair clapboard that is 28 ft above ground level? Why or why not? [14.6b]

5. Explain why possible solutions of radical equations must be checked. [14.5a]

6. Determine whether each of the following is true for all real numbers. Explain why or why not. [14.1f], [14.2a]

   a) $\sqrt{5x^2} = |x|\sqrt{5}$

   b) $\sqrt{b^2 - 4} = b - 2$

   c) $\sqrt{x^2 + 16} = x + 4$

Copyright © 2012 Pearson Education, Inc.

Test

For Extra Help

CHAPTER
Test Prep
VIDEOS

Step-by-step test solutions are found on the Chapter Test Prep Videos available via the Video Resources on DVD, in *MyMathLab* , and on YouTube (search "BittingerDevMath" and click on "Channels").

1. Find the square roots of 81.

Simplify.

2. $\sqrt{64}$

3. $-\sqrt{25}$

Approximate the expression involving square roots to three decimal places.

4. $\sqrt{116}$

5. $-\sqrt{87.4}$

6. $4\sqrt{5 \cdot 6}$

7. Identify the radicand in $8\sqrt{4 - y^3}$.

Determine whether each expression represents a real number. Write "yes" or "no."

8. $\sqrt{24}$

9. $\sqrt{-23}$

Simplify.

10. $\sqrt{a^2}$

11. $\sqrt{36y^2}$

Multiply.

12. $\sqrt{5}\sqrt{6}$

13. $\sqrt{x - 8}\sqrt{x + 8}$

Simplify by factoring.

14. $\sqrt{27}$

15. $\sqrt{25x - 25}$

16. $\sqrt{t^5}$

Multiply and simplify.

17. $\sqrt{5}\sqrt{10}$

18. $\sqrt{3ab}\sqrt{6ab^3}$

Simplify.

19. $\sqrt{\dfrac{27}{12}}$

20. $\sqrt{\dfrac{144}{a^2}}$

Rationalize the denominator.

21. $\sqrt{\dfrac{2}{5}}$

22. $\sqrt{\dfrac{2x}{y}}$

Divide and simplify.

23. $\dfrac{\sqrt{27}}{\sqrt{32}}$

24. $\dfrac{\sqrt{35x}}{\sqrt{80xy^2}}$

Add or subtract.

25. $3\sqrt{18} - 5\sqrt{18}$

26. $\sqrt{5} + \sqrt{\dfrac{1}{5}}$

Simplify.

27. $(4 - \sqrt{5})^2$

28. $(4 - \sqrt{5})(4 + \sqrt{5})$

29. Rationalize the denominator: $\dfrac{10}{4 - \sqrt{5}}$.

30. In a right triangle, $a = 8$ and $b = 4$. Find c. Give an exact answer and an approximation to three decimal places.

Solve.

31. $\sqrt{3x} + 2 = 14$

32. $\sqrt{6x + 13} = x + 3$

33. $\sqrt{1 - x} + 1 = \sqrt{6 - x}$

34. *Sighting to the Horizon.* The equation $D = \sqrt{2h}$ can be used to approximate the distance D, in miles, that a person can see to the horizon from a height h, in feet.

  a) How far to the horizon can you see through an airplane window at a height of 28,000 ft?

  b) Christina can see about 261 mi to the horizon through an airplane window. How high is the airplane?

35. *Lacrosse.* A regulation lacrosse field is 60 yd wide and 110 yd long. Find the length of a diagonal of such a field.

36. Rationalize the denominator: $\sqrt{\dfrac{2a}{5b}}$.

  A. $\dfrac{\sqrt{10ab}}{5b}$

  B. $\dfrac{a}{b}\sqrt{\dfrac{2b}{5a}}$

  C. $\dfrac{\sqrt{10}}{5}$

  D. $\dfrac{\sqrt{6a^3b}}{15ab}$

Synthesis

Simplify.

37. $\sqrt{\sqrt{\sqrt{625}}}$

38. $\sqrt{y^{16n}}$

Copyright © 2012 Pearson Education, Inc.

Appendixes

A

OBJECTIVES

a Convert from one American unit of length to another.

b Convert from one metric unit of length to another.

c Convert between American units of length and metric units of length.

Use the unit below to measure the length of each segment or object.

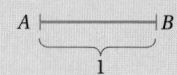

1.

2.

3.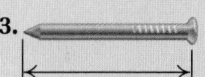

4.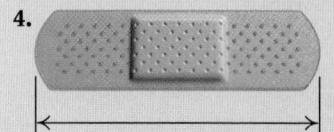

Linear Measures: American Units and Metric Units

Length, or distance, is one kind of measure. To find lengths, we start with some **unit segment** and assign to it a measure of 1. Suppose $\overline{AB}$ below is a unit segment.

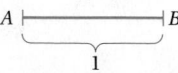

Let's measure segment $\overline{CD}$ below, using $\overline{AB}$ as our unit segment.

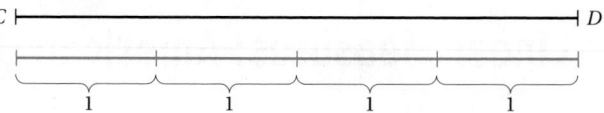

Since we can place 4 unit segments end to end along $\overline{CD}$, the measure of $\overline{CD}$ is 4.

Sometimes we need to use parts of units, called **subunits**. For example, the measure of the segment $\overline{MN}$ below is $1\frac{1}{2}$. We place one unit segment and one half-unit segment end to end.

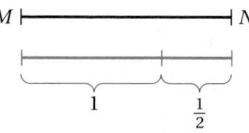

Do Exercises 1–4.

a American Measures

American units of length are related as follows.

AMERICAN UNITS OF LENGTH	
12 inches (in.) = 1 foot (ft)	3 feet = 1 yard (yd)
36 inches = 1 yard	5280 feet = 1 mile (mi)

(Actual size, in inches)

Answers

1. 2   **2.** 3   **3.** $1\frac{1}{2}$ **4.** $2\frac{1}{2}$

We can visualize comparisons of the units as follows:

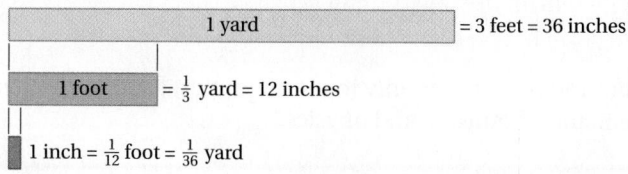

The symbolism 13 in. = 13″ and 27 ft = 27′ is also used for inches and feet. American units have also been called "English," or "British–American," because at one time they were used by both countries. Today, both Canada and England have officially converted to the metric system.

To change from certain American units to others, we make substitutions. Such a substitution is usually helpful when we are converting from a *larger* unit to a *smaller* one.

EXAMPLE 1 Complete: $7\frac{1}{3}$ yd = _____ in.

$$7\frac{1}{3}\,\text{yd} = 7\frac{1}{3} \times 1\,\text{yd} \qquad \text{We think of } 7\frac{1}{3}\,\text{yd as } 7\frac{1}{3} \times \text{yd, or } 7\frac{1}{3} \times 1\,\text{yd.}$$

$$= 7\frac{1}{3} \times 36\,\text{in.} \qquad \text{Substituting 36 in. for 1 yd}$$

$$= \frac{22}{3} \times 36\,\text{in.}$$

$$= 264\,\text{in.}$$

Do Exercises 5–7.

<aside>
Complete.

5. 8 yd = _____ in.

6. $2\frac{5}{6}$ yd = _____ ft

7. 3.8 mi = _____ in.
</aside>

Sometimes it helps to use multiplying by 1 in making conversions. For example, 12 in. = 1 ft, so

$$\frac{12\,\text{in.}}{1\,\text{ft}} = 1 \quad \text{and} \quad \frac{1\,\text{ft}}{12\,\text{in.}} = 1.$$

If we divide 12 in. by 1 ft or 1 ft by 12 in., we get 1 because the lengths are the same. Let's first convert from *smaller* units to *larger* units.

EXAMPLE 2 Complete: 48 in. = _____ ft.

We want to convert from "in." to "ft." We multiply by 1 using a symbol for 1 with "in." on the bottom and "ft" on the top to eliminate inches and to convert to feet:

$$48\,\text{in.} = \frac{48\,\text{in.}}{1} \times \frac{1\,\text{ft}}{12\,\text{in.}} \qquad \text{Multiplying by 1 using } \frac{1\,\text{ft}}{12\,\text{in.}} \text{ to eliminate in.}$$

$$= \frac{48\,\text{in.}}{12\,\text{in.}} \times 1\,\text{ft}$$

$$= \frac{48}{12} \times \frac{\text{in.}}{\text{in.}} \times 1\,\text{ft}$$

$$= 4 \times 1\,\text{ft} \qquad \text{The } \frac{\text{in.}}{\text{in.}} \text{ acts like 1, so we can omit it.}$$

$$= 4\,\text{ft.}$$

<aside>
Answers

5. 288   **6.** $8\frac{1}{2}$ **7.** 240,768
</aside>

We can also look at this conversion as "canceling" units:

$$48 \text{ in.} = \frac{48 \text{ in.}}{1} \times \frac{1 \text{ ft}}{12 \text{ in.}} = \frac{48}{12} \times 1 \text{ ft} = 4 \text{ ft.}$$

This method is used not only in mathematics, as here, but also in fields such as medicine, chemistry, and physics.

Do Exercises 8 and 9.

EXAMPLE 3 Complete: 25 ft = _____ yd.

Since we are converting from "ft" to "yd," we choose a symbol for 1 with "yd" on the top and "ft" on the bottom:

$$25 \text{ ft} = 25 \text{ ft} \times \frac{1 \text{ yd}}{3 \text{ ft}} \qquad 3 \text{ ft} = 1 \text{ yd, so } \frac{3 \text{ ft}}{1 \text{ yd}} = 1 \text{ and } \frac{1 \text{ yd}}{3 \text{ ft}} = 1.$$

We use $\dfrac{1 \text{ yd}}{3 \text{ ft}}$ to eliminate ft.

$$= \frac{25}{3} \times \frac{\text{ft}}{\text{ft}} \times 1 \text{ yd}$$

$$= 8\frac{1}{3} \times 1 \text{ yd} \qquad \text{The } \frac{\text{ft}}{\text{ft}} \text{ acts like 1, so we can omit it.}$$

$$= 8\frac{1}{3} \text{ yd, or } 8.\overline{3} \text{ yd.}$$

Again, in this example, we can consider conversion from the point of view of canceling:

$$25 \text{ ft} = 25 \text{ ft} \times \frac{1 \text{ yd}}{3 \text{ ft}} = \frac{25}{3} \times 1 \text{ yd} = 8\frac{1}{3} \text{ yd, or } 8.\overline{3} \text{ yd.}$$

Do Exercises 10 and 11.

EXAMPLE 4 Complete: 23,760 ft = _____ mi.

We choose a symbol for 1 with "mi" on the top and "ft" on the bottom:

$$23,760 \text{ ft} = 23,760 \text{ ft} \times \frac{1 \text{ mi}}{5280 \text{ ft}} \qquad 5280 \text{ ft} = 1 \text{ mi, so } \frac{1 \text{ mi}}{5280 \text{ ft}} = 1.$$

$$= \frac{23,760}{5280} \times \frac{\text{ft}}{\text{ft}} \times 1 \text{ mi}$$

$$= 4.5 \times 1 \text{ mi} \qquad\qquad \text{Dividing}$$

$$= 4.5 \text{ mi.}$$

Let's also consider this example using canceling:

$$23,760 \text{ ft} = 23,760 \text{ ft} \times \frac{1 \text{ mi}}{5280 \text{ ft}}$$

$$= \frac{23,760}{5280} \times 1 \text{ mi}$$

$$= 4.5 \times 1 \text{ mi} = 4.5 \text{ mi.}$$

Do Exercises 12 and 13.

Complete.
8. 72 in. = _____ ft

9. 17 in. = _____ ft

Complete.
10. 24 ft = _____ yd

11. 35 ft = _____ yd

Complete.
12. 26,400 ft = _____ mi

13. 2640 ft = _____ mi

Answers

8. 6   **9.** $1\frac{5}{12}$ **10.** 8   **11.** $11\frac{2}{3}$, or $11.\overline{6}$

12. 5   **13.** $\frac{1}{2}$, or 0.5

ⓑ Metric Measures

Although the **metric system** is used in most countries of the world, it is used very little in the United States. The metric system does not use inches, feet, pounds, and so on, but units for time and electricity are the same as those used now in the United States.

An advantage of the metric system is that it is easier to convert from one unit to another within this system than within the American system. That is because the metric system is based on the number 10.

The basic unit of length is the **meter**. It is just over a yard. In fact, 1 meter ≈ 1.1 yd.

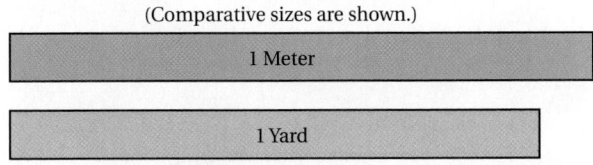

(Comparative sizes are shown.)

1 Meter

1 Yard

The other units of length are multiples of the length of a meter:

10 times a meter,   100 times a meter,   1000 times a meter,   and so on,

or fractions of a meter:

$\frac{1}{10}$ of a meter, $\frac{1}{100}$ of a meter, $\frac{1}{1000}$ of a meter,   and so on.

You should memorize the names and abbreviations listed in the table at right. Think of *kilo-* for 1000, *hecto-* for 100, *deka-* for 10, *deci-* for $\frac{1}{10}$, *centi-* for $\frac{1}{100}$, and *milli-* for $\frac{1}{1000}$. (The units dekameter and decimeter are not used often.) We will also use these prefixes when considering units of area, capacity, and mass.

METRIC UNITS OF LENGTH
1 *kilo*meter (km) = 1000 meters (m)
1 *hecto*meter (hm) = 100 meters (m)
1 *deka*meter (dam) = 10 meters (m)
1 meter (m)
1 *deci*meter (dm) = $\frac{1}{10}$ meter (m)
1 *centi*meter (cm) = $\frac{1}{100}$ meter (m)
1 *milli*meter (mm) = $\frac{1}{1000}$ meter (m)

Thinking Metric

To familiarize yourself with metric units, consider the following.

1 kilometer (1000 meters)   is slightly more than $\frac{1}{2}$ mile (0.6 mi).

1 meter   is just over a yard (1.1 yd).

1 centimeter (0.01 meter)   is a little more than the width of a paperclip (about 0.3937 inch).

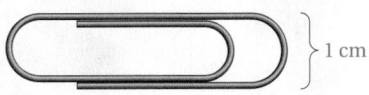

1 cm

1 cm

1 inch is about 2.54 centimeters.

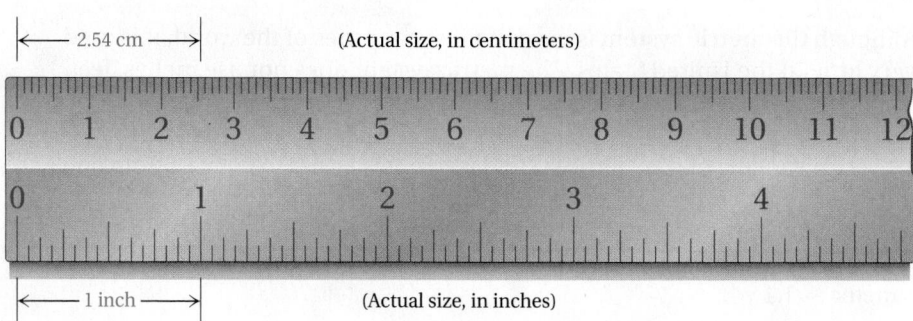

2.54 cm — (Actual size, in centimeters)

1 inch — (Actual size, in inches)

Using a centimeter ruler, measure each object.

14.

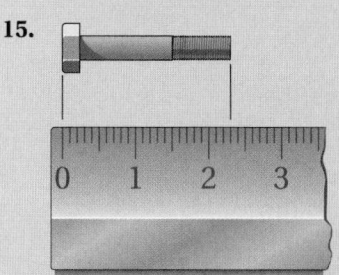

15.

16.

1 millimeter is about the diameter of paperclip wire.

1 mm

The millimeter (mm) is used to measure small distances, especially in industry.

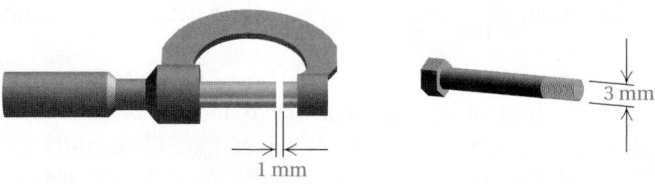

1 mm

3 mm

In many countries, the centimeter (cm) is used for body dimensions and clothing sizes.

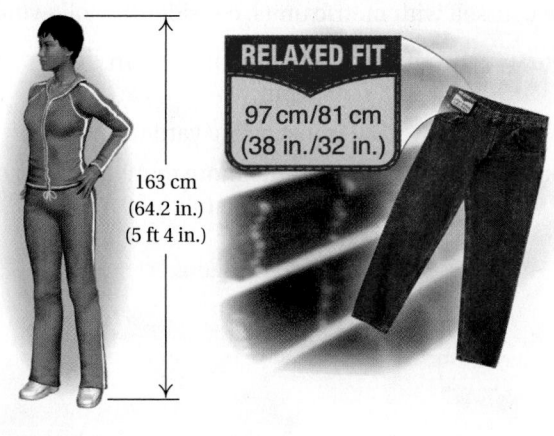

163 cm
(64.2 in.)
(5 ft 4 in.)

RELAXED FIT
97 cm/81 cm
(38 in./32 in.)

Do Exercises 14–16.

Answers

14. 2 cm, or 20 mm   **15.** 2.3 cm, or 23 mm
16. 4.4 cm, or 44 mm

The meter (m) is used for expressing dimensions of larger objects—say, the height of a diving board—and for shorter distances, like the length of a rug.

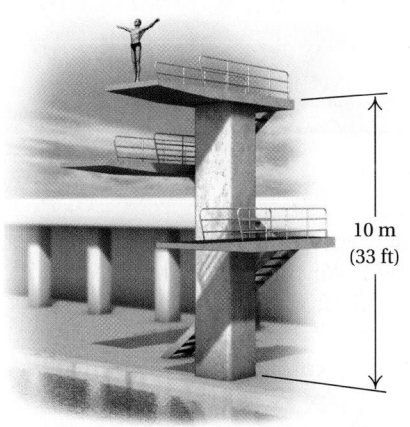

10 m
(33 ft)

3.7 m
(12 ft)

2.7 m
(9 ft)

The kilometer (km) is used for longer distances, mostly in cases in which miles are now being used.

1 mile is about 1.6 km.

| 1 km |
| 1 mi |

Do Exercises 17–22.

As with American units, when changing from a *larger* unit to a *smaller* unit, we usually make substitutions.

EXAMPLE 5 Complete: 4 km = _____ m.

Since we are converting from a *larger* unit to a *smaller* unit, we use substitution.

$$4 \text{ km} = 4 \times 1 \text{ km}$$
$$= 4 \times 1000 \text{ m} \quad \text{Substituting 1000 m for 1 km}$$
$$= 4000 \text{ m}$$

Do Exercises 23 and 24.

Since

$$\frac{1}{10} \text{ m} = 1 \text{ dm}, \quad \frac{1}{100} \text{ m} = 1 \text{ cm}, \quad \text{and} \quad \frac{1}{1000} \text{ m} = 1 \text{ mm},$$

it follows that

$$1 \text{ m} = 10 \text{ dm}, \quad 1 \text{ m} = 100 \text{ cm}, \quad \text{and} \quad 1 \text{ m} = 1000 \text{ mm}.$$

EXAMPLE 6 Complete: 93.4 m = _____ cm.

Since we are converting from a *larger* unit to a *smaller* unit, we use substitution. We substitute 100 cm for 1 m:

$$93.4 \text{ m} = 93.4 \times 1 \text{ m} = 93.4 \times 100 \text{ cm} = 9340 \text{ cm}.$$

Complete with mm, cm, m, or km.

17. A stick of gum is 7 _____ long.

18. New Orleans is 2941 _____ from San Diego.

19. A penny is 1 _____ thick.

20. The halfback ran 7 _____.

21. The book is 3 _____ thick.

22. The desk is 2 _____ long.

Complete.

23. 23 km = _____ m

24. 4 hm = _____ m

Answers

17. cm   18. km   19. mm   20. m
21. cm   22. m   23. 23,000   24. 400

EXAMPLE 7 Complete: 0.248 m = _____ mm.

Since we are converting from a *larger* unit to a *smaller* unit, we use substitution.

$$0.248 \text{ m} = 0.248 \times 1 \text{ m}$$
$$= 0.248 \times 1000 \text{ mm} \quad \text{Substituting 1000 mm for 1 m}$$
$$= 248 \text{ mm}$$

Do Exercises 25 and 26.

Complete.

25. 1.78 m = _____ cm

26. 9.04 m = _____ mm

We now convert from "m" to "km." Since we are converting from a *smaller* unit to a *larger* unit, we use multiplying by 1. We choose a symbol for 1 with "km" in the numerator and "m" in the denominator.

EXAMPLE 8 Complete: 2347 m = _____ km.

$$2347 \text{ m} = 2347 \text{ m} \times \frac{1 \text{ km}}{1000 \text{ m}} \quad \text{Multiplying by 1 using } \frac{1 \text{ km}}{1000 \text{ m}}$$

$$= \frac{2347}{1000} \times \frac{\text{m}}{\text{m}} \times 1 \text{ km} \quad \text{The } \frac{\text{m}}{\text{m}} \text{ acts like 1, so we omit it.}$$

$$= 2.347 \text{ km} \quad \begin{array}{l}\text{Dividing by 1000 moves the decimal} \\ \text{point three places to the left.}\end{array}$$

Using canceling, we can work this example as follows:

$$2347 \text{ m} = 2347 \text{ m̶} \times \frac{1 \text{ km}}{1000 \text{ m̶}} = \frac{2347}{1000} \times 1 \text{ km} = 2.347 \text{ km}.$$

Sometimes we multiply by 1 more than once.

EXAMPLE 9 Complete: 8.42 mm = _____ cm.

$$8.42 \text{ mm} = 8.42 \text{ mm} \times \frac{1 \text{ m}}{1000 \text{ mm}} \times \frac{100 \text{ cm}}{1 \text{ m}} \quad \begin{array}{l}\text{Multiplying by 1 using} \\ \frac{1 \text{ m}}{1000 \text{ mm}} \text{ and } \frac{100 \text{ cm}}{1 \text{ m}}\end{array}$$

$$= \frac{8.42 \times 100}{1000} \times \frac{\text{mm}}{\text{mm}} \times \frac{\text{m}}{\text{m}} \times 1 \text{ cm}$$

$$= \frac{842}{1000} \text{ cm} = 0.842 \text{ cm}$$

Do Exercises 27–30.

Complete.

27. 7814 m = _____ km

28. 7814 m = _____ dam

29. 9.67 mm = _____ cm

30. 89 km = _____ cm

Mental Conversion

Changing from one unit to another in the metric system amounts only to the movement of a decimal point. That is because the metric system is based on 10. Let's find a faster way to convert. Look at the following table.

1000 m	100 m	10 m	1 m	0.1 m	0.01 m	0.001 m
1 km	1 hm	1 dam	1 m	1 dm	1 cm	1 mm

Each place in the table has a value $\frac{1}{10}$ that to the left or 10 times that to the right. Thus moving one place in the table corresponds to moving one decimal place.

Answers

25. 178   **26.** 9040   **27.** 7.814
28. 781.4   **29.** 0.967   **30.** 8,900,000

Let's convert mentally.

EXAMPLE 10   Complete: 8.42 mm = _____ cm.

Think: To go from mm to cm in the table is a move of one place to the left. Thus we move the decimal point one place to the left.

1000 m	100 m	10 m	1 m	0.1 m	0.01 m	0.001 m
1 km	1 hm	1 dam	1 m	1 dm	1 cm	1 mm

1 place to the left

8.42   0.8.42   8.42 mm = 0.842 cm

EXAMPLE 11   Complete: 1.886 km = _____ cm.

Think: To go from km to cm in the table is a move of five places to the right. Thus we move the decimal point five places to the right.

1000 m	100 m	10 m	1 m	0.1 m	0.01 m	0.001 m
1 km	1 hm	1 dam	1 m	1 dm	1 cm	1 mm

5 places to the right

1.886   1.88600.   1.886 km = 188,600 cm

EXAMPLE 12   Complete: 3 m = _____ cm.

Think: To go from m to cm in the table is a move of two places to the right. Thus we move the decimal point two places to the right.

1000 m	100 m	10 m	1 m	0.1 m	0.01 m	0.001 m
1 km	1 hm	1 dam	1 m	1 dm	1 cm	1 mm

2 places to the right

3   3.00.   3 m = 300 cm

You should try to make metric conversions mentally as much as possible. The fact that conversions can be done so easily is an important advantage of the metric system. The most commonly used metric units of length are km, m, cm, and mm. We have purposely used these more often than the others in the exercises.

Do Exercises 31–34.

Complete. Try to do this mentally using the table.

31. 6780 m = _____ km

32. 9.74 cm = _____ mm

33. 1 mm = _____ cm

34. 845.1 mm = _____ dm

Answers

31. 6.78   **32.** 97.4   **33.** 0.1   **34.** 8.451

C Converting Units

We can make conversions between American units and metric units by using the following table. These listings are rounded approximations. Again, we either make a substitution or multiply by 1 appropriately.

AMERICAN	METRIC
1 in.	2.540 cm
1 ft	0.305 m
1 yd	0.914 m
1 mi	1.609 km
0.621 mi	1 km
1.094 yd	1 m
3.281 ft	1 m
39.370 in.	1 m

This table is set up to enable us to make conversions by substitution.

EXAMPLE 13 Complete: 26.2 mi = _____ km.
(The length of the Olympic marathon)

$$26.2 \text{ mi} = 26.2 \times 1 \text{ mi}$$
$$\approx 26.2 \times 1.609 \text{ km} \quad \text{Substituting 1.609 km for 1 mi}$$
$$= 42.1558 \text{ km}$$

EXAMPLE 14 Complete: 2.36 m = _____ in.
(The height of Bao Xishun, the world's tallest man)

$$2.36 \text{ m} = 2.36 \times 1 \text{ m}$$
$$\approx 2.36 \times 39.37 \text{ in.} \quad \text{Substituting 39.37 in. for 1 m}$$
$$= 92.9132 \text{ in.}$$

In an application like this one, the answer would probably be rounded to the nearest one, as 93 in.

EXAMPLE 15 Complete: 100 m = _____ ft.
(The length of the 100-meter dash)

$$100 \text{ m} = 100 \times 1 \text{ m}$$
$$\approx 100 \times 3.281 \text{ ft} \quad \text{Substituting 3.281 ft for 1 m}$$
$$= 328.1 \text{ ft}$$

EXAMPLE 16 Complete: 4544 km = _____ mi.
(The distance from New York to Los Angeles)

$$4544 \text{ km} = 4544 \times 1 \text{ km}$$
$$\approx 4544 \times 0.621 \text{ mi} \qquad \text{Substituting 0.621 mi for 1 km}$$
$$= 2821.824 \text{ mi}$$

In practical situations, we would probably round this answer to 2822 mi.

Do Exercises 35–37.

EXAMPLE 17 *Millau Viaduct.* The Millau viaduct is part of the E11 expressway connecting Paris, France, and Barcelona, Spain. The viaduct has the highest bridge piers ever constructed. The tallest pier is 804 ft high and the overall height including the pylon is 1122 ft, making this the highest bridge in the world. Convert 804 feet and 1122 feet to meters.

Source: www. abelard.org/france/viaduct-de-millau.php

We let P = the height of the pier and H = the overall height of the bridge. To convert feet to meters, we substitute 0.305 m for 1 ft.

$$P = 804 \text{ ft} \qquad\qquad H = 1122 \text{ ft}$$
$$= 804 \times 1 \text{ ft} \qquad\quad = 1122 \times 1 \text{ ft}$$
$$\approx 804 \times 0.305 \text{ m} \quad \approx 1122 \times 0.305 \text{ m}$$
$$= 245.22 \text{ m} \qquad\quad = 342.21 \text{ m}$$

Do Exercises 38 and 39.

EXAMPLE 18 Complete: 0.10414 mm = _____ in.
(The thickness of a $1 bill)

In this case, we must make two substitutions or multiply by two forms of 1 since the table on the preceding page does not provide an easy way to convert from millimeters to inches. Here we choose to multiply by forms of 1.

$$0.10414 \text{ mm} = 0.10414 \times 1 \text{ mm} \times \frac{1 \text{ cm}}{10 \text{ mm}}$$
$$= 0.010414 \text{ cm}$$
$$\approx 0.010414 \times 1 \text{ cm} \times \frac{1 \text{ in.}}{2.54 \text{ cm}}$$
$$= 0.0041 \text{ in.}$$

Do Exercise 40.

Complete.

35. 100 yd = _____ m
(The length of a football field excluding the end zones)

36. 2.5 mi = _____ km
(The length of the tri-oval track at Daytona International Speedway)

37. 2383 km = _____ mi
(The distance from St. Louis to Phoenix)

38. The distance from San Francisco to Las Vegas is 568 mi. Find the distance in kilometers.

39. The height of the Stratosphere Tower in Las Vegas, Nevada, is 1149 ft. Find the height in meters.

40. Complete: 3.175 mm = _____ in.
(The thickness of a quarter)

Answers

35. 91.4   **36.** 4.0225   **37.** 1479.843
38. 913.912   **39.** 350.445 m   **40.** 0.125

a Complete.

1. 1 ft = _____ in.

2. 1 yd = _____ ft

3. 1 in. = _____ ft

4. 1 mi = _____ yd

5. 1 mi = _____ ft

6. 1 ft = _____ yd

7. 3 yd = _____ in.

8. 10 yd = _____ ft

9. 84 in. = _____ ft

10. 48 ft = _____ yd

11. 18 in. = _____ ft

12. 29 ft = _____ yd

13. 5 mi = _____ ft

14. 5 mi = _____ yd

15. 63 in. = _____ ft

16. 11,616 ft = _____ mi

17. 10 ft = _____ yd

18. 9.6 yd = _____ ft

19. 7.1 mi = _____ ft

20. 31,680 ft = _____ mi

21. $4\frac{1}{2}$ ft = _____ yd

22. 48 in. = _____ ft

23. 45 in. = _____ yd

24. $6\frac{1}{3}$ yd = _____ in.

25. 330 ft = _____ yd

26. 5280 yd = _____ mi

27. 3520 yd = _____ mi

28. 25 mi = _____ ft

29. 100 yd = _____ ft

30. 480 in. = _____ ft

31. 360 in. = _____ ft

32. 720 in. = _____ yd

33. 1 in. = _____ yd

34. 25 in. = _____ ft

35. 2 mi = _____ in.

36. 63,360 in. = _____ mi

Copyright © 2012 Pearson Education, Inc.

b Complete. Do as much as possible mentally.

37. a) 1 km = _____ m
    b) 1 m = _____ km

38. a) 1 hm = _____ m
    b) 1 m = _____ hm

39. a) 1 dam = _____ m
    b) 1 m = _____ dam

40. a) 1 dm = _____ m
    b) 1 m = _____ dm

41. a) 1 cm = _____ m
    b) 1 m = _____ cm

42. a) 1 mm = _____ m
    b) 1 m = _____ mm

43. 6.7 km = _____ m

44. 27 km = _____ m

45. 98 cm = _____ m

46. 0.789 cm = _____ m

47. 8921 m = _____ km

48. 8664 m = _____ km

49. 56.66 m = _____ km

50. 4.733 m = _____ km

51. 5666 m = _____ cm

52. 869 m = _____ cm

53. 477 cm = _____ m

54. 6.27 mm = _____ m

55. 6.88 m = _____ cm

56. 6.88 m = _____ dm

57. 1 mm = _____ cm

58. 1 cm = _____ km

59. 1 km = _____ cm

60. 2 km = _____ cm

61. 14.2 cm = _____ mm

62. 25.3 cm = _____ mm

63. 8.2 mm = _____ cm

64. 9.7 mm = _____ cm

65. 4500 mm = _____ cm

66. 8,000,000 m = _____ km

67. 0.024 mm = _____ m

68. 60,000 mm = _____ dam

69. 6.88 m = _____ dam

70. 7.44 m = _____ hm

71. 2.3 dam = _____ dm

72. 9 km = _____ hm

73. 392 dam = _____ km

74. 0.056 mm = _____ dm

Complete the following table.

	OBJECT	MILLIMETERS (mm)	CENTIMETERS (cm)	METERS (m)
75.	Length of a calculator		18	
76.	Width of a calculator	85		
77.	Length of a piece of typing paper			0.278
78.	Length of a football field			109.09
79.	Width of a football field		4844	
80.	Width of a credit card	56		
81.	Length of 4 meter sticks			4
82.	Length of 3 meter sticks		300	
83.	Thickness of an index card	0.27		
84.	Thickness of a piece of cardboard		0.23	
85.	Height of the Willis Tower			442
86.	Height of the CN Tower (Toronto)	553,000		

C Complete.

87. 330 ft = _____ m
(The length of most baseball foul lines)

88. 12 in. = _____ cm
(The length of a common ruler)

89. 1171.4 km = _____ mi
(The distance from Cleveland to Atlanta)

90. 2 m = _____ ft
(The length of a desk)

91. 65 mph = _____ km/h
(A common speed limit in the United States)

92. 100 km/h = _____ mph
(A common speed limit in Canada)

93. 180 mi = _____ km
(The distance from Indianapolis to Chicago)

94. 141,600,000 mi = _____ km
(The farthest distance of Mars from the sun)

95. 70 mph = _____ km/h
(An interstate speed limit in Arizona)

96. 60 km/h = _____ mph
(A city speed limit in Canada)

97. 10 yd = _____ m
(The length needed for a first down in football)

98. 450 ft = _____ m
(The length of a long home run in baseball)

Copyright © 2012 Pearson Education, Inc.

99. 2.08 m = _____ in.
(The height of Amare Stoudemire of the Phoenix Suns)

100. 76 in. = _____ m
(The height of Jason Kidd of the Dallas Mavericks)

101. 381 m = _____ ft
(The height of the Empire State Building)

102. 1127 ft = _____ m
(The height of the John Hancock Center)

103. 15.7 cm = _____ in.
(The length of a $1 bill)

104. 7.5 in. = _____ cm
(The length of a pencil)

105. 2216 km = _____ mi
(The distance from Chicago to Miami)

106. 1862 mi = _____ km
(The distance from Seattle to Kansas City)

107. 13 mm = _____ in.
(The thickness of a plastic case for a DVD)

108. 0.25 in. = _____ mm
(The thickness of an eraser on a pencil)

Complete the following table. Answers may vary, depending on the conversion factor used.

	OBJECT	YARDS (yd)	CENTIMETERS (cm)	INCHES (in.)	METERS (m)	MILLIMETERS (mm)
109.	Width of a piece of typing paper			$8\frac{1}{2}$		
110.	Length of a football field	120				
111.	Width of a football field		4844			
112.	Width of a credit card					56
113.	Length of 4 yardsticks	4				
114.	Length of 3 meter sticks		300			
115.	Thickness of an index card				0.00027	
116.	Thickness of a piece of cardboard		0.23			
117.	Height of the Willis Tower				442	
118.	Height of Central Plaza, Hong Kong	409				

Synthesis

119. Develop a formula to convert from inches to millimeters.

120. Develop a formula to convert from millimeters to inches. How does it relate to the answer for Exercise 119?

Weight and Mass; Medical Applications

OBJECTIVES

a Convert from one American unit of weight to another.

b Convert from one metric unit of mass to another.

c Make conversions and solve applied problems concerning medical dosages.

There is a difference between **mass** and **weight**, but the terms are often used interchangeably. People sometimes use the word "weight" when, technically, they are referring to "mass." Weight is related to the force of gravity. The farther you are from the center of the earth, the less you weigh. Your mass stays the same no matter where you are.

a Weight: The American System

AMERICAN UNITS OF WEIGHT	
1 ton (T) = 2000 pounds (lb)	1 lb = 16 ounces (oz)

The term "ounce" used here for weight is different from the "ounce" we will use for capacity in Appendix C. We convert units of weight using the same techniques that we use with linear measures.

EXAMPLE 1 A well-known hamburger is called a "quarter-pounder." Find its name in ounces: a "_____ ouncer."

Since we are converting from a larger unit to a smaller unit, we use substitution.

$$\frac{1}{4} \text{ lb} = \frac{1}{4} \cdot 1 \text{ lb} = \frac{1}{4} \cdot 16 \text{ oz} \qquad \text{Substituting 16 oz for 1 lb}$$
$$= 4 \text{ oz}$$

A "quarter-pounder" can also be called a "four-ouncer."

EXAMPLE 2 Complete: 15,360 lb = _____ T.

Since we are converting from a smaller unit to a larger unit, we use multiplying by 1.

$$15,360 \text{ lb} = 15,360 \text{ lb} \times \frac{1 \text{ T}}{2000 \text{ lb}} \qquad \text{Multiplying by 1}$$
$$= \frac{15,360}{2000} \text{ T} = 7.68 \text{ T}$$

Do Exercises 1–3.

b Mass: The Metric System

The basic unit of mass is the **gram** (g), which is the mass of 1 cubic centimeter (1 cm^3) of water. Since a cubic centimeter is small, a gram is a small unit of mass.

$$1 \text{ g} = 1 \text{ gram} = \text{the mass of 1 cm}^3 \text{ of water}$$

Complete.

1. 5 lb = _____ oz

2. 8640 lb = _____ T

3. 1 T = _____ oz

1 g = 1 cm³ of water

The table at right lists the metric units of mass. The prefixes are the same as those for length.

Thinking Metric

One gram is about the mass of 1 raisin or 1 package of artificial sweetener. Since 1 kg is about 2.2 lb, 1000 kg is about 2200 lb, or 1 metric ton (t), which is just a little more than 1 American ton (T), which is 2000 lb.

METRIC UNITS OF MASS

1 metric ton (t) = 1000 kilograms (kg)

1 *kilo*gram (kg) = 1000 grams (g)

1 *hecto*gram (hg) = 100 grams (g)

1 *deka*gram (dag) = 10 grams (g)

1 gram (g)

$1\ deci\text{gram (dg)} = \dfrac{1}{10}$ gram (g)

$1\ centi\text{gram (cg)} = \dfrac{1}{100}$ gram (g)

$1\ milli\text{gram (mg)} = \dfrac{1}{1000}$ gram (g)

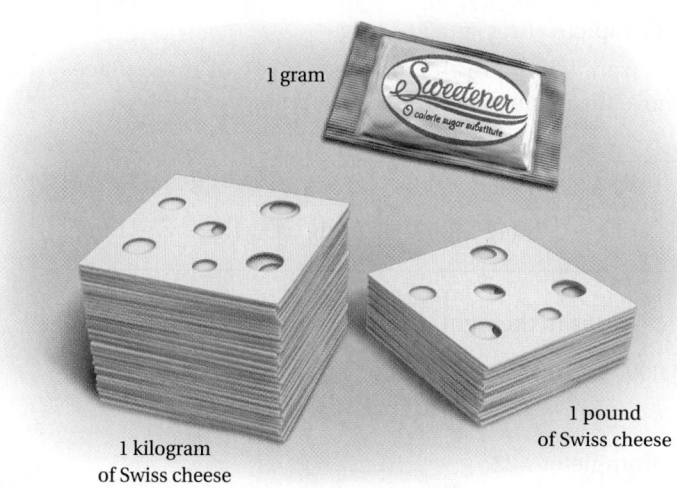

1 gram

1 pound
of Swiss cheese

1 kilogram
of Swiss cheese

Small masses, such as dosages of medicine and vitamins, may be measured in milligrams (mg). The gram (g) is used for objects ordinarily measured in ounces, such as the mass of a letter, a piece of candy, a coin, or a small package of food.

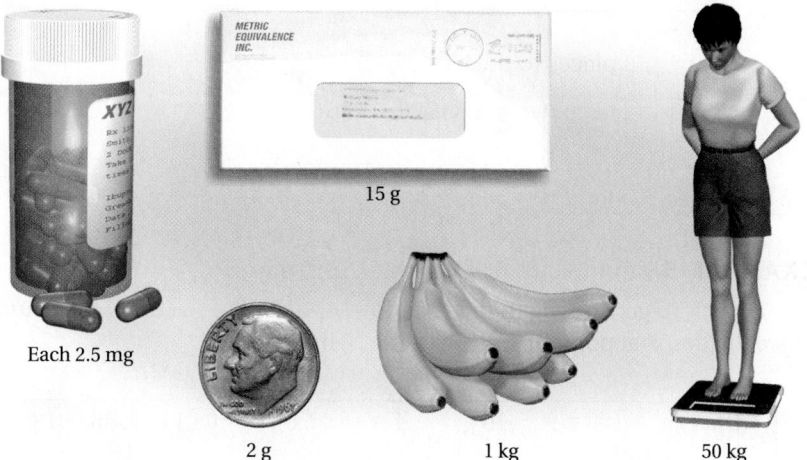

15 g

Each 2.5 mg

2 g

1 kg

50 kg

The kilogram (kg) is used for larger food packages, such as fruit, or for human body mass. The metric ton (t) is used for very large masses, such as the mass of an automobile, a truckload of gravel, or an airplane.

Do Exercises 4–8.

Complete with mg, g, kg, or t.

4. A laptop computer has a mass of 6 _____.

5. Eric has a body mass of 85.4 _____.

6. This is a 3-_____ vitamin.

7. A pen has a mass of 12 _____.

8. A sport utility vehicle has a mass of 3 _____.

Answers

4. kg   **5.** kg   **6.** mg   **7.** g   **8.** t

Changing Units Mentally

As before, changing from one metric unit to another amounts only to the movement of a decimal point. We use this table.

1000 g	100 g	10 g	1 g	0.1 g	0.01 g	0.001 g
1 kg	1 hg	1 dag	1 g	1 dg	1 cg	1 mg

EXAMPLE 3 Complete: 8 kg = _____ g.

Think: To go from kg to g in the table is a move of three places to the right. Thus we move the decimal point three places to the right.

1000 g	100 g	10 g	1 g	0.1 g	0.01 g	0.001 g
1 kg	1 hg	1 dag	1 g	1 dg	1 cg	1 mg

3 places to the right

8.0   8.000.   8 kg = 8000 g

EXAMPLE 4 Complete: 4235 g = _____ kg.

Think: To go from g to kg in the table is a move of three places to the left. Thus we move the decimal point three places to the left.

1000 g	100 g	10 g	1 g	0.1 g	0.01 g	0.001 g
1 kg	1 hg	1 dag	1 g	1 dg	1 cg	1 mg

3 places to the left

4235.0   4.235.0   4235 g = 4.235 kg

Complete.

9. 6.2 kg = _____ g

10. 304.8 cg = _____ g

> Do Exercises 9 and 10.

EXAMPLE 5 Complete: 6.98 cg = _____ mg.

Think: To go from cg to mg is a move of one place to the right. Thus we move the decimal point one place to the right.

1000 g	100 g	10 g	1 g	0.1 g	0.01 g	0.001 g
1 kg	1 hg	1 dag	1 g	1 dg	1 cg	1 mg

1 place to the right

6.98   6.9.8   6.98 cg = 69.8 mg

Answers

9. 6200 **10.** 3.048

The most commonly used metric units of mass are kg, g, cg, and mg. We have purposely used those more than the others in the exercises.

EXAMPLE 6 Complete: 89.21 mg = _____ g.

Think: To go from mg to g is a move of three places to the left. Thus we move the decimal point three places to the left.

1000 g	100 g	10 g	1 g	0.1 g	0.01 g	0.001 g
1 kg	1 hg	1 dag	1 g	1 dg	1 cg	1 mg

3 places to the left

89.21   0.089.21   89.21 mg = 0.08921 g

Do Exercises 11–13.

(C) Medical Applications

Another metric unit that is used in medicine is the microgram (mcg). It is defined as follows.

MICROGRAM

$$1 \text{ microgram} = 1 \text{ mcg} = \frac{1}{1,000,000} \text{ g} = 0.000001 \text{ g}$$

$$1,000,000 \text{ mcg} = 1 \text{ g}$$

EXAMPLE 7 Complete: 1 mg = _____ mcg.

We convert to grams and then to micrograms:

1 mg = 0.001 g

    = 0.001 × 1 g

    = 0.001 × 1,000,000 mcg   Substituting 1,000,000 mcg for 1 g

    = 1000 mcg.

Do Exercise 14.

EXAMPLE 8 *Medical Dosage.* Nitroglycerin sublingual tablets come in 0.4-mg tablets. How many micrograms are in each tablet?
Source: Steven R. Smith, M.D.

We are to complete: 0.4 mg = _____ mcg. Thus,

0.4 mg = 0.4 × 1 mg

    = 0.4 × 1000 mcg   From Example 7, substituting 1000 mcg for 1 mg

    = 400 mcg.

We can also do this problem in a manner similar to Example 7.

Do Exercise 15.

Complete.

11. 7.7 cg = _____ mg

12. 2344 mg = _____ cg

13. 67 dg = _____ mg

14. Complete:
    1 mcg = _____ mg.

15. Medical Dosage. A physician prescribes 500 mcg of alprazolam, an antianxiety medication. How many milligrams is this dosage?
Source: Steven R. Smith, M.D.

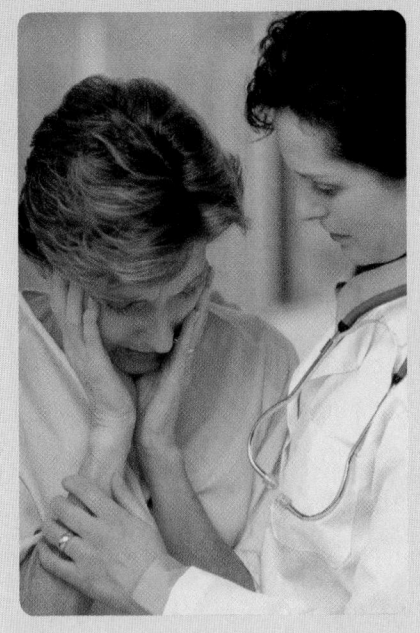

Answers

11. 77   **12.** 234.4   **13.** 6700   **14.** 0.001
15. 0.5 mg

a Complete.

1. 1 T = _____ lb

2. 1 lb = _____ oz

3. 6000 lb = _____ T

4. 8 T = _____ lb

5. 4 lb = _____ oz

6. 10 lb = _____ oz

7. 6.32 T = _____ lb

8. 8.07 T = _____ lb

9. 3200 oz = _____ T

10. 6400 oz = _____ T

11. 80 oz = _____ lb

12. 960 oz = _____ lb

13. *Excelsior.* Western Excelsior is a company that makes a packing material called excelsior. Excelsior is produced from the wood of aspen trees. The largest grove of aspen trees on record contained 13,000,000 tons of aspen. How many pounds of aspen were there?

Source: Western Excelsior Corporation, Mancos, Colorado

14. *Excelsior.* Western Excelsior buys 44,800 tons of aspen each year to make excelsior. How many pounds of aspen does it buy each year?

Source: Western Excelsior Corporation, Mancos, Colorado

b Complete.

15. 1 kg = _____ g

16. 1 hg = _____ g

17. 1 dag = _____ g

18. 1 dg = _____ g

19. 1 cg = _____ g

20. 1 mg = _____ g

21. 1 g = _____ mg

22. 1 g = _____ cg

23. 1 g = _____ dg

24. 25 kg = _____ g

25. 234 kg = _____ g

26. 9403 g = _____ kg

27. 5200 g = _____ kg

28. 1.506 kg = _____ g

29. 67 hg = _____ kg

Copyright © 2012 Pearson Education, Inc.

30. 45 cg = _____ g

31. 0.502 dg = _____ g

32. 0.0025 cg = _____ mg

33. 8492 g = _____ kg

34. 9466 g = _____ kg

35. 585 mg = _____ cg

36. 96.1 mg = _____ cg

37. 8 kg = _____ cg

38. 0.06 kg = _____ mg

39. 1 t = _____ kg

40. 2 t = _____ kg

41. 3.4 cg = _____ dag

42. 115 mg = _____ g

43. 60.3 kg = _____ t

44. 15.68 kg = _____ t

 Complete.

45. 1 mg = _____ mcg

46. 1 mcg = _____ mg

47. 325 mcg = _____ mg

48. 0.45 mg = _____ mcg

49. 210.6 mg = _____ mcg

50. 8000 mcg = _____ mg

51. 4.9 mcg = _____ mg

52. 0.075 mg = _____ mcg

Medical Dosage.   Solve each of the following. (None of these medications should be taken without consulting your own physician.)
Source: Steven R. Smith, M.D.

53. Digoxin is a medication used to treat heart problems. A physician orders 0.125 mg of digoxin to be taken once daily. How many micrograms of digoxin are there in the daily dosage?

54. Digoxin is a medication used to treat heart problems. A physician orders 0.25 mg of digoxin to be taken once a day. How many micrograms of digoxin are there in the daily dosage?

55. Triazolam is a medication used for the short-term treatment of insomnia. A physician advises her patient to take one of the 0.125-mg tablets each night for 7 nights. How many milligrams of triazolam will the patient have ingested over that 7-day period? How many micrograms?

56. Clonidine is a medication used to treat high blood pressure. The usual starting dose of clonidine is one 0.1-mg tablet twice a day. If a patient is started on this dose by his physician, how many total milligrams of clonidine will the patient have taken before he returns to see his physician 14 days later? How many micrograms?

57. Cephalexin is an antibiotic that frequently is prescribed in a 500-mg tablet form. A physician prescribes 2 g of cephalexin per day for a patient with a skin sore. How many 500-mg tablets would have to be taken in order to achieve this daily dosage?

58. Quinidine gluconate is a liquid mixture, part medicine and part water, that is administered intravenously. There are 80 mg of quinidine gluconate in each cubic centimeter (cc) of the liquid mixture. A physician orders 900 mg of quinidine gluconate to be administered daily to a patient with malaria. How much of the solution would have to be administered in order to achieve the recommended daily dosage?

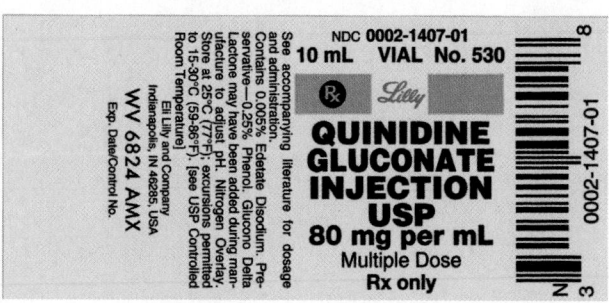

59. Amoxicillin is a common antibiotic prescribed for children. It is a liquid suspension composed of part amoxicillin and part water. In one formulation of amoxicillin suspension, there are 250 mg of amoxicillin in 5 cc of the liquid suspension. A physician prescribes 400 mg per day for a 2-year-old child with an ear infection. How much of the amoxicillin liquid suspension would the child's parent need to administer in order to achieve the recommended daily dosage of amoxicillin?

60. Albuterol is a medication used for the treatment of asthma. It comes in an inhaler that contains 17 mg of albuterol mixed with a liquid. One actuation (inhalation) from the mouthpiece delivers a 90-mcg dose of albuterol.

   a) A physician orders 2 inhalations 4 times per day. How many micrograms of albuterol does the patient inhale per day?

   b) How many actuations/inhalations are contained in one inhaler?

   c) Danielle is leaving for 4 months of college and wants to take enough albuterol to last for that time. Her physician has prescribed 2 inhalations 4 times per day. How many inhalers will Danielle need to take with her for the 4-month period?

Synthesis

61. A box of gelatin-mix packages weighs $15\frac{3}{4}$ lb. Each package weighs $1\frac{3}{4}$ oz. How many packages are in the box?

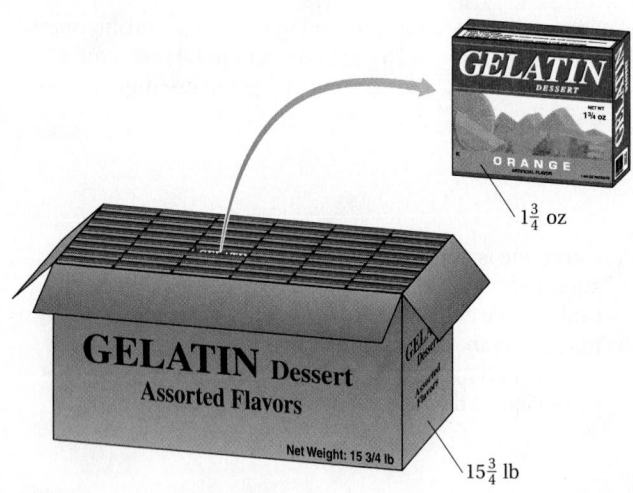

$1\frac{3}{4}$ oz

$15\frac{3}{4}$ lb

62. At $1.59 a dozen, the cost of eggs is $1.06 per pound. How much does an egg weigh?

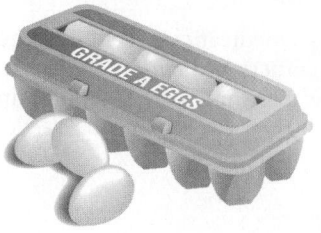

Copyright © 2012 Pearson Education, Inc.

C Capacity; Medical Applications

a Capacity

American Units

To answer a question like "How much soda is in the can?" we need measures of **capacity**. American units of capacity are fluid ounces, cups, pints, quarts, and gallons. These units are related as follows.

> **AMERICAN UNITS OF CAPACITY**
>
> 1 gallon (gal) = 4 quarts (qt)   1 pt = 2 cups
>   = 16 fluid ounces (fl oz)
>   1 qt = 2 pints (pt)   1 cup = 8 fluid oz

Fluid ounces, abbreviated fl oz, are often referred to as ounces, or oz.

EXAMPLE 1 Complete: 9 gal = _____ oz.

Since we are converting from a *larger* unit to a *smaller* unit, we use substitution:

$$9 \text{ gal} = 9 \cdot 1 \text{ gal} = 9 \cdot 4 \text{ qt}$$ Substituting 4 qt for 1 gal
$$= 9 \cdot 4 \cdot 1 \text{ qt} = 9 \cdot 4 \cdot 2 \text{ pt}$$ Substituting 2 pt for 1 qt
$$= 9 \cdot 4 \cdot 2 \cdot 1 \text{ pt} = 9 \cdot 4 \cdot 2 \cdot 16 \text{ oz}$$ Substituting 16 oz for 1 pt
$$= 1152 \text{ oz.}$$

EXAMPLE 2 Complete: 24 qt = _____ gal.

Since we are converting from a *smaller* unit to a *larger* unit, we multiply by 1 using 1 gal in the numerator and 4 qt in the denominator:

$$24 \text{ qt} = 24 \text{ qt} \cdot \frac{1 \text{ gal}}{4 \text{ qt}} = \frac{24}{4} \cdot 1 \text{ gal} = 6 \text{ gal.}$$

> Do Exercises 1 and 2.

Metric Units

One unit of capacity in the metric system is a **liter**. A liter is just a bit more than a quart. It is defined as follows.

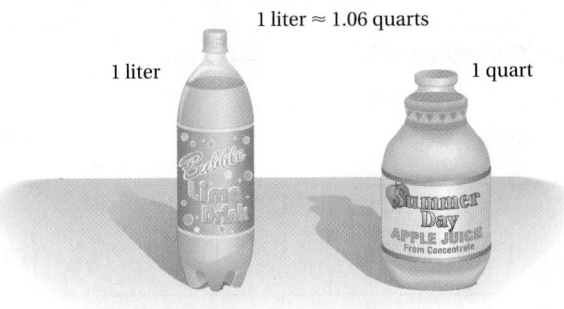

1 liter   1 liter ≈ 1.06 quarts   1 quart

Complete.

1. 5 gal = _____ pt

2. 80 qt = _____ gal

Answers

1. 40   **2.** 20

METRIC UNITS OF CAPACITY

> 1 liter (L) = 1000 cubic centimeters (1000 cm^3)
> The script letter ℓ is also used for "liter."

The metric prefixes are also used with liters. The most common is **milli-**. The milliliter (mL) is, then, $\frac{1}{1000}$ liter. Thus,

> 1 L = 1000 mL = 1000 cm^3;
> 0.001 L = 1 mL = 1 cm^3.

Although the other metric prefixes are rarely used for capacity, we display them in the following table as we did for linear measure.

1000 L	100 L	10 L	1 L	0.1 L	0.01 L	0.001 L
1 kL	1 hL	1 daL	1 L	1 dL	1 cL	1 mL (cc)

A preferred unit for drug dosage is the milliliter (mL) or the cubic centimeter (cm^3). The notation "cc" is also used for cubic centimeter, especially in medicine. The milliliter and the cubic centimeter represent the same measure of capacity. A milliliter is about $\frac{1}{5}$ of a teaspoon.

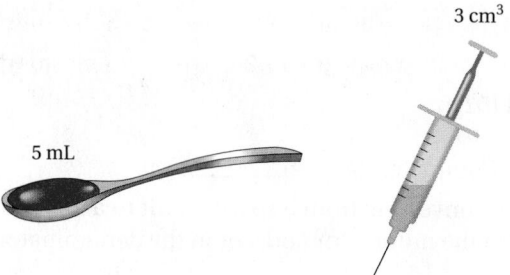

> 1 mL = 1 cm^3 = 1 cc

Volumes for which quarts and gallons are used are expressed in liters. Large volumes in business and industry are expressed using measures of cubic meters (m^3).

Do Exercises 3–6.

EXAMPLE 3 Complete: 4.5 L = _____ mL.

  4.5 L = 4.5 × 1 L = 4.5 × 1000 mL   Substituting 1000 mL for 1 L
    = 4500 mL

1000 L	100 L	10 L	1 L	0.1 L	0.01 L	0.001 L
1 kL	1 hL	1 daL	1 L	1 dL	1 cL	1 mL (cc)

3 places to the right

Complete with mL or L.

3. The patient received an injection of 2 _____ of penicillin.

4. There are 250 _____ in a coffee cup.

5. The gas tank holds 80 _____.

6. Bring home 8 _____ of milk.

Answers

3. mL   **4.** mL   **5.** L   **6.** L

EXAMPLE 4 Complete: 280 mL = _____ L.

$$280 \text{ mL} = 280 \times 1 \text{ mL}$$
$$= 280 \times 0.001 \text{ L} \qquad \text{Substituting 0.001 L for 1 mL}$$
$$= 0.28 \text{ L}$$

1000 L	100 L	10 L	1 L	0.1 L	0.01 L	0.001 L
1 kL	1 hL	1 daL	1 L	1 dL	1 cL	1 mL (cc)

3 places to the left

We do find metric units of capacity in frequent use in the United States—for example, in sizes of soda bottles and automobile engines.

Do Exercises 7 and 8.

Complete.

7. 0.97 L = _____ mL

8. 8990 mL = _____ L

b Medical Applications

The metric system is used extensively in medicine.

EXAMPLE 5 *Medical Dosage.* A physician orders 3.5 L of 5% dextrose in water (abbrev. D5W) to be administered over a 24-hr period. How many milliliters were ordered?

We convert 3.5 L to milliliters:

$$3.5 \text{ L} = 3.5 \times 1 \text{ L} = 3.5 \times 1000 \text{ mL} = 3500 \text{ mL}.$$

The physician ordered 3500 mL of D5W.

Do Exercise 9.

9. Medical Dosage. A physician orders 2400 mL of 0.9% saline solution to be administered intravenously over a 24-hr period. How many liters were ordered?

EXAMPLE 6 *Medical Dosage.* Liquids at a pharmacy are often labeled in liters or milliliters. Thus if a physician's prescription is given in ounces, it must be converted. For conversion, a pharmacist knows that 1 fluid oz ≈ 29.57 mL.* A prescription calls for 3 fluid oz of theophylline. For how many milliliters is the prescription?

We convert as follows:

$$3 \text{ oz} = 3 \times 1 \text{ oz} \approx 3 \times 29.57 \text{ mL} = 88.71 \text{ mL}.$$

The prescription calls for 88.71 mL of theophylline.

Do Exercise 10.

10. Medical Dosage. A prescription calls for 2 oz of theophylline.
a) For how many milliliters is the prescription?
b) For how many liters is the prescription?

*In practice, most pharmacists use 30 mL as an approximation to 1 oz.

Answers
7. 970   **8.** 8.99   **9.** 2.4 L
10. (a) About 59.14 mL; **(b)** about 0.059 L

a Complete.

1. 1 L = _____ mL = _____ cm^3

2. _____ L = 1 mL = _____ cm^3

3. 87 L = _____ mL

4. 806 L = _____ mL

5. 49 mL = _____ L

6. 19 mL = _____ L

7. 0.401 mL = _____ L

8. 0.816 mL = _____ L

9. 78.1 L = _____ cm^3

10. 99.6 L = _____ cm^3

11. 10 qt = _____ oz

12. 9.6 oz = _____ pt

13. 20 cups = _____ pt

14. 1 gal = _____ oz

15. 8 gal = _____ qt

16. 1 gal = _____ cups

17. 5 gal = _____ qt

18. 11 gal = _____ qt

19. 56 qt = _____ gal

20. 84 qt = _____ gal

21. 11 gal = _____ pt

22. 5 gal = _____ pt

Complete.

	OBJECT	GALLONS (gal)	QUARTS (qt)	PINTS (pt)	CUPS	OUNCES (oz)
23.	12-can package of 12-oz sodas					144
24.	6-bottle package of 16-oz sodas		3			
25.	Full tank of gasoline	16				
26.	Container of milk			8		
27.	Tropicana Punch				4	
28.	Dove shampoo					12
29.	Downy fabric softener					51
30.	Williams Electric Shave					7

Complete.

	OBJECT	LITERS (L)	MILLILITERS (mL)	CUBIC CENTIMETERS (cc)	CUBIC CENTIMETERS (cm^3)
31.	2-L bottle of soda	2			
32.	Heinz Vinegar		3755		
33.	Full tank of gasoline in Europe	64			
34.	Williams Electric Shave				207
35.	Dove shampoo			355	
36.	Newman's Own Salad Dressing		473		

Copyright © 2012 Pearson Education, Inc.

b *Medical Dosage.* Solve each of the following.
Source: Steven R. Smith, M.D.

37. An emergency-room physician orders 2.0 L of Ringer's lactate to be administered over 2 hr for a patient in shock. How many milliliters is this?

38. An emergency-room physician orders 2.5 L of 0.9% saline solution over 4 hr for a patient suffering from dehydration. How many milliliters is this?

39. A physician orders 320 mL of 5% dextrose in water (D5W) solution to be administered intravenously over 4 hr. How many liters of D5W is this?

40. A physician orders 40 mL of 5% dextrose in water (D5W) solution to be administered intravenously over 2 hr to an elderly patient. How many liters of D5W is this?

41. A physician orders 0.5 oz of magnesia and alumina oral suspension antacid 4 times per day for a patient with indigestion. How many milliliters of the antacid is the patient to ingest in a day?

42. A physician orders 0.25 oz of magnesia and alumina oral suspension antacid 3 times per day for a child with upper abdominal discomfort. How many milliliters of the antacid is the child to ingest in a day?

43. A physician orders 0.5 L of normal saline solution. How many milliliters are ordered?

44. A physician has ordered that his patient receive 60 mL per hour of normal saline solution intravenously. How many liters of the saline solution is the patient to receive in a 24-hr period?

45. A physician wants her patient to receive 3.0 L of normal saline intravenously over a 24-hr period. How many milliliters per hour must the nurse administer?

46. A physician tells a patient to purchase 0.5 L of hydrogen peroxide. Commercially, hydrogen peroxide is found on the shelf in bottles that hold 4 oz, 8 oz, and 16 oz. Which bottle comes closest to filling the prescription?

Medical Dosage. Because patients do not always have a working knowledge of the metric system, physicians often prescribe dosages in teaspoons (t or tsp) and tablespoons (T or Tbsp). The units are related to the metric system and to each other as follows:

$$5 \text{ mL} \approx 1 \text{ tsp}, \qquad 3 \text{ tsp} = 1 \text{ T}.$$

Complete.

47. 45 mL = _____ tsp

48. 3 T = _____ tsp

49. 1 mL = _____ tsp

50. 18.5 mL = _____ tsp

51. 2 T = _____ tsp

52. 8.5 tsp = _____ T

53. 1 T = _____ mL

54. 18.5 mL = _____ T

Synthesis

55. *Wasting Water.* Many people leave the water running while they are brushing their teeth. Suppose that 32 oz of water is wasted in such a way each day by one person. How much water, in gallons, is wasted in a week? in a month (30 days)? in a year (365 days)? Assuming each of the 306 million people in the United States wastes water in this way, estimate how much water is wasted in the United States in a day; in a year.

Time and Temperature

a Convert from one unit of time to another.

b Convert between Celsius and Fahrenheit temperatures using the formulas
$$F = \frac{9}{5} \cdot C + 32$$
and
$$C = \frac{5}{9} \cdot (F - 32).$$

a Time

A table of units of time is shown below. The metric system sometimes uses "h" for hour and "s" for second, but we will use the more familiar "hr" and "sec."

UNITS OF TIME	
1 day = 24 hours (hr)	1 year (yr) = $365\frac{1}{4}$ days
1 hr = 60 minutes (min)	
1 min = 60 seconds (sec)	1 week (wk) = 7 days

The earth revolves completely around the sun in $365\frac{1}{4}$ days. Since we cannot have $\frac{1}{4}$ day on the calendar, we give each year 365 days and every fourth year 366 days (a leap year), unless it is a year at the beginning of a century not divisible by 400.

EXAMPLE 1 Complete: 1 hr = _____ sec.

$$1 \text{ hr} = 60 \text{ min}$$
$$= 60 \cdot 1 \text{ min}$$
$$= 60 \cdot 60 \text{ sec} \quad \text{Substituting 60 sec for 1 min}$$
$$= 3600 \text{ sec}$$

EXAMPLE 2 Complete: 5 yr = _____ days.

$$5 \text{ yr} = 5 \cdot 1 \text{ yr}$$
$$= 5 \cdot 365\frac{1}{4} \text{ days} \quad \text{Substituting } 365\frac{1}{4} \text{ days for 1 yr}$$
$$= 5 \cdot \frac{1461}{4} \text{ days}$$
$$= \frac{7305}{4} \text{ days}$$
$$= 1826\frac{1}{4} \text{ days}$$

EXAMPLE 3 Complete: 4320 min = _____ days.

$$4320 \text{ min} = 4320 \text{ min} \cdot \frac{1 \text{ hr}}{60 \text{ min}} \cdot \frac{1 \text{ day}}{24 \text{ hr}} = \frac{4320}{60 \cdot 24} \text{ days} = 3 \text{ days}$$

Do Exercises 1–4.

Complete.

1. 2 hr = _____ min

2. 4 yr = _____ days

3. 1 day = _____ min

4. 168 hr = _____ wk

Answers

1. 120 **2.** 1461 **3.** 1440 **4.** 1

b Temperature

Below are two temperature scales: **Fahrenheit** for American measure and **Celsius** for metric measure.

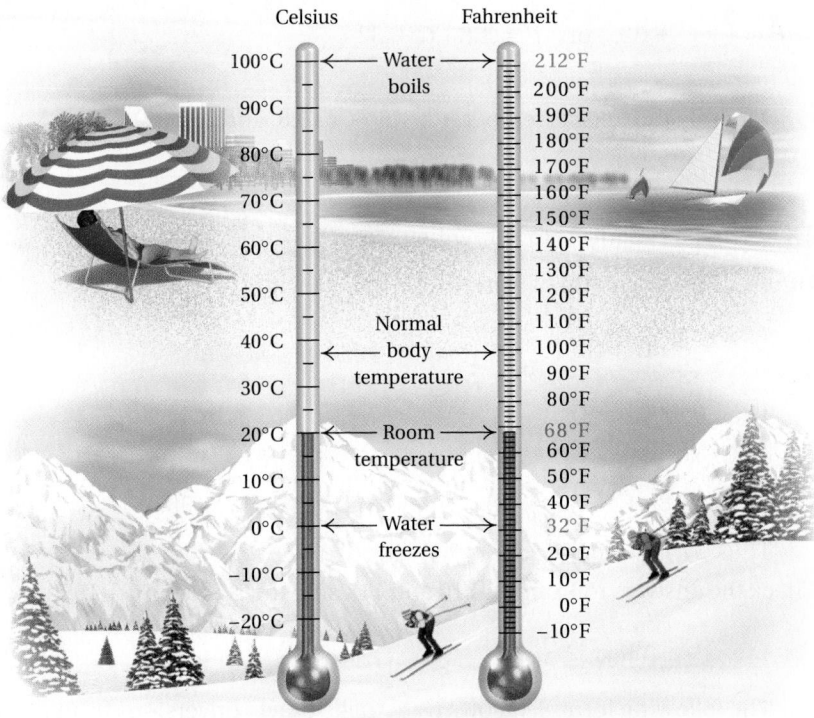

By laying a straight edge horizontally between the scales, we can make an approximate conversion from one measure of temperature to the other and get an idea of how the temperature scales compare.

EXAMPLES Convert to Celsius using the scales shown above. Approximate to the nearest ten degrees.

4. 212°F (Boiling point of water)   100°C   This is exact.

5. 32°F (Freezing point of water)   0°C   This is exact.

6. 105°F   40°C   This is approximate.

> Do Exercises 5–7.

EXAMPLES Make an approximate conversion to Fahrenheit using the scales shown above.

7. 44°C (Hot bath)   110°F   This is approximate.

8. 20°C (Room temperature)   68°F   This is exact.

9. 83°C   180°F   This is approximate.

> Do Exercises 8–10.

Convert to Celsius. Approximate to the nearest ten degrees.

5. 180°F (Brewing coffee)

6. 25°F (Cold day)

7. −10°F (Miserably cold day)

Convert to Fahrenheit. Approximate to the nearest ten degrees.

8. 25°C (Warm day at the beach)

9. 40°C (Temperature of a patient with a high fever)

10. 10°C (Cold bath)

Answers

5. 80°C   **6.** 0°C   **7.** −20°C   **8.** 80°F
9. 100°F   **10.** 50°F

The following formula allows us to make exact conversions from Celsius to Fahrenheit.

CELSIUS TO FAHRENHEIT

$$F = \frac{9}{5} \cdot C + 32, \quad \text{or} \quad F = 1.8 \cdot C + 32$$

$\left(\text{Multiply the Celsius temperature by } \frac{9}{5}, \text{ or } 1.8, \text{ and add } 32.\right)$

EXAMPLES Convert to Fahrenheit.

10. 0°C (Freezing point of water)

$$F = \frac{9}{5} \cdot C + 32 = \frac{9}{5} \cdot 0 + 32 = 0 + 32 = 32$$

Thus, 0°C = 32°F.

11. 37°C (Normal body temperature)

$$F = 1.8 \cdot C + 32 = 1.8 \cdot 37 + 32 = 66.6 + 32 = 98.6$$

Thus, 37°C = 98.6°F.

Check the answers to Examples 10 and 11 using the scales on p. 1195.

Convert to Fahrenheit.

11. 80°C

12. 35°C

Do Exercises 11 and 12.

The following formula allows us to make exact conversions from Fahrenheit to Celsius.

FAHRENHEIT TO CELSIUS

$$C = \frac{5}{9} \cdot (F - 32), \quad \text{or} \quad C = \frac{(F - 32)}{1.8}$$

$\left(\text{Subtract 32 from the Fahrenheit temperature and multiply by } \frac{5}{9} \text{ or divide by 1.8.}\right)$

EXAMPLES Convert to Celsius.

12. 212°F (Boiling point of water)   **13.** 77°F

$$C = \frac{5}{9} \cdot (F - 32) \qquad\qquad C = \frac{F - 32}{1.8}$$

$$= \frac{5}{9} \cdot (212 - 32) \qquad\qquad = \frac{77 - 32}{1.8}$$

$$= \frac{5}{9} \cdot 180 = 100 \qquad\qquad = \frac{45}{1.8} = 25$$

Thus, 212°F = 100°C.   Thus, 77°F = 25°C.

Check the answers to Examples 12 and 13 using the scales on p. 1195.

Convert to Celsius.

13. 95°F

14. 113°F

Answers

11. 176°F   **12.** 95°F   **13.** 35°C
14. 45°C

Do Exercises 13 and 14.

a   Complete.

1. 1 day = _____ hr

2. 1 hr = _____ min

3. 1 min = _____ sec

4. 1 wk = _____ days

5. 1 yr = _____ days

6. 2 yr = _____ days

7. 180 sec = _____ hr

8. 60 sec = _____ hr

9. 492 sec = _____ min
(The amount of time it takes for
the rays of the sun to reach the
earth)

10. 18,000 sec = _____ hr

11. 156 hr = _____ days

12. 444 hr = _____ days

13. 645 min = _____ hr

14. 375 min = _____ hr

15. 2 wk = _____ hr

16. 4 hr = _____ sec

17. 756 hr = _____ wk

18. 166,320 min = _____ wk

19. 2922 wk = _____ yr

20. 623 days = _____ wk

21. *Actual Time in a Day.*   Although we round it to 24 hr,
the actual length of a day is 23 hr, 56 min, and 4.2 sec.
How many seconds are there in an actual day?
Source: *The Handy Geography Answer Book*

22. *Time Length.*   What length of time is 86,400 sec? Is it
1 hr, 1 day, 1 week, or 1 month?

b   Convert to Fahrenheit. Use the formula $F = \dfrac{9}{5} \cdot C + 32$ or $F = 1.8 \cdot C + 32$.

23. 25°C

24. 85°C

25. 40°C

26. 90°C

27. 86°C

28. 93°C

29. 58°C

30. 35°C

31. 2°C   **32.** 78°C   **33.** 5°C   **34.** 15°C

35. 3000°C
(The melting point of iron)

36. 1000°C
(The melting point of gold)

Convert to Celsius. Use the formula $C = \dfrac{5}{9} \cdot (F - 32)$ or $C = \dfrac{F - 32}{1.8}$.

37. 86°F   **38.** 59°F   **39.** 131°F   **40.** 140°F

41. 178°F   **42.** 195°F   **43.** 140°F   **44.** 107°F

45. 68°F   **46.** 50°F   **47.** 44°F   **48.** 120°F

49. 98.6°F
(Normal body temperature)

50. 104°F
(High-fevered body temperature)

51. *Highest Temperatures.*   The highest temperature ever recorded in the world is 136°F in the desert of Libya in 1922. The highest temperature ever recorded in the United States is $56\frac{2}{3}$°C in California's Death Valley in 1913.

Source: *The Handy Geography Answer Book*

a) Convert each temperature to the other scale.
b) How much higher in degrees Fahrenheit was the world record than the U.S. record?

52. *Boiling Point and Altitude.*   The boiling point of water actually changes with altitude. The boiling point is 212°F at sea level, but lowers about 1°F for every 500 ft that the altitude increases above sea level.

Sources: *The Handy Geography Answer Book; The New York Times Almanac*

a) What is the boiling point at an elevation of 1500 ft above sea level?
b) The elevation of Tucson is 2564 ft above sea level and that of Phoenix is 1117 ft. What is the boiling point in each city?
c) How much lower is the boiling point in Denver, whose elevation is 5280 ft, than in Tucson?
d) What is the boiling point at the top of Mt. McKinley in Alaska, the highest point in the United States, at 20,320 ft?

53. *Record Low Temperature.*   The record low temperature in Hawaii as of August 2006 occurred on May 17, 1979. The record was 12°F at Mauna Kea Observatory. Convert 12°F to Celsius.

Source: National Climatic Data Center, NESDIS, NOAA, U.S. Department of Commerce

54. *Record High Temperature.*   The record high temperature in Utah as of August 2006 occurred on July 5, 1985. The record was 117°F at Saint George. Convert 117°F to Celsius.

Source: National Climatic Data Center, NESDIS, NOAA, U.S. Department of Commerce

Synthesis

55. Estimate the number of years in one million seconds.

56. Estimate the number of years in one billion seconds.

Copyright © 2012 Pearson Education, Inc.

Answers

CHAPTER 1

Exercise Set 1.1, p. 7

1. 5 thousands **3.** 5 hundreds **5.** 9 **7.** 7
9. 5 thousands + 7 hundreds + 0 tens + 2 ones, or
5 thousands + 7 hundreds + 2 ones
11. 9 ten thousands + 3 thousands + 9 hundreds + 8 tens +
6 ones **13.** 2 thousands + 0 hundreds + 5 tens + 8 ones, or
2 thousands + 5 tens + 8 ones **15.** 1 thousand +
5 hundreds + 7 tens + 6 ones **17.** 1 billion +
4 hundred millions + 2 ten millions + 4 millions +
1 hundred thousand + 6 ten thousands + 1 thousand +
9 hundreds + 4 tens + 8 ones **19.** 9 ten millions +
9 millions + 8 hundred thousands + 8 ten thousands +
6 thousands + 5 hundreds + 6 tens + 8 ones
21. 6 hundred thousands + 1 ten thousand + 7 thousands +
2 hundreds + 4 tens + 9 ones **23.** Eighty-five
25. Eighty-eight thousand **27.** One hundred twenty-three
thousand, seven hundred sixty-five **29.** Seven billion, seven
hundred fifty-four million, two hundred eleven thousand, five
hundred seventy-seven **31.** Seven hundred thousand, six
hundred thirty-four **33.** Three million, forty-eight thousand,
five **35.** 2,233,812 **37.** 8,000,000,000 **39.** 50,324
41. 632,896 **43.** 1,600,000,000 **45.** 64,186,000 **47.** <
49. > **51.** < **53.** > **55.** > **57.** >
59. 190,078 > 172,000, or 172,000 < 190,078
61. 1694 < 5249, or 5249 > 1694 **63.** 138

Calculator Corner, p. 12

1. 121 **2.** 1602 **3.** 1932 **4.** 864

Calculator Corner, p. 15

1. 28 **2.** 47 **3.** 67 **4.** 119 **5.** 2128 **6.** 2593

Exercise Set 1.2, p. 17

1. 387 **3.** 164 **5.** 5198 **7.** 6608 **9.** 8503 **11.** 5266
13. 34,432 **15.** 101,301 **17.** 18,424 **19.** 31,685
21. 1661 ft **23.** 570 ft **25.** 44 **27.** 533 **29.** 369
31. 26 **33.** 234 **35.** 417 **37.** 5382 **39.** 2778
41. 3069 **43.** 1089 **45.** 7748 **47.** 4144 **49.** 3831
51. 3749 **53.** 2191 **55.** 4418 **57.** 43,028 **59.** 95,974
61. 4206 **63.** 1305 **65.** 9989 **67.** 48,017
69. Six million, three hundred seventy-five thousand, six
hundred two **70.** 7 ten thousands **71.** 3; 4

Calculator Corner, p. 22

1. 448 **2.** 21,970 **3.** 6380 **4.** 39,564 **5.** 180,480
6. 2,363,754

Calculator Corner, p. 28

1. 28 **2.** 123 **3.** 323 **4.** 36

Exercise Set 1.3, p. 35

1. 520 **3.** 870 **5.** 1527 **7.** 64,603 **9.** 4770 **11.** 3995
13. 46,296 **15.** 14,652 **17.** 258,312 **19.** 798,408
21. 20,723,872 **23.** 362,128 **25.** 302,220 **27.** 49,101,136
29. 25,236,000 **31.** 20,064,048 **33.** 529,984 sq mi
35. 8100 sq ft **37.** 12 **39.** 1 **41.** 22 **43.** 0
45. Not defined **47.** 6 **49.** 55 R 2 **51.** 108
53. 307 **55.** 753 R 3 **57.** 74 R 1 **59.** 92 R 2
61. 1703 **63.** 987 R 5 **65.** 12,700 **67.** 127 **69.** 52 R 52
71. 29 R 5 **73.** 40 R 12 **75.** 90 R 22 **77.** 29 **79.** 105 R 3
81. 1609 R 2 **83.** 1007 R 1 **85.** 23 **87.** 107 R 1
89. 370 **91.** 609 R 15 **93.** 304 **95.** 3508 R 219
97. 8070 **99.** 50 **101.** 460 **103.** 730 **105.** 900
107. 100 **109.** 1000 **111.** 9100 **113.** 32,800
115. 6000 **117.** 8000 **119.** 45,000 **121.** 373,000
123. 80 + 90 = 170 **125.** 8070 − 2350 = 5720
127. 7300 + 9200 = 16,500 **129.** 6900 − 1700 = 5200
131. 10,000 + 5000 + 9000 + 7000 = 31,000
133. 92,000 − 23,000 = 69,000 **135.** 90 people
137. 50 · 70 = 3500 **139.** 30 · 30 = 900
141. 900 · 300 = 270,000 **143.** 400 · 200 = 80,000
145. 350 ÷ 70 = 5 **147.** 8450 ÷ 50 = 169
149. 1200 ÷ 200 = 6 **151.** 8400 ÷ 300 = 28 **153.** $11,200
155. $18,900; no **157.** Answers will vary depending on the
options chosen. **159.** Perimeter **160.** Minuend
161. Digits; periods **162.** Dividend **163.** Factors;
product **164.** Additive **165.** Multiplicative
166. Divisor; remainder; dividend **167.** 54, 122; 33, 2772; 4, 8
169. 30 buses **171.** 247,464 sq ft

Exercise Set 1.4, p. 46

1. 14 **3.** 0 **5.** 90,900 **7.** 450 **9.** 352 **11.** 25
13. 29 **15.** 0 **17.** 79 **19.** 45 **21.** 8 **23.** 14 **25.** 32
27. 143 **29.** 17,603 **31.** 37 **33.** 1035 **35.** 66
37. 324 **39.** 743 **41.** 175 **43.** 335 **45.** 18,252
47. 104 **49.** 45 **51.** 4056 **53.** 2847 **55.** 15 **57.** 205
59. 457 **61.** 142 R 5 **62.** 142 **63.** 334 **64.** 334 R 11
65. < **66.** > **67.** > **68.** < **69.** 6,376,000
70. 6,375,600 **71.** 347

Mid-Chapter Review: Chapter 1, p. 48

1. False   **2.** True   **3.** False   **4.** True   **5.** False
6.

95,406,237

Ninety-five million,

four hundred six thousand,

two hundred thirty-seven

7.
$$\begin{array}{r} \overset{5}{}\overset{9}{\cancel{6}}\overset{14}{\cancel{0}}\,4 \\ -\ \ 4\ 9\ 7 \\ \hline 1\ 0\ 7 \end{array}$$

8. 6 hundreds   **9.** 6 ten thousands

10. 6 thousands   **11.** 6 ones   **12.** 2   **13.** 6   **14.** 5   **15.** 1
16. 5 thousands + 6 hundreds + 0 tens + 2 ones, or
5 thousands + 6 hundreds + 2 ones
17. 6 ten thousands + 9 thousands + 3 hundreds + 4 tens +
5 ones   **18.** One hundred thirty-six   **19.** Sixty-four
thousand, three hundred twenty-five   **20.** 308,716
21. 4,567,216   **22.** >   **23.** <   **24.** <   **25.** >   **26.** 18
27. 22   **28.** 29   **29.** 3642   **30.** 798   **31.** 1030
32. 7922   **33.** 7534   **34.** 465   **35.** 339   **36.** 1854
37. 4328   **38.** 216   **39.** 15,876   **40.** 132,275
41. 5,679,870   **42.** 253   **43.** 112 R 5   **44.** 23 R 19
45. 144 R 31   **46.** 25 m   **47.** 8 sq in.   **48.** 600
49. 824,000   **50.** 180,000   **51.** By rounding prices and
estimating their sum, a shopper can estimate the total grocery
bill while shopping. This is particularly useful if the shopper
wants to spend no more than a certain amount.   **52.** Commas
separate the periods and make the numbers easier to read.
53. Answers will vary. Suppose one coat costs $150. Then the
multiplication 4 · $150 gives the cost of four coats. Or, suppose
one ream of copy paper costs $4. Then the multiplication $4 · 150
gives the cost of 150 reams.   **54.** If we use the definition of
division, $0 \div 0 = a$ such that $a \cdot 0 = 0$. We see that a could be
any number since $a \cdot 0 = 0$ for any number a. Thus we cannot say
that $0 \div 0 = 0$. This is why we agree not to allow division by 0.

Translating for Success, p. 59

1. E   **2.** M   **3.** D   **4.** G   **5.** A   **6.** O   **7.** F   **8.** K
9. J   **10.** H

Exercise Set 1.5, p. 60

1. 318 ft   **3.** 7450 ft   **5.** 95 milligrams   **7.** 18 rows
9. 1502 hr   **11.** 2054 mi   **13.** 2,073,600 pixels
15. 268,000 men   **17.** 168 hr   **19.** $23 per month
21. $233   **23.** $9276   **25.** 151,500   **27.** 1,190,000
motorcycles   **29.** $78   **31.** $40 per month   **33.** $24,456
35. 35 weeks; 2 episodes   **37.** 236 gal   **39.** 21 columns
41. (a) 4200 sq ft; (b) 268 ft   **43.** $247   **45.** 645 mi; 5 in.
47. 56 cartons   **49.** 32 $10 bills   **51.** $400   **53.** 525 min,
or 8 hr 45 min   **55.** 700 min, or 11 hr 40 min   **57.** 104 seats
59. 106 bones   **61.** 234,600   **62.** 234,560   **63.** 235,000
64. 22,000   **65.** 16,000   **66.** 4000   **67.** 8000   **68.** 320,000
69. 720,000   **70.** 46,800,000   **71.** 792,000 mi; 1,386,000 mi

Calculator Corner, p. 68

1. 243   **2.** 15,625   **3.** 20,736   **4.** 2048

Calculator Corner, p. 70

1. 49   **2.** 85   **3.** 36   **4.** 0   **5.** 73   **6.** 49

Exercise Set 1.6, p. 73

1. 3^4 **3.** 5^2 **5.** 7^5 **7.** 10^3 **9.** 49   **11.** 729
13. 20,736   **15.** 243   **17.** 22   **19.** 20   **21.** 100   **23.** 1
25. 49   **27.** 5   **29.** 434   **31.** 41   **33.** 88   **35.** 4
37. 303   **39.** 20   **41.** 70   **43.** 295   **45.** 32   **47.** 906
49. 62   **51.** 102   **53.** 32   **55.** $94   **57.** 401   **59.** 110
61. 7   **63.** 544   **65.** 708   **67.** 27   **69.** 452   **70.** 835

71. 13   **72.** 37   **73.** 2342   **74.** 4898   **75.** 25   **76.** 100
77. 104,286 mi^2 **78.** 98 gal   **79.** $24; 1 + 5 \cdot (4 + 3) = 36$
81. $7; 12 \div (4 + 2) \cdot 3 - 2 = 4$

Calculator Corner, p. 78

1. No   **2.** Yes   **3.** Yes   **4.** No

Exercise Set 1.7, p. 81

1. No   **3.** Yes   **5.** 1, 2, 3, 6, 9, 18   **7.** 1, 2, 3, 6, 9, 18, 27, 54
9. 1, 2, 4   **11.** 1   **13.** 1, 2, 7, 14, 49, 98   **15.** 1, 3, 5, 15, 17,
51, 85, 255   **17.** 4, 8, 12, 16, 20, 24, 28, 32, 36, 40   **19.** 20, 40,
60, 80, 100, 120, 140, 160, 180, 200   **21.** 3, 6, 9, 12, 15, 18, 21,
24, 27, 30   **23.** 12, 24, 36, 48, 60, 72, 84, 96, 108, 120
25. 10, 20, 30, 40, 50, 60, 70, 80, 90, 100   **27.** 9, 18, 27, 36, 45,
54, 63, 72, 81, 90   **29.** No   **31.** Yes   **33.** Yes   **35.** No
37. No   **39.** Neither   **41.** Composite   **43.** Prime
45. Prime   **47.** $2 \cdot 2 \cdot 2$ **49.** $2 \cdot 7$ **51.** $2 \cdot 3 \cdot 7$ **53.** $5 \cdot 5$
55. $2 \cdot 5 \cdot 5$ **57.** $13 \cdot 13$ **59.** $2 \cdot 2 \cdot 5 \cdot 5$ **61.** $5 \cdot 7$
63. $2 \cdot 2 \cdot 2 \cdot 3 \cdot 3$ **65.** $7 \cdot 11$ **67.** $2 \cdot 2 \cdot 7 \cdot 103$
69. $3 \cdot 17$ **71.** $2 \cdot 2 \cdot 2 \cdot 3 \cdot 5 \cdot 5$ **73.** $3 \cdot 7 \cdot 13$
75. $2 \cdot 3 \cdot 11 \cdot 17$ **77.** 26   **78.** 256   **79.** 425
80. 4200   **81.** 0   **82.** 22   **83.** 1   **84.** 3   **85.** $946
86. 201 min, or 3 hr 21 min   **87.** Row 1: 48, 90, 432, 63; row 2: 7,
2, 2, 10, 8, 6, 21, 10; row 3: 9, 18, 36, 14, 12, 11, 21; row 4: 29, 19, 42

Exercise Set 1.8, p. 87

1. 46, 224, 300, 36, 45,270, 4444, 256, 8064, 21,568
3. 224, 300, 36, 4444, 256, 8064, 21,568   **5.** 300, 36, 45,270,
8064   **7.** 36, 45,270, 711, 8064   **9.** 324, 42, 501, 3009, 75,
2001, 402, 111,111, 1005   **11.** 55,555, 200, 75, 2345, 35, 1005
13. 56, 784, 200   **15.** 200   **17.** 313,332, 7624, 111,126, 876,
1110, 5128, 64,000, 9990   **19.** 313,332, 111,126, 876, 1110,
9990   **21.** 9990   **23.** 1110, 64,000, 9990   **25.** 138
26. 139   **27.** 874   **28.** 56   **29.** 26   **30.** 13   **31.** 234
32. 4003   **33.** 45 gal   **34.** 4320 min
35. $2 \cdot 2 \cdot 2 \cdot 3 \cdot 5 \cdot 5 \cdot 13$ **37.** $2 \cdot 2 \cdot 3 \cdot 3 \cdot 7 \cdot 11$
39. 95,238

Exercise Set 1.9, p. 93

1. 4   **3.** 50   **5.** 40   **7.** 54   **9.** 150   **11.** 120   **13.** 72
15. 420   **17.** 144   **19.** 288   **21.** 30   **23.** 90   **25.** 72
27. 60   **29.** 36   **31.** 900   **33.** 48   **35.** 50   **37.** 143
39. 420   **41.** 378   **43.** 810   **45.** 2160   **47.** 9828
49. 6000   **51.** Every 60 yr   **53.** Every 420 yr
55. 659 tornadoes   **56.** 376,000,000   **57.** 39   **58.** 33,135
59. 6,356,118   **60.** 77,699   **61.** 5 in. by 24 in.

Summary and Review: Chapter 1, p. 95

Concept Reinforcement

1. True   **2.** True   **3.** False   **4.** False   **5.** True   **6.** False
7. True

Important Concepts

1. 2 thousands   **2.** <   **3.** 65,302   **4.** 3237   **5.** 225,036
6. 315 R 14   **7.** 36,500   **8.** 36,000   **9.** 36   **10.** 216
11. 1, 2, 4, 8, 13, 26, 52, 104   **12.** $2 \cdot 2 \cdot 2 \cdot 13$ **13.** 156

Review Exercises

1. 8 thousands   **2.** 3   **3.** 2 thousands + 7 hundreds +
9 tens + 3 ones   **4.** 5 ten thousands + 6 thousands +
0 hundreds + 7 tens + 8 ones, or 5 ten thousands +
6 thousands + 7 tens + 8 ones   **5.** 4 millions +
0 hundred thousands + 0 ten thousands + 7 thousands +
1 hundred + 0 tens + 1 one, or 4 millions +
7 thousands + 1 hundred + 1 one   **6.** Sixty-seven thousand,
eight hundred nineteen   **7.** Two million, seven hundred
eighty-one thousand, four hundred twenty-seven

8. 1,563,000,000 **9.** > **10.** < **11.** 14,272 **12.** 66,024
13. 21,788 **14.** 98,921 **15.** 5148 **16.** 1689 **17.** 2274
18. 17,757 **19.** 5,100,000 **20.** 6,276,800 **21.** 506,748
22. 27,589 **23.** 5,331,810 **24.** 12 R 3 **25.** 5 **26.** 913 R 3
27. 384 R 1 **28.** 4 R 46 **29.** 54 **30.** 452 **31.** 4389
32. 345,800 **33.** 345,760 **34.** 346,000 **35.** 300,000
36. $41,300 + 19,700 = 61,000$ **37.** $38,700 - 24,500 = 14,200$
38. $400 \cdot 700 = 280,000$ **39.** 8 **40.** 45 **41.** 58 **42.** 0
43. 4^3 **44.** 10,000 **45.** 36 **46.** 65 **47.** 233 **48.** 260
49. 165 **50.** $502 **51.** $484 **52.** 1982 **53.** $13,585
54. 14 beehives **55.** 98 sq ft; 42 ft **56.** 137 beakers; 13 mL
left over **57.** $27,598 **58.** 1, 2, 3, 4, 5, 6, 10, 12, 15, 20, 30, 60
59. 1, 2, 4, 8, 11, 16, 22, 44, 88, 176 **60.** 8, 16, 24, 32, 40, 48,
56, 64, 72, 80 **61.** Yes **62.** No **63.** Prime
64. Neither **65.** Composite **66.** $2 \cdot 5 \cdot 7$ **67.** $2 \cdot 3 \cdot 5$
68. $3 \cdot 3 \cdot 5$ **69.** $2 \cdot 3 \cdot 5 \cdot 5$ **70.** $2 \cdot 2 \cdot 2 \cdot 3 \cdot 3 \cdot 3 \cdot 3$
71. $2 \cdot 3 \cdot 5 \cdot 5 \cdot 5 \cdot 7$ **72.** 4344, 600, 93, 330, 255,555, 780,
2802, 711 **73.** 140, 182, 716, 2432, 4344, 600, 330, 780, 2802
74. 140, 716, 2432, 4344, 600, 780 **75.** 2432, 4344, 600
76. 140, 95, 475, 600, 330, 255,555, 780 **77.** 4344, 600, 330,
780, 2802 **78.** 255,555, 711 **79.** 140, 600, 330, 780
80. 36 **81.** 90 **82.** 30 **83.** 1404 **84.** B **85.** A
86. D **87.** $a = 8, b = 4$ **88.** 13, 11, 101, 37 **89.** 6 days

Understanding Through Discussion and Writing

1. $9432 = 9 \cdot 1000 + 4 \cdot 100 + 3 \cdot 10 + 2 \cdot 1 =$
$9(999 + 1) + 4(99 + 1) + 3(9 + 1) + 2 \cdot 1 =$
$9 \cdot 999 + 9 \cdot 1 + 4 \cdot 99 + 4 \cdot 1 + 3 \cdot 9 + 3 \cdot 1 + 2 \cdot 1.$ Since
999, 99, and 9 are each a multiple of 9, $9 \cdot 999$, $4 \cdot 99$, and $3 \cdot 9$
are multiples of 9. This leaves $9 \cdot 1 + 4 \cdot 1 + 3 \cdot 1 + 2 \cdot 1$, or
$9 + 4 + 3 + 2$. If $9 + 4 + 3 + 2$, the sum of the digits, is divisible
by 9, then 9432 is divisible by 9. **2.** Find the product of two
prime numbers. **3.** Answers will vary. Anthony is driving
from Kansas City to Minneapolis, a distance of 512 mi. He stops
for gas after driving 183 mi. How much farther must he drive?
4. The parentheses are not necessary in the expression
$9 - (4 \cdot 2)$. Using the rules for order of operations, the
multiplication would be performed before the subtraction even
if the parentheses were not present. The parentheses are
necessary in the expression $(3 \cdot 4)^2$; $(3 \cdot 4)^2 = 12^2 = 144$, but
$3 \cdot 4^2 = 3 \cdot 16 = 48$.

Test: Chapter 1, p. 101

1. [1.1a] 5 **2.** [1.1b] 8 thousands + 8 hundreds +
4 tens + 3 ones **3.** [1.1c] Thirty-eight million, four hundred
three thousand, two hundred seventy-seven **4.** [1.2a] 9989
5. [1.2a] 63,791 **6.** [1.2a] 3165 **7.** [1.2a] 10,515
8. [1.2c] 3630 **9.** [1.2c] 1039 **10.** [1.2c] 6848
11. [1.2c] 5175 **12.** [1.3a] 41,112 **13.** [1.3a] 5,325,600
14. [1.3a] 2405 **15.** [1.3a] 534,264 **16.** [1.3c] 3 R 3
17. [1.3c] 70 **18.** [1.3c] 97 **19.** [1.3c] 805 R 8
20. [1.5a] 83 calories **21.** [1.5a] 20 staplers **22.** [1.5a] $95
23. (a) [1.2b], [1.3b] 300 in., 5000 sq in.; 264 in., 3872 sq in.;
228 in., 2888 sq in.; **(b)** [1.5a] 2112 sq in. **24.** [1.3d] 35,000
25. [1.3d] 34,530 **26.** [1.3d] 34,500
27. [1.3e] $23,600 + 54,700 = 78,300$
28. [1.3e] $54,800 - 23,600 = 31,200$
29. [1.3e] $800 \cdot 500 = 400,000$ **30.** [1.4b] 46 **31.** [1.4b] 13
32. [1.4b] 14 **33.** [1.4b] 381 **34.** [1.6a] 12^4
35. [1.6b] 343 **36.** [1.6b] 100,000 **37.** [1.1d] >
38. [1.1d] < **39.** [1.6c] 31 **40.** [1.6c] 98 **41.** [1.6c] 2
42. [1.6c] 18 **43.** [1.6d] 216 **44.** [1.7c] Prime
45. [1.7c] Composite **46.** [1.7c] $2 \cdot 3 \cdot 3$
47. [1.7c] $2 \cdot 2 \cdot 3 \cdot 5$ **48.** [1.8a] Yes **49.** [1.8a] No
50. [1.8a] No **51.** [1.8a] Yes **52.** [1.9a] 48 **53.** [1.9a] 600
54. [1.6c] A **55.** [1.3b], [1.5a] 336 sq in. **56.** [1.6c]

CHAPTER 2

Calculator Corner, p. 112

1. $\frac{14}{15}$ **2.** $\frac{7}{8}$ **3.** $\frac{138}{167}$ **4.** $\frac{7}{25}$

Exercise Set 2.1, p. 113

1. Numerator: 3; denominator: 4 **3.** Numerator: 11;
denominator: 2 **5.** Numerator: 0; denominator: 7 **7.** $\frac{6}{12}$
9. $\frac{1}{8}$ **11.** $\frac{4}{3}$ **13.** $\frac{12}{16}$ **15.** $\frac{3}{4}$ **17.** $\frac{12}{12}$ **19.** $\frac{4}{3}$ **21.** $\frac{4}{8}$
23. (a) $\frac{2}{8}$; **(b)** $\frac{6}{8}$ **25. (a)** $\frac{3}{8}$; **(b)** $\frac{5}{8}$ **27.** 1 **29.** Not defined
31. 0 **33.** 7 **35.** Not defined **37.** 1 **39.** 0 **41.** $\frac{4}{15}$
43. $\frac{70}{9}$ **45.** $\frac{49}{64}$ **47.** $\frac{2}{15}$ **49.** $\frac{40}{21}$ **51.** $\frac{6}{5}$ **53.** $\frac{1}{6}$ **55.** $\frac{85}{6}$
57. $\frac{7}{100}$ **59.** $\frac{2}{5}$ **61.** $\frac{14}{39}$ **63.** $\frac{5}{8}$ **65.** $\frac{1}{40}$ **67.** $\frac{160}{27}$
69. $\frac{182}{285}$ **71.** $\frac{20}{32}$ **73.** $\frac{28}{32}$ **75.** $\frac{51}{54}$ **77.** $\frac{42}{132}$ **79.** $\frac{1}{2}$ **81.** $\frac{3}{4}$
83. $\frac{1}{5}$ **85.** 3 **87.** $\frac{3}{4}$ **89.** $\frac{7}{8}$ **91.** $\frac{6}{5}$ **93.** $\frac{1}{3}$ **95.** 6 **97.** $\frac{1}{3}$
99. $\frac{2}{3}$ **101.** $\frac{7}{90}$ **103.** $\frac{1}{6}$ **105.** $\frac{2}{16}$, or $\frac{1}{8}$

Exercise Set 2.2, p. 120

1. $\frac{1}{8}$ **3.** $\frac{1}{6}$ **5.** $\frac{27}{10}$ **7.** 1 **9.** 1 **11.** 1 **13.** 2 **15.** 4
17. 9 **19.** 9 **21.** $\frac{15}{2}$ **23.** 30 **25.** $\frac{1}{5}$ **27.** $\frac{9}{25}$ **29.** $\frac{11}{40}$
31. $\frac{5}{14}$ **33.** $\frac{6}{5}$ **35.** $\frac{1}{6}$ **37.** 6 **39.** $\frac{3}{10}$ **41.** $\frac{4}{5}$ **43.** $\frac{4}{15}$
45. 4 **47.** 2 **49.** $\frac{1}{8}$ **51.** $\frac{3}{7}$ **53.** 8 **55.** 35 **57.** 1
59. $\frac{2}{3}$ **61.** $\frac{9}{4}$ **63.** 144 **65.** 75 **67.** 2 **69.** $\frac{3}{5}$ **71.** 315
73. 204 **74.** 700 **75.** 3001 **76.** 204 R 8 **77.** 8 thousands
78. 8 millions **79.** 8 ones **80.** 8 hundreds **81.** $\frac{3}{8}$

Exercise Set 2.3, p. 128

1. 1 **3.** $\frac{3}{4}$ **5.** $\frac{3}{2}$ **7.** $\frac{7}{24}$ **9.** $\frac{3}{2}$ **11.** $\frac{19}{24}$ **13.** $\frac{9}{10}$ **15.** $\frac{29}{18}$
17. $\frac{31}{100}$ **19.** $\frac{41}{60}$ **21.** $\frac{189}{100}$ **23.** $\frac{7}{8}$ **25.** $\frac{13}{24}$ **27.** $\frac{17}{24}$
29. $\frac{3}{4}$ **31.** $\frac{437}{500}$ **33.** $\frac{53}{40}$ **35.** $\frac{391}{144}$ **37.** $\frac{2}{3}$ **39.** $\frac{3}{4}$ **41.** $\frac{5}{8}$
43. $\frac{1}{24}$ **45.** 2 **47.** $\frac{9}{14}$ **49.** $\frac{3}{5}$ **51.** $\frac{7}{10}$ **53.** $\frac{17}{60}$ **55.** $\frac{53}{100}$
57. $\frac{26}{75}$ **59.** $\frac{9}{100}$ **61.** $\frac{13}{24}$ **63.** $\frac{1}{24}$ **65.** $\frac{1}{24}$ **67.** $\frac{13}{16}$ **69.** $\frac{31}{75}$
71. $\frac{13}{75}$ **73.** < **75.** > **77.** < **79.** < **81.** >
83. > **85.** < **87.** $\frac{1}{15}$ **89.** $\frac{2}{15}$ **91.** $\frac{1}{2}$ **93.** 6,140,000 lb
94. About 12.8 billion, or 12,800,000,000, crayons **95.** 1
96. Not defined **97.** Not defined **98.** 4 **99.** $\frac{4}{21}$
100. $\frac{3}{2}$ **101.** 21 **102.** $\frac{1}{32}$ **103.** $\frac{21}{40}$ km **105.** $\frac{19}{24}$
107. $\frac{145}{144}$ **109.** >

Mid-Chapter Review: Chapter 2, p. 131

1. True **2.** False **3.** True **4.** False **5.** 25 **6.** 0
7. 1 **8.** 18
9. $\frac{11}{42} - \frac{3}{35} = \frac{11}{2 \cdot 3 \cdot 7} - \frac{3}{5 \cdot 7}$
$= \frac{11}{2 \cdot 3 \cdot 7} \cdot \left(\frac{5}{5}\right) - \frac{3}{5 \cdot 7} \cdot \left(\frac{2 \cdot 3}{2 \cdot 3}\right)$
$= \frac{11 \cdot 5}{2 \cdot 3 \cdot 7 \cdot 5} - \frac{3 \cdot 2 \cdot 3}{5 \cdot 7 \cdot 2 \cdot 3}$
$= \frac{55}{2 \cdot 3 \cdot 5 \cdot 7} - \frac{18}{2 \cdot 3 \cdot 5 \cdot 7}$
$= \frac{55 - 18}{2 \cdot 3 \cdot 5 \cdot 7} = \frac{37}{210}$
10. $x + \frac{1}{8} = \frac{2}{3}$
$x + \frac{1}{8} - \frac{1}{8} = \frac{2}{3} - \frac{1}{8}$
$x + 0 = \frac{2}{3} \cdot \frac{8}{8} - \frac{1}{8} \cdot \frac{3}{3}$
$x = \frac{16}{24} - \frac{3}{24}$
$x = \frac{13}{24}$
11. $\frac{8}{24}$, or $\frac{1}{3}$ **12.** $\frac{8}{6}$, or $\frac{4}{3}$ **13.** $\frac{2}{5}$ **14.** $\frac{11}{3}$ **15.** 1 **16.** 0
17. Not defined **18.** 0 **19.** $\frac{9}{31}$ **20.** $\frac{9}{5}$ **21.** $\frac{5}{42}$ **22.** $\frac{21}{29}$
23. $\frac{16}{45}$ **24.** $\frac{25}{12}$ **25.** 2 **26.** $\frac{19}{90}$ **27.** $\frac{40}{10}$ **28.** $\frac{1}{10}$ **29.** 1
30. $\frac{4}{15}$ **31.** $\frac{7}{240}$ **32.** $\frac{156}{10}$ **33.** 300 **34.** $\frac{6}{10}$ **35.** $\frac{13}{80}$
36. $\frac{7}{12}$ **37.** $\frac{1}{5}, \frac{2}{7}, \frac{3}{10}, \frac{4}{9}$ **38.** We multiply by 1, using the
notation n/n, to express each fraction in terms of the least
common denominator. **39.** Write $\frac{8}{5}$ as $\frac{16}{10}$ and $\frac{8}{2}$ as $\frac{40}{10}$ and since
taking 40 tenths away from 16 tenths would give a result less
than 0, it cannot possibly be $\frac{8}{5}$. You could also find the sum $\frac{8}{3} + \frac{8}{2}$
and show that it is not $\frac{8}{5}$. **40.** It is possible to cancel only when

identical *factors* appear in the numerator and the denominator of a fraction. Situations in which it is not possible to cancel include the occurrence of identical *addends* or *digits* in the numerator and the denominator.   **41.** No; since the only factors of a prime number are the number itself and 1, two different prime numbers cannot contain a common factor (other than 1).

Exercise Set 2.4, p. 139

1. $\frac{65}{2}, \frac{125}{6}, \frac{47}{4}$ **3.** $\frac{13}{8}$ **5.** $\frac{51}{4}$ **7.** $\frac{203}{100}$ **9.** $4\frac{1}{2}$ **11.** $7\frac{4}{7}$
13. $5\frac{7}{12}$ **15.** $28\frac{3}{4}$ **17.** $2\frac{11}{12}$ **19.** $14\frac{7}{12}$ **21.** $12\frac{1}{10}$ **23.** $16\frac{5}{12}$
25. $21\frac{1}{2}$ **27.** $27\frac{7}{8}$ **29.** $27\frac{13}{24}$ **31.** $1\frac{3}{5}$ **33.** $4\frac{1}{10}$ **35.** $21\frac{17}{24}$
37. $12\frac{1}{4}$ **39.** $15\frac{3}{8}$ **41.** $7\frac{5}{8}$ **43.** $13\frac{3}{8}$ **45.** $11\frac{5}{18}$ **47.** $22\frac{2}{3}$
49. $2\frac{5}{12}$ **51.** $8\frac{1}{6}$ **53.** $9\frac{31}{40}$ **55.** $24\frac{91}{100}$ **57.** $975\frac{4}{5}$ **59.** $6\frac{1}{4}$
61. $1\frac{1}{5}$ **63.** $3\frac{9}{16}$ **65.** $1\frac{1}{8}$ **67.** $1\frac{8}{43}$ **69.** $\frac{9}{40}$ **71.** 45,800
72. 45,770   **73.** Yes   **74.** No   **75.** No   **76.** Yes   **77.** No
78. Yes   **79.** Yes   **80.** Yes   **81.** $35\frac{57}{64}$ **83.** $1\frac{4}{5}$

Translating for Success, p. 152

1. O   **2.** K   **3.** F   **4.** D   **5.** H   **6.** G   **7.** L   **8.** E
9. M   **10.** J

Exercise Set 2.5, p. 153

1. 960 extension cords   **3.** 32 pairs   **5.** Food: $8400; housing: $10,500; clothing: $4200; savings: $3000; taxes: $8400; other expenses: $7500   **7.** $\frac{5}{12}$ hr   **9.** $\frac{37}{12}$ mi   **11.** $\frac{5}{8}$ in.   **13.** $48,280
15. 68°F   **17.** $\frac{27}{32}''$ **19.** $\frac{51}{32}$ in.   **21.** $343\frac{3}{8}$ lb   **23.** $\frac{11}{20}$ lb
25. $5\frac{7}{8}$ in.   **27.** $95\frac{1}{5}$ mi   **29.** $14\frac{13}{24}$ flats   **31.** $\frac{1}{4}$ tub
33. $4\frac{5}{6}$ ft $\times$ $10\frac{7}{12}$ ft   **35.** $\frac{1}{2}$ lb   **37.** $134\frac{1}{4}''$ **39.** $3\frac{4}{5}$ hr
41. $28\frac{3}{4}$ yd   **43.** $7\frac{5}{12}$ lb   **45.** 400 cu ft   **47.** About 690,000
49. 15 mpg   **51.** $5\frac{3}{8}$ yd   **53.** $59,538\frac{1}{8}$ sq ft   **55.** About 301,360,000   **57.** 16 L   **59.** $76\frac{1}{4}$ sq ft   **61.** 690 kg; $\frac{14}{23}$ cement; $\frac{5}{23}$ stone; $\frac{4}{23}$ sand; 1   **63.** $62\frac{1}{2}$ ft^2 **65.** $12\frac{4}{5}$ titles   **67.** Divisor; quotient; dividend   **68.** Common   **69.** Composite
70. Divisible; divisible   **71.** Multiplications; divisions; additions; subtractions   **72.** Addends   **73.** Numerator
74. Reciprocal   **75.** $\frac{4}{15}$; $320   **77.** $\frac{1}{12}$

Exercise Set 2.6, p. 164

1. $\frac{59}{30}$, or $1\frac{29}{30}$ **3.** $\frac{3}{20}$ **5.** $\frac{211}{8}$, or $26\frac{3}{8}$ **7.** $\frac{7}{16}$ **9.** $\frac{1}{36}$ **11.** $\frac{3}{8}$
13. $\frac{17}{6}$, or $2\frac{5}{6}$ **15.** $\frac{8395}{84}$, or $99\frac{79}{84}$ **17.** $\frac{37}{48}$ **19.** $\frac{25}{72}$
21. $\frac{103}{16}$, or $6\frac{7}{16}$ **23.** $16\frac{7}{96}$ mi   **25.** $9\frac{19}{40}$ lb   **27.** 0   **29.** 1
31. $\frac{1}{2}$ **33.** $\frac{1}{2}$ **35.** 0   **37.** 1   **39.** 3   **41.** 13   **43.** 2
45. $1\frac{1}{2}$ **47.** $\frac{1}{2}$ **49.** $271\frac{1}{2}$ **51.** 3   **53.** 100   **55.** $29\frac{1}{2}$
57. $\frac{8}{3}$ **58.** $\frac{3}{8}$ **59.** Prime: 5, 7, 23, 43; composite: 9, 14; neither: 1   **60.** 59 R 77   **61.** 16 people   **62.** 43 mg
63. $a = 2, b = 8$ **65.** The largest is $\frac{4}{3} + \frac{5}{2} = \frac{23}{6}$.

Summary and Review: Chapter 2, p. 167

Concept Reinforcement

1. True   **2.** True   **3.** False   **4.** True   **5.** False

Important Concepts

1. 0, 1, 18   **2.** $\frac{56}{96}$ **3.** $\frac{5}{14}$ **4.** $\frac{70}{9}$ **5.** $\frac{7}{10}$ **6.** $\frac{112}{180}$, or $\frac{28}{45}$ **7.** $\frac{4}{35}$
8. <   **9.** $\frac{59}{99}$ **10.** $\frac{26}{3}$ **11.** $7\frac{5}{6}$ **12.** $7\frac{27}{28}$ **13.** $14\frac{14}{25}$
14. $2\frac{37}{38}$ **15.** $\frac{7}{3}$ cups   **16.** $\frac{9}{2}$, or $4\frac{1}{2}$ **17.** $4\frac{1}{2}$

Review Exercises

1. Numerator: 2; denominator: 7   **2.** $\frac{3}{5}$ **3.** $\frac{7}{6}$ **4.** $\frac{2}{5}$ **5.** $\frac{1}{4}$
6. 1   **7.** $\frac{1}{3}$ **8.** $\frac{11}{23}$ **9.** Not defined   **10.** 0   **11.** $\frac{39}{40}$
12. 18   **13.** 6   **14.** $\frac{2}{7}$ **15.** $\frac{32}{225}$ **16.** $\frac{15}{100} = \frac{3}{20}, \frac{38}{100} = \frac{19}{50}$, $\frac{23}{100} = \frac{23}{100} \cdot \frac{24}{24} = \frac{6}{25}$ **17.** $\frac{3}{2}$ **18.** 56   **19.** $\frac{5}{2}$ **20.** 24
21. $\frac{2}{3}$ **22.** $\frac{1}{14}$ **23.** $\frac{2}{3}$ **24.** $\frac{1}{22}$ **25.** $\frac{3}{20}$ **26.** $\frac{10}{7}$

27. $\frac{5}{4}$ **28.** $\frac{1}{3}$ **29.** 9   **30.** $\frac{36}{47}$ **31.** $\frac{9}{2}$ **32.** 2   **33.** $\frac{11}{6}$
34. $\frac{1}{4}$ **35.** $\frac{9}{4}$ **36.** 300   **37.** 1   **38.** $\frac{4}{9}$ **39.** $\frac{63}{40}$ **40.** $\frac{19}{48}$
41. $\frac{25}{12}$ **42.** $\frac{891}{1000}$ **43.** $\frac{1}{3}$ **44.** $\frac{1}{8}$ **45.** $\frac{5}{27}$ **46.** $\frac{11}{18}$ **47.** >
48. >   **49.** <   **50.** >   **51.** $\frac{3}{10}$ **52.** 240   **53.** $\frac{19}{40}$
54. $\frac{2}{5}$ **55.** $\frac{15}{2}$ **56.** $\frac{67}{8}$ **57.** $\frac{13}{3}$ **58.** $\frac{75}{7}$ **59.** $2\frac{1}{3}$ **60.** $6\frac{3}{4}$
61. $12\frac{3}{5}$ **62.** $3\frac{1}{2}$ **63.** $10\frac{2}{3}$ **64.** $11\frac{11}{15}$ **65.** $10\frac{2}{3}$ **66.** $8\frac{1}{4}$
67. $7\frac{7}{9}$ **68.** $4\frac{11}{15}$ **69.** $4\frac{3}{20}$ **70.** $13\frac{3}{8}$ **71.** 16   **72.** $3\frac{1}{2}$
73. $2\frac{21}{50}$ **74.** 6   **75.** 12   **76.** $1\frac{7}{17}$ **77.** $\frac{1}{8}$ **78.** $\frac{9}{10}$
79. 9 days   **80.** About 22,800,000 metric tons   **81.** $4\frac{1}{4}$ yd
82. $177\frac{3}{4}$ in^2 **83.** $50\frac{1}{4}$ in^2 **84.** $1\frac{73}{100}$ in.   **85.** 24 lb
86. 1000 km   **87.** $13\frac{1}{4}$ in. $\times$ $13\frac{1}{4}$ in.: perimeter = 53 in., area = $175\frac{9}{16}$ sq in.; $13\frac{1}{4}$ in. $\times$ $3\frac{1}{4}$ in.: perimeter = 33 in., area = $43\frac{1}{16}$ sq in.   **88.** $\frac{1}{3}$ cup; 2 cups   **89.** $15   **90.** 60 bags
91. $850   **92.** $8\frac{3}{8}$ cups   **93.** $63\frac{2}{3}$ pies; $19\frac{1}{3}$ pies   **94.** 1
95. $\frac{7}{40}$ **96.** 3   **97.** $\frac{77}{240}$ **98.** $\frac{1}{2}$ **99.** 0   **100.** 1   **101.** 7
102. 10   **103.** $5\frac{1}{2}$ **104.** 0   **105.** $2\frac{1}{2}$ **106.** $28\frac{1}{2}$ **107.** A
108. B   **109.** D   **110.** D   **111.** $a = 11,176; b = 9887$
112. $\frac{6}{3} + \frac{5}{4} = 3\frac{1}{4}$

Understanding Through Discussion and Writing

1. No; if the sum of the fractional parts of the mixed numerals is n/n, then the sum of the mixed numerals is an integer. For example, $1\frac{1}{5} + 6\frac{4}{5} = 7\frac{5}{5} = 8$.   **2.** The student is probably multiplying the divisor by the reciprocal of the dividend rather than multiplying the dividend by the reciprocal of the divisor.
3. Taking $\frac{1}{2}$ of a number is equivalent to multiplying the number by $\frac{1}{2}$. Dividing by $\frac{1}{2}$ is equivalent to multiplying by the reciprocal of $\frac{1}{2}$, or 2. Thus taking $\frac{1}{2}$ of a number is not the same as dividing by $\frac{1}{2}$.   **4.** The student is multiplying the whole numbers to get the whole-number portion of the answer and multiplying fractions to get the fraction part of the answer. The student should have converted each mixed numeral to fraction notation, multiplied, simplified, and then converted back to a mixed numeral. The correct answer is $4\frac{6}{7}$.   **5.** Since $\frac{1}{7}$ is a smaller number than $\frac{2}{3}$, there are more $\frac{1}{7}$'s in 5 than $\frac{2}{3}$'s. Thus, $5 \div \frac{1}{7}$ is a greater number than $5 \div \frac{2}{3}$.   **6.** No; in order to simplify a fraction, we must be able to remove a factor of the type $\frac{n}{n}$, $n \neq 0$, where n is a factor that the numerator and the denominator have in common.

Test: Chapter 2, p. 175

1. [2.1a] $\frac{3}{4}$ **2.** [2.3c] >   **3.** [2.1b] 26   **4.** [2.1b] 1
5. [2.1b] Not defined   **6.** [2.1b] 0   **7.** [2.1e] $\frac{2}{3}$ **8.** [2.1c], [2.2a] 32
9. [2.1c], [2.2a] $\frac{3}{2}$ **10.** [2.2a] $\frac{5}{2}$ **11.** [2.2a] $\frac{2}{9}$ **12.** [2.2b] $\frac{8}{5}$
13. [2.2b] 4   **14.** [2.2b] $\frac{1}{18}$ **15.** [2.2c] $\frac{8}{5}$ **16.** [2.2c] 18
17. [2.2c] $\frac{18}{7}$ **18.** [2.3a] 3   **19.** [2.3a] $\frac{37}{24}$ **20.** [2.3a] $\frac{921}{1000}$
21. [2.3b] $\frac{1}{3}$ **22.** [2.3b] $\frac{1}{12}$ **23.** [2.3b] $\frac{77}{120}$ **24.** [2.3d] $\frac{15}{4}$
25. [2.2d] $\frac{7}{4}$ **26.** [2.4a] $4\frac{1}{2}$ **27.** [2.4a] $\frac{79}{8}$ **28.** [2.4b] $14\frac{1}{5}$
29. [2.4c] $4\frac{7}{24}$ **30.** [2.4d] $4\frac{1}{2}$ **31.** [2.4e] 2
32. [2.5a] **(a)** 3 in.; **(b)** $4\frac{1}{2}$ in.   **33.** [2.5a] 80 books
34. [2.5a] 5 qt   **35.** [2.5a] $\frac{1}{16}$ in.   **36.** [2.6a] $\frac{3}{4}$ **37.** [2.6b] 0
38. [2.6b] 1   **39.** [2.6b] 16   **40.** [2.6b] $1214\frac{1}{2}$ **41.** [2.5a] B
42. [2.6a] $\frac{7}{960}$ **43.** [2.5a] Rebecca walks $\frac{17}{56}$ mi farther.

CHAPTER 3

Exercise Set 3.1, p. 185

1. Four hundred eighty-six and thirty-four hundredths
3. One hundred forty-six thousandths   **5.** Two hundred forty-nine and eighty-nine hundredths   **7.** Three and seven hundred eighty-five thousandths   **9.** Twenty-seven and one thousand, two hundred forty-five ten-thousandths   **11.** $\frac{83}{10}$

13. $\frac{356}{100}$ **15.** $\frac{20,003}{1000}$ **17.** $\frac{10,008}{10,000}$ **19.** $\frac{372}{10}$ **21.** $\frac{13}{100,000}$
23. 0.8 **25.** 3.798 **27.** 8.89 **29.** 0.00019 **31.** 0.0078
33. 0.376193 **35.** 2.9 **37.** 3.098 **39.** 99.44 **41.** 2.1739
43. 0.58 **45.** 0.91 **47.** 0.001 **49.** 235.07 **51.** $\frac{4}{100}$
53. 0.4325 **55.** 0.1 **57.** 0.5 **59.** 2.7 **61.** 123.7
63. 0.89 **65.** 0.67 **67.** 1.00 **69.** 0.09 **71.** 0.325
73. 17.001 **75.** 10.101 **77.** 9.999 **79.** 800 **81.** 809.573
83. 810 **85.** 34.5439 **87.** 34.54 **89.** 35 **91.** $6\frac{3}{5}$
92. 54 **93.** 6170 **94.** 6200 **95.** 6000
96. $2 \cdot 2 \cdot 2 \cdot 2 \cdot 5 \cdot 5 \cdot 5$, or $2^4 \cdot 5^3$ **97.** $2 \cdot 3 \cdot 3 \cdot 5 \cdot 17$, or $2 \cdot 3^2 \cdot 5 \cdot 17$ **98.** $2 \cdot 7 \cdot 11 \cdot 13$ **99.** $2 \cdot 2 \cdot 2 \cdot 7 \cdot 7 \cdot 11$, or $2^3 \cdot 7^2 \cdot 11$ **101.** 2.000001, 2.0119, 2.018, 2.0302, 2.1, 2.108, 2.109 **103.** 6.78346 **105.** 0.03030

Calculator Corner, p. 190

1. 317.645 **2.** 506.553 **3.** 17.15 **4.** 49.08 **5.** 4.4
6. 33.83 **7.** 454.74 **8.** 0.99

Exercise Set 3.2, p. 193

1. 334.37 **3.** 1576.215 **5.** 132.560 **7.** 50.0248 **9.** 40.007
11. 977.955 **13.** 771.967 **15.** 8754.8221 **17.** 49.02
19. 85.921 **21.** 2.4975 **23.** 3.397 **25.** 8.85 **27.** 3.37
29. 1.045 **31.** 3.703 **33.** 0.9902 **35.** 99.66 **37.** 4.88
39. 0.994 **41.** 17.802 **43.** 51.13 **45.** 32.7386 **47.** 4.0622
49. 11.65 **51.** 384.68 **53.** 582.97 **55.** 15,335.3
57. The balance forward should read:
$ 9704.56
9677.12
10,677.12
10,553.17
10,429.15
10,416.72
12,916.72
12,778.94
12,797.82
9997.82
59. 35,000 **60.** 34,000 **61.** $\frac{1}{6}$ **62.** $\frac{34}{45}$ **63.** 6166 **64.** 5366
65. $16\frac{1}{2}$ servings **66.** $60\frac{1}{5}$ mi **67.** 345.8

Calculator Corner, p. 199

1. 48.6 **2.** 6930.5 **3.** 142.803 **4.** 0.5076 **5.** 7916.4
6. 20.4153

Exercise Set 3.3, p. 201

1. 60.2 **3.** 6.72 **5.** 0.252 **7.** 0.522 **9.** 237.6
11. 583,686.852 **13.** 780 **15.** 8.923 **17.** 0.09768
19. 0.782 **21.** 521.6 **23.** 3.2472 **25.** 897.6 **27.** 322.07
29. 55.68 **31.** 3487.5 **33.** 50.0004 **35.** 114.42902
37. 13.284 **39.** 90.72 **41.** 0.0028728 **43.** 0.72523
45. 1.872115 **47.** 45,678 **49.** 2888¢ **51.** 66¢ **53.** $0.34
55. $34.45 **57.** 47,300,000,000 **59.** 9,300,000
61. 23,400,000,000 **63.** $11\frac{1}{5}$ **64.** $\frac{35}{72}$ **65.** $2\frac{7}{15}$ **66.** $7\frac{2}{15}$
67. 342 **68.** 87 **69.** 4566 **70.** 1257 **71.** 87
72. 1176 R 14 **73.** $10^{21} = 1$ sextillion **75.** $10^{24} = 1$ septillion

Calculator Corner, p. 205

1. 14.3 **2.** 2.56 **3.** 0.064 **4.** 75.8

Exercise Set 3.4, p. 211

1. 2.99 **3.** 23.78 **5.** 7.48 **7.** 7.2 **9.** 1.143 **11.** 4.041
13. 56 **15.** 70 **17.** 20 **19.** 0.4 **21.** 0.41 **23.** 8.5
25. 9.3 **27.** 0.625 **29.** 0.26 **31.** 15.625 **33.** 2.34
35. 0.47 **37.** 0.2134567 **39.** 2.359 **41.** 4.26487 **43.** 169.4
45. 1023.7 **47.** 4256.1 **49.** 9.3 **51.** 0.0090678 **53.** 45.6
55. 2107 **57.** 303.003 **59.** 446.208 **61.** 24.14
63. 13.0072 **65.** 19.3204 **67.** 473.188278 **69.** 10.49
71. 911.13 **73.** 205 **75.** $1288.36 **77.** 5.42 million stays

79. $\frac{6}{7}$ **80.** $\frac{7}{8}$ **81.** $\frac{19}{73}$ **82.** $\frac{23}{31}$ **83.** $2 \cdot 2 \cdot 3 \cdot 3 \cdot 19$, or $2^2 \cdot 3^2 \cdot 19$ **84.** $2 \cdot 3 \cdot 3 \cdot 3 \cdot 3$, or $2 \cdot 3^4$ **85.** $3 \cdot 3 \cdot 223$, or $3^2 \cdot 223$ **86.** $5 \cdot 401$ **87.** $15\frac{1}{8}$ **88.** $5\frac{7}{8}$ **89.** 6.254194585
91. 1000 **93.** 100

Mid-Chapter Review: Chapter 3, p. 215

1. False **2.** True **3.** True
4.
$$y + 12.8 = 23.35$$
$$y + 12.8 - 12.8 = 23.35 - 12.8$$
$$y + 0 = 10.55$$
$$y = 10.55$$
5. $5.6 + 4.3 \times (6.5 - 0.25)^2 = 5.6 + 4.3 \times (6.25)^2$
$$= 5.6 + 4.3 \times 39.0625$$
$$= 5.6 + 167.96875$$
$$= 173.56875$$
6. Nine and sixty-nine hundredths **7.** 1,050,000 **8.** $\frac{453}{100}$
9. $\frac{287}{1000}$ **10.** 0.13 **11.** 5.2 **12.** 0.7 **13.** 6.39 **14.** 35.67
15. 8.002 **16.** 28.462 **17.** 28.46 **18.** 28.5 **19.** 28
20. 50.095 **21.** 1214.862 **22.** 5.228 **23.** 18.24 **24.** 272.19
25. 5.593 **26.** 15.55 **27.** 39.37 **28.** 4.14 **29.** 92.871
30. 8123.6 **31.** 2.937 **32.** 5.06 **33.** 3.2 **34.** 763.4
35. 0.914036 **36.** 2045¢ **37.** $1.47 **38.** 12.7 **39.** 8.4
40. 59.774 **41.** 33.33 **42.** The student probably rounded over successively from the thousandths place as follows: $236.448 \approx 236.45 \approx 236.5 \approx 237$. The student should have considered only the tenths place and rounded down.
43. The decimal points were not lined up before the subtraction was carried out. **44.** $10 \div 0.2 = \frac{10}{0.2} = \frac{10}{0.2} \cdot \frac{10}{10} = \frac{100}{2} = 100 \div 2$.
45. $0.247 \div 0.1 = \frac{247}{1000} \div \frac{1}{10} = \frac{247}{1000} \cdot \frac{10}{1} = \frac{247 \cdot 10}{10 \cdot 100} = \frac{247}{100} = 2.47 \neq 0.0247$;
$0.247 \div 10 = \frac{247}{1000} \div 10 = \frac{247}{1000} \cdot \frac{1}{10} = \frac{247}{10,000} = 0.0247 \neq 2.47$

Exercise Set 3.5, p. 222

1. 0.23 **3.** 0.6 **5.** 0.325 **7.** 0.2 **9.** 0.85 **11.** 0.375
13. 0.975 **15.** 0.52 **17.** 20.016 **19.** 0.25 **21.** 1.16
23. 1.1875 **25.** $0.2\overline{6}$ **27.** $0.\overline{3}$ **29.** $1.\overline{3}$ **31.** $1.1\overline{6}$
33. $0.\overline{571428}$ **35.** $0.91\overline{6}$ **37.** 0.3; 0.27; 0.267 **39.** 0.3; 0.33; 0.333 **41.** 1.3; 1.33; 1.333 **43.** 1.2; 1.17; 1.167 **45.** 0.6; 0.57; 0.571 **47.** 0.9; 0.92; 0.917 **49.** 0.2; 0.18; 0.182 **51.** 0.3; 0.28; 0.278 **53.** (a) 0.429; (b) 0.75; (c) 0.571; (d) 1.333
55. 15.8 mpg **57.** 17.8 mpg **59.** 15.2 mph **61.** $29.5625; $29.56 **63.** $27.875; $27.88 **65.** $31.484375; $31.48
67. 11.06 **69.** 8.4 **71.** $417.51\overline{6}$ **73.** 0 **75.** 2.8125
77. 0.20425 **79.** 317.14 **81.** 0.1825 **83.** 18 **85.** 2.736
87. 21 **88.** $238\frac{7}{8}$ **89.** 10 **90.** $\frac{43}{52}$ **91.** $50\frac{5}{24}$ **92.** $30\frac{7}{10}$
93. $1\frac{1}{2}$ **94.** $14\frac{13}{24}$ **95.** $1\frac{1}{24}$ cups **96.** $1\frac{33}{100}$ in. **97.** $0.\overline{142857}$
99. $0.\overline{428571}$ **101.** $0.\overline{714285}$ **103.** $0.\overline{1}$ **105.** $0.\overline{001}$

Exercise Set 3.6, p. 229

1. (d) **3.** (c) **5.** (a) **7.** (c) **9.** 1.6 **11.** 6 **13.** 60
15. 2.3 **17.** 180 **19.** (a) **21.** (c) **23.** (b) **25.** (b)
27. $1800 \div 9 = 200$ posts; answers may vary
29. $2 \cdot 12 = $24; answers may vary **31.** Repeating
32. Multiple **33.** Distributive **34.** Solution
35. Multiplicative **36.** Commutative **37.** Denominator; multiple **38.** Divisible; divisible **39.** Yes **41.** No
43. (a) $+, \times$; (b) $+, \times, -$

Translating for Success, p. 239

1. I **2.** C **3.** N **4.** A **5.** G **6.** B **7.** D **8.** O **9.** F
10. M

Exercise Set 3.7, p. 240

1. $43.1 billion **3.** 6.29 million passengers **5.** $151.1 million
7. $0.51 **9.** 102.8°F **11.** $64,333,333.33 **13.** Area: 8.125 sq cm; perimeter: 11.5 cm **15.** 22,691.5 mi **17.** 20.2 mpg
19. 11.9752 cu ft **21.** 78.1 cm **23.** 28.5 cm **25.** $24.33

27. 2.31 cm   **29.** 876 calories   **31.** \$1171.74   **33.** 227.75 sq ft
35. 0.364   **37.** 2152.56 sq yd   **39.** 10.8¢   **41.** \$906.50
43. 6.052 billion   **45.** 1.4°F   **47.** \$262,153   **49.** \$83,782
51. \$1,401,429   **53.** \$29,133   **55.** \$53.04   **57.** \$3745.41
59. \$1406.75   **61.** 6335   **62.** $\frac{31}{24}$ **63.** $6\frac{5}{6}$ **64.** $\frac{23}{15}$ **65.** $\frac{1}{24}$
66. 2803   **67.** $\frac{2}{15}$ **68.** $1\frac{5}{6}$ **69.** $\frac{129}{251}$ **70.** $\frac{5}{16}$ **71.** $\frac{13}{25}$ **72.** $\frac{25}{19}$
73. 28 min   **74.** $7\frac{1}{5}$ min   **75.** 186 calories   **76.** 30 calories
77. \$17.28

Summary and Review: Chapter 3, p. 247

Concept Reinforcement
1. True   **2.** False   **3.** True   **4.** False   **5.** True

Important Concepts
1. $\frac{5093}{100}$ **2.** 81.7   **3.** 42.159   **4.** 153.35   **5.** 38.611
6. 207.848   **7.** 19.11   **8.** 0.176   **9.** 60,437   **10.** 7.4
11. 0.047   **12.** 15,690

Review Exercises
1. 6,590,000   **2.** 3,100,000,000   **3.** Three and forty-seven
hundredths   **4.** Thirty-one thousandths   **5.** Twenty-seven and
one ten-thousandth   **6.** Nine tenths   **7.** $\frac{9}{100}$ **8.** $\frac{4561}{1000}$
9. $\frac{89}{1000}$ **10.** $\frac{30,227}{10,000}$ **11.** 0.034   **12.** 4.2603   **13.** 27.91
14. 867.006   **15.** 0.034   **16.** 0.91   **17.** 0.741   **18.** 1.041
19. 17.4   **20.** 17.43   **21.** 17.429   **22.** 17   **23.** 574.519
24. 0.6838   **25.** 229.1   **26.** 45.551   **27.** 29.2092   **28.** 790.29
29. 29.148   **30.** 70.7891   **31.** 12.96   **32.** 0.14442   **33.** 4.3
34. 0.02468   **35.** 7.5   **36.** 0.45   **37.** 45.2   **38.** 1.022
39. 0.2763   **40.** 1389.2   **41.** 496.2795   **42.** 6.95   **43.** 42.54
44. 4.9911   **45.** \$15.52   **46.** 1.9 lb   **47.** \$784.47   **48.** \$171.24
49. 14.5 mpg   **50. (a)** 106.2 lb; **(b)** 15.2 lb   **51.** 272   **52.** 216
53. \$125   **54.** 0.52   **55.** 0.45   **56.** 2.75   **57.** 3.25   **58.** $1.1\overline{6}$
59. $1.\overline{54}$ **60.** 1.5   **61.** 1.55   **62.** 1.545   **63.** \$82.73
64. \$4.87   **65.** 2493¢   **66.** 986¢   **67.** 1.8045   **68.** 57.1449
69. 15.6375   **70.** D   **71.** B   **72. (a)** $2.56 \times 6.4 \div 51.2 -$
$17.4 + 89.7 = 72.62$; **(b)** $(11.12 - 0.29) \times 3^4 = 877.23$
73. $1 = 3 \cdot \frac{1}{3} = 3(0.33333333\ldots) = 0.99999999\ldots$, or $0.\overline{9}$

Understanding Through Discussion and Writing
1. Count the number of decimal places. Move the decimal point
that many places to the right and write the result over a denominator of 1 followed by that many zeros.
2. $346.708 \times 0.1 = \frac{346,708}{1000} \times \frac{1}{10} = \frac{346,708}{10,000} = 34.6708 \neq 3467.08$
3. When the denominator of a fraction is a multiple of 10, long
division is not the fastest way to convert the fraction to decimal
notation. Many times when the denominator is a factor of some
multiple of 10, this is also the case. The latter situation occurs when
the denominator has only 2's or 5's or both as factors.   **4.** Multiply
by 1 to get a denominator that is a power of 10:

$$\frac{44}{125} = \frac{44}{125} \cdot \frac{8}{8} = \frac{352}{1000} = 0.352.$$

We can also divide to find that $\frac{44}{125} = 0.352$.

Test: Chapter 3, p. 252

1. [3.3b] 18,400,000   **2.** [3.3b] 13,100,000,000   **3.** [3.1a] Two and
thirty-four hundredths   **4.** [3.1a] One hundred five and five ten-
thousandths   **5.** [3.1b] $\frac{91}{100}$ **6.** [3.1b] $\frac{2769}{1000}$ **7.** [3.1b] 0.074
8. [3.1b] 3.7047   **9.** [3.1b] 756.09   **10.** [3.1b] 91.703
11. [3.1c] 0.162   **12.** [3.1c] 0.078   **13.** [3.1c] 0.9   **14.** [3.1d] 6
15. [3.1d] 5.68   **16.** [3.1d] 5.678   **17.** [3.1d] 5.7

18. [3.2a] 0.7902   **19.** [3.2a] 186.5   **20.** [3.2a] 1033.23
21. [3.2b] 48.357   **22.** [3.2b] 19.0901   **23.** [3.2b] 152.8934
24. [3.3a] 0.03   **25.** [3.3a] 0.21345   **26.** [3.3a] 73,962
27. [3.4a] 4.75   **28.** [3.4a] 30.4   **29.** [3.4a] 0.19
30. [3.4a] 0.34689   **31.** [3.4a] 34,689   **32.** [3.4b] 84.26
33. [3.2c] 8.982   **34.** [3.7a] \$133.99   **35.** [3.7a] 28.3 mpg
36. [3.7a] \$592.45   **37.** [3.7a] \$293.93   **38.** [3.7a] 67.44 million
passengers   **39.** [3.6a] 198   **40.** [3.6a] 4   **41.** [3.5a] 0.35
42. [3.5a] 0.88   **43.** [3.5a] 5.25   **44.** [3.5a] 0.75   **45.** [3.5a] $1.\overline{2}$
46. [3.5a] $2.\overline{142857}$ **47.** [3.5b] 2.1   **48.** [3.5b] 2.14
49. [3.5b] 2.143   **50.** [3.4c] 40.0065   **51.** [3.4c] 384.8464
52. [3.5c] 302.4   **53.** [3.3b] B   **54.** [3.7a] \$35
55. [3.1b, c] $\frac{2}{3}, \frac{5}{7}, \frac{15}{19}, \frac{11}{13}, \frac{17}{20}, \frac{13}{15}$

CHAPTER 4

Exercise Set 4.1, p. 267
1. $\frac{178}{572}$ **3.** $\frac{8\frac{3}{4}}{9\frac{5}{6}}$ **5.** $\frac{21}{4}, \frac{4}{21}$ **7.** $\frac{2}{3}$ **9.** $\frac{7}{9}$ **11.** $\frac{478}{213}, \frac{213}{478}$
13. 40 km/h   **15.** 7.48 mi/sec   **17.** 32 mpg
19. 43,728 people/sq mi   **21.** 186,000 mi/sec
23. 0.623 gal/ft^2 **25.** 124 km/h   **27.** No   **29.** Yes
31. Yes   **33.** No   **35.** 12   **37.** 20   **39.** 18   **41.** $\frac{28}{3}$, or $9\frac{1}{3}$
43. 2.7   **45.** 1.8   **47.** $\frac{3}{8}$ **49.** $\frac{16}{75}$ **51.** 0.7   **53.** $\frac{1}{20}$
55. 175 bulbs   **57.** 954 deer   **59.** 120 lb   **61.** 100 oz
63. 212.52 million, or 212,520,000
65. (a) About 122 gal; **(b)** 3080 mi   **67.** 880 calories
69. 58.1 mi   **71.** 64 cans   **73.** 4063 theaters
74. 281.4 million tracks   **75.** \$151,000

Calculator Corner, p. 274
1. 0.14   **2.** 0.00069   **3.** 0.438   **4.** 1.25

Exercise Set 4.2, p. 276
1. $\frac{90}{100}$; $90 \times \frac{1}{100}$; 90×0.01 **3.** $\frac{12.5}{100}$; $12.5 \times \frac{1}{100}$; 12.5×0.01
5. 0.67   **7.** 0.456   **9.** 0.5901   **11.** 0.1   **13.** 0.01   **15.** 2
17. 0.001   **19.** 0.0009   **21.** 0.0018   **23.** 0.2319
25. 0.14875   **27.** 0.565   **29.** 0.97   **31.** 0.07; 0.08
33. 0.548   **35.** 47%   **37.** 3%   **39.** 870%   **41.** 33.4%
43. 75%   **45.** 40%   **47.** 0.6%   **49.** 1.7%   **51.** 27.18%
53. 2.39%   **55.** 27%   **57.** 5.7%; 17.6%   **59.** 90.6%; 88%
61. 0.64; 0.3; 0.04; 0.02   **63.** $33\frac{1}{3}$ **64.** $37\frac{1}{2}$ **65.** $9\frac{3}{8}$
66. $18\frac{9}{16}$ **67.** $5\frac{11}{14}$ **68.** $111\frac{2}{3}$ **69.** $0.\overline{6}$ **70.** $0.\overline{3}$
71. $0.8\overline{3}$ **72.** $1.41\overline{6}$ **73.** $2.\overline{6}$ **74.** 0.9375   **75.** 50%
77. 70%   **79.** 20%

Calculator Corner, p. 279
1. 52%   **2.** 38.46%   **3.** 110.26%   **4.** 171.43%   **5.** 59.62%
6. 28.31%

Exercise Set 4.3, p. 283
1. 41%   **3.** 5%   **5.** 20%   **7.** 30%   **9.** 50%   **11.** 87.5%,
or $87\frac{1}{2}$%   **13.** 80%   **15.** 66.$\overline{6}$%, or $66\frac{2}{3}$%   **17.** 16.$\overline{6}$%, or
$16\frac{2}{3}$%   **19.** 18.75%, or $18\frac{3}{4}$%   **21.** 81.25%, or $81\frac{1}{4}$%
23. 16%   **25.** 5%   **27.** 34%   **29.** 8%; 59%   **31.** 22%
33. 12%   **35.** 15%   **37.** $\frac{17}{20}$ **39.** $\frac{5}{8}$ **41.** $\frac{1}{3}$ **43.** $\frac{1}{6}$ **45.** $\frac{29}{400}$
47. $\frac{1}{125}$ **49.** $\frac{203}{800}$ **51.** $\frac{176}{225}$ **53.** $\frac{711}{1100}$ **55.** $\frac{3}{2}$ **57.** $\frac{13}{40,000}$
59. $\frac{1}{3}$ **61.** $\frac{3}{50}$ **63.** $\frac{3}{25}$ **65.** $\frac{3}{4}$ **67.** $\frac{3}{20}$ **69.** $\frac{209}{1000}$

71.

Fraction Notation	Decimal Notation	Percent Notation
$\frac{1}{8}$	0.125	12.5%, or $12\frac{1}{2}$%
$\frac{1}{6}$	$0.1\overline{6}$	$16.\overline{6}$%, or $16\frac{2}{3}$%
$\frac{1}{5}$	0.2	20%
$\frac{1}{4}$	0.25	25%
$\frac{1}{3}$	$0.\overline{3}$	$33.\overline{3}$%, or $33\frac{1}{3}$%
$\frac{3}{8}$	0.375	37.5%, or $37\frac{1}{2}$%
$\frac{2}{5}$	0.4	40%
$\frac{1}{2}$	0.5	50%

73.

Fraction Notation	Decimal Notation	Percent Notation
$\frac{1}{2}$	0.5	50%
$\frac{1}{3}$	$0.\overline{3}$	$33.\overline{3}$%, or $33\frac{1}{3}$%
$\frac{1}{4}$	0.25	25%
$\frac{1}{6}$	$0.1\overline{6}$	$16.\overline{6}$%, or $16\frac{2}{3}$%
$\frac{1}{8}$	0.125	12.5%, or $12\frac{1}{2}$%
$\frac{3}{4}$	0.75	75%
$\frac{5}{6}$	$0.8\overline{3}$	$83.\overline{3}$%, or $83\frac{1}{3}$%
$\frac{3}{8}$	0.375	37.5%, or $37\frac{1}{2}$%

75. 70 **76.** 5 **77.** 400 **78.** 18.75 **79.** 23.125
80. 25.5 **81.** 4.5 **82.** 8.75 **83.** $33\frac{1}{3}$ **84.** $37\frac{1}{2}$ **85.** $83\frac{1}{3}$
86. $20\frac{1}{2}$ **87.** $43\frac{1}{8}$ **88.** $62\frac{1}{6}$ **89.** $18\frac{3}{8}$ **90.** $7\frac{4}{9}$ **91.** $\frac{18}{17}$
92. $\frac{209}{10}$ **93.** $\frac{203}{2}$ **94.** $\frac{259}{8}$ **95.** $11.\overline{1}$% **97.** $257.\overline{46317}$%
99. $0.01\overline{5}$ **101.** $1.04\overline{142857}$ **103.** $\frac{1}{6}$%, $\frac{2}{7}$%, 0.5%, $1\frac{1}{6}$%, 1.6%, $16\frac{1}{6}$%, 0.2, $\frac{1}{2}$, $0.\overline{54}$, 1.6

Calculator Corner, p. 290

1. $5.04 **2.** 0.0112 **3.** 450 **4.** $1000 **5.** 2.5% **6.** 12%

Exercise Set 4.4, p. 291

1. $a = 32\% \times 78$ **3.** $89 = p \times 99$ **5.** $13 = 25\% \times b$
7. 234.6 **9.** 45 **11.** $18 **13.** 1.9 **15.** 78% **17.** 200%
19. 50% **21.** 125% **23.** 40 **25.** $40 **27.** 88 **29.** 20
31. 6.25 **33.** $846.60 **35.** 1216 **37.** $\frac{9}{100}$ **38.** $\frac{179}{100}$
39. $\frac{875}{1000}$, or $\frac{7}{8}$ **40.** $\frac{125}{1000}$, or $\frac{1}{8}$ **41.** $\frac{9375}{10,000}$, or $\frac{15}{16}$ **42.** $\frac{6875}{10,000}$, or $\frac{11}{16}$
43. 0.89 **44.** 0.07 **45.** 0.3 **46.** 0.017 **47.** $800 (can vary); $843.20 **49.** $10,000 (can vary); $10,400 **51.** $1875

Exercise Set 4.5, p. 297

1. $\frac{37}{100} = \frac{a}{74}$ **3.** $\frac{N}{100} = \frac{4.3}{5.9}$ **5.** $\frac{25}{100} = \frac{14}{b}$ **7.** 68.4 **9.** 462
11. 40 **13.** 2.88 **15.** 25% **17.** 102% **19.** 25%
21. 93.75%, or $93\frac{3}{4}$% **23.** $72 **25.** 90 **27.** 88 **29.** 20
31. 25 **33.** $780.20 **35.** 200 **37.** 8 **38.** 4000 **39.** 8
40. 2074 **41.** 100 **42.** 15 **43.** $8.0\overline{4}$ **44.** $\frac{3}{16}$, or 0.1875
45. $\frac{43}{48}$ qt **46.** $\frac{1}{8}$ T **47.** $1170 (can vary); $1118.64

Mid-Chapter Review: Chapter 4, p. 299

1. False **2.** True **3.** False **4.** True
5. $\frac{1}{2}\% = \frac{1}{2} \cdot \frac{1}{100} = \frac{1}{200}$
6. $\frac{80}{1000} = \frac{8}{100} = 8\%$ **7.** $5.5\% = \frac{5.5}{100} = \frac{55}{1000} = \frac{11}{200}$
8. $0.375 = \frac{375}{1000} = \frac{37.5}{100} = 37.5\%$
9.
$$15 = p \times 80$$
$$\frac{15}{80} = \frac{p \times 80}{80}$$
$$\frac{15}{80} = p$$
$$0.1875 = p$$
$$18.75\% = p$$
10.
$$\frac{x}{4} = \frac{3}{6}$$
$$x \cdot 6 = 4 \cdot 3$$
$$\frac{x \cdot 6}{6} = \frac{4 \cdot 3}{6}$$
$$x = 2$$
11. $\frac{1}{3}$ **12.** $\frac{2}{7}$ **13.** 48.67 km/h **14.** 60.75 mi/hr, or 60.75 mph
15. 40 **16.** 9 **17.** 4.32 **18.** $\frac{1}{2}$ **19.** 49.917 ¢/oz
20. 11.611 ¢/oz **21.** 0.28 **22.** 0.0015 **23.** 0.05375
24. 2.4 **25.** 71% **26.** 9% **27.** 38.91% **28.** 18.75%, or $18\frac{3}{4}$% **29.** 0.5% **30.** 74% **31.** 600% **32.** $83.\overline{3}$%, or $83\frac{1}{3}$%
33. $\frac{17}{20}$ **34.** $\frac{3}{6250}$ **35.** $\frac{91}{400}$ **36.** $\frac{1}{6}$ **37.** 62.5%, or $62\frac{1}{2}$%
38. 45% **39.** 58 **40.** $16.\overline{6}$%, or $16\frac{2}{3}$% **41.** 2560
42. $50 **43.** 0.05%, 0.1%, $\frac{1}{2}$%, 1%, 5%, 10%, $\frac{13}{100}$, 0.275, $\frac{3}{10}$, $\frac{7}{20}$
44. B **45.** Some will say that the conversion will be done most accurately by first finding decimal notation. Others will say that it is more efficient to become familiar with some or all of the fraction and percent equivalents that appear inside the back cover and to make the conversion by going directly from fraction notation to percent notation. **46.** Since $40\% \div 10 = 4\%$, we can divide 36.8 by 10, obtaining 3.68. Since $400\% = 40\% \times 10$, we can multiply 36.8 by 10, obtaining 368. **47.** The student's approach will work. However, when we use the approach of equating cross products, we eliminate the need to find the least common denominator. **48.** They all represent the same number.

Translating for Success, p. 308

1. J **2.** M **3.** N **4.** E **5.** G **6.** H **7.** O **8.** C
9. D **10.** B

Exercise Set 4.6, p. 309

1. South Korea: 62,381 students; Japan: 35,272 students
3. $46,656 **5.** 140 items **7.** 940,000,000 acres **9.** $36,400
11. 74.4 items correct; 5.6 items incorrect **13.** Egypt: 24,596,374; United States: 62,315,472 **15.** About 17.3%
17. $230.10 **19.** About 612,000 fast-food cooks **21.** Alcohol: 43.2 mL; water: 496.8 mL **23.** Air Force: 25.2%; Army: 36.5%; Navy: 25.3%; Marines: 13.0% **25.** 5% **27.** 15% **29.** About 34.7% **31.** $33\frac{1}{3}$% **33.** About 49.5% **35.** About 59%
37. About 9.5% **39.** 34.375%, or $34\frac{3}{8}$% **41.** 15,081; 2.5%
43. 5,130,632; 20.2% **45.** 1,466,465; 13.3% **47.** 1.0%
49. $2.\overline{27}$ **50.** 0.44 **51.** 3.375 **52.** $4.\overline{7}$ **53.** 0.92 **54.** $0.8\overline{3}$
55. 0.4375 **56.** 2.317 **57.** 3.4809 **58.** 0.675 **59.** $42

Exercise Set 4.7, p. 320

1. $9.56 **3.** $1.62 **5.** $11.59; $171.39 **7.** 4%
9. $5600 **11.** $116.72 **13.** $276.28 **15.** $194.08
17. $2625 **19.** 12% **21.** $1380 **23.** 15% **25.** $355
27. $30; $270 **29.** $125; $112.50 **31.** 40%; $360
33. $849; 21.2% **35.** $0.\overline{5}$ **36.** $2.\overline{09}$ **37.** $0.91\overline{6}$
38. $1.\overline{857142}$ **39.** $2.\overline{142857}$ **40.** $1.58\overline{3}$
41. 4,030,000,000,000 **42.** 5,800,000 **43.** 42,700,000
44. 6,090,000,000,000 **45.** $17,700

Calculator Corner, p. 326

1. $16,357.18 **2.** $12,764.72

Exercise Set 4.8, p. 329

1. $8 **3.** $113.52 **5.** $925 **7.** $671.88 **9. (a)** $147.95;
(b) $10,147.95 **11. (a)** $84.14; **(b)** $6584.14 **13. (a)** $46.03;
(b) $5646.03 **15.** $441 **17.** $2802.50 **19.** $7853.38
21. $99,427.40 **23.** $4243.60 **25.** $28,225.00
27. $9270.87 **29.** $129,871.09 **31.** $4101.01
33. $1324.58 **35.** Interest: $20.88; amount applied to
principal: $4.69; balance after the payment: $1273.87
37. (a) $98; **(b)** interest: $86.56; amount applied to principal:
$11.44; **(c)** interest: $51.20; amount applied to principal: $46.80;
(d) At 12.6%, the principal is reduced by $35.36 more than at the
21.3% rate. The interest at 12.6% is $35.36 less than at 21.3%.
39. Reciprocals **40.** Divisible by 6 **41.** Additive
42. Quotient **43.** Perimeter **44.** Divisible by 3
45. Prime **46.** Proportional **47.** 9.38%

Summary and Review: Chapter 4, p. 332

Concept Reinforcement

1. True **2.** True **3.** True **4.** False **5.** True

Important Concepts

1. $\frac{17}{3}$ **2.** $7.50/hr **3.** Yes **4.** $\frac{27}{4}$ **5.** 175 mi
6. 0.62625 **7.** $63.\overline{63}$%, or $63\frac{7}{11}$% **8.** $\frac{17}{250}$ **9.** $4.1\overline{6}$%, or $4\frac{1}{6}$%
10. 10,000 **11.** About 15.3% **12.** 6% **13.** $185,000
14. Simple interest: $22.60; total amount due: $2522.60
15. $6594.26

Review Exercises

1. $\frac{47}{84}$ **2.** $\frac{46}{1.27}$ **3.** $\frac{83}{100}$ **4.** $\frac{0.72}{197}$ **5. (a)** $\frac{12,480}{16,640}$, or $\frac{3}{4}$;
(b) $\frac{16,640}{29,120}$, or $\frac{4}{7}$ **6.** $\frac{3}{4}$ **7.** $\frac{9}{16}$ **8.** 26 mpg
9. 6300 revolutions/min **10.** 0.638 gal/ft² **11.** Yes
12. No **13.** 32 **14.** 7 **15.** $\frac{1}{40}$ **16.** 24
17. 27 circuits **18. (a)** 267 Canadian dollars; **(b)** 46.82 U.S.
dollars **19.** 832 mi **20.** 27 acres **21.** About 3,418,140 lb
22. 6 in. **23.** About 13,644 lawyers **24.** 0.04; 0.144
25. 0.621; 0.842 **26.** 170% **27.** 6.5%
28. 37.5%, or $37\frac{1}{2}$% **29.** $33.\overline{3}$%, or $33\frac{1}{3}$% **30.** $\frac{6}{25}$
31. $\frac{63}{1000}$ **32.** $30.6 = p \times 90$; 34% **33.** $63 = 84\% \times b$; 75
34. $a = 38\frac{1}{2}\% \times 168$; 64.68 **35.** $\frac{24}{100} = \frac{16.8}{b}$; 70
36. $\frac{42}{30} = \frac{N}{100}$; 140% **37.** $\frac{10.5}{100} = \frac{a}{84}$; 8.82
38. 178 students; 84 students **39.** 46% **40.** 2500 mL
41. 12% **42.** 92 **43.** $24 **44.** 6% **45.** 11%
46. $42; $308 **47.** 14% **48.** $2940 **49.** About 18.3%
50. $36 **51. (a)** $394.52; **(b)** $24,394.52 **52.** $7575.25
53. $9504.80 **54. (a)** $129; **(b)** interest: $100.18; amount
applied to principal: $28.82; **(c)** interest: $70.72; amount applied
to principal; $58.28; **(d)** At 13.2%, the principal is decreased by
$29.46 more than at the 18.7% rate. The interest at 13.2% is
$29.46 less than at 18.7%. **55.** C **56.** C **57.** About 19%
58. Finishing paint: 11 gal; primer: 16.5 gal

Understanding Through Discussion and Writing

1. A 40% discount is better. When successive discounts are
taken, each is based on the previous discounted price rather
than on the original price. A 20% discount followed by a 22%
discount is the same as a 37.6% discount off the original
price. **2.** In terms of cost, a low faculty-to-student ratio is less
expensive than a high faculty-to-student ratio. In terms of
quality of education and student satisfaction, a high faculty-
to-student ratio is more desirable. A college president must
balance the cost and quality issues. **3.** No; the 10% discount
was based on the original price rather than on the sale price.
4. Let S = the original salary. After both raises have been given,
the two situations yield the same salary: $1.05 \cdot 1.1S =
1.1 \cdot 1.05S$. However, the first situation is better for the wage
earner, because $1.1S$ is earned the first year when a 10% raise is
given while in the second situation $1.05S$ is earned that year.
5. For a number n, 40% of 50% of n is $0.4(0.5n)$, or $0.2n$, or 20%
of n. Thus taking 40% of 50% of a number is the same as taking
20% of the number. **6.** The interest due on the 30-day loan
will be $41.10 while that due on the 60-day loan will be $131.51.
This could be an argument in favor of the 30-day loan. On the
other hand, the 60-day loan puts twice as much cash at the
firm's disposal for twice as long as the 30-day loan does. This
could be an argument in favor of the 60-day loan.

Test: Chapter 4, p. 340

1. [4.1a] $\frac{85}{97}$ **2.** [4.1a] $\frac{0.34}{124}$ **3.** [4.1a] $\frac{9}{10}$ **4.** [4.1a] $\frac{25}{32}$
5. [4.1b] $1\frac{1}{3}$ servings/lb **6.** [4.1b] 32 mpg **7.** [4.1c] Yes
8. [4.1c] No **9.** [4.1d] 100 **10.** [4.1d] 360
11. [4.1e] 525 mi **12.** [4.1e] **(a)** 3501.45 Hong Kong dollars;
(b) $102.17 **13.** [4.1e] About $59.17 **14.** [4.1e] 4.8 min
15. [4.2b] 0.147 **16.** [4.2b] 38% **17.** [4.3a] 137.5%
18. [4.3b] $\frac{13}{20}$ **19.** [4.4a, b] $a = 40\% \cdot 55$; 22
20. [4.5a, b] $\frac{N}{100} = \frac{65}{80}$; 81.25% **21.** [4.6a] 16,692 kidney
transplants; 6224 liver transplants; 2263 heart transplants
22. [4.6a] About 611 at-bats **23.** [4.6b] 6.7%
24. [4.6a] 60.6% **25.** [4.7a] $25.20; $585.20 **26.** [4.7b] $630
27. [4.7c] $40; $160 **28.** [4.8a] $8.52 **29.** [4.8a] $5356
30. [4.8b] $1110.39 **31.** [4.6b] Plumber: 757,000, 7.4%;
veterinary assistant: 29,000, 40.8%; motorcycle repair: 21,000,
14.3%; fitness professional: 235,000, 63,000
32. [4.8b] $11,580.07 **33.** [4.7c] $50; about 14.3%
34. [4.8c] Interest: $36.73; amount applied to the principal:
$17.27; balance after payment: $2687 **35.** [4.4a, b], [4.5a, b] B
36. [4.1b] C **37.** [4.7b] $194,600 **38.** [4.7b], [4.8b] $2546.16

CHAPTER 5

Exercise Set 5.1, p. 351

1. Average: $36.\overline{5}$; median: 21; mode: 2 **3.** Average: 21; median:
18.5; mode: 29 **5.** Average: 21; median: 20; modes: 5, 20
7. Average: 5.38; median: 5.7; no mode exists
9. Average: 239.5; median: 234; mode: 234 **11.** 23 mpg
13. 2.7 **15.** Average: $4.19; median: $3.99; mode:
$3.99 **17.** 90 **19.** 263 days **21.** Bulb A: average
time = 1171.25 hr; bulb B: average time ≈ 1251.58 hr;
bulb B is better **23.** 225.05 **24.** 126.0516 **25.** $\frac{3}{35}$
26. $\frac{14}{15}$ **27.** 118.75% **28.** 68.75% **29.** 51.2%
30. 97.81% **31.** $a = 30$; $b = 58$ **33.** $3475

Exercise Set 5.2, p. 357

1. 100 calories **3.** Boca All American Flame Grilled Meatless;
Franklin Farms Portabella Fresh; Gardenburger Portabella
5. Average: 3.5 g; median: 3 g; mode: 3 g **7.** Most expensive:
Lightlife Meatless Light; least expensive: Boca All American
Flame Grilled Meatless **9.** Greatest fat: Veggie Patch Garlic

Portabella; least fat: Franklin Farms Portabella Fresh and Lightlife Meatless Light   **11.** 92°   **13.** 108°   **15.** 85°, 60%; 90°, 40%; 100°, 10%   **17.** 90° and higher   **19.** 30% and higher   **21.** 90% − 40% = 50%   **23.** 483,612,200 mi   **25.** Neptune   **27.** All   **29.** 11 Earth diameters   **31.** Average: 31,191.75 mi; median: 19,627.5 mi; no mode exists   **33.** White rhino   **35.** About 1350 rhinos   **37.** About 4100 rhinos   **39.** Cabinets: $13,444; countertops: $4033.20; appliances: $2151.04; fixtures: $806.64   **40.** Cabinets: $3597.55; countertops: $1276.55; labor: $2901.25; flooring: $696.30

Mid-Chapter Review: Chapter 5, p. 361

1. True   **2.** True   **3.** False
4. $\frac{60 + 45 + 115 + 15 + 35}{5} = \frac{270}{5} = 54$ **5.** 2.1, 4.8, 6.3, 8.7, 11.3, 14.5; 6.3 and 8.7; $\frac{6.3 + 8.7}{2} = \frac{15}{2} = 7.5$; the median is 7.5.
6. Average: 83; median: 45; mode: 29   **7.** Average: 18.45; median: 13.895; no mode   **8.** Average: $\frac{1}{2}$; median: $\frac{5}{10}$; no mode   **9.** Average: 126; median: 116; no mode   **10.** Average: $6.09; median: $5.24; modes: $4.96 and $5.24   **11.** Average: $\frac{27}{32}$; median: $\frac{13}{16}$; no mode   **12.** Average: 6; median: 7; modes: 5 and 7   **13.** Average: 38.2; median: 38.2; no mode   **14.** 8 oz   **15.** 6%   **16.** Hershey's Special Dark chocolate bar   **17.** 7 oz   **18.** Nabisco Chips Ahoy cookies   **19.** 90 guns per 100 civilians   **20.** 60 more guns per 100 civilians   **21.** 45 guns per 100 civilians; 55 guns per 100 civilians   **22.** India   **23.** 47.5 guns per 100 civilians   **24.** 50 guns per 100 civilians   **25.** At an average speed of 20 mph, the trip would take $1\frac{1}{2}$ hr (30 mi ÷ 20 mph = $1\frac{1}{2}$ hr). But the driver could have driven at a speed of 75 mph for a brief period during that time.   **26.** Answers may vary. Some would ask for the average salary since it is a center point that places equal emphasis on all the salaries in the firm. Some would ask for the median salary since it is a center point that deemphasizes the extremely high and extremely low salaries. Some would ask for the mode of the salaries since it might indicate the salary you are most likely to earn.

Exercise Set 5.3, p. 369

1. Miniature tall bearded   **3.** About 23.2 in.   **5.** 16 in. to 26 in.   **7.** Tall bearded   **9.** 25 in.   **11.** 185 calories   **13.** 1 slice of chocolate cake with fudge frosting   **15.** 1 cup of premium chocolate ice cream   **17.** About 125 calories   **19.** 1950 and 1970   **21.** About 175,000 bachelor's degrees

23.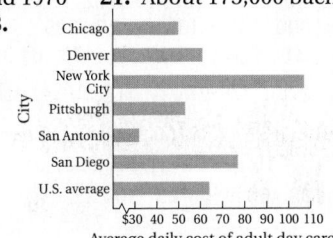
Average daily cost of adult day care

25. Chicago, Denver, Pittsburgh, and San Antonio   **27.** $43 higher   **29.** New York City   **31.** 27 min   **33.** 3.2 million tourists; 4.3 million tourists   **35.** 2007 to 2008
37. 9–11 A.M.   **39.** About 300 bank crimes
41.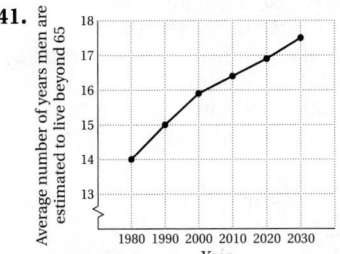

43. 25%   **45.** 10.1%   **46.** Natural   **47.** Add; divide   **48.** Simple   **49.** Marked price; rate of discount; discount; sale price   **50.** Compound   **51.** Repeating   **52.** Subtrahend   **53.** Terminating

Translating for Success, p. 376

1. D   **2.** B   **3.** J   **4.** K   **5.** I   **6.** F   **7.** N   **8.** E   **9.** L   **10.** M

Exercise Set 5.4, p. 377

1. 11%   **3.** 93,750 students   **5.** Japan   **7.** 18%   **9.** 38%, or about 390 people
11.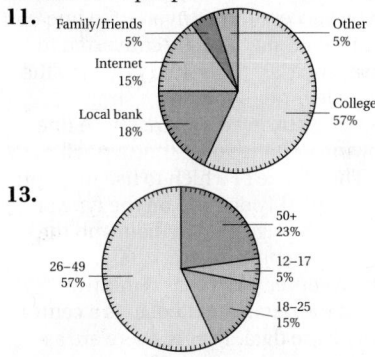

13.
(pie chart: 50+ 23%; 12–17 5%; 18–25 15%; 26–49 57%)

Summary and Review: Chapter 5, p. 379

Concept Reinforcement

1. False   **2.** True   **3.** True

Important Concepts

1. Average: 8; median: 8; mode: 8   **2.** Quaker Organic Maple & Brown Sugar; $0.54 per serving   **3.** 12 g   **4.** Arrowhead Stadium and Candlestick Park   **5.** About $110 million more   **6.** 80 yr and older   **7.** 27%

Review Exercises

1. 38.5   **2.** 13.4   **3.** 1.55   **4.** 1840   **5.** $16.$\overline{6}$ **6.** 321.$\overline{6}$ **7.** 96   **8.** 28 mpg   **9.** 3.1   **10.** 38.5   **11.** 14   **12.** 1.8   **13.** 1900   **14.** $17   **15.** 375   **16.** Average: $260; median: $228   **17.** 26   **18.** 11 and 17   **19.** 0.2   **20.** 700 and 800   **21.** $17   **22.** 20   **23.** Battery A: average ≈ 43.04 hr; battery B: average ≈ 41.55 hr; battery A is better.   **24.** $30.37   **25.** $10.85   **26.** $3.76   **27.** 18 champions   **28.** 30–34 years   **29.** 19 more champions   **30.** 2004, 2007, 2008   **31.** 60%   **32.** About 52%   **33.** 2006   **34.** 2001   **35.** 2007   **36.** 2001, 2004, 2009   **37.** 2004, 2009   **38.** 24 higher   **39.** 281   **40.** 283   **41.** 36%   **42.** Marines   **43.** 350,000   **44.** 10% more   **45.** D   **46.** A
47.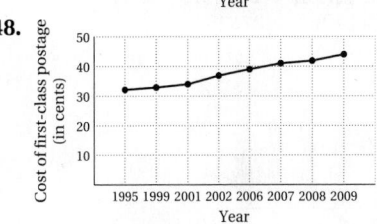

48.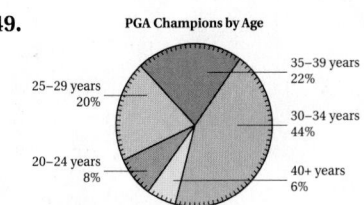

49.
PGA Champions by Age
(pie chart: 35–39 years 22%; 30–34 years 44%; 40+ years 6%; 20–24 years 8%; 25–29 years 20%)

50. $a = 316, b = 349$

Understanding Through Discussion and Writing

1. The equation could represent a person's average income during a 4-yr period. Answers may vary. **2.** Bar graphs that show change over time can be successfully converted to line graphs. Other bar graphs cannot be successfully converted to line graphs. **3.** We can use circle graphs to visualize how the numbers of items in various categories compare in size. **4.** A bar graph is convenient for showing comparisons. A line graph is convenient for showing a change over time as well as to indicate patterns or trends. The choice of which to use to graph a particular set of data would probably depend on the type of data analysis desired. **5.** The average, the median, and the mode are "center points" that characterize a set of data. You might use the average to find a center point that is midway between the extreme values of the data. The median is a center point that is in the middle of all the data. That is, there are as many values less than the median as there are values greater than the median. The mode is a center point that represents the value or values that occur most frequently. **6.** Circle graphs are similar to bar graphs in that both allow us to tell at a glance how items in various categories compare in size. They differ in that circle graphs show percents whereas bar graphs show actual numbers of items in a given category.

Test: Chapter 5, p. 385

1. [5.1a] 49.5 **2.** [5.1a] 2.6 **3.** [5.1a] 15.5
4. [5.1b, c] 50.5; no mode exists **5.** [5.1b, c] 3; 1 and 3
6. [5.1b, c] 17.5; 17 and 18 **7.** [5.1a] 33 mpg
8. [5.1a] 76 **9.** [5.1a] 2.9 **10.** [5.1d] Bar A: average ≈ 8.417; bar B: average ≈ 8.417; equal quality **11.** [5.2a] 179 lb **12.** [5.2a] 5 ft 3 in.; medium frame **13.** [5.2a] 9 lb **14.** [5.2a] 32 lb
15. [5.2b] Spain **16.** [5.2b] Norway and the United States **17.** [5.2b] 900 lb **18.** [5.2b] 1000 lb
19. [5.3b]

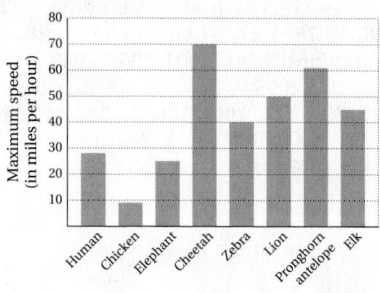

20. [5.2a], [5.3a] 61 mph **21.** [5.2a], [5.3a] No; the zebra can run 12 mph faster than a human. **22.** [5.1a], [5.2a], [5.3a] 41 mph
23. [5.1b], [5.2a], [5.3a] 42.5 mph **24.** [5.3c] 53%
25. [5.3c] 41% **26.** [5.3c] 1967 **27.** [5.3c] 2006
28. [5.3b]

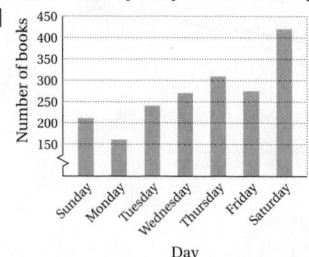

29. [5.3d]

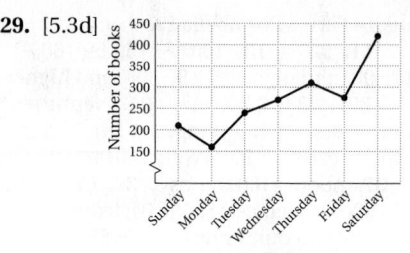

30. [5.4b]

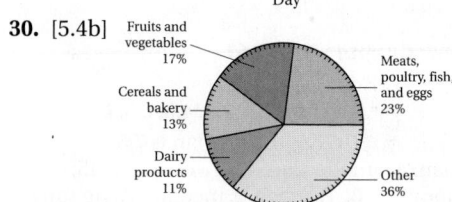

31. [5.4a] C **32.** [5.1a, b] $a = 74$, $b = 111$

CHAPTER 6

Exercise Set 6.1, p. 397

1. $\overset{\longleftrightarrow}{G \quad H}$, $\overline{GH}, \overline{HG}$
3. $\overset{\bullet \longrightarrow}{Q \qquad D}$, $\overrightarrow{QD}$ **5.** $\overleftrightarrow{DE}, \overleftrightarrow{ED}, \overleftrightarrow{DF}, \overleftrightarrow{FD}, \overleftrightarrow{EF}, \overleftrightarrow{FE},$ l
7. Angle GHI, angle IHG, $\angle GHI$, $\angle IHG$, or $\angle H$ **9.** 10° **11.** 180°
13. 130° **15.** Obtuse **17.** Acute **19.** Straight
21. Obtuse **23.** Acute **25.** Obtuse **27.** Not perpendicular
29. Perpendicular **31.** Scalene; obtuse **33.** Scalene; right
35. Equilateral; acute **37.** Scalene; obtuse **39.** Quadrilateral
41. Pentagon **43.** Triangle **45.** Pentagon **47.** Hexagon
49. 1440° **51.** 900° **53.** 2160° **55.** 3240° **57.** 46°
59. 120° **61.** 43° **63.** $160 **64.** $22.50 **65.** $148
66. $1116.67 **67.** $33,597.91 **68.** $413,458.31
69. $641,566.26 **70.** $684,337.34 **71.** $m\angle ACB = 50°$;
$m\angle CAB = 40°$; $m\angle EBC = 50°$; $m\angle EBA = 40°$; $m\angle AEB = 100°$;
$m\angle ADB = 50°$

Exercise Set 6.2, p. 404

1. 17 mm **3.** 15.25 in. **5.** 18 km **7.** 30 ft **9.** 16 yd
11. 88 ft **13.** 182 mm **15.** 27 ft **17.** 122 cm
19. 172 in., or 14 ft 4 in. **21.** (a) 228 ft; (b) $1046.52
23. $19.20 **24.** $96 **25.** 1000 **26.** 1331 **27.** 225
28. 484 **29.** 49 **30.** 64 **31.** 5% **32.** 11% **33.** 64 in.

Exercise Set 6.3, p. 412

1. 15 km² **3.** 1.4 in² **5.** $6\frac{1}{4}$ yd² **7.** 8100 ft² **9.** 50 ft²
11. 169.883 cm² **13.** $41\frac{2}{9}$ in² **15.** 484 ft² **17.** 3237.61 km²
19. $28\frac{57}{64}$ yd² **21.** 32 cm² **23.** 60 in² **25.** 104 ft²
27. 45.5 in² **29.** 8.05 cm² **31.** 297 cm² **33.** 7 m²
35. 1197 m² **37.** (a) About 8473 ft²; (b) about $102
39. 630.36 ft² **41.** (a) 819.75 ft²; (b) 3 gal; (c) $74.85
43. 80 cm² **45.** 675 cm² **47.** 21 cm² **49.** 144 ft²
51. Three **52.** Parallel **53.** Perpendicular **54.** Prime
55. Angle **56.** Cents; dollars **57.** Perimeter
58. Multiplicative; additive **59.** 16,914 in²

Calculator Corner, p. 419

1. Left to the student **2.** Left to the student

Exercise Set 6.4, p. 422

1. 14 cm; 44 cm; 154 cm² **3.** $1\frac{1}{2}$ in.; $4\frac{5}{7}$ in.; $1\frac{43}{56}$ in²
5. 16 ft; 100.48 ft; 803.84 ft² **7.** 0.7 cm; 4.396 cm; 1.5386 cm²

9. Diameter: 12.74 ft; circumference: about 40 ft; area: about 127.41 ft^2; about 46.67 ft^2 larger than the medium net and about 19.76 ft^2 larger than the large net   **11.** About 30.96 in^2 larger
13. About 24,889 mi   **15.** Maximum circumference of barrel: $8\frac{9}{14}$ in.; minimum circumference of handle: $2\frac{86}{14}$ in.
17. 65.94 yd^2 **19.** 45.68 ft   **21.** 26.84 yd   **23.** 45.7 yd
25. 100.48 m^2 **27.** 6.9972 cm^2 **29.** 64.4214 in^2 **31.** 16
32. 289   **33.** 37.5%, or $37\frac{1}{2}$%   **34.** 66.$\overline{6}$%, or $66\frac{2}{3}$%
35. 5 lb   **36.** $730   **37.** 43,560 ft^2; 1311.6 ft; $599.96
39. 43,595.47395 ft^2; 739.9724 ft; $449.97
41. 43,560 ft^2; 844 ft; $449.97

Mid-Chapter Review: Chapter 6, p. 426

1. True   **2.** True   **3.** False   **4.** True
5. $A = \frac{1}{2} \cdot 12\,\text{cm} \cdot 8\,\text{cm}$ **6.** $C \approx 3.14 \cdot 10.2$ in.
$A = \frac{12 \cdot 8}{2}\,\text{cm}^2$ $C = 32.028$ in.;
$A = \frac{96}{2}\,\text{cm}^2$, or 48 cm^2 $A \approx 3.14 \cdot 5.1\,\text{in.} \cdot 5.1\,\text{in.}$
   $A = 81.6714\,\text{in}^2$
7. 3060°   **8.** 15°   **9.** Hexagon   **10.** Scalene; right
11. Isosceles; obtuse   **12.** Equilateral; acute   **13.** 76 mm
14. $P = 50\frac{2}{3}$ ft; $A = 160\frac{4}{9}$ ft^2 **15.** 800 in^2 **16.** $\frac{9}{16}$ yd^2
17. 66 km^2 **18.** $C = 43.96$ in.; $A = 153.86$ in^2
19. $C = 27.004$ cm; $A = 58.0586$ cm^2 **20.** Area of a circle with radius 4 ft: $16 \cdot \pi$ ft^2; Area of a square with side 4 ft: 16 ft^2; Circumference of a circle with radius 4 ft: $8 \cdot \pi$ ft; Area of a rectangle with length 8 ft and width 4 ft: 32 ft^2; Area of a triangle with base 4 ft and height 8 ft: 16 ft^2; Perimeter of a square with side 4 ft: 16 ft; Perimeter of a rectangle with length 8 ft and width 4 ft: 24 ft   **21.** The area of a 16-in.-diameter pizza is approximately $3.14 \cdot 8$ in. $\cdot$ 8 in., or 200.96 in^2. At $16.25, its unit price is $\frac{\$16.25}{200.96\,\text{in}^2}$, or about $0.08/in^2. The area of a 10-in.-diameter pizza is approximately $3.14 \cdot 5$ in. $\cdot$ 5 in., or 78.5 in^2. At $7.85, its unit price is $\frac{\$7.85}{78.5\,\text{in}^2}$, or $0.10/in^2. Since the 16-in.-diameter pizza has the lower unit price, it is a better buy.
22. No; let l and w represent the length and the width of the smaller rectangle. Then $3 \cdot l$ and $3 \cdot w$ represent the length and the width of the larger rectangle. The area of the first rectangle is $l \cdot w$, but the area of the second is $3 \cdot l \cdot 3 \cdot w = 3 \cdot 3 \cdot l \cdot w = 9 \cdot l \cdot w$, or 9 times the area of the smaller rectangle.   **23.** Yes; let s represent the length of a side of the larger square. Then $\frac{1}{2}s$ represents the length of a side of the smaller square. The perimeter of the larger square is $4 \cdot s$, and the perimeter of the smaller square is $4 \cdot \frac{1}{2}s = 2s$, or $\frac{1}{2}$ the perimeter of the larger square.   **24.** For a rectangle with length l and width w,
$$P = l + w + l + w$$
$$= (l + w) + (l + w)$$
$$= 2 \cdot (l + w).$$
We also have
$$P = l + w + l + w$$
$$= (l + l) + (w + w)$$
$$= 2 \cdot l + 2 \cdot w.$$
25. See p. 408 of the text.   **26.** No; let r = radius of the smaller circle. Then its area is $\pi \cdot r \cdot r$, or πr^2. The radius of the larger circle is $2r$, and its area is $\pi \cdot 2r \cdot 2r$, or $4\pi r^2$, or $4 \cdot \pi r^2$. Thus the area of the larger circle is 4 times the area of the smaller circle.

Exercise Set 6.5, p. 434

1. 768 cm^3; 512 cm^2 **3.** 45 in^3; 87 in^2 **5.** 75 m^3; 145 m^2
7. $357\frac{1}{2}$ yd^3; $311\frac{1}{2}$ yd^2 **9.** 803.84 in^3 **11.** 353.25 cm^3
13. 41,580,000 yd^3 **15.** 4,186,666.67 in^3 **17.** 124.72 m^3

19. $1950\frac{101}{168}$ ft^3 **21.** 113,982 ft^3 **23.** 24.64 cm^3 **25.** $\frac{33}{40}$ yd^3
27. 4747.68 cm^3 **29.** About 904 ft^3 **31.** 143.72 cm^3
33. 259,988,380,000 mi^3 **35.** About 77.7 in^3 **37.** 61,600 m^3
39. 5832 yd^3 **41.** 646.74 cm^3 **43.** $\frac{6}{25}$ **44.** $\frac{171}{200}$ **45.** $\frac{51}{400}$
46. $\frac{2}{3}$ **47.** $\frac{7}{20}$ **48.** $\frac{5}{8}$ **49.** $\frac{3}{8}$ **50.** $\frac{9}{2}$ **51.** $\frac{5}{6}$ **52.** $\frac{19}{200}$
53. $\frac{1}{200}$ **54.** $\frac{1}{6}$ **55.** 1064 mi^3 **56.** 24,360 mi^2
57. 260.4 ft   **58.** 1087.8 mi^3 **59.** 3540.68 km^3
61. 0.477 m^3

Exercise Set 6.6, p. 447

1. 79°   **3.** 23°   **5.** 32°   **7.** 61°   **9.** 177°   **11.** 41°
13. 95°   **15.** 78°   **17.** Not congruent   **19.** Congruent
21. $m\angle 2 = 67°$, $m\angle 3 = 33°$, $m\angle 4 = 80°$, $m\angle 6 = 33°$
23. **(a)** $\angle 1$ and $\angle 3$, $\angle 2$ and $\angle 4$, $\angle 8$ and $\angle 6$, $\angle 7$ and $\angle 5$;
(b) $\angle 2$, $\angle 3$, $\angle 6$, and $\angle 7$; **(c)** $\angle 2$ and $\angle 6$, $\angle 3$ and $\angle 7$
25. $m\angle 6 = m\angle 2 = m\angle 8 = 125°$, $m\angle 5 = m\angle 3 = m\angle 7 = m\angle 1 = 55°$ **27.** $\angle ABE \cong \angle DCE$, 95°; $\angle BAE \cong \angle CDE$; $\angle AEB \cong \angle DEC$; $\angle BED \cong \angle AEC$ **29.** $\angle AEC \cong \angle DCE$, 50°; $\angle BED \cong \angle EDC$, 41°   **31.** $\frac{45}{4}$, or $11\frac{1}{4}$ **32.** $\frac{129}{8}$, or $16\frac{1}{8}$
33. 118   **34.** $\frac{44}{3}$, or $14\frac{2}{3}$

Exercise Set 6.7, p. 456

1. $\angle A \cong \angle R$, $\angle B \cong \angle S$, $\angle C \cong \angle T$; $\overline{AB} \cong \overline{RS}$, $\overline{AC} \cong \overline{RT}$, $\overline{BC} \cong \overline{ST}$ **3.** $\angle D \cong \angle G$, $\angle E \cong \angle H$, $\angle F \cong \angle K$; $\overline{DE} \cong \overline{GH}$, $\overline{DF} \cong \overline{GK}$, $\overline{EF} \cong \overline{HK}$ **5.** $\angle X \cong \angle U$, $\angle Y \cong \angle V$, $\angle Z \cong \angle W$; $\overline{XY} \cong \overline{UV}$, $\overline{XZ} \cong \overline{UW}$, $\overline{YZ} \cong \overline{VW}$ **7.** $\angle A \cong \angle F$, $\angle C \cong \angle D$, $\angle B \cong \angle E$; $\overline{AC} \cong \overline{FD}$, $\overline{AB} \cong \overline{FE}$, $\overline{CB} \cong \overline{DE}$ **9.** $\angle M \cong \angle Q$, $\angle N \cong \angle P$, $\angle O \cong \angle S$; $\overline{MN} \cong \overline{QP}$, $\overline{MO} \cong \overline{QS}$, $\overline{NO} \cong \overline{PS}$
11. No   **13.** Yes   **15.** Yes   **17.** No   **19.** Yes   **21.** Yes
23. Yes   **25.** Yes   **27.** Yes   **29.** ASA   **31.** SAS
33. SSS or SAS   **35.** $\overline{PR} \cong \overline{TR}$, $\overline{SR} \cong \overline{QR}$, $\angle PRQ \cong \angle TRS$ (vertical angles); $\triangle PRQ \cong \triangle TRS$ by SAS
37. $m\angle GLK = m\angle GLM = 90°$, $\angle GLK \cong \angle GLM$, $\overline{GL} \cong \overline{GL}$, $\overline{KL} \cong \overline{ML}$; $\triangle KLG \cong \triangle MLG$ by SAS   **39.** $\overline{AE} \cong \overline{CD}$, $\overline{AB} \cong \overline{CB}$, $\overline{EB} \cong \overline{DB}$; $\triangle AEB \cong \triangle CDB$ by SSS
41. $\triangle LKH \cong \triangle GKJ$ by SAS; $\angle HLK \cong \angle JGK$, $\angle LHK \cong \angle GJK$, $\overline{LH} \cong \overline{GJ}$ **43.** $\triangle PED \cong \triangle PFG$ by ASA. As corresponding parts, $\overline{EP} \cong \overline{FP}$; thus P is the midpoint of $\overline{EF}$.
45. $m\angle A = 70°$, $m\angle D = m\angle B = 110°$
47. $m\angle M = 71°$, $m\angle J = m\angle L = 109°$ **49.** $TU = 9$, $NU = 15$
51. $KL = 3\frac{1}{2}$, $ML = JK = 7\frac{1}{2}$ **53.** $AC = 28$, $ED = 38$
55. 45.2%   **56.** $33\frac{1}{3}$%   **57.** 55%   **58.** 88%   **59.** $\frac{2.7}{13.1}$; $\frac{13.1}{2.7}$
60. $\frac{1}{4}$; $\frac{3}{4}$ **61.** 1.75   **62.** 2.34   **63.** 0.234   **64.** 0.0234
65. 13.85

Translating for Success, p. 466

1. K   **2.** G   **3.** B   **4.** H   **5.** O   **6.** M   **7.** E   **8.** A
9. D   **10.** I

Exercise Set 6.8, p. 467

1. $\angle R \leftrightarrow \angle A$, $\angle S \leftrightarrow \angle B$, $\angle T \leftrightarrow \angle C$, $\overline{RS} \leftrightarrow \overline{AB}$, $\overline{RT} \leftrightarrow \overline{AC}$, $\overline{ST} \leftrightarrow \overline{BC}$ **3.** $\angle C \leftrightarrow \angle W$, $\angle B \leftrightarrow \angle J$, $\angle S \leftrightarrow \angle Z$, $\overline{CB} \leftrightarrow \overline{WJ}$, $\overline{CS} \leftrightarrow \overline{WZ}$, $\overline{BS} \leftrightarrow \overline{JZ}$
5. $\angle A \cong \angle R$, $\angle B \cong \angle S$, $\angle C \cong \angle T$; $\frac{AB}{RS} = \frac{AC}{RT} = \frac{BC}{ST}$
7. $\angle M \cong \angle C$, $\angle E \cong \angle L$, $\angle S \cong \angle F$; $\frac{ME}{CL} = \frac{MS}{CF} = \frac{ES}{LF}$
9. $\frac{PS}{ND} = \frac{SQ}{DM} = \frac{PQ}{NM}$ **11.** $\frac{TA}{GF} = \frac{TW}{GC} = \frac{AW}{FC}$
13. $QR = 10$, $PR = 8$ **15.** $EC = 18$ **17.** 36 ft   **19.** 100 ft
21. $\frac{147}{5}$, or $29\frac{2}{5}$ **22.** 0.244   **23.** 78   **24.** 61.1611

Summary and Review: Chapter 6, p. 469

Concept Reinforcement

1. True   **2.** False   **3.** False   **4.** True   **5.** True

Important Concepts

1. Angle WAQ, angle QAW, $\angle WAQ$, $\angle QAW$, or $\angle A$; 26°
2. (a) Straight; **(b)** acute; **(c)** obtuse; **(d)** right
3. (a) Isosceles, right; **(b)** equilateral, acute; **(c)** scalene, acute;
(d) scalene, obtuse **4.** 87° **5.** 1260° **6.** 27.8 ft; 46.74 ft²
7. 15.5 m² **8.** 8.75 ft² **9.** 80 m² **10.** 37.68 in.
11. 616 cm² **12.** 1683.3 m³ **13.** $30\frac{6}{35}$ ft³
14. 1696.537813 cm³ **15.** 26.49375 ft³
16. Complement: 52°; supplement: 142°
17. $m\angle 7 = 60°; m\angle 9 = 55°; m\angle 10 = 60°; m\angle 11 = 65°$
18. $m\angle 4 = m\angle 1 = m\angle 8 = 105°;$
$m\angle 6 = m\angle 3 = m\angle 2 = m\angle 7 = 75°$ **19. (a)** SAS;
(b) ASA **20.** $BC = 45.5, AB = DC = 73; m\angle A = 30°,$
$m\angle B = m\angle D = 150°$ **21.** $ZA = 15$ and $AT = 30$

Review Exercises

1. 54° **2.** 180° **3.** 140° **4.** 90° **5.** Acute **6.** Straight
7. Obtuse **8.** Right **9.** 60° **10.** Scalene **11.** Right
12. 720° **13.** 23 ft **14.** 4.4 m **15.** 228 ft; 2808 ft²
16. 36 ft; 81 ft² **17.** 17.6 cm; 12.6 cm² **18.** 60 cm²
19. 35 mm² **20.** 22.5 m² **21.** 29.64 yd² **22.** 88 cm²
23. $145\frac{5}{9}$ in² **24.** 840 ft² **25.** 8 m **26.** $\frac{14}{11}$ in., or $1\frac{3}{11}$ in.
27. 14 ft **28.** 20 cm **29.** 50.24 m **30.** 8 in.
31. 200.96 m² **32.** $5\frac{1}{11}$ in² **33.** 1038.555 ft³
34. 26.28 ft²; 20.28 ft **35.** 93.6 yd³; 150 m²
36. 193.2 cm³; 240.4 cm² **37.** 31,400 ft³ **38.** 33.49$\overline{3}$ cm³
39. 4.71 in³ **40.** 942 cm³ **41.** 49° **42.** 8° **43.** 85°
44. 147° **45.** 47° **46.** $m\angle 2 = 105°, m\angle 3 = 37°,$
$m\angle 4 = 38°, m\angle 6 = 37°$ **47. (a)** $\angle 1$ and $\angle 5, \angle 4$ and $\angle 8,$
$\angle 3$ and $\angle 7, \angle 2$ and $\angle 6$; **(b)** $\angle 4, \angle 5, \angle 2$, and $\angle 7$; **(c)** $\angle 4$ and $\angle 7,$
$\angle 2$ and $\angle 5$ **48.** $m\angle 1 = m\angle 3 = m\angle 7 = m\angle 5 = 45°,$
$m\angle 6 = m\angle 2 = m\angle 8 = 135°$ **49.** $\angle D \cong \angle R, \angle H \cong \angle Z,$
$\angle J \cong \angle K; \overline{DH} \cong \overline{RZ}, \overline{DJ} \cong \overline{RK}, \overline{HJ} \cong \overline{ZK}$ **50.** $\angle A \cong \angle G,$
$\angle B \cong \angle D, \angle C \cong \angle F, \overline{AB} \cong \overline{GD}, \overline{AC} \cong \overline{GF}, \overline{BC} \cong \overline{DF}$ **51.** ASA
52. SSS **53.** None **54.** $\overline{IJ} \cong \overline{KJ}, \angle HJI \cong \angle LJK,$
$\angle HIJ \cong \angle LKJ; \triangle JIH \cong \triangle JKL$ by ASA
55. $m\angle C = 63°, m\angle B = m\angle D = 117°; BC = 23, CD = 13$
56. $\angle C \cong \angle F, \angle Q \cong \angle A, \angle W \cong \angle S; \dfrac{CQ}{FA} = \dfrac{CW}{FS} = \dfrac{QW}{AS}$
57. $MO = 14$ **58.** B **59.** B **60.** 100 ft²
61. 7.83998704 m² **62.** 47.25 cm²

Understanding Through Discussion and Writing

1. Add 90° to the measure of the angle's complement.
2. This could be done using the technique in Example 8 of
Section 6.5. We could also approximate the volume with the
volume of a similarly shaped rectangular solid. Another method
is to break the egg and measure the capacity of its contents.
3. Linear measure is one-dimensional, area is two-dimensional,
and volume is three-dimensional.
4. Divide the figure into 3 triangles.

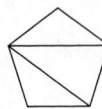

The sum of the measures of the angles of each triangle is 180°,
so the sum of the measures of the angles of the figure is $3 \cdot 180°$,
or 540°. **5.** The volume of the cone is half the volume of the
dome. It can be argued that a cone-cap is more energy-efficient
since there is less air under it to be heated and cooled.
6. Volume of two spheres, each with radius r: $2\left(\frac{4}{3}\pi r^3\right) = \frac{8}{3}\pi r^3$;
volume of one sphere with radius $2r$: $\frac{4}{3}\pi(2r)^3 = \frac{32}{3}\pi r^3$. The
volume of the sphere with radius $2r$ is four times the volume of
the two spheres, each with radius r: $\frac{32}{3}\pi r^3 = 4 \cdot \frac{8}{3}\pi r^3$.

Test: Chapter 6, p. 481

1. [6.1b] 90° **2.** [6.1b] 35° **3.** [6.1b] 180°
4. [6.1b] 113° **5.** [6.1c] Right **6.** [6.1c] Acute
7. [6.1c] Straight **8.** [6.1c] Obtuse **9.** [6.1f] 35°
10. [6.1e] Isosceles **11.** [6.1e] Obtuse **12.** [6.1f] 540°
13. [6.2a], [6.3a] 32.82 cm; 65.894 cm²
14. [6.2a], [6.3a] $19\frac{1}{2}$ in.; $23\frac{49}{64}$ in²
15. [6.3b] 25 cm² **16.** [6.3b] 12 m² **17.** [6.3b] 18 ft²
18. [6.4a] $\frac{1}{4}$ in. **19.** [6.4a] 9 cm **20.** [6.4b] $\frac{11}{14}$ in.
21. [6.4c] 254.34 cm² **22.** [6.4d] 65.46 km; 103.815 km²
23. [6.5a] 84 cm³; 142 cm² **24.** [6.5e] 420 in³
25. [6.5b] 1177.5 ft³ **26.** [6.5c] 4186.$\overline{6}$ yd³
27. [6.5d] 113.04 cm³ **28.** [6.6a] Complement: 25°;
supplement: 115° **29.** [6.6c] $m\angle 2 = 110°, m\angle 3 = 8°,$
$m\angle 4 = 62°, m\angle 6 = 8°$ **30.** [6.6d] $m\angle 6 = m\angle 2 =$
$m\angle 8 = 120°, m\angle 5 = m\angle 3 = m\angle 7 = m\angle 1 = 60°$
31. [6.7a] $\angle C \cong \angle A, \angle W \cong \angle T, \angle S \cong \angle Z, \overline{CW} \cong \overline{AT},$
$\overline{WS} \cong \overline{TZ}, \overline{SC} \cong \overline{ZA}$ **32.** [6.7a] SAS **33.** [6.7a] None
34. [6.7a] ASA **35.** [6.7a] None **36.** [6.7b] $m\angle G = 105°,$
$m\angle D = m\angle F = 75°; EF = 11, DE = GF = 20$
37. [6.7b] $LJ = 6.4, KM = 6$ **38.** [6.8a] $\angle E \cong \angle T, \angle R \cong \angle G,$
$\angle S \cong \angle F; \dfrac{ER}{TG} = \dfrac{RS}{GF} = \dfrac{SE}{FT}$ **39.** [6.8b] $EK = 18, ZK = 27$
40. [6.5c] D **41.** [6.3a] 2 ft² **42.** [6.3b] 1.875 ft²
43. [6.5a] 0.65 ft³ **44.** [6.5d] 0.033 ft³ **45.** [6.5b] 0.055 ft³

CHAPTER 7

Exercise Set 7.1, p. 490

1. 32 min; 69 min; 81 min **3.** 1935 m² **5.** 260 mi
7. 24 ft² **9.** 56 **11.** 8 **13.** 1 **15.** 6 **17.** 2
19. $b + 7$, or $7 + b$ **21.** $c - 12$ **23.** $q + 4$, or $4 + q$
25. $a + b$, or $b + a$ **27.** $x \div y$, or $\dfrac{x}{y}$, or x/y, or $x \cdot \dfrac{1}{y}$
29. $x + w$, or $w + x$ **31.** $n - m$ **33.** $x + y$, or $y + x$
35. $2z$ **37.** $3m$ **39.** $4a + 6$, or $6 + 4a$ **41.** $xy - 8$
43. $2t - 5$ **45.** $3n + 11$, or $11 + 3n$ **47.** $4x + 3y$, or
$3y + 4x$ **49.** $89\%s$, or $0.89s$, where s is the salary
51. $s + 0.05s$ **53.** $65t$ miles **55.** $\$50 - x$ **57.** $\$8.50n$
59. $2 \cdot 3 \cdot 3 \cdot 3$ **60.** $2 \cdot 2 \cdot 2 \cdot 2 \cdot 2$ **61.** $2 \cdot 2 \cdot 3 \cdot 3 \cdot 3$
62. $2 \cdot 2 \cdot 2 \cdot 2 \cdot 2 \cdot 2 \cdot 3$ **63.** $3 \cdot 11 \cdot 31$ **64.** 18
65. 96 **66.** 60 **67.** 96 **68.** 396 **69.** $\frac{1}{4}$ **71.** 0

Calculator Corner, p. 497

1. 8.717797887 **2.** 17.80449381 **3.** 67.08203932
4. 35.4807407 **5.** 3.141592654 **6.** 91.10618695
7. 530.9291585 **8.** 138.8663978

Calculator Corner, p. 498

1. −0.75 **2.** −0.45 **3.** −0.125 **4.** −1.8 **5.** −0.675
6. −0.6875 **7.** −3.5 **8.** −0.76

Calculator Corner, p. 500

1. 5 **2.** 17 **3.** 0 **4.** 6.48 **5.** 12.7 **6.** 0.9 **7.** $\frac{5}{7}$ **8.** $\frac{4}{3}$

Exercise Set 7.2, p. 502

1. −282 **3.** 24; −2 **5.** 3,600,000,000; −460
7. Alley Cats: −34; Strikers: 34
9. $\frac{10}{3}$ (number line from −6 to 6)
11. −5.2 (number line from −6 to 6)
13. $-4\frac{2}{5}$ (number line from −6 to 6)
15. −0.875 **17.** 0.8$\overline{3}$
19. −1.1$\overline{6}$ **21.** 0.$\overline{6}$ **23.** 0.1 **25.** −0.5 **27.** 0.16

29. $>$ **31.** $<$ **33.** $<$ **35.** $<$ **37.** $>$ **39.** $<$ **41.** $>$
43. $<$ **45.** $<$ **47.** $>$ **49.** $<$ **51.** $<$ **53.** $x < -6$
55. $y \geq -10$ **57.** False **59.** True **61.** True
63. False **65.** 3 **67.** 10 **69.** 0 **71.** 30.4 **73.** $\frac{2}{3}$
75. 0 **77.** 2.65 **79.** $7\frac{4}{5}$ **80.** 0.238 **81.** 0.63
82. 0.2276 **83.** 1.1 **84.** 125% **85.** 52% **86.** 59.375%,
or $59\frac{3}{8}$% **87.** $83.\overline{3}$%, or $83\frac{1}{3}$% **89.** $-\frac{2}{3}, -\frac{2}{5}, -\frac{1}{3}, -\frac{2}{7}, -\frac{1}{7}, \frac{1}{3}, \frac{2}{5}, \frac{9}{8}$
91. $-100, -8\frac{7}{8}, -8\frac{5}{8}, -\frac{67}{8}, -5, 0, 1^7, |3|, \frac{14}{4}, 4, |-6|, 7^1$ **93.** $\frac{1}{1}$

Exercise Set 7.3, p. 510

1. -7 **3.** -6 **5.** 0 **7.** -8 **9.** -7 **11.** -27
13. 0 **15.** -42 **17.** 0 **19.** 0 **21.** 3 **23.** -9
25. 7 **27.** 0 **29.** 35 **31.** -3.8 **33.** -8.1 **35.** $-\frac{1}{5}$
37. $-\frac{7}{9}$ **39.** $-\frac{3}{8}$ **41.** $-\frac{19}{24}$ **43.** $\frac{1}{24}$ **45.** $\frac{8}{15}$ **47.** $\frac{16}{45}$
49. 37 **51.** 50 **53.** -1409 **55.** -24 **57.** 26.9
59. -8 **61.** $\frac{13}{8}$ **63.** -43 **65.** $\frac{4}{3}$ **67.** 24 **69.** $\frac{3}{8}$
71. 13,796 ft **73.** -3°F **75.** $-$\$20,300 **77.** He owes \$85.
79. 0.713 **80.** 0.92875 **81.** 12.5% **82.** 40.625% **83.** $\frac{8}{5}$
84. $\frac{1}{4}$ **85.** All positive numbers **87.** B

Exercise Set 7.4, p. 516

1. -7 **3.** -6 **5.** 0 **7.** -4 **9.** -7 **11.** -6 **13.** 0
15. 14 **17.** 11 **19.** -14 **21.** 5 **23.** -1 **25.** 18
27. -3 **29.** -21 **31.** 5 **33.** -8 **35.** 12 **37.** -23
39. -68 **41.** -73 **43.** 116 **45.** 0 **47.** -1 **49.** $\frac{1}{12}$
51. $-\frac{17}{12}$ **53.** $\frac{1}{8}$ **55.** 19.9 **57.** -8.6 **59.** -0.01
61. -193 **63.** 500 **65.** -2.8 **67.** -3.53 **69.** $-\frac{1}{2}$
71. $\frac{6}{7}$ **73.** $-\frac{41}{30}$ **75.** $-\frac{2}{15}$ **77.** $-\frac{1}{48}$ **79.** $-\frac{43}{60}$ **81.** 37
83. -62 **85.** -139 **87.** 6 **89.** 108.5 **91.** $\frac{1}{4}$
93. 2319 m **95.** \$347.94 **97.** 5676 ft **99.** 381 ft
101. 1130°F **103.** 100.5 **104.** 226 **105.** 13
106. 50 **107.** $\frac{11}{12}$ **108.** $\frac{41}{64}$ **109.** False; $3 - 0 \neq 0 - 3$
111. True **113.** True

Mid-Chapter Review: Chapter 7, p. 520

1. True **2.** False **3.** True **4.** False
5. $-x = -(-4) = 4$;
$-(-x) = -(-(-4)) = -(4) = -4$
6. $5 - 13 = 5 + (-13) = -8$ **7.** $-6 - 7 = -6 + (-7) = -13$
8. 4 **9.** 11 **10.** $3y$ **11.** $n - 5$ **12.** 450; -79
13.

$$\begin{array}{c} \overset{-3.5}{\underset{-6\,-5\,-4\,-3\,-2\,-1\ \ 0\ \ 1\ \ 2\ \ 3\ \ 4\ \ 5\ \ 6}{\bullet}} \end{array}$$

14. -0.8 **15.** $2.\overline{3}$ **16.** $<$
17. $>$ **18.** False **19.** True **20.** $5 > y$ **21.** $t \leq -3$
22. 15.6 **23.** 18 **24.** 0 **25.** $\frac{12}{5}$ **26.** 5.6 **27.** $-\frac{7}{4}$
28. 0 **29.** 49 **30.** 19 **31.** 2.3 **32.** -2 **33.** $-\frac{1}{8}$
34. 0 **35.** -17 **36.** $-\frac{11}{24}$ **37.** -8.1 **38.** -9 **39.** -2
40. -10.4 **41.** 16 **42.** $\frac{7}{20}$ **43.** -12 **44.** -4 **45.** $-\frac{4}{3}$
46. -1.8 **47.** 13 **48.** 9 **49.** -23 **50.** 75 **51.** 14
52. 33°C **53.** \$54.80 **54.** Answers may vary. Three
examples are $\frac{6}{13}, -23.8,$ and $\frac{43}{5}$. These are rational numbers
because they can be named in the form $\dfrac{a}{b}$, where a and b are
integers and b is not 0. They are not integers, however, because
they are neither whole numbers nor the opposites of whole
numbers. **55.** Answers may vary. Three examples are $\pi, -\sqrt{7}$,
and $0.31311311131111.\ldots$ Irrational numbers cannot be
written as the quotient of two integers. Real numbers that are not
rational are irrational. Decimal notation for rational numbers
either terminates or repeats. Decimal notation for irrational
numbers neither terminates nor repeats. **56.** Answers may
vary. If we think of the addition on the number line, we start at 0,
move to the left to a negative number, and then move to the left
again. This always brings us to a point on the negative portion of
the number line. **57.** Yes; consider $m - (-n)$, where both
m and n are positive. Then $m - (-n) = m + n$. Now $m + n$,
the sum of two positive numbers, is positive.

Exercise Set 7.5, p. 526

1. -8 **3.** -48 **5.** -24 **7.** -72 **9.** 16 **11.** 42
13. -120 **15.** -238 **17.** 1200 **19.** 98 **21.** -72
23. -12.4 **25.** 30 **27.** 21.7 **29.** $-\frac{2}{5}$ **31.** $\frac{1}{12}$
33. -17.01 **35.** $-\frac{5}{12}$ **37.** 420 **39.** $\frac{2}{7}$ **41.** -60
43. 150 **45.** $-\frac{2}{45}$ **47.** 1911 **49.** 50.4 **51.** $\frac{10}{189}$ **53.** -960
55. 17.64 **57.** $-\frac{5}{784}$ **59.** 0 **61.** -720 **63.** $-30,240$
65. 1 **67.** 16, -16; 16, -16 **69.** 441; -147 **71.** 20; 20
73. -2; 2 **75.** -20 lb **77.** -54°C **79.** \$12.71
81. -32 m **83.** 38°F **85.** 180
86. $2 \cdot 2 \cdot 2 \cdot 2 \cdot 2 \cdot 2 \cdot 2 \cdot 2 \cdot 2 \cdot 3 \cdot 3$ **87.** $\frac{2}{3}$ **88.** $\frac{8}{9}$ **89.** $\frac{6}{11}$
90. $\frac{41}{265}$ **91.** $\frac{11}{32}$ **92.** $\frac{37}{67}$ **93.** $\frac{1}{24}$ **94.** 6 **95.** A
97.

$$\begin{array}{c} \overset{x-2y \quad -y \quad -x \quad x-y \qquad\qquad 2x \quad x+y \ \ 3x \ \ 2y}{\xrightarrow{}} \\ \underset{0 \qquad x \quad y}{} \end{array}$$

Calculator Corner, p. 534

1. -4 **2.** -0.3 **3.** -12 **4.** -9.5 **5.** -12 **6.** 2.7
7. -2 **8.** -5.7 **9.** -32 **10.** -1.8 **11.** 35
12. 14.44 **13.** -2 **14.** -0.8 **15.** 1.4 **16.** 4

Exercise Set 7.6, p. 535

1. -8 **3.** -14 **5.** -3 **7.** 3 **9.** -8 **11.** 2 **13.** -12
15. -8 **17.** Not defined **19.** 0 **21.** $\frac{7}{15}$ **23.** $-\frac{13}{47}$
25. $\frac{1}{13}$ **27.** $-\frac{1}{32}$ **29.** -7.1 **31.** 9 **33.** $4y$ **35.** $\frac{3b}{2a}$
37. $4 \cdot \left(\frac{1}{17}\right)$ **39.** $8 \cdot \left(-\frac{1}{13}\right)$ **41.** $13.9 \cdot \left(-\frac{1}{1.5}\right)$ **43.** $\frac{2}{3} \cdot \left(-\frac{5}{4}\right)$
45. $x \cdot y$ **47.** $(3x + 4)\left(\frac{1}{5}\right)$ **49.** $-\frac{9}{8}$ **51.** $\frac{5}{3}$ **53.** $\frac{9}{14}$
55. $\frac{9}{64}$ **57.** $-\frac{5}{4}$ **59.** $-\frac{27}{5}$ **61.** $\frac{11}{13}$ **63.** -2
65. -16.2 **67.** -2.5 **69.** -1.25 **71.** Not defined
73. 23.5% **75.** -3.3% **77.** 33 **78.** 129 **79.** 1
80. 1296 **81.** $\frac{22}{39}$ **82.** 0.477 **83.** 87.5% **84.** $\frac{2}{3}$ **85.** $\frac{9}{8}$
86. $\frac{128}{625}$ **87.** $\frac{1}{-10.5}$; -10.5, the reciprocal of the reciprocal
is the original number. **89.** Negative **91.** Positive
93. Negative

Exercise Set 7.7, p. 547

1. $\frac{3y}{5y}$ **3.** $\frac{10x}{15x}$ **5.** $\frac{2x}{x^2}$ **7.** $-\frac{3}{2}$ **9.** $-\frac{7}{6}$ **11.** $\frac{4s}{3}$ **13.** $8 + y$
15. nm **17.** $xy + 9$, or $9 + yx$ **19.** $c + ab$, or $ba + c$
21. $(a + b) + 2$ **23.** $8(xy)$ **25.** $a + (b + 3)$ **27.** $(3a)b$
29. $2 + (b + a), (2 + a) + b, (b + 2) + a$; answers may vary
31. $(5 + w) + v, (v + 5) + w, (w + v) + 5$; answers may vary
33. $(3x)y, y(x \cdot 3), 3(yx)$; answers may vary
35. $a(7b), b(7a), (7b)a$; answers may vary **37.** $2b + 10$
39. $7 + 7t$ **41.** $30x + 12$ **43.** $7x + 28 + 42y$
45. $7x - 21$ **47.** $-3x + 21$ **49.** $\frac{2}{3}b - 4$ **51.** $7.3x - 14.6$
53. $-\frac{3}{5}x + \frac{3}{5}y - 6$ **55.** $45x + 54y - 72$
57. $-4x + 12y + 8z$ **59.** $-3.72x + 9.92y - 3.41$
61. $4x, 3z$ **63.** $7x, 8y, -9z$ **65.** $2(x + 2)$ **67.** $5(6 + y)$
69. $7(2x + 3y)$ **71.** $7(2t - 1)$ **73.** $8(x - 3)$
75. $6(3a - 4b)$ **77.** $-4(y - 8)$, or $4(-y + 8)$
79. $5(x + 2 + 3y)$ **81.** $8(2m - 4n + 1)$
83. $4(3a + b - 6)$ **85.** $2(4x + 5y - 11)$ **87.** $a(x - 1)$
89. $a(x - y - z)$ **91.** $-6(3x - 2y - 1)$, or $6(-3x + 2y + 1)$
93. $\frac{1}{3}(2x - 5y + 1)$ **95.** $6(6x - y + 3z)$ **97.** $19a$ **99.** $9a$
101. $8x + 9z$ **103.** $7x + 15y^2$ **105.** $-19a + 88$
107. $4t + 6y - 4$ **109.** b **111.** $\frac{13}{4}y$ **113.** $8x$ **115.** $5n$
117. $-16y$ **119.** $17a - 12b - 1$ **121.** $4x + 2y$
123. $7x + y$ **125.** $0.8x + 0.5y$ **127.** $\frac{35}{6}a + \frac{3}{2}b - 42$
129. 144 **130.** 72 **131.** 144 **132.** 60 **133.** 32
134. 72 **135.** 90 **136.** 108 **137.** $\frac{89}{48}$ **138.** $\frac{5}{24}$ **139.** $-\frac{5}{24}$
140. 30% **141.** Not equivalent; $3 \cdot 2 + 5 \neq 3 \cdot 5 + 2$
143. Equivalent; commutative law of addition
145. $q(1 + r + rs + rst)$

Calculator Corner, p. 555

1. -11 **2.** 9 **3.** 114 **4.** $117{,}649$ **5.** $-1{,}419{,}857$
6. $-1{,}124{,}864$ **7.** $-117{,}649$ **8.** $-1{,}419{,}857$ **9.** $-1{,}124{,}864$
10. -4 **11.** -2 **12.** 787

Translating for Success, p. 556

1. N **2.** I **3.** A **4.** K **5.** J
6. F **7.** M **8.** B **9.** G **10.** E

Exercise Set 7.8, p. 557

1. $-2x - 7$ **3.** $-8 + x$ **5.** $-4a + 3b - 7c$
7. $-6x + 8y - 5$ **9.** $-3x + 5y + 6$ **11.** $8x + 6y + 43$
13. $5x - 3$ **15.** $-3a + 9$ **17.** $5x - 6$ **19.** $-19x + 2y$
21. $9y - 25z$ **23.** $-7x + 10y$ **25.** $37a - 23b + 35c$
27. 7 **29.** -40 **31.** 19 **33.** $12x + 30$ **35.** $3x + 30$
37. $9x - 18$ **39.** $-4x - 64$ **41.** -7 **43.** -7 **45.** -16
47. -334 **49.** 14 **51.** 1880 **53.** 12 **55.** 8 **57.** -86
59. 37 **61.** -1 **63.** -10 **65.** -67 **67.** -7988
69. -3000 **71.** 60 **73.** 1 **75.** 10 **77.** $-\frac{13}{45}$ **79.** $-\frac{23}{18}$
81. -122 **83.** Integers **84.** Additive inverses
85. Commutative law **86.** Identity property of 1
87. Associative law **88.** Associative law **89.** Multiplicative
inverses **90.** Identity property of 0
91. $6y - (-2x + 3a - c)$ **93.** $6m - (-3n + 5m - 4b)$
95. $-2x - f$ **97. (a)** $52; 52; 28.130169;$
(b) $-24; -24; -108.307025$ **99.** -6

Summary and Review: Chapter 7, p. 561

Concept Reinforcement

1. True **2.** True **3.** False **4.** False

Important Concepts

1. 14 **2.** $<$ **3.** $\frac{5}{4}$ **4.** -8.5 **5.** -2 **6.** 56 **7.** -8
8. $\frac{9}{20}$ **9.** $\frac{5}{3}$ **10.** $5x + 15y - 20z$ **11.** $9(3x + y - 4z)$
12. $5a - 2b$ **13.** $4a - 4b$ **14.** -2

Review Exercises

1. 4 **2.** $19\%x$, or $0.19x$ **3.** $-45, 72$ **4.** 38 **5.** 126
6. **7.**
8. $<$ **9.** $>$ **10.** $>$ **11.** $<$ **12.** $x > -3$ **13.** True
14. False **15.** -3.8 **16.** $\frac{3}{4}$ **17.** $\frac{8}{3}$ **18.** $-\frac{1}{7}$ **19.** 34
20. 5 **21.** -3 **22.** -4 **23.** -5 **24.** 1 **25.** $-\frac{7}{5}$
26. -7.9 **27.** 54 **28.** -9.18 **29.** $-\frac{2}{7}$ **30.** -210
31. -7 **32.** -3 **33.** $\frac{3}{4}$ **34.** 40.4 **35.** -2 **36.** 2
37. -2 **38.** 8-yd gain **39.** $-\$130$ **40.** $\$4.64$
41. $\$18.95$ **42.** $15x - 35$ **43.** $-8x + 10$ **44.** $4x + 15$
45. $-24 + 48x$ **46.** $2(x - 7)$ **47.** $-6(x - 1)$, or $6(-x + 1)$
48. $5(x + 2)$ **49.** $-3(x - 4y + 4)$, or $3(-x + 4y - 4)$
50. $7a - 3b$ **51.** $-2x + 5y$ **52.** $5x - y$ **53.** $-a + 8b$
54. $-3a + 9$ **55.** $-2b + 21$ **56.** 6 **57.** $12y - 34$
58. $5x + 24$ **59.** $-15x + 25$ **60.** D **61.** B **62.** $-\frac{5}{8}$
63. -2.1 **64.** 1000 **65.** $4a + 2b$

Understanding Through Discussion and Writing

1. The sum of each pair of opposites such as -50 and 50, -49 and 49, and so on is 0. The sum of these sums and the remaining integer, 0, is 0. **2.** The product of an even number of negative numbers is positive, and the product of an odd number of negative numbers is negative. Now $(-7)^8$ is the product of 8 factors of -7 so it is positive, and $(-7)^{11}$ is the product of 11 factors of -7 so it is negative. **3.** Consider $\frac{a}{b} = q$,

where a and b are both negative numbers. Then $q \cdot b = a$, so q must be a positive number in order for the product to be

negative. **4.** Consider $\frac{a}{b} = q$, where a is a negative number

and b is a positive number. Then $q \cdot b = a$, so q must be a negative number in order for the product to be negative.
5. We use the distributive law when we collect like terms even though we might not always write this step. **6.** Jake expects the calculator to multiply 2 and 3 first and then divide 18 by that product. This procedure does not follow the rules for order of operations.

Test: Chapter 7, p. 567

1. [7.1a] 6 **2.** [7.1b] $x - 9$ **3.** [7.2d] $>$ **4.** [7.2d] $<$
5. [7.2d] $>$ **6.** [7.2d] $-2 > x$ **7.** [7.2e] True **8.** [7.2e] 7
9. [7.2e] $\frac{9}{4}$ **10.** [7.2e] 2.7 **11.** [7.3b] $-\frac{2}{3}$ **12.** [7.3b] 1.4
13. [7.6b] $-\frac{1}{2}$ **14.** [7.6b] $\frac{7}{4}$ **15.** [7.3b] 8 **16.** [7.4a] 7.8
17. [7.3a] -8 **18.** [7.3a] $\frac{7}{40}$ **19.** [7.4a] 10 **20.** [7.4a] -2.5
21. [7.4a] $\frac{7}{8}$ **22.** [7.5a] -48 **23.** [7.5a] $\frac{3}{16}$ **24.** [7.6a] -9
25. [7.6c] $\frac{3}{4}$ **26.** [7.6c] -9.728 **27.** [7.8d] -173
28. [7.8d] -5 **29.** [7.3c], [7.4b] Up 15 points **30.** [7.4b] $14°F$
31. [7.5b] $16{,}080$ **32.** [7.6d] $-0.75°C$ each minute
33. [7.7c] $18 - 3x$ **34.** [7.7c] $-5y + 5$
35. [7.7d] $2(6 - 11x)$ **36.** [7.7d] $7(x + 3 + 2y)$
37. [7.4a] 12 **38.** [7.8b] $2x + 7$ **39.** [7.8b] $9a - 12b - 7$
40. [7.8c] $68y - 8$ **41.** [7.8d] -4 **42.** [7.8d] 448
43. [7.2d] B **44.** [7.2e], [7.8d] 15 **45.** [7.8c] $4a$
46. [7.7e] $4x + 4y$

CHAPTER 8

Exercise Set 8.1, p. 574

1. Yes **3.** No **5.** No **7.** Yes **9.** Yes **11.** No **13.** 4
15. -20 **17.** -14 **19.** -18 **21.** 15 **23.** -14 **25.** 2
27. 20 **29.** -6 **31.** $6\frac{1}{2}$ **33.** 19.9 **35.** $\frac{7}{3}$ **37.** $-\frac{7}{4}$
39. $\frac{41}{24}$ **41.** $-\frac{1}{20}$ **43.** 5.1 **45.** 12.4 **47.** -5 **49.** $1\frac{5}{6}$
51. $-\frac{10}{21}$ **53.** -11 **54.** 5 **55.** $-\frac{5}{12}$ **56.** $\frac{1}{3}$ **57.** $-\frac{3}{2}$
58. -5.2 **59.** $-\frac{1}{24}$ **60.** 172.72 **61.** $\$83 - x$ **62.** $65t$ miles
63. 342.246 **65.** $-\frac{26}{15}$ **67.** -10 **69.** All real numbers
71. $-\frac{5}{17}$ **73.** $13, -13$

Exercise Set 8.2, p. 580

1. 6 **3.** 9 **5.** 12 **7.** -40 **9.** 1 **11.** -7 **13.** -6
15. 6 **17.** -63 **19.** -48 **21.** 36 **23.** -9 **25.** -21
27. $-\frac{3}{5}$ **29.** $-\frac{3}{2}$ **31.** $\frac{9}{2}$ **33.** 7 **35.** -7 **37.** 8 **39.** 15.9
41. -50 **43.** -14 **45.** $7x$ **46.** $-x + 5$ **47.** $8x + 11$
48. $-32y$ **49.** $x - 4$ **50.** $-5x - 23$ **51.** $-10y - 42$
52. $-22a + 4$ **53.** $8r$ miles **54.** $\frac{1}{2}b \cdot 10$ m^2, or $5b$ m^2
55. -8655 **57.** No solution **59.** No solution
61. $\dfrac{b}{3a}$ **63.** $\dfrac{4b}{a}$

Calculator Corner, p. 585

1. Left to the student

Exercise Set 8.3, p. 589

1. 5 **3.** 8 **5.** 10 **7.** 14 **9.** -8 **11.** -8 **13.** -7
15. 12 **17.** 6 **19.** 4 **21.** 6 **23.** -3 **25.** 1 **27.** 6
29. -20 **31.** 7 **33.** 2 **35.** 5 **37.** 2 **39.** 10 **41.** 4
43. 0 **45.** -1 **47.** $-\frac{4}{3}$ **49.** $\frac{2}{5}$ **51.** -2 **53.** -4 **55.** $\frac{4}{5}$
57. $-\frac{28}{27}$ **59.** 6 **61.** 2 **63.** No solution **65.** All real
numbers **67.** 6 **69.** 8 **71.** 1 **73.** All real numbers
75. No solution **77.** 17 **79.** $-\frac{5}{3}$ **81.** -3 **83.** 2
85. $\frac{4}{7}$ **87.** No solution **89.** All real numbers **91.** $-\frac{51}{31}$
93. -6.5 **94.** -75.14 **95.** $7(x - 3 - 2y)$
96. $8(y - 11x + 1)$ **97.** -160 **98.** $-17x + 18$
99. $91x - 242$ **100.** 0.25 **101.** $-\frac{5}{32}$ **103.** $\frac{52}{45}$

Exercise Set 8.4, p. 597

1. (a) $57{,}000$ Btu's; **(b)** $a = \dfrac{B}{30}$ **3. (a)** 1.6 mi; **(b)** $t = 5M$

5. (a) 1423 students; **(b)** $n = 15f$ **7.** 10.5 calories per ounce
9. 42 games   **11.** $x = \dfrac{y}{5}$ **13.** $c = \dfrac{a}{b}$ **15.** $m = n - 11$
17. $x = y + \dfrac{3}{5}$ **19.** $x = y - 13$ **21.** $x = y - b$
23. $x = 5 - y$ **25.** $x = a - y$ **27.** $y = \dfrac{5x}{8}$, or $\dfrac{5}{8}x$
29. $x = \dfrac{By}{A}$ **31.** $t = \dfrac{W - b}{m}$ **33.** $x = \dfrac{y - c}{b}$ **35.** $h = \dfrac{A}{b}$
37. $w = \dfrac{P - 2l}{2}$, or $\dfrac{1}{2}P - l$ **39.** $a = 2A - b$
41. $b = 3A - a - c$ **43.** $t = \dfrac{A - b}{a}$ **45.** $x = \dfrac{c - By}{A}$
47. $a = \dfrac{F}{m}$ **49.** $c^2 = \dfrac{E}{m}$ **51.** $t = \dfrac{3k}{v}$ **53.** 0.92   **54.** -90
55. -9.325 **56.** 44   **57.** -13.2 **58.** $-21a + 12b$
59. 0.031   **60.** 0.671   **61.** $\frac{1}{6}$ **62.** $-\frac{3}{2}$
63. (a) 1901 calories;

(b) $a = \dfrac{917 + 6w + 6h - K}{6}$;

$\quad h = \dfrac{K - 917 - 6w + 6a}{6}$;

$\quad w = \dfrac{K - 917 - 6h + 6a}{6}$

65. $b = \dfrac{Ha - 2}{H}$, or $a - \dfrac{2}{H}$; $a = \dfrac{2 + Hb}{H}$, or $\dfrac{2}{H} + b$
67. A quadruples.   **69.** A increases by $2h$ units.

Mid-Chapter Review: Chapter 8, p. 601

1. False   **2.** True   **3.** True   **4.** False
5.
$\quad x + 5 = -3$
$\quad x + 5 - 5 = -3 - 5$
$\quad x + 0 = -8$
$\quad x = -8$

6.
$\quad -6x = 42$
$\quad \dfrac{-6x}{-6} = \dfrac{42}{-6}$
$\quad 1 \cdot x = -7$
$\quad x = -7$

7.
$\quad 5y + z = t$
$\quad 5y + z - z = t - z$
$\quad 5y = t - z$
$\quad \dfrac{5y}{5} = \dfrac{t - z}{5}$
$\quad y = \dfrac{t - z}{5}$

8. 6   **9.** -12 **10.** 7   **11.** -10 **12.** 20   **13.** 5   **14.** $\frac{3}{4}$
15. -1.4 **16.** 6   **17.** -17 **18.** -9 **19.** 17   **20.** 21
21. 18   **22.** -15 **23.** $-\frac{3}{2}$ **24.** 1   **25.** -3 **26.** $\frac{3}{2}$
27. -1 **28.** 3   **29.** -7 **30.** 4   **31.** 2   **32.** $\frac{9}{8}$ **33.** $-\frac{21}{5}$
34. 9   **35.** -2 **36.** 0   **37.** All real numbers
38. No solution   **39.** $-\frac{13}{2}$ **40.** All real numbers   **41.** $b = \dfrac{A}{4}$
42. $x = y + 1.5$ **43.** $m = s - n$ **44.** $t = \dfrac{9w}{4}$
45. $t = \dfrac{B + c}{a}$ **46.** $y = 2M - x - z$ **47.** Equivalent
expressions have the same value for all possible replacements
for the variable(s). Equivalent equations have the same
solution(s).   **48.** The equations are not equivalent because
they do not have the same solutions. Although 5 is a solution of
both equations, -5 is a solution of $x^2 = 25$ but not of $x = 5$.
49. For an equation $x + a = b$, add the opposite of a (or
subtract a) on both sides of the equation.   **50.** The student
probably added $\frac{1}{3}$ on both sides of the equation rather than
adding $-\frac{1}{3}$ (or subtracting $\frac{1}{3}$) on both sides. The correct solution is
-2.   **51.** For an equation $ax = b$, multiply by $1/a$ (or divide by a)

on both sides of the equation.   **52.** Answers may vary.
A walker who knows how far and how long she walks each day
wants to know her average speed each day.

Exercise Set 8.5, p. 607

1. 20%   **3.** 150   **5.** 546   **7.** 24%   **9.** 2.5   **11.** 5%
13. 25%   **15.** 84   **17.** 24%   **19.** 16%   **21.** $46\frac{2}{3}$ **23.** 0.8
25. 5   **27.** 40   **29.** $16.1   **31.** $2.1   **33.** About 12%
35. $2.646 billion   **37.** $390   **39. (a)** 16%; **(b)** $29
41. (a) $3.75; **(b)** $28.75   **43. (a)** $30; **(b)** $34.50   **45.** About
85,821 acres   **47.** About 22.6%   **49.** 800%   **51.** 10%
53. About 144%   **55.** 181.52   **56.** 0.4538   **57.** 12.0879
58. 844.1407   **59.** $a + c$ **60.** $7x - 9y$ **61.** -3.9
62. $-6\frac{1}{8}$ **63.** Division; subtraction   **64.** Exponential;
division; subtraction   **65.** 6 ft 7 in.

Translating for Success, p. 622

1. B   **2.** H   **3.** G   **4.** N   **5.** J   **6.** C   **7.** L   **8.** E
9. F   **10.** D

Exercise Set 8.6, p. 623

1. 3113 manatees   **3.** 180 in.; 60 in.   **5.** $16.56   **7.** $699\frac{1}{3}$ mi
9. 1204 and 1205   **11.** 41, 42, 43   **13.** 61, 63, 65   **15.** Length:
48 ft; width: 14 ft   **17.** $75   **19.** $85   **21.** 11 visits
23. 28°, 84°, 68°   **25.** 33°, 38°, 109°   **27.** $350   **29.** $852.94
31. 12 mi   **33.** $36   **35.** $25 and $50   **37.** -12 **39.** $-\frac{47}{40}$
40. $-\frac{17}{40}$ **41.** $-\frac{3}{10}$ **42.** $-\frac{32}{15}$ **43.** -10 **44.** 1.6
45. 409.6   **46.** -9.6 **47.** -41.6 **48.** 0.1   **49.** 120 apples
51. About 0.65 in.   **53.** $9.17, not $9.10

Exercise Set 8.7, p. 636

1. (a) Yes; **(b)** yes; **(c)** no; **(d)** yes; **(e)** yes
3. (a) No; **(b)** no; **(c)** no; **(d)** yes; **(e)** no
5.

$x > 4$

7.
$t < -3$

9.
$m \geq -1$

11.
$-3 < x \leq 4$

13.
$0 < x < 3$

15. $\{x \mid x > -5\}$;

17. $\{x \mid x \leq -18\}$;

19. $\{y \mid y > -5\}$

21. $\{x \mid x > 2\}$ **23.** $\{x \mid x \leq -3\}$ **25.** $\{x \mid x < 4\}$
27. $\{t \mid t > 14\}$ **29.** $\{y \mid y \leq \frac{1}{4}\}$ **31.** $\{x \mid x > \frac{7}{12}\}$
33. $\{x \mid x < 7\}$;

35. $\{x \mid x < 3\}$;

37. $\{y \mid y \geq -\frac{2}{5}\}$ **39.** $\{x \mid x \geq -6\}$ **41.** $\{y \mid y \leq 4\}$
43. $\{x \mid x > \frac{17}{3}\}$ **45.** $\{y \mid y < -\frac{1}{14}\}$ **47.** $\{x \mid x \leq \frac{3}{10}\}$
49. $\{x \mid x < 8\}$ **51.** $\{x \mid x \leq 6\}$ **53.** $\{x \mid x < -3\}$
55. $\{x \mid x > -3\}$ **57.** $\{x \mid x \leq 7\}$ **59.** $\{x \mid x > -10\}$
61. $\{y \mid y < 2\}$ **63.** $\{y \mid y \geq 3\}$ **65.** $\{y \mid y > -2\}$
67. $\{x \mid x > -4\}$ **69.** $\{x \mid x \leq 9\}$ **71.** $\{y \mid y \leq -3\}$
73. $\{y \mid y < 6\}$ **75.** $\{m \mid m \geq 6\}$ **77.** $\{t \mid t < -\frac{5}{3}\}$
79. $\{r \mid r > -3\}$ **81.** $\{x \mid x \geq -\frac{57}{34}\}$ **83.** $\{x \mid x > -2\}$
85. -74 **86.** 4.8   **87.** $-\frac{5}{8}$ **88.** -1.11 **89.** -38 **90.** $-\frac{7}{8}$
91. -9.4 **92.** 1.11   **93.** 140   **94.** 41   **95.** $-2x - 23$
96. $37x - 1$ **97. (a)** Yes; **(b)** yes; **(c)** no; **(d)** no; **(e)** no; **(f)** yes;
(g) yes   **99.** No solution

Exercise Set 8.8, p. 643

1. $n \geq 7$ **3.** $w > 2 \, \text{kg}$ **5.** $90 \, \text{mph} < s < 110 \, \text{mph}$
7. $w \leq 20 \, \text{hr}$ **9.** $c \geq \$1.50$ **11.** $x > 8$ **13.** $y \leq -4$
15. $n \geq 1300$ **17.** $W \leq 500 \, \text{L}$ **19.** $3x + 2 < 13$
21. $\{x \mid x \geq 84\}$ **23.** $\{C \mid C < 1063°\}$ **25.** $\{Y \mid Y \geq 1935\}$
27. $\{L \mid L \geq 5 \, \text{in.}\}$ **29.** 15 or fewer copies **31.** 5 min or
more **33.** 2 courses **35.** 4 servings or more **37.** Lengths
greater than or equal to 92 ft; lengths less than or equal to 92 ft
39. Lengths less than 21.5 cm **41.** The blue-book value is
greater than or equal to \$10,625. **43.** It has at least 16 g of fat.
45. Dates at least 6 weeks after July 1 **47.** Heights greater
than or equal to 4 ft **49.** 21 calls or more **51.** Even
52. Odd **53.** Additive **54.** Multiplicative **55.** Equivalent
56. Addition principle **57.** Multiplication principle; is
reversed **58.** Solution **59.** Temperatures between $-15°C$
and $-9\frac{4}{9}°C$ **61.** They contain at least 7.5 g of fat per serving.

Summary and Review: Chapter 8, p. 648

Concept Reinforcement
1. True **2.** True **3.** False **4.** True

Important Concepts

1. -12 **2.** All real numbers **3.** No solution **4.** $b = \dfrac{2A}{h}$

5.
$x > 1$
6.
$x \leq -1$
7. $\{y \mid y > -4\}$

Review Exercises

1. -22 **2.** 1 **3.** 25 **4.** 9.99 **5.** $\frac{1}{4}$ **6.** 7 **7.** -192
8. $-\frac{7}{3}$ **9.** $-\frac{15}{64}$ **10.** -8 **11.** 4 **12.** -5 **13.** $-\frac{1}{3}$ **14.** 3
15. 4 **16.** 16 **17.** All real numbers **18.** 6 **19.** -3
20. 28 **21.** 4 **22.** No solution **23.** Yes **24.** No
25. Yes **26.** $\{y \mid y \geq -\frac{1}{2}\}$ **27.** $\{x \mid x \geq 7\}$ **28.** $\{y \mid y > 2\}$
29. $\{y \mid y \leq -4\}$ **30.** $\{x \mid x < -11\}$ **31.** $\{y \mid y > -7\}$
32. $\{x \mid x > -\frac{9}{11}\}$ **33.** $\{x \mid x \geq -\frac{1}{12}\}$
34.
$x < 3$
35.
$-2 < x \leq 5$
36.
$y > 0$
37. $d = \dfrac{C}{\pi}$ **38.** $B = \dfrac{3V}{h}$

39. $a = 2A - b$ **40.** $x = \dfrac{y - b}{m}$ **41.** Length: 365 mi; width:
275 mi **42.** 345, 346 **43.** \$2117 **44.** 27 subscriptions
45. $35°, 85°, 60°$ **46.** 15 **47.** 18.75% **48.** 600
49. About 18% **50.** \$220 **51.** \$53,400 **52.** \$138.95
53. 86 **54.** $\{w \mid w > 17 \, \text{cm}\}$ **55.** C **56.** A **57.** 23, -23
58. 20, -20 **59.** $a = \dfrac{y - 3}{2 - b}$

Understanding Through Discussion and Writing
1. The end result is the same either way. If s is the original
salary, the new salary after a 5% raise followed by an 8% raise is
$1.08(1.05s)$. If the raises occur the other way around, the new
salary is $1.05(1.08s)$. By the commutative and associative laws of
multiplication, we see that these are equal. However, it would be
better to receive the 8% raise first, because this increase yields a
higher salary initially than a 5% raise.
2. No; Erin paid 75% of the original price and was offered credit
for 125% of this amount, not to be used on sale items. Now,
125% of 75% is 93.75%, so Erin would have a credit of 93.75% of
the original price. Since this credit can be applied only to non-
sale items, she has less purchasing power than if the amount
she paid were refunded and she could spend it on sale items.
3. The inequalities are equivalent by the multiplication

principle for inequalities. If we multiply on both sides of one
inequality by -1, the other inequality results.
4. For any pair of numbers, their relative position on the number line is reversed when both are multiplied by the same negative number. For example, -3 is to the left of 5 on the number
line ($-3 < 5$), but 12 is to the right of -20 ($-3(-4) > 5(-4)$).
5. Answers may vary. Fran is more than 3 years older than Todd.
6. Let n represent "a number." Then "five more than a number"
translates to the *expression* $n + 5$, or $5 + n$, and "five is more
than a number" translates to the *inequality* $5 > n$.

Test: Chapter 8, p. 653

1. [8.1b] 8 **2.** [8.1b] 26 **3.** [8.2a] -6 **4.** [8.2a] 49
5. [8.3b] -12 **6.** [8.3a] 2 **7.** [8.3a] -8 **8.** [8.1b] $-\frac{7}{20}$
9. [8.3c] 7 **10.** [8.3c] $\frac{5}{3}$ **11.** [8.3b] $\frac{5}{2}$
12. [8.3c] No solution **13.** [8.3c] All real numbers
14. [8.7c] $\{x \mid x \leq -4\}$ **15.** [8.7c] $\{x \mid x > -13\}$
16. [8.7d] $\{x \mid x \leq 5\}$ **17.** [8.7d] $\{y \mid y \leq -13\}$
18. [8.7d] $\{y \mid y \geq 8\}$ **19.** [8.7d] $\{x \mid x \leq -\frac{1}{20}\}$
20. [8.7e] $\{x \mid x < -6\}$ **21.** [8.7e] $\{x \mid x \leq -1\}$
22. [8.7b]
$y \leq 9$
23. [8.7b, e]
$x < 1$
24. [8.7b]
$-2 \leq x \leq 2$
25. [8.5a] 18
26. [8.5a] 16.5% **27.** [8.5a] 40,000 **28.** [8.5a] About 25.8%
29. [8.6a] Width: 7 cm; length: 11 cm **30.** [8.5a] About \$310 billion
31. [8.6a] 2509, 2510, 2511 **32.** [8.6a] \$880 **33.** [8.6a] 3 m, 5 m
34. [8.8b] $\{l \mid l \leq 174 \, \text{yd}\}$ **35.** [8.8b] $\{b \mid b \leq \$105\}$
36. [8.8b] $\{c \mid c \leq 143,750\}$ **37.** [8.4b] $r = \dfrac{A}{2\pi h}$
38. [8.4b] $x = \dfrac{y - b}{8}$ **39.** [8.5a] D **40.** [8.4b] $d = \dfrac{1 - ca}{-c}$,
or $\dfrac{ca - 1}{c}$ **41.** [7.2e], [8.3a] 15, -15 **42.** [8.6a] 60 tickets

CHAPTER 9

Calculator Corner, p. 660
1. Left to the student

Calculator Corner, p. 666
1. $y = 2x + 1$
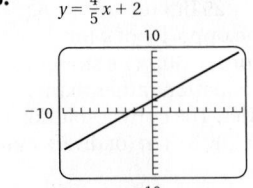

2. $y = -3x + 1$
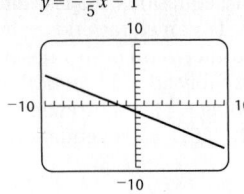

3. $y = -5x + 3$

4. $y = 4x - 5$

5. $y = \frac{4}{5}x + 2$

6. $y = -\frac{3}{5}x - 1$

7. $y = 2.085x + 5.08$

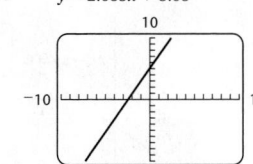

8. $y = -3.45x - 1.68$

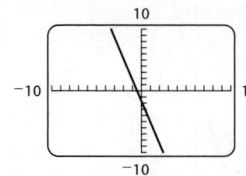

Exercise Set 9.1, p. 667

1.

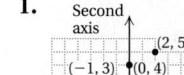

3. II **5.** IV **7.** III
9. On an axis, not in a quadrant
11. II **13.** IV **15.** II
17. I, IV **19.** I, III

21. A: $(3, 3)$; B: $(0, -4)$; C: $(-5, 0)$; D: $(-1, -1)$; E: $(2, 0)$
23. No **25.** No **27.** Yes

29.

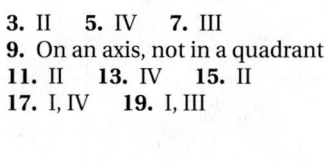

$$\begin{array}{c} y = x - 5 \\ \hline -1 \; ? \; 4 - 5 \\ \quad -1 \quad \text{TRUE} \end{array}$$

$$\begin{array}{c} y = x - 5 \\ \hline -4 \; ? \; 1 - 5 \\ \quad -4 \quad \text{TRUE} \end{array}$$

31.

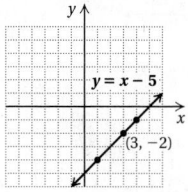

$$\begin{array}{c} y = \tfrac{1}{2}x + 3 \\ \hline 5 \; ? \; \tfrac{1}{2} \cdot 4 + 3 \\ 2 + 3 \\ 5 \quad \text{TRUE} \end{array}$$

$$\begin{array}{c} y = \tfrac{1}{2}x + 3 \\ \hline 2 \; ? \; \tfrac{1}{2}(-2) + 3 \\ -1 + 3 \\ 2 \quad \text{TRUE} \end{array}$$

33.

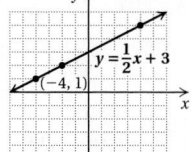

$$\begin{array}{c} 4x - 2y = 10 \\ \hline 4 \cdot 0 - 2(-5) \; ? \; 10 \\ 0 + 10 \\ 10 \quad \text{TRUE} \end{array}$$

$$\begin{array}{c} 4x - 2y = 10 \\ \hline 4 \cdot 4 - 2 \cdot 3 \; ? \; 10 \\ 16 - 6 \\ 10 \quad \text{TRUE} \end{array}$$

35.

x	y
−2	−1
−1	0
0	1
1	2
2	3
3	4

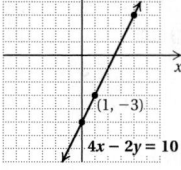

37.

x	y
−2	−2
−1	−1
0	0
1	1
2	2
3	3

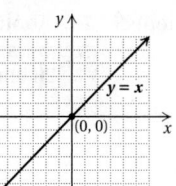

39.

x	y
−2	−1
0	0
4	2

41.

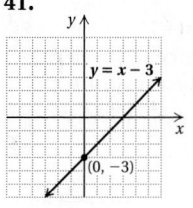

43.

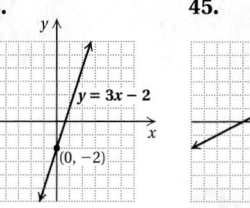

45.

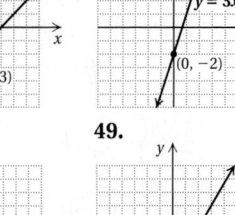

47.

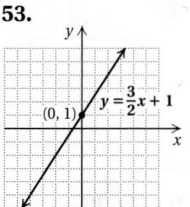

49.

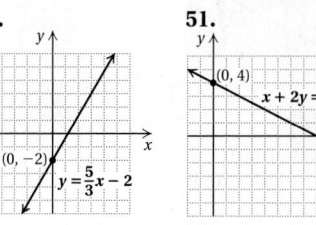

51.

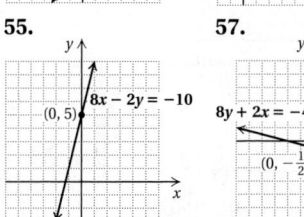

53.

55.

57.

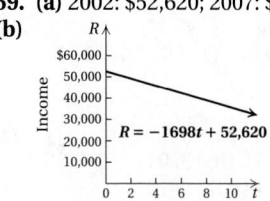

59. (a) 2002: $52,620; 2007: $44,130; 2010: $39,036;
(b)

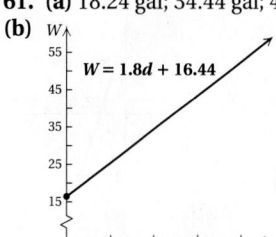

about $47,500;
(c) 9 yr after 2002, or in 2011

61. (a) 18.24 gal; 34.44 gal; 43.44 gal;
(b)

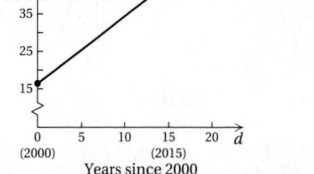

about 31 gal;
(c) 11 yr after 2000, or in 2011

63. 12 **64.** 4.89 **65.** 0 **66.** $\tfrac{4}{5}$ **67.** 3.4 **68.** $\sqrt{2}$ **69.** $\tfrac{2}{3}$

70. $\frac{7}{8}$ **71.** 48 patients   **72.** About 30.7%   **73.** $(-1, -5)$, , answers may vary   **77.** 26 linear units

75.

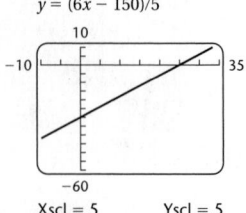

Calculator Corner, p. 675

1. y-intercept: $(0, -15)$; x-intercept: $(-2, 0)$;
$y = -7.5x - 15$

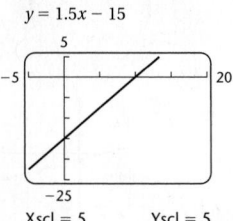

Xscl = 1   Yscl = 5

2. y-intercept: $(0, 43)$; x-intercept: $(-20, 0)$;
$y = 2.15x + 43$

Xscl = 5   Yscl = 5

3. y-intercept: $(0, -30)$; x-intercept: $(25, 0)$;
$y = (6x - 150)/5$

Xscl = 5   Yscl = 5

4. y-intercept: $(0, -4)$; x-intercept: $(20, 0)$;
$y = 0.2x - 4$

Xscl = 5   Yscl = 1

5. y-intercept: $(0, -15)$; x-intercept: $(10, 0)$;
$y = 1.5x - 15$

Xscl = 5   Yscl = 5

6. y-intercept: $\left(0, -\frac{1}{2}\right)$; x-intercept: $\left(\frac{2}{5}, 0\right)$;
$y = (5x - 2)/4$

Xscl = 0.25   Yscl = 0.25

Visualizing for Success, p. 678

1. E   **2.** C   **3.** G   **4.** A   **5.** I   **6.** D   **7.** F   **8.** J
9. B   **10.** H

Exercise Set 9.2, p. 679

1. (a) $(0, 5)$; (b) $(2, 0)$ **3.** (a) $(0, -4)$; (b) $(3, 0)$
5. (a) $(0, 3)$; (b) $(5, 0)$ **7.** (a) $(0, -14)$; (b) $(4, 0)$
9. (a) $\left(0, \frac{10}{3}\right)$; (b) $\left(-\frac{5}{2}, 0\right)$ **11.** (a) $\left(0, -\frac{1}{3}\right)$; (b) $\left(\frac{1}{2}, 0\right)$

13.

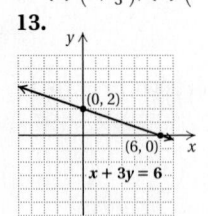

15.

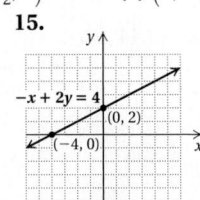

17.

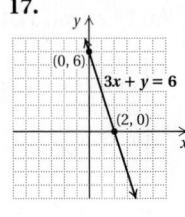

19.

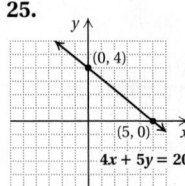

21.

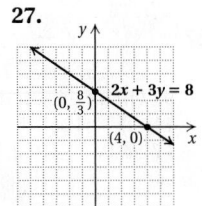

23.

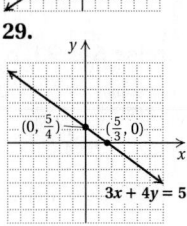

25.

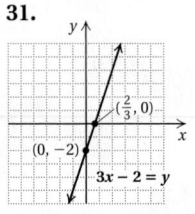

27.

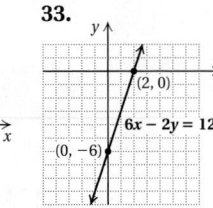

29.

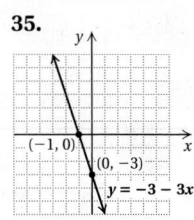

31.

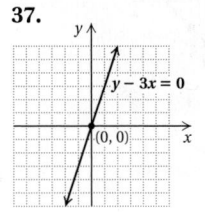

33.

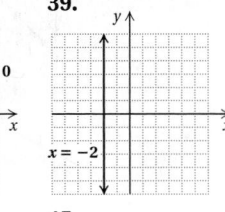

35.

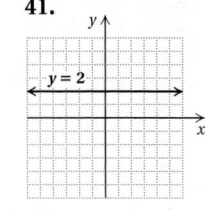

37.

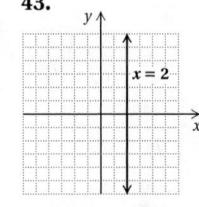

39.

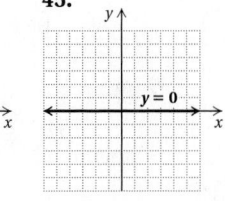

41.

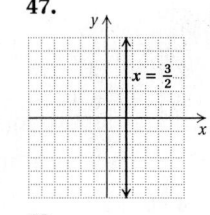

43.

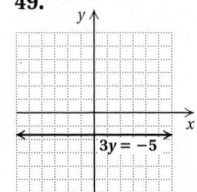

45.

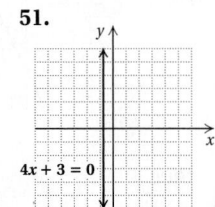

47.

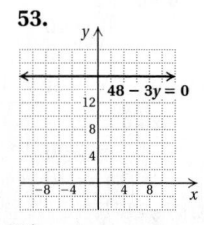

49.

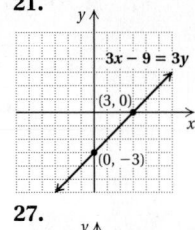

51.

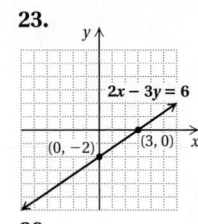

53.

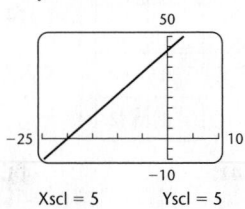

55. $y = -1$ **57.** $x = 4$ **59.** $\{x|x > -40\}$
60. $\{x|x \le -7\}$ **61.** $\{x|x < 1\}$ **62.** $\{x|x \ge 2\}$
63. $\{x|x \le 7\}$ **64.** $\{x|x > 1\}$ **65.** About 89,434
66. $43,200   **67.** $y = -4$ **69.** $k = 12$

Calculator Corner, p. 687

1. This line will pass through the origin and slant up from left to right. This line will be steeper than $y = 10x$.   **2.** This line will pass through the origin and slant up from left to right. This line will be less steep than $y = \frac{5}{32}x$.   **3.** This line will pass through the origin and slant down from left to right. This line will be steeper than $y = -10x$.   **4.** This line will pass through the origin and slant down from left to right. This line will be less steep than $y = -\frac{5}{32}x$.

Exercise Set 9.3, p. 690

1. $-\frac{3}{7}$ 3. $\frac{2}{3}$ 5. $\frac{3}{4}$ 7. 0

9. $-\frac{4}{5}$;

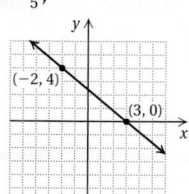

11. 3;

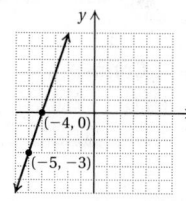

13. $-\frac{2}{3}$;

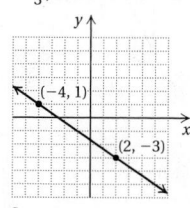

15. $\frac{7}{8}$;

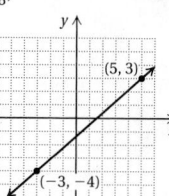

17. $\frac{2}{3}$ 19. Not defined 21. $-\frac{5}{13}$ 23. 0 25. -10
27. 3.78 29. 3 31. $-\frac{1}{5}$ 33. $-\frac{3}{2}$ 35. Not defined
37. -1 39. 3 41. $\frac{5}{4}$ 43. 0 45. $\frac{4}{3}$ 47. $-\frac{21}{8}$ 49. $\frac{12}{41}$
51. $\frac{28}{129}$ 53. 3.0%; yes 55. About $-2{,}170{,}000$ acres per year
57. About 82,900 people per year 59. 19,000 tons per year
61. $\frac{4}{25}$ 62. $\frac{1}{3}$ 63. $\frac{3}{8}$ 64. $\frac{3}{4}$ 65. \$3.57 66. \$48.60
67. 20% 68. \$18 69. \$45.15 70. \$55 71. $y = -x + 5$
73. $y = x + 2$

Exercise Set 9.4, p. 699

1. Slope: -4; y-intercept: $(0, -9)$ 3. Slope: 1.8; y-intercept: $(0, 0)$
5. Slope: $-\frac{8}{7}$; y-intercept: $(0, -3)$ 7. Slope: $\frac{4}{9}$; y-intercept:
$\left(0, -\frac{7}{9}\right)$ 9. Slope: $-\frac{3}{2}$; y-intercept: $\left(0, -\frac{1}{2}\right)$ 11. Slope: 0;
y-intercept: $(0, -17)$ 13. $y = -7x - 13$ 15. $y = 1.01x - 2.6$
17. $y = -5$ 19. $y = -2x - 6$ 21. $y = \frac{3}{4}x + \frac{5}{2}$
23. $y = x - 8$ 25. $y = -3x + 3$ 27. $y = x + 4$
29. $y = -\frac{1}{2}x + 4$ 31. $y = -\frac{3}{2}x + \frac{13}{2}$ 33. $x = 4$
35. $y = -4x - 11$ 37. $y = \frac{1}{4}$ 39. (a) $H = \frac{551}{175}x + 44.50$, or
$H = 3.15x + 44.50$; (b) an increase of \$3.15 per year; (c) \$79.15
41. $\frac{53}{7}$ 42. $\frac{3}{8}$ 43. 6 44. $\frac{42}{5}$ 45. $\frac{24}{19}$ 46. $\frac{125}{7}$ 47. $\frac{1}{3}$
48. $-\frac{1}{12}$ 49. $\frac{42}{25}$ 50. $\frac{5}{7}$ 51. $y = 3x - 9$ 53. $y = \frac{3}{2}x - 2$

Mid-Chapter Review: Chapter 9, p. 701

1. False 2. True 3. True 4. False
5. (a) The y-intercept is $(0, -3)$. (b) The x-intercept is $(-3, 0)$.
(c) The slope is $\dfrac{-3 - 0}{0 - (-3)} = \dfrac{-3}{3} = -1$. (d) The equation of the
line in $y = mx + b$ form is
$$y = -1x + -3, \text{ or } -x - 3.$$
6. (a) The x-intercept is $(c, 0)$. (b) The y-intercept is $(0, d)$.
(c) The slope is $\dfrac{d - 0}{0 - c} = \dfrac{d}{-c} = -\dfrac{d}{c}$. (d) The equation of the line
in $y = mx + b$ form is
$$y = -\frac{d}{c}x + d.$$
7. No 8. Yes 9. x-intercept: $(-6, 0)$; y-intercept: $(0, 9)$
10. x-intercept: $\left(\frac{1}{2}, 0\right)$; y-intercept: $\left(0, -\frac{1}{20}\right)$
11.

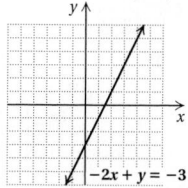

12.

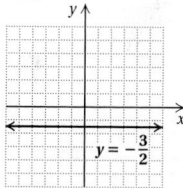

13.

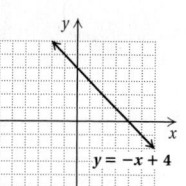

14.

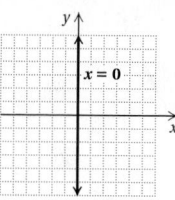

15. $-\frac{40}{9}$ 16. $-\frac{1}{2}$ 17. 0 18. 13 19. Not defined
20. $-30{,}200$ people per year 21. D 22. C 23. B
24. E 25. A 26. $y = -3x + 2$ 27. $x = \frac{1}{2}$
28. $y = -\frac{1}{5}x - \frac{17}{5}$ 29. $y = -4$ 30. No; an equation
$x = a, a \neq 0$, does not have a y-intercept. 31. Most would
probably say that the second equation would be easier to graph
because it has been solved for y. This makes it more efficient to find
the y-value that corresponds to a given x-value. 32. $A = 0$. If the
line is horizontal, then the equation is of the form $y =$ a constant.
Thus, Ax must be 0 and, hence, $A = 0$. 33. Any ordered pair
$(7, y)$ is a solution of $x = 7$. Thus all points on the graph are
7 units to the right of the x-axis, so they lie on a vertical line.

Exercise Set 9.5, p. 705

1.

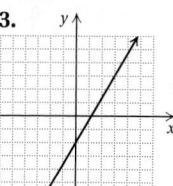

3.

5.

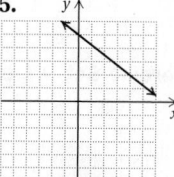

7.

9.

11.

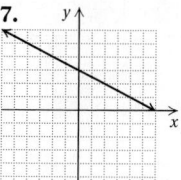

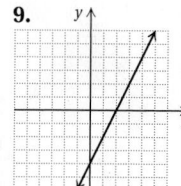

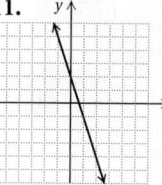

13.

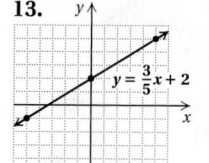

$y = \frac{3}{5}x + 2$

15.

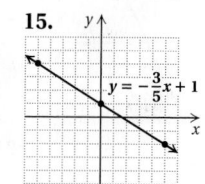

$y = -\frac{3}{5}x + 1$

17.

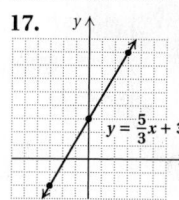

$y = \frac{5}{3}x + 3$

19.

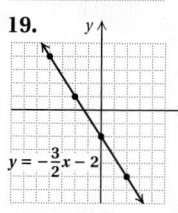

$y = -\frac{3}{2}x - 2$

21.

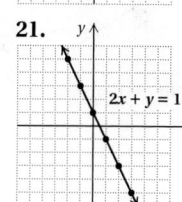

$2x + y = 1$

23.

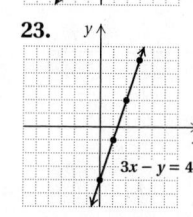

$3x - y = 4$

25.

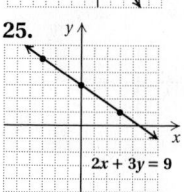

$2x + 3y = 9$

27.

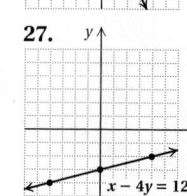

$x - 4y = 12$

29.

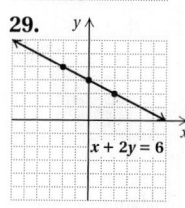

$x + 2y = 6$

31. $\frac{13}{10}$ 32. $-\frac{1}{6}$ 33. $\frac{69}{100}$, or 0.69 34. $-\frac{3}{5}$, or -0.6 35. 0
36. Not defined 37. Not defined 38. 0 39. Increase of
about 484 kidney transplants per year; 484 40. Increase of
about 251 liver transplants per year; 251 41. $y = 1.5x + 16$

43.

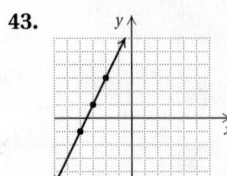

Exercise Set 9.6, p. 712

1. Yes **3.** No **5.** No **7.** No **9.** Yes **11.** Yes **13.** No
15. Yes **17.** Yes **19.** Yes **21.** No **23.** Yes **25.** Parallel
27. Neither **29.** Equivalent equations **30.** Addition
principle **31.** Multiplication principle **32.** Horizontal
33. Vertical **34.** Slope **35.** x-intercept **36.** y-intercept
37. $y = 3x + 6$ **39.** $y = -3x + 2$ **41.** $y = \frac{1}{2}x + 1$
43. 16 **45.** A: $y = \frac{4}{3}x - \frac{7}{3}$; B: $y = -\frac{3}{4}x - \frac{1}{4}$

Calculator Corner, p. 717

1. Left to the student

Visualizing for Success, p. 718

1. D **2.** H **3.** E **4.** A **5.** J **6.** F **7.** C **8.** B
9. I **10.** G

Exercise Set 9.7, p. 719

1. No **3.** Yes

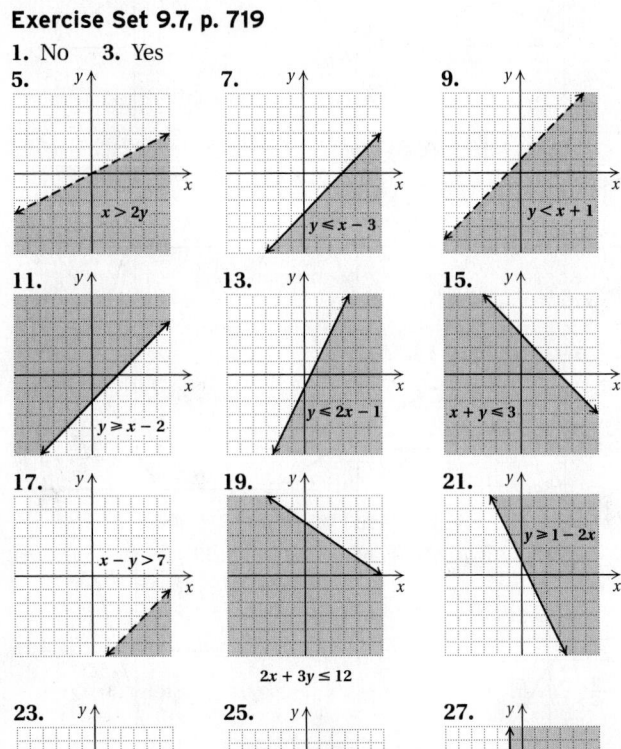

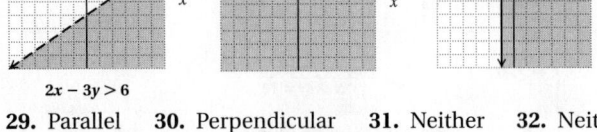

29. Parallel **30.** Perpendicular **31.** Neither **32.** Neither
33. $35c + 75a > 1000$

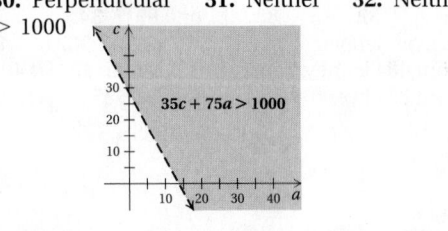

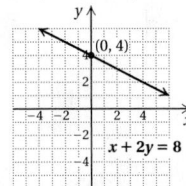

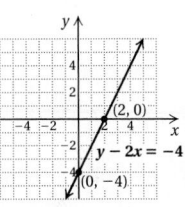

Summary and Review: Chapter 9, p. 721

Concept Reinforcement

1. True **2.** False **3.** True **4.** False **5.** True **6.** False
7. False

Important Concepts

1. $F: (2, 4)$; $G: (-2, 0)$; $H: (-3, -5)$
2.

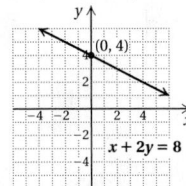

3.

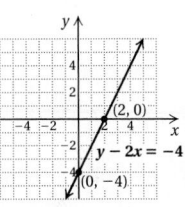

4.

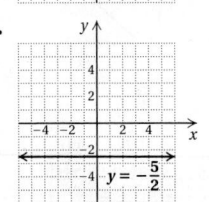

5.

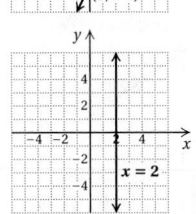

6. m is not defined. **7.** $\frac{3}{2}$ **8.** 0 **9.** m is not defined.
10. -2 **11.** 0 **12.** $y = 6x + 7$ **13.** $y = -\frac{1}{6}x - \frac{11}{6}$
14. Perpendicular **15.** Parallel
16.

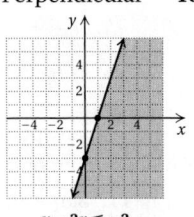

Review Exercises

1. $(-5, -1)$ **2.** $(-2, 5)$ **3.** $(3, 0)$
4.–6. **7.** IV **8.** III **9.** I **10.** No
11. Yes

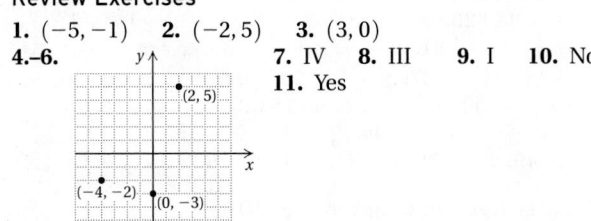

12.

$$2x - y = 3$$
$$\overline{2 \cdot 0 - (-3) \;?\; 3}$$
$$0 + 3 \;|\;$$
$$3 \;|\; \quad \text{TRUE}$$

$$2x - y = 3$$
$$\overline{2 \cdot 2 - 1 \;?\; 3}$$
$$4 - 1 \;|\;$$
$$3 \;|\; \quad \text{TRUE}$$

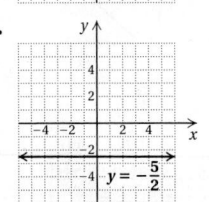

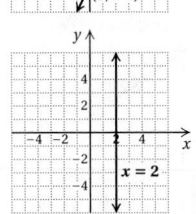

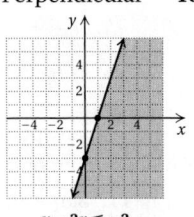

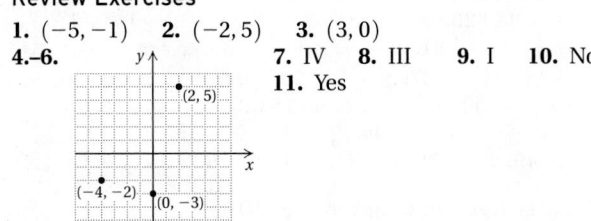

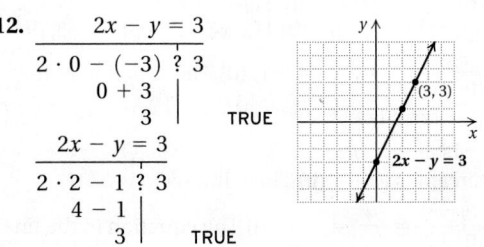

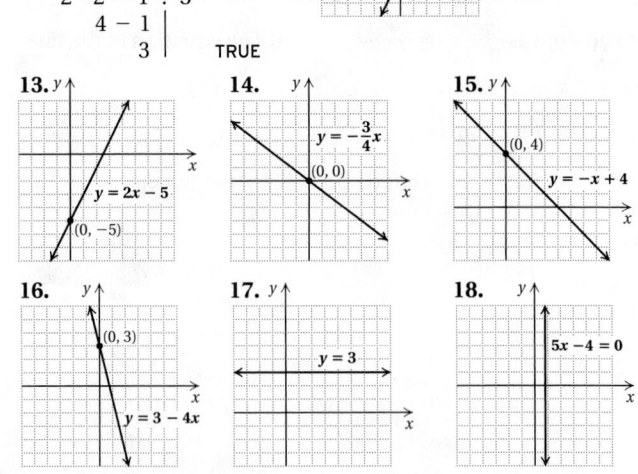

19.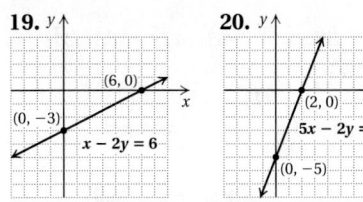

20.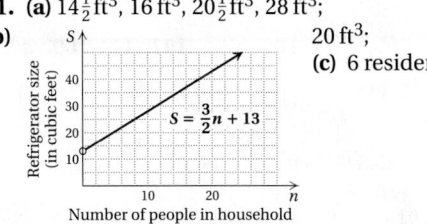

21. (a) $14\frac{1}{2}$ ft³, 16 ft³, $20\frac{1}{2}$ ft³, 28 ft³;
(b) 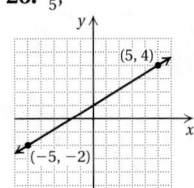 20 ft³;
(c) 6 residents

22. (a) 2.4 driveways per hour; (b) 25 minutes per driveway
23. 4 manicures per hour **24.** $\frac{1}{3}$ **25.** $-\frac{1}{3}$
26. $\frac{3}{5}$; **27.** -1;

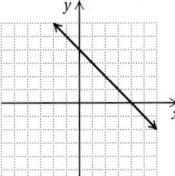 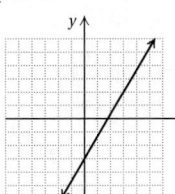

28. 7% **29.** $-\frac{5}{8}$ **30.** $\frac{1}{2}$ **31.** Not defined **32.** 0
33. Slope: -9; y-intercept: $(0, 46)$ **34.** Slope: -1; y-intercept: $(0, 9)$ **35.** Slope: $\frac{3}{5}$; y-intercept: $\left(0, -\frac{4}{5}\right)$
36. $y = -2.8x + 19$ **37.** $y = \frac{5}{8}x - \frac{7}{8}$ **38.** $y = 3x - 1$
39. $y = \frac{2}{3}x - \frac{11}{3}$ **40.** $y = -2x - 4$ **41.** $y = x + 2$
42. $y = \frac{1}{2}x - 1$ **43.** (a) $y = 119.9x + 2316$;
(b) 119.9 million prescriptions per year; (c) 3395.1 million prescriptions, or 3,395,100,000 prescriptions

44. 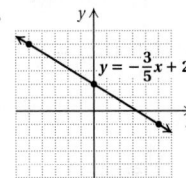 **45.**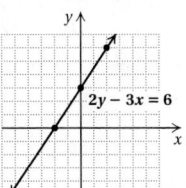

46. 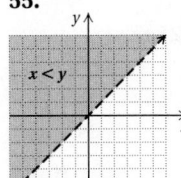 **47.**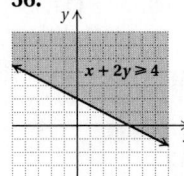

48. Parallel **49.** Perpendicular **50.** Parallel **51.** Neither
52. No **53.** No **54.** Yes
55. 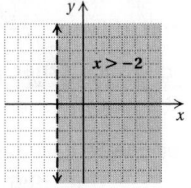 **56.** **57.**

58. D **59.** C **60.** 45 square units; 28 linear units
61. (a) 239.58$\overline{3}$ ft per minute; (b) about 0.004 min per foot

Understanding Through Discussion and Writing

1. If one equation represents a vertical line (that is, it is of the form $x = a$) and the other represents a horizontal line (that is, it is of the form $y = b$), then the graphs are perpendicular. If neither line is of one of the forms above, then solve each equation for y in order to determine the slope of each. Then, if the product of the slopes is -1, the graphs are perpendicular.
2. If $b > 0$, then the y-intercept of $y = mx + b$ is on the positive y-axis and the graph of $y = mx + b$ lies "above" the origin. Using $(0, 0)$ as a test point, we have the false inequality $0 > b$, so the region above $y = mx + b$ is shaded.
　　If $b = 0$, the line $y = mx + b$ or $y = mx$ passes through the origin. Testing a point above the line, such as $(1, m + 1)$, we have the true inequality $m + 1 > m$, so the region above the line is shaded.
　　If $b < 0$, then the y-intercept of $y = mx + b$ is on the negative y-axis and the graph of $y = mx + b$ lies "below" the origin. Using $(0, 0)$ as a test point, we get the true inequality $0 > b$, so the region above $y = mx + b$ is shaded.
　　Thus we see that in any case the graph of any inequality of the form $y > mx + b$ is always shaded above the line $y = mx + b$. **3.** The y-intercept is the point at which the graph crosses the y-axis. Since a point on the y-axis is neither left nor right of the origin, the first or x-coordinate of the point is 0.
4.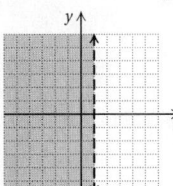

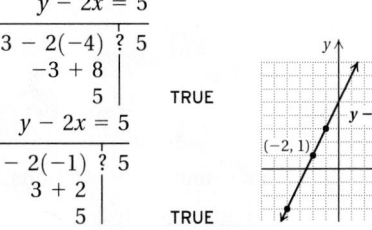 The graph of $x < 1$ on the number line consists of the points in the set $\{x | x < 1\}$. The graph of $x < 1$ on a plane consists of the points, or ordered pairs, in the set $\{(x, y) | x + 0 \cdot y < 1\}$. This is the set of ordered pairs with first coordinate less than 1.

5. First, plot the y-intercept, $(0, 2458)$. Then, thinking of the slope as $\frac{37}{100}$, plot a second point on the line by moving up 37 units and to the right 100 units from the y-intercept. Next, thinking of the slope as $\frac{-37}{-100}$, start at the y-intercept and plot a third point by moving down 37 units and to the left 100 units. Finally, draw a line through the three points.
6. If the equations are of the form $x = p$ and $x = q$, where $p \neq q$, then the graphs are parallel vertical lines. If neither equation is of the form $x = p$, then solve each for y in order to determine the slope and the y-intercept of each. If the slopes are the same and the y-intercepts are different, the lines are parallel.

Test: Chapter 9, p. 729
1. [9.1a] II **2.** [9.1a] III **3.** [9.1b] $(-5, 1)$
4. [9.1b] $(0, -4)$
5. [9.1c]

$$\begin{array}{c|c} y - 2x = 5 \\ \hline -3 - 2(-4) \;?\; 5 \\ -3 + 8 \\ 5 & \text{TRUE} \end{array}$$

$$\begin{array}{c|c} y - 2x = 5 \\ \hline 3 - 2(-1) \;?\; 5 \\ 3 + 2 \\ 5 & \text{TRUE} \end{array}$$

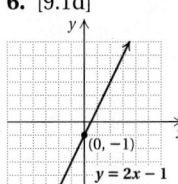

6. [9.1d] **7.** [9.1d] **8.** [9.2b]

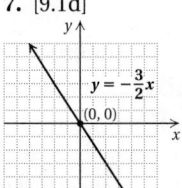 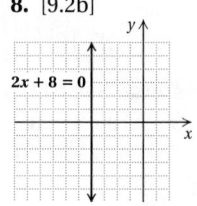

9. [9.2b]
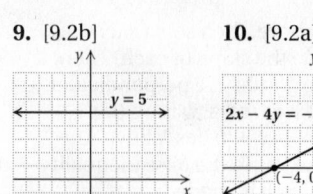

10. [9.2a]
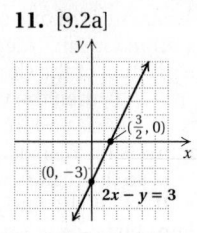

11. [9.2a]

12. [9.1e] **(a)** 1990: $7800; 1996: $12,000; 2005: $18,300; 2010: $21,800
(b)
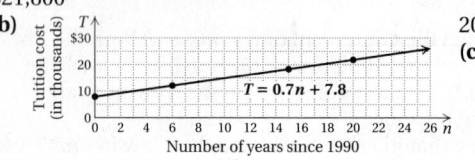
2015: $25,000 **(c)** 2020

13. [9.3c] **(a)** 14.5 floors per minute; **(b)** $4\frac{4}{29}$ seconds per floor
14. [9.3c] 87.5 mph   **15.** [9.3a] -2
16. [9.3a] $\frac{3}{8}$;
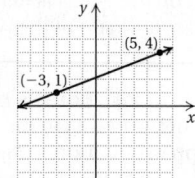

17. [9.3b] **(a)** $\frac{2}{5}$; **(b)** not defined   **18.** [9.3c] $-\frac{1}{20}$
19. [9.5a]   **20.** [9.5a]
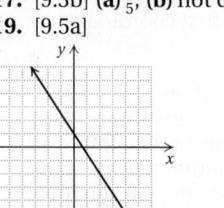   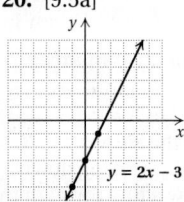

21. [9.4a] Slope: 2; y-intercept: $\left(0, -\frac{1}{4}\right)$ **22.** [9.4a] Slope: $\frac{4}{3}$; y-intercept: $(0, -2)$ **23.** [9.4a] $y = 1.8x - 7$
24. [9.4a] $y = -\frac{3}{8}x - \frac{1}{8}$ **25.** [9.4b] $y = x + 2$
26. [9.4b] $y = -3x - 6$ **27.** [9.4c] $y = -3x + 4$
28. [9.4c] $y = \frac{1}{4}x - 2$ **29.** [9.4c] **(a)** $y = 1.03x + 84.7$;
(b) 1.03 billion eggs per year; **(c)** 97.06 billion eggs
30. [9.6a, b] Parallel   **31.** [9.6a, b] Neither   **32.** [9.6a, b] Perpendicular   **33.** [9.7a] No   **34.** [9.7a] Yes
35. [9.7b]   **36.** [9.7b]
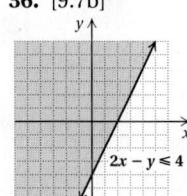   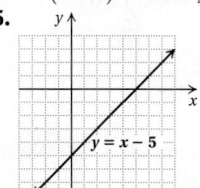

37. [9.6a, b] A   **38.** [9.1a] 25 square units; 20 linear units
39. [9.6b] 3

CHAPTER 10

Exercise Set 10.1, p. 740

1. $3 \cdot 3 \cdot 3 \cdot 3$ **3.** $(-1.1)(-1.1)(-1.1)(-1.1)(-1.1)$
5. $\left(\frac{2}{3}\right)\left(\frac{2}{3}\right)\left(\frac{2}{3}\right)\left(\frac{2}{3}\right)$ **7.** $(7p)(7p)$ **9.** $8 \cdot k \cdot k \cdot k$
11. $-6 \cdot y \cdot y \cdot y \cdot y$ **13.** 1   **15.** b **17.** 1   **19.** -7.03
21. 1   **23.** ab **25.** a **27.** 27   **29.** 19   **31.** -81
33. 256   **35.** 93   **37.** 136   **39.** 10; 4   **41.** 3629.84 ft^2
43. $\frac{1}{3^2} = \frac{1}{9}$ **45.** $\frac{1}{10^3} = \frac{1}{1000}$ **47.** $\frac{1}{a^3}$ **49.** $8^2 = 64$ **51.** y^4

53. $\frac{5}{z^4}$ **55.** $\frac{x}{y^2}$ **57.** 4^{-3} **59.** x^{-3} **61.** a^{-5} **63.** 2^7
65. 8^{14} **67.** x^5 **69.** 9^{38} **71.** $(3y)^{12}$ **73.** $(7y)^{17}$
75. 3^3 **77.** 1   **79.** x^{17} **81.** $\frac{1}{x^{13}}$ **83.** $\frac{1}{a^{10}}$ **85.** $s^3 t^7$
87. 7^3 **89.** y^8 **91.** $\frac{1}{16^6}$ **93.** $\frac{1}{m^6}$ **95.** $\frac{1}{(8x)^4}$ **97.** 1
99. x^2 **101.** x^9 **103.** $\frac{1}{z^4}$ **105.** x^3 **107.** 1   **109.** $a^3 b^2$
111. $5^2 = 25$; $5^{-2} = \frac{1}{25}$; $\left(\frac{1}{5}\right)^2 = \frac{1}{25}$; $\left(\frac{1}{5}\right)^{-2} = 25$; $-5^2 = -25$; $(-5)^2 = 25$; $-\left(-\frac{1}{5}\right)^2 = -\frac{1}{25}$; $\left(-\frac{1}{5}\right)^{-2} = 25$ **113.** 8 in.; 4 in.
114. 228, 229   **115.** 25,543.75 ft^2 **116.** $51°, 27°, 102°$
117. $\frac{23}{14}$ **118.** $\frac{11}{10}$ **119.** $4(x - 3 + 6y)$
120. $2(128 - a - 2b)$ **121.** No   **123.** No   **125.** y^{5x}
127. a^{4t} **129.** 1   **131.** $>$ **133.** $<$ **135.** $-\frac{1}{10,000}$
137. No; for example, $(3 + 4)^2 = 49$, but $3^2 + 4^2 = 25$.

Calculator Corner, p. 748
1. 1.3545×10^{-4} **2.** 3.2×10^5 **3.** 3×10^{-6} **4.** 8×10^{-26}

Exercise Set 10.2, p. 751

1. 2^6 **3.** $\frac{1}{5^6}$ **5.** x^{12} **7.** $\frac{1}{a^{18}}$ **9.** t^{18} **11.** $\frac{1}{t^{12}}$ **13.** x^8
15. $a^3 b^3$ **17.** $\frac{1}{a^3 b^3}$ **19.** $\frac{1}{m^3 n^6}$ **21.** $16x^6$ **23.** $\frac{9}{x^8}$
25. $\frac{1}{x^{12}y^{15}}$ **27.** $x^{24}y^8$ **29.** $\frac{a^{10}}{b^{35}}$ **31.** $\frac{25t^6}{r^8}$ **33.** $\frac{b^{21}}{a^{15}c^6}$
35. $\frac{9x^6}{y^{16}z^6}$ **37.** $\frac{16x^6}{y^4}$ **39.** $a^{12}b^8$ **41.** $\frac{y^6}{4}$ **43.** $\frac{a^8}{b^{12}}$
45. $\frac{8}{y^6}$ **47.** $49x^6$ **49.** $\frac{x^6 y^3}{z^3}$ **51.** $\frac{c^2 d^6}{a^4 b^2}$ **53.** 2.8×10^{10}
55. 9.07×10^{17} **57.** 3.04×10^{-6} **59.** 1.8×10^{-8}
61. 10^{11} **63.** 4.19854×10^8 **65.** 2.4×10^9
67. 87,400,000   **69.** 0.00000005704   **71.** 10,000,000
73. 0.00001   **75.** 6×10^9 **77.** 3.38×10^4
79. 8.1477×10^{-13} **81.** 2.5×10^{13} **83.** 5.0×10^{-4}
85. 3.0×10^{-21} **87.** Approximately 1.325×10^{14} ft^3
89. The mass of Jupiter is 3.18×10^2 times the mass of Earth.
91. 1×10^{22} **93.** 7.5×10^{-7} m   **95.** 4.375×10^2 days
97. $9(x - 4)$ **98.** $2(2x - y + 8)$ **99.** $3(s + t + 8)$
100. $-7(x + 2)$ **101.** $\frac{7}{4}$ **102.** 2   **103.** $-\frac{12}{7}$ **104.** $-\frac{11}{2}$
105.   **106.**
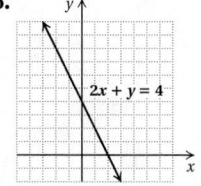

107. 2.478125×10^{-1} **109.** $\frac{1}{5}$ **111.** 3^{11} **113.** 7
115. $\frac{1}{0.4}$, or 2.5   **117.** False   **119.** False   **121.** True

Calculator Corner, p. 758
1. 3; 2.25; -27 **2.** 44; 0; 9.28

Exercise Set 10.3, p. 763
1. -18; 7   **3.** 19; 14   **5.** -12; -7 **7.** $\frac{13}{3}$; 5   **9.** 9; 1
11. 56; -2 **13.** 1112 ft   **15.** $18,750; $24,000
17. $-4, 4, 5, 2.75, 1$ **19. (a)** 2728.4 billion kilowatt-hours; 3521.8 billion kilowatt-hours; 4315.2 billion kilowatt-hours; 5108.6 billion kilowatt-hours; 5902 billion kilowatt-hours;
(b) left to the student   **21.** 9 words   **23.** 6   **25.** 15

27. $2, -3x, x^2$ **29.** $-2x^4, \frac{1}{3}x^3, -x, 3$ **31.** $6x^2$ and $-3x^2$
33. $2x^4$ and $-3x^4$; $5x$ and $-7x$ **35.** $3x^5$ and $14x^5$; $-7x$
and $-2x$; 8 and -9 **37.** $-3, 6$ **39.** $5, \frac{3}{4}, 3$ **41.** $-5, 6,$
$-2.7, 1; -2$ **43.** $-3x$ **45.** $-8x$ **47.** $11x^3 + 4$ **49.** $x^3 - x$
51. $4b^5$ **53.** $\frac{3}{4}x^5 - 2x - 42$ **55.** x^4 **57.** $\frac{15}{16}x^3 - \frac{7}{6}x^2$
59. $x^5 + 6x^3 + 2x^2 + x + 1$ **61.** $15y^9 + 7y^8 + 5y^3 - y^2 + y$
63. $x^6 + x^4$ **65.** $13x^3 - 9x + 8$ **67.** $-5x^2 + 9x$
69. $12x^4 - 2x + \frac{1}{4}$ **71.** $1, 0; 1$ **73.** $2, 1, 0; 2$
75. $3, 2, 1, 0; 3$ **77.** $2, 1, 6, 4; 6$
79.

Term	Coefficient	Degree of the Term	Degree of the Polynomial
$-7x^4$	-7	4	
$6x^3$	6	3	
$-x^2$	-1	2	4
$8x$	8	1	
-2	-2	0	

81. x^2, x **83.** x^3, x^2, x^0 **85.** None missing
87. $x^3 + 0x^2 + 0x - 27; x^3 \qquad - 27$
89. $x^4 + 0x^3 + 0x^2 - x + 0x^0; x^4 \qquad\qquad - x$
91. None missing   **93.** Trinomial   **95.** None of these
97. Binomial   **99.** Monomial   **101.** 27 apples   **102.** -19
103. $-\frac{17}{24}$ **104.** $\frac{5}{8}$ **105.** -2.6 **106.** $\frac{15}{2}$ **107.** $b = \frac{C + r}{a}$
108. 45%; 37.5%; 17.5%   **109.** $3(x - 5y + 21)$ **111.** $3x^6$
113. 10   **115.** $-4, 4, 5, 2.75, 1$ **117.** 9

Calculator Corner, p. 772
1. Yes   **2.** Yes   **3.** No   **4.** Yes   **5.** No   **6.** Yes

Exercise Set 10.4, p. 773
1. $-x + 5$ **3.** $x^2 - \frac{11}{2}x - 1$ **5.** $2x^2$ **7.** $5x^2 + 3x - 30$
9. $-2.2x^3 - 0.2x^2 - 3.8x + 23$ **11.** $6 + 12x^2$
13. $-\frac{1}{2}x^4 + \frac{2}{3}x^3 + x^2$ **15.** $0.01x^5 + x^4 - 0.2x^3 +$
$0.2x + 0.06$ **17.** $9x^8 + 8x^7 - 6x^4 + 8x^2 + 4$
19. $1.05x^4 + 0.36x^3 + 14.22x^2 + x + 0.97$ **21.** $5x$
23. $x^2 - \frac{3}{2}x + 2$ **25.** $-12x^4 + 3x^3 - 3$ **27.** $-3x + 7$
29. $-4x^2 + 3x - 2$ **31.** $4x^4 - 6x^2 - \frac{3}{4}x + 8$ **33.** $7x - 1$
35. $-x^2 - 7x + 5$ **37.** -18 **39.** $6x^4 + 3x^3 - 4x^2 + 3x - 4$
41. $4.6x^3 + 9.2x^2 - 3.8x - 23$ **43.** $\frac{3}{4}x^3 - \frac{1}{2}x$
45. $0.06x^3 - 0.05x^2 + 0.01x + 1$ **47.** $3x + 6$
49. $11x^4 + 12x^3 - 9x^2 - 8x - 9$ **51.** $x^4 - x^3 + x^2 - x$
53. $\frac{23}{2}a + 12$ **55.** $5x^2 + 4x$ **57.** $(r + 11)(r + 9)$;
$9r + 99 + 11r + r^2$, or $r^2 + 20r + 99$
59. $(x + 3)(x + 3)$, or $(x + 3)^2; x^2 + 3x + 9 + 3x$,
or $x^2 + 6x + 9$ **61.** $\pi r^2 - 25\pi$ **63.** $18z - 64$ **65.** 6
66. -19 **67.** $-\frac{7}{22}$ **68.** 5   **69.** 5   **70.** 1   **71.** $\frac{39}{2}$ **72.** $\frac{37}{2}$
73. $\{x | x \geq -10\}$ **74.** $\{x | x < 0\}$ **75.** $20w + 42$
77. $2x^2 + 20x$ **79.** $y^2 - 4y + 4$ **81.** $12y^2 - 23y + 21$
83. $-3y^4 - y^3 + 5y - 2$

Mid-Chapter Review: Chapter 10, p. 777
1. True   **2.** False   **3.** False   **4.** True
5. $4w^3 + 6w - 8w^3 - 3w = (4 - 8)w^3 + (6 - 3)w =$
$-4w^3 + 3w$ **6.** $(3y^4 - y^2 + 11) - (y^4 - 4y^2 + 5) =$
$3y^4 - y^2 + 11 - y^4 + 4y^2 - 5 = 2y^4 + 3y^2 + 6$ **7.** z **8.** 1
9. -32 **10.** 1   **11.** 5^7 **12.** $(3a)^9$ **13.** $\frac{1}{x^3}$ **14.** 1
15. 7^4 **16.** $\frac{1}{x^2}$ **17.** w^8 **18.** $\frac{1}{y^4}$ **19.** 3^{15} **20.** $\frac{x^{18}}{y^{12}}$

21. $\frac{a^{24}}{5^6}$ **22.** $\frac{x^2 z^4}{4y^6}$ **23.** 2.543×10^7 **24.** 1.2×10^{-4}
25. 0.000036   **26.** 144,000,000   **27.** 6×10^3 **28.** 5×10^{-7}
29. 16; 1   **30.** -16; 9   **31.** $-2x^5 - 5x^2 + 4x + 2$
32. $8x^6 + 2x^3 - 8x^2$ **33.** 3, 1, 0; 3   **34.** 1, 4, 6; 6
35. Binomial   **36.** Trinomial   **37.** $8x^2 + 5$
38. $5x^3 - 2x^2 + 2x - 11$ **39.** $-4x - 10$
40. $-0.4x^2 - 3.4x + 9$ **41.** $3y + 3y^2$ **42.** The area of the
smaller square is x^2, and the area of the larger square is $(3x)^2$, or
$9x^2$, so the area of the larger square is nine times the area of the
smaller square.   **43.** The volume of the smaller cube is x^3, and
the volume of the larger cube is $(2x)^3$, or $8x^3$, so the volume of
the larger cube is eight times the volume of the smaller cube.
44. Exponents are added when powers with like bases are
multiplied. Exponents are multiplied when a power is raised
to a power.   **45.** $3^{-29} = \frac{1}{3^{29}}$ and $2^{-29} = \frac{1}{2^{29}}$. Since $3^{29} > 2^{29}$,
we have $\frac{1}{3^{29}} < \frac{1}{2^{29}}$.   **46.** It is better to evaluate a polynomial after
like terms have been collected, because there are fewer terms
to evaluate.   **47.** Yes; consider the following: $(x^2 + 4) +$
$(4x - 7) = x^2 + 4x - 3$.

Calculator Corner, p. 782
1. Correct   **2.** Correct   **3.** Not correct   **4.** Not correct

Exercise Set 10.5, p. 783
1. $40x^2$ **3.** x^3 **5.** $32x^8$ **7.** $0.03x^{11}$ **9.** $\frac{1}{15}x^4$ **11.** 0
13. $-24x^{11}$ **15.** $-2x^2 + 10x$ **17.** $-5x^2 + 5x$
19. $x^5 + x^2$ **21.** $6x^3 - 18x^2 + 3x$ **23.** $-6x^4 - 6x^3$
25. $18y^6 + 24y^5$ **27.** $x^2 + 9x + 18$ **29.** $x^2 + 3x - 10$
31. $x^2 + 3x - 4$ **33.** $x^2 - 7x + 12$ **35.** $x^2 - 9$
37. $x^2 - 16$ **39.** $3x^2 + 11x + 10$ **41.** $25 - 15x + 2x^2$
43. $4x^2 + 20x + 25$ **45.** $x^2 - 6x + 9$ **47.** $x^2 - \frac{21}{10}x - 1$
49. $x^2 + 2.4x - 10.81$ **51.** $(x + 2)(x + 6)$, or $x^2 + 8x + 12$
53. $(x + 1)(x + 6)$, or $x^2 + 7x + 6$
55.   **57.**   **59.**
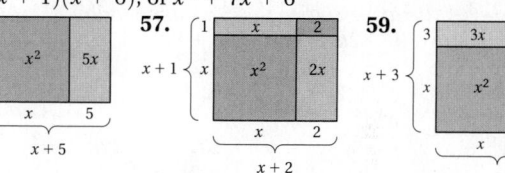
61. $x^3 - 1$ **63.** $4x^3 + 14x^2 + 8x + 1$
65. $3y^4 - 6y^3 - 7y^2 + 18y - 6$ **67.** $x^6 + 2x^5 - x^3$
69. $-10x^5 - 9x^4 + 7x^3 + 2x^2 - x$ **71.** $-1 - 2x - x^2 + x^4$
73. $6t^4 + t^3 - 16t^2 - 7t + 4$ **75.** $x^9 - x^5 + 2x^3 - x$
77. $x^4 - 1$ **79.** $x^4 + 8x^3 + 12x^2 + 9x + 4$
81. $2x^4 - 5x^3 + 5x^2 - \frac{19}{10}x + \frac{1}{5}$ **83.** $-\frac{3}{4}$ **84.** 6.4   **85.** 96
86. 32   **87.** $3(5x - 6y + 4)$ **88.** $4(4x - 6y + 9)$
89. $-3(3x + 15y - 5)$ **90.** $100(x - y + 10a)$
91.
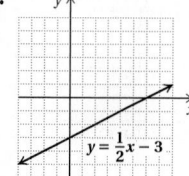
92. $\frac{23}{19}$ **93.** $75y^2 - 45y$
95. $V = (4x^3 - 48x^2 + 144x)$ in^3; $S = (-4x^2 + 144)$ in^2
97. 5   **99.** $(x^3 + 2x^2 - 210)$ m^3 **101.** 0   **103.** 0

Visualizing for Success, p. 792
1. E, F   **2.** B, O   **3.** K, S   **4.** G, R   **5.** D, M   **6.** J, P
7. C, L   **8.** N, Q   **9.** A, H   **10.** I, T

Exercise Set 10.6, p. 793

1. $x^3 + x^2 + 3x + 3$ **3.** $x^4 + x^3 + 2x + 2$ **5.** $y^2 - y - 6$
7. $9x^2 + 12x + 4$ **9.** $5x^2 + 4x - 12$ **11.** $9t^2 - 1$
13. $4x^2 - 6x + 2$ **15.** $p^2 - \frac{1}{16}$ **17.** $x^2 - 0.01$
19. $2x^3 + 2x^2 + 6x + 6$ **21.** $-2x^2 - 11x + 6$
23. $a^2 + 14a + 49$ **25.** $1 - x - 6x^2$ **27.** $\frac{9}{64}y^2 - \frac{5}{8}y + \frac{25}{36}$
29. $x^5 + 3x^3 - x^2 - 3$ **31.** $3x^6 - 2x^4 - 6x^2 + 4$
33. $13.16x^2 + 18.99x - 13.95$ **35.** $6x^7 + 18x^5 + 4x^2 + 12$
37. $8x^6 + 65x^3 + 8$ **39.** $4x^3 - 12x^2 + 3x - 9$
41. $4y^6 + 4y^5 + y^4 + y^3$ **43.** $x^2 - 16$ **45.** $4x^2 - 1$
47. $25m^2 - 4$ **49.** $4x^4 - 9$ **51.** $9x^8 - 16$ **53.** $x^{12} - x^4$
55. $x^8 - 9x^2$ **57.** $x^{24} - 9$ **59.** $4y^{16} - 9$ **61.** $\frac{25}{64}x^2 - 18.49$
63. $x^2 + 4x + 4$ **65.** $9x^4 + 6x^2 + 1$ **67.** $a^2 - a + \frac{1}{4}$
69. $9 + 6x + x^2$ **71.** $x^4 + 2x^2 + 1$ **73.** $4 - 12x^4 + 9x^8$
75. $25 + 60t^2 + 36t^4$ **77.** $x^2 - \frac{5}{4}x + \frac{25}{64}$ **79.** $9 - 12x^3 + 4x^6$
81. $4x^3 + 24x^2 - 12x$ **83.** $4x^4 - 2x^2 + \frac{1}{4}$ **85.** $9p^2 - 1$
87. $15t^5 - 3t^4 + 3t^3$ **89.** $36x^8 + 48x^4 + 16$
91. $12x^3 + 8x^2 + 15x + 10$ **93.** $64 - 96x^4 + 36x^8$
95. $t^3 - 1$ **97.** $25; 49$ **99.** $56; 16$ **101.** $a^2 + 2a + 1$
103. $t^2 + 10t + 24$ **105.** Lamps: 500 watts; air conditioner:
2000 watts; television: 50 watts **106.** $\frac{28}{27}$ **107.** $-\frac{41}{7}$
108. $\frac{27}{4}$ **109.** $y = \frac{3x - 12}{2}$, or $y = \frac{3}{2}x - 6$
110. $a = \frac{5d + 4}{3}$, or $a = \frac{5}{3}d + \frac{4}{3}$ **111.** $30x^3 + 35x^2 - 15x$
113. $a^4 - 50a^2 + 625$ **115.** $81t^{16} - 72t^8 + 16$ **117.** -7
119. First row: 90, −432, −63; second row: 7, −18, −36, −14, 12,
−6, −21, −11; third row: 9, −2, −2, 10, −8, −8, −8, −10, 21;
fourth row: −19, −6 **121.** Yes **123.** No

Exercise Set 10.7, p. 801

1. −1 **3.** −15 **5.** 240 **7.** −145 **9.** 3.715 L **11.** 205.9 m
13. 44.46 in^2 **15.** 63.78125 in^2 **17.** Coefficients: 1, −2, 3, −5;
degrees: 4, 2, 2, 0; 4 **19.** Coefficients: 17, −3, −7; degrees: 5, 5,
0; 5 **21.** $-a - 2b$ **23.** $3x^2y - 2xy^2 + x^2$ **25.** $20au + 10av$
27. $8u^2v - 5uv^2$ **29.** $x^2 - 4xy + 3y^2$ **31.** $3r + 7$
33. $-b^2a^3 - 3b^3a^2 + 5ba + 3$ **35.** $ab^2 - a^2b$
37. $2ab - 2$ **39.** $-2a + 10b - 5c + 8d$
41. $6z^2 + 7zu - 3u^2$ **43.** $a^4b^2 - 7a^2b + 10$ **45.** $a^6 - b^2c^2$
47. $y^6x + y^4x + y^4 + 2y^2 + 1$ **49.** $12x^2y^2 + 2xy - 2$
51. $12 - c^2d^2 - c^4d^4$ **53.** $m^3 + m^2n - mn^2 - n^3$
55. $x^9y^9 - x^6y^6 + x^5y^5 - x^2y^2$ **57.** $x^2 + 2xh + h^2$
59. $9a^2 + 12ab + 4b^2$ **61.** $r^6t^4 - 8r^3t^2 + 16$
63. $p^8 + 2m^2n^2p^4 + m^4n^4$ **65.** $3a^3 - 12a^2b + 12ab^2$
67. $m^2 + 2mn + n^2 - 6m - 6n + 9$ **69.** $a^2 - b^2$
71. $4a^2 - b^2$ **73.** $c^4 - d^2$ **75.** $a^2b^2 - c^2d^4$
77. $x^2 + 2xy + y^2 - 9$ **79.** $x^2 - y^2 - 2yz - z^2$
81. $a^2 + 2ab + b^2 - c^2$
83. $3x^4 - 7x^2y + 3x^2 - 20y^2 + 22y - 6$ **85.** IV **86.** III
87. I **88.** II
89. 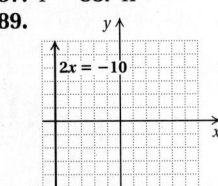 **90.**

91. 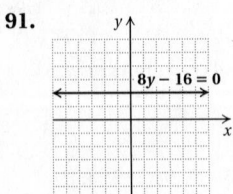 **92.**

93. $4xy - 4y^2$ **95.** $2xy + \pi x^2$

97. $2\pi nh + 2\pi mh + 2\pi n^2 - 2\pi m^2$ **99.** 16 gal
101. $12,351.94

Exercise Set 10.8, p. 810

1. $3x^4$ **3.** $5x$ **5.** $18x^3$ **7.** $4a^3b$ **9.** $3x^4 - \frac{1}{2}x^3 + \frac{1}{8}x^2 - 2$
11. $1 - 2u - u^4$ **13.** $5t^2 + 8t - 2$ **15.** $-4x^4 + 4x^2 + 1$
17. $6x^2 - 10x + \frac{3}{2}$ **19.** $9x^2 - \frac{5}{2}x + 1$ **21.** $6x^2 + 13x + 4$
23. $3rs + r - 2s$ **25.** $x + 2$ **27.** $x - 5 + \dfrac{-50}{x - 5}$
29. $x - 2 + \dfrac{-2}{x + 6}$ **31.** $x - 3$ **33.** $x^4 - x^3 + x^2 - x + 1$
35. $2x^2 - 7x + 4$ **37.** $x^3 - 6$ **39.** $t^2 + 1$
41. $y^2 - 3y + 1 + \dfrac{-5}{y + 2}$ **43.** $3x^2 + x + 2 + \dfrac{10}{5x + 1}$
45. $6y^2 - 5 + \dfrac{-6}{2y + 7}$ **47.** Product **48.** Monomial
49. Multiplication; equivalent **50.** $x = a$ **51.** Trinomial
52. Quotient **53.** Absolute value **54.** Slope **55.** $x^2 + 5$
57. $a + 3 + \dfrac{5}{5a^2 - 7a - 2}$ **59.** $2x^2 + x - 3$
61. $a^5 + a^4b + a^3b^2 + a^2b^3 + ab^4 + b^5$ **63.** −5 **65.** 1

Summary and Review: Chapter 10, p. 813

Concept Reinforcement

1. True **2.** False **3.** False **4.** True

Important Concepts

1. z^8 **2.** a^2b^6 **3.** $\dfrac{y^6}{27x^{12}z^9}$ **4.** 7.63×10^5 **5.** 0.0003
6. 6×10^4 **7.** $2x^4 - 4x^2 - 3$ **8.** $3x^4 + x^3 - 2x^2 + 2$
9. $x^6 - 6x^4 + 11x^2 - 6$ **10.** $2y^2 + 11y + 12$ **11.** $x^2 - 25$
12. $9w^2 + 24w + 16$ **13.** $-2a^3b^2 - 5a^2b + ab^2 - 2ab$
14. $y^2 - 4y + \frac{8}{5}$ **15.** $x - 9 + \dfrac{48}{x + 5}$

Review Exercises

1. $\dfrac{1}{7^2}$ **2.** y^{11} **3.** $(3x)^{14}$ **4.** t^8 **5.** 4^3 **6.** $\dfrac{1}{a^3}$ **7.** 1
8. $9t^8$ **9.** $36x^8$ **10.** $\dfrac{y^3}{8x^3}$ **11.** t^{-5} **12.** $\dfrac{1}{y^4}$
13. 3.28×10^{-5} **14.** 8,300,000 **15.** 2.09×10^4
16. 5.12×10^{-5} **17.** 1.54468×10^{10} slices **18.** 10
19. $-4y^5, 7y^2, -3y, -2$ **20.** x^2, x^0 **21.** 3, 2, 1, 0; 3
22. Binomial **23.** None of these **24.** Monomial
25. $-2x^2 - 3x + 2$ **26.** $10x^4 - 7x^2 - x - \frac{1}{2}$
27. $x^5 - 2x^4 + 6x^3 + 3x^2 - 9$
28. $-2x^5 - 6x^4 - 2x^3 - 2x^2 + 2$ **29.** $2x^2 - 4x$
30. $x^5 - 3x^3 - x^2 + 8$ **31.** Perimeter: $4w + 6$; area: $w^2 + 3w$
32. $(t + 3)(t + 4)$, $t^2 + 7t + 12$ **33.** $x^2 + \frac{7}{6}x + \frac{1}{3}$
34. $49x^2 + 14x + 1$ **35.** $12x^3 - 23x^2 + 13x - 2$
36. $9x^4 - 16$ **37.** $15x^7 - 40x^6 + 50x^5 + 10x^4$
38. $x^2 - 3x - 28$ **39.** $9y^4 - 12y^3 + 4y^2$ **40.** $2t^4 - 11t^2 - 21$
41. 49 **42.** Coefficients: 1, −7, 9, −8; degrees: 6, 2, 2, 0; 6
43. $-y + 9w - 5$ **44.** $m^6 - 2m^2n + 2m^2n^2 + 8n^2m - 6m^3$
45. $-9xy - 2y^2$ **46.** $11x^3y^2 - 8x^2y - 6x^2 - 6x + 6$
47. $p^3 - q^3$ **48.** $9a^8 - 2a^4b^3 + \frac{1}{9}b^6$ **49.** $5x^2 - \frac{1}{2}x + 3$
50. $3x^2 - 7x + 4 + \dfrac{1}{2x + 3}$ **51.** 0, 3.75, −3.75, 0 **52.** B
53. D **54.** $\frac{1}{2}x^2 - \frac{1}{2}y^2$ **55.** $400 - 4a^2$ **56.** $-28x^8$
57. $\frac{94}{13}$ **58.** $x^4 + x^3 + x^2 + x + 1$ **59.** 80 ft by 40 ft

Understanding Through Discussion and Writing

1. 578.6×10^{-7} is not in scientific notation because 578.6 is not
a number greater than or equal to 1 and less than 10.

2. When evaluating polynomials, it is essential to know the order in which the operations are to be performed. **3.** We label the figure as shown.

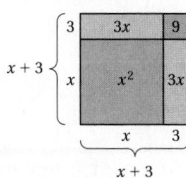

Then we see that the area of the figure is $(x + 3)^2$, or $x^2 + 3x + 3x + 9 \neq x^2 + 9$. **4.** Emma did not divide *each* term of the polynomial by the divisor. The first term was divided by $3x$, but the second was not. Multiplying Emma's "quotient" by the divisor $3x$, we get $12x^3 - 18x^2 \neq 12x^3 - 6x$. This should convince her that a mistake has been made. **5.** Yes; for example, $(x^2 + xy + 1) + (3x - xy + 2) = x^2 + 3x + 3$. **6.** Yes; consider $a + b + c + d$. This is a polynomial in 4 variables but it has degree 1.

Test: Chapter 10, p. 819

1. [10.1d, f] $\frac{1}{6^5}$ **2.** [10.1d] x^9 **3.** [10.1d] $(4a)^{11}$ **4.** [10.1e] 3^3

5. [10.1e, f] $\frac{1}{x^5}$ **6.** [10.1b, e] 1   **7.** [10.2a] x^6 **8.** [10.2a, b] $-27y^6$

9. [10.2a, b] $16a^{12}b^4$ **10.** [10.2b] $\frac{a^3b^3}{c^3}$

11. [10.1d], [10.2a, b] $-216x^{21}$ **12.** [10.1d], [10.2a, b] $-24x^{21}$
13. [10.1d], [10.2a, b] $162x^{10}$ **14.** [10.1d], [10.2a, b] $324x^{10}$

15. [10.1f] $\frac{1}{5^3}$ **16.** [10.1f] y^{-8} **17.** [10.2c] 3.9×10^9

18. [10.2c] 0.00000005   **19.** [10.2d] 1.75×10^{17}
20. [10.2d] 1.296×10^{22} **21.** [10.2e] 1.5×10^4 files
22. [10.3a] -43 **23.** [10.3d] $\frac{1}{3}, -1, 7$ **24.** [10.3g] 3, 0, 1, 6; 6
25. [10.3i] Binomial   **26.** [10.3e] $5a^2 - 6$
27. [10.3e] $\frac{7}{4}y^2 - 4y$ **28.** [10.3f] $x^5 + 2x^3 + 4x^2 - 8x + 3$
29. [10.4a] $4x^5 + x^4 + 2x^3 - 8x^2 + 2x - 7$
30. [10.4a] $5x^4 + 5x^2 + x + 5$ **31.** [10.4c] $-4x^4 + x^3 - 8x - 3$
32. [10.4c] $-x^5 + 0.7x^3 - 0.8x^2 - 21$
33. [10.5b] $-12x^4 + 9x^3 + 15x^2$ **34.** [10.6c] $x^2 - \frac{2}{3}x + \frac{1}{9}$
35. [10.6b] $9x^2 - 100$ **36.** [10.6a] $3b^2 - 4b - 15$
37. [10.6a] $x^{14} - 4x^8 + 4x^6 - 16$ **38.** [10.6a] $48 + 34y - 5y^2$
39. [10.5d] $6x^3 - 7x^2 - 11x - 3$ **40.** [10.6c] $25t^2 + 20t + 4$
41. [10.7c] $-5x^3y - y^3 + xy^3 - x^2y^2 + 19$
42. [10.7e] $8a^2b^2 + 6ab - 4b^3 + 6ab^2 + ab^3$
43. [10.7f] $9x^{10} - 16y^{10}$ **44.** [10.8a] $4x^2 + 3x - 5$

45. [10.8b] $2x^2 - 4x - 2 + \frac{17}{3x + 2}$

46. [10.3a] 3, 1.5, -3.5, -5, -5.25
47. [10.4d] $(t + 2)(t + 2)$, $t^2 + 4t + 4$ **48.** [10.4d] B
49. [10.5b], [10.6a] $V = l^3 - 3l^2 + 2l$ **50.** [8.3b], [10.6b, c] $-\frac{61}{12}$

CHAPTER 11

Exercise Set 11.1, p. 829

1. x **3.** x^2 **5.** 2   **7.** $17xy$ **9.** x **11.** x^2y^2
13. $x(x - 6)$ **15.** $2x(x + 3)$ **17.** $x^2(x + 6)$
19. $8x^2(x^2 - 3)$ **21.** $2(x^2 + x - 4)$
23. $17xy(x^4y^2 + 2x^2y + 3)$ **25.** $x^2(6x^2 - 10x + 3)$
27. $x^2y^2(x^3y^3 + x^2y + xy - 1)$
29. $2x^3(x^4 - x^3 - 32x^2 + 2)$
31. $0.8x(2x^3 - 3x^2 + 4x + 8)$
33. $\frac{1}{3}x^3(5x^3 + 4x^2 + x + 1)$ **35.** $(x + 3)(x^2 + 2)$
37. $(3z - 1)(4z^2 + 7)$ **39.** $(3x + 2)(2x^2 + 1)$
41. $(2a - 7)(5a^3 - 1)$ **43.** $(x + 3)(x^2 + 2)$
45. $(x + 3)(2x^2 + 1)$ **47.** $(2x - 3)(4x^2 + 3)$

49. $(3p - 4)(4p^2 + 1)$ **51.** $(x - 1)(5x^2 - 1)$
53. $(x + 8)(x^2 - 3)$ **55.** $(x - 4)(2x^2 - 9)$
57. $\{x | x > -24\}$ **58.** $\{x | x \leq \frac{14}{5}\}$ **59.** 27
60. $p = 2A - q$ **61.** $y^2 + 12y + 35$ **62.** $y^2 + 14y + 49$
63. $y^2 - 49$ **64.** $y^2 - 14y + 49$

65. 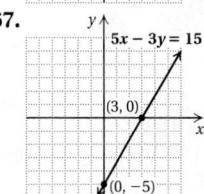   **66.**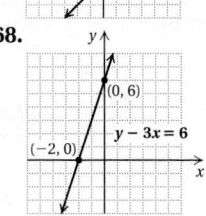

67.   **68.**

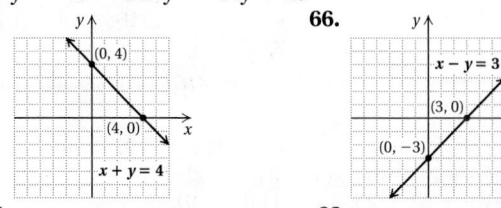

69. $(2x^2 + 3)(2x^3 + 3)$ **71.** $(x^5 + 1)(x^7 + 1)$
73. Not factorable by grouping

Exercise Set 11.2, p. 837

1.

Pairs of Factors	Sums of Factors
1, 15	16
$-1, -15$	-16
3, 5	8
$-3, -5$	-8

$(x + 3)(x + 5)$

3.

Pairs of Factors	Sums of Factors
1, 12	13
$-1, -12$	-13
2, 6	8
$-2, -6$	-8
3, 4	7
$-3, -4$	-7

$(x + 3)(x + 4)$

5.

Pairs of Factors	Sums of Factors
1, 9	10
$-1, -9$	-10
3, 3	6
$-3, -3$	-6

$(x - 3)^2$

7.

Pairs of Factors	Sums of Factors
$-1, 14$	13
$1, -14$	-13
$-2, 7$	5
$2, -7$	-5

$(x + 2)(x - 7)$

9.

Pairs of Factors	Sums of Factors
1, 4	5
$-1, -4$	-5
2, 2	4
$-2, -2$	-4

$(b + 1)(b + 4)$

11.

Pairs of Factors	Sums of Factors
$\frac{1}{3}, \frac{1}{3}$	$\frac{2}{3}$
$-\frac{1}{3}, -\frac{1}{3}$	$-\frac{2}{3}$
$1, \frac{1}{9}$	$\frac{10}{9}$
$-1, -\frac{1}{9}$	$-\frac{10}{9}$

$\left(x + \frac{1}{3}\right)^2$

13. $(d - 2)(d - 5)$ **15.** $(y - 1)(y - 10)$ **17.** Prime
19. $(x - 9)(x + 2)$ **21.** $x(x - 8)(x + 2)$
23. $y(y - 9)(y + 5)$ **25.** $(x - 11)(x + 9)$
27. $(c^2 + 8)(c^2 - 7)$ **29.** $(a^2 + 7)(a^2 - 5)$
31. $(x - 6)(x + 7)$ **33.** Prime **35.** $(x + 10)^2$
37. $2z(z - 4)(z + 3)$ **39.** $3t^2(t^2 + t + 1)$
41. $x^2(x - 25)(x + 4)$ **43.** $(x - 24)(x + 3)$
45. $(x - 9)(x - 16)$ **47.** $(a + 12)(a - 11)$ **49.** $3(t + 1)^2$
51. $w^2(w - 4)^2$ **53.** $-1(x - 10)(x + 3)$, or
$(-x + 10)(x + 3)$, or $(x - 10)(-x - 3)$
55. $-1(a - 2)(a + 12)$, or $(-a + 2)(a + 12)$, or
$(a - 2)(-a - 12)$ **57.** $(x - 15)(x - 8)$
59. $-1(x + 12)(x - 9)$, or $(-x - 12)(x - 9)$, or
$(x + 12)(-x + 9)$ **61.** $(y - 0.4)(y + 0.2)$
63. $(p + 5q)(p - 2q)$ **65.** $-1(t + 14)(t - 6)$, or
$(-t - 14)(t - 6)$, or $(t + 14)(-t + 6)$ **67.** $(m + 4n)(m + n)$
69. $(s + 3t)(s - 5t)$ **71.** $6a^8(a + 2)(a - 7)$
73. $16x^3 - 48x^2 + 8x$ **74.** $28w^2 - 53w - 66$
75. $49w^2 + 84w + 36$ **76.** $16w^2 - 88w + 121$
77. $16w^2 - 121$ **78.** $y^3 - 3y^2 + 5y$
79. $6x^2 + 11xy - 35y^2$ **80.** $27x^{12}$ **81.** $\frac{8}{3}$ **82.** $-\frac{7}{2}$
83. 1743 arrests **84.** $100°, 25°, 55°$
85. $15, -15, 27, -27, 51, -51$ **87.** $\left(x + \frac{1}{4}\right)\left(x - \frac{3}{4}\right)$
89. $(x + 5)\left(x - \frac{5}{7}\right)$ **91.** $(b^n + 5)(b^n + 2)$
93. $2x^2(4 - \pi)$

Calculator Corner, p. 842

1. Correct **2.** Correct **3.** Not correct **4.** Not correct

Exercise Set 11.3, p. 846

1. $(2x + 1)(x - 4)$ **3.** $(5x + 9)(x - 2)$
5. $(3x + 1)(2x + 7)$ **7.** $(3x + 1)(x + 1)$
9. $(2x - 3)(2x + 5)$ **11.** $(2x + 1)(x - 1)$
13. $(3x - 2)(3x + 8)$ **15.** $(3x + 1)(x - 2)$
17. $(3x + 4)(4x + 5)$ **19.** $(7x - 1)(2x + 3)$
21. $(3x + 2)(3x + 4)$ **23.** $(3x - 7)^2$, or $(7 - 3x)^2$
25. $(24x - 1)(x + 2)$ **27.** $(5x - 11)(7x + 4)$
29. $-2(x - 5)(x + 2)$, or $2(-x + 5)(x + 2)$, or
$2(x - 5)(-x - 2)$ **31.** $4(3x - 2)(x + 3)$
33. $6(5x - 9)(x + 1)$ **311.** $2(3y + 5)(y - 1)$
37. $(3x - 1)(x - 1)$ **39.** $4(3x + 2)(x - 3)$
41. $(2x + 1)(x - 1)$ **43.** $(3x + 2)(3x - 8)$
45. $5(3x + 1)(x - 2)$ **47.** $p(3p + 4)(4p + 5)$
49. $-1(3x + 2)(3x - 8)$, or $(-3x - 2)(3x - 8)$, or
$(3x + 2)(-3x + 8)$ **51.** $-1(5x - 3)(3x - 2)$, or
$(-5x + 3)(3x - 2)$, or $(5x - 3)(-3x + 2)$
53. $x^2(7x - 1)(2x + 3)$ **55.** $3x(8x - 1)(7x - 1)$
57. $(5x^2 - 3)(3x^2 - 2)$ **59.** $(5t + 8)^2$
61. $2x(3x + 5)(x - 1)$ **63.** Prime **65.** Prime
67. $(4m + 5n)(3m - 4n)$ **69.** $(2a + 3b)(3a - 5b)$
71. $(3a + 2b)(3a + 4b)$ **73.** $(5p + 2q)(7p + 4q)$
75. $6(3x - 4y)(x + y)$ **77.** $q = \dfrac{A + 7}{p}$

78. $x = \dfrac{y - b}{m}$ **79.** $y = \dfrac{6 - 3x}{2}$ **80.** $q = p + r - 2$

81. $\{x \mid x > 4\}$ 82. $\left\{ x \mid x \le \frac{8}{11} \right\}$
81. $\{x \mid x > 4\}$ **82.** $\left\{ x \mid x \le \frac{8}{11} \right\}$
83.

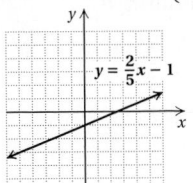

84. y^8 **85.** y-intercept: $(0, -4)$; x-intercept: $(16, 0)$
86. y-intercept: $(0, 4)$; x-intercept: $(16, 0)$
87. y-intercept: $(0, -5)$; x-intercept: $(6.5, 0)$
88. y-intercept: $\left(0, \frac{2}{3}\right)$; x-intercept: $\left(\frac{5}{8}, 0\right)$
89. y-intercept: $(0, 4)$; x-intercept: $\left(\frac{4}{5}, 0\right)$
90. y-intercept: $(0, -5)$; x-intercept: $\left(\frac{5}{2}, 0\right)$
91. $(2x^n + 1)(10x^n + 3)$ **93.** $(x^{3a} - 1)(3x^{3a} + 1)$
95.–103. Left to the student

Exercise Set 11.4, p. 851

1. $(x + 2)(x + 7)$ **3.** $(x - 4)(x - 1)$
5. $(3x + 2)(2x + 3)$ **7.** $(3x - 4)(x - 4)$
9. $(7x - 8)(5x + 3)$ **11.** $(2x + 3)(2x - 3)$
13. $(x^2 + 3)(2x^2 + 5)$ **15.** $(2x - 1)(x + 4)$
17. $(3x + 5)(x - 3)$ **19.** $(2x + 7)(3x + 1)$
21. $(3x - 1)(x - 1)$ **23.** $(2x + 3)(2x - 5)$
25. $(2x - 1)(x + 1)$ **27.** $(3x + 2)(3x - 8)$
29. $(3x - 1)(x + 2)$ **31.** $(3x - 4)(4x - 5)$
33. $(7x + 1)(2x - 3)$ **35.** $(3x + 2)(3x + 4)$
37. $(3x - 7)^2$, or $(7 - 3x)^2$ **39.** $(24x + 1)(x - 2)$
41. $-1(3a - 1)(3a + 5)$, or $(-3a + 1)(3a + 5)$, or
$(3a - 1)(-3a - 5)$ **43.** $-2(x - 5)(x + 2)$, or
$2(-x + 5)(x + 2)$, or $2(x - 5)(-x - 2)$
45. $4(3x - 2)(x + 3)$ **47.** $6(5x - 9)(x + 1)$
49. $2(3y + 5)(y - 1)$ **51.** $(3x - 1)(x - 1)$
53. $4(3x + 2)(x - 3)$ **55.** $(2x + 1)(x - 1)$
57. $(3x - 2)(3x + 8)$ **59.** $5(3x + 1)(x - 2)$
61. $p(3p + 4)(4p + 5)$ **63.** $-1(5x - 4)(x + 1)$, or
$(-5x + 4)(x + 1)$, or $(5x - 4)(-x - 1)$
65. $-3(2t - 1)(t - 5)$, or $3(-2t + 1)(t - 5)$, or
$3(2t - 1)(-t + 5)$ **67.** $x^2(7x - 1)(2x + 3)$
69. $3x(8x - 1)(7x - 1)$ **71.** $(5x^2 - 3)(3x^2 - 2)$
73. $(5t + 8)^2$ **75.** $2x(3x + 5)(x - 1)$ **77.** Prime
79. Prime **81.** $(4m + 5n)(3m - 4n)$
83. $(2a + 3b)(3a - 5b)$ **85.** $(3a - 2b)(3a - 4b)$
87. $(5p + 2q)(7p + 4q)$ **89.** $6(3x - 4y)(x + y)$
91. $-6x(x - 5)(x + 2)$, or $6x(-x + 5)(x + 2)$, or
$6x(x - 5)(-x - 2)$ **93.** $x^3(5x - 11)(7x + 4)$
95. $\{x \mid x < -100\}$ **96.** $\{x \mid x \ge 217\}$
97. $\{x \mid x \le 8\}$ **98.** $\{x \mid x < 2\}$ **99.** $\left\{ x \mid x \ge \frac{20}{3} \right\}$
100. $\{x \mid x > 17\}$ **101.** $\left\{ x \mid x > \frac{26}{7} \right\}$ **102.** $\left\{ x \mid x \ge \frac{77}{17} \right\}$
103. About 6369 km, or 3949 mi **104.** $40°$ **105.** $(3x^5 - 2)^2$
107. $(4x^5 + 1)^2$ **109.–117.** Left to the student

Mid-Chapter Review: Chapter 11, p. 855

1. True **2.** False **3.** True **4.** False
5. $10y^3 - 18y^2 + 12y = 2y \cdot 5y^2 - 2y \cdot 9y + 2y \cdot 6$
$\qquad\qquad\qquad\qquad = 2y(5y^2 - 9y + 6)$
6. $a \cdot c = 2 \cdot (-6) = -12;$
$\quad -x = -4x + 3x;$
$\quad 2x^2 - x - 6 = 2x^2 - 4x + 3x - 6$
$\qquad\qquad\qquad = 2x(x - 2) + 3(x - 2)$
$\qquad\qquad\qquad = (x - 2)(2x + 3)$
7. x **8.** x^2 **9.** $6x^3$ **10.** 4 **11.** $5x^2y$ **12.** x^2y^2
13. $x(x^2 - 8)$ **14.** $3x(x + 4)$ **15.** $2(y^2 + 4y - 2)$
16. $t^3(3t^3 - 5t - 2)$ **17.** $(x + 1)(x + 3)$ **18.** $(z - 2)^2$
19. $(x + 4)(x^2 + 3)$ **20.** $8y^3(y^2 - 6)$

21. $6xy(x^2 + 4xy - 7y^2)$ **22.** $(4t - 3)(t - 2)$
23. $(z - 1)(z + 5)$ **24.** $(z + 4)(2z^2 + 5)$
25. $(3p - 2)(p^2 - 3)$ **26.** $5x^3(2x^5 - 5x^3 - 3x^2 + 7)$
27. $(2w + 3)(w^2 - 3)$ **28.** $x^2(4x^2 - 5x + 3)$
29. $(6y - 5)(y + 2)$ **30.** $3(x - 3)(x + 2)$
31. $(3x + 2)(2x^2 + 1)$ **32.** $(w - 5)(w - 3)$
33. $(2x + 5)(4x^2 + 1)$ **34.** $(5z + 2)(2z - 5)$
35. $(2x + 1)(3x + 2)$ **36.** $(x - 6y)(x - 4y)$
37. $(2z + 1)(3z^2 + 1)$ **38.** $a^2b^3(ab^4 + a^2b^2 - 1 + a^3b^3)$
39. $(4y + 5z)(y - 3z)$ **40.** $3x(x + 2)(x + 5)$
41. $(x - 3)(x^2 - 2)$ **42.** $(3y + 1)^2$ **43.** $(y + 2)(y + 4)$
44. $3(2y + 5)(y + 3)$ **45.** $(x - 7)(x^2 + 4)$
46. $-1(y - 4)(y + 1)$, or $(-y + 4)(y + 1)$, or $(y - 4)(-y - 1)$
47. $4(2x + 3)(2x - 5)$ **48.** $(5a - 3b)(2a - b)$
49. $(2w - 5)(3w^2 - 5)$ **50.** $y(y + 6)(y + 3)$
51. $(4x + 3y)(x + 2y)$ **52.** $-1(3z - 2)(2z + 3)$, or
$(-3z + 2)(2z + 3)$, or $(3z - 2)(-2z - 3)$
53. $(3t + 2)(4t^2 - 3)$ **54.** $(y - 4z)(y + 5z)$
55. $(3x - 4y)(3x + 2y)$ **56.** $(3z - 1)(z + 3)$
57. $(m - 8n)(m + 2n)$ **58.** $2(w - 3)^2$
59. $2t(3t - 2)(3t - 1)$ **60.** $(z + 3)(5z^2 + 1)$
61. $(t - 2)(t + 7)$ **62.** $(2t - 5)^2$ **63.** $(t - 2)(t + 6)$
64. $-1(2z + 3)(z - 4)$, or $(-2z - 3)(z - 4)$, or
$(2z + 3)(-z + 4)$ **65.** $-1(y - 6)(y + 2)$, or $(-y + 6)(y + 2)$,
or $(y - 6)(-y - 2)$ **66.** Find the product of two binomials.
For example, $(2x^2 + 3)(x - 4) = 2x^3 - 8x^2 + 3x - 12$.
67. There is a finite number of pairs of numbers with the
correct product, but there are infinitely many pairs with the
correct sum.   **68.** Since both constants are negative, the
middle term will be negative so $(x - 17)(x - 18)$ cannot be a
factorization of $x^2 + 35x + 306$.   **69.** No; both $2x + 6$ and
$2x + 8$ contain a factor of 2, so $2 \cdot 2$, or 4, must be factored out
to reach the complete factorization. In other words, the largest
common factor is 4, not 2.

Exercise Set 11.5, p. 863

1. Yes   **3.** No   **5.** No   **7.** Yes   **9.** $(x - 7)^2$
11. $(x + 8)^2$ **13.** $(x - 1)^2$ **15.** $(x + 2)^2$ **17.** $(y + 6)^2$
19. $(t - 4)^2$ **21.** $(q^2 - 3)^2$ **23.** $(4y + 7)^2$ **25.** $2(x - 1)^2$
27. $x(x - 9)^2$ **29.** $3(2q - 3)^2$ **31.** $(7 - 3x)^2$, or $(3x - 7)^2$
33. $5(y^2 + 1)^2$ **35.** $(1 + 2x^2)^2$ **37.** $(2p + 3q)^2$
39. $(a - 3b)^2$ **41.** $(9a - b)^2$ **43.** $4(3a + 4b)^2$ **45.** Yes
47. No   **49.** No   **51.** Yes   **53.** $(y + 2)(y - 2)$
55. $(p + 3)(p - 3)$ **57.** $(t + 7)(t - 7)$
59. $(a + b)(a - b)$ **61.** $(5t + m)(5t - m)$
63. $(10 + k)(10 - k)$ **65.** $(4a + 3)(4a - 3)$
67. $(2x + 5y)(2x - 5y)$ **69.** $2(2x + 7)(2x - 7)$
71. $x(6 + 7x)(6 - 7x)$ **73.** $\left(\frac{1}{4} + 7x^4\right)\left(\frac{1}{4} - 7x^4\right)$
75. $(0.3y + 0.02)(0.3y - 0.02)$ **77.** $(7a^2 + 9)(7a^2 - 9)$
79. $(a^2 + 4)(a + 2)(a - 2)$ **81.** $5(x^2 + 9)(x + 3)(x - 3)$
83. $(1 + y^4)(1 + y^2)(1 + y)(1 - y)$
85. $(x^6 + 4)(x^3 + 2)(x^3 - 2)$ **87.** $\left(y + \frac{1}{4}\right)\left(y - \frac{1}{4}\right)$
89. $\left(5 + \frac{1}{7}x\right)\left(5 - \frac{1}{7}x\right)$ **91.** $(4m^2 + t^2)(2m + t)(2m - t)$
93. -11 **94.** 400   **95.** $-\frac{5}{6}$ **96.** -0.9 **97.** 2   **98.** -160
99. $x^2 - 4xy + 4y^2$ **100.** $\frac{1}{2}\pi x^2 + 2xy$ **101.** y^{12}
102. $25a^4b^6$
103.   **104.**

105. Prime   **107.** $(x + 11)^2$ **109.** $2x(3x + 1)^2$

111. $(x^4 + 2^4)(x^2 + 2^2)(x + 2)(x - 2)$
113. $3x^3(x + 2)(x - 2)$ **115.** $2x\left(3x + \frac{2}{5}\right)\left(3x - \frac{2}{5}\right)$
117. $p(0.7 + p)(0.7 - p)$ **119.** $(0.8x + 1.1)(0.8x - 1.1)$
121. $x(x + 6)$ **123.** $\left(x + \frac{1}{x}\right)\left(x - \frac{1}{x}\right)$
125. $(9 + b^{2k})(3 - b^k)(3 + b^k)$ **127.** $(3b^n + 2)^2$
129. $(y + 4)^2$ **131.** 9   **133.** Not correct   **135.** Not correct

Exercise Set 11.6, p. 871

1. $3(x + 8)(x - 8)$ **3.** $(a - 5)^2$ **5.** $(2x - 3)(x - 4)$
7. $x(x + 12)^2$ **9.** $(x + 3)(x + 2)(x - 2)$
11. $3(4x + 1)(4x - 1)$ **13.** $3x(3x - 5)(x + 3)$
15. Prime   **17.** $x(x^2 + 7)(x - 3)$ **19.** $x^3(x - 7)^2$
21. $-2(x - 2)(x + 5)$, or $2(-x + 2)(x + 5)$, or
$2(x - 2)(-x - 5)$ **23.** Prime
25. $4(x^2 + 4)(x + 2)(x - 2)$
27. $(1 + y^4)(1 + y^2)(1 + y)(1 - y)$ **29.** $x^3(x - 3)(x - 1)$
31. $\frac{1}{9}\left(\frac{1}{3}x^3 - 4\right)^2$ **33.** $m(x^2 + y^2)$ **35.** $9xy(xy - 4)$
37. $2\pi r(h + r)$ **39.** $(a + b)(2x + 1)$
41. $(x + 1)(x - 1 - y)$ **43.** $(n + 2)(n + p)$
45. $(2q - 1)(3q + p)$ **47.** $(2b - a)^2$, or $(a - 2b)^2$
49. $(4x + 3y)^2$ **51.** $(7m^2 - 8n)^2$ **53.** $(y^2 + 5z^2)^2$
55. $\left(\frac{1}{2}a + \frac{1}{3}b\right)^2$ **57.** $(a + b)(a - 2b)$
59. $(m + 20n)(m - 18n)$ **61.** $(mn - 8)(mn + 4)$
63. $r^3(rs - 2)(rs - 8)$ **65.** $a^3(a - b)(a + 5b)$
67. $\left(a + \frac{1}{5}b\right)\left(a - \frac{1}{5}b\right)$ **69.** $(x + y)(x - y)$
71. $(4 + p^2q^2)(2 + pq)(2 - pq)$
73. $(1 + 4x^6y^6)(1 + 2x^3y^3)(1 - 2x^3y^3)$
75. $(q + 8)(q + 1)(q - 1)$ **77.** $ab(2ab + 1)(3ab - 2)$
79. $(m + 1)(m - 1)(m + 2)(m - 2)$ **81.** $(t + 1)^2(t - 1)^2$
82. $y = 8x - 4$ **83.** $y = -3x - 12$ **84.** $y = -0.28x - 1.16$
85. $y = -\frac{2}{3}x + \frac{7}{3}$ **86.** $25x^2 - 10xt + t^2$ **87.** $-\frac{14}{11}$
88. $\{x | x < 32\}$ **89.** $X = \dfrac{A + 7}{a + b}$ **91.** $(x - 5)(x + 2)(x - 2)$
93. $(3.5x - 1)^2$ **95.** $(5x + 4)(x + 1.8)$
97. $(y - 2)(y + 3)(y - 3)$ **99.** $(x - 1)(x + 2)(x - 2)$
101. Prime   **103.** $(y - 1)^3$ **105.** $(y + 4 + x)^2$

Calculator Corner, p. 880

1. Left to the student

Exercise Set 11.7, p. 881

1. $-4, -9$ **3.** $-3, 8$ **5.** $-12, 11$ **7.** $0, -3$ **9.** $0, -18$
11. $-\frac{5}{2}, -4$ **13.** $-\frac{1}{5}, 3$ **15.** $4, \frac{1}{4}$ **17.** $0, \frac{2}{3}$ **19.** $-\frac{1}{10}, \frac{1}{27}$
21. $\frac{1}{3}, -20$ **23.** $0, \frac{2}{3}, \frac{1}{2}$ **25.** $-5, -1$ **27.** $-9, 2$ **29.** $3, 5$
31. $0, 8$ **33.** $0, -18$ **35.** $-4, 4$ **37.** $-\frac{2}{3}, \frac{2}{3}$ **39.** -3
41. 4 **43.** $0, \frac{6}{5}$ **45.** $-1, \frac{5}{3}$ **47.** $-\frac{1}{4}, \frac{2}{3}$ **49.** $-1, \frac{2}{3}$
51. $-\frac{7}{10}, \frac{7}{10}$ **53.** $-2, 9$ **55.** $\frac{4}{5}, \frac{3}{2}$ **57.** $(-4, 0), (1, 0)$
59. $\left(-\frac{5}{2}, 0\right), (2, 0)$ **61.** $(-3, 0), (5, 0)$ **63.** $-1, 4$
65. $-1, 3$ **67.** $(a + b)^2$ **68.** $a^2 + b^2$ **69.** -16
70. -4.5 **71.** $-\frac{10}{3}$ **72.** $\frac{3}{10}$ **73.** $-5, 4$ **75.** $-3, 9$
77. $-\frac{1}{8}, \frac{1}{8}$ **79.** $-4, 4$ **81.** Answers may vary.
(a) $x^2 - x - 12 = 0$; **(b)** $x^2 + 7x + 12 = 0$; **(c)** $4x^2 - 4x + 1 = 0$;
(d) $x^2 - 25 = 0$; **(e)** $40x^3 - 14x^2 + x = 0$ **83.** $2.33, 6.77$
85. $0, 2.74$

Translating for Success, p. 890

1. O   **2.** M   **3.** K   **4.** I   **5.** G   **6.** E   **7.** C   **8.** A
9. H   **10.** B

Exercise Set 11.8, p. 891

1. Length: 42 in.; width: 14 in.   **3.** Length: 12 ft; width: 2 ft
5. Height: 4 cm; base: 14 cm   **7.** Base: 8 m; height: 16 m

9. 182 games **11.** 12 teams **13.** 4950 handshakes
15. 25 people **17.** 20 people **19.** 14 and 15
21. 12 and 14; −12 and −14 **23.** 15 and 17; −15 and −17
25. Hypotenuse: 17 ft; leg: 15 ft **27.** 32 ft **29.** 9 ft
31. Dining room: 12 ft by 12 ft; kitchen: 12 ft by 10 ft
33. 4 sec **35.** 5 and 7 **37.** Factor **38.** Factor
39. Product **40.** Common factor **41.** Trinomial
42. Quotient rule **43.** y-intercept **44.** Slope
45. 35 ft **47.** 5 ft **49.** 30 cm by 15 cm **51.** 7 in.

Summary and Review: Chapter 11, p. 897

Concept Reinforcement
1. False **2.** True **3.** False **4.** True

Important Concepts
1. $4xy$ **2.** $9x^2(3x^3 - x + 2)$ **3.** $(z - 3)(z^2 + 4)$
4. $(x + 2)(x + 4)$ **5.** $3(z - 4)(2z + 1)$
6. $(3y - 1)(2y + 3)$ **7.** $(2x + 1)^2$ **8.** $2(3x + 2)(3x - 2)$
9. $-5, 1$

Review Exercises
1. $5y^2$ **2.** $12x$ **3.** $5(1 + 2x^3)(1 - 2x^3)$ **4.** $x(x - 3)$
5. $(3x + 2)(3x - 2)$ **6.** $(x + 6)(x - 2)$ **7.** $(x + 7)^2$
8. $3x(2x^2 + 4x + 1)$ **9.** $(x + 1)(x^2 + 3)$
10. $(3x - 1)(2x - 1)$ **11.** $(x^2 + 9)(x + 3)(x - 3)$
12. $3x(3x - 5)(x + 3)$ **13.** $2(x + 5)(x - 5)$
14. $(x + 4)(x^3 - 2)$ **15.** $(4x^2 + 1)(2x + 1)(2x - 1)$
16. $4x^4(2x^2 - 8x + 1)$ **17.** $3(2x + 5)^2$ **18.** Prime
19. $x(x - 6)(x + 5)$ **20.** $(2x + 5)(2x - 5)$ **21.** $(3x - 5)^2$
22. $2(3x + 4)(x - 6)$ **23.** $(x - 3)^2$ **24.** $(2x + 1)(x - 4)$
25. $2(3x - 1)^2$ **26.** $3(x + 3)(x - 3)$ **27.** $(x - 5)(x - 3)$
28. $(5x - 2)^2$ **29.** $(7b^5 - 2a^4)^2$ **30.** $(xy + 4)(xy - 3)$
31. $3(2a + 7b)^2$ **32.** $(m + 5)(m + t)$
33. $32(x^2 - 2y^2z^2)(x^2 + 2y^2z^2)$ **34.** $1, -3$ **35.** $-7, 5$
36. $-4, 0$ **37.** $\frac{2}{3}, 1$ **38.** $-8, 8$ **39.** $-2, 8$
40. $(-5, 0), (-4, 0)$ **41.** $\left(-\frac{3}{2}, 0\right), (5, 0)$
42. Height: 6 cm; base: 5 cm **43.** −18 and −16; 16 and 18
44. −19 and −17; 17 and 19 **45.** On the ground: 4 ft; on the
tree: 3 ft **46.** 6 km **47.** B **48.** A **49.** 2.5 cm **50.** 0, 2
51. Length: 12 in.; width: 6 in. **52.** No solution **53.** $2, -3, \frac{5}{2}$
54. $-2, \frac{5}{4}, 3$ **55.** $x^2(\pi - 2)$

Understanding Through Discussion and Writing
1. Although $x^3 - 8x^2 + 15x$ can be factored as
$(x^2 - 5x)(x - 3)$, this is not a complete factorization of the
polynomial since $x^2 - 5x = x(x - 5)$. Gwen should always look
for a common factor first. **2.** Josh is correct, because answers
can easily be checked by multiplying.
3. For $x = -3$:
$$(x - 4)^2 = (-3 - 4)^2 = (-7)^2 = 49;$$
$$(4 - x)^2 = [4 - (-3)]^2 = 7^2 = 49.$$
For $x = 1$:
$$(x - 4)^2 = (1 - 4)^2 = (-3)^2 = 9;$$
$$(4 - x)^2 = (4 - 1)^2 = 3^2 = 9.$$
In general, $(x - 4)^2 = [-(-x + 4)]^2 = [-(4 - x)]^2 =$
$(-1)^2(4 - x)^2 = (4 - x)^2$.
4. The equation is not in the form $ab = 0$. The correct
procedure is
$$(x - 3)(x + 4) = 8$$
$$x^2 + x - 12 = 8$$
$$x^2 + x - 20 = 0$$
$$(x + 5)(x - 4) = 0$$
$$x + 5 = 0 \quad or \quad x - 4 = 0$$
$$x = -5 \quad or \quad x = 4.$$
The solutions are −5 and 4.

5. One solution of the equation is 0. Dividing both sides of the
equation by x, leaving the solution $x = 3$, is equivalent to
dividing by 0. **6.** She could use the measuring sticks to draw
a right angle as shown below. Then she could use the 3-ft and
4-ft sticks to extend one leg to 7 ft and the 4-ft and 5-ft sticks to
extend the other leg to 9 ft.

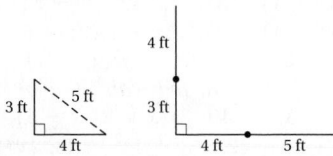

Next, she could draw another right angle with either the 7-ft
side or the 9-ft side as a side.

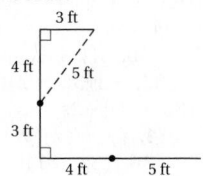

Then she could use the sticks to extend the other side to the
appropriate length. Finally, she would draw the remaining side
of the rectangle.

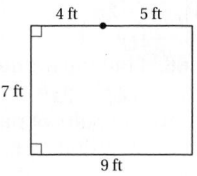

Test: Chapter 11, p. 903
1. [11.1a] $4x^3$ **2.** [11.2a] $(x - 5)(x - 2)$ **3.** [11.5b] $(x - 5)^2$
4. [11.1b] $2y^2(2y^2 - 4y + 3)$ **5.** [11.1c] $(x + 1)(x^2 + 2)$
6. [11.1b] $x(x - 5)$ **7.** [11.2a] $x(x + 3)(x - 1)$
8. [11.3a], [11.4a] $2(5x - 6)(x + 4)$
9. [11.5d] $(2x + 3)(2x - 3)$ **10.** [11.2a] $(x - 4)(x + 3)$
11. [11.3a], [11.4a] $3m(2m + 1)(m + 1)$
12. [11.5d] $3(w + 5)(w - 5)$ **13.** [11.5b] $5(3x + 2)^2$
14. [11.5d] $3(x^2 + 4)(x + 2)(x - 2)$ **15.** [11.5b] $(7x - 6)^2$
16. [11.3a], [11.4a] $(5x - 1)(x - 5)$ **17.** [11.1c] $(x + 2)(x^3 - 3)$
18. [11.5d] $5(4 + x^2)(2 + x)(2 - x)$
19. [11.3a], [11.4a] $3t(2t + 5)(t - 1)$ **20.** [11.7b] 0, 3
21. [11.7b] −4, 4 **22.** [11.7b] −4, 5 **23.** [11.7b] $-5, \frac{3}{2}$
24. [11.7b] −4, 7 **25.** [11.7b] $(-5, 0), (7, 0)$
26. [11.7b] $\left(\frac{2}{3}, 0\right), (1, 0)$ **27.** [11.8a] Length: 8 m; width: 6 m
28. [11.8a] Height: 4 cm; base: 14 cm **29.** [11.8a] 5 ft
30. [11.5d] A **31.** [11.8a] Length: 15 m; width: 3 m
32. [11.2a] $(a - 4)(a + 8)$ **33.** [11.7b] $-\frac{8}{3}, 0, \frac{2}{5}$
34. [10.6b], [11.5d] D

CHAPTER 12

Exercise Set 12.1, p. 912
1. 0 **3.** 8 **5.** $-\frac{5}{2}$ **7.** −4, 7 **9.** −5, 5 **11.** None
13. $\dfrac{(4x)(3x^2)}{(4x)(5y)}$ **15.** $\dfrac{2x(x - 1)}{2x(x + 4)}$ **17.** $\dfrac{(3 - x)(-1)}{(4 - x)(-1)}$
19. $\dfrac{(y + 6)(y - 7)}{(y + 6)(y + 2)}$ **21.** $\dfrac{x^2}{4}$ **23.** $\dfrac{8p^2q}{3}$ **25.** $\dfrac{x - 3}{x}$
27. $\dfrac{m + 1}{2m + 3}$ **29.** $\dfrac{a - 3}{a + 2}$ **31.** $\dfrac{a - 3}{a - 4}$ **33.** $\dfrac{x + 5}{x - 5}$
35. $a + 1$ **37.** $\dfrac{x^2 + 1}{x + 1}$ **39.** $\dfrac{3}{2}$ **41.** $\dfrac{6}{t - 3}$ **43.** $\dfrac{t + 2}{2(t - 4)}$
45. $\dfrac{t - 2}{t + 2}$ **47.** −1 **49.** −1 **51.** −6 **53.** $-x - 1$

55. $\dfrac{56x}{3}$ 57. $\dfrac{2}{dc^2}$ 59. 1   61. $\dfrac{(a+3)(a-3)}{a(a+4)}$

63. $\dfrac{2a}{a-2}$ 65. $\dfrac{(t+2)(t-2)}{(t+1)(t-1)}$ 67. $\dfrac{x+4}{x+2}$ 69. $\dfrac{5(a+6)}{a-1}$

71. 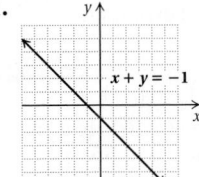   72.

73. 18 and 20; -20 and -18 74. 3.125 L
75. $(x-8)(x+7)$ 76. $(a-8)^2$ 77. $x^3(x-7)(x+5)$
78. $(2y^2+1)(y-5)$ 79. $(2+t)(2-t)(4+t^2)$
80. $10(x+7)(x+1)$ 81. $(x-7)(x-2)$ 82. Prime
83. $(4x-5y)^2$ 84. $(a-7b)(a-2b)$ 85. $x+2y$
87. $\dfrac{(t-9)^2(t-1)}{(t^2+9)(t+1)}$ 89. $\dfrac{x-y}{x-5y}$

91. $\dfrac{5(2x+5)-25}{10}=\dfrac{10x+25-25}{10}$
$$=\dfrac{10x}{10}$$
$$=x$$

You get the same number you selected. To do a number trick, ask someone to select a number and then perform these operations. The person will probably be surprised that the result is the original number.

Exercise Set 12.2, p. 919

1. $\dfrac{x}{4}$ 3. $\dfrac{1}{x^2-y^2}$ 5. $a+b$ 7. $\dfrac{x^2-4x+7}{x^2+2x-5}$ 9. $\dfrac{3}{10}$

11. $\dfrac{1}{4}$ 13. $\dfrac{b}{a}$ 15. $\dfrac{(a+2)(a+3)}{(a-3)(a-1)}$ 17. $\dfrac{(x-1)^2}{x}$ 19. $\dfrac{1}{2}$

21. $\dfrac{15}{8}$ 23. $\dfrac{15}{4}$ 25. $\dfrac{a-5}{3(a-1)}$ 27. $\dfrac{(x+2)^2}{x}$ 29. $\dfrac{3}{2}$

31. $\dfrac{c+1}{c-1}$ 33. $\dfrac{y-3}{2y-1}$ 35. $\dfrac{x+1}{x-1}$ 37. $\{x|x\geq 77\}$

38. Height: 7 in.; base: 10 in.   39. $8x^3-11x^2-3x+12$
40. $-2p^2+4pq-4q^2$ 41. $\dfrac{4y^8}{x^6}$ 42. $\dfrac{125x^{18}}{y^{12}}$ 43. $\dfrac{4x^6}{y^{10}}$

44. $\dfrac{1}{a^{15}b^{20}}$ 45. $-\dfrac{1}{b^2}$ 47. $\dfrac{a+1}{5ab^2(a^2+4)}$

Exercise Set 12.3, p. 923

1. 108   3. 72   5. 126   7. 360   9. 500   11. $\dfrac{65}{72}$
13. $\dfrac{29}{120}$ 15. $\dfrac{23}{180}$ 17. $12x^3$ 19. $18x^2y^2$ 21. $6(y-3)$
23. $t(t+2)(t-2)$ 25. $(x+2)(x-2)(x+3)$
27. $t(t+2)^2(t-4)$ 29. $(a+1)(a-1)^2$
31. $(m-3)(m-2)^2$ 33. $(2+3x)(2-3x)$
35. $10v(v+4)(v+3)$ 37. $18x^3(x-2)^2(x+1)$
39. $6x^3(x+2)^2(x-2)$ 41. $120w^6$ 43. $(x-3)^2$
44. $2x(3x+2)$ 45. $(x+3)(x-3)$ 46. $(x+7)(x-3)$
47. $(x+3)^2$ 48. $(x-7)(x+3)$ 49. $120x^4;8x^3;960x^7$
50. $48x^6;16x^5;768x^{11}$ 51. $20x^2;10x;200x^3$
52. $48ab^3;4ab;192a^2b^4$ 53. $120x^3;2x^2;240x^5$
54. $a^{15};a^5;a^{20}$ 55. The product of the LCM and the GCF is the product of the two expressions.

Exercise Set 12.4, p. 929

1. 1   3. $\dfrac{6}{3+x}$ 5. $\dfrac{-4x+11}{2x-1}$ 7. $\dfrac{2x+5}{x^2}$ 9. $\dfrac{41}{24r}$

11. $\dfrac{2(2x+3y)}{x^2y^2}$ 13. $\dfrac{4+3t}{18t^3}$ 15. $\dfrac{x^2+4xy+y^2}{x^2y^2}$

17. $\dfrac{6x}{(x-2)(x+2)}$ 19. $\dfrac{11x+2}{3x(x+1)}$ 21. $\dfrac{x(x+6)}{(x+4)(x-4)}$

23. $\dfrac{6}{z+4}$ 25. $\dfrac{3x-1}{(x-1)^2}$ 27. $\dfrac{11a}{10(a-2)}$

29. $\dfrac{2(x^2+4x+8)}{x(x+4)}$ 31. $\dfrac{7a+6}{(a-2)(a+1)(a+3)}$

33. $\dfrac{2(x^2-2x+17)}{(x-5)(x+3)}$ 35. $\dfrac{3a+2}{(a+1)(a-1)}$

37. $\dfrac{1}{4}$ 39. $-\dfrac{1}{t}$ 41. $\dfrac{-x+7}{x-6}$, or $\dfrac{7-x}{x-6}$, or $\dfrac{x-7}{6-x}$

43. $y+3$ 45. $\dfrac{2(b-7)}{(b+4)(b-4)}$ 47. $a+b$ 49. $\dfrac{5x+2}{x-5}$

51. -1 53. $\dfrac{-x^2+9x-14}{(x-3)(x+3)}$ 55. $\dfrac{2(x+3y)}{(x+y)(x-y)}$

57. $\dfrac{a^2+7a+1}{(a+5)(a-5)}$ 59. $\dfrac{5t-12}{(t+3)(t-3)(t-2)}$ 61. x^2-1

62. $13y^3-14y^2+12y-73$ 63. $\dfrac{1}{8x^{12}y^9}$ 64. $\dfrac{x^6}{25y^2}$

65. $\dfrac{1}{x^{12}y^{21}}$ 66. $\dfrac{25}{x^4y^6}$ 67.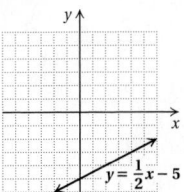

68.   69.   70.

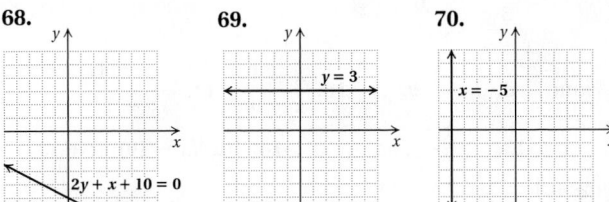

71. -8 72. $\dfrac{5}{6}$ 73. $3,5$ 74. $-2,9$ 75. Perimeter: $\dfrac{16y+28}{15}$; area: $\dfrac{y^2+2y-8}{15}$ 77. $\dfrac{(z+6)(2z-3)}{(z+2)(z-2)}$

79. $\dfrac{11z^4-22z^2+6}{(z^2+2)(z^2-2)(2z^2-3)}$

Exercise Set 12.5, p. 937

1. $\dfrac{4}{x}$ 3. 1   5. $\dfrac{1}{x-1}$ 7. $\dfrac{-a-4}{10}$ 9. $\dfrac{7z-12}{12z}$

11. $\dfrac{4x^2-13xt+9t^2}{3x^2t^2}$ 13. $\dfrac{2(x-20)}{(x+5)(x-5)}$ 15. $\dfrac{3-5t}{2t(t-1)}$

17. $\dfrac{2s-st-s^2}{(t+s)(t-s)}$ 19. $\dfrac{y-19}{4y}$ 21. $\dfrac{-2a^2}{(x+a)(x-a)}$

23. $\dfrac{8}{3}$ 25. $\dfrac{13}{a}$ 27. $\dfrac{8}{y-1}$ 29. $\dfrac{x-2}{x-7}$

31. $\dfrac{4}{(a+5)(a-5)}$ 33. $\dfrac{2(x-2)}{x-9}$ 35. $\dfrac{3(3x+4)}{(x+3)(x-3)}$

37. $\dfrac{1}{2}$ 39. $\dfrac{x-3}{(x+3)(x+1)}$ 41. $\dfrac{18x+5}{x-1}$ 43. 0

45. $\dfrac{-9}{2x-3}$ 47. $\dfrac{20}{2y-1}$ 49. $\dfrac{2a-3}{2-a}$ 51. $\dfrac{z-3}{2z-1}$

53. $\dfrac{2}{x+y}$ 55. x^5 56. $30x^{12}$ 57. $\dfrac{b^{20}}{a^8}$ 58. $18x^3$

59. $\dfrac{6}{x^3}$ 60. $\dfrac{10}{x^3}$ 61. $-\dfrac{11}{35}$ 62. 10   63. $x^2-9x+18$

64. $(4-\pi)r^2$ 65. $\dfrac{30}{(x-3)(x+4)}$

67. $\dfrac{x^2 + xy - x^3 + x^2y - xy^2 + y^3}{(x^2 + y^2)(x + y)^2(x - y)}$

69. Missing side: $\dfrac{-2a - 15}{a - 6}$; area: $\dfrac{-2a^3 - 15a^2 + 12a + 90}{2(a - 6)^2}$

Mid-Chapter Review: Chapter 12, p. 941

1. False **2.** True **3.** True **4.** False **5.** True

6.
$$\dfrac{x - 1}{x - 2} - \dfrac{x + 1}{x + 2} - \dfrac{x - 6}{4 - x^2}$$
$$= \dfrac{x - 1}{x - 2} - \dfrac{x + 1}{x + 2} - \dfrac{x - 6}{4 - x^2} \cdot \dfrac{-1}{-1}$$
$$= \dfrac{x - 1}{x - 2} - \dfrac{x + 1}{x + 2} - \dfrac{6 - x}{x^2 - 4}$$
$$= \dfrac{x - 1}{x - 2} - \dfrac{x + 1}{x + 2} - \dfrac{6 - x}{(x - 2)(x + 2)}$$
$$= \dfrac{x - 1}{x - 2} \cdot \dfrac{x + 2}{x + 2} - \dfrac{x + 1}{x + 2} \cdot \dfrac{x - 2}{x - 2} - \dfrac{6 - x}{(x - 2)(x + 2)}$$
$$= \dfrac{x^2 + x - 2}{(x - 2)(x + 2)} - \dfrac{x^2 - x - 2}{(x - 2)(x + 2)} - \dfrac{6 - x}{(x - 2)(x + 2)}$$
$$= \dfrac{x^2 + x - 2 - x^2 + x + 2 - 6 + x}{(x - 2)(x + 2)}$$
$$= \dfrac{3x - 6}{(x - 2)(x + 2)}$$
$$= \dfrac{3(x - 2)}{(x - 2)(x + 2)} = \dfrac{x - 2}{x - 2} \cdot \dfrac{3}{x + 2}$$
$$= \dfrac{3}{x + 2}$$

7. None **8.** 3, 8 **9.** $\dfrac{7}{2}$ **10.** $\dfrac{x - 1}{x - 3}$ **11.** $\dfrac{2(y + 4)}{y - 1}$

12. -1 **13.** $\dfrac{1}{-x + 3}$, or $\dfrac{1}{3 - x}$ **14.** $10x^3(x - 10)^2(x + 10)$

15. $\dfrac{a + 1}{a - 3}$ **16.** $\dfrac{y}{(y - 2)(y - 3)}$ **17.** $x + 11$ **18.** $\dfrac{1}{x - y}$

19. $\dfrac{a^2 + 5ab - b^2}{a^2b^2}$ **20.** $\dfrac{2(3x^2 - 4x + 6)}{x(x + 2)(x - 2)}$ **21.** E **22.** A

23. D **24.** B **25.** F **26.** C **27.** If the numbers have a common factor, then their product contains that factor more than the greatest number of times it occurs in any one factorization. In this case, their product is not their least common multiple. **28.** Yes; consider the product $\dfrac{a}{b} \cdot \dfrac{c}{d} = \dfrac{ac}{bd}$. The reciprocal of the product is $\dfrac{bd}{ac}$. This is equal to the product of the reciprocals of the two original factors: $\dfrac{bd}{ac} = \dfrac{b}{a} \cdot \dfrac{d}{c}$.

29. Although multiplying the denominators of the expressions being added results in a common denominator, it is often not the *least* common denominator. Using a common denominator other than the LCD makes the expressions more complicated, requires additional simplification after the addition has been performed, and leaves more room for error.

30. Their sum is 0. Another explanation is that $-\left(\dfrac{1}{3 - x}\right) = \dfrac{1}{-(3 - x)} = \dfrac{1}{x - 3}$.

31. $\dfrac{x + 3}{x - 5}$ is undefined for $x = 5$, $\dfrac{x - 7}{x + 1}$ is undefined for $x = -1$, and $\dfrac{x + 1}{x - 7}$ (the reciprocal of $\dfrac{x - 7}{x + 1}$) is undefined for $x = 7$.

32. The binomial is a factor of the trinomial.

Calculator Corner, p. 946

1.–2. Left to the student

Study Tips, p. 947

1. Rational expression **2.** Solutions **3.** Rational expression **4.** Rational expression **5.** Rational expression **6.** Solutions **7.** Rational expression **8.** Solutions **9.** Solutions **10.** Solutions **11.** Rational expression **12.** Solutions **13.** Rational expression

Exercise Set 12.6, p. 948

1. $\dfrac{6}{5}$ **3.** $\dfrac{40}{29}$ **5.** $\dfrac{47}{2}$ **7.** -6 **9.** $\dfrac{24}{7}$ **11.** $-4, -1$
13. $-4, 4$ **15.** 3 **17.** $\dfrac{14}{3}$ **19.** 5 **21.** 5 **23.** $\dfrac{5}{2}$ **25.** -2
27. $-\dfrac{13}{2}$ **29.** $\dfrac{17}{2}$ **31.** No solution **33.** -5 **35.** $\dfrac{5}{3}$
37. $\dfrac{1}{2}$ **39.** No solution **41.** No solution **43.** 4
45. No solution **47.** $-2, 2$ **49.** 7 **51.** Quotient
52. Product **53.** Reciprocals **54.** Factoring
55. Greatest **56.** Not **57.** Subtract **58.** Additive
inverses **59.** $-\dfrac{1}{6}$ **61.** Left to the student

Translating for Success, p. 960

1. K **2.** E **3.** C **4.** N **5.** D **6.** O **7.** F **8.** H
9. B **10.** A

Exercise Set 12.7, p. 961

1. $2\dfrac{2}{9}$ hr **3.** $25\dfrac{5}{7}$ min **5.** $3\dfrac{15}{16}$ hr **7.** $22\dfrac{2}{9}$ min **9.** $3\dfrac{3}{4}$ min
11. Sarah: 30 km/h; Rick: 70 km/h **13.** Passenger: 80 mph;
freight: 66 mph **15.** 20 mph **17.** Hank: 14 km/h;
Kelly: 19 km/h **19.** Ralph: 5 km/h; Bonnie: 8 km/h **21.** 3 hr
23. $\dfrac{10}{3}$ students/teacher **25.** 2.3 km/h **27.** 66 g **29.** 1.92 g
31. 1.75 lb **33.** $1\dfrac{11}{39}$ kg **35.** **(a)** 0.269; **(b)** 168 hits;
(c) 188 hits **37.** 22 in.; 55.8 cm **39.** $7\dfrac{1}{4}$; 57.9 cm
41. $7\dfrac{1}{2}$; $23\dfrac{3}{5}$ in. **43.** 287 trout **45.** 200 duds
47. **(a)** 4.8 tons; **(b)** 48 lb **49.** $\dfrac{21}{2}$ **51.** $\dfrac{8}{3}$ **53.** $\dfrac{35}{3}$
55. 15 ft **57.** $y = -2x + \dfrac{7}{4}$ **58.** $y = \dfrac{2}{5}x + \dfrac{34}{5}$
59. x^{11} **60.** x **61.** $\dfrac{1}{x^{11}}$ **62.** $\dfrac{1}{x}$

63. **64.** **65.**

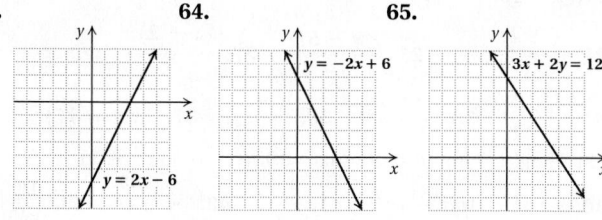

66. **67.** **68.**

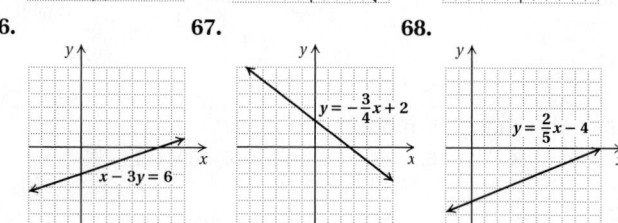

69. Ann: 6 hr; Betty: 12 hr **71.** $27\dfrac{3}{11}$ min

73. $t = \dfrac{ab}{b + a}$

Exercise Set 12.8, p. 972

1. $\dfrac{25}{4}$ **3.** $\dfrac{1}{3}$ **5.** -6 **7.** $\dfrac{1 + 3x}{1 - 5x}$ **9.** $\dfrac{2x + 1}{x}$ **11.** 8

13. $x - 8$ **15.** $\dfrac{y}{y - 1}$ **17.** $-\dfrac{1}{a}$ **19.** $\dfrac{ab}{b - a}$

21. $\dfrac{p^2 + q^2}{q + p}$ **23.** $\dfrac{2a(a + 2)}{5 - 3a^2}$ **25.** $\dfrac{15(4 - a^3)}{14a^2(9 + 2a)}$

27. $\dfrac{ac}{bd}$ **29.** 1 **31.** $\dfrac{4x + 1}{5x + 3}$ **33.** $\{x | x \leq 96\}$

34. $\left\{b | b > \dfrac{22}{9}\right\}$ **35.** $\{x | x < -3\}$ **36.** $\left\{m | m \geq \dfrac{22}{25}\right\}$

37. $4x^4 + 3x^3 + 2x - 7$ **38.** 0 **39.** $(p - 5)^2$
40. $(p + 5)^2$ **41.** $50(p^2 - 2)$ **42.** $5(p + 2)(p - 10)$
43. 14 yd   **44.** 12 ft, 5 ft   **45.** $\dfrac{(x - 1)(3x - 2)}{5x - 3}$ **47.** $\dfrac{5x + 3}{3x + 2}$

Exercise Set 12.9, p. 980

1. $y = 4x; 80$ **3.** $y = 1.6x; 32$ **5.** $y = 3.6x; 72$
7. $y = \frac{25}{3}x; \frac{500}{3}$ **9.** (a) $P = 12H$; (b) $\$420$
11. (a) $C = 11.25S$; (b) $\$101.25$ **13.** (a) $M = \frac{1}{6}E$;
(b) $18.\overline{3}$ lb; (c) 30 lb   **15.** (a) $N = 80{,}000S$;
(b) $16{,}000{,}000$ instructions/sec   **17.** $93\frac{1}{3}$ servings
19. $y = \dfrac{75}{x}; \frac{15}{2}$, or 7.5 **21.** $y = \dfrac{80}{x}; 8$ **23.** $y = \dfrac{1}{x}; \frac{1}{10}$
25. $y = \dfrac{2100}{x}; 210$ **27.** $y = \dfrac{0.06}{x}; 0.006$ **29.** (a) Direct;
(b) $69\frac{3}{8}$ players   **31.** (a) Inverse; (b) $4\frac{1}{2}$ hr
33. (a) $N = \dfrac{280}{P}$; (b) 10 gal   **35.** (a) $I = \dfrac{1920}{R}$;
(b) 32 amperes   **37.** (a) $m = \dfrac{40}{n}$; (b) 10 questions
39. 8.25 ft   **41.** $16x^2 - 2x + \frac{1}{16}$ **42.** $\frac{1}{9}x^2 - 36$
43. $x^3 - x^2 + 2x + 4$ **44.** $25x^2 + 30x + 9$
45. $\left(7x + \frac{1}{4}\right)\left(7x - \frac{1}{4}\right)$ **46.** $(13x + 1)^2$
47. $(5x - 7)(x + 3)$ **48.** $(10x - 9)^2$
49. $\frac{8}{5}$ **50.** 11 **51.** $9, 16$ **52.** $-12, -9$
53. $\frac{2}{5}, \frac{4}{7}$ **54.** $-\frac{1}{7}, \frac{3}{2}$ **55.** $\frac{1}{3}$ **56.** $\frac{47}{20}$ **57.** -1 **58.** 49
59. The y-values become larger.   **61.** $P^2 = kt$ **63.** $P = kV^3$

Summary and Review: Chapter 12, p. 985

Concept Reinforcement
1. True   **2.** False   **3.** True   **4.** True   **5.** False

Important Concepts
1. $\dfrac{x - 1}{2(x + 5)}$ **2.** $\dfrac{y + 5}{5(y + 3)}$ **3.** $\dfrac{b + 7}{b + 8}$ **4.** -1
5. $\dfrac{x^2 - 4x - 10}{(x + 2)(x + 1)(x - 1)}$ **6.** 1 **7.** $\dfrac{3(2y - 5)}{5(9 - y)}$
8. $y = 150x; y = 300$ **9.** $y = \dfrac{225}{x}; y = 22.5$

Review Exercises
1. 0 **2.** 6 **3.** $-6, 6$ **4.** $-6, 5$ **5.** -2 **6.** None
7. $\dfrac{x - 2}{x + 1}$ **8.** $\dfrac{7x + 3}{x - 3}$ **9.** $\dfrac{y - 5}{y + 5}$ **10.** $\dfrac{a - 6}{5}$
11. $\dfrac{6}{2t - 1}$ **12.** $-20t$ **13.** $\dfrac{2x(x - 1)}{x + 1}$ **14.** $30x^2y^2$
15. $4(a - 2)$ **16.** $(y - 2)(y + 2)(y + 1)$ **17.** $\dfrac{-3(x - 6)}{x + 7}$
18. -1 **19.** $\dfrac{2a}{a - 1}$ **20.** $d + c$ **21.** $\dfrac{4}{x - 4}$ **22.** $\dfrac{x + 5}{2x}$
23. $\dfrac{2x + 3}{x - 2}$ **24.** $\dfrac{-x^2 + x + 26}{(x - 5)(x + 5)(x + 1)}$ **25.** $\dfrac{2(x - 2)}{x + 2}$
26. $\dfrac{z}{1 - z}$ **27.** $c - d$ **28.** 8 **29.** $-5, 3$ **30.** $5\frac{1}{7}$ hr
31. 95 mph, 175 mph   **32.** 240 km/h, 280 km/h
33. 160 defective calculators   **34.** (a) $\frac{12}{13}$ c; (b) $4\frac{1}{5}$ c; (c) $9\frac{1}{3}$ c
35. $10{,}000$ blue whales   **36.** 6 **37.** $y = 3x; 60$
38. $y = \frac{4}{5}x; 16$ **39.** $y = \dfrac{30}{x}; 6$ **40.** $y = \dfrac{1}{x}; \frac{1}{5}$ **41.** $y = \dfrac{0.65}{x}; 0.13$
42. $\$288.75$ **43.** 1 hr   **44.** C   **45.** A   **46.** $\dfrac{5(a + 3)^2}{a}$
47. They are equivalent proportions.

Understanding Through Discussion and Writing

1. No; when we are adding, no sign changes are required so the result is the same regardless of use of parentheses. When we are subtracting, however, the sign of each term of the expression being subtracted must be changed and parentheses are needed to make sure this is done.   **2.** Graph each side of the equation and determine the number of points of intersection of the graphs.   **3.** Canceling removes a factor of 1, allowing us to rewrite $a \cdot 1$ as a.   **4.** Inverse variation; the greater the average gain per play, the smaller the number of plays required.
5. Form a rational expression that has factors of $x + 3$ and $x - 4$ in the denominator.   **6.** If we multiply both sides of a rational equation by a variable expression in order to clear fractions, it is possible that the variable expression is equal to 0. Thus an equivalent equation might not be produced.

Test: Chapter 12, p. 991
1. [12.1a] 0 **2.** [12.1a] -8 **3.** [12.1a] $-7, 7$ **4.** [12.1a] $1, 2$
5. [12.1a] 1 **6.** [12.1a] None   **7.** [12.1c] $\dfrac{3x + 7}{x + 3}$
8. [12.1d] $\dfrac{a + 5}{2}$ **9.** [12.2b] $\dfrac{(5x + 1)(x + 1)}{3x(x + 2)}$
10. [12.3a] $(y - 3)(y + 3)(y + 7)$ **11.** [12.4a] $\dfrac{23 - 3x}{x^3}$
12. [12.5a] $\dfrac{2(4 - t)}{t^2 + 1}$ **13.** [12.4a] $\dfrac{-3}{x - 3}$ **14.** [12.5a] $\dfrac{2x - 5}{x - 3}$
15. [12.4a] $\dfrac{8t - 3}{t(t - 1)}$ **16.** [12.5a] $\dfrac{-x^2 - 7x - 15}{(x + 4)(x - 4)(x + 1)}$
17. [12.5b] $\dfrac{x^2 + 2x - 7}{(x - 1)^2(x + 1)}$ **18.** [12.8a] $\dfrac{3y + 1}{y}$
19. [12.6a] 12 **20.** [12.6a] $-3, 5$ **21.** [12.9a] $y = 2x; 50$
22. [12.9a] $y = 0.5x; 12.5$ **23.** [12.9c] $y = \dfrac{18}{x}; \frac{9}{50}$
24. [12.9c] $y = \dfrac{22}{x}; \frac{11}{50}$ **25.** [12.9b] 240 km   **26.** [12.9d] $1\frac{1}{5}$ hr
27. [12.7b] 16 defective spark plugs   **28.** [12.7b] 50 zebras
29. [12.7a] 12 min   **30.** [12.7a] Craig: 65 km/h; Marilyn: 45 km/h
31. [12.7b] 15 **32.** [12.6a] D   **33.** [12.7a] Rema: 4 hr; Reggie: 10 hr
34. [12.8a] $\dfrac{3a + 2}{2a + 1}$

CHAPTER 13

Calculator Corner, p. 998
1. $(-1, 3)$ **2.** $(0, 5)$ **3.** $(2, -3)$ **4.** $(-4, 1)$ **5.** $(3, 2)$
6. $(1.4, -1.8)$

Exercise Set 13.1, p. 999
1. Yes   **3.** No   **5.** Yes   **7.** Yes   **9.** Yes   **11.** $(4, 2)$
13. $(4, 3)$ **15.** $(-3, -3)$ **17.** No solution   **19.** $(2, 2)$
21. $\left(\frac{1}{2}, 1\right)$ **23.** Infinite number of solutions   **25.** $(5, -3)$
27. $\dfrac{2x^2 - 1}{x^2(x + 1)}$ **28.** $\dfrac{-4}{x - 2}$ **29.** $\dfrac{3(3x + 4)}{(x - 4)(x + 4)}$
30. $\dfrac{2x + 5}{x + 3}$ **31.** Trinomial   **32.** Binomial   **33.** Monomial
34. None of these   **35.** $A = 2, B = 2$ **37.** $x + 2y = 2$,
$x - y = 8$ **39.–41.** Left to the student

Exercise Set 13.2, p. 1005
1. $(-2, 1)$ **3.** $(2, -4)$ **5.** $(4, 3)$ **7.** $(2, -3)$ **9.** $(1, 9)$
11. $(4, -3)$ **13.** $(2, -4)$ **15.** $\left(\frac{17}{3}, \frac{16}{3}\right)$ **17.** $(6, 3)$
19. $\left(\frac{25}{8}, -\frac{11}{4}\right)$ **21.** $(-4, 3)$ **23.** $(-3, 0)$ **25.** Length: $3\frac{1}{2}$ in.; width: $1\frac{1}{2}$ in.   **27.** Length: 365 mi; width: 275 mi

29. Length: 40 ft; width: 20 ft   **31.** Length: 110 yd; width: 60 yd   **33.** 16 and 21   **35.** 12 and 40   **37.** Length: 94 ft; width: 50 ft   **39.** 20 and 8

41. 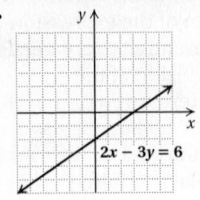   **42.**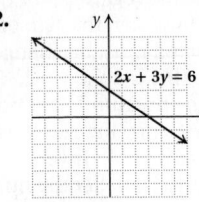

43. 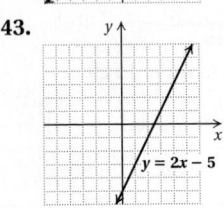   **44.**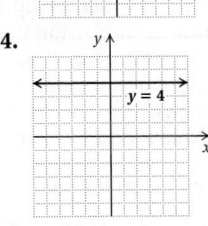

45. $(3x - 2)(2x - 3)$ **46.** $(4p + 3)(p - 1)$ **47.** Not factorable   **48.** $(3a - 5)(3a + 5)$ **49.** x^3 **50.** x^7

51. $\dfrac{1}{x^7}$ **52.** $\dfrac{b^3}{a^3}$ **53.** $(5.\overline{6}, 0.\overline{6})$ **55.** $(4.38, 4.33)$

57. Baseball: 30 yd; softball: 20 yd

Exercise Set 13.3, p. 1013

1. $(6, -1)$ **3.** $(3, 5)$ **5.** $(2, 5)$ **7.** $\left(-\tfrac{1}{2}, 3\right)$ **9.** $\left(-1, \tfrac{1}{5}\right)$
11. No solution   **13.** $(-1, -6)$ **15.** $(3, 1)$ **17.** $(8, 3)$
19. $(4, 3)$ **21.** $(1, -1)$ **23.** $(-3, -1)$ **25.** $(3, 2)$
27. $(50, 18)$ **29.** Infinite number of solutions   **31.** $(2, -1)$
33. $\left(\tfrac{231}{202}, \tfrac{117}{202}\right)$ **35.** $(-38, -22)$ **37.** Slope; y-intercepts
38. Perpendicular   **39.** Solution   **40.** Direct
41. Horizontal   **42.** Inverse   **43.** Slope–intercept
44. Graph   **45.–63.** Left to the student   **65.** $(5, 2)$
67. $(0, -1)$ **69.** $(0, 3)$ **71.** $x = \dfrac{c - b}{a - 1}, y = \dfrac{ac - b}{a - 1}$

Mid-Chapter Review: Chapter 13, p. 1016

1. False   **2.** False   **3.** True   **4.** True
5. $x + x - 3 = -1$
$\qquad 2x - 3 = -1$
$\qquad\quad 2x = -1 + 3$
$\qquad\quad 2x = 2$
$\qquad\quad\ x = 1$

$y = 1 - 3$
$y = -2$

The solution is $(1, -2)$.
6. $2x - 3y = 7$
$\quad\ \underline{x + 3y = -10}$
$\quad 3x + 0y = -3$
$\quad 3x \qquad\ = -3$
$\qquad\quad x = -1$

$-1 + 3y = -10$
$\qquad\ 3y = -9$
$\qquad\ \ y = -3$

The solution is $(-1, -3)$.
7. Yes   **8.** No   **9.** No   **10.** Yes   **11.** $(3, -2)$ **12.** $(-2, 3)$
13. Infinite number of solutions   **14.** No solution
15. $(5, -3)$ **16.** $(-2, -1)$ **17.** $\left(\tfrac{5}{3}, -\tfrac{2}{3}\right)$ **18.** $\left(\tfrac{1}{4}, \tfrac{3}{2}\right)$
19. No solution   **20.** $(0, -1)$ **21.** $(-4, 3)$ **22.** Infinite number of solutions   **23.** Length: 5 ft; width: 4 ft
24. 52 and -34 **25.** 12 and 8   **26.** We know that the first coordinate of the point of intersection is 2. We substitute 2 for x in either $y = 3x - 1$ or $y = 9 - 2x$ and find y, the second

coordinate of the point of intersection, 5. Thus the graphs intersect at $(2, 5)$.   **27.** The coordinates of the point of intersection of the graphs are not integers, so it is difficult to determine the solution from the graph.   **28.** The equations have the same coefficients of x and y but different constant terms. This means that their graphs have the same slope but different y-intercepts. Thus they have no points in common and the system of equations has no solution.   **29.** This is not the best approach, in general. If the first equation has x alone on one side, for instance, or if the second equation has a variable alone on one side, solving for y in the first equation is inefficient. This procedure could also introduce fractions in the computations unnecessarily.

Exercise Set 13.4, p. 1025

1. Adults: 90; children: 230   **3.** 4×6 prints: 30; 5×7 prints: 6
5. Two-pointers: 35; three-pointers: 5   **7.** \$50 bonds: 13; \$100 bonds: 6   **9.** Cardholders: 128; non-cardholders: 75
11. Solution A: 40 L; solution B: 60 L   **13.** Hay: 10 lb; grain: 5 lb
15. Dimes: 70; quarters: 33   **17.** Brazilian: 200 lb; Turkish: 100 lb
19. 28% fungicide: 100 L; 40% fungicide: 200 L   **21.** Large type: 4 pages; small type: 8 pages   **23.** 70% cashews: 36 lb; 45% cashews: 24 lb   **25.** Type A: 12; type B: 4; 180
27. Kuyatts': 32 yr; Marconis': 16 yr   **29.** Randy: 24; Marie: 6
31. $50°, 130°$ **33.** $28°, 62°$ **35.** 87-octane: 12 gal; 93-octane: 6 gal   **37.** Dr. Zeke's: $53\tfrac{1}{3}$ oz; Vitabrite: $26\tfrac{2}{3}$ oz
39. $(5x + 9)(5x - 9)$ **40.** $(6 + a)(6 - a)$ **41.** $4(x^2 + 25)$
42. $4(x + 5)(x - 5)$

43. 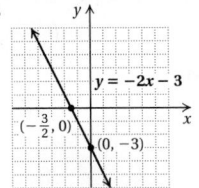   **44.**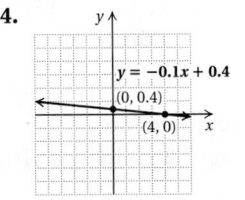

45. 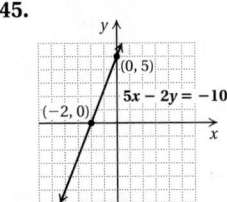   **46.**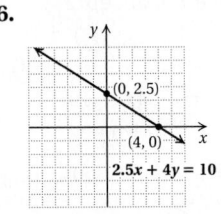

47. $\dfrac{x - 3}{x + 2}$ **48.** $\dfrac{x + 5}{x - 5}$ **49.** $\dfrac{-x^2 - 7x + 23}{(x + 3)(x - 4)}$
50. $\dfrac{-2(x - 5)}{(x + 1)(x - 1)}$ **51.** 43.75 L   **53.** $4\tfrac{4}{7}$ L   **55.** 54

Translating for Success, p. 1035

1. C   **2.** A   **3.** G   **4.** E   **5.** J   **6.** I   **7.** B   **8.** L
9. O   **10.** F

Exercise Set 13.5, p. 1036

1.

Speed	Time
30	t
46	t

4.5 hr

3.

Speed	Time	
72	$t + 3$	→ $d = 72(t + 3)$
120	t	→ $d = 120t$

$4\tfrac{1}{2}$ hr

5.

Speed	Time	
$r+6$	4	$\rightarrow d = (r+6)4$
$r-6$	10	$\rightarrow d = (r-6)10$

14 km/h

7. 384 km   **9. (a)** 24 mph; **(b)** 90 mi   **11.** $1\frac{23}{43}$ min after the toddler starts running, or $\frac{23}{43}$ min after the mother starts running

13. 15 mi   **15.** $\dfrac{x}{3}$ **16.** $\dfrac{x^5y^3}{2}$ **17.** $\dfrac{a+3}{2}$ **18.** $\dfrac{x-2}{4}$

19. 2   **20.** $\dfrac{1}{x^2+1}$ **21.** $\dfrac{x+2}{x+3}$ **22.** $\dfrac{3(x+4)}{x-1}$ **23.** $\dfrac{x+3}{x+2}$

24. $\dfrac{x^2+25}{x^2-25}$ **25.** $\dfrac{x+2}{x-1}$ **26.** $\dfrac{x^2+2}{2x^2+1}$ **27.** Approximately 3603 mi   **29.** $5\frac{1}{3}$ mi

Summary and Review: Chapter 13, p. 1038

Concept Reinforcement
1. False   **2.** True   **3.** True   **4.** False

Important Concepts
1. Yes   **2.** $(4,-2)$ **3.** $(-2,1)$ **4.** $(4,-3)$

Review Exercises
1. No   **2.** Yes   **3.** Yes   **4.** No   **5.** $(5,-2)$ **6.** Infinite number of solutions   **7.** No solution   **8.** $(0,5)$ **9.** $(-3,9)$
10. $(3,-1)$ **11.** $(1,4)$ **12.** $(-2,4)$ **13.** $(1,-2)$
14. $(3,1)$ **15.** $(1,4)$ **16.** No solution   **17.** $(-2,4)$
18. $(-2,-6)$ **19.** $(3,2)$ **20.** $(2,-4)$ **21.** Infinite number of solutions   **22.** $(-4,1)$ **23.** Length: 37.5 cm; width: 10.5 cm
24. Orchestra: 297; balcony: 211   **25.** 40 L of each
26. Asian: 4800 kg; African: 7200 kg   **27.** Peanuts: 8 lb; fancy nuts: 5 lb   **28.** 87-octane: 2.5 gal; 95-octane: 7.5 gal   **29.** Jeff: 39; his son: 13   **30.** $32°, 58°$ **31.** $77°, 103°$ **32.** 135 km/h
33. 412.5 mi   **34.** D   **35.** A   **36.** $C=1, D=3$
37. $(2,0)$ **38.** $960   **39.** $y=-x+5, y=\frac{2}{3}x$
40. $x+y=4, x+y=-3$ **41.** Rabbits: 12; pheasants: 23

Understanding Through Discussion and Writing
1. The second equation can be obtained by multiplying both sides of the first equation by -2. Thus the equations have the same graph, so the system of equations has an infinite number of solutions.   **2.** The multiplication principle might be used to obtain a pair of terms that are opposites. The addition principle is used to eliminate a variable. Once a variable has been eliminated, the multiplication and addition principles are also used to solve for the remaining variable and, after a substitution, are used again to find the variable that was eliminated   **3.** Answers will vary.   **4.** A chart allows us to see the given information and the missing information clearly and to see the relationships that yield equations.

Test: Chapter 13, p. 1043
1. [13.1a] No   **2.** [13.1b]

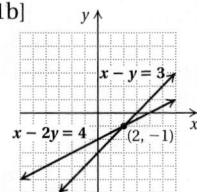

3. [13.2a] $(8,-2)$ **4.** [13.2b] $(-1,3)$ **5.** [13.2a] $(1,3)$
6. [13.3a] $(1,-5)$ **7.** [13.3b] No solution   **8.** [13.3b] $\left(\frac{1}{2}, -\frac{2}{3}\right)$
9. [13.3b] $(5,1)$ **10.** [13.2c] Length: 2108.5 yd; width: 2024.5 yd
11. [13.4a] Solution A: 40 L; solution B: 20 L   **12.** [13.5a] 40 km/h

13. [13.2c] Concessions: $2850; rides: $1425
14. [13.2c] Hay: 415 acres; oats: 235 acres   **15.** [13.2c] $45°, 135°$
16. [13.4a] 87-octane: 4 gal; 93-octane: 8 gal   **17.** [13.4a] 20 min
18. [13.5a] 11 hr   **19.** [13.1b], [13.2b], [13.3b] D
20. [13.1a] $C=-\frac{19}{2}; D=\frac{14}{3}$ **21.** [13.4a] 5 people
22. [9.4c], [13.1b] $y=\frac{1}{5}x+\frac{17}{5}, y=-\frac{3}{5}x+\frac{9}{5}$
23. [9.4c], [13.1b] $x=3, y=-2$

CHAPTER 14

Calculator Corner, p. 1047
1. 6.557   **2.** 10.050   **3.** 102.308   **4.** 0.632   **5.** -96.985
6. -0.804

Exercise Set 14.1, p. 1051
1. $2, -2$ **3.** $3, -3$ **5.** $10, -10$ **7.** $13, -13$ **9.** $16, -16$
11. 2   **13.** -3 **15.** -6 **17.** -15 **19.** 19   **21.** 2.236
23. 20.785   **25.** -18.647 **27.** 2.779   **29.** -168.375
31. (a) About 3029 GPM; **(b)** about 4601 GPM   **33.** 0.977 sec
35. 0.888 sec   **37.** 200   **39.** x **41.** t^2+1 **43.** $\dfrac{3}{x+2}$
45. No   **47.** Yes   **49.** No   **51.** c **53.** $3x$ **55.** $8p$
57. ab **59.** $34d$ **61.** $x+3$ **63.** $a-5$ **65.** $2a-5$
67. $11y-9$ **69.** $61°, 119°$ **70.** $38°, 52°$ **71.** $10,660
72. $\dfrac{1}{x+3}$ **73.** 1   **74.** $\dfrac{(x+2)(x-2)}{(x+1)(x-1)}$ **75.** 1.7, 2.2, 2.6
77. $16, -16$ **79.** $7, -7$

Calculator Corner, p. 1057
1. False   **2.** False   **3.** False   **4.** True

Exercise Set 14.2, p. 1058
1. $2\sqrt{3}$ **3.** $5\sqrt{3}$ **5.** $2\sqrt{5}$ **7.** $10\sqrt{6}$ **9.** $9\sqrt{6}$
11. $3\sqrt{x}$ **13.** $4\sqrt{3x}$ **15.** $4\sqrt{a}$ **17.** $8y$ **19.** $x\sqrt{13}$
21. $2t\sqrt{2}$ **23.** $6\sqrt{5}$ **25.** $12\sqrt{2y}$ **27.** $2x\sqrt{7}$
29. $x-3$ **31.** $\sqrt{2}(2x+1)$, or $(2x+1)\sqrt{2}$
33. $\sqrt{y}(6+y)$, or $(6+y)\sqrt{y}$ **35.** t^3 **37.** x^6
39. $x^2\sqrt{x}$ **41.** $t^9\sqrt{t}$ **43.** $(y-2)^4$ **45.** $2(x+5)^5$
47. $6m\sqrt{m}$ **49.** $2a^2\sqrt{2a}$ **51.** $2p^8\sqrt{26p}$ **53.** $8x^3y\sqrt{7y}$
55. $3\sqrt{6}$ **57.** $3\sqrt{10}$ **59.** $6\sqrt{7x}$ **61.** $6\sqrt{xy}$
63. 13   **65.** $5b\sqrt{3}$ **67.** $2t$ **69.** $a\sqrt{bc}$ **71.** $2xy\sqrt{2xy}$
73. 18   **75.** $\sqrt{10x-5}$ **77.** $x+2$ **79.** $6xy^3\sqrt{3xy}$
81. $10x^2y^3\sqrt{5xy}$ **83.** $33p^4q^2\sqrt{2pq}$ **85.** $16a^3b^3c^5\sqrt{3abc}$
87. $(-2,4)$ **88.** $\left(\frac{1}{8}, \frac{9}{8}\right)$ **89.** $(2,1)$ **90.** $(10,3)$
91. 10 mph   **92.** 360 ft^2 **93.** 211 adults and 171 children
94. 30% insecticide: 80 L; 50% insecticide: 120 L
95. $\sqrt{5}\sqrt{x-1}$ **97.** $\sqrt{x+6}\sqrt{x-6}$ **99.** $x\sqrt{x-2}$
101. 0.5   **103.** 2   **105.** $6(x-2)^2\sqrt{10}$ **107.** $2^{54}x^{158}\sqrt{2x}$
109. $a^2-5\sqrt{a}$

Exercise Set 14.3, p. 1065
1. 3   **3.** 6   **5.** $\sqrt{5}$ **7.** $\frac{1}{5}$ **9.** $\frac{2}{5}$ **11.** 2   **13.** $3y$ **15.** $\frac{4}{7}$
17. $\frac{1}{6}$ **19.** $-\frac{4}{9}$ **21.** $\frac{8}{17}$ **23.** $\frac{13}{14}$ **25.** $\dfrac{5}{x}$ **27.** $\dfrac{3a}{25}$
29. $\dfrac{5}{y^5}$ **31.** $\dfrac{x^9}{7}$ **33.** $\dfrac{\sqrt{10}}{5}$ **35.** $\dfrac{\sqrt{14}}{4}$ **37.** $\dfrac{\sqrt{3}}{6}$
39. $\dfrac{\sqrt{10}}{6}$ **41.** $\dfrac{3\sqrt{5}}{5}$ **43.** $\dfrac{2\sqrt{6}}{3}$ **45.** $\dfrac{\sqrt{3x}}{x}$ **47.** $\dfrac{\sqrt{xy}}{y}$
49. $\dfrac{x\sqrt{5}}{10}$ **51.** $\dfrac{\sqrt{3}}{3}$ **53.** $\dfrac{3\sqrt{2}}{4}$ **55.** $\dfrac{\sqrt{55}}{5}$ **57.** $\sqrt{2}$
59. $\dfrac{\sqrt{55}}{11}$ **61.** $\dfrac{\sqrt{21}}{6}$ **63.** $\dfrac{\sqrt{6}}{2}$ **65.** 5   **67.** $\dfrac{\sqrt{3x}}{x}$
69. $\dfrac{4y\sqrt{5}}{5}$ **71.** $\dfrac{a\sqrt{2a}}{4}$ **73.** $\dfrac{\sqrt{42x}}{3x}$ **75.** $\dfrac{3\sqrt{6}}{8c}$

77. $\dfrac{y\sqrt{xy}}{x}$ **79.** $\dfrac{3n\sqrt{10}}{8}$ **81.** $(4, 2)$ **82.** $(10, 30)$
83. No solution   **84.** Infinite number of solutions
85. $\left(-\frac{5}{2}, -\frac{9}{2}\right)$ **86.** $\left(\frac{26}{23}, \frac{44}{23}\right)$ **87.** $\dfrac{(x+7)^2}{x-7}$
88. $\dfrac{(x-2)(x-5)}{(x-3)(x-4)}$ **89.** $\dfrac{a-5}{2}$ **90.** $\dfrac{x-3}{x-2}$ **91.** $9x^2 - 49$
92. $16a^2 - 25b^2$ **93.** 1.57 sec; 3.14 sec; 1.01 sec   **95.** $\dfrac{\sqrt{5}}{40}$
97. $\dfrac{\sqrt{3xy}}{ax^2}$ **99.** $\dfrac{y-x}{xy}$

Mid-Chapter Review: Chapter 14, p. 1069

1. True   **2.** False   **3.** False   **4.** True
5. $\sqrt{3x^2 - 48x + 192} = \sqrt{3(x^2 - 16x + 64)}$
$\qquad\qquad = \sqrt{3(x-8)^2}$
$\qquad\qquad = \sqrt{3}\sqrt{(x-8)^2}$
$\qquad\qquad = \sqrt{3}(x-8)$

6. $\sqrt{30}\sqrt{40y} = \sqrt{30 \cdot 40y}$
$\qquad\qquad = \sqrt{1200y}$
$\qquad\qquad = \sqrt{100 \cdot 12 \cdot y}$
$\qquad\qquad = \sqrt{100 \cdot 4 \cdot 3 \cdot y}$
$\qquad\qquad = \sqrt{100}\sqrt{4}\sqrt{3y}$
$\qquad\qquad = 10 \cdot 2\sqrt{3y}$
$\qquad\qquad = 20\sqrt{3y}$

7. $\sqrt{18ab^2}\sqrt{14a^2b^4} = \sqrt{18ab^2 \cdot 14a^2b^4}$
$\qquad\qquad = \sqrt{2 \cdot 3 \cdot 3 \cdot 2 \cdot 7 \cdot a^3 \cdot b^6}$
$\qquad\qquad = \sqrt{2^2 \cdot 3^2 \cdot 7 \cdot a^2 \cdot a \cdot b^6}$
$\qquad\qquad = \sqrt{2^2}\sqrt{3^2}\sqrt{a^2}\sqrt{b^6}\sqrt{7a}$
$\qquad\qquad = 2 \cdot 3 \cdot a \cdot b^3\sqrt{7a}$
$\qquad\qquad = 6ab^3\sqrt{7a}$

8. $\sqrt{\dfrac{3y^2}{44}} = \sqrt{\dfrac{3y^2}{2 \cdot 2 \cdot 11}} = \sqrt{\dfrac{3y^2}{2 \cdot 2 \cdot 11} \cdot \dfrac{11}{11}}$
$\qquad = \sqrt{\dfrac{33y^2}{2^2 \cdot 11^2}} = \dfrac{y\sqrt{33}}{2 \cdot 11} = \dfrac{y\sqrt{33}}{22}$

9. $-11, 11$ **10.** $\dfrac{x-3}{7}$ **11. (a)** No; **(b)** yes   **12.** $8r^3s^3\sqrt{2r}$
13. $5(x-3)$ **14.** $\frac{1}{10}$ **15.** -6 **16.** $-\frac{25}{7}$ **17.** 15
22. $4q^5\sqrt{2q}$ **18.** $10y$ **19.** $2x - 1$ **20.** $20\sqrt{2x}$ **21.** $\frac{1}{4}$
23. $\dfrac{9}{z}$ **24.** 25 **25.** $\frac{3}{7}$ **26.** 8 **27.** $10c^2d^5\sqrt{6c}$
28. $12x^3y^5z\sqrt{10yz}$ **29.** $2\sqrt{15xy}$ **30.** $7a\sqrt{15}$ **31.** $\dfrac{y^{12}}{5}$

32.

$\dfrac{x}{\sqrt{3}}$	$\dfrac{3\sqrt{x}}{x}$
$\sqrt{\dfrac{3}{x}}$	$\dfrac{\sqrt{3x}}{3}$
$\dfrac{3}{\sqrt{x}}$	$\dfrac{x\sqrt{3}}{3}$
$\dfrac{3x}{\sqrt{3}}$	$\sqrt{3}$
$\dfrac{3}{\sqrt{3}}$	$\dfrac{\sqrt{3x}}{x}$
$\sqrt{\dfrac{x}{3}}$	$x\sqrt{3}$

33. The square root of 100 is the principal, or positive, square root, which is 10. **A** square root of 100 could refer to either the positive square root or the negative square root, 10 or -10.
34. It is incorrect to take the square roots of the terms in the numerator individually—that is, $\sqrt{a+b}$ and $\sqrt{a} + \sqrt{b}$ are not equivalent. The following is correct:
$$\sqrt{\dfrac{9 + 100}{25}} = \dfrac{\sqrt{9+100}}{\sqrt{25}} = \dfrac{\sqrt{109}}{5}.$$
35. In general, $\sqrt{a^2 - b^2} \neq \sqrt{a^2} - \sqrt{b^2}$. In this case, let $x = 13$. Then $\sqrt{x^2 - 25} = \sqrt{13^2 - 25} = \sqrt{169 - 25} = \sqrt{144} = 12$, but $\sqrt{x^2} - \sqrt{25} = \sqrt{13^2} - \sqrt{25} = 13 - 5 = 8$.
36. (1) If necessary, rewrite the expression as $\sqrt{a}/\sqrt{b}$.
(2) Simplify the numerator and the denominator, if possible, by taking the square roots of perfect square factors.   **(3)** Multiply by a form of 1 that produces an expression without a radical in the numerator.

Exercise Set 14.4, p. 1075

1. $16\sqrt{3}$ **3.** $4\sqrt{5}$ **5.** $13\sqrt{x}$ **7.** $-9\sqrt{d}$
9. $25\sqrt{2}$ **11.** $\sqrt{3}$ **13.** $\sqrt{5}$ **15.** $13\sqrt{2}$ **17.** $3\sqrt{3}$
19. $2\sqrt{2}$ **21.** 0 **23.** $(2 + 9x)\sqrt{x}$, or $\sqrt{x}(2 + 9x)$
25. $(3 - 2x)\sqrt{3}$ **27.** $3\sqrt{2x+2}$ **29.** $(x+3)\sqrt{x^3 - 1}$
31. $(4a^2 + a^2b - 5b)\sqrt{b}$ **33.** $\frac{2}{3}\sqrt{3}$, or $\dfrac{2\sqrt{3}}{3}$
35. $\frac{13}{2}\sqrt{2}$, or $\dfrac{13\sqrt{2}}{2}$ **37.** $\frac{1}{6}\sqrt{6}$, or $\dfrac{\sqrt{6}}{6}$ **39.** $\sqrt{15} - \sqrt{3}$
41. $10 + 5\sqrt{3} - 2\sqrt{7} - \sqrt{21}$ **43.** $9 - 4\sqrt{5}$ **45.** -62
47. 1 **49.** $13 + \sqrt{5}$ **51.** $x - 2\sqrt{xy} + y$ **53.** $-\sqrt{3} - \sqrt{5}$
55. $5 - 2\sqrt{6}$ **57.** $\dfrac{4\sqrt{10} - 4}{9}$ **59.** $5 - 2\sqrt{7}$
61. $\dfrac{12 - 3\sqrt{x}}{16 - x}$ **63.** $\dfrac{24 + 3\sqrt{x} + 8\sqrt{2} + \sqrt{2x}}{64 - x}$
65. $\dfrac{2\sqrt{a} - a - 1}{1 - a}$ **67.** $\dfrac{4\sqrt{a} + 4\sqrt{t} + \sqrt{3a} + \sqrt{3t}}{a - t}$ **69.** $\frac{5}{11}$
70. $-\frac{38}{13}$ **71.** $-1, 6$ **72.** $2, 5$ **73.** $\dfrac{x^6}{3}$ **74.** $\dfrac{x-3}{4(x+3)}$
75. $14{,}270$ ft   **76.** $-9, -2, -5, -17, -0.678375$ **77.** $\sqrt{13}, 5$
79. Not correct   **81.** $\dfrac{-4\sqrt{6}}{5}$
83. True; $(3\sqrt{x+2})^2 = (3\sqrt{x+2})(3\sqrt{x+2}) = (3 \cdot 3)(\sqrt{x+2} \cdot \sqrt{x+2}) = 9(x+2)$

Calculator Corner, p. 1081

1. Left to the student   **2.** Left to the student

Exercise Set 14.5, p. 1083

1. 36 **3.** 18.49 **5.** 165 **7.** $\frac{621}{2}$ **9.** 5 **11.** 3 **13.** $\frac{17}{4}$
15. No solution   **17.** No solution   **19.** 9 **21.** 12
23. $1, 5$ **25.** 3 **27.** 5 **29.** No solution   **31.** $-\frac{10}{3}$ **33.** 3
35. No solution   **37.** 9 **39.** 1 **41.** 8 **43.** 256
45. About 232 mi   **47.** $16{,}200$ ft   **49.** 211.25 ft; 281.25 ft
51. Slope; y-intercepts   **52.** Square root   **53.** Principal square root   **54.** Positive; direct   **55.** Quotient
56. Positive; inverse   **57.** Quotient   **58.** Product
59. $-2, 2$ **61.** $-\frac{57}{16}$ **63.** 13 **65.** Left to the student
67. Left to the student

Translating for Success, p. 1090

1. J   **2.** K   **3.** N   **4.** H   **5.** G   **6.** E   **7.** O   **8.** D
9. B   **10.** C

Exercise Set 14.6, p. 1091

1. 17 **3.** $\sqrt{32} \approx 5.657$ **5.** 12 **7.** 4 **9.** 26
11. 12 **13.** 2 **15.** $\sqrt{2} \approx 1.414$ **17.** 5 **19.** 3

21. $\sqrt{1850}$ yd ≈ 43.012 yd **23.** About 21.2 ft
25. $\sqrt{75}$ m ≈ 8.660 m **27.** $\sqrt{26,900}$ yd ≈ 164.012 yd
29. $\left(-\frac{3}{2}, -\frac{1}{16}\right)$ **30.** $\left(\frac{8}{5}, 9\right)$ **31.** $\left(-\frac{9}{19}, \frac{91}{38}\right)$ **32.** $(-10, 1)$
33. $-\frac{1}{3}$ **34.** $\frac{5}{8}$ **35.** $12 - 2\sqrt{6} \approx 7.101$

Summary and Review: Chapter 14, p. 1093

Concept Reinforcement
1. True **2.** True **3.** True **4.** False

Important Concepts
1. $y^2 - 3$ **2.** (a) Yes; (b) no **3.** $20y\sqrt{3}$
4. $5a^6b^4\sqrt{7b}$ **5.** $4x^3y^2\sqrt{6x}$ **6.** $b\sqrt{3b}$ **7.** $\frac{5}{9}$
8. $\frac{a\sqrt{2}}{5}$ **9.** $(x + 6)\sqrt{x - 1}$ **10.** $9 + \sqrt{26}$
11. $\frac{47 - 14\sqrt{2}}{79}$ **12.** 6 **13.** 9, 81 **14.** $a = \sqrt{657} \approx 25.632$

Review Exercises
1. $8, -8$ **2.** $20, -20$ **3.** 6 **4.** -13 **5.** 1.732
6. 9.950 **7.** -17.892 **8.** 0.742 **9.** -2.055
10. 394.648 **11.** $x^2 + 4$ **12.** x **13.** $4 - x$
14. $\frac{2}{y - 7}$ **15.** Yes **16.** No **17.** No **18.** Yes
19. m **20.** $x - 4$ **21.** $4x$ **22.** $2p - 3$ **23.** $4\sqrt{3}$
24. $4t\sqrt{2}$ **25.** $t - 7$ **26.** $x + 8$ **27.** x^4 **28.** $5a^3\sqrt{3a}$
29. $\sqrt{21}$ **30.** $\sqrt{x^2 - 9}$ **31.** $2\sqrt{15}$ **32.** $2x\sqrt{10}$
33. $5xy\sqrt{2}$ **34.** $10a^2b\sqrt{ab}$ **35.** $\frac{5}{8}$ **36.** $\frac{7}{t}$ **37.** $\frac{c^4}{4}$
38. $\frac{\sqrt{2}}{2}$ **39.** $\frac{x\sqrt{15x}}{15}$ **40.** $\frac{\sqrt{5y}}{y}$ **41.** $\frac{b^3\sqrt{ab}}{a}$
42. $\frac{\sqrt{15}}{5}$ **43.** $\frac{x\sqrt{30}}{6}$ **44.** $13\sqrt{5}$ **45.** $\sqrt{5}$
46. $\frac{1}{2}\sqrt{2}$, or $\frac{\sqrt{2}}{2}$ **47.** $7 + 4\sqrt{3}$ **48.** 1 **49.** $8 - 4\sqrt{3}$
50. 52 **51.** No solution **52.** 0, 3 **53.** 9
54. (a) About 63 mph; (b) 405 ft **55.** 20
56. $\sqrt{3} \approx 1.732$ **57.** $\sqrt{2,600,000,000}$ ft $\approx 50,990$ ft
58. 9 ft **59.** B **60.** C **61.** $\sqrt{1525}$ mi ≈ 39.051 mi
62. $b = \pm\sqrt{A^2 - a^2}$ **63.** 6

Understanding Through Discussion and Writing
1. It is necessary for the signs to differ to ensure that the product of the conjugates will be free of radicals.
2. Since $\sqrt{11 - 2x}$ cannot be negative, the statement $\sqrt{11 - 2x} = -3$ cannot be true for any value of x, including 1.
3. We often use the rules for manipulating exponents "in reverse" when simplifying radical expressions. For example, we might write x^5 as $x^4 \cdot x$ or y^6 as $(y^3)^2$. **4.** No; consider the clapboard's height above ground level to be one leg of a right triangle. Then the length of the ladder is the hypotenuse of that triangle. Since the length of the hypotenuse must be greater than the length of a leg, a 28-ft ladder cannot be used to repair a clapboard that is 28 ft above ground level. **5.** The square of a number is equal to the square of its opposite. Thus, while squaring both sides of a radical equation allows us to find the solutions of the original equation, this procedure can also introduce numbers that are not solutions of the original equation. **6.** (a) $\sqrt{5x^2} = \sqrt{5}\sqrt{x^2} = \sqrt{5} \cdot |x| = |x|\sqrt{5}$. The given statement is correct.
(b) Let $b = 3$. Then $\sqrt{b^2 - 4} = \sqrt{3^2 - 4} = \sqrt{9 - 4} = \sqrt{5}$, but $b - 2 = 3 - 2 = 1$. The given statement is false.
(c) Let $x = 3$. Then $\sqrt{x^2 + 16} = \sqrt{3^2 + 16} = \sqrt{9 + 16} = \sqrt{25} = 5$, but $x + 4 = 3 + 4 = 7$. The given statement is false.

Test: Chapter 14, p. 1099
1. [14.1a] $9, -9$ **2.** [14.1a] 8 **3.** [14.1a] -5 **4.** [14.1b] 10.770
5. [14.1b] -9.349 **6.** [14.1b] 21.909 **7.** [14.1d] $4 - y^3$
8. [14.1e] Yes **9.** [14.1e] No **10.** [14.1f] a **11.** [14.1f] $6y$
12. [14.2c] $\sqrt{30}$ **13.** [14.2c] $\sqrt{x^2 - 64}$ **14.** [14.2a] $3\sqrt{3}$
15. [14.2a] $5\sqrt{x - 1}$ **16.** [14.2b] $t^2\sqrt{t}$ **17.** [14.2c] $5\sqrt{2}$
18. [14.2c] $3ab^2\sqrt{2}$ **19.** [14.3b] $\frac{3}{2}$ **20.** [14.3b] $\frac{12}{a}$
21. [14.3c] $\frac{\sqrt{10}}{5}$ **22.** [14.3c] $\frac{\sqrt{2xy}}{y}$ **23.** [14.3a, c] $\frac{3\sqrt{6}}{8}$
24. [14.3a] $\frac{\sqrt{7}}{4y}$ **25.** [14.4a] $-6\sqrt{2}$ **26.** [14.4a] $\frac{6}{5}\sqrt{5}$, or $\frac{6\sqrt{5}}{5}$
27. [14.4b] $21 - 8\sqrt{5}$ **28.** [14.4b] 11 **29.** [14.4c] $\frac{40 + 10\sqrt{5}}{11}$
30. [14.6a] $\sqrt{80} \approx 8.944$ **31.** [14.5a] 48 **32.** [14.5a] $-2, 2$
33. [14.5b] -3 **34.** [14.5c] (a) About 237 mi; (b) 34,060.5 ft
35. [14.6b] $\sqrt{15,700}$ yd ≈ 125.300 yd **36.** A **37.** [14.1a] $\sqrt{5}$
38. [14.2b] y^{8n}

CHAPTER 15

Calculator Corner, p. 1107
1. 0.6, 1 **2.** $-1.5, 5$ **3.** 3, 8 **4.** 2, 4

Exercise Set 15.1, p. 1108
1. $x^2 - 3x + 2 = 0; a = 1, b = -3, c = 2$ **3.** $7x^2 - 4x + 3 = 0$; $a = 7, b = -4, c = 3$ **5.** $2x^2 - 3x + 5 = 0; a = 2, b = -3, c = 5$
7. $0, -5$ **9.** $0, -2$ **11.** $0, \frac{2}{5}$ **13.** $0, -1$ **15.** 0, 3
17. $0, \frac{1}{5}$ **19.** $0, \frac{3}{14}$ **21.** $0, \frac{81}{2}$ **23.** $-12, 4$ **25.** $-5, -1$
27. $-9, 2$ **29.** 3, 5 **31.** -5 **33.** 4 **35.** $-\frac{2}{3}, \frac{1}{2}$
37. $-\frac{2}{3}, 4$ **39.** $-1, \frac{5}{3}$ **41.** $-5, -1$ **43.** $-2, 7$ **45.** $-5, 4$
47. 4 **49.** $-2, 1$ **51.** $-\frac{2}{5}, 10$ **53.** $-4, 6$ **55.** 1
57. 2, 5 **59.** No solution **61.** $-\frac{5}{2}, 1$ **63.** 35 diagonals
65. 7 sides **67.** 8 **68.** -13 **69.** $2\sqrt{2}$ **70.** $2\sqrt{3}$
71. $2\sqrt{5}$ **72.** $2\sqrt{22}$ **73.** $9\sqrt{5}$ **74.** $2\sqrt{255}$ **75.** 2.646
76. 4.796 **77.** 1.528 **78.** 22.908 **79.** $-\frac{1}{3}, 1$ **81.** $0, \frac{\sqrt{5}}{5}$
83. $-1.7, 4$ **85.** $-1.7, 3$ **87.** $-2, 3$ **89.** 4

Exercise Set 15.2, p. 1116
1. $11, -11$ **3.** $\sqrt{7}, -\sqrt{7}$ **5.** $\frac{\sqrt{15}}{5}, -\frac{\sqrt{15}}{5}$ **7.** $\frac{5}{2}, -\frac{5}{2}$
9. $\frac{7\sqrt{3}}{3}, -\frac{7\sqrt{3}}{3}$ **11.** $\sqrt{3}, -\sqrt{3}$ **13.** $\frac{8}{7}, -\frac{8}{7}$ **15.** $-7, 1$
17. $-3 \pm \sqrt{21}$ **19.** $-13 \pm 2\sqrt{2}$ **21.** $7 \pm 2\sqrt{3}$
23. $-9 \pm \sqrt{34}$ **25.** $\frac{-3 \pm \sqrt{14}}{2}$ **27.** $-5, 11$ **29.** $-15, 1$
31. $-2, 8$ **33.** $-21, -1$ **35.** $1 \pm \sqrt{6}$ **37.** $11 \pm \sqrt{19}$
39. $-5 \pm \sqrt{29}$ **41.** $\frac{7 \pm \sqrt{57}}{2}$ **43.** $-7, 4$ **45.** $\frac{-3 \pm \sqrt{17}}{4}$
47. $\frac{-3 \pm \sqrt{145}}{4}$ **49.** $\frac{-2 \pm \sqrt{7}}{3}$ **51.** $-\frac{1}{2}, 5$ **53.** $-\frac{5}{2}, \frac{2}{3}$
55. About 13.0 sec **57.** About 9.2 sec **59.** Product
60. Quadratic; equivalent **61.** Principal square root
62. Square root **63.** Quotient **64.** Product **65.** Quotient
66. Power; multiply **67.** $-12, 12$ **69.** $-16\sqrt{2}, 16\sqrt{2}$
71. $-2\sqrt{c}, 2\sqrt{c}$ **73.** $49.896, -49.896$ **75.** $-9, 9$

Calculator Corner, p. 1122
1. The equations $x^2 + x = -1$ and $x^2 + x + 1 = 0$ are equivalent. The graph of $y = x^2 + x + 1$ has no x-intercepts, so the equation $x^2 + x = -1$ has no real-number solutions.

Exercise Set 15.3, p. 1123

1. $-3, 7$ **3.** 3 **5.** $-\frac{4}{3}, 2$ **7.** $-\frac{5}{2}, \frac{3}{2}$ **9.** $-3, 3$

11. $1 \pm \sqrt{3}$ **13.** $5 \pm \sqrt{3}$ **15.** $-2 \pm \sqrt{7}$ **17.** $\dfrac{-4 \pm \sqrt{10}}{3}$

19. $\dfrac{5 \pm \sqrt{33}}{4}$ **21.** $\dfrac{1 \pm \sqrt{3}}{2}$ **23.** No real-number solutions

25. $\dfrac{5 \pm \sqrt{73}}{6}$ **27.** $\dfrac{3 \pm \sqrt{29}}{2}$ **29.** $-\sqrt{5}, \sqrt{5}$ **31.** $-2 \pm \sqrt{3}$

33. $\dfrac{5 \pm \sqrt{37}}{2}$ **35.** $-1.3, 5.3$ **37.** $-0.2, 6.2$ **39.** $-1.2, 0.2$

41. $0.3, 2.4$ **43.** $3\sqrt{10}$ **44.** $\sqrt{6}$ **45.** $2\sqrt{2}$
46. $(9x - 2)\sqrt{x}$ **47.** $4\sqrt{5}$ **48.** $3x^2\sqrt{3x}$ **49.** $30x^5\sqrt{10}$

50. $\dfrac{\sqrt{21}}{3}$ **51.** $y = \dfrac{141}{x}$ **52.** $3\frac{1}{3}$ hr **53.** $0, 2$

55. $\dfrac{3 \pm \sqrt{5}}{2}$ **57.** $\dfrac{-7 \pm \sqrt{61}}{2}$ **59.** $\dfrac{-2 \pm \sqrt{10}}{2}$ **61.** Yes

63.–69. Left to the student

Mid-Chapter Review: Chapter 15, p. 1125

1. True **2.** False **3.** True
4. $x^2 - 6x - 2 = 0$
$$x^2 - 6x = 2$$
$$x^2 - 6x + 9 = 2 + 9$$
$$(x - 3)^2 = 11$$
$$x - 3 = \pm\sqrt{11}$$
$$x = 3 \pm \sqrt{11}$$
5. $3x^2 = 8x - 2$
$3x^2 - 8x + 2 = 0$ Standard form
$a = 3, \quad b = -8, \quad c = 2$
We substitute for $a, b,$ and c in the quadratic formula:
$$x = \frac{-b \pm \sqrt{b^2 - 4ac}}{2a} \quad \text{Quadratic formula}$$
$$x = \frac{-(-8) \pm \sqrt{(-8)^2 - 4 \cdot 3 \cdot 2}}{2 \cdot 3} \quad \text{Substituting}$$
$$x = \frac{8 \pm \sqrt{64 - 24}}{6} = \frac{8 \pm \sqrt{40}}{6} = \frac{8 \pm \sqrt{4 \cdot 10}}{6}$$
$$x = \frac{8 \pm 2\sqrt{10}}{6} = \frac{2(4 \pm \sqrt{10})}{2 \cdot 3} = \frac{4 \pm \sqrt{10}}{3}$$
6. $a = 1; b = -5; c = 10$ **7.** $a = 1; b = 14; c = -4$
8. $a = 3; b = -17; c = 0$ **9.** $0, \frac{1}{3}$ **10.** $-2, 5$ **11.** $0, 1$
12. 7 **13.** $-2, 0$ **14.** $-\frac{4}{3}, \frac{1}{6}$ **15.** $0, 22$ **16.** $2, 3$
17. $-\frac{7}{8}, 5$ **18.** $-3, 1$ **19.** $\dfrac{9 \pm \sqrt{57}}{2}$ **20.** $\dfrac{7 \pm \sqrt{113}}{4}$

21. $8, 10$ **22.** $\dfrac{-3 \pm \sqrt{33}}{4}$ **23.** No real-number solutions

24. $-8, 8$ **25.** No real-number solutions **26.** $3 \pm \sqrt{2}$

27. $-\frac{3}{2}, \frac{1}{2}$ **28.** $\pm\sqrt{3}$ **29.** $\dfrac{1 \pm \sqrt{5}}{2}$ **30.** $-8, 12$

31. No real-number solutions **32.** $\dfrac{1 \pm \sqrt{5}}{2}$ **33.** $-5, 5$

34. $\dfrac{1 \pm \sqrt{11}}{2}$ **35.** No real-number solutions **36.** $-2.4, 3.4$

37. $-3.4, -0.1$ **38.** A **39.** B **40.** A **41.** C **42.** B
43. C **44.** B **45.** Mark does not recognize that the $\pm$ sign yields two solutions, one in which the radical is added to 3 and the other in which the radical is subtracted from 3. **46.** The addition principle should be used at the outset to get 0 on one side of the equation. Since this was not done in the given procedure, the principle of zero products was not applied correctly. **47.** The first coordinates of the x-intercepts of the graph of $y = (x - 2)(x + 3)$ are the solutions of the equation $(x - 2)(x + 3) = 0$. **48.** The quadratic formula would not be the easiest way to solve a quadratic equation when the equation can be solved by factoring or by using the principle of square roots. **49.** Answers will vary. Any equation of the form $ax^2 + bx + c = 0$, where $b^2 - 4ac < 0$, will do. Then the graph of the equation $y = ax^2 + bx + c$ will not cross the x-axis.
50. If $x = -5$ or $x = 7$, then $x + 5 = 0$ or $x - 7 = 0$. Thus the equation $(x + 5)(x - 7) = 0$, or $x^2 - 2x - 35 = 0$, has solutions -5 and 7.

Exercise Set 15.4, p. 1130

1. $I = \dfrac{VQ}{q}$ **3.** $m = \dfrac{Sd^2}{kM}$ **5.** $d^2 = \dfrac{kmM}{S}$ **7.** $W = \sqrt{\dfrac{10t}{T}}$

9. $t = \dfrac{A}{a + b}$ **11.** $x = \dfrac{y - c}{a + b}$ **13.** $a = \dfrac{bt}{b - t}$

15. $p = \dfrac{qf}{q - f}$ **17.** $b = \dfrac{2A}{h}$ **19.** $h = \dfrac{S - 2\pi r^2}{2\pi r}$, or

$h = \dfrac{S}{2\pi r} - r$ **21.** $R = \dfrac{r_1 r_2}{r_2 + r_1}$ **23.** $Q = \dfrac{P^2}{289}$

25. $E = \dfrac{mv^2}{2g}$ **27.** $r = \dfrac{1}{2}\sqrt{\dfrac{S}{\pi}}$ **29.** $A = \dfrac{-m + \sqrt{m^2 + 4kP}}{2k}$

31. $a = \sqrt{c^2 - b^2}$ **33.** $t = \dfrac{\sqrt{s}}{4}$

35. $r = \dfrac{-\pi h + \sqrt{\pi^2 h^2 + \pi A}}{\pi}$ **37.** $v = 20\sqrt{\dfrac{F}{A}}$

39. $a = \sqrt{c^2 - b^2}$ **41.** $a = \dfrac{2h\sqrt{3}}{3}$

43. $T = \dfrac{2 + \sqrt{4 - a(m - n)}}{a}$ **45.** $T = \dfrac{v^2\pi m}{8k}$

47. $x = \dfrac{d\sqrt{3}}{3}$ **49.** $n = \dfrac{1 + \sqrt{1 + 8N}}{2}$ **51.** $b = \dfrac{a}{3S - 1}$

53. $B = \dfrac{A}{QA + 1}$ **55.** $n = \dfrac{S + 360}{180}$, or $n = \dfrac{S}{180} + 2$

57. $t = \dfrac{A - P}{Pr}$ **59.** $D = \dfrac{BC}{A}$ **61.** $a = \dfrac{-b}{C - K}$, or $a = \dfrac{b}{K - C}$

63. $\sqrt{65} \approx 8.062$ **64.** $\sqrt{75} \approx 8.660$ **65.** $\sqrt{41} \approx 6.403$
66. $\sqrt{44} \approx 6.633$ **67.** $\sqrt{1084} \approx 32.924$ **68.** $\sqrt{5} \approx 2.236$
69. $\sqrt{424}$ ft ≈ 20.591 ft **70.** $\sqrt{12{,}500}$ yd ≈ 111.803 yd
71. $3x\sqrt{2}$ **72.** $8x^2\sqrt{3x}$ **73.** $3t$ **74.** $x^3\sqrt{x}$

75. (a) $r = \dfrac{C}{2\pi}$; **(b)** $A = \dfrac{C^2}{4\pi}$; **(c)** $C = 2\sqrt{A\pi}$

Translating for Success, p. 1136

1. M **2.** G **3.** F **4.** L **5.** D **6.** N **7.** J **8.** E
9. B **10.** C

Exercise Set 15.5, p. 1137

1. Length: 19 ft; width: 4 ft **3.** 16 in.; 24 in. **5.** Length: 14.8 yd; width; 4.6 yd **7.** Length: 20 cm; width: 16 cm **9.** 4.6 m; 6.6 m **11.** Length: 5.6 in.; width: 3.6 in. **13.** Length: 6.4 cm; width: 3.2 cm **15.** 3 cm **17.** 7 km/h **19.** 2 km/h **21.** 0 km/h (no wind) or 40 km/h **23.** 8 mph
25. 1 km/h **27.** $8\sqrt{2}$ **28.** $12\sqrt{10}$ **29.** $(2x - 7)\sqrt{x}$

30. $-\sqrt{6}$ **31.** $\dfrac{3\sqrt{2}}{2}$ **32.** $\dfrac{2\sqrt{3}}{3}$ **33.** $5\sqrt{6} - 4\sqrt{3}$

34. $(9x + 2)\sqrt{x}$ **35.** y-intercept: $(0, 4)$; x-intercept: $\left(\frac{1}{2}, 0\right)$
36. y-intercept: $(0, -9)$; x-intercept: $(15, 0)$
37. $12\sqrt{2}$ in. ≈ 16.97 in.; two 12-in. pizzas

Visualizing for Success, p. 1145

1. J **2.** F **3.** H **4.** G **5.** B **6.** E **7.** D **8.** I
9. C **10.** A

Exercise Set 15.6, p. 1146

1. 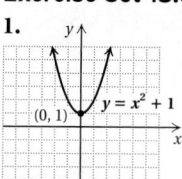 $y = x^2 + 1$ (0, 1)

3. 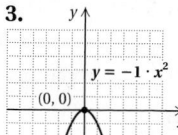 $y = -1 \cdot x^2$ (0, 0)

5. 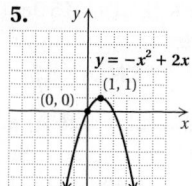 $y = -x^2 + 2x$ (1, 1) (0, 0)

7. 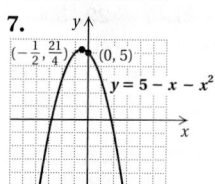 $\left(-\frac{1}{2}, \frac{21}{4}\right)$ (0, 5) $y = 5 - x - x^2$

9. 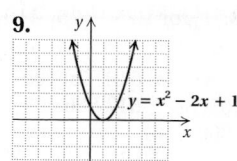 $y = x^2 - 2x + 1$

11. 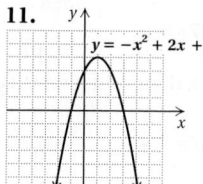 $y = -x^2 + 2x + 3$

13. 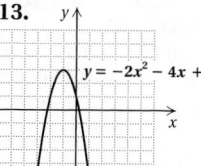 $y = -2x^2 - 4x + 1$

15. 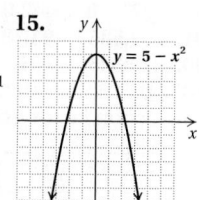 $y = 5 - x^2$

17. 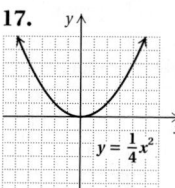 $y = \frac{1}{4}x^2$

19. 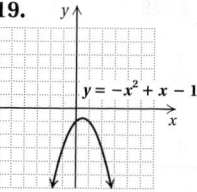 $y = -x^2 + x - 1$

21. 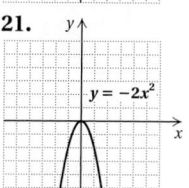 $y = -2x^2$

23. 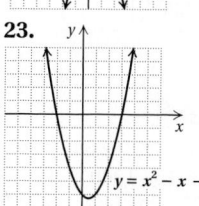 $y = x^2 - x - 6$

25. $(-\sqrt{2}, 0)$; $(\sqrt{2}, 0)$ **27.** $(-5, 0)$; $(0, 0)$ **29.** $\left(\frac{-1 - \sqrt{33}}{2}, 0\right)$; $\left(\frac{-1 + \sqrt{33}}{2}, 0\right)$ **31.** $(3, 0)$ **33.** $(-2 - \sqrt{5}, 0)$; $(-2 + \sqrt{5}, 0)$

35. None **37.** $22\sqrt{2}$ **38.** $25y^2\sqrt{y}$ **39.** $y = \frac{29.76}{x}$ **40.** 35

41. $\frac{47}{60}$ **42.** 49.55 **43. (a)** After 2 sec; after 4 sec; **(b)** after 3 sec; **(c)** after 6 sec **45.** 16; two real solutions
47. -161.91; no real solutions

Calculator Corner, p. 1152

1. -12.8 **2.** -9.2 **3.** -2 **4.** 20

Exercise Set 15.7, p. 1156

1. Yes **3.** Yes **5.** No **7.** Yes **9.** Yes **11.** Yes
13. A relation but not a function **15. (a)** 9; **(b)** 12; **(c)** 2; **(d)** 5;
(e) 7.4; **(f)** $5\frac{2}{3}$ **17. (a)** -21; **(b)** 15; **(c)** 42; **(d)** 0; **(e)** 2; **(f)** -162.6
19. (a) 7; **(b)** -17; **(c)** 24.1; **(d)** 4; **(e)** -26; **(f)** 6 **21. (a)** 0; **(b)** 5;
(c) 2; **(d)** 170; **(e)** 65; **(f)** 230 **23. (a)** 1; **(b)** 3; **(c)** 3; **(d)** 4; **(e)** 11;
(f) 23 **25. (a)** 0; **(b)** -1; **(c)** 8; **(d)** 1000; **(e)** -125; **(f)** -1000
27. (a) 159.48 cm; **(b)** 153.98 cm **29.** $1\frac{20}{33}$ atm; $1\frac{10}{11}$ atm; $4\frac{1}{33}$ atm
31. 1.792 cm; 2.8 cm; 11.2 cm

33. 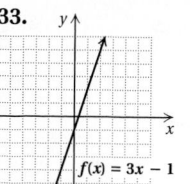 $f(x) = 3x - 1$

35. 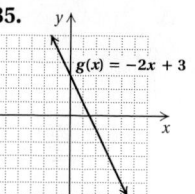 $g(x) = -2x + 3$

37. 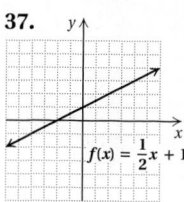 $f(x) = \frac{1}{2}x + 1$

39. 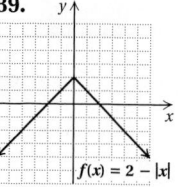 $f(x) = 2 - |x|$

41. 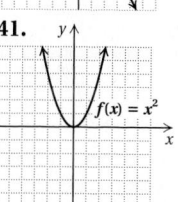 $f(x) = x^2$

43. 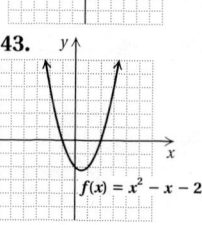 $f(x) = x^2 - x - 2$

45. Yes **47.** Yes **49.** No **51.** No **53.** About 75 per 10,000 men **55.** No **56.** Yes **57.** No solution
58. Infinite number of solutions

59. 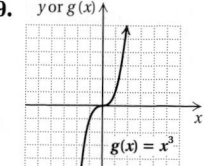 y or $g(x)$ $g(x) = x^3$

61. 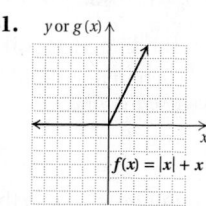 y or $g(x)$ $f(x) = |x| + x$

Summary and Review: Chapter 15, p. 1160

Concept Reinforcement

1. False **2.** True **3.** True **4.** True

Important Concepts

1. $-\frac{4}{5}, 2$ **2.** $-\frac{\sqrt{77}}{7}, \frac{\sqrt{77}}{7}$ **3.** $2 \pm \sqrt{3}$ **4.** $\frac{3 \pm \sqrt{21}}{4}$

5. 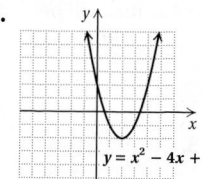 $y = x^2 - 4x + 2$ **6.** Yes

7. (a) $h(5) = 9$; **(b)** $f(0) = -4$

Review Exercises

1. $-\sqrt{3}, \sqrt{3}$ **2.** $-2\sqrt{2}, 2\sqrt{2}$ **3.** $\frac{3}{5}, 1$ **4.** $-2, \frac{1}{3}$
5. $-8 \pm \sqrt{13}$ **6.** 0 **7.** $0, \frac{7}{5}$ **8.** $1 \pm \sqrt{11}$ **9.** $\frac{1 \pm \sqrt{10}}{3}$
10. $-3 \pm 3\sqrt{2}$ **11.** $\frac{2 \pm \sqrt{3}}{2}$ **12.** $\frac{3 \pm \sqrt{33}}{2}$ **13.** No real-
number solutions **14.** $0, \frac{4}{3}$ **15.** $-5, 3$ **16.** 1 **17.** $2 \pm \sqrt{2}$
18. $-1, \frac{5}{3}$ **19.** 0.4, 4.6 **20.** $-1.9, -0.1$ **21.** $T = L(4V^2 - 1)$
22. 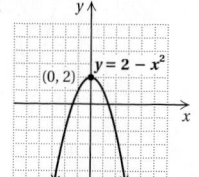 (0, 2) $y = 2 - x^2$

23. 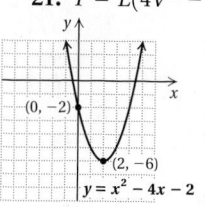 (0, -2) (2, -6) $y = x^2 - 4x - 2$

24. $(-\sqrt{2}, 0)$; $(\sqrt{2}, 0)$ **25.** $(2 - \sqrt{6}, 0)$; $(2 + \sqrt{6}, 0)$
26. 4.7 cm, 1.7 cm **27.** 15 ft **28.** About 8.1 sec
29. $-1, -7, 2$ **30.** 0, 0, 19 **31.** 2700 calories

32.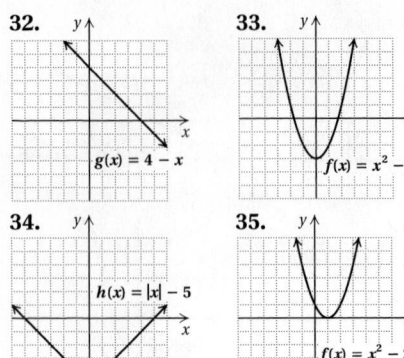
$g(x) = 4 - x$

33.
$f(x) = x^2 - 3$

34.
$h(x) = |x| - 5$

35.
$f(x) = x^2 - 2x + 1$

36. No **37.** Yes **38.** D **39.** A **40.** 31 and 32; −32 and −31 **41.** $5\sqrt{\pi}$ in., or about 8.9 in. **42.** 25 **43.** −4, −2 **44.** −5, −1 **45.** −6, 0 **46.** −3

Understanding Through Discussion and Writing

1. The second line should be $x + 6 = \sqrt{16}$ or $x + 6 = -\sqrt{16}$. Then we would have

$$x + 6 = 4 \quad or \quad x + 6 = -4$$
$$x = -2 \quad or \quad x = -10.$$

Both numbers check so the solutions are −2 and −10.
2. No; since each input has exactly one output, the number of outputs cannot exceed the number of inputs. **3.** Find the average, v, of the x-coordinates of the x-intercepts, $v = \dfrac{a_1 + a_2}{2}$.
Then the equation of the line of symmetry is $x = v$. The number v is also the first coordinate of the vertex. We substitute this value for x in the equation of the parabola to find the y-coordinate of the vertex. **4.** If $a > 0$, the graph opens up. If $a < 0$, the graph opens down. **5.** The solutions will be rational numbers because each is the solution of a linear equation of the form $mx + b = 0$.

Test: Chapter 15, p. 1165

1. [15.2a] $-\sqrt{5}, \sqrt{5}$ **2.** [15.1b] $-\frac{8}{7}, 0$ **3.** [15.1c] $-8, 6$
4. [15.1c] $-\frac{1}{3}, 2$ **5.** [15.2b] $8 \pm \sqrt{13}$ **6.** [15.3a] $\dfrac{1 \pm \sqrt{13}}{2}$
7. [15.3a] $\dfrac{3 \pm \sqrt{37}}{2}$ **8.** [15.3a] $-2 \pm \sqrt{14}$ **9.** [15.3a] $\dfrac{7 \pm \sqrt{37}}{6}$
10. [15.1c] $-1, 2$ **11.** [15.1c] $-4, 2$ **12.** [15.2c] $2 \pm \sqrt{14}$
13. [15.3b] $-1.7, 5.7$ **14.** [15.4a] $n = \dfrac{-b + \sqrt{b^2 + 4ad}}{2a}$
15. [15.6b] $\left(\dfrac{1 - \sqrt{21}}{2}, 0\right), \left(\dfrac{1 + \sqrt{21}}{2}, 0\right)$
16. [15.6a]
$y = 4 - x^2$ (0, 4)
17. [15.6a]
(0, 5) $\left(\frac{1}{2}, \frac{21}{4}\right)$
$y = -x^2 + x + 5$
18. [15.7b] 1; $1\frac{1}{2}$; 2 **19.** [15.7b] 1; 3; −3 **20.** [15.5a] Length: 6.5 m; width: 2.5 m **21.** [15.5a] 24 km/h **22.** [15.7e] 25.86 min
23. [15.7c]
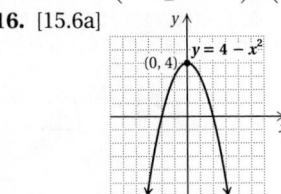
$h(x) = x - 4$
24. [15.7c]
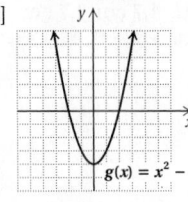
$g(x) = x^2 - 4$

25. [15.7d] Yes **26.** [15.7d] No **27.** [15.7b] D **28.** [15.5a] $5 + 5\sqrt{2}$
29. [13.2b], [15.3a] $(1 + \sqrt{5}, -1 + \sqrt{5}), (1 - \sqrt{5}, -1 - \sqrt{5})$

APPENDIXES

Exercise Set A, p. 1178

1. 12 **3.** $\frac{1}{12}$ **5.** 5280 **7.** 108 **9.** 7 **11.** $1\frac{1}{2}$, or 1.5
13. 26,400 **15.** $5\frac{1}{4}$, or 5.25 **17.** $3\frac{1}{3}$ **19.** 37,488
21. $1\frac{1}{2}$, or 1.5 **23.** $1\frac{1}{4}$, or 1.25 **25.** 110 **27.** 2 **29.** 300
31. 30 **33.** $\frac{1}{36}$ **35.** 126,720 **37.** (a) 1000; (b) 0.001
39. (a) 10; (b) 0.1 **41.** (a) 0.01; (b) 100 **43.** 6700 **45.** 0.98
47. 8.921 **49.** 0.05666 **51.** 566,600 **53.** 4.77 **55.** 688
57. 0.1 **59.** 100,000 **61.** 142 **63.** 0.82 **65.** 450
67. 0.000024 **69.** 0.688 **71.** 230 **73.** 3.92 **75.** 180; 0.18
77. 278; 27.8 **79.** 48,440; 48.44 **81.** 4000; 400 **83.** 0.027; 0.00027 **85.** 442,000; 44,200 **87.** 100.65 **89.** 727.4394
91. 104.585 **93.** 289.62 **95.** 112.63 **97.** 9.14
99. 81.8896 **101.** 1250.061 **103.** 6.18109 **105.** 1376.136
107. 0.51181 **109.–119.** Answers may vary, depending on the conversion factor used.

	yd	cm	in.	m	mm
109.	0.2361	21.59	$8\frac{1}{2}$	0.2159	215.9
111.	52.95934	4844	1907.0828	48.44	48,440
113.	4	365.6	144	3.656	3656
115.	0.000295	0.027	0.0106299	0.00027	0.27
117.	483.548	44,200	17,401.54	442	442,000

119. 1 in. = 25.4 mm

Exercise Set B, p. 1186

1. 2000 **3.** 3 **5.** 64 **7.** 12,640 **9.** 0.1 **11.** 5
13. 26,000,000,000 lb **15.** 1000 **17.** 10 **19.** $\frac{1}{100}$, or 0.01
21. 1000 **23.** 10 **25.** 234,000 **27.** 5.2 **29.** 6.7
31. 0.0502 **33.** 8.492 **35.** 58.5 **37.** 800,000 **39.** 1000
41. 0.0034 **43.** 0.0603 **45.** 1000 **47.** 0.325 **49.** 210,600
51. 0.0049 **53.** 125 mcg **55.** 0.875 mg; 875 mcg
57. 4 tablets **59.** 8 cc **61.** 144 packages

Exercise Set C, p. 1192

1. 1000; 1000 **3.** 87,000 **5.** 0.049 **7.** 0.000401
9. 78,100 **11.** 320 **13.** 10 **15.** 32 **17.** 20
19. 14 **21.** 88

	gal	qt	pt	cups	oz
23.	1.125	4.5	9	18	144
25.	16	64	128	256	2048
27.	0.25	1	2	4	32
29.	0.3984375	1.59375	3.1875	6.375	51

	L	mL	cc	cm³
31.	2	2000	2000	2000
33.	64	64,000	64,000	64,000
35.	0.355	355	355	355

37. 2000 mL **39.** 0.32 L **41.** 59.14 mL **43.** 500 mL
45. 125 mL/hr **47.** 9 **49.** $\frac{1}{5}$ **51.** 6 **53.** 15

55. 1.75 gal/week; 7.5 gal/month; 91.25 gal/year; 76.5 million gal/day; 27.9225 billion gal/year

Exercise Set D, p. 1197

1. 24 **3.** 60 **5.** $365\frac{1}{4}$ **7.** 0.05 **9.** 8.2 **11.** 6.5
13. 10.75 **15.** 336 **17.** 4.5 **19.** 56 **21.** 86,164.2 sec
23. 77°F **25.** 104°F **27.** 186.8°F **29.** 136.4°F
31. 35.6°F **33.** 41°F **35.** 5432°F **37.** 30°C **39.** 55°C
41. $81.\overline{1}$°C **43.** 60°C **45.** 20°C **47.** $6.\overline{6}$°C **49.** 37°C
51. (a) 136°F = 57.$\overline{7}$°C, $56\frac{2}{3}$°C = 134°F; **(b)** 2°F **53.** 53.$\overline{3}$°C
55. About 0.03 yr

Exercise Set E, p. 1201

1. $\{3, 4, 5, 6, 7, 8\}$ **3.** $\{41, 43, 45, 47, 49\}$ **5.** $\{-3, 3\}$
7. False **9.** True **11.** True **13.** True **15.** True
17. False **19.** $\{c, d, e\}$ **21.** $\{1, 10\}$ **23.** $\{\ \}$, or $\varnothing$
25. $\{a, e, i, o, u, q, c, k\}$ **27.** $\{0, 1, 7, 10, 2, 5\}$
29. $\{a, e, i, o, u, m, n, f, g, h\}$ **31.** $\{x | x \text{ is an integer}\}$
33. $\{x | x \text{ is real number}\}$ **35.** $\{\ \}$, or $\varnothing$ **37. (a)** A; **(b)** A;
(c) A; **(d)** $\{\ \}$, or $\varnothing$ **39.** True

Exercise Set F, p. 1205

1. $(z + 3)(z^2 - 3z + 9)$ **3.** $(x - 1)(x^2 + x + 1)$
5. $(y + 5)(y^2 - 5y + 25)$ **7.** $(2a + 1)(4a^2 - 2a + 1)$
9. $(y - 2)(y^2 + 2y + 4)$ **11.** $(2 - 3b)(4 + 6b + 9b^2)$
13. $(4y + 1)(16y^2 - 4y + 1)$ **15.** $(2x + 3)(4x^2 - 6x + 9)$
17. $(a - b)(a^2 + ab + b^2)$ **19.** $\left(a + \frac{1}{2}\right)\left(a^2 - \frac{1}{2}a + \frac{1}{4}\right)$
21. $2(y - 4)(y^2 + 4y + 16)$ **23.** $3(2a + 1)(4a^2 - 2a + 1)$
25. $r(s + 4)(s^2 - 4s + 16)$ **27.** $5(x - 2z)(x^2 + 2xz + 4z^2)$
29. $(x + 0.1)(x^2 - 0.1x + 0.01)$
31. $8(2x^2 - t^2)(4x^4 + 2x^2t^2 + t^4)$
33. $2y(y - 4)(y^2 + 4y + 16)$
35. $(z - 1)(z^2 + z + 1)(z + 1)(z^2 - z + 1)$
37. $(t^2 + 4y^2)(t^4 - 4t^2y^2 + 16y^4)$ **39.** 1; 19; 19; 7; 1
41. $(x^{2a} + y^b)(x^{4a} - x^{2a}y^b + y^{2b})$
43. $3(x^a + 2y^b)(x^{2a} - 2x^ay^b + 4y^{2b})$
45. $\frac{1}{3}\left(\frac{1}{2}xy + z\right)\left(\frac{1}{4}x^2y^2 - \frac{1}{2}xyz + z^2\right)$ **47.** $y(3x^2 + 3xy + y^2)$
49. $4(3a^2 + 4)$

Exercise Set G, p. 1210

1. $y = 4x - 18$ **3.** $y = -2x + 12$ **5.** $y = 3x + 4$
7. $y = -3x - 6$ **9.** $y = 4$ **11.** $y = -\frac{4}{5}x + \frac{23}{5}$
13. $y = x + 3$ **15.** $y = x$ **17.** $y = \frac{5}{3}x - 5$
19. $y = 3x + 5$ **21.** $y = -\frac{7}{4}x$ **23.** $y = \frac{2}{11}x + \frac{91}{66}$
25. $y = 5x + 3$

Exercise Set H, p. 1213

1. $\{-3, 3\}$ **3.** $\varnothing$ **5.** $\{0\}$ **7.** $\{-9, 15\}$ **9.** $\left\{-\frac{1}{2}, \frac{7}{2}\right\}$
11. $\left\{-\frac{5}{4}, \frac{23}{4}\right\}$ **13.** $\{-11, 11\}$ **15.** $\{-291, 291\}$
17. $\{-8, 8\}$ **19.** $\{-7, 7\}$ **21.** $\{-2, 2\}$ **23.** $\{-7, 8\}$
25. $\{-12, 2\}$ **27.** $\left\{-\frac{5}{2}, \frac{7}{2}\right\}$ **29.** $\varnothing$ **31.** $\left\{-\frac{13}{54}, -\frac{7}{54}\right\}$
33. $\{x | x \geq -5\}$, or $[-5, \infty)$ **35.** $\left\{1, -\frac{1}{4}\right\}$

Exercise Set I, p. 1216

1. 5 **3.** $\sqrt{29} \approx 5.385$ **5.** $\sqrt{648} \approx 25.456$ **7.** 7.1
9. $\frac{\sqrt{41}}{7} \approx 0.915$ **11.** $\frac{9}{4}$ **13.** $\sqrt{6970} \approx 83.487$
15. $\sqrt{a^2 + b^2}$ **17.** $\frac{2}{5}$ **19.** $\sqrt{17 + 2\sqrt{14} + 2\sqrt{15}} \approx 5.677$
21. $\sqrt{9,672,400} \approx 3110.048$ **23.** $\left(\frac{3}{2}, \frac{7}{2}\right)$ **25.** $\left(0, \frac{11}{2}\right)$
27. $\left(-1, -\frac{17}{2}\right)$ **29.** $(-0.25, -0.3)$ **31.** $\left(-\frac{1}{12}, \frac{1}{24}\right)$
33. $\left(\frac{\sqrt{2} + \sqrt{3}}{2}, \frac{3}{2}\right)$ **35.** $(-4, 0)$ **37.** $\sqrt{49 + k^2}$
39. $8\sqrt{m^2 + n^2}$ **41.** Yes **43.** $(2, 4\sqrt{2})$

Exercise Set J, p. 1225

1. $4, -4$ **3.** $12, -12$ **5.** $20, -20$ **7.** $-\frac{7}{6}$ **9.** 14
11. 0.06 **13.** Does not exist as a real number **15.** 18.628
17. 1.962 **19.** $y^2 + 16$ **21.** $\frac{x}{y - 1}$ **23.** $4|x|$ **25.** $12|c|$
27. $|p + 3|$ **29.** $|x - 2|$ **31.** 3 **33.** $-4x$ **35.** -6
37. $0.7(x + 1)$ **39.** -5 **41.** $-\frac{2}{3}$ **43.** $|x|$ **45.** $5|a|$
47. 6 **49.** $|a + b|$ **51.** y **53.** $x - 2$ **55.** $\sqrt[7]{y}$ **57.** 2
59. $\sqrt[5]{a^3b^3}$ **61.** 8 **63.** 343 **65.** $17^{1/2}$ **67.** $18^{1/3}$
69. $(xy^2z)^{1/5}$ **71.** $(3mn)^{3/2}$ **73.** $(8x^2y)^{5/7}$ **75.** $\frac{1}{1000}$
77. $\frac{3}{x^{1/4}}$ **79.** $\frac{1}{(2rs)^{3/4}}$ **81.** $\left(\frac{8yz}{7x}\right)^{3/5}$ **83.** $\frac{5ac^{1/2}}{3}$
85. $5^{7/8}$ **87.** $7^{1/4}$ **89.** $4.9^{1/2}$ **91.** $6^{3/28}$ **93.** $a^{23/12}$

Exercise Set K, p. 1230

1. $(-\infty, 5)$ **3.** $[-3, 3]$ **5.** $(-8, -4)$ **7.** $(-2, 5)$
9. $(-\sqrt{2}, \infty)$
11. $\{x | x > -1\}$, or $(-1, \infty)$

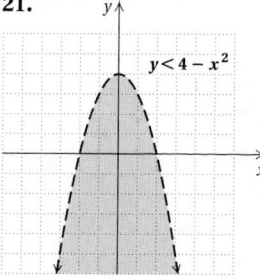

13. $\{x | x > 3\}$, or $(3, \infty)$

15. $\{x | x < -60\}$, or $(-\infty, -60)$

17. $\{a | a \leq -22\}$, or $(-\infty, -22]$

19. $\{x | x \leq 0.9\}$, or $(-\infty, 0.9]$ **21.** $\left\{x | x \leq \frac{5}{6}\right\}$, or $\left(-\infty, \frac{5}{6}\right]$
23. $\{x | x < 6\}$, or $(-\infty, 6)$ **25.** $\{y | y \leq -3\}$, or $(-\infty, -3]$
27. $\left\{y | y > \frac{2}{3}\right\}$, or $\left(\frac{2}{3}, \infty\right)$

Exercise Set L, p. 1235

1. $\{x | x < -2 \text{ or } x > 6\}$, or $(-\infty, -2) \cup (6, \infty)$
3. $\{x | -2 \leq x \leq 2\}$, or $[-2, 2]$ **5.** $\{x | -1 \leq x \leq 4\}$, or $[-1, 4]$
7. $\{x | -1 < x < 2\}$, or $(-1, 2)$ **9.** All real numbers, or
$(-\infty, \infty)$ **11.** $\{x | 2 < x < 4\}$, or $(2, 4)$
13. $\{x | x < -2 \text{ or } 0 < x < 2\}$, or $(-\infty, -2) \cup (0, 2)$
15. $\{x | -9 < x < -1 \text{ or } x > 4\}$, or $(-9, -1) \cup (4, \infty)$
17. $\{x | x < -3 \text{ or } -2 < x < 1\}$, or $(-\infty, -3) \cup (-2, 1)$
19.

21.

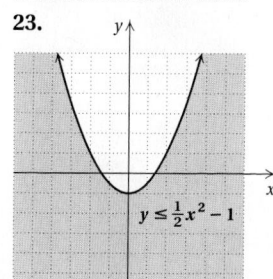

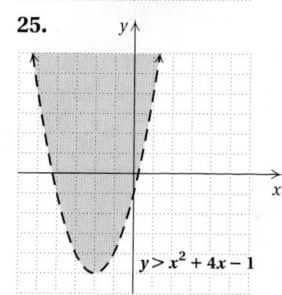

23.

25.

27.

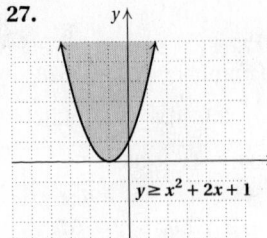

$y \geq x^2 + 2x + 1$

29.

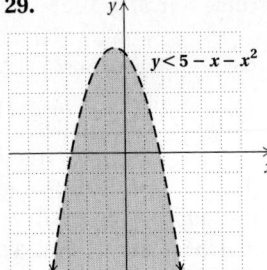

$y < 5 - x - x^2$

31.

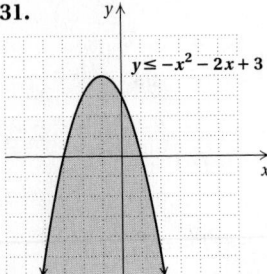

$y \leq -x^2 - 2x + 3$

33.

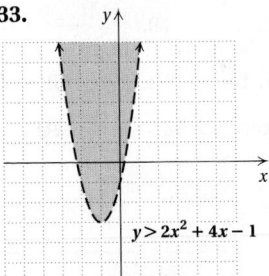

$y > 2x^2 + 4x - 1$

Exercise Set M, p. 1241

1.

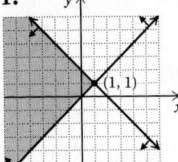

(1, 1)

3.

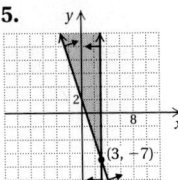

$\left(\frac{1}{2}, \frac{1}{2}\right)$

5.

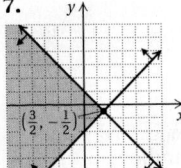

(3, −7)

7.

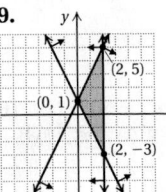

$\left(\frac{3}{2}, -\frac{1}{2}\right)$

9.

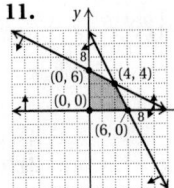

(2, 5), (0, 1), (2, −3)

11.

(0, 6), (4, 4), (0, 0), (6, 0)

1. 0.57, 0.43   **3.** 0.075, 0.134, 0.057, 0.071, 0.030   **5.** 0.633
7. 52   **9.** $\frac{1}{4}$ **11.** $\frac{1}{2}$ **13.** $\frac{2}{13}$ **15.** $\frac{2}{7}$ **17.** 0   **19.** $\frac{5}{36}$
21. $\frac{5}{36}$ **23.** $\frac{1}{36}$

1. $i\sqrt{35}$, or $\sqrt{35}i$ **3.** $4i$ **5.** $-2i\sqrt{3}$, or $-2\sqrt{3}i$
7. $i\sqrt{3}$, or $\sqrt{3}i$ **9.** $9i$ **11.** $7i\sqrt{2}$, or $7\sqrt{2}i$ **13.** $-7i$
15. $4 - 2\sqrt{15}i$, or $4 - 2i\sqrt{15}$ **17.** $12 - 4i$ **19.** $9 - 5i$
21. $7 + 4i$ **23.** $-4 - 4i$ **25.** $-1 + i$ **27.** $11 + 6i$
29. -18 **31.** $-\sqrt{14}$ **33.** 21 **35.** $-6 + 24i$ **37.** $1 + 5i$
39. $18 + 14i$ **41.** $38 + 9i$ **43.** $2 - 46i$ **45.** $5 - 12i$
47. $-24 + 10i$ **49.** $-i$ **51.** 1 **53.** -1 **55.** i **57.** -1
59. $-125i$ **61.** 8 **63.** $1 - 23i$ **65.** 0 **67.** 0 **69.** 1
71. $5 - 8i$ **73.** $2 - \dfrac{\sqrt{6}}{2}i$ **75.** $\frac{9}{10} + \frac{13}{10}i$ **77.** $-i$
79. $-\frac{3}{7} - \frac{8}{7}i$ **81.** $\frac{6}{5} - \frac{2}{5}i$ **83.** $-\frac{8}{41} + \frac{10}{41}i$ **85.** $-\frac{4}{3}i$
87. $-\frac{1}{2} - \frac{1}{4}i$ **89.** $-\frac{3}{5} + \frac{4}{5}i$
91.

$$x^2 - 2x + 5 = 0$$
$$(1 - 2i)^2 - 2(1 - 2i) + 5 \ \overset{?}{\vphantom{|}} \ 0$$
$$1 - 4i + 4i^2 - 2 + 4i + 5$$
$$1 - 4i - 4 - 2 + 4i + 5$$
$$0 \ \bigg| \ \text{TRUE}$$

Yes

93.

$$x^2 - 4x - 5 = 0$$
$$(2 + i)^2 - 4(2 + i) - 5 \ \overset{?}{\vphantom{|}} \ 0$$
$$4 + 4i + i^2 - 8 - 4i - 5$$
$$4 + 4i - 1 - 8 - 4i - 5$$
$$-10 \ \bigg| \ \text{FALSE}$$

No

95. $\pm\frac{5}{3}i$ **97.** $7 \pm 2i$ **99.** $\frac{5}{4} \pm \frac{\sqrt{39}}{4}i$ **101.** $-\frac{1}{2} \pm \frac{\sqrt{7}}{2}i$
103. $2 \pm 3i$ **105.** $1 \pm 2\sqrt{2}i$ **107.** $-1 \pm 2i$ **109.** $2 \pm i$
111. $\frac{1}{2} \pm \frac{3}{2}i$ **113.** $1, -\frac{1}{2} \pm \frac{\sqrt{3}}{2}i$

Glossary

A

Abscissa   The first coordinate in an ordered pair of numbers

Absolute value   The distance that a number is from 0 on the number line

ac-method   A method for factoring trinomials of the type $ax^2 + bx + c, a \neq 1$, involving the product, ac, of the leading coefficient a and the last term c; also called the *grouping method*

Acute angle   An angle whose measure is greater than 0° and less than 90°

Acute triangle   A triangle in which all three angles are acute

Addends   In addition, the numbers being added

Additive identity   The number 0

Additive inverse   A number's opposite; two numbers are additive inverses of each other if their sum is zero.

Additive inverse of a polynomial   Two polynomials are additive inverses, or opposites, of each other if their sum is zero.

Algebraic expression   A number or variable or a collection of numbers and variables on which operations are performed

Angle   A set of points consisting of two rays (half-lines) with a common endpoint (vertex)

Area   The number of square units that fill a plane region

Arithmetic mean   A center point of a set of numbers found by adding the numbers and dividing by the number of items of data; also called the *average* or the *mean*

Arithmetic numbers   The set of whole numbers and positive fractions; also called *nonnegative rational numbers*

Ascending order   When a polynomial is written with the exponents of the variable increasing as read from left to right, it is said to be in ascending order.

Associative law of addition   The statement that when three numbers are added, regrouping the addends gives the same sum

Associative law of multiplication   The statement that when three numbers are multiplied, regrouping the factors gives the same product

Average   A center point of a set of numbers found by adding the numbers and dividing by the number of items of data; also called the *mean* or the *arithmetic mean*

Axes   Two perpendicular number lines used to identify points in a plane

B

Bar graph   A graphic display of data using bars proportional in length to the numbers represented

Base   In exponential notation, the number being raised to a power

Binomial   A polynomial containing two terms

C

Celsius   A temperature scale in which water freezes at 0° and water boils at 100°

Circle   The set of all points in a plane that are a given distance (radius) from a given point (center)

Circle graph   A graphic display of data using a divided circle to show the percent of a quantity in each of several categories; also called *pie chart*

Circumference   The distance around a circle

Coefficient   The numeric multiplier of a variable

Commission   A percent of total sales paid to a salesperson

Commutative law of addition   The statement that when two numbers are added, changing the order in which the numbers are added does not affect the sum

Commutative law of multiplication   The statement that when two numbers are multiplied, changing the order in which the numbers are multiplied does not affect the product

Complementary angles   Two angles for which the sum of their measures is 90°

Completing the square   Adding a particular constant to an expression so that the resulting sum is a perfect square

Complex fraction expression   A rational expression that has one or more rational expressions within its numerator and/or denominator

Complex number Any number that can be named $a + bi$, where a and b are any real numbers

Complex-number system A number system that contains the real-number system and is designed so that negative numbers have defined square roots

Complex rational expression A rational expression that has one or more rational expressions within its numerator and/or denominator

Composite number A natural number, other than 1, that is not prime

Compound interest Interest computed on the sum of an original principal and the interest previously accrued by that principal

Congruent angles Two angles that have the same measure

Congruent segments Two line segments that have the same length

Congruent triangles Triangles in which corresponding angles and sides are congruent

Conjugate of a complex number The conjugate of $a + bi$ is $a - bi$, and the conjugate of $a - bi$ is $a + bi$.

Conjugates Pairs of radical terms, like $\sqrt{a} + \sqrt{b}$ and $\sqrt{a} - \sqrt{b}$ or $c + \sqrt{d}$ and $c - \sqrt{d}$, for which the product does not have a radical term

Consecutive even integers Even integers that are two units apart

Consecutive integers Integers that are one unit apart

Consecutive odd integers Odd integers that are two units apart

Constant A number or letter that stands for just one number

Constant of proportionality The constant in an equation of direct or inverse variation

Coordinates The numbers in an ordered pair

Coplanar lines Lines in the same plane

Cross products Given an equation with a single fraction on each side, the products formed by multiplying the left numerator and the right denominator, and the left denominator and the right numerator

Cube root The number c is called a cube root of a, written $\sqrt[3]{a}$, if $c^3 = a$.

D

Decimal notation A representation of a number containing a decimal point

Degree of a polynomial The degree of the term of highest degree in a polynomial

Degree of a term The sum of the exponents of the variables

Denominator The number below the fraction bar in a fraction

Descending order When a polynomial is written with the exponents of the variable decreasing as read from left to right, it is said to be in descending order.

Diagonal of a quadrilateral A line segment that joins two opposite vertices

Diameter A line segment that passes through the center of a circle and has its endpoints on the circle

Difference The result of subtracting one number from another

Difference of cubes An expression that can be written in the form $A^3 - B^3$

Difference of squares An expression that can be written in the form $A^2 - B^2$

Digit A number 0, 1, 2, 3, 4, 5, 6, 7, 8, or 9 that names a place-value location

Direct variation A situation that translates to an equation of the form $y = kx$, with k a positive constant

Discount The amount subtracted from the original price of an item to find the sale price

Discriminant The radicand, $b^2 - 4ac$, from the quadratic formula

Distance formula The equation $d = \sqrt{(x_2 - x_1)^2 + (y_2 - y_1)^2}$ that represents the distance between two points, (x_1, y_1) and (x_2, y_2), on the coordinate plane

Distributive law of multiplication over addition The statement that multiplying a factor by the sum of two numbers gives the same result as multiplying the factor by each of the two numbers and then adding

Distributive law of multiplication over subtraction The statement that multiplying a factor by the difference of two numbers gives the same result as multiplying the factor by each of the two numbers and then subtracting

Dividend In division, the number being divided

Divisible The number b is said to be divisible by another number a if b is a multiple of a.

Divisor In division, the number dividing another number

Domain The set of all first coordinates of the ordered pairs in a function

E

Elimination method An algebraic method that uses the addition principle to solve a system of equations

Empty set The set without members

Equation A number sentence that says that the expressions on either side of the equals sign, =, represent the same number

Equation of direct variation An equation, described by $y = kx$ with k a positive constant, used to represent direct variation

Equation of inverse variation An equation, described by $y = \dfrac{k}{x}$ with k a positive constant, used to represent inverse variation

Equiangular triangle A triangle in which all angles are congruent

Equilateral triangle A triangle in which all sides are the same length

Equivalent equations Equations with the same solutions

Equivalent expressions Expressions that have the same value for all allowable (or meaningful) replacements

Equivalent fractions Two different fractions that represent the same number

Equivalent inequalities Inequalities that have the same solution set

Evaluate To substitute a value for each occurrence of a variable in an expression

Even root A root with an even index

Event A set of outcomes

Exponent In expressions of the form a^n, the number n is an exponent.

Exponential notation A representation of a number using a base raised to a power

F

Factor *Verb*: to write an equivalent expression that is a product; *Noun*: a multiplier

Factoring Writing an expression as a product

Factorization A number expressed as a product of two or more numbers

Factorization of a polynomial An expression that names the polynomial as a product

Fahrenheit A temperature scale in which water freezes at 32° and water boils at 212°

FOIL To multiply two binomials by multiplying the First terms, the Outside terms, the Inside terms, and then the Last terms

Formula An equation that uses numbers or letters to represent a relationship between two or more quantities

Fraction equation An equation containing one or more rational expressions; also called a *rational equation*

Fraction expression A quotient, or ratio, of two polynomials; also called a *rational expression*

Fraction notation A number written using a numerator and a denominator

Function A correspondence between a first set, called the domain, and a second set, called the range, such that each member of the domain corresponds to *exactly one* member of the range

G

Geometric figure A set of points

Grade The measure of a road's steepness

Grade point average (GPA) The average of the grade point values for each credit hour taken

Graph A picture or diagram of the data in a table; a line, curve, or collection of points that represents all the solutions of an equation

Greatest common factor (GCF) The common factor of a polynomial with the largest possible coefficient and the largest possible exponent(s)

H

Hypotenuse In a right triangle, the side opposite the right angle

I

Identity property of 1 The statement that the product of a number and 1 is always the original number

Identity property of 0 The statement that the sum of a number and 0 is always the original number

Imaginary number A number that can be named bi, where b is some real number and $b \neq 0$

Index In the expression $\sqrt[k]{a}$, the number k is called the index.

Inequality A mathematical sentence using $<, >, \leq, \geq,$ or $\neq$

Input A member of the domain of a function

Integers The whole numbers and their opposites; $\ldots, -4, -3, -2, -1, 0, 1, 2, 3, 4, \ldots$

Intercept The point at which a graph intersects the x- or y-axis

Interest A percentage of an amount invested or borrowed

Interest rate The percent at which interest is calculated on a principal

Intersecting lines Lines that cross each other at a common point

Intersection of sets A and B The set of all elements that are common to *both* A and B, denoted $A \cap B$

Inverse variation A situation that translates to an equation of the form $y = \dfrac{k}{x}$, with k a positive constant

Irrational number A real number that cannot be named as a ratio of two integers

Isosceles triangle A triangle in which two or more sides are the same length

L

Leading coefficient The coefficient of the term of highest degree in a polynomial

Leading term The term of highest degree in a polynomial

Least common denominator (LCD) The least common multiple of the denominators of two or more fractions

Least common multiple (LCM) The smallest number that is a multiple of two or more numbers

Legs In a right triangle, the two sides that form the right angle

Like radicals Radicals that have the same index and the same radicand

Like terms Terms that have exactly the same variable factors

Line Two rays that have common points and continue in opposite directions

Line of symmetry A line that can be drawn through a graph such that the part of the graph on one side of the line is an exact reflection of the part on the opposite side

Line graph A graph in which quantities are represented as points connected by straight-line segments

Linear equation   Any equation that can be written in the form $Ax + By = C$, where x and y are variables

Linear function   A function that can be described by an equation of the form $y = mx + b$, where x and y are variables

Linear inequality   An inequality whose related equation is a linear equation

M

Marked price   The original price of an item

Mean   A center point of a set of numbers found by dividing the sum of the numbers by the number of items of data; also called the *average* or the *arithmetic mean*

Median   In a set of data listed in order from smallest to largest, the middle number if there is an odd number of data items, or the average of the two middle numbers if there is an even number of data items

Metric system   A measurement system used in most countries of the world, but very little in the United States

Midpoint formula   The formula $\left(\dfrac{x_1 + x_2}{2}, \dfrac{y_1 + y_2}{2}\right)$. If the endpoints of a segment are (x_1, y_1) and (x_2, y_2), then this represents the coordinates of the midpoint.

Minuend   The number from which another number is being subtracted

Mixed numeral   A number represented by a whole number and a fraction less than 1

Mode   The number or numbers that occur most often in a set of data

Monomial   An expression of the type ax^n, where a is a real-number constant and n is a nonnegative integer

Multiple of a number   A product of the number and some natural number

Multiplication property of 0   The statement that the product of 0 and any real number is 0

Multiplicative identity   The number 1

Multiplicative inverses   Reciprocals; two numbers whose product is 1

N

Natural numbers   The counting numbers: 1, 2, 3, 4, 5, …

Negative integers   Integers to the left of zero on the number line

Nonnegative rational numbers   The set of whole numbers and positive fractions; also called *arithmetic numbers*

Numerator   The number above the fraction bar in a fraction

O

Obtuse angle   An angle whose measure is greater than 90° and less than 180°

Obtuse triangle   A triangle in which one angle is an obtuse angle

Odd root   A root with an odd index

Opposite   The opposite, or additive inverse, of a number x is written $-x$. Opposites are the same distance from 0 on the number line but on different sides of 0.

Opposite of a polynomial   Two polynomials are opposites, or additive inverses, of each other if their sum is zero.

Ordered pair   A pair of numbers of the form (a, b) for which the order in which the numbers are listed is important

Ordinate   The second coordinate in an ordered pair of numbers

Origin   The point $(0, 0)$ on a graph where the two axes intersect

Original price   The price of an item before a discount is deducted

Outcome   The result of an experiment

Output   A member of the range of a function

P

Palindrone prime   A prime number that remains a prime number when its digits are reversed

Parabola   The graph of a quadratic equation

Parallel lines   Lines in the same plane that never intersect; two lines are parallel if they have the same slope.

Parallelogram   A four-sided polygon with two pairs of parallel sides

Percent notation   A representation of a number as n parts per 100; $n\%$

Perfect square   A rational number p for which there exists a number a for which $a^2 = p$

Perfect-square trinomial   A trinomial that is the square of a binomial

Perimeter   The distance around an object or the sum of the lengths of its sides

Periods   Groups of three digits, separated by commas

Perpendicular lines   Two lines that intersect to form a right angle; two lines are perpendicular if the product of their slopes is -1.

Pi (π)   The number that results when the circumference of a circle is divided by its diameter; $\pi \approx 3.14$, or $\frac{22}{7}$

Pictograph   A graphic means of displaying information using symbols to represent the amounts

Pie chart   A graphic display of data using a divided circle to show the percent of a quantity in each of several categories; also called *circle graph*

Point–slope equation   The equation $y - y_1 = m(x - x_1)$, where x_1, y_1, and m are real numbers and m is the slope and (x_1, y_1) is a point that lies on the graph of the equation

Polygon   A closed geometric figure with three or more line segments as sides

Polynomial   A monomial or a combination of sums and/or differences of monomials

Polynomial equation An equation in which two polynomials are set equal to each other

Positive integers Integers to the right of zero on the number line

Prime factorization A factorization of a composite number as a product of prime numbers

Prime number A natural number that has exactly two *different* factors: itself and 1

Prime polynomial A polynomial that cannot be factored using only integer coefficients

Principal An amount of money that is invested or borrowed

Principal square root The nonnegative square root of a number

Principle of zero products The statement that an equation $ab = 0$ is true if and only if $a = 0$ is true or $b = 0$ is true, or both are true

Product The result when one number is multiplied by another

Proportion An equation stating that two ratios are equal

Proportional numbers Two pairs of numbers having the same ratio

Protractor A device used to measure and draw angles

Purchase price The price of an item before sales tax is added

Pythagorean equation The equation $a^2 + b^2 = c^2$, where a and b are lengths of the legs of a right triangle and c is the length of the hypotenuse

Pythagorean theorem In any right triangle, if a and b are the lengths of the legs and c is the length of the hypotenuse, then $a^2 + b^2 = c^2$.

Q

Quadrants The four regions into which the axes divide a plane

Quadratic equation An equation of the form $ax^2 + bx + c = 0$, where $a \neq 0$

Quadratic formula The solutions of $ax^2 + bx + c = 0$, $a \neq 0$, are given by the equation $x = \dfrac{-b \pm \sqrt{b^2 - 4ac}}{2a}$.

Quadratic function A second-degree polynomial function in one variable

Quadratic inequality An inequality whose related equation is a quadratic equation

Quotient The result when one number is divided by another

R

Radical equation An equation that has variables in one or more radicands

Radical expression An algebraic expression in which a radical symbol appears

Radical symbol The symbol $\sqrt{}$

Radicand The expression under the radical

Radius A line segment with one endpoint on the center of a circle and the other endpoint on the circle

Range The set of all second coordinates of the ordered pairs in a function

Rate A ratio used to compare two different kinds of measure

Ratio The quotient of two quantities; the ratio of a to b is $\dfrac{a}{b}$, also written $a:b$

Rational equation An equation containing one or more rational expressions; also called a *fraction equation*

Rational expression A quotient, or ratio, of two polynomials; also called a *fraction expression*

Rational numbers Any number that can be written as the ratio of two integers $\dfrac{a}{b}$, where $b \neq 0$

Rationalizing the denominator A procedure for finding an equivalent expression without a radical in the denominator

Ray A part of a line consisting of one endpoint and all the points on the line on one side of the endpoint

Real numbers All rational and irrational numbers; the set of all numbers corresponding to points on the number line

Reciprocal A multiplicative inverse; two numbers are reciprocals if their product is 1

Rectangle A four-sided polygon with four 90° angles

Relation A correspondence between a first set, called the domain, and a second set, called the range, such that each member of the domain corresponds to *at least one* member of the range

Repeating decimal A decimal in which a number pattern repeats indefinitely

Right angle An angle whose measure is 90°

Right triangle A triangle in which one angle is a right angle

Rise The change in the second coordinate between two points on a line

Roster notation A way of naming sets by listing all the elements in the set

Rounding Approximating the value of a number; used when estimating

Run The change in the first coordinate between two points on a line

S

Sale price The price of an item after a discount has been deducted

Sales tax A tax added to the purchase price of an item

Sample space The set of all possible outcomes

Scalene triangle A triangle in which all sides are of different lengths

Scientific notation A number written in the form $M \times 10^n$, where n is an integer, $1 \leq M < 10$, and M is expressed in decimal notation

Segment A geometric figure consisting of two points, called endpoints, and all points between them

Set A collection of objects

Set-builder notation The naming of a set by describing basic characteristics of the elements in the set

Similar figures Figures with the same shape, but not necessarily the same size

Similar triangles Triangles in which corresponding angles have the same measure and the lengths of corresponding sides are proportional

Simple interest A percentage of an amount P invested or borrowed for t years, computed by calculating principal $\times$ interest rate $\times$ time in years

Simplify To rewrite an expression in an equivalent, abbreviated form

Slope The ratio of the rise to the run for any two points on a line

Slope–intercept equation An equation of the form $y = mx + b$, where x and y are variables, the slope is m, and the y-intercept is $(0, b)$

Solution of an equation A replacement for the variable that makes the equation true

Solution of a system of equations An ordered pair that makes both equations true

Solution set The set of all solutions of an equation, an inequality, or a system of equations or inequalities

Solve To find all solutions of an equation, an inequality, or a system of equations or inequalities; to find the solution(s) of a problem

Sphere The set of all points in space that are a given distance (radius) from a given point (center)

Square A four-sided polygon with four right angles and all sides of equal length

Square of a number A number multiplied by itself

Square root The number c is a square root of a if $c^2 = a$.

Square-root symbol The symbol $\sqrt{}$

Standard form of a linear equation An equation written in the form $Ax + By = C$

Standard form of a quadratic equation An equation written in the form $ax^2 + bx + c = 0, a > 0$, where a, b, and c are real-number constants

Statistic A number that describes a set of data

Straight angle An angle whose measure is 180°

Subsets Sets that are parts of other sets

Substitute To replace a variable with a number

Substitution method An algebraic method for solving systems of equations

Subtrahend In subtraction, the number being subtracted

Sum The result in addition

Sum of cubes An expression that can be written in the form $A^3 + B^3$

Sum of squares An expression that can be written in the form $A^2 + B^2$

Supplementary angles Two angles for which the sum of their measures is 180°

Surface area The sum of the areas of all of the faces of a three-dimensional figure

System of equations A set of two or more equations that are to be solved simultaneously

T

Table A method of presenting data in rows and columns

Term A number, a variable, or a product or a quotient of numbers and/or variables

Terminating decimal A decimal that can be written using a finite number of decimal places

Total price The sum of the purchase price of an item and the sales tax on the item

Transversal A line that intersects two or more coplanar lines in different points

Trapezoid A polygon with four sides, two of which, the bases, are parallel to each other

Triangle A three-sided polygon

Trinomial A polynomial containing three terms

Trinomial square The square of a binomial expressed as three terms

U

Union of sets A and B The set of all elements belonging to *either* A or B, denoted $A \cup B$

V

Value The numerical result after a number has been substituted into an expression

Variable A letter that represents an unknown number

Variation constant The constant in an equation of direct or inverse variation

Vertex The common endpoint of two rays that form an angle; the point at which the graph of a quadratic equation crosses its axis of symmetry

Vertical angles Two non-straight angles formed by two pairs of opposite rays

Vertical-line test The statement that a graph represents a function if it is impossible to draw a vertical line that intersects the graph more than once

Volume The number of cubic units needed to fill a three-dimensional figure

W

Whole numbers The natural numbers and 0: $0, 1, 2, 3, 4, 5, \ldots$

X

x-intercept The point at which a graph crosses the x-axis

Y

y-intercept The point at which a graph crosses the y-axis

Index

Triangles, similar, 958, 959
Trillions period, 2
Trinomial square, 857
   factoring, 858, 897
Trinomials, 763
   factoring, 831–836, 841–845
True equation, 6, 570
True inequality, 6, 628
Two, divisibility by, 83

U

Undefined rational expression, 906
Undefined slope, 687
Union of sets, 1200
Unit angle, 392
Unit cube, 428
Unit segment, 1168

V

Value
   of an expression, 507
   of a function, 1151
   of a polynomial, 756
Value feature on a graphing
      calculator, 1152
Variable, 42, 486
   substituting for, 487
Variation
   constant, 974, 977
   direct, 974
   inverse, 977

Vertex, 391, 1141, 1142, 1160
Vertical angle property, 442
Vertical angles, 442
Vertical lines, 676
   slope, 687
Vertical-line test, 1153, 1154
Volume
   of a circular cone, 432, 469
   of a circular cylinder, 431, 469
   of a rectangular solid, 428, 469
   of a sphere, 431, 469

W

Water flow of fire hose, 1051
Week, 1194
Whole numbers, 3, 493
   addition, 11, 12
   division, 25, 28
   expanded notation, 3
   fraction notation, 107
   multiplication, 20, 22
   order, 6
   rounding, 30
   standard notation, 3
   subtraction, 14
   word names for, 4
Wind chill temperature, 1053
Word names
   for decimal notation, 179
   for whole numbers, 4
Work principle, 954
Work problems, 952

X

x-intercept, 673, 1144

Y

Yard, 1168
Year, 1194
y-intercept, 662, 673

Z

Zero
   degree of, 762
   dividend of, 26, 530
   division by, 26, 530
   as exponent, 735
   fraction notation for, 107
   identity property, 506, 538, 561
   multiplication property of, 523
   in quotients, 29
   reciprocal, 117
   slope of, 687
Zero feature on a graphing
      calculator, 880
Zero products, principle of, 875,
      876, 897